Selected Papers on

UV, VUV, and X-Ray Lasers

Books in SPIE's Milestone Series
Brian J. Thompson, *General Editor*

Published

Acousto-Optics (A. Korpel)
Applications of Polarized Light (B.H. Billings)
Architectural Lighting (M.S. Rea)
Automatic Object Recognition (H. Nasr)
Characterization of Optical Coatings (M.R. Jacobson)
CO_2 Lasers (J.D. Evans)
Coherence and Fluctuations of Light (E. Wolf, L. Mandel)
Coherent Optical Processing (F.T.S. Yu, S. Yin)
Computer-Controlled Optical Surfacing (R.A. Jones)
Computer-Generated Holograms and Diffractive Optics (S.H. Lee)
Deposition of Optical Coatings (M.R. Jacobson)
Design of Optical Coatings (M.R. Jacobson)
Digital Image Processing (M.M. Trivedi)
Digital Image Restoration (M.I. Sezan)
Dye Lasers (F.J. Duarte)
Ellipsometry (R.M.A. Azzam)
Fiber Optic Gyroscopes (R.B. Smith)
Free-Space Laser Communications (D.L. Begley)
High-Power Lasers (J.M. Soures)
Holographic and Diffractive Lenses and Mirrors (T.W. Stone, B.J. Thompson)
Holographic Particle Diagnostics (C.S. Vikram)
Image Coding and Compression (M. Rabbani)
Image Tubes (I.P. Csorba)
Infrared Design (R.B. Johnson, W.L. Wolfe)
Infrared Fiber Optics (J.A. Harrington)
Interferometry (P. Hariharan)
Laser Damage in Optical Materials (R.M. Wood)
Laser Design (H. Weichel)
Laser Scanning and Recording (L. Beiser)
Light Scattering (M. Kerker)
Liquid Crystals for Optics (S.D. Jacobs)
Multiple Scattering in Plane Parallel Atmospheres and Oceans: Methods (G.W. Kattawar)
Natural Optical Activity (A. Lakhtakia)
Nonlinear Optics (H.E. Brandt)
Optical Computing (H.J. Caulfield, G. Gheen)
Optical Fiber Technology (D.B. Keck)
Optical Fibers in Medicine (A. Katzir)
Optical Microlithography (H. Stover)
Optical Moiré and Applications (G. Indebetouw, R. Czarnek)
Optical Shop Metrology (D. Malacara)
Optical Storage (G.T. Sincerbox, J.M. Zavislan)
Optical Tolerancing (G.E. Wiese)
Optical Transfer Function: Foundation and Theory (L. Baker)
Optical Transfer Function: Measurement (L. Baker)
Optomechanical Design (D.C. O'Shea)
Photoconductivity (N.V. Joshi)
Photon Statistics and Coherence in Nonlinear Optics (J. Peřina)
Polarization (B.H. Billings)
Quasielastic Light Scattering (B. Chu)
Radiometry (I.J. Spiro)
Rare-Earth-Doped Fiber Laser Sources and Amplifiers (M.J.F. Digonnet)
Scalar Wave Diffraction (K.E. Oughstun)
Scanning Acoustic Microscopy (B. Khuri-Yakub, C. Quate)
Scattering in the Atmosphere (C.F. Bohren)
Schlieren Optics (J.R. Meyer-Arendt)
Semiconductor Diode Lasers (J.J. Coleman)
Semiconductor Infrared Detectors (A. Rogalski)
Solid State Lasers (R.C. Powell)
Special Significance to Optometry (W.M. Rosenblum, W.J. Benjamin)
Speckle Metrology (R.S. Sirohi)
Surface-enhanced Raman Scattering (M. Kerker)
Turbulence in a Refractive Medium (E L Andreas)
Ultrafast Laser Technology (T.R. Gosnell, A.J. Taylor)
UV, VUV, and X-Ray Lasers (R.W. Waynant, M.N. Ediger)
Visual Communication (T.R. Hsing, A.G. Tescher)

Forthcoming

Adaptive Optics for Atmospheric Compensation (J.E. Pearson, F. L. Ebright)
Astronomical Optics (D.J. Schroeder)
Color—Fundamentals (D.L. MacAdam)
Coupled-Mode Theory in Guided-Wave Optics (D. G. Hall)
Diffraction Gratings (D. Maystre)
Effects of Aberrations in Optical Imaging (V.N. Mahajan, R. Singh)
Electron Optics (P.W. Hawkes)
Fiber Optic Communications (L. D. Hutcheson, S. C. Mettler)
Fundamentals of Lasers (W.T. Silfvast)
Fundamentals of Optoelectronics (G.R. Little)
Gaussian Beam Mode Optics for MM-Wave & Terahertz Systems (J.C.G. Lesurf)
Geometrical Aspects of Scattering (P. L. Marston)
Gradient Index Optics (D. Moore)
Instrumentation in Astronomy (W. Livingston)
Laser Doppler Velocimetry and Its Applications (R. J. Adrian)
Laser Safety (D.H. Sliney)
Model-Based Vision (H. Nasr)
Nonimaging Optics (R. Winston)
Optical Chaos (F. T. Arecchi, R. G. Harrison)
Optical Correlators (S. Jutamulia)
Optical Fiber Networking (E.G. Rawson)
Performance Evaluation of Signal & Image Processing Systems (F. Sadjadi)
Photochemistry (D. Neckers)
Photodynamic Therapy (D. Kessel)
Prisms and Mirrors—Design and Fabrication (R. Hradaynath)
Solar Radiation and Solar Thermal Systems (D. Osborn)
UV Optics and Technology (R. E. Huffman)

SPIE Milestone Series
Volume MS 71

Selected Papers on UV, VUV, and X-Ray Lasers

Ronald W. Waynant
Marwood N. Ediger, *Editors*
Food Drug Administration
Center for Devices and Radiological Health

Brian J. Thompson
General Editor, SPIE Milestone Series

SPIE Optical Engineering Press

A Publication of SPIE—The International Society for Optical Engineering
Bellingham, Washington USA

Library of Congress Cataloging-in-Publication Data

Selected papers on UV, VUV, and x-ray lasers / Ronald W. Waynant, Marwood N. Ediger.
p. cm. — (SPIE milestone series ; v. MS 71)
Includes index.
ISBN 0-8194-1125-6 (hardbound). — ISBN 0-8194-1126-4 (softbound)
1. X-ray lasers. 2. Ultraviolet radiation. 3. Gas lasers.
4. Excimer lasers. I. Waynant, Ronald W. II. Ediger, Marwood N.,
1958- . III. Series.
TA1707.S45 1993
621.36`6—dc20 92-33721
CIP

ISBN 0-8194-1125-6 (hardbound)
ISBN 0-8194-1126-4 (softbound)

Published by
SPIE—The International Society for Optical Engineering
P.O. Box 10, Bellingham, Washington 98227-0010 USA
Telephone 206/676-3290 (Pacific Time) • Telex 46-7053

This book is a compilation of outstanding papers selected from the world literature on optical and optoelectronic science, engineering, and technology. SPIE Optical Engineering Press acknowledges with appreciation the authors and publishers who have given their permission to reprint material included in this volume. An earnest effort has been made to contact the copyright holders of all papers reproduced herein.

Printed in the United States of America

Introduction to the Series

There is no substitute for reading the original papers on any subject even if that subject is mature enough to be critically written up in a textbook or a monograph. Reading a well-written book only serves as a further stimulus to drive the reader to seek the original publications. The problems are, which papers and in what order?

As a serious student of a field, do you really have to search through all the material for yourself, and read the good with the not-so-good, the important with the not-so-important, and the milestone papers with the merely pedestrian offerings? The answer to all these questions is usually yes, unless the authors of the textbooks or monographs that you study have been very selective in their choices of references and bibliographic listings. Even in that all-too-rare circumstance, the reader is then faced with finding the original publications, many of which may be in obscure or not widely held journals.

From time to time and in many disparate fields, volumes appear that are collections of reprints that represent the milestone papers in the particular field. Some of these volumes have been produced for specific topics in optical science, but as yet no systematic set of volumes has been produced that covers connected areas of optical science and engineering.

The editors of each individual volume in the series have been chosen for their deep knowledge of the world literature in their fields; hence, the selection of reprints chosen for each book has been made with authority and care.

On behalf of SPIE, I thank the individual editors for their diligence, and we all hope that you, the reader, will find these volumes invaluable additions to your own working library.

Brian J. Thompson
University of Rochester

Selected Papers on

UV, VUV, and X-Ray Lasers

Contents

†Dagger indicates review paper.

Section Three

Excimer UV Lasers—Rare Gas Halide

Section Six

Gamma Ray Lasers

†Dagger indicates review paper.

Preface

This collection of papers is intended to serve as a useful resource for both the new researcher and the established worker in the field of UV, VUV, and x-ray lasers. The papers herein are believed to be among the most valuable journal articles published. They are arranged chronologically within each topic area so that the influence of progress and new results can be seen in the papers that follow.

Included among the research papers are several review papers (indicated by a dagger preceding their title in the table of contents) that give a summary of the field at various times. The beginner would do well to turn to these papers at the start of his study of the subject. A list of additional important resources in the form of books or extensive material has been placed in Appendix I; a number of the journal articles would have been reprinted here if space had been available. Appendix II is a list of the currently existing spectral lines below 4000 Å on which lasing has been observed. This list will be updated occasionally in SPIE's journal *Optical Engineering*; additions and corrections should be brought to the attention of the editors.

The papers presented here do not represent a complete and exhaustive collection. However, the several review papers, together with the additional resources of Appendix I, do contain reference to almost all the pertinent literature. The objective in selecting papers to be reproduced here was to choose the most important papers consistent with the availability of the material for reproduction. Some valuable references were omitted because the rights to reproduce could not be obtained or because the material was too extensive.

The editors would like to thank the Naval Research Laboratory for its long-term support of much of the VUV and UV laser research that contributed to early results included here, to the competence to acquire and assemble these papers, and to the assistance in finding many sources cited here. The assistance of Marcia W. Patchan in collecting many of the latest references is especially appreciated. Eve Protic's help in assembling the entire document was invaluable to the final completed volume. The assistance of several members of the IEEE LEOS Technical Committee on Gas and Short Wavelength Lasers, who reviewed the contents of the volume and made helpful suggestions, is appreciated as well.

Ronald W. Waynant
Marwood N. Ediger
FDA Center for Devices
and Radiological Health
December 1992

Section One

UV and VUV Lasers

In their classic paper describing the possibility of lasers, Schawlow and Townes point out the difficulty of building x-ray lasers. The first laser, by Maiman, was in the red, and much early laser also was confined to the red or infrared. The first UV work published was in 1963 by Heard, who also was responsible, I believe, for the famous statement that "telephone poles would lase if pumped hard enough." The 1960s were characterized by new laser lines and new sources for pumping them.

Some of the earliest ultraviolet laser work was done by Bridges and Chester and by Cheo and Cooper, who between them discovered hundreds of lines in the UV. Avco Research Laboratories picked up on Heard's nitrogen and developed a low inductance discharge that improved the peak power. Shipman refined the Avco work on the N_2 laser and showed the potential of high voltage traveling-wave pumping.

Bazhulin, Knyazev, and Petrash contributed the idea of a VUV molecular hydrogen laser, which was realized independently by Waynant and Hodgson using the Shipman concept of transverse traveling-wave pumping. Both the nitrogen and hydrogen discharge pumped lasers worked at pressures of a few tens of Torr, emitted at most a few millijoules of energy, and had such high gain that a resonant cavity was not necessary. These traveling-wave amplified spontaneous emission (ASE) devices were so difficult to excite that very little development has taken place yet. Nitrogen, of course, is easier to excite and has been developed further than hydrogen.

Reprinted with permission from *Nature*, Vol. 200(4907), p. 667 (November 16, 1963).

PHYSICS

Ultra-violet Gas Laser at Room Temperature

ULTRA-VIOLET coherent light has been generated directly at room temperature in a pulsed nitrogen-gas laser. A group of 20 strong simultaneous lines have been observed in the ultra-violet. Thirty lines have been identified. These range in the ultra-violet spectrum from 3000 Å to 4000 Å. The strongest line has been observed at 3371 Å; the strongest visible line is at 3400 Å. The output radiation is believed to be produced as the result of inversion in the triplet state of nitrogen, resulting in subsequent emission in the second positive group, $C^3\pi_u \rightarrow B^3\pi_g$. The beam has a full angular width of 1 milliradian, as measured 100 ft. from the confocal laser cavity.

The plasma is excited with a 100–150-kV pulse of sub-μsec duration. The coherent-light pulse width is as short as 20 nsec. Despite the short pulse duration the output spot of the laser is exceedingly brilliant. The output spot for the confocal Fabry–Perot cavity does not contain the usual mode structure associated with single line operation, a characteristic that is noted when several sets of transitions compete simultaneously.

Output powers of the order of 10-W peak have been obtained summing over the lines. The plasma tube has a 48-in. discharge-length. Cold cathode excitation is used. The silver-coated flint glass end mirrors are spaced at 150 cm. The radius of curvature of the mirrors is approximately 400 cm. One mirror is heavily silvered, whereas the other transmits 2·5 per cent.

The infra-red nitrogen band spectra[1], which can be produced with 40-kV. 30-amp pulses of 1 μsec duration, are not observed when high-voltage pulses are applied.

H. G. HEARD

Energy Systems Inc.,
Palo Alto, California.

1. Mathias, L., and Parker, J. T., *J. App. Phys. Letters*, 3, 16 (1963).

Reprinted with the permission of the Optical Society of America from *Applied Optics,* Vol. 4(5), pp. 573-580 (May 1965).

Visible and uv Laser Oscillation at 118 Wavelengths in Ionized Neon, Argon, Krypton, Xenon, Oxygen, and Other Gases

William B. Bridges and Arthur N. Chester

Laser oscillation has been observed at one hundred and eighteen wavelengths in ionized neon, argon, krypton, xenon, oxygen, and other gases in the spectral range 2677 Å to 7993 Å. Of these lines, ninety-six have been definitely identified, and arise from singly, doubly, and triply ionized atoms. A 2-m, pulsed dc discharge was employed. Measured and calculated wavelengths and level classifications are tabulated. The majority of the laser lines observed are shown by comparison with calculated relative line strengths to be the strong lines predicted by *L-S* coupling that possess lower levels optically connected to the ion ground state. The rules $\Delta S = 0$, $\Delta J = \Delta L = +1$ are reasonably well obeyed, although violations of *L-S* restrictions on core change and multiplicity are also observed. Evidence of upper level population by electron collision with ground-state ions is presented. The time dependence of laser output under pulsed excitation is discussed.

Introduction

Laser action in argon, krypton, and xenon ions has been previously reported for a number of wavelengths in the visible spectrum.[1,2] This paper summarizes our observations to date in these gases and in neon, in the spectral range 2600 Å to 8000 Å, and also reports laser oscillations in oxygen, nitrogen, and carbon ions which were obtained incidentally during the study. A total of one hundred and eighteen lines has been observed; of these, ninety-six have been definitely classified as arising from singly, doubly, and triply ionized species. Figure 1 gives a compact summary of these wavelengths, with the strongest and most characteristic indicated by arrowheads. The *miscellaneous* column lists carbon, nitrogen, and those lines observed that could not definitely be ascribed to the noble gases or oxygen.

Equipment

Oscillation was obtained on all the wavelengths reported in the present work with a pulsed dc discharge in a 2-m long, 3-mm diam Pyrex tube. All of the stronger lines will oscillate in much shorter tubes (10 cm or less), and continuous operation has already been reported for many of them.[3] In retrospect, it appears that such a long tube is not necessary; in fact, it is undesirable, even for spectroscopy, because the discharge is sometimes difficult to maintain at low gas pressures. A large oxide cathode was used to supply the high currents necessary for ion laser operation. A reasonably satisfactory and inexpensive source of cathodes was realized in the Type 5C22 hydrogen thyratrons, with a cathode area of about 6 cm². Operation at peak currents in excess of 300 A or at low gas pressures disintegrated the oxide coating and required the occasional replacement of a cathode (disintegrated cathode coating, incidentally, supplied the oxygen for the first observations of the oxygen ion lines). A simple capacitor of 0.25 μF to 10 μF was charged to voltages as high as 10 kV (but usually 2 kV to 4 kV) and discharged into the laser at repetition rates of 10 pps to 100 pps. Triggering was achieved with a thyratron-driven spark coil, capacitively coupled through the tube wall near the cathode. The exact conditions varied between observations (which were made over several months), but laser oscillation was usually obtainable over a wide range of discharge parameters, so that none of the parameters appears to be particularly critical; the only exceptions to this were the triply ionized lines, which required the maximum obtainable discharge current. Gas pressures over the range 200 mtorr to less than 1 mtorr were used, with the heavier gases generally favoring the lower pressures.

Four sets of dielectric coated quartz mirrors of 2-m radius were used to observe the transitions of shorter wavelengths. Their ranges and reflectivities are as follows: (a) 90% at 2600 Å and 2800 Å, 80% at 2400 Å and 2900 Å; (b) 94% at 3100 Å, 90% at 2700 Å and 3300 Å; (c) 93% at 3600 Å, 90% at 3300 Å and 3800 Å; (d) 95% at 3700 Å and 4300 Å, 90% at 3400 Å and 4400 Å. In addition, three sets of dielectric coated glass mirrors of 487-cm radius described previously[1] were used to

The authors are with Hughes Research Laboratories, Malibu, California.

Received 13 August 1964.

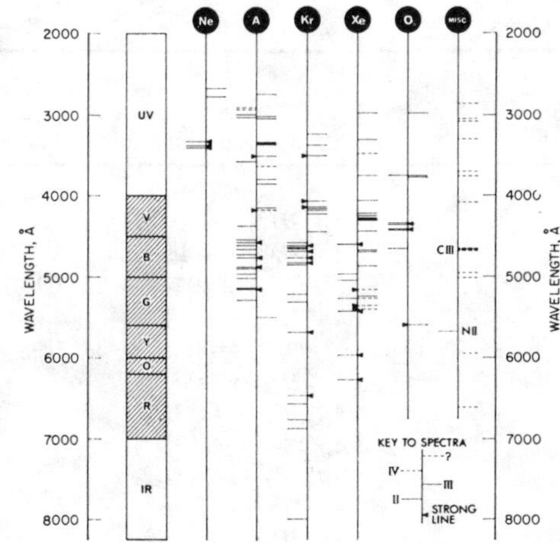

Fig. 1. Summary of ion laser lines observed in the visible and uv.

cover the longer wavelength range; we repeat their transmission properties here: (e) 1% at 4100 Å and 5000 Å, 3% at 4000 Å and 5100 Å; (f) 1% at 4900 Å and 5600 Å, 3% at 4600 Å and 6000 Å; (g) 1% at 5700 Å and 7800 Å, 3% at 5600 Å and 7900 Å. It was always possible to find a line that would oscillate with mirrors of adjacent wavelength ranges, so that mirror alignment could be *bootstrapped* through the spectrum. (In fact, in the 2-m tube the line Ar II 4880 Å would oscillate with any set of mirrors, the measured gain being >10 dB/m.)

Term Assignments

Tables I to IV give measured and calculated wavelengths (in air) and the identification of those laser lines which can confidently be assigned to noble gas ions. These tables also include the laser lines previously reported.[1,2] The strongest or most characteristic lines in each gas are designated by an asterisk (*). The term notation used is standard for *L-S* coupling.[4] In addition, Table V lists a number of oxygen ion lines that were observed and identified during the study; Table VI lists observed lines yet to be identified, along with a few identified miscellaneous lines. Wavelengths for which a probable error of 0.1Å or less is quoted were measured with a 2-m, dual-grating Bausch & Lomb spectrograph, with 4 Å/mm dispersion, and an iron arc reference spectrum. Other wavelengths were measured with a 0.5-m Jarrell-Ash spectrometer.

To assist in making term assignments, tables of allowed transitions similar to those described by Faust *et al.*[5] were computed using an IBM 7090. All possible differences were taken between known term values,[4] excluding combinations having no parity change or having $|\Delta J|>1$. These were converted to wavelengths in air using Edlén's formula[6] and arranged in order of increasing wavelength. Except for the lines Ne III 2678 Å and Kr II 4650 Å, all assignments could be made unambiguously on the basis of the measured wavelength alone. The computer program was not used in the case of neon, the identification being made instead from emission spectra reported by deBruin.[7]

Table I, Neon

Insufficient accuracy was obtained on the line Ne III 2678 Å to discriminate between the two possible assignments. The 2677.90 would seem more likely based on the empirically observed rule $\Delta J = \Delta L = +1$ (discussed later). The line Ne II 3327.17 Å was first thought to be a ghost in the Jarrell-Ash 0.5-m spectrometer, since it was much weaker and occurred in the vicinity of strong lines; such ghosts were quite common because of the lack of optics and consequent poor illumination of the grating in this instrument. Observations of threshold and pulse shape in both first and second order confirmed this as an independent laser line, despite its less likely lower level (see later discussion of mechanisms). Of the six lines tabulated, no violations of *L-S* selection rules against core or multiplicity change occur.

Table II, Argon

The line 2753.6 Å has been observed by Minnhagen and Stigmark[8] and classified as Ar III on the basis of behavior with excitation. The line does not arise from energy levels tabulated in ref. 4. The transitions responsible for Ar IV 2912.8 Å and Ar IV 2926.8 Å nicely fit the requirements for strongest laser action (shown later), namely, that $\Delta J = \Delta L = +1$ and that the lower level be optically connected to the ion ground state. Since these required the highest current available, it is quite reasonable that these were the only Ar IV lines observed. The lines 3002.5 Å and 3047 Å, although not measured sufficiently accurately to make a firm identification, are quite likely the newly classified $f \rightarrow d'$ transitions reported by Minnhagen.[9] The excitation mechanism proposed by Bennett *et al.*[10] predicts p excited levels; however, other non-p upper levels have been observed, e.g., the Ar II 3576.9 Å $d \rightarrow p$ transition, which terminates on the upper level of a strong laser line, Ar II 5145 Å. It seems likely that $p \rightarrow s$ and $p \rightarrow d$ transitions are favored not so much because the population mechanism preferentially excites p upper levels, but rather because the lower levels must have allowed transitions to the ion ground state, a p state. Other measurements of argon ion laser characteristics support this model of a three-level system, originally proposed by Gordon *et al.*[11] which will be discussed in a later section. Clearly the definite classification of these possible $f \rightarrow d'$ lines is desirable.

Table I. Neon Ion Laser Lines

Observed wavelength (Å)	Calculated wavelength (Å)	Spectrum	Identification
2678 ± 0.5	2678.64	III	$3p\ ^3P_1 \rightarrow 3s\ ^3S^\circ_1$
	2677.90	III	$3p\ ^3P_{0,2} \rightarrow 3s\ ^3S^\circ_1$
2777.5 ± 0.5	2777.65	III	$3p'\ ^3D_3 \rightarrow 3s'\ ^3D^\circ_3$
3324 ± 0.5	*3323.77	II	$3p\ ^2P^\circ_{3/2} \rightarrow 3s\ ^2P_{3/2}$
3327.5 ± 0.5	3327.17	II	$3p\ ^4D^\circ_{3/2} \rightarrow 3s\ ^4P_{3/2}$
3378.5 ± 0.5	*3378.30	II	$3p\ ^2P^\circ_{1/2} \rightarrow 3s\ ^2P_{1/2}$
3392 ± 0.5	*3392.86	II	$3p\ ^2P^\circ_{3/2} \rightarrow 3s\ ^2P_{1/2}$

Table II. Argon Ion Laser Lines

Observed wavelength (Å)	Calculated wavelength (Å)	Spectrum	Identification
2753.6 ± 0.5	—[a]	III	—
2912.8 ± 0.5	2913.00	IV	$4p\ ^2D^\circ_{5/2} \rightarrow 4s\ ^2P_{3/2}$
2926.8 ± 0.5	2926.27	IV	$4p\ ^2D^\circ_{3/2} \rightarrow 4s\ ^2P_{1/2}$
3002.5 ± 0.5	(3002.961)[b]	II	(?) $(^3P_1)\ 5f[2]^\circ_{5/2} \rightarrow 3d'\ ^2D_{3/2}$
3024 ± 0.5	3024.05	III	$4p''\ ^3D_3 \rightarrow 4s''\ ^3P^\circ_2$
3047 ± 1	(3047.053)[b]	II	(?) $(^3P_1)\ 4f[3]^\circ_{5/2} \rightarrow 3d'\ ^2F_{7/2}$
3054.8 ± 0.5	3054.84	III	$4p''\ ^3D_2 \rightarrow 4s''\ ^3P^\circ_1$
3336 ± 0.5	3336.13	III	$4p'\ ^3F_4 \rightarrow 4s'\ ^3D^\circ_3$
3344.5 ± 0.5	3344.72	III	$4p'\ ^3F_3 \rightarrow 4s'\ ^3D^\circ_2$
3358.3 ± 0.5	3358.49	III	$4p'\ ^3F_2 \rightarrow 4s'\ ^3D^\circ_1$
3511.13 ± 0.06	*3511.12	III	$4p\ ^3P_2 \rightarrow 4s\ ^3S^\circ_1$
3514.15 ± 0.06	3514.18	III	$4p\ ^3P_1 \rightarrow 4s\ ^3S^\circ_1$
3576.9 ± 0.5	(3576.611)[c]	II	$4d\ ^4F^\circ_{7/2} \rightarrow 4p\ ^4D_{5/2}$
3637.86 ± 0.04	3637.89[d]	—	—
3795.28 ± 0.06	3795.32	III	$4p''\ ^3D_3 \rightarrow 3d''\ ^3P^\circ_2$
3858.26 ± 0.06	3858.29	III	$4p''\ ^3D_2 \rightarrow 3d''\ ^3P^\circ_1$
4146.60 ± 0.04	4146.71	III	$4p'\ ^3P_2 \rightarrow 4s''\ ^3P^\circ_2$
4182.92 ± 0.06	*—[e]	—	—
4370.73 ± 0.06	4370.75	II	$4p'\ ^2D^\circ_{3/2} \rightarrow 3d\ ^2D_{3/2}$
4545.04 ± 0.1	4545.04	II	$4p\ ^2P^\circ_{3/2} \rightarrow 4s\ ^2P_{3/2}$
4579.36 ± 0.16	*4579.34	II	$4p\ ^2S^\circ_{1/2} \rightarrow 4s\ ^2P_{1/2}$
4609.57 ± 0.1	4609.55	II	$4p'\ ^2F^\circ_{7/2} \rightarrow 4s'\ ^2D_{5/2}$
4657.95 ± 0.02	4657.89	II	$4p\ ^2P^\circ_{1/2} \rightarrow 4s\ ^2P_{3/2}$
4726.89 ± 0.04	4726.85	II	$4p\ ^2D^\circ_{3/2} \rightarrow 4s\ ^2P_{3/2}$
4764.88 ± 0.04	*4764.86	II	$4p\ ^2P^\circ_{3/2} \rightarrow 4s\ ^2P_{1/2}$
4879.86 ± 0.04	*4879.86	II	$4p\ ^2D^\circ_{5/2} \rightarrow 4s\ ^2P_{3/2}$
4889.06 ± 0.06	4889.03	II	$4p\ ^2P_{1/2} \rightarrow 4s\ ^2P_{1/2}$
4965.09 ± 0.02	4965.07	II	$4p\ ^2D^\circ_{3/2} \rightarrow 4s\ ^2P_{1/2}$
5017.17 ± 0.02	5017.15	II	$4p'\ ^2F^\circ_{5/2} \rightarrow 3d\ ^2D_{3/2}$
5141.8 ± 0.5	5141.78	II	$4p'\ ^2F^\circ_{7/2} \rightarrow 3d\ ^2D_{5/2}$
5145.27 ± 0.06	*5145.30	II	$4p\ ^4D^\circ_{5/2} \rightarrow 4s\ ^2P_{3/2}$
5287 ± 1	5286.88	II	$4p\ ^4D^\circ_{3/2} \rightarrow 4s\ ^2P_{1/2}$
5502.2 ± 0.5	5502.20	III	$4p'\ ^3D_3 \rightarrow 4s''\ ^3P^\circ_2$

[a] Minnhagen and Stigmark[8] identifies as Ar III.
[b] Measured and classified by Minnhagen.[9] Racah notation used for upper level.
[c] Measured and classified by Minnhagen.[9] Note that lower level is upper level of the strong laser transition 5145.30.
[d] MIT tables[12] list as argon (3637.89).
[e] Very strong and repeatable; probably Ar III.

The line 3637.89 Å is identified by the MIT wavelength tables[12] as argon. McFarlane[13] has suggested that this line is Ar III $4p'\ ^1F_3 \rightarrow 4s'^1D^\circ_2$, by comparison of the three lines Ar III 3511 Å, Ar III 3514 Å, Ar 3637.89 Å with the isoelectronic laser lines observed by him in Cl II. This assignment seems quite reasonable, although the existence of other unclassified lines in argon discharges in the same wavelength vicinity (e.g., Table VI, 3705.2 Å) may raise some question. The line 4182.92 is included in Table II rather than under miscellaneous lines because it is so strong and repeatable that there is little doubt that it is argon. Two new Ar II lines, Ar II 4889.03 Å and Ar II 5141.78 Å, lying within the range covered by our previous investigation[1] are reported; both lines are quite weak and required higher excitation currents. We have also corrected here a transcribing error in the classification of Ar II 4879.86 Å which appeared in ref. 1 and was called to our attention by Bennett *et al.*[10]

Of the thirty classified lines listed in Table II, five have core changes, two have multiplicity changes, and two explicitly do not fit the *L-S* model.

Table III, Krypton

The only doubtful assignment is Kr II 4650.16; McFarlane has observed the line C III 4650.16, $3p^3P^\circ_1 \rightarrow 3s^3S_1$, which he reports as very persistent.[14] Since other carbon ion lines were observed in the discharge at the same time (see Table VI), it was impossible to tell whether the observed line is Kr II or C III. No doubt the source of carbon in this case was also the cathode.

Of the twenty-six lines tabulated in Table III, two have core changes and seven have multiplicity changes.

Table IV, Xenon

The most unusual feature of the xenon ion laser is the existence of four strong and characteristic lines,

Table III. Krypton Ion Laser Lines

Observed wavelength (Å)	Calculated wavelength (Å)	Spectrum	Identification
3239.2 ± 0.5	3239.51	III	$5p'' \, {}^1D_2 \rightarrow 5s'' \, {}^1P^\circ_1$
3375.0 ± 0.5	3374.96	III	$5p'' \, {}^3D_3 \rightarrow 5s'' \, {}^3P^\circ_2$
3507.42 ± 0.06	*3507.42	III	$5p \; {}^3P_2 \rightarrow 5s \; {}^3S^\circ_1$
4067.36 ± 0.06	*4067.37	III	$5p' \, {}^1F_3 \rightarrow 5s' \, {}^1D^\circ_2$
4131.38 ± 0.06	*4131.33	III	$5p \; {}^5P_2 \rightarrow 5s \; {}^3S^\circ_1$
4154.45 ± 0.04	4154.44	III	$5p' \, {}^3F_3 \rightarrow 5s' \, {}^1D^\circ_2$
4171.81 ± 0.1	4171.79	III	$5p \; {}^5P_1 \rightarrow 5s \; {}^3S^\circ_1$
4226.51 ± 0.06	4226.58	III	$5p' \, {}^3F_2 \rightarrow 4d' \, {}^3D^\circ_1$
4443.28 ± 0.04	4443.29	III	$5p' \, {}^3D_2 \rightarrow 4d' \, {}^3D^\circ_1$
4577.20 ± 0.1	4577.20	II	$5p' \, {}^2F^\circ_{7/2} \rightarrow 5s' \, {}^2D_{5/2}$
4619.17 ± 0.1	*4619.15	II	$5p \; {}^2D^\circ_{5/2} \rightarrow 5s \; {}^2P_{3/2}$
4633.92 ± 0.06	4633.86	II	$5p' \, {}^2F^\circ_{5/2} \rightarrow 5s' \, {}^2D_{3/2}$
4650.16 ± 0.1	4650.16	II[a]	$5p \; {}^2P^\circ_{1/2} \rightarrow 5s \; {}^4P_{1/2}$
4680.45 ± 0.06	*4680.41	II	$5p \; {}^2S^\circ_{1/2} \rightarrow 5s \; {}^2P_{1/2}$
4762.44 ± 0.06	*4762.43	II	$5p \; {}^2D^\circ_{3/2} \rightarrow 5s \; {}^2P_{1/2}$
4765.71 ± 0.1	4765.73	II	$5p \; {}^4D^\circ_{5/2} \rightarrow 5s \; {}^4P_{3/2}$
4825.18 ± 0.06	*4825.17	II	$5p \; {}^4S^\circ_{3/2} \rightarrow 5s \; {}^2P_{1/2}$
4846.66 ± 0.06	4846.59	II	$5p \; {}^2P^\circ_{1/2} \rightarrow 5s \; {}^2P_{3/2}$
5208.32 ± 0.04	5208.31	II	$5p \; {}^4P^\circ_{3/2} \rightarrow 5s \; {}^4P_{3/2}$
5308.68 ± 0.04	5308.65	II	$5p \; {}^4P^\circ_{5/2} \rightarrow 5s \; {}^4P_{3/2}$
5681.92 ± 0.04	*5681.88	II	$5p \; {}^4D^\circ_{5/2} \rightarrow 5s \; {}^2P_{3/2}$
6471.0 ± 0.5	*6470.88	II	$5p \; {}^4P^\circ_{5/2} \rightarrow 5s \; {}^2P_{3/2}$
6570.0 ± 0.5	6570.12	II	$5p' \, {}^2D^\circ_{5/2} \rightarrow 4d \; {}^2F_{5/2}$
6764.57 ± 0.06	6764.42	II	$5p \; {}^4P^\circ_{1/2} \rightarrow 5s \; {}^2P_{1/2}$
6870.96 ± 0.06	6870.84	II	$5p' \, {}^2F^\circ_{5/2} \rightarrow 4d \; {}^2P_{3/2}$
7993.0 ± 0.5	7993.22	II	$5p \; {}^4P^\circ_{3/2} \rightarrow 4d \; {}^4D_{1/2}$

[a] Assignment in doubt; could be C III $3p \; {}^3P^\circ_1 \rightarrow 3s \; {}^3S_1$ (4650.16 Å).

5159.04 Å, 5260.17 Å, 5352.89 Å, and 5394.59 Å (also obtained in short tubes) that are unidentified on the basis of known energy levels. One $s' \rightarrow p'$ transition is observed (Xe II 4965.08 Å) which, as in the case of Ar II 3576.9 Å, terminates on the upper level of a strong laser line, Xe II 5971.11 Å. Similarly, the transition Xe III 3306.53 Å x' (unclassified) $\rightarrow p'$ terminates on the upper level of Xe III 4285.88 Å and Xe III 4305.85 Å. Of the twenty-one classified lines listed in Table IV, one exhibits a core change, two have multiplicity changes, and three arise from partially unclassified levels.

Table V, Oxygen

All these lines were originally observed with oxygen introduced by the breakdown of cathode coating during bombardment at very low noble gas pressures. Most of these lines could be reproduced by simply letting a few tenths of mtorr of air into the discharge tube. McFarlane[14] has independently observed and identified all but O III 2984.61 Å and O II 4649.14 Å. No changes in core and only one change in multiplicity occur in the ten lines listed in Table V.

Table VI, Miscellaneous

We list here the remainder of the laser lines observed during the course of the study. It is perhaps appropriate to specify first the criteria used to determine whether a line lased or not. If the mode structure was clearly visible on a piece of white paper (smeared with vacuum grease for ultraviolet lines) at a distance of a meter or so in a dimly lighted room, or if the line appeared on a spectrographic plate with exposure times appropriate to the unquestionable laser lines (the spectrograph was 60 m from the laser and no collimating optics were used), then the line was classified as a laser line. There were no questionable cases. Even the strongest lines observed in spontaneous emission failed to meet these criteria unless they also lased.

The comments in the remarks column are for the most part self-explanatory. The identification of the lines labeled "Ne IV?" and "Xe IV?" is based on their similarity in time behavior and current dependence to

Table IV. Xenon Ion Laser Lines

Observed wavelength (Å)	Calculated wavelength (Å)	Spectrum	Identification
2983.7 ± 0.5	2983.85	III	$6p'' \, 32_1 \rightarrow 6s'' \, {}^3P^\circ_0$
3306.4 ± 0.5	3306.53	III	$nx' \, 37_{3,2} \rightarrow 6p' \, {}^3D_3$
3781.01 ± 0.1	3780.97	III	$6p \; {}^3P_2 \rightarrow 6s \; {}^3S^\circ_1$
4060.48 ± 0.06	4060.41	III	$6p'' \, 32_1 \rightarrow 5d'' \, 25^\circ_1$
4214.05 ± 0.06	4214.01	III	$6p' \, {}^3P_2 \rightarrow 5d' \, {}^3D^\circ_3$
4240.26 ± 0.1	4240.24	III	$6p' \, {}^1D_2 \rightarrow 5d'' \, 17^\circ_3$
4272.60 ± 0.06	4272.59	III	$6p' \, {}^3F_4 \rightarrow 5d' \, {}^3D^\circ_3$
4285.92 ± 0.06	4285.88	III	$6p' \, {}^3D_3 \rightarrow 6s' \, {}^1D^\circ_2$
4305.77 ± 0.06	4305.85	III	$6p' \, {}^3D_3 \rightarrow 5d' \, {}^3D^\circ_3$
4434.22 ± 0.1	4434.15	III	$6p' \, {}^3F_2 \rightarrow 5d' \, {}^3D^\circ_1$
4603.02 ± 0.04	*4603.02	II	$6p \; {}^4D^\circ_{3/2} \rightarrow 6s \; {}^4P_{3/2}$
4673.73 ± 0.06	4673.68	III	$6p' \, {}^1F_3 \rightarrow 6s' \, {}^1D^\circ_2$
4683.57 ± 0.06	4683.54	III	$6p \; {}^5P_2 \rightarrow 6s \; {}^3S^\circ_1$
4869.48 ± 0.06	4869.46	III	$6p' \, {}^3F_3 \rightarrow 5d' \, {}^3D^\circ_2$
4965.00 ± 0.06	4965.08	II	$7s' \, {}^2D_{3/2} \rightarrow 6p' \, {}^2P^\circ_{3/2}$
5044.89 ± 0.06	5044.92	II	$6p' \, {}^2P^\circ_{1/2} \rightarrow 6s' \, {}^2D_{3/2}$
5159.04 ± 0.04	*—	II(?)[a]	—
5238.89 ± 0.06	5238.93	III	$6p' \, {}^3P_2 \rightarrow 5d'' \, 13^\circ_1$
5260.17 ± 0.06	—	II(?)[a]	—
5261.5 ± 1	5261.95	II	$6p' \, {}^2D^\circ_{3/2} \rightarrow 6s' \, {}^2D^*_{3/2}$
5352.89 ± 0.06	*—	II(?)[a]	—
5394.59 ± 0.06	*—	II(?)[a]	—
5419.16 ± 0.06	*5419.15	II	$6p \; {}^4D^\circ_{5/2} \rightarrow 6s \; {}^4P_{3/2}$
5971.12 ± 0.06	*5971.11	II	$6p' \, {}^2P^\circ_{3/2} \rightarrow 6s' \, {}^2D_{3/2}$
6270.90 ± 0.1	6270.81	II	$6p' \, {}^2F^\circ_{5/2} \rightarrow 6s' \, {}^2D_{3/2}$

[a] Strong, repeatable lines; also obtained in short laser tubes at modest currents.

Table V. Oxygen Ion Laser Lines

Observed wavelength (Å)	Calculated wavelength (Å)	Spectrum	Identification
2984.3 ± 0.5	2984.61	III	$4p \; {}^5P^\circ_2 \rightarrow 3d \; {}^3D_2$
3749.49 ± 0.04	3749.49	II	$3p \; {}^4S^\circ_{3/2} \rightarrow 3s \; {}^4P_{5/2}$
3754.70 ± 0.04	3754.67	III	$3p \; {}^3D_2 \rightarrow 3s \; {}^3P^\circ_1$
3759.85 ± 0.04	3759.88	III	$3p \; {}^3D_3 \rightarrow 3s \; {}^3P^\circ_2$
4347.39 ± 0.06	*4347.38	II	$3p' \, {}^2D^\circ_{3/2} \rightarrow 3s' \, {}^2D_{3/2}$
4351.26 ± 0.04	*4351.28	II	$3p' \, {}^2D^\circ_{5/2} \rightarrow 3s' \, {}^2D_{5/2}$
4414.91 ± 0.04	*4414.28	II	$3p \; {}^2D^\circ_{5/2} \rightarrow 3s \; {}^2P_{3/2}$
4416.92 ± 0.1	*4416.97	II	$3p \; {}^2D^\circ_{3/2} \rightarrow 3s \; {}^2P_{1/2}$
4649.08 ± 0.1	4649.14	II	$3p \; {}^4D^\circ_{7/2} \rightarrow 3s \; {}^4P_{5/2}$
5592.37 ± 0.06	*5592.37	III	$3p \; {}^1P_1 \rightarrow 3s \; {}^1P^\circ_1$

Table VI. Miscellaneous Laser Lines

Measured wavelength (Å)	Discharge in which observed	Probable identification	Remarks
2866.8 ± 1	neon	Ne IV?	lases at peak of highest current pulse
3050 ± 1	krypton	—	elusive, low pressure, impurity likely
3079.7 ± 0.3	xenon	Xe IV?	lases at peak of highest current pulse
3330.8 ± 0.3	xenon	Xe IV?	lases at peak of highest current pulse
3483.6 ± 0.5	xenon	Xe	reproducible, moderately strong
3705.2 ± 0.5	argon	Ar II, III	reproducible, favors higher pressures
3760.00 ± 0.04	xenon	—	weak, favors low pressures, impurity likely
4088.90 ± 0.1	argon	Si IV (4088.86) $4p\ ^2P^\circ_{3/2} \rightarrow 4s\ ^2S_{1/2}$	weak, low pressure
4645.3 ± 0.5	argon	—	weak
4647.40 ± 0.04	air; krypton, xenon	C III (4647.40)[a] $3p\ ^3P^\circ_2 \rightarrow 3s\ ^3S_1$	
4650.40 ± 0.1	xenon	—[b]	
4954.10 ± 0.06	xenon	—	
5007.72 ± 0.04	xenon	—	
5679.6 ± 0.3	air	N II (5679.56) $3p\ ^3D_3 \rightarrow 3s\ ^3P^\circ_2$	
5852.5 ± 1	neon–argon (helium)	(?) Ne I (5852.488) $2p_1 \rightarrow 1s_2$	requires trace of Ar in He–Ne mixture
5955.73 ± 0.04	air; xenon	O?	
6577.45 ± 0.12	helium, neon	(?) O III (6577.50)[c] $3d\ ^5F_2 \rightarrow 4d\ ^3D^\circ_3$	
7503.5 ± 1	argon–neon (helium)	(?) Ar I (7503.867) $2p_1 \rightarrow 1s_2$	favors very low Ar pressures

[a] Identification is from McFarlane,[14] who reports this line as very persistent.
[b] This line is distinct from the line 4650.16 listed in Table III. [c] Identification doubtful; not reported in spontaneous emission.

the identified Ar IV lines. A number of these lines could reasonably be listed under the appropriate noble gas. The line 4088.90 Å, observed in an argon discharge, is tentatively identified as Si IV (4088.86 Å), a very strong line in spontaneous emission. Intense erosion of the discharge walls during this observation was most likely the source of silicon. We are indebted to McFarlane for the identification of C III 4647.40 Å. Carbon was not intentionally introduced into the tube, but some evidently remains in the form of unconverted cathode coating. McFarlane reports this line to be very persistent. The line measured as 4650.40 Å was definitely not the line 4650.16 Å (Kr II or C III). The one nitrogen line N II 5679.56 Å observed was obtained by letting air into the discharge tube (to reproduce the O II, O III lines). Only one set of mirrors was used, and no search was made for other N lines. McFarlane[14] reports six others at shorter wavelengths.

The lines Ne I 5852.488 Å and Ar I 7503.867 Å, although not ion lines, are nevertheless interesting, and will be discussed in another paper. We report them here because they occur under the same gas pressures and excitation conditions as the ion lines. Both are very strong lines in spontaneous emission, of course, and ordinarily they do not oscillate under neutral gas laser conditions. The presence of some argon is necessary to obtain the Ne I 5852.488 Å line, which is consistent with the mechanism originally proposed by Javan[15] for destroying neon metastables in helium–neon lasers.

Comparison with Theory

To make the regularities among the observed laser lines evident, we have organized the information contained in Tables I to IV in a number of different ways. Figures 2 and 3 show the relative occurrence of laser transitions among the various supermultiplet groups for singly and doubly ionized atoms. The number beside each indicated supermultiplet group is the number of observed laser transitions belonging to that group. The figures are drawn for argon, with the schematic level placed at the center of the levels which make up that group; it is intended to be schematic

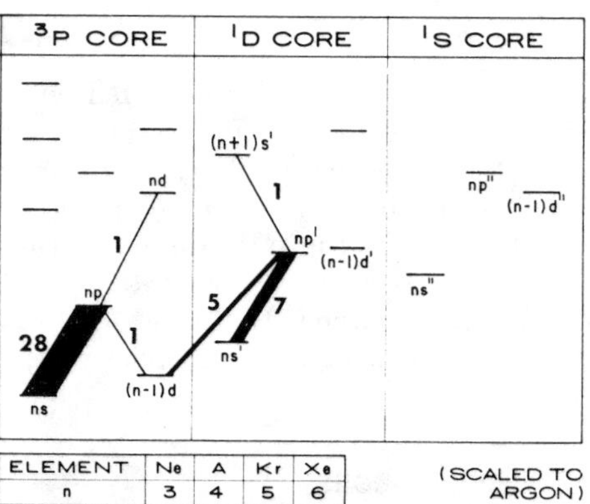

Fig. 2. Generalized energy level diagram for singly ionized noble gas atoms. The number shown beside each supermultiplet group is the number of laser transitions in that group.

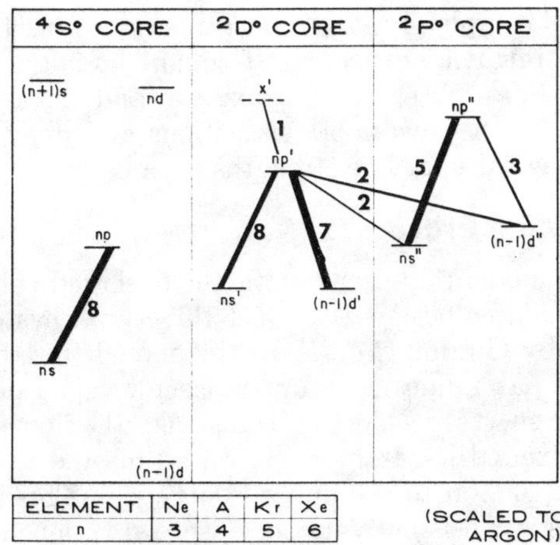

Fig. 3. Generalized energy level diagram for doubly ionized noble gas atoms. The number shown beside each supermultiplet group is the number of laser transitions in that group.

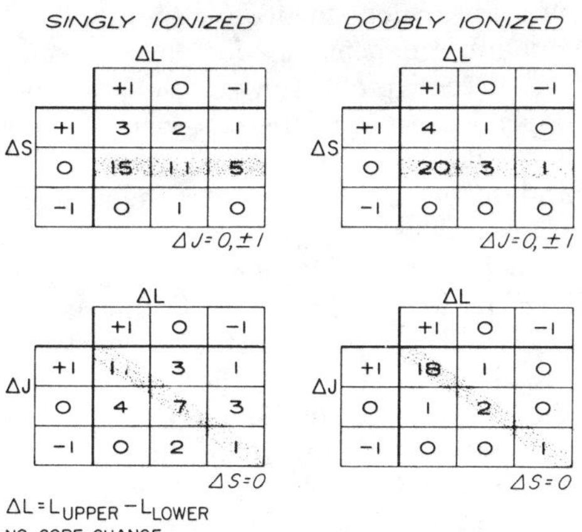

SINGLY IONIZED

ΔS \ ΔL	+1	0	−1
+1	3	2	1
0	15	11	5
−1	0	1	0

ΔJ = 0, ±1

DOUBLY IONIZED

ΔS \ ΔL	+1	0	−1
+1	4	1	0
0	20	3	1
−1	0	0	0

ΔJ = 0, ±1

ΔJ \ ΔL	+1	0	−1
+1	11	3	1
0	4	7	3
−1	0	2	1

ΔS = 0

ΔJ \ ΔL	+1	0	−1
+1	18	1	0
0	1	2	0
−1	0	0	1

ΔS = 0

$\Delta L = L_{UPPER} - L_{LOWER}$
NO CORE CHANGE

Fig. 4. Summary of ΔS, ΔL, ΔJ for observed laser transitions in neon, argon, krypton, and xenon, except those exhibiting core changes. The selection rules $\Delta S = 0$ and $\Delta J = \Delta L$ are shown shaded.

only, since in a particular case the actual levels may be reversed in order, may fall far outside the wavelength range studied, or may not even exist [e.g., $(n - 1)d$ in neon]. The lines Ar II 3002.96 Å and Ar II 3047.05 Å are not shown, since J_c-l rather than L-S coupling seems to give a more appropriate description of their upper levels.[9] The prevalence of $p \rightarrow s$ and $p \rightarrow d$ transitions is clearly seen. The only other transitions are those terminating on a (strong) laser line.

Some further regularities among the observed lines appear when they are tabulated as in Fig. 4. Here, the changes in total spin ΔS, total orbital angular momentum ΔL, and total angular momentum ΔJ are given for the observed lines (Δ = upper-lower). The shading indicates the rules $\Delta S = 0$, $\Delta J = \Delta L$, the same rules which L-S coupling predicts for the greatest spectral line strengths. There appears to be a strong tendency for $\Delta S = 0$, $\Delta J = \Delta L = +1$. (The lines involving a spin change are not shown in the $\Delta J - \Delta L$ tables because they clearly violate L-S coupling, and it would be misleading to suggest that they should follow the same rules; nevertheless, it turns out that of the twelve noble gas ion lines observed which have $\Delta S \neq 0$, eight satisfy $\Delta J = \Delta L$.) Transitions involving a core change are omitted from Fig. 4.

In view of this observed tendency for the laser transitions to satisfy the L-S selection rules, it is appropriate to compare the number of transitions observed in the noble gases with the relative line strengths obtained assuming perfect L-S coupling. A similar treatment has been given by Faust *et al.*[5] for the neutral neon atom using the appropriate J_c-l coupling scheme. However, since we are comparing here transitions observed in different gases rather than between levels of different n in the same gas, we should not expect such overwhelming agreement as in ref. 5. The relatively restricted wavelength range 2500 Å to 8000 Å also works against a complete comparison between theory and observations, since many likely transitions lie outside the range.

The line strength is proportional to the transition probability between two atomic states and is given by the matrix element of the electric dipole moment between these states. For atoms satisfying the model of L-S coupling this may be written[16]

$$S = F(S,J,L_c,l,L;S',J',L_c',l',L')s^2e^2, \qquad (1)$$

where s is the radial matrix element

$$s = (4\lambda^2 - 1)^{-1/2}\int_0^\infty rR(nl)R(n'l')\,dr. \qquad (2)$$

Here the orbital angular momentum of the core, of the jumping electron, and of the atom as a whole are denoted L_c, l, and L for the upper level, and $\lambda = \max(l,l')$. The radial matrix element may be calculated by some convenient method, such as the Coulomb approximation.[17] Since this multiplier varies from gas to gas we have chosen to tabulate only the angular factors.

The angular parts of the matrix element (the F's) are tabulated in Figs. 5 and 6 for those multiplets in which

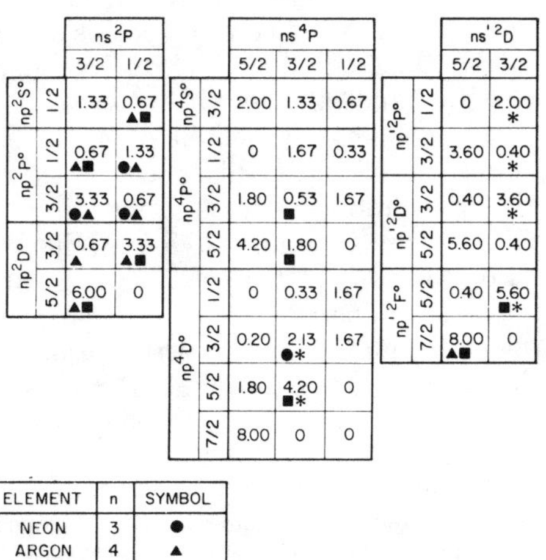

		$ns\,^2P$ 3/2	$ns\,^2P$ 1/2
$np\,^2S^o$	1/2	1.33	0.67 ▲■
$np\,^2P^o$	1/2	0.67 ▲■	1.33 ●▲
$np\,^2P^o$	3/2	3.33 ●▲	0.67 ●▲
$np\,^2D^o$	3/2	0.67 ▲	3.33 ▲■
$np\,^2D^o$	5/2	6.00 ▲■	0

		$ns\,^4P$ 5/2	$ns\,^4P$ 3/2	$ns\,^4P$ 1/2
$np\,^4S^o$	3/2	2.00	1.33	0.67
$np\,^4P^o$	1/2	0	1.67	0.33
$np\,^4P^o$	3/2	1.80	0.53 ■	1.67
$np\,^4P^o$	5/2	4.20	1.80 ■	0
$np\,^4D^o$	1/2	0	0.33	1.67
$np\,^4D^o$	3/2	0.20	2.13 ●*	1.67
$np\,^4D^o$	5/2	1.80	4.20 ■*	0
$np\,^4D^o$	7/2	8.00	0	0

		$ns'\,^2D$ 5/2	$ns'\,^2D$ 3/2
$np'\,^2P^o$	1/2	0	2.00 *
$np'\,^2P^o$	3/2	3.60	0.40 *
$np'\,^2D^o$	3/2	0.40	3.60 *
$np'\,^2D^o$	5/2	5.60	0.40
$np'\,^2F^o$	5/2	0.40	5.60 ■*
$np'\,^2F^o$	7/2	8.00 ▲■	0

ELEMENT	n	SYMBOL
NEON	3	●
ARGON	4	▲
KRYPTON	5	■
XENON	6	*

Fig. 5. Calculated relative line strengths of transitions in singly ionized noble gas atoms. The observed laser lines are indicated with the appropriate symbol in each block.

	J	$ns\,^3S^o$ 1
$np\,^3P$	0	1.00
	1	3.00 ▲
	2	5.00 ▲■*

	J	$ns'\,^3D^o$ 3	2	1	$(n-1)d'\,^3D^o$ 3	2	1
$np'\,^3P$	0	0	0	0.33	0	0	3.50
	1	0	0.75	0.25	0	7.88	2.63
	2	1.40	0.25	0.02	14.70 *	2.63	0.18
$np'\,^3D$	1	0	0.75	2.25	0	2.63	7.88
	2	0.78	3.47	0.75	2.72	12.15	2.63 ■
	3	6.22 ●	0.78	0	21.78 *	2.72	0
$np'\,^3F$	2	0.02	0.78	4.20 ▲	0.01	0.22	1.20 ■*
	3	0.78	6.22 ▲	0	0.22	1.78 *	0
	4	9.00 ▲	0	0	2.57 *	0	0

	J	$ns''\,^3P^o$ 2	1	0	$(n-1)d''\,^3P^o$ 2	1	0
$np''\,^3D$	1	0.08	1.25	1.67	0.002	0.04	0.05
	2	1.25	3.75 ▲	0	0.04	0.11 ▲	0
	3	7.00 ▲■	0	0	0.20 ▲	0	0

ELEMENT	n	SYMBOL
NEON	3	●
ARGON	4	▲
KRYPTON	5	■
XENON	6	*

Fig. 6. Calculated relative line strengths of transitions in doubly ionized noble gas atoms. The observed laser lines are indicated with the appropriate symbol in each block.

a number of laser lines were observed in the singly and doubly ionized noble gases. Since the radial matrix elements for $np \rightarrow (n-1)d$ transitions are ordinarily somewhat less than for $np \rightarrow ns$ transitions, we should not attempt to compare these two groups with each other. Comparison among transitions of a single multiplet, or in some cases a supermultiplet, should be meaningful, however.* Despite notable discrepancies (i.e., strong laser lines that do not fit the system), it is evident that there is a reasonable correlation between the predicted line strengths and the occurrence of observed laser transitions.

A number of $6s \rightarrow 5p$ lines have been observed in singly ionized krypton by Laures *et al.*;[18] however, these were obtained with 10 torr of helium in the discharge tube, which will suppress all of the ion lines reported here. The upper state excitation in their experiment was most likely by collision with the helium $2s^3S_1$ metastable, which is reasonably coincident with (and above) the observed $6s$ upper states. Enhancement by helium of Ar II laser lines having upper levels near this energy has also been observed by Gordon.[19] It is interesting that the observed $6s \rightarrow 5p$ lines also have large line strengths predicted on the basis of *L-S* coupling (Fig. 5) and, for the most part, terminate on laser levels reported here.

The observation of a number of transitions involving a core change or a change in the total spin of the atom demonstrates, of course, that *L-S* coupling cannot be trusted completely to predict transitions for which laser action might be expected. It might be noted that the other lines observed (in oxygen and nitrogen) are generally the lowest *p-s* transitions and obey the *L-S* coupling rules for line strengths even better.

Excitation Processes

The model that seems to fit the observed behavior of the ion laser best is that of a three-level system, proposed by Gordon *et al.*[11] In this model (for the singly ionized laser lines) the upper laser level is populated by two successive electron collisions; the first produces an unexcited ion from a neutral atom, and the second excites the ion to the upper laser level. This two-step process is consistent with the observed I^2 dependence of spontaneous emission from the singly ionized laser upper levels and the I^4 dependence of power output.[3] Direct excitation from the neutral atom ground state as proposed by Bennett *et al.*,[10] would presumably result in a linear dependence for spontaneous emission and a quadratic dependence for power output. If the model of successive electron collisions is correct, then an I^3 dependence should be observed for spontaneous emission of doubly ionized lines, I^4 for triply ionized lines, and so on. These measurements will be made shortly.

The depopulation of the lower laser level occurs by vacuum ultraviolet radiation to the ion ground state; this suggests a lifetime for the lower level roughly $(\lambda_{\mathrm{vac\ uv}}/\lambda_{\mathrm{laser}})^3$ shorter than the upper level. The ultraviolet radiation can be increasingly trapped as the ion density builds up, however; such an effect is exhibited in Fig. 7, which shows the time behavior of the Ar II 5145 Å-line as the pulsed current is increased

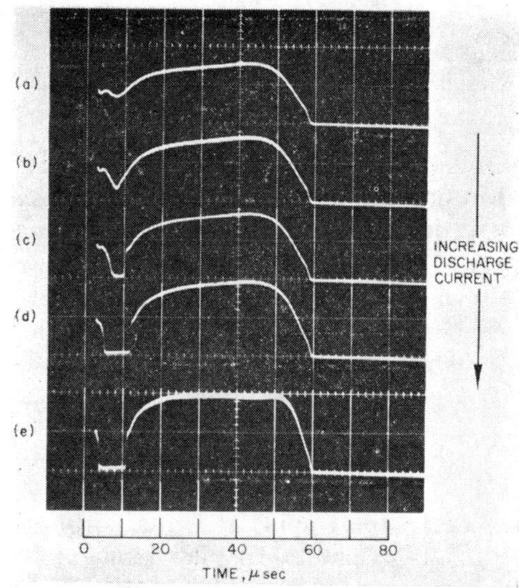

Fig. 7. Time behavior of pulsed laser oscillation at Ar II 5145 Å. A four-section artificial delay line produced a reasonably square, 60-μsec current pulse, increasing from about 30 A in (a) to about 60 A in (e). The laser tube used was 30-cm long by 2.5-mm diam, filled with argon at 60 mtorr. A 1P42 vacuum photodiode was used with a compensated connecting cable to achieve a rise time faster than 0.2 μsec. Peak laser power is about 0.5 W at 5145 Å.

* The *best* approximations to the radial matrix element implicitly use further information concerning the angular momenta (e.g., by introducing the experimentally observed energy levels of the atoms partially to repair the deficiency of the *L-S* coupling approximation). However, such approximations do not allow simple comparisons, but require both radial and angular calculations in order to compare the gases with each other.

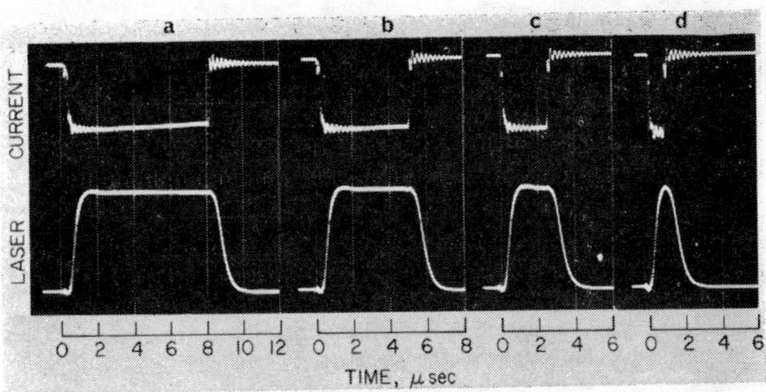

Fig. 8. Time behavior of pulsed laser oscillation at Ar II 4880 Å. A hard-tube pulser was used to produce 35-A pulses (shown negative) with pulse lengths decreasing from 8 μsec at (a) to about 1 μsec at (d). The laser tube was 1-m long and 4 mm in diameter. The laser pulse follows the current pulse within the capability of the photomultiplier channel (about 0.5-μsec rise time).

(from top to bottom). The *dead* region which develops at higher currents is a region of high attenuation (Gordon *et al.* have made actual attenuation measurements in an oscillator–amplifier configuration) presumed to be caused by radiation trapping. The return of laser oscillation following this region indicates a reduction in the trapping. One explanation for this change is that the ultraviolet line is greatly broadened by gas heating through collisions. The details of the mechanism will appear shortly.[11]

For lower currents or shorter pulse lengths this effect is not observed and the laser pulse follows the current pulse exactly, as shown in Fig. 8 for the Ar II 4880-Å line.

Comments and Future Work

Further spectroscopic work is needed to identify the remaining lines, particularly those which we have tentatively identified as $f \rightarrow d$ transitions. The more laser lines that are classified, of course, the clearer the internal mechanism and the requirements for laser action will become. It also seems reasonably evident from the relative ease with which oscillation is obtained in ions that many other materials will eventually exhibit laser action; the wealth of lines available should allow a careful choice of desirable properties for practical devices. The list of ion laser materials at present contains neon, argon, krypton, xenon, mercury,[20] chlorine,[13] iodine,[21] oxygen, nitrogen, and carbon. Some of our unidentified lines may, indeed, arise from other elements present as impurities, e.g., silicon.

Continuous operation has been reported for ten lines of Ar II (ref. 3) and has been observed on many of the stronger lines of Kr II and Xe II. A systematic study of which lines will oscillate continuously and the optimum conditions for such operation will constitute a separate investigation.

The authors gratefully acknowledge the enthusiasm and assistance of their colleagues, particularly R. B. Hodge, R. A. Hubach, F. J. McClung, and J. K. Neeland. We also thank E. I. Gordon of Bell Telephone Laboratories for many fruitful discussions, and R. A. McFarlane of Bell Telephone Laboratories and P. Laures, L. Dana, and C. Frapard of Compagnie General d'Electricité for supplying us with preprints of their papers.

References

1. W. B. Bridges, Appl. Phys. Letters **4,** 128 (1964).
2. W. B. Bridges, Proc. IEEE (c) **52,** 843 (1964).
3. E. I. Gordon, E. F. Labuda, and W. B. Bridges, Appl. Phys. Letters **4,** 178 (1964).
4. C. E. Moore, *Atomic Energy Levels*, Natl. Bur. Std. (U.S.), Circ. No. 467, Vol. I (1949), Vol. II (1952), Vol. III (1958).
5. W. L. Faust, R. A. McFarlane, C. K. N. Patel, and C. G. B. Garrett, Phys. Rev. **133,** A1476 (1964).
6. C. D. Coleman, W. R. Bozman, and W. F. Meggers, Natl. Bur. Std. (U.S.), Monograph No. 3 (1960).
7. T. L. deBruin and C. J. Bakker, Z. Physik **69,** 19 (1931); T. L. deBruin, Z. Physik **77,** 505 (1932).
8. L. Minnhagen and L. Stigmark, Arkiv Fysik **13,** 27 (1957).
9. L. Minnhagen, Arkiv Fysik **25,** 203 (1963).
10. W. R. Bennett, Jr., J. W. Knutson, Jr., G. N. Mercer, and J. L. Detch, Appl. Phys. Letters **4,** 180 (1964).
11. E. I. Gordon, E. F. Labuda, and R. C. Miller, to be published.
12. G. R. Harrison, *MIT Wavelength Tables* (Wiley, New York, 1939).
13. R. A. McFarlane, Appl. Opt. **3,** 1196 (1964).
14. R. A. McFarlane, Appl. Phys. Letters **5,** 91 (1964).
15. A. Javan, Phys. Rev. Letters **3,** 87 (1959).
16. E. U. Condon and G. H. Shortley, *Theory of Atomic Spectra* (Cambridge Univ. Press, New York, 1953), pp. 237–245. Also see ref. 17.
17. D. R. Bates and A. Damgaard, Phil. Trans. Roy. Soc. London **A242,** 101 (1949).
18. P. Laures, L. Dana, and C. Frapard, Compt. Rend. **258,** 6363 (1964).
19. E. I. Gordon, private communication.
20. W. E. Bell, Appl. Phys. Letters **4,** 34 (1964).
21. G. R. Fowles and R. C. Jensen, Proc. IEEE **(c) 52,** 851 (1964).

Note Added in Proof. C. J. Humphreys of the Naval Ordnance Laboratory, Corona, California (private communication) has observed the Xe lines 5394.59, 5352.88, 5159.06 (Table IV) and 5007.78, 4954.16 (Table VI) in spontaneous emission; they were unidentified and were therefore not reported in his monographs [J. Res. Natl. Bur. Std. (U. S.) **16,** 639 (1936), **22,** 19 (1939)]. His observations and further work in our laboratory indicate that these are strong Xe III lines. More accurate wavelength measurements of uv laser lines by P. K. Cheo and H. G. Cooper of Bell Telephone Laboratories, Whippany, New Jersey (private communication) rule out the *f-d* assignments for the two Ar lines (Table II); they obtain 3002.64 ± 0.06 and 3047.13 ± 0.06, the latter being a strong O line present as an impurity. Cheo and Cooper also point out that the first line in Table V should be O III 2983.78 $3p^1D_2 \rightarrow 3s^1p^0{}_1$, a much more reasonable assignment. It is also possible that this strong O line is responsible for the first Xe entry in Table IV; this line appeared to favor high Xe pressures, however, so that the assignment given could still be correct.

Reprinted with permission from *Journal of Applied Physics*, Vol. 36(6), pp. 1862-1865 (June 1965). ©1965 American Institute of Physics.

Ultraviolet Ion Laser Transitions between 2300 and 4000 Å

P. K. Cheo and H. G. Cooper
Bell Telephone Laboratories, Inc., Whippany, New Jersey
(Received 1 December 1964)

Fifty-five ultraviolet laser transitions in the wavelength region 2300–4000 Å have been observed from the ions of N, O, Ne, Ar, Kr, and Xe. The electron transition is $p \rightarrow s$ for all identified lines, with the exception of two xenon transitions which are $p \rightarrow d$. Threshold currents for laser action in a 4-mm-bore tube were in the ranges 10–100, 100–500, and >400 A, respectively, for singly, doubly, and triply ionized atoms. Current saturation and current quenching of laser action both were observed. Results with two tube bores show that the usual inverse relation between gain and tube diameter does not hold in ultraviolet ion lasers.

INTRODUCTION

LASER oscillations have been reported previously in ionized atoms of the noble[1–4] and atmospheric[2,5] gases in the 2600–8000 Å wavelength range. Most of these lines were identified with known term values of singly or doubly ionized species and only a very few were assigned to triply ionized atoms or not identified. We have observed 55 ultraviolet laser transitions in ionized N, O, Ne, Ar, Kr, and Xe in the 2300–4000 Å spectral range using pulse excitation. Approximately two-thirds of these lines have been identified, nearly all of which are assigned to doubly or triply ionized species. The unidentified transitions are believed to originate largely from terms not yet determined in atoms ionized triply or higher.

An interesting feature of the observed ion laser transitions is that the upper level belongs to the p electron configuration. The excitation mechanism that provides an excess population at an upper p level is not fully understood. We have studied the current dependence of the laser output power with the hope of isolating the dominant mechanism. The results were insufficient to yield a definite conclusion, but they did provide useful information concerning current threshold, current saturation, and effects of tube bore.

[1] W. B. Bridges, Appl. Phys. Letters 4, 128 (1964).
[2] W. B. Bridges and A. N. Chester, Appl. Opt. (to be published).
[3] P. Laures, L. Dana, and C. Frapard, Compt. Rend. **258**, 6363 (1964).
[4] P. Laures, L. Dana, and C. Frapard, Compt. Rend. **259**, 745 (1964).
[5] R. A. McFarlane, Appl. Phys. Letters **5**, 91 (1964).

EXPERIMENTAL PROCEDURE

Pulse currents in the range 5 to 2000 A and 10^{-3} to 10^{-5} sec in duration at voltages of 3 to 12 kV were generated by discharging a 0.65-μF capacitor through the laser tube with a thyratron. Current was measured with a copper cup covered with a nichrome disk[6] that had been calibrated against a coaxial resistive load. Cold electrodes on side tubes were employed and breakdown was initiated with an rf trigger. The laser tube bore was 4 mm and discharge length 1 m. A tube of the same length but with 2-mm bore also was investigated. The only laser transitions observed with the latter tube were those from singly ionized atoms. The resonant cavity was near confocal, consisting of aluminized mirrors having a 1-m radius of curvature and separated by 1.3 m. Gas pressure for optimum laser intensity, p_{opt}, ranged from 1 to 100 μ, depending on gas type and wavelength. For the noble gases, p_{opt} decreased monotonically with increasing atomic number. In general, shorter laser wavelengths were observed with higher

[6] H. M. Brady (private communication).

discharge currents and to a lesser extent with larger E/p values, were E is the axial electric field. Pressure was monitored with Pirani and thermocouple gauges calibrated for each gas type studied.

All wavelengths were determined spectrographically with a $1\frac{1}{2}$-m long Bausch & Lomb instrument. Spectrograms were restricted to second order in the 2300–3700 Å range by a Corning 7-54 filter and first order was used above 3700 Å. The nominal accuracy was ± 0.06 Å in the second order achieved by interpolation with an iron spectrum. For some of the identified lines, the discrepancy between observed and calculated wavelengths exceeds this error due to line broadening or insufficient number of iron lines nearby, but the assignments still are believed to be correct. To ascertain stimulated rather than spontaneous emission, two exposures were made on the same film, one with a high Q cavity and the other with the cavity resonance spoiled by tilting the mirror nearest to the spectrograph. The exposure time of the first spectra was about one-tenth of the latter. A number of spontaneous lines appeared on the spectrographic plate, even though the mirror transmission was $\sim 0.1\%$. A second check for stimulated emission was made with a monochromator, photomultiplier, and oscilloscope. Rotation of the mirror caused the laser lines to disappear on the scope display. A number of weaker laser transitions observed with the spectrograph, but not detected with the photomultiplier, are not reported.

Measurements of the current dependence of the laser output power were made for a number of the lines. The discharge current was varied by adding a resistor in series with the laser tube, while keeping E/p constant for a given sequence of measurements.

TABLE I. Observed ultraviolet laser transitions (identified).

Species	λ_{obs}[a]	λ_{calc}[a]	Assignment
N III	3367.32	3367.34	$3p^4P_{5/2}\ -3s^4P_{5/2}{}^0$
N IV	3478.70	3478.67	$3p^3P_2{}^0\ -3s^3S_1$
N IV	3483.02	3482.96	$3p^3P_1{}^0\ -3s^3S_1$
O III	2983.86	2983.78	$3p^1D_2\ -3s^1P_1{}^0$
O III	3047.15	3047.13	$3p^3P_2\ -3s^3P_2{}^0$
O IV	3063.46	3063.45	$3p^2P_{3/2}{}^0-3s^2S_{1/2}$
O IV	3381.34	3381.33[b]	$3p^4D_{3/2}\ -3s^4P_{1/2}{}^0$
O IV	3385.54	3385.54	$3p^4D_{7/2}\ -3s^4P_{5/2}{}^0$
O II	3749.50	3749.49	$3p^4S_{3/2}{}^0-3s^4P_{5/2}$
O III	3754.43	3754.67	$3p^3D_2\ -3s^3P_1{}^0$
O III	3759.82	3759.88	$3p^3D_3\ -3s^3P_2{}^0$
Ne IV[c]	2358.00	2357.96	$3p^4D_{7/2}{}^0-3s^4P_{5/2}$
Ne III	2677.98	2677.90	$3p^3P_{2,0}\ -3s^3S_1{}^0$
Ne III	2678.68	2678.64	$3p^3P_1\ -3s^3S_1{}^0$
Ne II	3319.84	3319.75	$3p'^2P_{1/2}{}^0-3s'^2D_{3/2}$
Ne II	3323.79	3323.77	$3p^2P_{3/2}{}^0-3s^2P_{3/2}$
Ne II	3345.50	3345.52	$3p'^2P_{3/2}{}^0-3s'^2D_{5/2}$
Ne II	3378.33	3378.30	$3p^2P_{1/2}{}^0-3s^2P_{1/2}$
Ne II	3392.86	3392.86	$3p^2P_{3/2}{}^0-3s^2P_{1/2}$
Ar IV	2624.90	2624.93	$4p'^2D_{5/2}{}^0-4s'^2D_{5/2}$
Ar III	2884.24	2884.16	$4p'^3P_2\ -4s'^3D_3{}^0$
Ar IV	2912.92	2913.00	$4p^2D_{5/2}{}^0-4s^2P_{3/2}$
Ar IV	2926.24	2926.27	$4p^2D_{3/2}{}^0-4s^2P_{1/2}$
Ar III	3336.21	3336.13	$4p'^3F_4\ -4s'^3D_3{}^0$
Ar III	3344.79	3344.72	$4p'^3F_3\ -4s'^3D_2{}^0$
Ar III	3358.52	3358.49	$4p'^3F_2\ -4s'^3D_1{}^0$
Ar III	3511.21	3511.12	$4p^3P_2\ -4s^3S_1{}^0$
Kr III	3124.43	3124.38	$5p'^1D_2\ -5s'^1D_2{}^0$
Kr III	3239.43	3239.51	$5p''^1D_2\ -5s''^1P_1{}^0$
Kr III	3507.36	3507.42	$5p^3P_2\ -5s^3S_1{}^0$
Kr III	3564.20	3564.23	$5p^3P_1\ -5s^3S_1{}^0$
Xe III	3246.94	3246.84	$6p''^3D_3\ -5d'^3D_3{}^0$
Xe III	3454.23	3454.24	$6p'^1D_2\ -6s'^1D_2{}^0$
Xe III	3745.73	3745.71	$6p'^1D_2\ -5d'^1D_2{}^0$
Xe III	3780.99	3780.97	$6p^3P_2\ -6s^3S_1{}^0$

[a] Wavelength in air.
[b] Another possible assignment is $3p^4D_{5/2} \rightarrow 3s^4P_{3/2}{}^0$ with $\lambda_{calc}=3381.28$ Å.
[c] See Ref. 9.

TABLE II. Observed ultraviolet laser transitions (unidentified).

Species	λ_{obs}[a]	Species	λ_{obs}[a]
Ne III[b]	2473.50	Xe	2691.82
Ne	2866.88	Xe (II[e])	3079.78
Ar III[c]	2753.91	Xe (III or IV[e])	3305.92
Ar	3002.64[d]	Xe	3330.82
Ar	3637.96	Xe	3350.04
Kr	2649.41	Xe	3482.96
Kr	2664.50	Xe	3645.46
Kr	2741.51	Xe	3669.20
Kr	3049.74	Xe	3803.27
Xe	2477.18	Xe	3972.93

[a] Wavelength in air.
[b] See Ref. 15.
[c] See Ref. 10.
[d] The wavelength discrepancy between this and the 3002.96 Å $f \rightarrow d$ transition in Ar II identified by Minnhagen (see Ref. 11) indicates that they are two distinct lines.
[e] See Ref. 12.

RESULTS

A. Observed Laser Transitions

Thirty-five identified and 20 unidentified laser transitions are listed in Tables I and II for the six gases studied. These two tables are intended to include only the highest gain lines in the 2300–4000 Å region. Many additional ultraviolet laser frequencies are expected with dielectrically coated mirrors. Particularly good

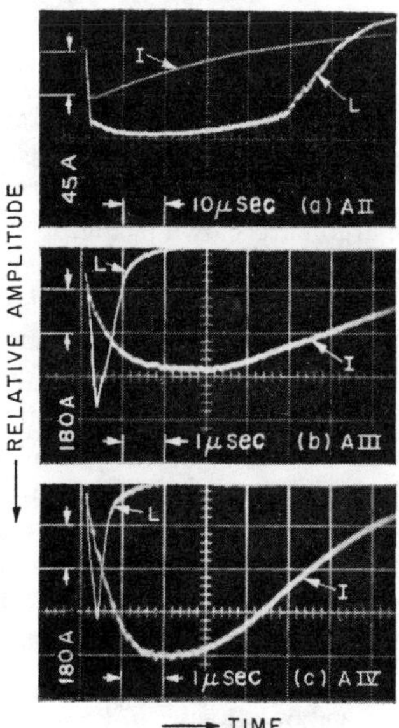

FIG. 1. Laser intensity L and discharge current I vs time for the lines (a) 4880 Å of Ar II, (b) 3511 Å of Ar III, and (c) 2913 Å of Ar IV.

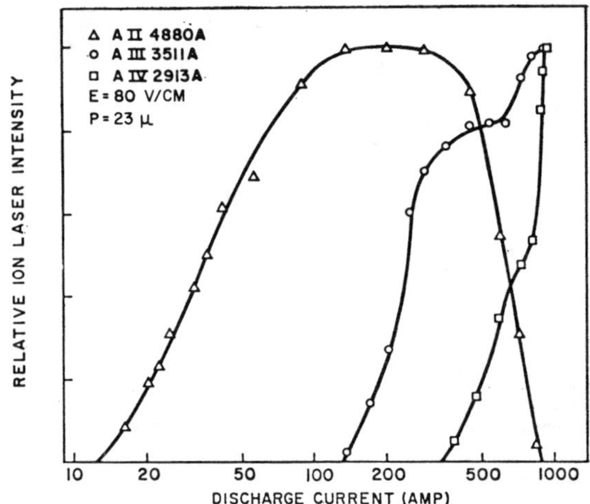

FIG. 2. Peak laser intensity vs peak current for the argon ion laser.

candidates are those lines, not reported here, which appeared only on the spectrographic plates but were not strong enough to be detected with the monochromator and photomultiplier. To expedite identification, allowed transitions between known term levels[7] were computed and refractive index corrections[8] made. The large number of unidentified transitions are attributed primarily to incomplete data on term values, especially for noble gases ionized triply or higher. A search of recent literature on ion spectra yielded identification of only one additional line, the 2358 Å of Ne IV.[9] The work of Minnhagen and Stigmark[10] and Minnhagen[11,12] allowed determination of the ion type for the 2754-Å Ar, 3080-Å Xe, and 3306-Å Xe lines. The substantial list of unidentified lines in Table II suggests that the laser will provide a means for detecting ultraviolet spectra not observable by conventional techniques.

B. Time and Current Dependence

No time delay between the current and laser pulses was detected. Typical current and laser pulse waveforms for lines from the three different stages of ionization in argon are shown in Fig. 1. Similar behavior was observed for the three ion types in other gases. The laser pulse width was ~ 0.1 to 1 μsec for all lines from doubly and triply ionized atoms that were studied. Ultraviolet laser pulses from singly ionized species generally were longer in duration, as long as the current was maintained above the threshold value. This suggests possible operation of the ultraviolet laser in the cw mode[13] for the singly ionized species, but not for the doubly and triply ionized atoms. Another effect observed with singly ionized laser transitions is a double peak over a limited current range near threshold. Similar phenomena have been reported by others.[2,14] Current saturation and quenching, as discussed in the next paragraph, almost certainly are involved here, in addition to transients resulting from gas breakdown and current buildup.

Dependence of the peak laser intensity on peak current is illustrated in Fig. 2 for lines from Ar II, Ar III, and Ar IV and in Fig. 3 for lines from Ne II, Ne III, and Ne IV. The axial electric field E and gas pressure p were held constant while taking the data shown in Figs. 2 and 3. When E/p was varied over a wide range, the threshold currents were modified slightly but the general shapes of the three curves were essentially unchanged. As expected,[10] the current required for laser threshold increased with the degree of ionization. It may be noted that the Ar II line saturates before the Ar III line reaches the threshold current. It is totally quenched when the Ar III radiation saturates and the Ar IV line is near threshold. Quenching did not occur for the Ne II line, presumably because of insufficient current, but saturation is apparent from the inflections on both the Ne II and Ne III curves. A general feature of both the Ar II and Ne II curves, but less evident in the latter, is that the laser intensity increases very nearly as the first power of the current during much of the rise prior to saturation. Near threshold, the laser intensity increases at a much faster rate with current for the singly ionized species. For lines from the doubly and triply ionized atoms, however, the shape depends strongly on experimental conditions and no simple power law dependence of the laser intensity with current was obtained. One reason for the lack of a well-defined power law relationship is that all three ion species are present simultaneously at large discharge currents. Consequently, the simple differential equations, which are assumed for the presence of only one ion type, no longer hold and a more complex model of coupled equations presumably is required.

DISCUSSION

The 3479 and 3483 Å lines of N IV constitute a $^3P_{1,2} \rightarrow {}^3S_1$ doublet. This doublet is characteristic of the dominant $p \rightarrow s$ electron configuration change in ion lasers and appears also in Ne III, Ar III,[2] and Kr III. Two assignments are possible for the 3381-Å O IV line; the $^4D_{3/2} \rightarrow {}^4P_{1/2}{}^0$ transition agrees slightly better with the observed wavelength. The five oxygen lines below 3400 Å are all extremely strong. They were observed in noble gas discharges, especially Xe, due to evolution of oxygen gas from the laser tube at high pump power levels. The shortest wavelength obtained in all of the gases studied was the 2358-Å Ne IV line. Similar current threshold behavior was observed for both the 2473- and 2358-Å Ne lines, which indicates that the 2473-Å transition also may be fron Ne IV. Previously de Bruin[15] assigned 2473 Å to $a^3D_3 \rightarrow 3p^3P_2$ in Ne III, but the a^3D_3 term level is in doubt since it is not listed

[7] C. E. Moore, Natl. Bur. Stds, Circ. No. 467 Vols. I, II, and III.
[8] Table of Wave Numbers, Vol. I, Natl. Bur. Stds. (1960).
[9] S. Goldsmith and A. S. Kaufman, Proc. Phys. Soc. (London) **81**, 544 (1963).
[10] L. Minnhagen and L. Stigmark, Arkiv Fysik **13**, 27 (1957).
[11] L. Minnhagen, Arkiv Fysik **25**, 203 (1964).
[12] L. Minnhagen (private communication).
[13] E. I. Gordon, E. F. Labuda, and W. B. Bridges, Appl. Phys. Letters **4**, 178 (1964).
[14] R. A. McFarlane, Appl. Opt. **3**, 1196 (1964).
[15] T. de Bruin, Z. Physik **77**, 507 (1932).

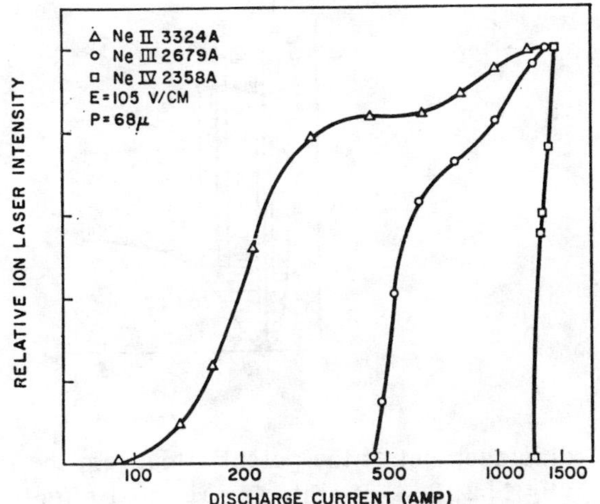

FIG. 3. Peak laser intensity vs peak current for the neon ion laser.

by Moore.[7] Four lines of Ne III, in the range 2590–2610 Å, appeared on the spectrograms, but further experiments established that the emission was spontaneous. Because of the low working pressure of the Xe pulsed ion laser, $\sim 1\,\mu$, laser lines from contaminants often were observed. Special precautions, therefore, were taken to insure that the laser oscillations were not from impurities. A check made on each of the Xe laser transitions was to introduce into the laser tube xenon and atmospheric gases alternately. It is believed that all of the unidentified Xe lines listed in Table II are accurately labeled, although they are the ones most in doubt with regard to the parent gas.

All lines identified in Table I originate from a p level and, with the exception of two Xe lines, terminate at an s level consistent with the $p \rightarrow s$ selection rule suggested by McFarlane.[5] A possible reason for $p \rightarrow d$ Xe transitions is that the $5d$ levels lie relatively lower, compared to the lowest lying $6s$ states, than do the analogous s and d levels in the other gases. Bridges and Chester,[2] using dielectrically coated mirrors, also observed $p \rightarrow d$ ultraviolet lines in argon. They did not appear in our work, apparently because of insufficient gain with aluminum mirrors.

The result that the electron configuration of the upper level is p for all identified lines is rather curious. For all species except N IV, the ground state is p also. Consequently, the lower laser state, s or d, is optically connected to the ground state, a situation favorable for maintaining an inverted population. For the N IV ion laser, and C III[14] also, the electron configuration is s for both the ground state and lower laser level, seemingly unfavorable for a $p \rightarrow s$ laser transition. However, depopulation of the lower laser s level may be achieved in this case by decaying to a lower lying p state. The mechanism for production of an excess population at the upper p level still requires further explanation.

Two possible excitation mechanisms for the production of an upper laser p level, proposed previously,[16,17] are (a) "direct," as described by the one-step process,

$$A^{m+}(p)+e \rightarrow [A^{(m+1)+}(p)]^{*}+2e \qquad (1)$$

and (b) "stepwise," consisting of the two successive interactions

$$A^{m+}+e \rightarrow A^{(m+1)+}+2e \qquad (2a)$$

and

$$A^{(m+1)+}+e \rightarrow [A^{(m+1)+}(p)]^{*}+e, \qquad (2b)$$

where $m=0$, 1, and 2 for laser action in ions II, III, and IV, respectively. Attempts to determine conclusively from our data which of the two mechanisms is dominant in the pulsed ultraviolet ion laser were unsuccessful. The nearly linear dependence of laser power on current for A II and Ne II, that was noted above, is consistent with the direct process. For the III and IV species, however, the results are not conclusive because of the added complexities introduced at high pump power levels by the simultaneous presence of species of various stages of ionization.

Current saturation and quenching of laser lines from the singly ionized atoms could arise from total ionization of the gas with subsequent depletion by excitation to doubly or triply ionized types. A simple calculation shows that the gas in our tube would be fully ionized at the pressure and current values used in our experiments. Saturation of the Ar II line intensity of Fig. 2 occurs near the threshold current for the Ar III line and the Ar III curve has a break near the Ar IV threshold, all consistent with the picture of saturation by total ionization. Similar behavior is exhibited by Ne in Fig. 3.

Dependence of the gain G on tube bore d appears to be considerably different in the ultraviolet laser from that in other gas lasers. The relation $G \propto 1/d$, found in the He–Ne laser, did not hold for the 2- and 4-mm bore tubes used in our experiments. Preliminary measurements showed that laser action could be obtained only for singly ionized atoms with the 2-mm tube, even though the mirrors and cavity dimensions were the same as with the larger tube bore. The average current density was comparable in both sizes of tubes at the same E/p ratio. A possible explanation for this tube bore effect in the ultraviolet region is that ion recombination at the walls, enhanced by the low pressures used in these lasers, precludes creation of a sufficient density of doubly and triply ionized species in the discharge for onset of stimulated emission.

ACKNOWLEDGMENTS

The authors are indebted to R. A. McFarlane for valuable discussions, to A. M. Wittenberg for his advice and contributions in connection with the spectroscopic analysis, to W. B. Bridges for a preprint of his paper, and to Professor L. Minnhagen of Lund Institute of Technology for unpublished results on spectra identification. We are grateful to B. R. Rapacki and H. A. Youngman for technical assistance.

[16] W. R. Bennett, Jr., J. W. Knutson, Jr., G. N. Mercer, and J. L. Detch, Appl. Phys. Letters 4, 180 (1964).

[17] R. C. Miller, E. I. Gordon, and E. F. Labuda, paper presented at the Conference on Electron Device Research, Cornell University, June, 1964.

ON THE POSSIBILITY OF STIMULATED EMISSION IN THE FAR ULTRAVIOLET

P. A. BAZHULIN, I. N. KNYAZEV and G. G. PETRASH

Lebedev Institute of Physics of the Academy of Sciences of the U.S.S.R.

Submitted to JETP editor December 7, 1964

J. Exptl. Theoret. Phys. (U.S.S.R.) 48, 975-976 (March, 1965)

WE have previously observed [1] stimulated emission in the infrared using the H_2 molecule, and we have discussed the possible mechanisms responsible for the inversion, based on the Franck-Condon principle. The experimental results, as well as similar data on other molecules [2], in general bear out this mechanism very well. On this basis one may find many molecular transitions for which population inversion is possible under certain excitation conditions. In the present note we wish to deal only with the possibility of obtaining stimulated emission in transitions between resonance and ground electronic states of molecules. This possibility is of particular interest. The mechanism considered is similar to one described in [1] and is in principle applicable to many molecules having similar dispositions of their potential energy curves.

As an example we choose the simplest molecule, H_2. As upper and lower states of the active medium we consider the electronic state $2p\pi\,{}^1\Pi_u$ and the ground state $1s\sigma^{2}\,{}'\Sigma_g^+$, which will be designated in what follows by C and X respectively (one might equally well choose the $2p\sigma\,{}'\Sigma_u^+$ state as the upper level). The dipole transition C ⟷ X corresponds to the Werner bands observed in the far ultraviolet [3]. The potential curve for the ground state is calculated in [4]. A Morse function gives a sufficiently good approximation to the lowest vibrational levels of the C state. Both of these curves are shown in the figure.

Because of the large magnitude of the vibrational quanta, only the lowest vibrational level $v'' = 0$ in the ground state is occupied at room temperature. During the initial moments of discharge, excitation of the vibrational levels of the states X and C occurs primarily via electron collisions with molecules in the ground state. Since the Franck-Condon principle applies to electron excitation [5], it is seen that, owing to the

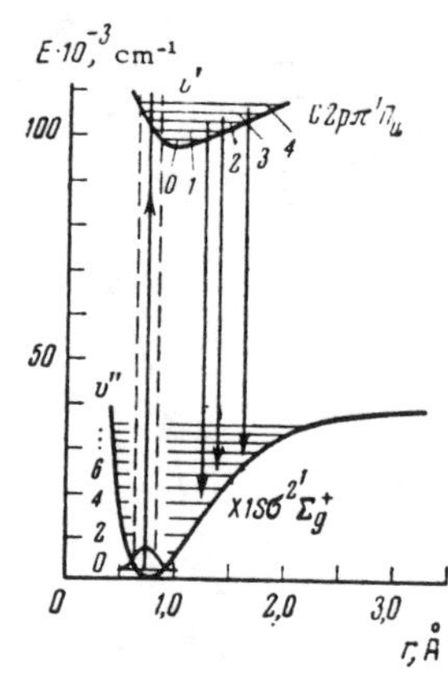

displacement of the potential curves, the levels $v' = 1, 2, 3, 4$ of state C are most effectively populated. Transitions from these levels to ground state $v'' = 0$ have relatively large probability. From these levels there are, besides transitions to the ground state $v'' = 0$, rather large probabilities for making transitions to the upper vibrational levels of the ground state (the Werner bands seen in emission). Population of these latter vibrational levels by electron collisions from the ground state $v'' = 0$ is very unlikely, since no change in the electronic state is involved. Thus during the initial moments of the discharge one should observe inversion between the states C ($v' = 1$-4) and X ($v'' > 1$). For sufficiently intense excitation one should obtain stimulated emission on several bands of the Werner system in the wavelength region from 1100 Å (1-1) to 1250 Å (4-8). The corresponding transitions are shown by arrows in the figure. Owing to the symmetry of the H_2 molecule, radiative transitions between vibrational levels are forbidden and the lifetime of the upper vibrational levels of the ground state is determined by collisions with other molecules. In practical cases it will obviously be very long. This will make continuous operation of the laser impossible and will limit the obtainable pulse repetition rate.

This mechanism has two special features which make its implementation particularly attractive. In the first place it allows one to obtain laser action in the so far unattainable region of very short wavelengths. Secondly, such a procedure for obtaining stimulated emission should give a very large efficiency and very high peak powers. This is related to the fact that, in distinction to the known gaseous systems, we are here using transitions between the lowest resonance levels which, because of the large cross-section for the electron excitation, are populated much more strongly than the others. Moreover, the use of transitions terminating in the ground electronic state is very efficient, since in this case a very large fraction of the energy given to the active medium by fast electrons is converted to quanta of stimulated emission.

[1] Bazhulin, Knyazev, and Petrash, JETP 47, 1590 (1964), Soviet Phys. JETP 20, 1068 (1965).

[2] L. E. S. Mathias, and J. T. Parker, Appl. Phys. Lett. 3, 16 (1963). H. G. Heard, Nature 200, 667 (1963). L. E. S. Mathias and J. T. Parker, Phys. Lett. 7, 194 (1963).

[3] G. R. Jeppersen, Phys. Rev. 44 165 (1933). O. W. Richardson, Molecular Hydrogen and its Spectrum, Yale University Press, London, 1934.

[4] J. Tobias and J. T. Vanderslice, J. Chem. Phys. 35, 1852 (1961).

[5] G. Herzberg, Spectra and Structure of Diatomic Molecules, (Russ. Transl.) IIL, 1949. H. S. W. Massey and E. H. S. Burhop, Electronic and Ionic Impact Phenomena, Oxford, 1952.

Translated by J. A. Armstrong
138

Reprinted with the permission of the American Institute of Physics from *Applied Physics Letters,* Vol. 10(1), pp. 3-4 (January 1, 1967).

TRAVELING WAVE EXCITATION OF HIGH POWER GAS LASERS*

John D. Shipman, Jr.
Plasma Physics Division
Naval Research Laboratory
Washington, D. C.
(Received 4 November 1966)

Experiments are described in which nitrogen and neon lasers are excited by a wave of current excitation which effectively travels from one end of the laser to the other with its velocity matching that of the stimulated emission. This type of excitation is accomplished with a low-impedance flat-plate Blumlein pulse generator. The power output in the direction of the wave of excitation is at least ten times that in the other direction. A 2.5-MW pulse of about 4-nsec duration is obtained with nitrogen and a 190-kW pulse of about 1.5 nsec with neon.

Leonard and Gerry[1,2] demonstrated that the pulsed N_2 laser (3371 Å), discovered by Heard,[3] could be operated with an output power of several hundred kilowatts in a pulse lasting ~20 nsec. The pulse duration is necessarily short because of the metastability of the lower laser level, which obviates inversion for times greater than the radiative lifetime of the upper laser level. The transient inverted population arises because the excitation rate of the upper level by electron impact is large compared to the excitation rate of the lower level when the electron temperature exceeds a few electron volts.

Leonard and Gerry anticipated that megawatt power levels could be achieved with a faster (low inductance) discharge. This was confirmed at NRL with a flat-plate Blumlein pulse line circuit (Fig. 1) which generates 500 kA in 4 nsec (when the solid dielectric switches are fired simultaneously). The generator and plasma load geometry results in a subnanohenry load inductance which together with subnanohenry switching[4] achieves $dI/dt \sim 10^{14}$ A/sec. As in the Leonard-Gerry experiments, the current flows perpendicular to the axis of the discharge tube. With a lasing volume 0.3-cm high, 10-cm wide, 183-cm long and initial pressure of 30 torr, a 1.2-MW pulse of radiation having a width at half power of 5 nsec was observed at each end.[5] The pulse duration is small compared to the radiative lifetime because of the rapid cooling of the electron gas by ionization when the electron density approaches $\sim 10^{15}$ electrons/cm^3 (ref. 6).

Because of their high gain, lasers of this type do not require feedback from mirrors. In such a super-radiant mode of operation spontaneous emission noise is amplified everywhere throughout the discharge.

Experimentally, it was found that there was no measurable time delay (<1 nsec) between the current and light output. This result led to an experiment (suggested in principal by G. Gould) designed to improve the coherence and make the output unidirectional. The lasing plasma was inverted by a traveling wave of excitation current starting from one end and progressing toward the other or output end with a velocity equal to the velocity of light. Thus a plasma element at the starting end would emit spontaneous radiation isotropically but subsequent elements would be preferentially stimulated to emit toward the output end by the amplified emission of the first element before having time to emit very much spontaneous radiation in other directions. This traveling excitation wave was generated by firing the solid dielectric switches sequentially at precise intervals. As a result, the electromagnetic wave in the Blumlein line crosses the discharge tube at an angle such that the excitation (inversion) current wave travels down the tube with a phase velocity equal to the velocity of light.

This traveling wave excitation mode of operation

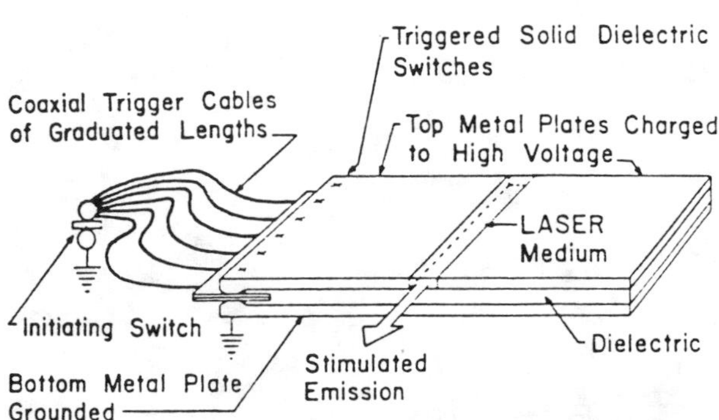

Fig. 1. Schematic of the Blumlein pulse generator with flat-plate transmission lines used to pump molecular nitrogen and neon lasers. Bottom plate: 183-cm wide and 366-cm long. Dielectric: 0.15-cm thick Mylar submerged in water. Generator impedance: 0.3 Ω; voltage applied to top plates: ~75 kV.

*Sponsored by Advanced Research Projects Agency.

resulted in a 10:1 ratio in the power emitted from the two ends. A peak power of 2.5 MW with a pulse width of 4 nsec was observed with electrical parameters similar to those employed for the super-radiant mode (see Fig. 1).

The experiment was repeated with neon since it also has self-terminating characteristics similar to molecular nitrogen.[7,8] A power of 190 kW was observed at 5401 Å, again with at least a 10:1 power ratio from the two ends. However, in this case the pulse width at half amplitude was only 1.5 nsec, (Fig. 2), which was somewhat lengthened by the resolution of the detection system.[5] Here again it is expected that the short pulse is due to cooling of the electron gas. (Higher temperatures are needed for neon, relative to N_2, because of the higher excitation energy.)

The traveling wave excitation method reported here could also be accomplished in alternative ways, i.e., by feeding the discharge tube with a large number of coaxial cables of properly graduated lengths in parallel, fed through a single switch.

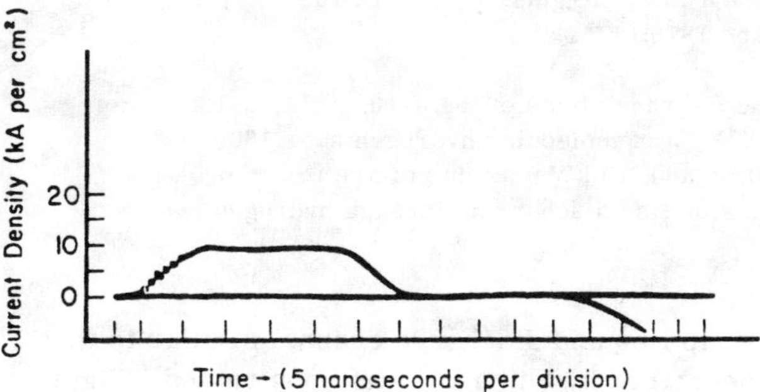

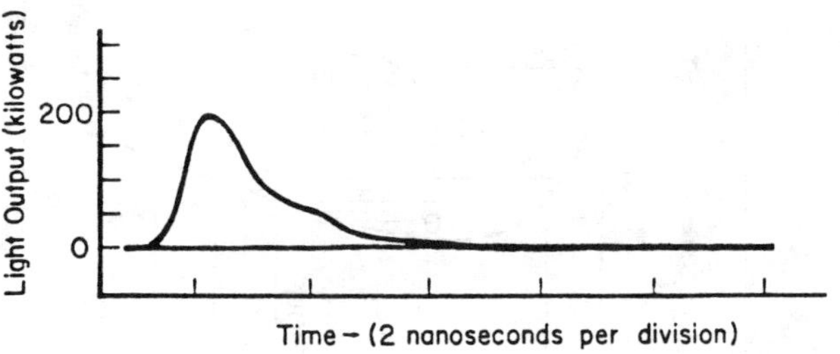

Fig. 2. Current density and light output (5401 Å) pulses on a neon laser shot.

[1] D. A. Leonard, *Appl. Phys. Letters* **7,** 4 (1965).

[2] E. T. Gerry, *Appl. Phys. Letters* **7,** 6 (1965).

[3] H. G. Heard, *Nature* **200,** 667 (1963).

[4] Following J. C. Martin, A.W.R.E. Aldermaston, England, (private communication), six solid dielectric switches were employed. The jitter is no more than a few-tenths nanosecond.

[5] The detecting equipment consisted of Optics Technology neutral-density filters, a TRG 105 B phototube housing with a calibrated ITT phototube having S-5 response, coaxial transmission line, and a Tektronix 519 oscilloscope. Overall response of the system to a delta function input was about 0.5 nsec at half amplitude.

[6] J. D. Shipman and A. C. Kolb, *IEEE J. Quantum Electronics* **QE-2,** 298 (1966).

[7] D. A. Leonard, R. A. Neal, and E. T. Gerry, *Appl. Phys. Letters* **7,** 175 (1965).

[8] D. M. Clunie, R. S. A. Thorn, and K. E. Trezise, *Phys. Letters* **14,** 28 (1965).

Reprinted with permission from *Physical Review Letters,* Vol. 25(8), pp. 494-497 (August 24, 1970). ©(1970 American Physical Society.

VACUUM-ULTRAVIOLET LASER ACTION OBSERVED IN THE LYMAN BANDS OF MOLECULAR HYDROGEN

R. T. Hodgson
IBM Thomas J. Watson Research Center, Yorktown Heights, New York 10598
(Received 5 June 1970)

Stimulated emission has been observed in the P-branch lines of the 3-10, 4-11, 5-12, 6-13, and 7-13 Lyman bands (v'-v'', $B\,^1\Sigma_u^+ \rightarrow X\,^1\Sigma_g^+$) of molecular hydrogen near 1600 Å. Light pulses of approximately 2 nsec duration and 1.5 kW maximum power were produced using a Blumlein parallel-plate transmission line discharging through hydrogen gas at pressures between 20 and 150 Torr.

The first observation of stimulated emission in the vacuum-ultraviolet spectral range is reported in this Letter. The wavelengths of the laser light near 1600 Å are the shortest wavelengths achieved to this time, and the pulse power and energies available should make this type of laser useful for studying the interaction of high-energy photons with matter.

The lasing action is produced by inverting the population of an excited electronic state of a diatomic molecule with respect to the high vibrational-rotational levels of the ground state. This general scheme was in fact proposed by Bazhulin, Knyazev, and Petrash[1] in 1965. Figure 1 shows an energy-level diagram of the hydrogen molecule. A fast electrical discharge in hydrogen gas was used to excite the $B\,^1\Sigma_u^+$ vibrational-rotational levels. The dashed vertical lines represent the electron-collision-induced transitions between the zeroth vibrational level of the $X^1\Sigma_g^+$ ground state and the v' levels of the upper states. Since the high-energy electron collisions populate the electronic states much more efficiently than the upper vibrational levels of the ground state, inversion densities and gain were high enough to produce stimulated emission without mirrors in P-branch lines of the 3-10, 4-11, 5-12, 6-13, and 7-13 Lyman bands ($B\,^1\Sigma_u^+ \rightarrow X^1\Sigma_g^+$). These transitions are indicated by the solid vertical lines in Fig. 1.

In order to generate the high-power fast-pulsed electrical discharge needed to produce a large inversion and high gain at vacuum-ultraviolet wavelengths, a Blumlein circuit parallel-plate strip line and discharge channel similar to that described by Shipman[2] was constructed. Figure

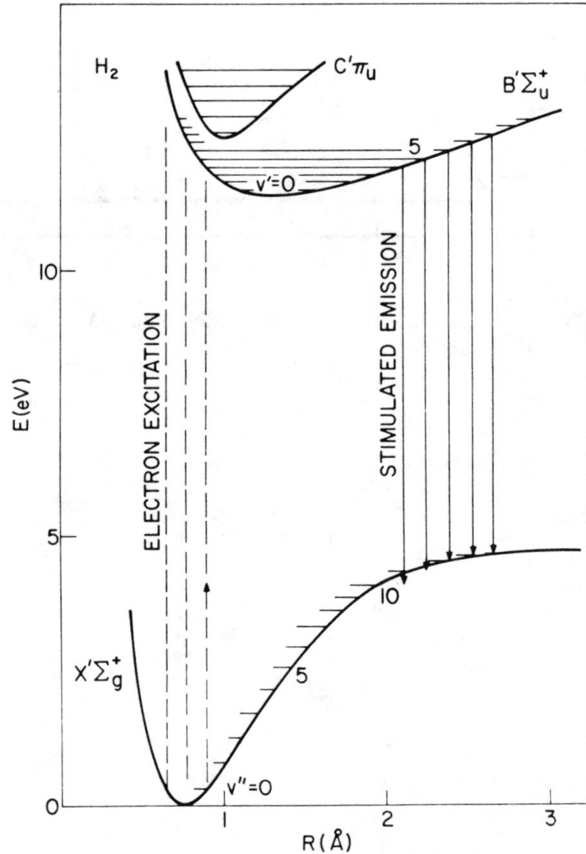

FIG. 1. Potential energy curves for the $X\,^1\Sigma_g^+$, $B\,^1\Sigma_u^+$, and $C\,^1\Pi_u$ states of the hydrogen molecule. The potential energy in electron volts is plotted as a function of internuclear distance in Å.

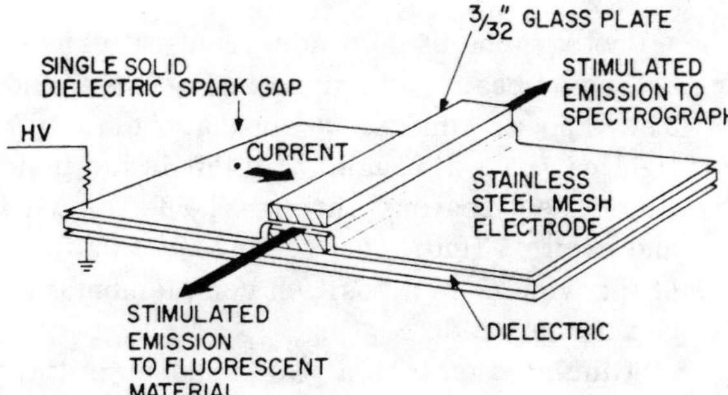

FIG. 2. Blumlein circuit flat-plate transmission line and discharge-tube arrangement. Electrode dimensions are 40×80 cm^2. 0.040-cm Mylar was used as the dielectric to hold off 30 kV dc. Torr-seal epoxy was used to cement the 23-cm mesh between the two glass plates forming the sides of the discharge channel.

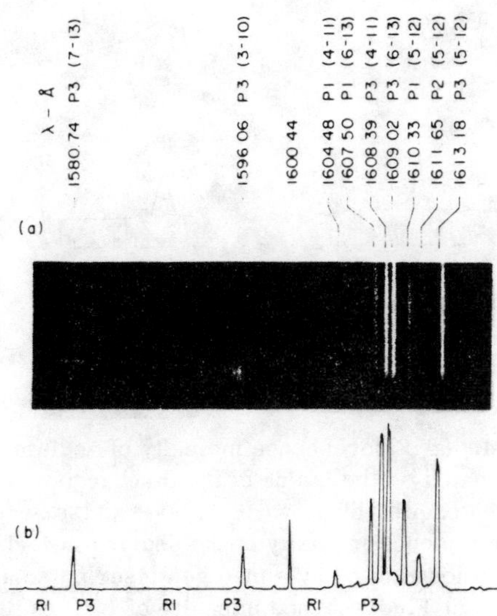

FIG. 3. (a) Stimulated emission spectra showing some of the P-branch lines of the 3-10, 4-11, 5-12, 6-13, and 7-13 Lyman bands ($B\,^1\Sigma_u^+ \rightarrow X\,^1\Sigma_g^+$) of molecular hydrogen. (b) Microdensitometer trace of this spectrum. Some of the missing $R(1)$ line positions are also noted along with their corresponding $P(3)$ lines.

2 shows the experimental arrangement. The discharge was contained in a $120\times1.2\times0.04$ cm^3 channel made by sandwiching the high-voltage current-carrying electrodes between two long thin glass plates. Stainless-steel mesh was used for these electrodes so that the cut edges would provide lines of sharp metal points in the gas to make the breakdown and discharge more uniform.[3] A single mechanically ruptured solid dielectric switch was used to initiate the discharge.

Figure 3(a) shows a spectrum of the laser emission taken in the first order using a McPherson model 225 1-m normal-incidence vacuum monochromator equipped with a film holder and a 1200-line/mm grating. Wavelengths were measured absolutely to within 1 Å using a zero-order mark and the monochromator setting. Relative wavelengths agreed to within the 0.05-Å measuring error with Herzberg and Howe's[4] measured wavelengths for the assigned lines.

The stimulated emission spectrum shown in Fig. 3(a) and the microdensitometer trace shown in Fig. 3(b) can be explained using Spindler's[5] published Franck-Condon factors for the molecular hydrogen Lyman band intensities in conjunction with the intensity and selection rules for $J' \rightarrow J''$ transitions within each band.[6]

The probability of exciting a hydrogen molecule in the $v''=0$ level of the $X\,^1\Sigma_g^+$ ground state to a given vibrational level v' of the $B\,^1\Sigma_u^+$ state is proportional to the v'-0 Franck-Condon factors. These factors increase[5] with v' until they reach 0.074 at $v'=7$. For each v', the probability of exciting the various rotational levels can be predicted since excitations of odd-to-odd rotational levels are forbidden by symmetry.[6] Thus, since two-thirds of the hydrogen molecules are in the $X\,^1\Sigma_g^+$, $v''=0, J''=1$ orthohydrogen state[6] in equilibrium at room temperature, we would expect most electron collisions to populate the v', $J'=2$, and $J'=0$ levels of the higher-energy electronic states. If the electron-collision transition probabilities are determined by the same statistical weight arguments as the optical transition probabilities, the ratio[6] would in fact be 2:1. Now, the $J'=2$ levels can only radiate to the $J''=3$ or the $J''=1$ levels of the various ground electronic vibrational states [the $P(3)$ and $R(1)$ lines of the bands]. The branching ratio[6] for emission from these lines is determined by the statistical weights of the rotational levels and is numerically equal to 1.5:1 for the $P(3)$ and $R(1)$ lines. In fact, only a single $P(3)$ line from each $J'=2$ level is seen, and that line belongs to the band with the largest Franck-Condon factor. This perturbation of emission intensities from that seen in spontaneous emission proves that the $J'=2$ states have been stimulated to emit in the $P(3)$ lines. With highest discharge powers, sufficient population builds up in the $J'=0$ level of the $v'=5$ and 6 vibrational states and the $J'=1$, $v'=5$ level that emission is stimulated in the $P(1)$ lines of the 5-12 and 6-13 bands, and in the $P(2)$ line of the 5-12 band.

Estimates of laser energy, pulse length, and power were made by converting the ultraviolet pulses to visible radiation using fluorescent scintillators coated on the inside of the discharge

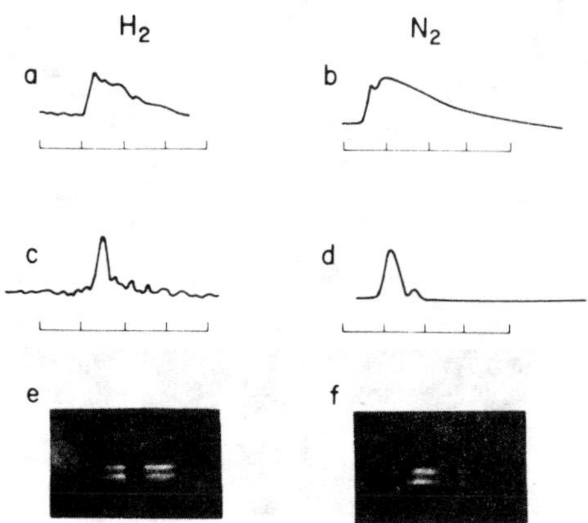

FIG. 4. (a) Fluorescence intensity of sodium salicylate coated on the inside of the discharge tube window when excited by a hydrogen laser pulse at ~1600 Å. (b) Fluorescence intensity of the sodium salicylate coating when excited by a nitrogen laser pulse at 3371 Å. (c) Fluorescence intensity of BBO excited by a hydrogen laser pulse. (d) Intensity of N_2 laser pulse measured directly as a function of time with no fluorescent window in place. The measuring apparatus risetime is less than $\frac{1}{2}$ nsec. (e) Fluorescence pattern observed with H_2 laser pulse. (f) Fluorescence pattern observed with N_2 laser pulse. The 3371-Å light can pass through a gap in the scintillator coated on the inside of the window, through the Pyrex, and excite the scintillator coated on the outside. Horizontal scale: 1 div = 5 nsec.

tube window. Figures 4(a) and 4(b) can be used to compare the response of sodium salicylate excited by the ~1600-Å light pulse [4(a)] with that excited by a 3371-Å light pulse from a molecular nitrogen laser [4(b)]. A trace of the intensity of fluorescence excited in BBO (2, 5-dibiphenylyloxazole) reproduced in Fig. 4(c) shows the hydrogen laser pulse shape more clearly than the sodium salicylate because its fluorescence lifetime is of the order of 1 nsec.[7] The nitrogen laser pulse height and width were directly measured with a biplanar photodiode, and intensity-versus-time traces such as that given in Fig. 4(d) were used to calibrate the response of the sodium salicylate to fast light pulses of 3371-Å wavelength. Since the quantum efficiency of the scintillator is constant[8] between 400 and 3400 Å, the total energy contained in the hydrogen laser pulse could be estimated to be about 3 μJ.

The pulse energies plotted as a function of hydrogen pressure showed a broad maximum near 60 Torr. At about 20 and 150 Torr, the fluorescent intensity dropped below the detection level of our TRG 105B, *S*-20 response, biplanar photodiode, and Tektronix 119 oscilloscope combination.

The pulse length was estimated to be ~2 nsec by measuring the risetime of the sodium salicylate fluorescence. These estimated values of energy and pulse length correspond to a power of 1.5 kW.

Photographs of the fluorescent patterns of the two laser beams are given in Figs. 4(e) and 4(f). They appear similar except that the 3371-Å laser light can pass through a gap left in the inside fluorescent coating, through the Pyrex window, and excite a fluoresent strip coated on the outside of the window in a position complementary to the gap in the inside coating.

Stimulated emission was proposed initially by Bazhulin, Knyazev, and Petrash[1] on the $C\,^1\Pi_u \to X\,^1\Sigma_g^+$ Werner band transitions in hydrogen in the 1100-Å region. They pointed out that a diatomic molecular system with the minimum of the ground-state- and excited-state-potential curves at different internuclear distances implied large probabilities of emission to high vibrational levels. Ali and Kolb[9] simulated the discharge parameters of Shipman's[2] device with a computer, and predicted lasing action on the Werner bands in the region 1025-1239 Å. They did not treat the excitation of the $B\,^1\Sigma_u^+$ in detail. In fact, the Franck-Condon factors for the Lyman bands are lower than for the Werner bands. In the discharge, however, more electrons have sufficient energy to excite the $B\,^1\Sigma_u^+$, $v' = 1$-7 vibrational levels than the $C\,^1\Pi_u$ state since the threshold energies are smaller. This would explain the fact that no stimulated emission on the Werner bands is seen, and that the power output in the $v' = 7$ band is less than the $v' = 5$ band.

Stimulating discussions with P. P. Sorokin and J. A. Armstrong, and the technical assistance of S. Baliozian are gratefully acknowledged.

[1]P. A. Bazhulin, I. N. Knyazev, and G. G. Petrash, Zh. Eksp. Teor. Fiz. 48, 975 (1965) [Sov. Phys.—JETP 21, 649 (1965)].

[2]J. D. Shipman, Jr., Appl. Phys. Lett. 10, 3 (1967).

[3]H. W. Furamoto and H. L. Ceccon, Appl. Opt. 8, 1613 (1969).

[4]G. Herzberg and L. L. Howe, Can. J. Phys. 37, 636 (1959).

[5]R. J. Spindler, AVSSD 0287-66-RR, NASA Report No. CR 72107.

[6]G. Herzberg, *Molecular Spectra and Molecular Structure: I. Spectra of Diatomic Molecules* (Van Nostrand, Princeton, N. J., 1950).

[7]I. B. Berlman, *Handbook of Fluorescence Spectra of Aromatic Molecules* (Academic, New York, 1965).

[8]J. A. R. Samson, *Techniques of Vacuum Ultraviolet Spectroscopy* (Wiley, New York, 1967).

[9]A. W. Ali and A. C. Kolb, Appl. Phys. Lett. 13, 259 (1968).

[10]H. S. W. Massey, *Electronic and Ionic Impact Phenomena* (Clarendon, Oxford, England, 1969).

Reprinted with the permission of the American Institute of Physics from *Applied Physics Letters,* Vol. 17(9), pp. 383-384 (November 1, 1970).

VACUUM ULTRAVIOLET LASER EMISSION FROM MOLECULAR HYDROGEN

R. W. Waynant, * J. D. Shipman, Jr., R. C. Elton, and A. W. Ali

Naval Research Laboratory, Washington, D. C. 20390
(Received 19 August 1970; in final form 15 September 1970)

Using a short-risetime traveling-wave discharge system, lasing has been produced in molecular hydrogen in the 1600-Å region and confirmed by direct observation of extensive amplification in the direction of travel. Pulsewidths and powers on the order of 1 nsec and hundreds of kilowatts, respectively, are observed. The ten H_2 lines resolved extend from 1567 to 1613 Å in the Lyman band. The laser lines originate from transitions between the vibrational levels of the state $B(2p\sigma\,^1\Sigma_u^+)$ and the higher vibrational levels of the ground state $X(1s\,^1\Sigma_g^+)$.

The possibility of obtaining laser action in the vacuum ultraviolet spectral region by electron impact excitation of molecular hydrogen was originally suggested by Bazhulin *et al.*[1] Ali and Kolb[2] followed with a rate equation analysis showing the feasibility of a device and predicting the laser power to be generated in the Werner band (1000–1200 Å). Ali[3] later extended the predictions to the Lyman band (1400-1650 Å). While attempting to realize these predictions in the laboratory, we have observed laser lines in the Lyman band between 1567 and 1613 Å.

Using a smaller version of the parallel-plate Blumlein system built by Shipman[4] to produce lasing in N_2, excitation currents of hundreds of kiloamperes (and voltages of about 100 kV) are generated with a risetime of 2.5 nsec. The gas is confined to a channel between the electrodes measuring 0.3 cm×1.2 cm×100 cm long. The solid dielectric switches used to short circuit one transmission line are fired sequentially to prodce an excitation wave (transverse to the channel length) that reaches the gas initially at one end and subsequently travels in the longitudinal direction at the velocity of light in the gas. In this manner the gas is excited at the speed of light by the traveling wave and the inverted population is swept out by stimulation at the same rate, so that the light output is primarily from one end. Since the gain is high, no optical cavity is required for lasing to take place. A lithium fluoride window is used between the laser itself and the necessary vacuum transmission path required for propagation of the short wavelengths to the detection devices.

Identification of the emission from H_2 was done with a McPherson model 225 1-m scanning spectrometer equipped with a Bausch and Lomb 600 grooves/mm grating blazed at 1500 Å and a film cassette. Kodak 101-01 film was used and 800-Å regions of the spectrum were investigated on each exposure. The most pronounced lines observed on the film were in the region of 1600 Å. Accurate (±0.2 Å) wavelength identification was accomplished by comparing the second order of these lines with Hg and He glow discharge spectra (in air). One shot from the laser system with N_2 fill gas provided additional calibration lines near 3000 Å and also a reference for estimation of the power, after the peak power of the N_2 system was measured at 1 MW. Taking into account the relative sensitivity of the system for shorter wavelengths and then comparing the exposure of H_2 with the exposure of N_2, an order-of-magnitude estimate of the power is about 100 kW.

All other line and continuum features between 1000 and 3600 Å were absent on the spectrogram, even when as many as ten shots were superimposed, whereas other workers[5,6] with fast-discharge hydrogen lamps have observed a continuum of emission peaked at 2200 Å with an intensity of about 30% of the radiation at 1600 Å. We view the absence of this continuum—even when the main peak is overexposed—as an indication of amplification of the observed lines. (The decrease in instrument sensitivity from 1600 to 2200 Å is not expected to be greater than a factor of 2.)

Additional confirmation of lasing is obtained by observation of the increased emission from one end of the laser with respect to the other as a consequence of the traveling-wave excitation. Using an ITT 4018 photodiode with a liumogen phosphor (decay time ≈2.5 nsec[7]), time-resolved observations were made at each end of the laser. The amplitude of the 1600-Å pulse of ~1-nsec duration recorded at the end toward which the excitation proceeded was greater than ten times that at the opposite end. Since only amplification could produce this effect, amplification by stimulated emission is confirmed.

At room temperature, the hydrogen molecule is mainly in the zeroth vibrational level of the ground electronic state. The molecules are distributed among the rotation levels, $J''=0, 1, 2,$ and 3 of this vibrational level in the percentages 13, 66, 12, and 8%, respectively. By far the largest percentage is in the $J''=1$ rotational state. Electron collisions with molecules in this state will lead to population of even-numbered rotational

TABLE I. Wavelengths and vibrational transitions for H_2 lines observed. Relative film densities on a scale of 1 to 10 are indicated in parentheses.

Transition $B(v') - X(v'')$	wavelength Å $P(1)$	$P(3)$	$R(1)$
2-9	1571.8 (1)	...	...
3-10	1591.5 (4)	1596.1 (8)	...
4-11	1604.7 (6)	1608.6 (10)	...
5-12	...	1613.3 (10)	...
6-13	1607.4 (8)	...	...
7-13	...	1580.5 (6)	1577.1 (5)
8-14	1567.3 (1)	...	...

levels in the B state ($J' = 0, 2$) with $J' = 2$ preferred. Frank-Condon factors calculated by Spindler[8] suggest that the $v' = 2$ to 11 levels of the B state will be preferentially populated. Since the upper vibrational levels on the ground state are essentially empty, stimulated emission can occur between $B(v' = 2$ to $11;\ J' = 0, 2)$ and $X(v'' = 9$ to $14;\ J'' = 1, 3)$.

Table I lists the observed lines. Comparison of these lines with the identification of Herzberg and Howe[9] suggests the transitions that are involved. Transitions between $(J', J'') = (0, 1)$, $(2, 3)$, and $(2, 1)$ are designated $P(1)$, $P(3)$, and $R(1)$, respectively.

The technical assistance of L. J. Verna is gratefully acknowledged.

Note added September 11, 1970. Since submission of this paper, the obtainment of a hydrogen spectrum similar to that reported here has been reported in Phys. Rev. Letters 25, 494 (1970). Although Blumlein circuitry is used in both experiments, in our opinion the traveling-wave excitation method described here provides the convincing proof of lasing.

*The material in this article will be used in part towards a Ph. D. thesis at Catholic University of America.

[1]P. A. Bazhulin, I. N. Knyazev, and G. G. Petrash, Soviet Phys. JETP 21, 649 (1965).

[2]A. W. Ali and A. C. Kolb, Appl. Phys. Letters 13, 259 (1968).

[3]A. W. Ali, the Catholic University of America, Dept. of Space Science and Applied Physics Report No. 68-009, 1968 (unpublished).

[4]J. D. Shipman, Jr., Appl. Phys. Letters 10, 3 (1967).

[5]S. I. Levikov and L. P. Shishatskaya, Opt. Spektrosc. 11, 371 (1961).

[6]I. B. Berlman, O. J. Stiengraber, and M. J. Benson, Rev. Sci. Instr. 39, 54 (1968).

[7]R. W. Waynant and R. C. Elton, Proceedings of the International Conference on Organic Scintillators and Liquid Scintillation Counting, 1970 (unpublished).

[8]R. J. Spindler, Jr., J. Quant. Spectry. Radiative Transfer 9, 597 (1969).

[9]G. Herzberg and L. L. Howe, Can. J. Phys. 37, 636 (1959).

Reprinted with permission from *Journal of Chemical Physics,* Vol. 55(11), pp. 5378-5379 (December 1, 1971).

Vacuum-Ultraviolet Lasing Action Observed in CO: 1800–2000 Å

R. T. Hodgson

IBM Watson Research Center, Yorktown Heights, New York 10598

(Received 9 August 1971)

Stimulated emission has been observed on Q and R branch lines of five bands of the CO fourth positive group ($A\,^1\Pi \rightarrow X\,^1\Sigma^+$) in the wavelength range 1810–1970 Å. Superradiant 1.5-nsec 6-W pulses were produced using a Blumlein circuit parallel plate transmission line discharging through a tube containing carbon monoxide at 60 torr pressure. The order of appearance of the lines and their relative intensities are in agreement with a simple model. The model supposes single electron impact excitation of the ground state molecules to the lowest energy excited singlet state, followed by stimulated emission of those transitions of highest gain to the initially unpopulated, highly excited vibrational levels of the ground electronic state. No stimulated emission from highly perturbed rotational levels is seen.

Observations of lasing action in the vacuum-uv spectral region have recently been published.[1–3] This communication reports observations of stimulated emission from transitions in carbon monoxide similar to the molecular hydrogen transitions reported in Refs. 1 and 2.

High-energy electrons have a higher probability of exciting a ground state diatomic molecule to excited electronic states than to the lower energy excited vibrational levels of the ground electronic state. For a short time at the beginning of an electrical discharge in a diatomic molecular gas, then, it is possible to have a population inversion between these molecular states. If sufficient population can be built up in an excited electronic state in a time comparable to the spontaneous emission time (spontaneous emission populates the excited vibrational levels of the ground state and reduces the inversion), the gain may be high enough that the spontaneous emission is highly amplified in the length of the discharge, and a "superradiant" pulse of largely stimulated emission can be produced. No mirrors need be used in such a case. This is an advantage since these types of transitions normally lie in the far-uv spectral region where mirror reflectivities are low.

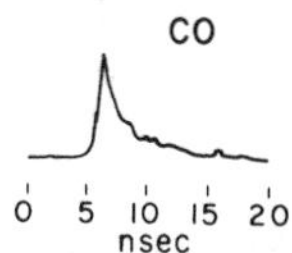

Fig. 1. Oscillogram of stimulated emission power as a function of time from a discharge in 60 torr carbon monoxide. The measuring system used an ITT biplanar photodiode with a sapphire window and an S-20 response photocathode, and a Tektronix 519 oscilloscope.

A Blumlein circuit, parallel-plate transmission line similar to that described in Ref. 1 was used to discharge a very high current into a $0.05\times1.2\times120$ cm^3 tube containing flowing Matheson research grade carbon monoxide at 60 torr pressure. A single shot solid-dielectric spark gap switch was mechanically ruptured to short the transmission line and initiate the discharge. The light output was detected with an ITT biplanar photodiode with a sapphire window, and also with a McPherson model-225 1-m vacuum spectrograph.

A typical oscilloscope trace of the photodiode output power is shown in Fig. 1. The pulse height corresponds to 6 W, and the pulse width at half-maximum is 1.5 nsec.

Figures 2(a) and 2(b) show single shot stimulated emission spectra compared with the normal carbon monoxide spontaneous emission spectra excited by a Tesla coil discharge shown in Figs. 2(c) and 2(d). The exposure times for Figs. 2(c) and 2(d) were 10 and 60 sec, respectively. Figure 3 shows a microdensitometer tracing of the 2–8 band stimulated emission, high-resolution spectra. The P, Q, and R branch line positions and spontaneous emission intensities are given by the positions and lengths of the lines drawn over the microdensitometer tracing. The measured wavelengths agree with the assignment wavelengths, as calculated from Krupenie's monograph,[4] to within the measuring accuracy of 0.05 Å. The wavelengths and assignments are listed in Table I.

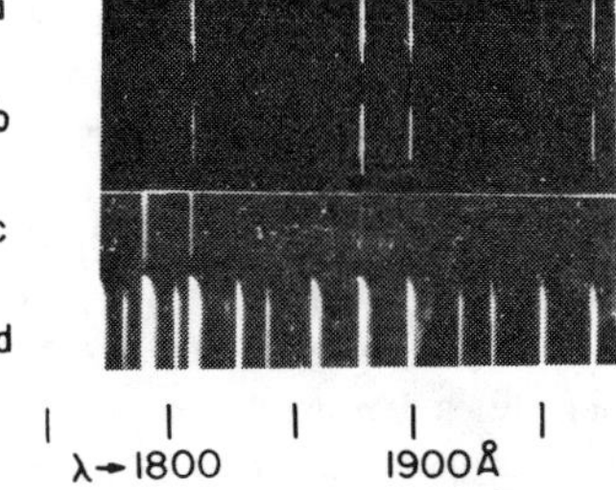

Fig. 2. (a) and (b) Single shot exposures of 1.5-nsec pulses of stimulated emission spectra from discharges in 60 torr carbon monoxide. (c) Spontaneous emission spectrum of a Tesla coil discharge in carbon monoxide. (d) Same conditions as (c) with 6 times longer exposure.

The high-resolution stimulated emission spectra show that the Q branch lines are most intense, the R branch lines are much less intense, or, in one band, missing, and the P branch lines are missing. The $Q7$ line is missing in the 2–8 band and appears to be weak or missing in the 2–6 and 2–7 bands as well.

The spectra can be qualitatively explained by considering the electron impact excitation of carbon monoxide, the stimulated emission coefficients of the P, Q, and R branch transitions from the excited states, and the effect of perturbations and molecular collisions on the level populations.

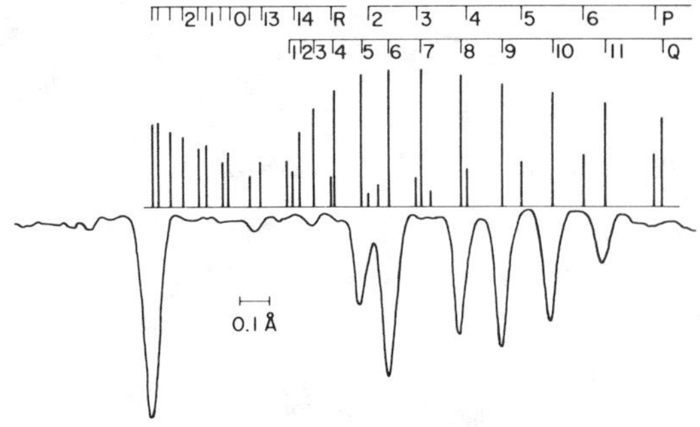

FIG. 3. Microdensitometer tracing of the 2–8 band stimulated emission spectrum. The positions and intensities of the spontaneous emission lines are given by the positions and lengths of the lines drawn over the microdensitometer tracing.

TABLE I. Stimulated emission spectrum of CO fourth positive group $A\ ^1\Pi \rightarrow X\ ^1\Sigma^+$.

Band λ_{Head} (Å)	$v'-v''$	Lines	Remarks
1810.85	2–6	Q5–13 R2–9	Not all resolved—Q7 missing all R lines would be blended
1878.31	2–7	Q5–13 R2–9	Not resolved—Q7 probably missing blended
1950.06	2–8	Q5–11 R2–9	All resolved—Q7 missing blended
1897.84	3–8	Q5–12 R2–9	All resolved blended
1970.13	3–9	Q5–11	All resolved R lines missing

Optical selection and intensity rules can be used to predict the resulting excited states when a molecule is bombarded with electrons if the electron energy is much greater than threshold energy. We have used these rules[5] to estimate the relative probabilities of exciting the closely spaced rotational levels of the $A\ ^1\Pi$ vibrational states by direct electron impact excitation from the equilibrium ground state population. The model predicts that the upper and lower Λ states of each rotational level are nearly equally populated and the inversion densities for the P, Q, and R branch lines from each rotational level are nearly equal. Since the P, Q, and R branch spontaneous emission coefficients are proportional[5] to J', $2J'+1$, and $J'+1$, however, the gain for the Q branch transitions will be highest, and the lower Λ states will be stimulated to emit Q branch radiation. The inversion density and gain for neighboring P and R branch lines is then reduced since the lower energy states have been populated by the Q branch transitions. In addition, if molecular collisions had collision cross sections of 10^{-14} cm^2, they could change upper to lower Λ states on a nanosecond time scale, and reduce the P and R branch inversion still further.

In a sufficiently powerful discharge, the inversion densities between the upper Λ states and the rotational levels of the $^1\Sigma^+$ ground state could be high enough for high gain. Since the R branch transitions have the higher gain, they would be stimulated, and the gain for the P branch lines would be reduced. The model predicts strong Q branch radiation, weaker R branch radiation, and no P branch radiation, in agreement with the observations.

The lower Λ level of the $J'=7$, $v'=2$, $^1\Pi$ state (the origin of the Q 7 line of the 2–6, 2–7, and 2–8 bands) is perturbed by a rotational level[5] of a $^1\Sigma^-$ state. It may be that near-resonant molecular collisions depopulate the $^1\Pi$ state, and reduce the gain for the Q7 lines. This mechanism may explain why no stimulated emission is seen from any of the $v'=1$ rotational levels since they are all perturbed by a $^3\Delta$ state.[6]

The carbon monoxide, vacuum-uv laser system is analogous to the molecular hydrogen system in that the final laser state is an excited vibrational level of the ground electronic state of a diatomic molecule. The lower power produced in the carbon monoxide laser is probably due to electron energy losses to triplet molecular states which have energies slightly lower than the $A\ ^1\Pi$ state.

ACKNOWLEDGMENTS

Useful discussions with Robert Field and M. J. Mumma, and technical assistance from S. Baliozian are gratefully acknowledged.

[1] R. T. Hodgson, Phys. Rev. Letters **25**, 494 (1970).

[2] R. W. Waynant, J. D. Shipman, Jr., R. C. Elton, and A. W. Ali, Appl. Phys. Letters **17**, 383 (1970).

[3] N. G. Basov, V. A. Danilychev, Yu. M. Popov, and D. D. Khodkevich, ZhETF Pis. Red. **12**, 473 (1970) [JETP Letters **12**, 329 (1970)].

[4] P. H. Krupenie, Natl. Std. Ref. Data Ser., Natl. Bur. Std. (U.S.), **5** (1966).

[5] G. Herzberg, *Molecular Spectra and Molecular Structure: I. Spectra of Diatomic Molecules* (Van Nostrand, Princeton, N.J., 1950), p. 208.

[6] J. D. Simmons, A. M. Bass, and S. G. Tilford, Astrophys. J. **155**, 345 (1969).

ELECTRON-BEAM EXCITATION OF VACUUM ULTRAVIOLET HYDROGEN LASER

R. T. HODGSON and R. W. DREYFUS
IBM Thomas J. Watson Research Center, Yorktown Heights, N.Y. 10598, USA

Received 6 December 1971

Stimulated emission of the Lyman-Band transitions of H_2 near 1600 Å has been achieved using a commercial electron-beam generator as an energy source. A 10^4 A. 3 ns pulse of 400 keV electrons propagated 1.5m through H_2 at pressures of 10-100 torr. Electron-molecule collisions produced inversion and superradiance at the kW power level.

The power needed to pump lasers rises drastically as the wavelength decreases to the vacuum ultraviolet range. In part, this increase reflects the frequency dependence of the Einstein stimulated emission coefficient, and in part the increase is due to the lack of good mirrors for low loss optical cavities. The first reported vacuum uv lasers [1, 2] solved the technical problem of introducing high powers into laser systems by using discharge tubes, strip lines, and condenser configurations custom-made for low circuit inductance and high discharge power. This letter reports another approach that has been successful in producing vacuum uv laser action using a commercially available and well engineered high-power laboratory instrument.

A 3 ns pulse of electrons from a Febetron 706 electron-beam gun * was confined by an axial 2-10 kG magnetic field to propagate down a 1.75 m long 1.9 cm I.D. stainless stell tube filled with hydrogen gas at 50 torr pressure (fig. 1). The electron-beam parameters were: 10^4 A maximum current, 400 keV energy, and 1 cm^2 initial beam cross section.

The light emitted by the H_2 was analyzed by a McPherson Model 225 vacuum spectrograph. The spectra, recorded on Kodak Pathé SC7 film, clearly showed the stimulated emission of the Lyman bands ($B^1\Sigma_u^+ \rightarrow X^1\Sigma_g^+$) of H_2 near 1600 Å [1]. Spectra identical with that given in fig. 3 of ref. [1] shows that the energy is emitted into the higher gain P3 transitions, which are over 10^3 times as intense as the corresponding R1 transitions. In spontaneous emission, the intensity ratio of these two transitions is 1.5 : 1.

The altered intensity ratio of the lines from the same upper state is proof of stimulated emission, as discussed previously [1], and is analo-

* Field Emission Corp., McMinnville, Ore., USA.

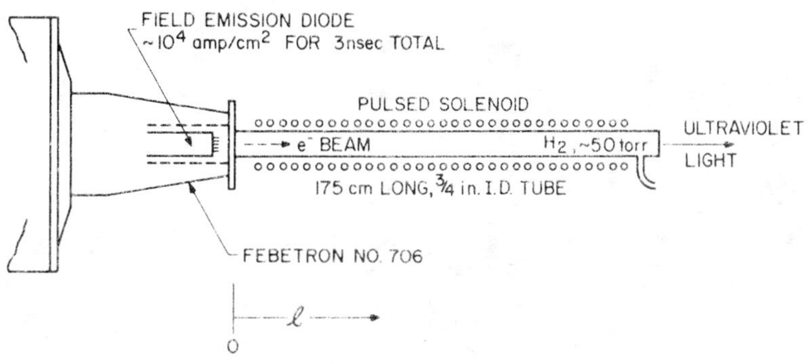

Fig. 1. Sketch of experimental apparatus.

gous to stimulated emission line narrowing where most of the radiation is emitted in the wavelength range of highest gain.

The power output was estimated by attenuating ** the ~ 1600 Å light with O_2 and measuring the film density [4]. Preliminary results indicate that the three strongest lines exposed the film with an energy density ranging from 5 to 10 erg/cm^2.

The H_2 laser pulse length and beam cross sectional area have not been measured. However, if the same pulse length (1 ns) and beam cross sectional area (0.1 cm^2) as a 3371 Å N_2 laser [5] produced in the same system are assumed the energy density of 10 erg/cm^2 in a 1 ns pulse over a 0.1 cm^2 cross sectional area gives an estimated power of ~ 100 W spectral line.

The laser action exhibited a fairly sharp threshold effect at about 7000 A/cm^2 initial beam current with a 2 kG magnetic field. Increasing the magnetic field up to 10 kG increased the laser power slightly. Weak laser action was even noted with highest electron-beam power and no magnetic field. Laser action was recorded from 20 to 100 torr, with a broad maximum at 50 torr.

Laser action was first predicted [6] to occur in the Werner-Band system ($C^1\Pi_u \rightarrow X^1\Sigma_g^+$) of transitions of H_2 around 1200 Å. However, only weak spontaneous emission spectra were presently recorded from 1050 to 1250 Å. The measured energy density was $< 10^{-2}$ erg/cm^2 and was taken as evidence that stimulated emission is not present in the Werner-Band system.

Clearly, only a very small proportion of the original 4×10^9 W beam energy is being transformed to laser light. (At an H_2 pressure of 50 torr, for example, a single 400 keV electron loses only 22 eV/cm.) Measurements made with a Faraday cup in N_2 indicate that only about 2000 A/cm^2 of the initial beam current propagates as fas as 1 m down the tube at optimum pressure for laser action. When the pressure is raised, the beam disappears, and evidence of current instabilities appears on the measured beam current traces. These instabilities prohibit raising the gas pressure and laser power at this time.

Technical assistance of S. Baliozian and R. Linn is gratefully acknowledged.

** The spectrograph was filled with a known pressure of O_2 gas, and the resultant attenuation was calculated from ref. [3].

References

[1] R. T. Hodgson, Phys. Rev. Letters 25 (1970) 494.
[2] R. W. Waynant, J. D. Shipman Jr., R. C. Elton and A. W. Ali, Appl. Phys. Letters 17 (1970) 383.
[3] K. Watanabe, E. C. Y. Inn and M. Zelikoff, J. Chem. Phys. 21 (1953) 1026.
[4] M. J. B. Fairhead and D. W. Heddle, J. Phys. E. 4 (1971) 89.
[5] R. W. Dreyfus and R. T. Hodgson, to be published.
[6] P. A. Bazhulin, I. N. Knyazev and G. G. Petrash, Zh. Eksp. Teor. Fiz. 48 (1965) 975, Sov. Phys., JETP 21 (1965) 649.

Reprinted with the permission of the American Physical Society from *Physical Review Letters,* Vol. 28(9), pp. 533-535 (February 28, 1972).

Observations of Gain by Stimulated Emission in the Werner Band of Molecular Hydrogen

Ronald W. Waynant
Naval Research Laboratory, Washington, D. C. 20390
(Received 29 November 1971)

Stimulated emission of vacuum ultraviolet radiation has been observed on two $Q1$ lines in the Werner band ($C^1\Pi_u \rightarrow X^1\Sigma_g^+$) of molecular hydrogen. These lines, 1161 and 1230 Å, contain 5 kW peak power and were produced by a traveling-wave discharge system. Using this excitation principle, evidence of gain has been obtained by observations of optimum velocity matching at pulse velocities less than c.

Observation and verification of amplification by the stimulated emission of radiation at photon energies above 10 eV have been made for the first time. The availability of such short-wavelength photons in an intense, directional beam is of immediate importance particularly in such fields as photochemistry, photofragment spectroscopy, and photoionization. Stimulated emission of these highly energetic photons has been produced in molecular hydrogen by rapid inversion of the vibrational levels of the $C^1\Pi_u$ excited electronic state with respect to the upper vibrational levels of the $X^1\Sigma_g^+$ ground state.

Speculation on the possibility of laser emission from the Werner band ($C^1\Pi_u$-$X^1\Sigma_g^+$ was first published by Bazhulin, Knyazev, and Petrash.[1] Figure 1 shows a greatly simplified energy-level diagram for the hydrogen molecule. A fast-rising current can produce an electron energy distribution which will preferentially populate the upper electronic states, inverting the vibrational levels with respect to the upper vibrational levels of the $X^1\Sigma_g^+$ ground state. A detailed rate-equation analysis of the Werner band for such a discharge was carried out by Ali and Kolb.[2] This analysis predicted lasing on several vibrational transitions with peak power density of about 20 kW/cm^3 for the strongest vibrational band. It

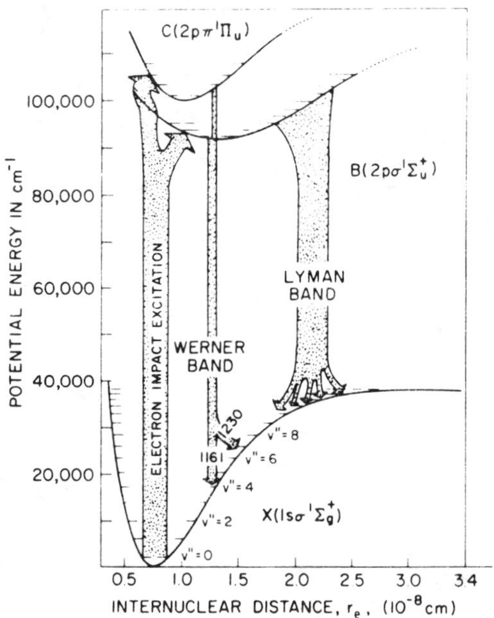

FIG. 1. Energy levels of H_2 from which lasing has been observed.

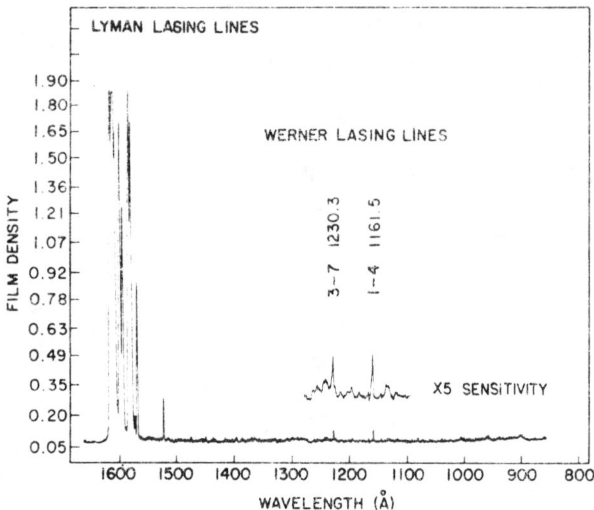

FIG. 2. Densitometer trace showing both Lyman- and Werner-band lasing lines. The new Werner-band lines are shown on an increased sensitivity scale for added clarity; the smaller linelike structure shown on this scale is film noise and not additional emission.

must be realized that this power would be divided among several rotational lines.

Experimentally, vacuum-ultraviolet laser action in H_2 was observed initially in the Lyman band at 1600 Å.[3,4] The traveling-wave discharge system of Shipman had been used previously[3] in the Lyman band to produce total peak powers of several megawatts in a short (~1 nsec) pulse. This traveling-wave system, with several lossy optical components removed from the vacuum optical transmission path, has been used to generate the shorter-wavelength (1161–1230 Å) Werner-band lasing first reported here. These higher-energy photons were detected by passsing the unfocused laser emission through a 1.5-m, 10-mm-diam vacuum path and then through the 0.025-mm slits of a 1-m vacuum monochromator equipped with a film holder and a 600-line/mm platinum-coated grating. Kodak 101-01 film was used to record the superimposed emission from several pulses, and a microdensitometer trace for the 800–1600-Å region is presented in Fig. 2. The monochromator was wavelength calibrated in the first order using argon and atomic hydrogen lines. The identified lines have no more than a ±0.3-Å uncertainty when examined by comparator.

The traveling-wave excitation system explained in detail previously[3] has the capability of varying the propagation velocity of the excitation wave longitudinally down the laser channel. Casperson and Yariv[5] have recently shown that the laser-pulse propagation velocity is gain dependent and is less than c when gain is present. It was previously shown[6] experimentally that maximum laser output was obtained both in N_2 and in the Lyman band of H_2 when the excitation wave velocity was less than c. This velocity-matching technique has now been extended to the newly observed Werner-band lines. It has been seen that these lines do not appear on film when the excitation wave travels at a phase velocity of c or greater, but do appear for excitation phase velocities less than c. This output enhancement by velocity matching is taken as evidence that the pulse traveling in the excited (inverted) gas region is being amplified, is traveling at a velocity less than c, and is showing a greater intensity for $v_p < c$ because of a reduction in spontaneous-emission losses which occur between the excitation wavefront and the laser pulse.

Estimates of the peak power in the two Werner lines were made by comparing the film densities with those of the Lyman band, where power has been measured more accurately by a photoelectric technique. These lines each appear to contain about 5 kW, based on the assumption that the pulse width remains about 1 nsec at these shorter wavelengths. Direct pulse-width measurements have been hampered by the low photon flux available after wavelength selection and by the lack of fast, sensitive detectors in this wavelength region. The 5-kW peak power observed here was emitted from a 36-cm^3 volume of H_2 at 20 Torr pressure. The measurement was made through a LiF window which can be expected to attenuate 50% or more at these wavelengths. This corresponds to an observed power density of 250–300 W cm^{-3} or more.

The identification of the two new Werner-band lines was facilitated by using the Franck-Condon factors calculated by Spindler.[7] If the Franck-Condon factor for exciting transitions from the $v''=0$ vibrational level of the $X^1\Sigma_g^+$ state to any vibrational level of the $C^1\Pi_u$ state (i.e., $q_{0v'}$) is multiplied by the Franck-Condon factor for the emissive transition from v' of $C^1\Pi_u$ to v'' of $X^1\Sigma_g^+$ (i.e., $q_{v'v''}$), the product $q_{0v'}q_{v'v''}$ gives a relative strength of the emission within the Werner band. Table I shows the vibrational transitions and the product $q_{0v'}q_{v'v''}$ in numerical order of the expected intensity for the nine most likely laser levels. As shown, the 1-4 transition would be expected to be the strongest followed by 2-5, 3-7, and 2-6.

Rotational levels must also be taken into account. Since 66% of the molecules are in the $J''=1$ rotational level at room temperature, the upper rotational levels $J'=1$ and $J'=2$ would be populated most heavily by excitation. For transitions involving $\Delta\Lambda=1$, P, Q, and R rotational lines are allowed with Q lines most probable, based on Hönl-London formulas. Table I gives wavelengths for the $Q1$ transitions according to the values given by Richardson.[8] With the use of wavelengths, the two lines observed correspond to the $Q1$ lines of 1-4 and 3-7. The observation of the $Q1$ transitions corresponds to the rotational line expected. Although the $J'=1$ and $J'=2$ levels would receive equal excitation, the $Q1$ ($J'=1 \rightarrow J''=1$) transition dominates during emission according to the Hönl-London formulas. The $R1$, $P3$, and $Q2$ rotational lines all have a lower transition probability and would require a higher gain in order to be observed. The 1-4 transition is observed to be strongest, in agreement with the calculated Franck-Condon factors. The 3-7 transition should, however, appear somewhat less intense than 2-5 according to Franck-Condon factors, but it was seen in the Lyman-band laser emission spectrum[3] that the intensities did not strictly obey these guidelines. With increased laser power or detection sensitivity, more of the other lines in Table I are expected to show up.

TABLE I. Relative probability of emission in the Werner band according to the Franck-Condon factors calculated by Spindler (Ref. 7), and the resulting wavelengths of the Q1 transition as given by Richardson (Ref. 8).

$v'-v''$	$q_{0v'}q_{v'v''}$	Q1 (Å)
1-4	0.0571	1161.32
2-5	0.0546	1175.87
3-7	0.0462	1229.98
2-6	0.0436	1218.94
0-2	0.0414	1099.45
1-3	0.0413	1116.34
0-1	0.0406	1054.18
4-8	0.0380	1239.53
3-6	0.0297	1189.38

The author gratefully acknowledges helpful discussions with R. C. Elton and P. S. Julienne, and the technical assistance of L. J. Verna.

[1]P. A. Bazhulin, I. N. Knyazev, and G. G. Petrash, Zh. Eksp. Teor. Fiz. 48, 975 (1965) [Sov. Phys. JETP 21, 649 (1965)].

[2]A. W. Ali and A. C. Kolb, Appl. Phys. Lett. 13, 259 (1968).

[3]R. W. Waynant, J. D. Shipman, Jr., R. C. Elton, and A. W. Ali, Appl. Phys. Lett. 17, 383 (1970), and Proc. IEEE 59, 679 (1971).

[4]R. T. Hodgson, Phys. Rev. Lett. 25, 494 (1970).

[5]L. Casperson and A. Yariv, Phys. Rev. Lett. 26, 293 (1971).

[6]R. W. Waynant and R. C. Elton, Bull. Amer. Phys. Soc. 16, 593 (1971).

[7]R. J. Spindler, Jr., J. Quant. Spectrosc. Radiat. Transfer 9, 597 (1969).

[8]O. W. Richardson, *Molecular Hydrogen and Its Spectrum* (Yale Univ. Press, New Haven, Conn., 1934).

Reprinted with permission from *Physical Review Letters,* Vol. 28(9), pp. 536-539 (February 28, 1972). ©1972 American Physical Society.

Vacuum-uv Laser Action Observed in H_2 Werner Bands: 1161–1240 Å

R. T. Hodson and R. W. Dreyfus
IBM Thomas J. Watson Research Center, Yorktown Heights, New York 10598
(Received 20 December 1971)

Stimulated emission has been observed in the $Q1$ and some $P3$ lines of the $v' \to v'' = 1$-4, 2-5, 2-6, and 3-7 Werner bands ($C^1\Pi_u \to X^1\Sigma_g^+$) of molecular hydrogen near 1200 Å. Light pulses of approximately 1 nsec duration were produced by bombarding hydrogen gas with ~400-keV electrons from a commercial electron-beam generator.

Observations of laser action in the vacuum-ultraviolet spectral region near 1600 Å have been published.[1-3] This Letter reports stimulated emission of even more energetic transitions in the H_2 Werner bands ($C^1\Pi_u$-$X^1\Sigma_g^+$). The wavelengths of the light, from 1161 to 1240 Å, are the shortest laser wavelengths achieved to this time, and the ~10-eV photons can be used for photochemistry, photodissociation, and photoionization investigations of most molecules.

The threshold power needed for lasing action in the vacuum-uv increases drastically as the frequency is raised. In order to introduce high power into hydrogen gas on a nonosecond time scale, the devices used[1,2] to produce lasing near 1600 Å were essentially capacitors, strip lines, and discharge tubes optimized for low inductance. Unfortunately, these devices did not excite sufficient molecules to the $C^1\Pi_u$ state to show high gain and super-radiant laser action on the Werner-band system. In addition, the device described in Ref. 1 has not been engineered to be a reliable laboratory instrument. For these reasons, a field-emission electron-beam generator[4] which delivers 5×10^9 W in a 3-nsec pulse is presently used as a power source for shorter-wavelength lasers.

Figure 1 shows a sketch of the apparatus which produces stimulated emission on the H_2 Werner bands. A 1-cm-i.d. stainless steel tube is bolted to the front face of a Febetron[4] 706 electron-beam generator. The generator consists of a Marx circuit followed by a Blumlein-circuit voltage doubler and pulse sharpener which delivers a 600-kV-peak pulse to a 50-Ω load. The voltage is applied between a number of etched tungsten needles and a 1-mil-thick Ti anode. Electrons are pulled off the cathode by field emission and accelerated across the vacuum gap to the anode. They pass through the anode (losing about 10% of their energy) and are available to excite and ionize the hydrogen gas at a pressure of 20–100 Torr in the tube.

A pulsed magnetic field of 6 kG confines the electrons to a small cross-sectional area in the line of sight. An electron-beam current of ~ 4000 A/cm^2 follows the field lines to the end of the field coil 2.3 m away from the anode, where it diverges into the tube wall 20 cm away from the entrance slit of the vacuum monochromator.

A slightly different version of this setup has already been successful in producing laser action in the H_2 Lyman bands,[5,6] the N_2 laser system at 3371 Å,[7] and in a number of lines of Ne I and Ne II.[8] It may also be commented that the present improvements over the system described in Ref. 6 increased laser powers to ~400 kW/cm^2 on several of the Lyman-band lines.

In all these electron-beam–pumped gas lasers, the high-energy primary, secondary, and cascade electrons induce transitions between the ground

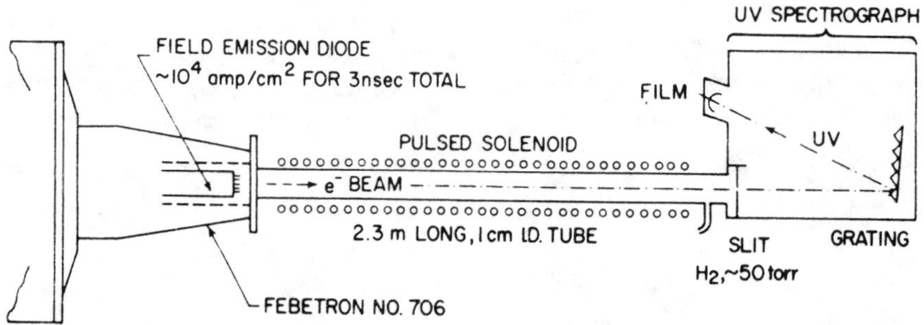

FIG. 1. Sketch of experimental arrangement. The 1-m McPherson monochromator is equipped with a 1200-line/mm Al + MgF_2 coated grating blazed at 1500 Å. Spectra are recorded using Kodak Pathé SC 7 film.

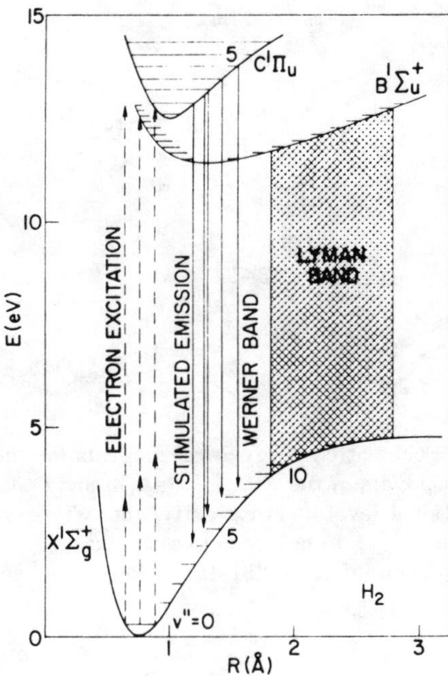

FIG. 2. Potential-energy curves for the $X^1\Sigma_g{}^+$, $B^1\Sigma_u{}^+$, and $C^1\Pi_u$ states of H_2. The dashed vertical lines represent the electron-collision–induced transitions between the zeroth vibrational level of the ground molecular state and the v' levels of the upper states. Solid vertical lines indicate the stimulated transitions of the Werner bands. The cross-hatched area is the region of previously observed stimulated emission in the Lyman bands; see Refs. 1 and 2.

electronic state and the excited electronic states. In H_2 the (v') vibrational levels of the $B^1\Sigma_u{}^+$ and $C^1\Pi_u$ states are excited more efficiently than the upper vibrational levels of the ground electronic state. These upward transitions are indicated by the dashed vertical lines on the potential-energy diagram (Fig. 2). The very high-power, nanosecond electron pulse produces a large inversion density before the spontaneous emission can populate the upper vibrational levels of the ground electronic state. The gain is then high enough for stimulated emission (without mirrors) on the downward transitions indicated by the solid lines of Fig. 2.

The principal diagnostic method used for the present work is spectral analysis of the light emitted from the H_2 under electron-beam bombardment. Figure 3 shows a microdensitometer trace of the Werner-band emission spectrum with sufficient resolution (0.25 Å) to resolve most of the lines of the emission spectrum. The relative wavelengths of the lines agree to within the 0.05-Å measuring error with Jeppeson's[9] measured wavelength for the assignments. The

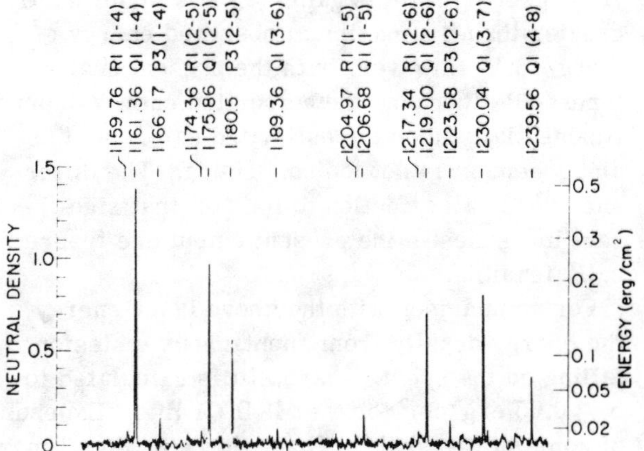

FIG. 3. Microdensitometer trace of the Werner-band stimulated-emission spectrum. The measured neutral density is plotted on the left as a function of the wavelength, and the corresponding film exposure in erg/cm^2 calculated from Ref. 10 is indicated on the right.

spectrum shown in Fig. 3 was exposed in a single shot with no window between the tube and the film so that the spectrum below 1050 Å (the cutoff of the LiF window) could be exposed. Spectra exposed with the window in place are identical to that in Fig. 3, and are completely different from the normal spontaneous emission spectra. It will be shown later that this difference proves that stimulated emission, and not spontaneous emission, is occurring.

From the neutral densities of the lines recorded on the left side of Fig. 3, the exposures (in erg/cm^2) are calculated using the work of Burton, Hatter, and Ridgeley.[10] Assuming the same 1-nsec pulse length measured[7] for N_2 or H_2 (near 1600 Å), these measured exposures indicate power densities of up to 50 W/cm^2. In fact, subsequent exposures gave maximum powers of 500 W/cm^2 in the (1-4) $Q1$ line. These estimates are quite conservative, since the efficiency of the 1200-line/mm grating and the LiF-window losses have not been taken into account.

The power output from an electron-beam-pumped gas laser can be estimated by estimating the inversion number density and calculating the gain. This was done by assuming that the ratio of excited-electronic-state density to ion density equals the ratio of excitation to ionization collision cross sections[11,12] for high-energy electrons, and by using measured ion production coefficients.[13] An inversion number density of 6×10^{11} was obtained this way, which indicates a relatively low gain of 7×10^{-2} cm^{-1} for the strongest transition. We can calculate that the energy should be about

10^3 erg/cm^2 with this gain. This is significantly greater than the maximum observed energy of 5 erg/cm^2. However, with the present near threshold situation, the calculated energy depends exponentially upon the estimated gain, and the disagreement is not too surprising. The difference does call attention to the fact that significant increases in the present output are theoretically feasible.

For comparison with the above laser energy, the energy density from spontaneous emission falling on the spectrograph slit is calculated to be <0.05 erg/cm^2 for the (1-4) $Q1$ line. Exposure of some of the weakest lines shown in Fig. 3 may well be due to spontaneous emission.

The stimulated-emission power available is not higher because most electrons lose only a negligible fraction of their energy before they hit the tube walls. As the pressure is raised to increase this fraction, evidence of beam instability is noted[7] and the laser power drops. If this problem can be overcome, the new developments in electron-beam technology can be applied to make these electron-beam pumped gas lasers relatively convenient and useful.

Stimulated emission of several transitions of the Werner-band system can be proven by a variation of a "spectral-line-narrowing" argument. The two energy levels of the $C^1\Pi_u$ state expected on the basis of intensity rules[14] to be most highly populated are the $J'=1$ lower Λ level and the $J'=2$ upper Λ level of the $v'=1$ vibrational state (Fig. 4). The branching ratios for spontaneous emission from these states are determined[14] by the v'-v'' Franck-Condon factors,[15] the selection rules, and the statistical weights of the rotational levels. Only transitions with $\Delta J=0$ (Q branch lines) are allowed from the lower Λ levels, while only transitions with $\Delta J=+1$ and -1 (P and R branch lines) are allowed from the upper Λ levels.[14]

The $Q1$ line of the $v'=1$ to $v''=4$ band is expected[14,15] to be 1.4 times as intense as another transition from the same upper state, the $Q1$ line of the 1-3 band at 1116 Å. However, in the spectrum recorded, the 1-4-band $Q1$ line is at least 50 times as intense as the 1-3-band line, which is too weak to detect. The only explanation for such anomalous intensity ratios is that the $v'=1$, $J'=1$ lower Λ level has been stimulated to emit on the higher gain (1-4) $Q1$ transition.

A different example, again on the 1-4 band, can be seen by referring to Fig. 4. The $Q1$ transition gain is expected[14] to be $\frac{5}{3}$ as great as the gain on

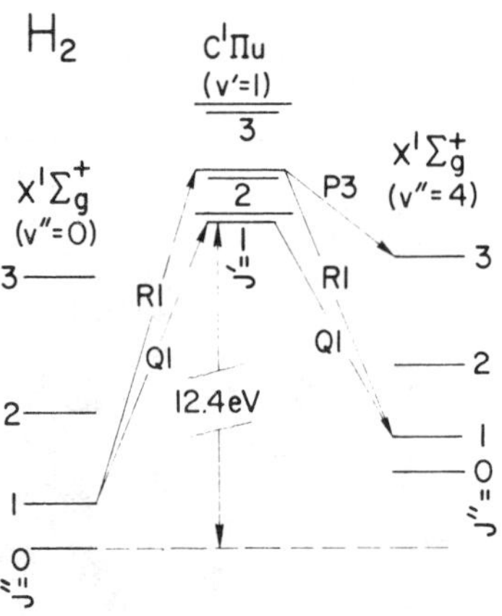

FIG. 4. Schematic energy-level diagram for the rotational sublevels of the $X^1\Sigma_g^+$ ($v''=0, 4$) and $C^1\Pi_u$ ($v'=1$) vibrational levels. For clarity, the Λ-type doubling of the $^1\Pi_u$ state has been greatly exaggerated and the energy scale of each vibrational level has been shifted.

the $R1$ transition, and $\frac{5}{2}$ as great as the gain on the $P3$ transition from the $J'=2$ upper Λ level. If, in fact, the $Q1$ emission is stimulated, the $J''=1$ level will "fill up" and the population inversion and gain on the $R1$ transition will be reduced. The $J'=2$ upper Λ level will then at some point be stimulated to emit on the $P3$ transition. Figure 3 shows, for example, that the $P3$ line of the 1-4 band is at least 3 times more intense than the $R1$ line. In spontaneous emission, the $R1$ line is the stronger in the ratio 3:2. Such an altered intensity ratio is even more striking in the 2-5 band where the $P3$:$R1$-line intensity ratio is greater than 10:1.

No trace is seen of the $P3$ line of the strong 3-7 band. The $P3$ and $R1$ lines are known to be perturbed by a level of the $B^1\Sigma_u^+$ state, and the effect seems to be identical to the stimulated emission of the CO fourth positive bands,[16] where sets of perturbed rotational lines are missing.

In summary, we have shown that stimulated emission of the shortest-wavelength (1161 Å) laser light reported to date can be produced using an electron beam to pump H_2 gas.

Technical assistance from R. Linn and S. R. Baliozian is gratefully acknowledged.

---

[1]R. T. Hodgson, Phys. Rev. Lett. 25, 494 (1970).

[2]R. W. Waynant, J. D. Shipman, Jr., R. C. Elton, and A. W. Ali, Appl. Phys. Lett. 17, 383 (1970).

[3]N. G. Basov, V. A. Danilychev, Yu. M. Popov, and D. D. Khodkevich, Pis'ma Zh. Eksp. Teor. Fiz. 12,

473 (1970) [JETP Lett. 12, 329 (1970)].

[4]Field Emission Corp., McMinnville, Ore.

[5]R. T. Hodgson and R. W. Dreyfus, in Proceedings of the Twenty-Fourth Gaseous Electronics Conference, Gainesville, Florida, 5-8 October 1971 (to be published).

[6]R. T. Hodgson and R. W. Dreyfus, "Electron-Beam Excitation of a Vacuum-Ultraviolet Hydrogen Laser" (to be published).

[7]R. W. Dreyfus and R. T. Hodgson, Appl. Phys. Lett. 20, 195 (1972); M. Clerc and M. Schmidt, C. R. Acad. Sci., Ser. B 272, 668 (1971).

[8]R. W. Dreyfus and R. T. Hodgson, to be published.

[9]C. R. Jeppeson, Phys. Rev. 44, 165 (1933).

[10]W. M. Burton, A. T. Hatter, and A. Ridgeley, Amer. Astronaut. Soc. Photo-Bull. 1, 27 (1971).

[11]E. J. Stone and E. C. Zipf, to be published.

[12]H. S. W. Massey, *Electronic and Ionic Impact Phenomena* (Oxford Univ. Press, Oxford, England, 1969), Vol. II, p. 910.

[13]R. D. Evans, *The Atomic Nucleus* (McGraw-Hill, New York, 1955), Chap. 18, Eq. 2.22.

[14]G. Herzberg, *Molecular Spectra and Molecular Structure: I, Spectra of Diatomic Molecules* (Van Nostrand, Princeton, N. J., 1950).

[15]R. J. Spindler, Jr., J. Quant. Spectrosc. Radiat. Transfer 9, 627 (1969).

[16]R. T. Hodgson, J. Chem. Phys. 55, 5378 (1971).

Reprinted with permission from *IEEE Journal of Quantum Electronics,* Vol. QE-10(2), pp. 153-174 (February 1974). ©1974 IEEE.

Review of Ultraviolet Laser Physics

CHARLES K. RHODES

***Abstract*—A review of the status and properties of coherent sources of ultraviolet radiation is presented. This includes a wide range of developments concerning atomic and molecular systems useful for generating wavelengths below 4000 Å, as well as progress in alternative methods of ultraviolet production. Particular emphasis is placed on recent advances in molecular bound-free systems whose operation is enhanced at high densities. It is believed that some of these systems may be scalable to sufficiently high-energy outputs to be useful in controlled fusion applications. A brief prognosis and discussion of future developments tending to the X-ray region are given.**

I. INTRODUCTION

SINCE the invention of the optical maser in 1960 by T. H. Maiman [1], the field has undergone a rapid and extensive development impacting a wide area of both pure science and the technology of applications. Pacing these developments has been the generation of a vast number of coherent sources spanning the far infrared from several hundred microns to the ultraviolet up to nearly 1100 Å. On balance, however, the major fraction of source development has centered on the visible and infrared spectral regions, and excursions into the domain of the ultraviolet have been scarce and meager in comparison to the overall tidal wave of progress. For the purposes of this review, we define as ultraviolet all wavelengths less than 4000 Å. The comprehensive fund of experience strongly indicates that developments in the ultraviolet require patience, special techniques, and a certain element of serendipity. We observe that, in their original analysis [2] of infrared and optical masers, Schawlow and Townes appraised the difficulties associated with the extension of the maser concept to ultraviolet and shorter wavelengths. In addition to the general unavailability of satisfactory transmitting or reflecting optical materials below ~ 1000 Å, Schawlow and Townes indicated the severe frequency dependence of the excitation power required to establish useful inversion densities and optical gains at these shorter wavelengths. The essence of this result is illustrated as follows. The linear optical gain at line center g can be expressed as

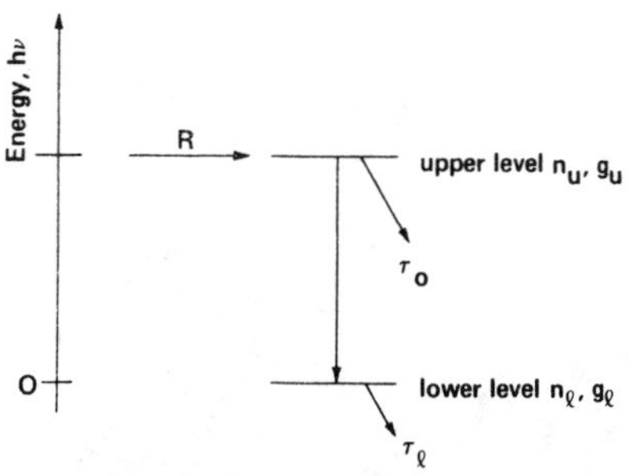

Fig. 1. Simple model of a two-level system. The quantities n_u, g_u, and n_l, g_l represent the densities and degeneracies, respectively, of the upper and lower states. The parameter R denotes the pumping rate of the upper level, while τ_0^{-1}, and τ^{-1}, and τ_l^{-1} describe the decay rates for the paths indicated.

$$g = \left(\frac{4\pi^2}{3\hbar c}\right)\mu^2 \, \Delta n \, \frac{\nu}{\Delta\nu} \tag{1}$$

where μ is the transition matrix element, Δn represents the inversion density,[1] ν designates the transition frequency, and $\Delta\nu$ is the linewidth. If we consider the two-level system shown in Fig. 1, then the inversion density can be related

Manuscript received June 27, 1973. This work was supported by the U.S. Atomic Energy Commission.

The author is with the Lawrence Livermore Laboratory, University of California, Livermore, Calif. 94550.

[1] More precisely, the quantity Δn is defined as $(n_u/g_u - n_l/g_l)$ where n_u and n_l denote the population densities of the upper and lower states, respectively, and g_u and g_l represent the corresponding degeneracies of these levels.

to the upper level excitation rate R by the expression

$$\Delta n = \frac{R\tau_u}{g_u}\left(1 - \frac{g_u}{g_l}\frac{\tau_l}{\tau}\right) \tag{2}$$

where τ_u is defined by

$$\frac{1}{\tau_u} \equiv \frac{1}{\tau} + \frac{1}{\tau_0}. \tag{3}$$

In this simple example we have assumed that only the upper level is populated by a rate R and that the decay rate of n_u to n_l is given by τ^{-1}, the decay of n_u to all other levels is given by τ_0^{-1}, and that the decay rate of n_l equals τ_l^{-1}. If we further assume that the upper state has a statistical weight of unity and that $\tau_l/\tau << 1$, then

$$\Delta n \simeq R\tau_u. \tag{4}$$

Under circumstances in which τ_u is determined primarily by the spontaneous radiative rate between the upper and lower levels, $\tau_u \simeq \tau$ and scales as ν^{-3}, giving

$$\tau_u \simeq \gamma\nu^{-3} \tag{5}$$

where γ is the appropriate collection of constants.[2] Two examples are of interest: 1) a Doppler-broadened transition; 2) a radiatively broadened transition. In the former case the linewidth[3] $\Delta\nu$ is proportional to ν, while in the latter it is proportional to ν^3. These considerations, convolved with expressions (1), (4), and (5), lead to the following expressions for the gain g:

$g \propto R\nu^{-3}$ Doppler broadened
$g \propto R\nu^{-5}$ radiatively broadened.

Therefore, for some fixed gain g_0, the required pump power[4] scales as ν^4 in the Doppler broadened case and as ν^6 in the radiatively broadened example.

Since the linewidth $\Delta\nu$ has a strong influence on the optical gain of a given transition, we explore this issue in somewhat greater depth. Processes which will contribute to the width of a bound–bound resonance[5] are the following: 1) Doppler effect,[3] which reflects atomic motion and scales in proportion to the frequency ν and the atomic mean speed; 2) radiative broadening, which scales according to ν^3; 3) collisional broadening, [3] which is dependent primarily upon density; 4) stark broadening, [4] which is determined largely by the plasma density; and 5) Auger effect [5], [6], which is a rapid lifetime broadening mechanism caused by electron–electron interaction and is operative in systems with inner shell vacancies.

Fig. 2 illustrates graphically the relative frequency dependence of the Doppler, radiative, and collisional broadening contributions for the assumed conditions corresponding to a density of ~ 10^{17} cm^{-3} and average thermal speed v such that $v/c \simeq 10^{-6}$. The radiative rate is scaled from that obtained for the hydrogen $L\alpha$ line and thus represents the case of a fully allowed electric dipole amplitude. The diagram in Fig. 2 indicates three separate regions which are distinguished in wavelength by the approximate conditions:[6] $\lambda \gtrsim 50\mu$, 300 Å $\leq \lambda \lesssim 50\mu$, and $\lambda \leq$ 300 Å in which the linewidths are dominated by the collisional, Doppler, and radiative effects, respectively. Notice the steepening slope of the envelope curve which selectively conspires against the generation of optical gain at short wavelengths. Although not shown in Fig. 2, Auger rates are important at shorter wavelengths involving inner shell transitions. We note incidentally that the competition between the Auger rate and the corresponding radiative rate determines the fluorescent yield. Typically, Auger rates are more important for lower Z as fluorescent yields generally increase [6] with greater Z (e.g., $\omega \sim 85$ percent for a K-shell vacancy in xenon), and for fixed Z are more influential for higher shells. This point relates principally to the possibility of achieving coherent oscillation on inner shell transitions where fast Auger rates may represent a severe loss.

Recognition of these fundamental considerations opposing the generation of optical amplification at ultraviolet and shorter wavelengths inspires an examination of the need for coherent radiation in this spectral region. We observe that copious fluxes of incoherent ultraviolet and X-ray quanta are available through the use of laser-produced plasmas [7], synchrotron radiation [8], or vacuum sparks [9]. Certain applications seem imperative. Clearly, the precise control of optical energy over narrow frequency bands in the ultraviolet will enable a detailed examination of electronic structure of atoms and molecules paralleling the studies of molecular vibrational structure permitted by the development of infrared sources. Raman scattering studies will be facilitated, since Raman cross sections are generally larger and detection more efficient in the ultraviolet spectral region. Moreover, these sources will be useful in a vast array of photochemical processes, which implies the development of efficient methods for isotope separation and other wavelength selective chemical syntheses. Since the divergence angle decreases with wavelength for a fixed aperture, communication between distant points such as two synchronous satellites is facilitated with the use of short wavelength radiation. The low solar content of radiation, particularly for

[2] Since the Einstein A coefficient is given by $(64\pi^4/3hc^3)\,\mu^2\nu^3$ where μ is the relevant matrix element, γ is given by $3hc^3/64\pi^4\mu^2$.

[3] For an analysis of the Doppler effect, see E. Fermi, *Rev. Mod. Phys.*, vol. 4, p. 87, 1932. However, we must bear in mind that generally there is a complicated interplay between the Doppler effect and broadening caused by particle–particle interactions.

[4] Recall that R is a particle rate, so that the corresponding energy rate goes at $h\nu R$, which adds another power of the frequency to the ν^3 and ν^5 dependencies.

[5] For the moment we will restrict ourselves to bound–bound transitions; as we will discuss in a later section, the linewidths of bound-free transitions are more easily considered from a different perspective.

[6] Clearly, in any given case, the precise values of the various contributions to the linewidth depend upon the specific collision broadening cross section, the mass of the radiator, the kinetic temperature, and the matrix element of the transition. These are issues of quantitative detail; the qualitative aspects remain unchanged.

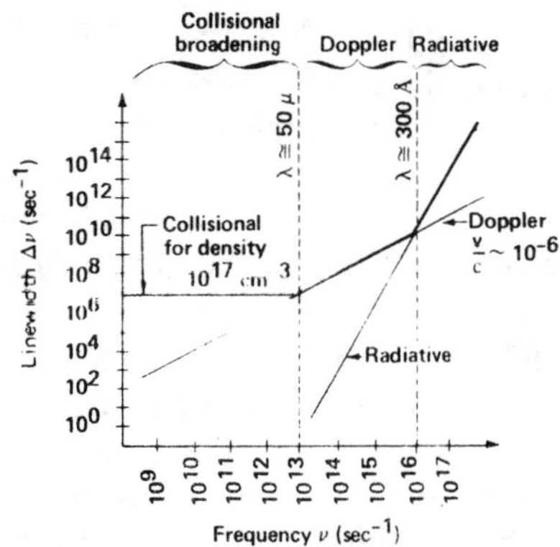

Fig. 2. The dependence of the contributions to the linewidth $\Delta\nu$ due to collisional processes (assuming a density $\sim 10^{17}$ cm^{-3}), the Doppler effect (for $v/c \sim 10^{-6}$), and spontaneous radiative decay on frequency ν. For this density and velocity three separate regions are distinguished: $\lambda \gtrsim 50\ \mu$, 300 Å $\lesssim \lambda\ 50\ \mu$, and $\lambda \lesssim 300$ Å in which the linewidths are dominated by the collisional, Doppler, and radiative effects, respectively. Notice the steepening slope of the envelope curve.

wavelengths less than 2000 Å, is an important consideration for space communications [10]. The region around 2700 Å would be very useful for earth communications applications because of the high-altitude ozone shield [11]. It has also been shown [12] that X-ray point sources are useful for high-resolution subnanosecond X-ray radiography. A truly coherent source would considerably extend this capability. Finally, since the inverse bremsstrahlung absorption rate in a plasma scales [13] very nearly as $1/\lambda^2$, ultraviolet lasers appear well suited for the heating of high-density plasmas for thermonuclear fusion applications. A bright future certainly awaits the practical development of these systems.

II. Classes of Systems

A. Atomic Systems

Stimulated emission in the ultraviolet region between 1548–4000 Å has been observed in a wide variety of ionized atomic systems. Table I in the Appendix, which contains a list of the transitions and radiating species, is observed to include the materials Ne, Ar, Kr, Xe, F, Cl, C, O, N, P, B, S, Pb, and Cd in various states of ionization. Species having ionization stages as high as quadruply ionized have been observed in stimulated emission.

1) Systems Excited by Electron Collisions: With the exception of the ionic cadmium line at 3250 Å, the majority of the other systems mentioned above characteristically operate in pulsed low-pressure high-current discharges. However, we will note later an example of continuous-wave operation on the 3638- and 3511-Å transitions of Ar III. From the observed temporal behavior of the output radiation in relation to the current pulse, it was clear that in most cases the inversions were generated by direct or successive inelastic collisions with electrons [14]–[17] as well as radiative cascade processes [17], [18]. However, it was often found difficult to discriminate clearly between alternative channels of excitation. Collisional transfer from excited atomic systems, a common process in neutral maser systems, appeared to play no role. For species X, the direct amplitude is represented by

$$X + e^- \rightarrow X^{+*} + e^- + e^- \qquad (6)$$

while an example of the stepwise process is given by the sequence

$$X + e^- \rightarrow X^+ + e^- + e^- \qquad (7)$$

and

$$X^+ + e^- \rightarrow X^{+*} + e^-. \qquad (8)$$

In addition, excitation of metastable neutral atomic species by electrons to excited ionic states may also be an important process. Such two-step processes generate an upper laser level population which is proportional to the square of the excitation current, a mechanism important in certain continuous-wave ion lasers [17].

In spite of the complexity of the current dependence, an interesting regularity concerning the electron configurations of the transitions emerged. It was found in many cases that the upper laser level, in either singly, doubly, or triply ionized atoms, involved an excited p-electron which would undergo transition to a lower s-orbital. This general p–s feature has been found to be characteristic of the rare gas ion systems [19]–[22], as well as neutral neon [23]. A plausible explanation of this selection rule has beeen given by Bennett *et al.* [20] as follows: In the sudden approximation the amplitude for the process (6) can be estimated by assuming that the wave function of the ion core Φ_0 remains unchanged during the collision. This assumption should be valid provided that the electron–atom collision time τ_c is sufficiently less than the electronic readjustment time τ_e of the ionic core. We may estimate τ_e as being roughly equal to the orbital period of an outer electron. The inequality

$$\frac{\tau_c}{\tau_e} < 1 \qquad (9)$$

is satisfied provided that incident electron energy exceeds the ionization potential of the resulting ion by approximately a few electronvolts. For singly ionized material, this condition is met, with the exception of He, for electrons with an incident energy greater than 25 eV. With these conditions in mind, we may expand the wave function Φ_0 of the initially produced core state in terms of a complete set of functions representing the states ϕ_i^+ of the ion core systems X^+. This leads to the expression

$$\Phi_0 = \sum_i c_i \phi_i^+ \qquad (10)$$

where c_i are the appropriate expansion coefficients. Since the coefficients c_i are evaluated by

$$c_i = \int \phi_i^{+*}\Phi_0 \, d^3r \tag{11}$$

this analysis predicts that the excited ions will be produced in configurations which have the same parity as the ionic ground state. Configurations with the opposite parity have vanishing amplitudes by virtue of the right-hand side of expression (11) and are, therefore, not excited.

In the majority of cases, observations support this simple picture. Consider the examples of the 3749-Å transition [14] of O II and the 3323-Å transition [15] of Ne II, as illustrated in Fig. 3. In both cases the ground-state ions are odd parity with the electron configurations $2p^3$ and $2p^5$, respectively. The lowest excitation which changes the principal quantum number of a p-electron and conserves parity is a transition to the $3p$ shell. The upper states of the O II and Ne II transitions are the $^4S^0$ and $^2P^0$ terms of the $2p^23p$ and $2p^43p$ configurations, respectively, both with odd parity in agreement with the corresponding ionic ground-state term values. The result in both cases is an inversion on p–s transitions, the lower states of which decay rapidly by spontaneous emission of a deep ultraviolet photon [24] (539 Å for O II, and 446 Å for Ne II) to the ionic ground state. Provided that the ion densities are sufficiently low so that this spontaneous emission is untrapped, this rapid decay of the lower states enhances the tendency for the generation of population inversions. However, we note that radiation trapping has been observed to have an important influence on the spontaneous decay of argon ionic states in the Ar II system [17].

In addition to the wide variety of pulsed sources, there exist some important examples of continuous-wave operation of ionized atomic systems in the ultraviolet. Two such cases involve the 3638- and 3511-Å transitions of Ar III with reported outputs of ~ 5 W. For further details, the reader should consult the comprehensive review of atomic ion systems given by Bridges *et al.* [17].

2) Penning Ionization Excitation: The He–Cd system [25]–[28], which operates on the $4d^95s^2\,^2D_{3/2} \rightarrow 4d^{10}5p\,^2P_{1/2}^0$ 3250-Å transition of Cd II as shown in Fig. 4, relies on an entirely different physical mechanism for the production of the inverted population. We present below a brief description of the essential aspects of this system. It has been established [29], [30] that the dominant mechanism leading to excitation of the $^2D_{3/2}$ state is Penning ionization according to the process

$$\mathrm{He}(2^3S_1) + \mathrm{Cd}(^1S_0) \rightarrow \mathrm{He}(1^1S_0) + \mathrm{Cd}^+(^2D_{3/2}) + e^-. \tag{12}$$

The electron easily carries off the exothermicity due to its small mass. The measured cross sections for this reaction are 6.5×10^{-15} cm^2 and $4.5 \pm 0.2 \times 10^{-15}$ cm^2 as determined, respectively, by Collins *et al.* [30] and Schearer and Padovani [29]. The difference in these values has been attributed to slightly different assessments of the cadmium vapor pressure [30]. The large amplitude for this Penning

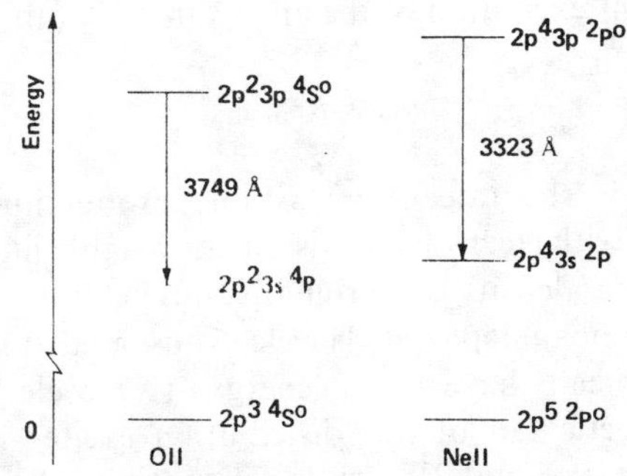

Fig. 3. Partial energy-level diagrams of O II and Ne II illustrating the 3749- and 3323-Å transitions.

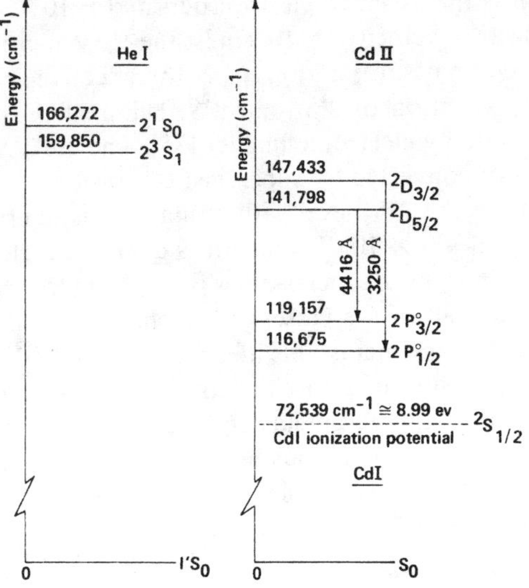

Fig. 4. The partial energy-level diagrams of He I, Cd I, and Cd II relevant to the 3250-Å transition of the He–Cd oscillator.

process is interesting since it is observed that the helium changes multiplicity as a result of the collision. Normally, a transition of this nature in light atoms is anticipated to be weak. However, an electron exchange mechanism completely relaxes this selection rule. There is considerable evidence that reaction (12) occurs almost entirely through electron exchange [31], [32]. This is, of course, similar fundamentally to exchange processes which occur in electron scattering except that the incident electron is now bound rather than free.

The radiative lifetimes of the Cd II $^2D_{3/2}$ and $^2P_{1/2}$ levels, which are ~ 260 × 10^{-9} s [28], [33] and ~ 0.5 × 10^{-9} s [34], when combined with the selective transfer to the ^2D level by the near resonant Penning ionization result in a clear tendency to produce a population inversion through preferential population of upper level and rapid decay of the lower state.

It is possible to make a rough estimate of the inversion density generated by the Penning process which incorporates the known Penning-ionization cross section in conjunction with the cross section of electron impact excitation of metastable helium. For this we assume an effective electron density of approximately 10^{10} cm^{-3}. The density of helium metastables n_{He} is given by (ignoring subsequent excitation of the metastables to other levels)

$$n_{He} \approx R\tau_{He}n_{He}^0 \tag{13}$$

where R is the rate of metastable production through collisions with electrons, τ_{He} is the metastable lifetime, and n_{He}^0 is the density of ground-state helium, which we assume to be undepleted. The electrons created by the discharge typically have a mean energy of a few electronvolts. The energetic tail of this distribution excites He to the metastable 2^1S_0 and 2^3S_1 levels. The rate R is evaluated as

$$R \simeq n_e\sigma_{e-He}v_e \tag{14}$$

where n_e is the assumed electron density ($\approx 10^{10}$ cm^{-3}), v_e is the electron velocity ($\approx 10^8$ cm/s; the He velocity is very slow in comparison), and σ_{e-He} is the effective cross section for excitation of 2^1S_0 and 2^3S_1 helium from the 1^1S ground state by electronic impact [35]. The He 2^1S_0 states are rapidly converted by superelastic collisions with slow electrons to the 2^3S_1 level with a characteristic cross section [36] of $\sim 3 \times 10^{-14}$ cm^2. If it is assumed further that the lifetime of the He metastables is due primarily to diffusion to the wall of the vessel with a characteristic dimension of 1 mm, the metastable lifetime is around 10^{-6} s. For a helium pressure of 2 torr the combination of these factors gives an estimated metastable density of $n_{He} \approx 1.2 \times 10^{11}$ cm^{-3}. By an analogous argument, this excited state population density is coupled to the corresponding population density of excited ionic ^2D states $n_{Cd^+}{}^*$ by the relation

$$n_{Cd^+}{}^* \approx \tfrac{1}{2}n_{He}n_{Cd}v_{He}\sigma_{He-Cd}\tau_{Cd^+} \tag{15}$$

where n_{Cd} is the density of atomic cadmium ground-state species, v_{He} is the helium velocity ($\approx 10^5$ cm/s; cadmium atoms are slowly moving in comparison), σ_{He-Cd} is the Penning cross section ($\approx 6.5 \times 10^{-15}$ cm^2), and τ_{Cd^+} is the lifetime of the ionic state which is taken to be 260×10^{-9} s. We use the cross section obtained by Collins *et al.* [30] and assume in expression (15) that one half of the Penning transfer goes into the upper ^2D level, the state relevant in the 3250-Å transition. At a cadmium vapor pressure of 10^{-2} torr, the resulting excited ionic density is $\approx 1.5 \times 10^9$ cm^{-3}. Although the ^2P states will also be populated by the Penning effect, their short lifetimes ($\approx 10^{-9}$ s) prevent the generation of an appreciable density in these levels. This leads to an inversion density which is roughly equivalent to the upper level density of 5×10^9 cm^{-3}, a value which is in very good accord with the density determined experimentally by Hodges [28].

Cadmium has eight naturally occurring isotopes, six of which with atomic mass numbers (A = 110, 111, 112, 113, 114, and 116) have appreciable and roughly comparable natural abundances. Since the isotope shift is of the order of the Doppler width of the resonance, the line has an inhomogeneous width which is considerably greater than the Doppler width of a single species. The usefulness of this laser for high-resolution spectroscopy is therefore considerably enhanced by the use of a single cadmium isotope.

Under typical operating conditions the cadmium vapor pressure is in the vicinity of 10^{-2} torr, while the helium pressure is in the range of 1–2 torr. The vapor pressure of the cadmium is controlled by the operating temperature of the plasma tube.

B. Molecular Systems

Stimulated emission in both the near ultraviolet and vacuum ultraviolet regions has been obtained from several molecular species. In contrast to the atomic systems which generally involve ionized material, the molecular systems observed to date all correspond to neutral molecules. The relatively rapid dissociative recombination [37] channel, available for molecular ions but not for atomic ions, may play a role in explaining this observation.

The molecular ultraviolet systems can be divided into two categories according to the nature of the transition involved. These classifications are represented by systems operating on bound–bound and bound–free molecular transitions. The former correspond to the traditional level schemes associated with laser devices in which both the upper and lower states represent different bound configurations of the radiating system. In the latter, however, the lower level is in the continuum of positive energy states describing free motion at infinity of fragments of the bound upper state system. As a result of the continuum nature of these transitions, the linewidths of the bound–free systems are typically many orders of magnitude greater than those normally associated with bound–bound transitions.

1) Bound–Bound Systems: Oscillation in the ultraviolet has been observed between various bound states in H_2, HD, D_2, CO, and N_2. In H_2, HD, and D_2 stimulated emission has been observed [38]–[42] from the Lyman bands ($B^1\Sigma_u^+ \rightarrow X^1\Sigma_g^+$); Werner band ($C^1\Pi_u$ $X^1\Sigma_g^+$) transitions [43]–[44] have been observed in H_2 yielding the shortest wavelength (λ = 1161 Å) so far observed in stimulated emission; oscillation [45] $\sim$ 1900 Å on the CO fourth positive band ($A^1\Pi \rightarrow X^1\Sigma^+$) has been generated experimentally; and the second positive system of N_2 ($C^3\Pi_u \rightarrow B^3\Pi_g$) at $\sim$ 3371 Å has been seen [46], [47] in stimulated emission. The theory of the pulsed nitrogen system has been considered by Ali *et al.* [48]. A general rate equation analysis for three-level ultraviolet systems has been discussed by Elton *et al.* [49] and a treatment of the H_2 Lyman and Werner bands has been given by Ali and Kepple [50]. Similar aspects have been considered by Ali and Kolb [51].

The first suggestion that H_2 was a suitable candidate for vacuum ultraviolet laser was published by Bazhulin *et al.* [52]. Fig. 5 illustrates the energy levels relevant to oscillation on the Lyman band of hydrogen. Consideration of the Werner band system is similar except that the $C^1\Pi_u$ state serves as the upper level rather than the $B^1\Sigma_u^+$. For hydrogen gas at room temperature, only the $\nu = 0, j = 0$, 1 states of the $X^1\Sigma_g^+$ ground state are appreciably pop-

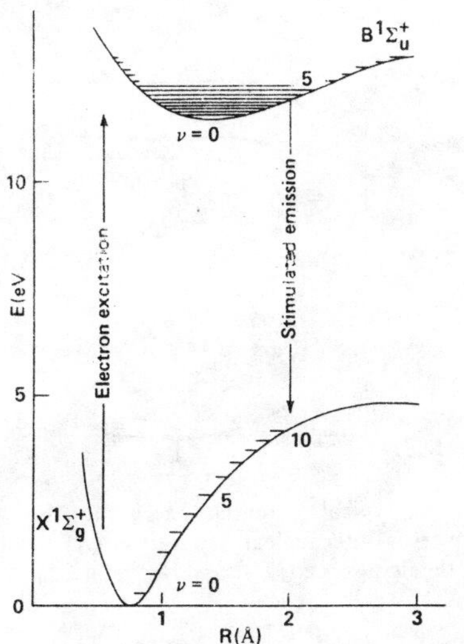

Fig. 5. A partial energy-level diagram of molecular hydrogen illustrating the potential curves as a function of internuclear distance R for the $X^1\Sigma_g^+$ and $B^1\Sigma_u^+$ states relevant to stimulated emission on the Lyman band. The vibrational levels of the electronic states are indexed by ν.

ulated.[7] The excitation from these states to the appropriate levels of the $B^1\Sigma_u^+$ is achieved through the action of a fast rise time, high current electric discharge [38], or relativistic electron-beam source [40] which produces [41] a large density of energetic electrons and subsequent secondary electrons. In the relativistic electron-beam case, since all the relevant cross sections are small at the high primary beam energies ($\geq$ 500 keV), the slower secondaries provide the main excitation of the gas. These electrons, through collisions with the ground-state H_2 molecules, generate populations in the $B^1\Sigma_u^+$, ν = 3, 4, 5, 6, 7, j = 0, 1, 2, levels. Electron-impact excited fluorescence studies and electron energy loss spectra [53], [54] in H_2 gas show that this excitation satisfies dipole selection rules and that the probability of excitation is proportional to the Franck–Condon overlap factors connecting the $\nu = 0$ vibrational level of the lower $X^1\Sigma_g^+$ state with the vibrational levels of the upper $B^1\Sigma_u^+$ state. On the other hand, the excited ν = 3, 4, 5, 6, 7 vibrational levels of the $B^1\Sigma_g^+$ state have large Franck–Condon factors [55] connecting them to the ν = 10, 11, 12, 13 levels of the $X^1\Sigma_g^+$ ground state. Since the vibrational states of the lower $X^1\Sigma_g^+$ state are not appreciably excited [56] on the time scale of the radiative lifetime of the upper $B^1\Sigma_u^+$ state, an inversion and subsequent oscillation occurs on the P (j) transitions of the 3–10, 4–11, 5–12, 6–13, and 7–13 Lyman bands [57] ($B^1\Sigma_u^+ \rightarrow X^1\Sigma_g^+$) where j = 3, 2, 1 depending upon the particular band (not all those possible have been observed). Because of nuclear statistics, the adjacent rotational lines should have alternating intensities as has been confirmed by observation. This system provides a distinct example of excitation by direct electron impact and a manifestation of optical selection rules.

Inversions based on the Franck–Condon principle will occur generally along the lines described above under conditions where the potential minima of the upper and lower potential curves surfaces are sufficiently displaced. Such displacements are anticipated whenever an electron is promoted from one orbital to another orbital with different bonding characteristics. For example, excitation from a bonding orbital to a nonbonding or antibonding orbital generally significantly increases the equilibrium internuclear separation.[8] It is clear that these considerations are also valid for polyatomic systems where changes in molecular conformation are commonly associated with excited electronic states.[9]

The same basic mechanisms are operative in the Werner band system of H_2. This oscillator has produced the shortest wavelength so far reported of 1161.36 Å on the $Q1$ (1–4) transition. We point out that since the upper level is not a Σ state, the spectrum of the Werner band has the interesting complication of Λ-doubling [43].

The N_2 second positive system [46], [47] at 3371 Å is another important example of a transient inversion established by electron collisions. Superradiant oscillation has been observed on this transition ($C^3\Pi_u \rightarrow B^3\Pi_g$) at power levels in excess of 2 MW [58] for pulses of a nominal length of 10 ns. The calculations of Cartwright [59] indicate that preferential excitation of the nitrogen $C^3\Pi_u$ state may be obtained by electron collisions over a relatively broad electron-energy range at approximately 20 eV. The peak cross section for excitation of the $C^3\Pi_u$ state $\sim \pi a_0^2$ is near 15 eV. Since the lower state of this transition is metastable on the time scale of interest, a rapidly rising high E/P discharge is required. In addition to direct excitation by collisions, refined theoretical treatments of the nitrogen second positive system have included the effects of collisional ionization of the upper $C^3\Pi_u$ state [48]. Finally, we observe that the N_2 second positive band ($C^3\Pi_u - B^3\Pi_g$) at $\sim$ 3371 Å occurs in the triplet manifold of states, whereas the ground $X^1\Sigma_g^+$ state of N_2 is a singlet configuration. This suggests that exchange processes are involved in the excitation scheme of this system.

2) Bound-Free Systems:

a) General discussion: The use of molecular bound-free transitions in laser systems was initially proposed by Houtermans [60] in connection with the continua of H_2 and Hg_2. Nevertheless, only relatively recently has genuine stimulated emission utilizing transitions of this genre been observed on the molecular continua of xenon [61] at $\sim$ 1722 Å and krypton [62] at $\sim$ 1457 Å.

[7] This arises from the large vibrational and rotational spacings characteristic of the H_2 system. For spectroscopic details, see G. Herzberg, *Molecular Spectra and Molecular Structure*, vol. 1, *Spectra of Diatomic Molecules*. Princeton, N.J.: Van Nostrand, 1950.

[8] These influences are shown clearly in the molecular potential curves of N_2, O_2, NO, and their corresponding ions presented in F. R. Gilmore, *J. Quant. Spectrosc. Radiat. Transfer*, vol. 5, p. 369, 1965.

[9] For example, the excited $\tilde{A}\ ^1A_2''$ state of NH_8 corresponds to the D_{3h} point group rather than the C_{3v} point group of the $\tilde{X}\ ^1A_1$ ground state. For further details, the reader is referred to the following volumes. G. Herzberg, *Molecular Spectra and Molecular Structure*, vol. 1, *Spectra of Diatomic Molecules*. Princeton, N. J.: Van Nostrand, 1950. G. Herzberg, *Molecular Spectra and Molecular Structure*, vol. 2, *Infrared and Raman Spectra of Polyatomic Molecules*. Princeton, N. J.: Van Nostrand, 1945. G. Herzberg, *Molecular Spectra and Molecular Structure*, vol. 3, *Electronic Spectra and Electronic Structure of Polyatomic Molecules*. Princeton, N. J.: Van Nostrand, 1966.

The rare gas molecular continua represent a subset of the much larger class of bound–free systems. Additional members of this larger group are the well-known examples [63]–[66] Zn_2, Cd_2, Hg_2, HeH, NeH, and LiXe, among others. In spite of the relatively long history concerning the molecular continua of some of these systems (the ultraviolet continua of the excited rare gas systems have been known since the 1930's), much detailed and fundamental knowledge of the properties of these molecules currently is lacking. In this context it is interesting to recall Finkelnburg's early discussion [63] in 1938 of the continuous spectrum of Hg_2 which contains the following statement: "Bei der Mannigfaltigkeit der Erscheinungen, die von Temperatur, Druck und Anregungsbedingungen so stark abhangig sind, ist es nicht moglich, durch wenige Aufnahmen ein Bild der Spektren zu geben." It is not clear that the present situation is vastly different. Certainly one source of interpretive difficulties with continuous spectra stems directly from the absence of two basic tools generally used in the analysis of molecular electronic transitions; viz., vibrational and rotational progressions. Among the simplest systems representing the prototype of molecular bound–free transitions, and for which there exists a considerable literature concerning its properties, is He_2. The complex nature of these molecular systems is immediately illuminated by the fact that over 60 electronic states are currently known even for this elementary system [67].

For simplicity in the following discussion, we will focus on the properties of the homonuclear rare gas systems [68]. To a very good approximation, these excited molecular dimers can be regarded as Rydberg states. In this view the molecular configurations are then comprised of two parts: the molecular ion core (e.g., He_2^+), and a single excited electron orbiting largely outside of the region occupied by the core. One then has a relatively simple Rydberg series [69] characteristic of that core state. This model predicts that the equilibrium internuclear separation R_0, the molecular vibrational frequency, and the molecular moment of inertia are determined largely by the corresponding properties of the molecular ionic core. The potential curves given by Ginter and Battino [67] for He_2^* quite strikingly indicate the validity of this approximate model. It would appear that this feature introduces a very desirable simplification into an otherwise rather complicated situation, since it should be possible to formulate meaningful estimates of matrix elements on the basis of an essentially one-electron picture.

For typical cases of interest the excited state is characterized by a potential function $V^*(R)$ which has a substantial potential minimum at an internuclear separation R_0 and which supports several vibrational levels. In contrast, the ground-state interatomic potential $V(R)$ is generally strongly repulsive for $R \sim R_0$, although it does exhibit a relatively shallow van der Waals minimum at internuclear distances substantially greater than R_0. Fig. 6 schematically illustrates these potential curves. It is characteristic that the triplet state lie somewhat below the singlet level due to exchange energy. We also observe that

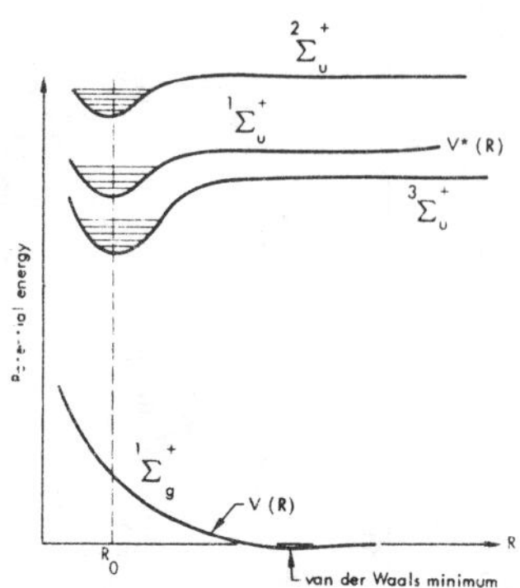

Fig. 6. Plot of typical potential energy for homonuclear rare gas molecules versus internuclear separation (R) illustrating the ground $^1\Sigma_g^+$ state, the first excited $^3\Sigma_u^+$ and $^1\Sigma_u^+$ states, and the $^2\Sigma_u^+$ ionic core state.

in the rare gas systems the lowest excited state is characteristically located so that a photon arising from the $^3\Sigma_u^+ \rightarrow {}^1\Sigma_g^+$ transition is sufficiently energetic to photoionize into the $^2\Sigma_u^+$ continuum.

An interesting property of these systems derives from the fact that certain of these continuous bands are observed with very similar characteristics in all three phases—gas, liquid, and solid. For example, the argon continuum centered near 1300 Å resulting from excitation by americium α particles exhibits essentially identical line shapes (within $\sim$ 10 percent) for all three phases [70]. On the basis of this observation, one is strongly motivated to conclude that the excited species in all cases very closely resemble the gaseous dimer which is only negligibly influenced by the weak van der Waals forces of the surrounding neighbors in the liquid and solid. This immediately suggests the possibility that these systems may be successfully operated at liquid or solid density. In this connection it is useful to note that, at an active density of 2×10^{19} cm^{-3} ($\sim$1 atm) and assuming roughly one Rydberg per system, the stored energy density corresponds to nearly 50 kJ/l. However, as we will indicate later, exciton–exciton mutual annihilation processes will generally limit exciton densities to values far less than this figure.

b) Discussion of kinetic mechanisms: Although the rare gases are normally considered to comprise one of the simplest classes of materials, a complicated chain comprised of several processes contributes to the kinetic scheme which leads to neutral molecular formation. We illustrate, with the example of xenon, some of the processes that are operative when high-pressure rare gases are excited with relativistic electron beams. They are the following:

$$e^- + \text{Xe} \rightarrow e^- + \text{Xe}^* \quad (16)$$

$$e^- + \text{Xe} \rightarrow e^- + e^- + \text{Xe}^+ \quad (17)$$

$$\text{Xe}^* + \text{Xe} + \text{Xe} \rightarrow \text{Xe}_2^* + \text{Xe} \quad (18)$$

$$\text{Xe}^+ + \text{Xe} + \text{Xe} \rightarrow \text{Xe}_2^+ + \text{Xe} \quad (19)$$

$$\text{Xe}_2^+ + e^- \rightarrow \text{Xe}^* + \text{Xe} \quad (20)$$

$$Xe_2^* \rightarrow \gamma + Xe + Xe \tag{21}$$

$$Xe^{**} + Xe \rightarrow Xe^* + Xe \tag{22}$$

$$Xe_2^*(\nu) + Xe \rightarrow Xe_2^*(\nu') + Xe \tag{23}$$

$$Xe^{**} + e^- \rightarrow Xe^* + e^- \tag{24}$$

$$\gamma + Xe_2^* \rightarrow Xe_2^+ + e^- \tag{25}$$

$$Xe_2^* + Xe_2^* \rightarrow Xe_2^+ + e^- + Xe + Xe \tag{26}$$

$$Xe^* + e^- \rightarrow Xe^+ + e^- + e^-. \tag{27}$$

Reactions (16) and (17) represent the excitation and ionization generated by both the high-energy primary electrons as well as the sufficiently energetic secondaries. Electrons can also lose energy radiatively. However, for the ~1-MeV electron energies of interest, this loss is low, being less than ~8 percent in the highest Z case, xenon [71]. Of course, for the lighter materials this figure is even smaller and radiative energy loss for the electrons may be neglected. These excited and ionized atoms will then subsequently combine in three-body processes to form the corresponding molecule and molecular ion as represented by reactions (18) and (19). It is important to note that the rates of these three-body processes will scale like the square of the ground-state atom density. We also note that at elevated temperatures the inverse reactions of processes (18) and (19) become important and must be taken into account through the principle of detailed balance. The dissociative recombination process (20) then provides a channel to convert the ionized material into excited atomic species. For the rare gases this process is quite fast except in the case of helium.[10] The abnormally slow rate for helium is believed to be related to the lack of an appropriate curve crossing of a dissociative neutral molecular state with the ionic bound potential curve [37].

Process (21) illustrates a spontaneous radiative bound–free transition of the molecular system corresponding, for example, to the $^3\Sigma_u^+ \rightarrow {}^1\Sigma_g^+$ transition shown in Fig. 6. This transition is an allowed electric dipole process through spin-orbit coupling. Indeed, in the higher Z materials (e.g., Kr_2^* and Xe_2^*) it is anticipated that the spin selection rule will be at least partially broken as it is in the atomic case.[11] It could also represent the fully allowed $^1\Sigma_u^+ \rightarrow {}^1\Sigma_g^+$ transition as well. However, some caution must be exercised on this point as there is some evidence in the case of xenon that the radiative lifetime of the molecular triplet state is substantially longer than a simple estimate based on the corresponding atomic triplet-state lifetime [72]. There is evidence in the literature [73], [74] that the triplet state of xenon may have a radiative lifetime as great as 500 ns. Nevertheless, a fluorescence lifetime of approximately 5×10^{-9} s has been observed in liquid xenon [75]. This issue requires further clarification. Actually, because of this point, there is some suspicion at the present time that the stimulated emission observed in xenon and krypton may be entirely due to the singlet manifold rather than the corresponding triplet states.

Atomic and molecular relaxation processes are indicated in (22)–(24). In the atomic case it is desired to collapse the manifold of excited states of $^3P_2$ level which correlates with lowest molecular excited state[12] ($^1S_0 + {}^3P_2 \leftrightarrow {}^3\Sigma_u^+$). Both electrons and atoms can participate in these processes. Slow electrons can be very important, particularly involving magnetic transitions and transitions requiring a change in the electronic spin state. For instance in neon, Phelps [76] has determined the relaxation rates of $^3P_1 \rightarrow {}^3P_2$ through collisions with neon atoms and electrons. For the atomic collision partners the cross section is of the order of $\sim 10^{-19}$ cm^2, while for the electrons the cross section is $\sim 10^{-13}$ cm^2, which is essentially the theoretical maximum imposed by unitarity[13] for s-wave scattering of thermal electrons. Molecular vibrational relaxation is illustrated by reaction (23). It is anticipated that this may be a very efficient process requiring only a few gas kinetic collisions because of the possibility of resonant atom exchange. Helium, however, apparently constitutes an exception to this expectation. Callear and Hedges [77] report that the vibrational relaxation of the He_2 [$a^3\Sigma_u^+$, $\nu = 1$) state is "abnormally slow." A long-range repulsive potential which keeps the atom and molecule at relatively large distances, and thus prevents the exchange process, could account for this observation in helium. Finally, processes (25) and (26) illustrate photoionization and Penning ionization of the excited dimer states. Taken together, these reactions represent losses of both photons and radiating molecular systems. Since the lowest excited molecular state is more than halfway up from the molecular ground state to the convergence of the Rydberg series at the

[10] For these rates see H. J. Oskam and V. R. Mittelstadt, *Phys. Rev.*, vol. 132, p. 1445, 1963. They are reported in this work to be $< 4 \times 10^{-9}$, $(2.2 \pm 0.2) \times 10^{-7}$, $(6.7 \pm 0.5) \times 10^{-7}$, $(1.2 \pm 0.1) \times 10^{-6}$, and $(1.4 \pm 0.1) \times 10^{-6}$ cm^3/s for He_2^+, Ne_2^+, Ar_2^+, and Xe_2^+, respectively. Since the measurements detect the total recombination rate, these numbers are upper bounds on the dissociative process. More recent data on He_2^+ are reported in A. W. Johnson and J. B. Gerardo, *Phys. Rev. Lett.*, vol. 28, p. 1096, 1972. The temperature dependence of the recombination coefficient has been considered in T. F. O'Malley, *Phys. Rev.*, vol. 185, p. 101, 1969.

[11] The atomic g-values of the low-lying atomic resonance lines of Kr and Xe are close to one another and near the j–j limit. See P. G. Wilkinson, *Can. J. Phys.*, vol. 45, p. 1709, 1967.

[12] Information relating to the Xe_2 potential curves appears in R. S. Mulliken, *J. Chem. Phys.*, vol. 52, p. 5170, 1970. It is now believed, however, that the equilibrium internuclear separation of ~2.85 Å indicated by Mulliken is too small and that a larger value between ~3.1–3.4 Å is more appropriate (A. V. Phelps, private communication; D. C. Lorents and R. M. Hill, private communication). The potential energy curves of the ground $^1\Sigma^+$ states of the rare gas systems, with the exception of the species involving xenon, have been computed in R. G. Gordon and Y. S. Kim, *J. Chem. Phys.*, vol. 56, p. 3122, 1972. Systems with xenon have also been calculated (B. Schneider, private communication). Ground-state data are also known experimentally from beam studies (R. B. Bernstein and J. T. Muckerman, *Intermolecular Forces, Advances in Chemical Physics*, vol. 12, J. O. Hirschfelder, Ed. New York: Interscience, 1969, p. 389. *Molecular Beams, Advances in Chemical Physics*, vol. 10, J. Ross, Ed. New York: Interscience, 1966).

[13] This is simply a statement of the conservation of probability.

ground molecular ionic state,[14] the frequency of the $^3\Sigma_u^+ \rightarrow {}^1\Sigma_g^+$ transition is sufficient to photoionize the $^3\Sigma_u^+$ state. This will then be a stimulated loss process diminishing the optical gain on the $^3\Sigma_u^+ \rightarrow {}^1\Sigma_g^+$ transition. The Penning process is also undesirable. Given a time scale for pumping, the rate of the Penning process will establish an upper bound on the attainable energy density storage. Although these cross sections are not presently known for the rare gas systems, the rate has been measured for the process[15]

$$\mathrm{He}\,(2^3S_1) + \mathrm{He}\,(2^3S_1) \rightarrow \mathrm{He}^+\,(1^2S_{1/2}) + \mathrm{He}\,(1^1S_0) + e^- \quad (28)$$

involving the helium metastable He (2^3S_1) giving a cross section $\sigma \simeq 10^{-14}$ cm^2. For the moment, assume that the molecular process (26) possesses a similar value and that the available pumping time τ is $\sim 50 \times 10^{-9}$ s. We may then roughly estimate the bound on the excited particle density n by equating $nv\sigma \simeq 1/\tau$, where v is the mean relative intermolecular speed. This gives $n \simeq 10^{17}$ cm^{-3} which, assuming a Rydberg per system, corresponds to only ~250 J/l. This is a fundamental limitation which emphasizes the need for a rapid means of excitation. We will return to this point later in the discussion.

The loss processes (25) and (26) may be considered from a unified point of view. Diagrammatically, the photoionization process (25) can be represented as shown in Fig. 7, where I denotes the appropriate intermediate autoionizing state. In a similar manner the amplitude for the Penning reaction (26) may be symbolized as shown in Fig. 8, in which the photon now appears as a propagator rather than as an external line. In a certain sense, the latter may be regarded as a photoionization process quite similar to the former, but with the photon not necessarily on the mass shell (i.e., $\omega \neq c\,|\mathbf{k}|$). We remark that the amplitude for the photoionizing process (25) may not be negligible in comparison with the amplitude for stimulated emission in process (21). Since no direct measurements of the photoionization cross sections of the relevant Xe_2^* dimer states have been made, estimates must be made on the basis of similar processes in other systems. Recent calculations [78] for the Rydberg states of H_2 give values for photoionization cross sections in the range 1–2×10^{-17} cm^2. In addition, measured values as great as 9×10^{-18} cm^2 have been reported for the photoionization of metastable 2^1S_0 and 2^3S_1 He atoms [79]. On the other hand, the structural similarity between the excited rare gas atoms and the neighboring alkali atoms (core plus lone outer s-electron) indicates that cross sections as low as $\sim 10^{-18}$ cm^2 may apply [80]. Finally, reaction (27) represents the loss of excited xenon atoms (or dimers) through

[14] The molecular configurations have an excited-state structure not greatly different from the rare gas atoms themselves; that is, a large energy gap from the ground state to the first excited state followed by a relatively narrow band of excited states from there to the first ion level.

[15] A. V. Phelps and J. P. Molnar, *Phys. Rev.*, vol. 89, p. 1202, 1953. A rate of $(4.5 \pm 1.0) \times 10^{-9}$ cm^3/s is given by more recent measurements reported by A. W. Johnson and J. B. Gerardo, *Phys. Rev.*, vol. A7, p. 925, 1973.

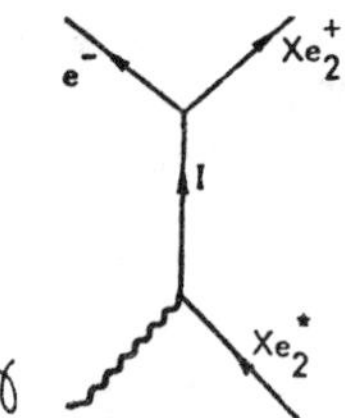

Fig. 7. Diagram of photoionization of the excited Xe_2^* dimer.

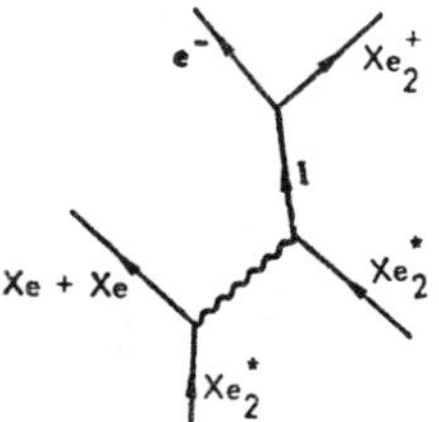

Fig. 8. Diagram of mutual exciton–exciton annihilation of Xe_2^* dimers by Penning ionization.

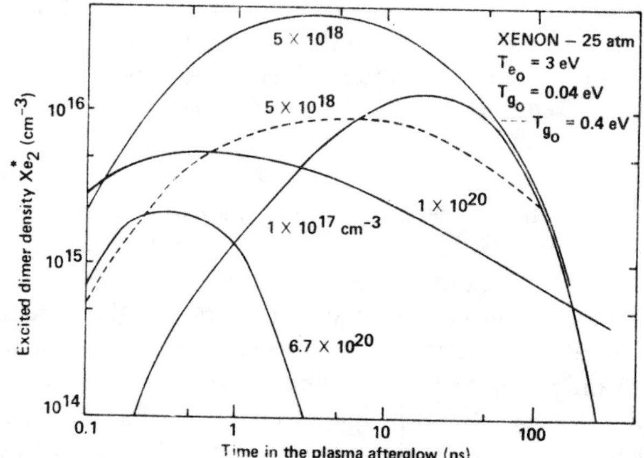

Fig. 9. The calculated temporal evolution in the afterglow of the excited dimer density corresponding to the Xe_2 ($^3\Sigma_u^+$) state for various values of initial electron density $n_e(0)$ ranging from 10^{17} cm^{-3} to 6.7×10^{20} cm^{-3}. These results are from the calculations George and Rhodes in [78].

collisions with relatively low-energy electrons. These low-energy electrons can excite an excited xenon atom to either a higher bound level or to the ionized state. For example, electrons with kinetic energies greater than ~3.81 eV can ionize the lowest excited state of atomic xenon ($^3P_2$). Wojaczek [81] has examined the electron collisional ionization of the metastable $(3p^54s)^3\,P$ states of argon and determined a cross section, using the classical method of Gryzinski [82], of $\sim 10^{-15}$ cm^2 for this process.

Detailed calculations based on this kinetic model have been performed [83]. Fig. 9 illustrates the temporal behavior of the excited dimer density in the afterglow for various values of initial electron density n_e (0). From the previous discussion, reactions (18) and (19) represent two key processes in the kinetic chain. In these calculations the rate for reaction (18) was taken [74] as 2.5×10^{-32} cm^6/s, while the rate constant for process (19) was taken to be $(3.57 \pm 0.17) \times 10^{-31}$ cm^6/s as determined from recent measurements [84]. It is interesting to observe that there is an optimum initial electron density of ~5×10^{18} cm^{-3} for the stated conditions. The study found that the most favorable circumstances for population inversion occurred for a plasma that is initially ~1-percent ionized with cold gas atoms. Both plasma heating and higher levels of plasma ionization inhibit dimer formation.

The role of destructive processes such as reactions (26) and (27) is shown in Fig. 10. Their presence dramatically alters the temporal evolution of the electron density n_e, the electron temperature T_e, and the gas kinetic temperature T_g. The electron creation processes maintain the electron density and temperature at significantly higher values than would occur otherwise. This energy density is eventually transmitted to the kinetic mode of the gas leading to an increase in the gas temperature T_g. Dissociative recombination, of course, also contributes to gas heating since hot atoms with as much as 1 eV of energy may be produced [37]. Studies of dissociative recombination in Ne and Ar definitely establishing the production of kinetically hot atoms by the dissociative recombination mechanism have been reported by Connor and Biondi [85] and Frommhold and Biondi [86]. Gas heating has an adverse effect on both the kinetic processes generating the excited dimers and collision-induced absorption from *ground-state* molecular species. We will explore this latter issue in greater detail in a subsequent section.

c) Molecular xenon system: The use of the rare gases for the generation of coherent vacuum ultraviolet radiation was initially proposed by Basov [87] and Moltchanov *et al.* [88]. Early luminescence experiments were conducted on condensed material with excitation by fast electrons [89] and X-rays [90]. Coherent oscillation ~1760 Å in liquid xenon excited with an electron beam was subsequently reported by the Russian group [91]. Further reports of oscillation in xenon, including the observation of stimulated emission in high-pressure xenon gas at ~1720 Å followed [61]. More recently it has been suggested that high-pressure noble gas systems could be operated in a conventional discharge [92]. The presence of optical gain and coherent oscillation have been conclusively demonstrated for the xenon dimer system. We outline below the experimental observations of Hoff *et al.* [61] leading to this conclusion.

The essential observations demonstrating unequivocally the presence of a coherent stimulated process are the measurement of spectral line narrowing (a necessary but insufficient condition), the observation of spatial coherence via the resulting spatially directed beam, the existence of a sharp oscillator threshold, a time dependence of the directed output radiation radically different from the spontaneous emission observed below threshold, and a dip in the spontaneous emission viewed perpendicular to the laser axis. Since the excited xenon dimers are strong spontaneous radiators, great care must be taken to assure that the radiation from this system truly represents a coherent process [2].

The experimental apparatus giving rise to laser emission at 1722 ±1 Å in relativistic electron-beam excited material over a range of xenon gas pressures near 200 psia is il-

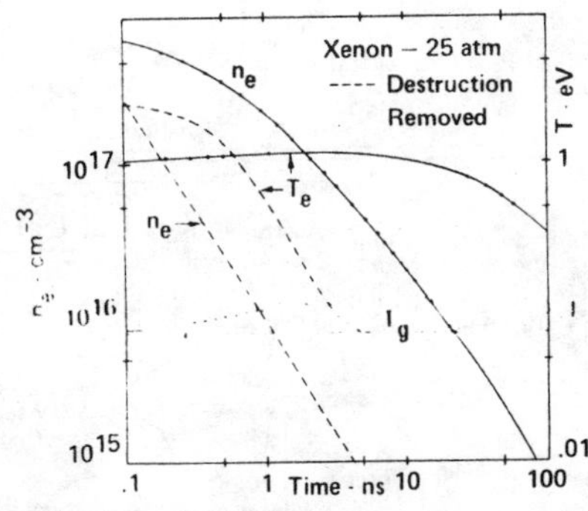

Fig. 10. The calculated temporal evolution in the afterglow of electron density n_e, electron temperature T_e, and gas kinetic temperature T_g for xenon gas at 25 atm. The dashed curves correspond to the results when the rates of the destructive processes are set to zero.

lustrated in Fig. 11. A high-pressure gas cell with internal mirrors and mode-limiting optical apertures was attached to a Febetron 705 relativistic electron-beam generator which emits a 40-ns pulse in a 10-kA beam with a nominal energy of 1.5 MeV over a 2-cm-diam aperture. The electron-beam current density penetrating the diaphragm and incident on the gas was ~300 A/cm^2 as measured by a calibrated Faraday cup. The optical cavity consisted of two 1-m-radius-of-curvature mirrors separated by 5 cm. The mirrors were fabricated from highly polished MgF_2 substrates which were Al coated and MgF_2 overcoated. The reflectance and transmittance of the mirrors at 1700 Å were measured to be 80 and 8 percent, respectively. The 2-mm-diam intracavity apertures limited the field of view of the diagnostic systems essentially to the volume contained in the cylinder defined by the apertures. The spectral composition of the radiation along the optical axis was detected by an 0.75-m Seya–Namioka spectrograph. The temporal characteristics were observed using an ITT 4115 photodiode with a 2-ns rise time. Spatial propagation studies were performed by replacing the photodiode with SWR film mounted on a variable length line-of-sight pipe, and attenuation in this pipe was accomplished with calibrated sapphire attenuators. The spontaneous radiation emitted perpendicular to the cavity axis was monitored using an 0.82-m Czerny–Turner spectrometer with a typical bandpass of 5 Å about a center wavelength of 1715 Å.

Fig. 12 illustrates the typical spectral output of the laser for conditions above and below threshold along with a calibration spectrum. The spectral linewidth (measured photographically) narrowed from ~160 Å (as observed without mirrors) to a half-width of ~15 Å with the optical cavity. In addition to the spectral narrowing, marked changes in the time dependence of the directed output radiation were observed for conditions above and below the oscillation threshold. This dramatic change in the temporal pulse shape is seen as an intense ~10-ns pulse as shown in Fig. 13. Spectral line narrowing was observed only in conjunction with this fast pulse.

Since spectral narrowing is not a sufficient condition demonstrating optical gain, a measurement of the spatial coherence of the emitted radiation is imperative. In this case the radiation was spatially coherent as observed

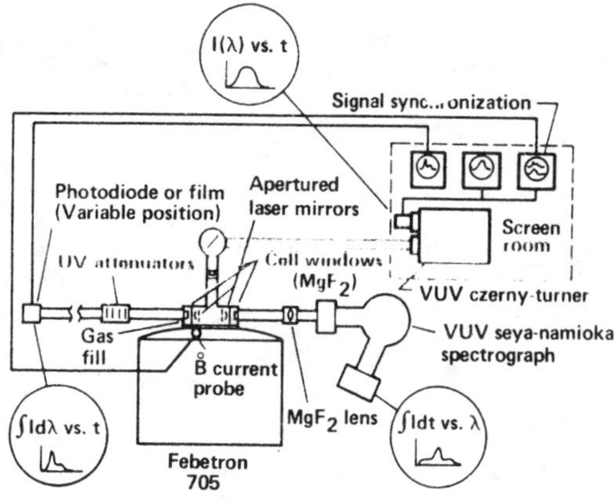

Fig. 11. Schematic of the experimental apparatus illustrating the three diagnostic systems: Seya–Namioka spectrograph for time-integrated spectral determinations; a photodiode to record the directed emission, and a Czerny–Turner spectrometer equipped with a photomultiplier to view the spontaneous emission side light.

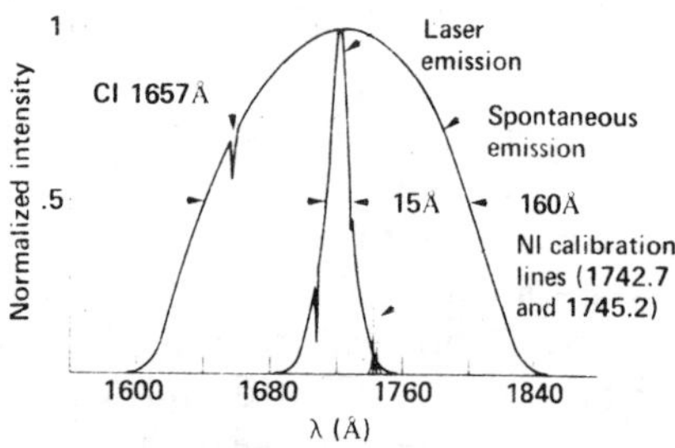

Fig. 12. Time-integrated spectral output of the xenon oscillator (linear vertical scale) from spectrograph for 1) conditions below threshold and 2) conditions above threshold showing NI calibration lines. Two unidentified absorption lines appear at 1708 and 1726 Å. Above threshold the emission narrows to ~ 15 Å at ~ 1720 Å.

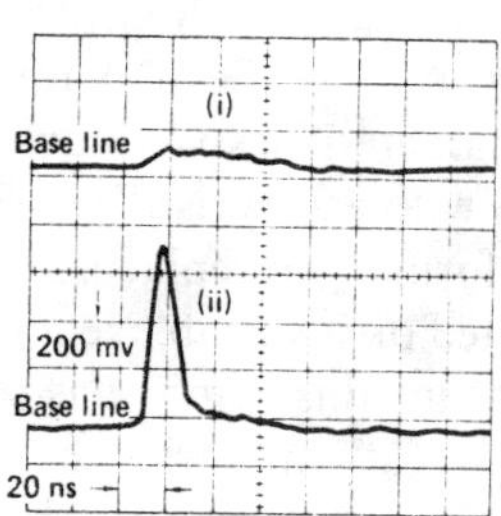

Fig. 13. Spectrally integrated photodiode output as a function of time for (i) conditions below threshold and (ii) conditions above threshold.

photographically by positioning film at various distances from the laser cavity. The half-angle of divergence so determined was 5 mrad, which is a factor of 9 larger than the divergence of the fundamental mode (0.6 mrad). Since the ratio of the diameter of a higher order mode to the fundamental mode is a constant [93], the divergence of the higher order mode is larger by this constant factor. In this example, the diameter of the fundamental mode at the 2-mm aperture is 0.186 mm. Assuming that the highest order mode is the size of the aperture, the diameter ratio is 10.7, which agrees well with observation.

Finally, it was observed that a definite oscillation threshold depending on xenon gas pressure existed. Fig. 14 illustrates the dependence of the peak laser output on xenon pressure. Sharp threshold phenomena are observed at ~ 110 and ~ 375 psia.

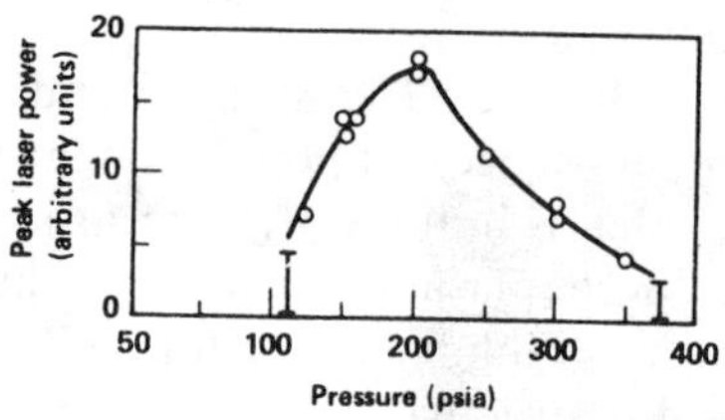

Fig. 14. Laser peak power versus xenon pressure. Note the existence of thresholds at ~ 110 and ~ 375 psia. The maximum standard deviation of the data points was 0.612.

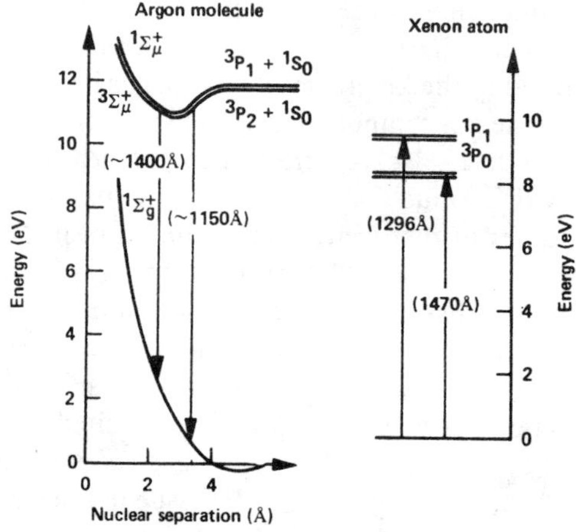

Fig. 15. Partial energy-level diagrams of Ar_2 and Xe relevant to the resonant energy transfer. The xenon energy-level scale is offset vertically to match the Xe $^1S_0 \rightarrow {}^1P_1$ 1296-Å transition to the ~ 1300-Å molecular bound–free transition of the argon dimer.

Because of the rapid energy transfer processes known to occur between iertain rare gas atoms and molecules in the gas [94], liquid [70], and solid [70] phases, these studies have been extended to include rare gas mixtures. Of particular interest is the resonant energy transfer process [94]

$$Ar_2(^{1,3}\Sigma_u^+) + Xe(^1S_0) \rightarrow Ar(^1S_0) + Ar(^1S_0) + Xe(^1P_1) \qquad (29)$$

which efficiently quenches the 1300-Å argon continuum and leads to the generation of the xenon continuum at ~ 1700 Å through a strong coupling of the argon and xenon kinetic chains in argon/xenon mixtures. There are also similarly impressive atom–atom amplitudes in the argon/xenon and krypton/xenon systems [94]. The energy-level diagram relevant to this process is shown in Fig. 15. Since the excited xenon atom is not pure singlet, the apparent violation of the Wigner–Witmer rule [95] for $Ar_2(^3\Sigma_u^+)$ is not considered important.

This energy transfer process has been examined experimentally with a pulsed high-current relativistic electron beam [68]. Fig. 16(a) illustrates the emission observed by Krawetz and Rhodes [68] at 1300 Å from pure argon at 850-torr pressure. Considerable radiation attributable[16] to the lower vibrational levels of the $^1\Sigma_u^+ \rightarrow {}^1\Sigma_g^+$ transition of Ar_2^*

[16] Y. Yanaka and K. Yoshino, *J. Chem Phys.*, vol. 53, p. 2012, 1970. It is interesting to note that this assignment does not agree with the earlier work reported by G. S. Hurst, T. E. Bortner, and T. D. Stickler, *Phys. Rev.*, vol. 178, p. 4, 1969.

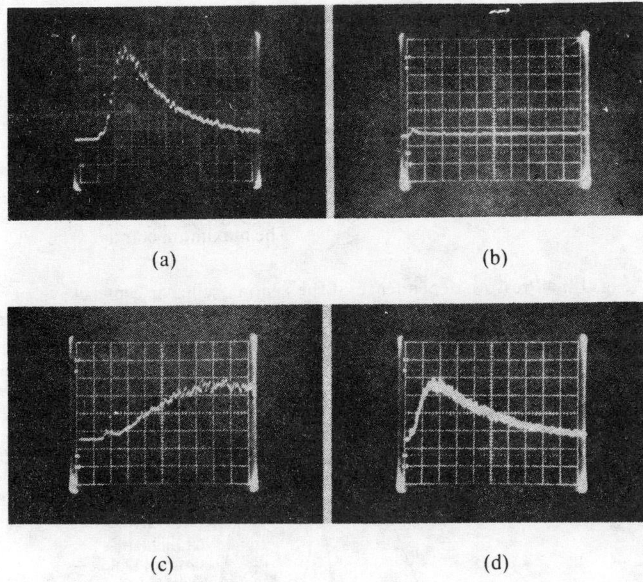

Fig. 16. (a) Time dependence of 1300 Å (± 5 Å) argon continuum emission at a pressure of 850 torr. Vertical scale: 400 mV/cm; horizontal scale: 100 ns/cm. (b) Time dependence of 1300 Å (± 5 Å) argon continuum emission from a mixture of 820-torr argon and 30-torr xenon. Vertical scale: 200 mV/cm; horizontal scale: 100 ns/cm. This result is to be compared to that of Fig. 16(a). (c) Time dependence of 1700 Å (± 5 Å) continuum emission arising from Xe_2^* produced in a mixture of 820-torr argon and 30-torr xenon. The conditions of the experiment are the same as for Fig. 16(b). Vertical scale: 200 mV/cm; horizontal scale: 100 ns/cm. (d) Time dependence of 1700 Å (± 5 Å) continuum emission from Xe_2^* which is identical to Fig. 16(c) except that the horizontal sweep rate is reduced. Vertical scale: 200 mV/cm; horizontal scale: 500 ns/cm.

is present.[17] Tanaka and Yoshino[16] conclude that the contribution of the ${}^3\Sigma_u^+ \rightarrow {}^1\Sigma_g^+$ transition should be small in argon. The influence of the addition of 30 torr of xenon to 820 torr of argon on the intensity of the 1300-Å argon continuum is illustrated in Fig. 16(b). All other parameters including the vertical sensitivity are identical to those of Fig. 16(a). The argon molecular continuum is essentially eliminated by the presence of the xenon additive. The xenon atoms, once excited to the ${}^1P_1$ level, are strongly trapped[17] and should eventually relax by both collisional quenching to the triplet states and by molecular formation of Xe_2^* in the process[18]

$$Xe^* + Xe({}^1S_0) + Ar({}^1S_0) \rightarrow Xe_2^* + Ar({}^1S_0). \tag{30}$$

Observe that this reaction is quite similar to process (18) except that the third body is argon instead of xenon. In the approximation that the third body participates largely through the relatively long-range van der Waals interaction, it should be possible to estimate the ratio of the rates for (18) and (30), since the van der Waals force involves the atomic polarizabilities in a known manner [96]. This aspect is presently under examination.[19] It is important to note that this rate can be made sufficiently rapid even at relatively low xenon densities by a corresponding increase in the argon density. The signature of Xe_2^* formation is the appearance of the molecular xenon emission at ~ 1700 Å. Since the xenon partial pressure is considerably less than that of the argon, it is anticipated that the formation rate of the Xe_2^* species will be less than for the Ar_2^* observed without xenon present. Fig. 16(c) shows the time dependence of the emission observed at 1700 Å in the mixture consisting of 30-torr Xe and 820-torr Ar. These conditions are identical to those existing in Fig. 16(b). Fig. 16(d) illustrates the data of Fig. 16(c) with a reduced horizontal sweep of 500 ns/cm enabling observation of the complete time development of the emission at 1700 Å. These data are completely consistent with the conclusions of Gedanken *et al.* [94] concerning the efficient energy transfer process (29). It is significant in this connection to observe that the curve in Fig. 16(c) very closely approximates the integral of the trace shown in Fig. 16(a). This is consistent with an efficient transfer from the Ar_2^* to the Xe atoms generating a population of ${}^3P_2$ Xe atoms through collisional cascade from the ${}^1P_1$ level.

The existence of such a rapid energy transfer mechanism suggests the operation of the xenon laser system in argon/xenon mixtures in which the xenon is actually the minority constituent. For reasons to be examined later, a reduction in the xenon density can have a beneficial influence on the properties of the oscillator. Preliminary experimental [62] results show that energy transfer processes can be used to substantially increase the output power of the xenon laser at ~1720 Å in argon/xenon mixtures. Experimentally observed enhancements at the output are approximately a factor of 2 in both peak power and energy, as shown in Fig. 17. This effect is illustrated in Fig. 17, which displays both the output peak power and energy for pure xenon and argon/xenon mixtures. The mixture data refers to a fixed xenon pressure of 100 psia. In this case, the enhancement is measured by the relative peaks of the two pairs of curves. Note that for pure xenon the maximum output energy occurs at a xenon pressure of ~200 psia, while the corresponding maximum of the mixture falls at 100 psia xenon and ~200 psia argon. For these conditions the output is essentially doubled, although the stopping power [71] of the mixture is somewhat lower than the pure xenon case. This indicates an improvement in the efficiency as well. In addition, the use of argon/xenon mixtures results in a reduction of the oscillation threshold in terms of xenon partial pressure. Oscillation on the xenon molecular transition has been observed in mix-

[17] The radiating ${}^1P_1$ and ${}^3P_1$ levels are completely trapped, while the ${}^3P_0$ and ${}^3P_2$ are radiatively metastable. For single photon processes the ${}^3P_0$ can decay by M1 and E2 radiation to the ${}^3P_1$ and ${}^3P_2$ levels, respectively, with the ${}^3P_0 \rightarrow {}^1S_0$ channel strictly forbidden; the lowest order process for ${}^3P_2 \rightarrow {}^1S_0$ decay is M2. For data on neon, argon, and krypton, see R. S. Van Dyck, Jr., C. E. Johnson, and H. A. Shugart, *Phys. Rev.*, vol. A5, p. 991, 1972.

[18] The formation of heteronuclear dimers such as ArXe* cannot be completely ruled out in these mixtures. Recent experimental studies provide no evidence for the formation of ArXe*, although a band ~ 1530 Å was tentatively attributed to a heteronuclear KrXe* dimer. For details, see O. Chestnovsky, B. Raz, and J. Jortner, *J. Chem. Phys.*, to be published. Earlier work indicating the possible formation of heteronuclear systems appears in E. Kugler, *Ann. Phys.*, vol. 14, p. 137, 1964.

[19] The rate constant for reaction (30) has been measured preliminarily to have the value $(1.8 \pm 0.2) \times 10^{-32}$ cm^6/s at ~ 300 K. (P. W. Hoff and P. J. Kelly, private communication.) This result compares reasonably with an estimate based on the polarizabilities of the interacting systems.

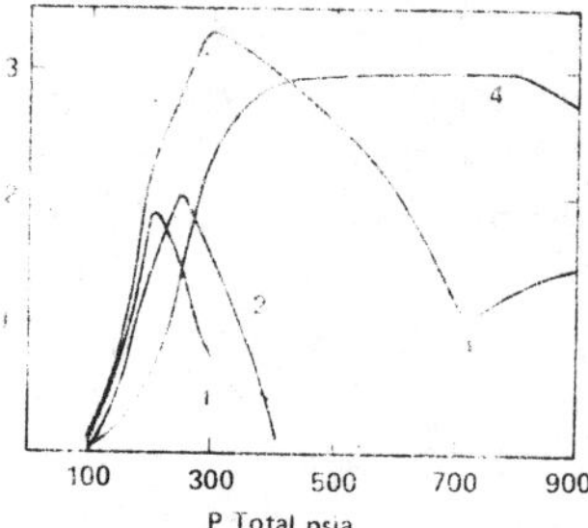

Fig. 17. Dependence of pulse energy and pulse peak power versus total pressure for the xenon laser at ~ 1720 Å operating on pure xenon and argon–xenon mixtures: 1) pulse energy for pure xenon; 2) peak power for pure xenon; 3) pulse energy for 100 psia xenon with added argon; 4) peak power for 100 psia xenon with added argon. An enhancement of approximately a factor of 2 is seen for both quantities.

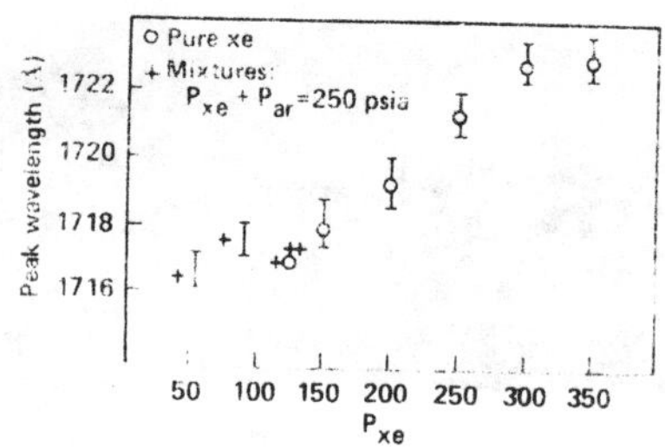

Fig. 18. Pressure dependence of the xenon oscillator center wavelength on xenon partial pressure for both argon/xenon mixtures and pure xenon.

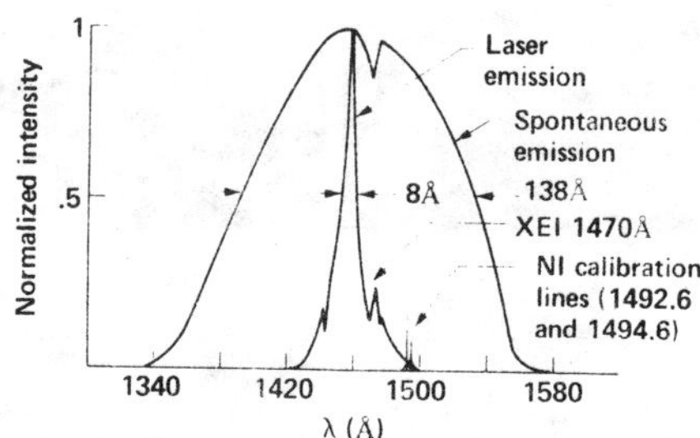

Fig. 19. Time-integrated spectral output of the high-pressure krypton oscillator (linear vertical scale) showing NI calibration lines for: 1) conditions below threshold, and 2) conditions above threshold. Above threshold the transition narrows to ~ 8 Å at 1457 ± 1 Å. Minor absorption bands are tentatively attributed to the $X^1\Sigma_g^+ \rightarrow A^1\Pi$ transition of CO present as an impurity in addition to the xenon resonance absorption at 1470 Å.

tures of 50 psia xenon and 400 psia argon where the xenon is truly the minority constituent. It is important to realize, however, that these data pertain to an oscillator configuration which contained no control of the mode volume. Calibrated sapphire attenuators were used to prevent detector saturation over the full dynamic range of measurements. Among the several factors which may contribute to the increased oscillator output are: 1) the possibility of lower excited-state–excited-state collisional loss rates in the argon kinetic chain as compared to the corresponding xenon kinetic processes. For fixed Xe_2* excimer density, the excited-state losses will be the same; therefore for this process to be operative the differential losses would have to occur higher in the kinetic chain. 2) Lower collisionally induced absorption [97]–[100] arising from xenon–xenon encounters (at fixed temperature and wavelength, this effect scales as the square of the xenon density). 3) Oscillation over a large effective mode volume due to the decrease in the optical losses noted in 2) above, or due to a more beneficial electron-energy deposition in the gas. Internal apertures are necessary to limit the mode volume in order to separate these geometrical averaging effects from increases in localized inversion density.

It is interesting that this improved performance has been observed in conjunction with a blue shift of the mixture spectrum in comparison to the case of pure xenon. Although short of a proof, this is a significant indication that reduced collisionally induced absorption originating from xenon–xenon collisions[20] may be an important factor in the increased output. A frequency shift of this nature is expected since the collision-induced absorption is strongly frequency dependent [97], [98]. Assuming that the Ar-Xe potential curves are such that collision-induced absorption from this system is negligible at wavelengths ~ 1720 Å so that the optical losses arise solely from Xe–Xe encounters and that it is possible to generate essentially the same xenon exciton densities as developed in the pure xenon case under conditions of substantially reduced total xenon density, a greater optical gain should result. This occurs since the optical losses are dependent only on the total *xenon* density, and will be lower under these conditions. The actual data of the experimentally determined frequency shifts are illustrated in Fig. 18. Frequency shifts as large as 7 Å are observed, and the shift is *independent* of argon pressure supporting the assumption made above. In Sections II-B, 2 (e) and II-B, 2 (f) we will consider a very simple model which indicates the interplay between exciton formation and destruction rates, collision-induced absorption, and dynamical gas heating.

d) Molecular krypton system: The molecular continuum of krypton arising from bound–free transitions of the excited krypton dimer Kr_2* and centered at ~1500 Å is analogous to the corresponding spectral feature in xenon at ~ 1700 Å. As a first approximation, the level structure of the Kr_2 system can be understood *mutatis mutandis* from the published data[12,21] on Xe_2. Kinetically, the system should also strongly resemble the xenon case as modeled by processes (16)–(27). This similarity is reflected in the fact that strong stimulated emission has been observed [62] on this transition in krypton at 1457 ± 1 Å with a linewidth of 8 Å, as shown by the spectrum in Fig. 19. The experimental arrangement was identical to that used in the xenon experiments of Hoff *et al.* [61]. This emission occurred in a ~ 8-ns pulse observed on the photodiode and displayed in Fig. 20. Due to a small but unavoidable impurity of xenon in the krypton sample, the xenon 1470-Å resonance line is a prominent ab-

[20] At ~ 1700 Å there is also the possibility of a component due to argon–xenon collisions which would scale like the product of the argon and xenon densities. The importance of this effect depends upon the details of the molecular potential curves for the ArXe system.

[21] These larger diatomics should be considered within the framework of Hund's case (*c*) coupling.

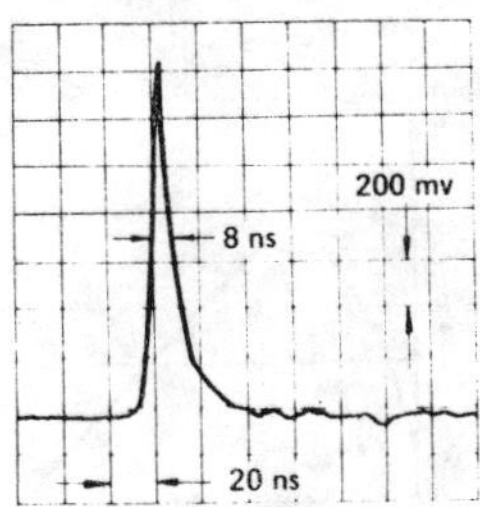

Fig. 20. Spectrally integrated photodiode output signal illustrating the time dependence of the krypton laser output at ~ 1457 Å for conditions well above threshold (500 psia). The pulse rise time may be limited by the 2-ns detectors response time.

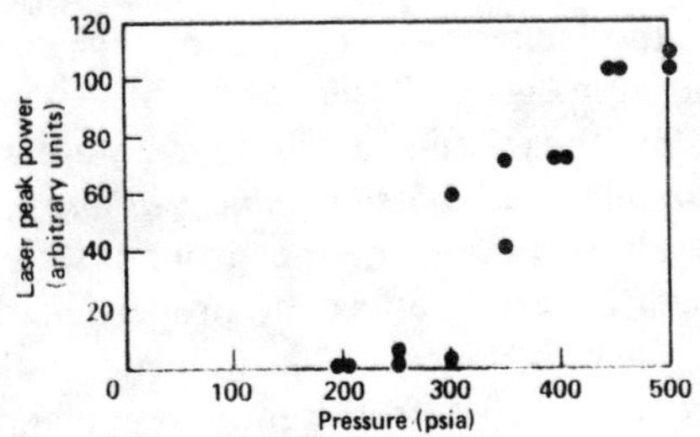

Fig. 21. The pressure dependence of the krypton oscillator output. Note the threshold at ~ 260 psia.

sorptive feature in the spectrum. Moreover, the observations indicate that this absorptive loss dominates the optical losses of the system and easily prevents oscillation unless considerable care is taken to limit contamination from xenon. Furthermore, since the 1470-Å xenon resonance line absorption has a strong wavelength dependence in the region which overlaps the wavelength of the observed stimulated emission, it is expected that the precise values of the krypton stimulated emission center frequency and bandwidth will be dependent on the xenon impurity level. The pressure dependence of the peak power (detected with an ITT 4115 photodiode) is illustrated in Fig. 21. A threshold for oscillation was observed at ~ 250 psia; pressure cell limitations prevented an examination of the region above 500 psia. In the case of krypton, no wavelength shift was observed with krypton pressure in significant contrast to the observations on the xenon system.

e) Competition between excimer formation and destruction: In this section, we consider a very simple geometric model examining the competition between excimer formation and decay. Of course, the full kinetic treatment always applies, this is done merely for simple illustrative purposes. Consider the formation of an excimer $(ab)^*$ which correlates with an excited species a^* and partner b. Under a wide range of circumstances the excited $(ab)^*$ systems are formed primarily by three-body collisions of a^*, b, and a third species denoted in the following as c, in the process

$$a^* + b + c \rightarrow (ab)^* + c \tag{31}$$

which in the previously described kinetic model corresponds to process (18). At sufficiently high excimer densities, an important destructive path can be mutual excimer–excimer annihilation[22] by the reactions

$$(ab)^* + (ab)^* \rightarrow \text{nonexcimer species} \tag{32}$$

which, for example, may be a Penning process as illustrated earlier by process (26).

It is physically reasonable that states $(ab)^*$ characterized by large-scale lengths (molecular dimensions) will have substantial amplitudes for excimer formation by process (31). This follows since the extended structure implies a sizable interaction radius of the a^*–b system, and, consequently, increases the probability of a favorable three-body encounter. On the other hand, destructive channels illustrated by reaction (32) above may also be correspondingly large for such states again as a direct consequence of their size. Since the excimer density is determined by the balance between production and destruction mechanisms, we formulate below a statement of the competition between reactions (31) and (32) within the framework of a very approximate and simple model. This model consists entirely of the basic assumption that the relevant reactions are governed by a single amplitude r_0 which is determined by scale length of the $(ab)^*$ complex. This sweeping statement establishes a relationship between the kinetic rates and a property of the *free* $(ab)^*$ system and thus constitutes a simple criterion for comparison of $(ab)^*$ alternatives.[23]

We now analyze the competition between these processes. For this purpose the densities n^*, n_a, n_b, and n_c denote the $(ab)^*$, a^*, b, and c species, respectively. The quantity v represents the relative velocity of the collision partners and r_0 is the scale length mentioned above. With these definitions it is easily seen that the equation of motion for the excimer density n^* takes the form

$$\dot{n}^* = n_a n_b n_c v r_0^5 - n^{*2} v r_0^2. \tag{33}$$

The three-body rate is essentially a two-body rate modified by a multiplicative factor consisting of the product of the two-body collision frequency and the duration of an encounter. The steady-state condition[24] ($\dot{n}^* = 0$) is then equivalent to

$$n^* = (n_a n_b n_c r_0^3)^{1/2} \tag{34}$$

in which it is observed that the velocity factor fails to appear.[25] On this basis it seems that the larger systems such as Xe_2^* [98][12] and $LiXe^*$ [66], [98] are favored. For fixed n_a, the situation is improved with the product $n_b n_c r_0^3$. We observe that if n_a is proportional to the excitation rate a ten-fold increase in n^* necessitates a hundred-fold in-

[22] For an excimer density of ~ 10^{17} cm^{-3} and a cross section of ~ 10^{-14} cm^2, the relaxation time is ~ 50 ns. Since we are primarily interested here in the influence of the excimer–excimer process, we ignore the radiative channel in this analysis. The radiative process is incorporated in a later section.

[23] This assumption can easily be relaxed in any specific case by incorporating the actual rate constants for the relevant processes.

[24] Provided that the time scale of the kinetic chain is sufficiently short in comparison to the time scale of variations in the source of excitation, the steady-state analysis is a reasonable approximation which leads to an adiabatic response of n^* to n_a, n_b, and n_c. Since this condition is valid for the questions of interest, we will make this assumption throughout.

[25] This simple model leads to a temperature independence of expression (34) provided the "interaction radius" r_0 is not energy dependent.

crease in the excitation rate. This unfavorable scaling condition is the general signature of loss mechanisms associated with excited-state–excited-state loss channels.

f) Ground-state collision-induced absorption: Collision-induced absorption from the ground state of the (*ab*) system can adversely affect the properties of bound–free systems. There is evidence of its influence in the stimulated emission at ~ 1720 Å from xenon by the appearance of a red shift in the stimulated emission spectrum which depends on the xenon density as shown in Fig. 18. At a specific wavelength λ the absorption coefficient β is proportional to the factor [98], [100] $\rho_a \rho_b e^{-\Delta(\lambda)/kT}$ where ρ_a and ρ_b are the densities of the appropriate ground-state species, $\Delta(\lambda)$ is a characteristic energy dependent upon the wavelength λ through the details of the potential energy surfaces, and T is the kinetic temperature of the gas. Since $\Delta(\lambda)/kT >> 1$ for conditions of interest, the exponential factor has very strong temperature dependence. There is an additional temperature-dependent factor which is weakly varying in comparison to the exponential and which for simplicity we will neglect here [98]. In addition, if the density factor $\rho_a \rho_b$ strongly varies with temperature, as it would, for example, in the Hg, Cd, or Zn systems [63], then these two effects combine in the generation of a severe temperature dependence. The result is an absorption coefficient running amok. From this standpoint, high densities of hot material represent the worst case.

Within the framework of the previously stated kinetic model, one can formulate a simple statement concerning the density dependence and scaling laws of the optical gain exhibited by the excited material. In this way we establish a relationship between the kinetic processes generating the desired excited species and the unwanted optical losses. For this purpose, it is useful to modify the rate equation given by expression (33) by the inclusion of a radiative decay term ($-n^*/\tau$) on the right-hand side. The revised equation then reads

$$\dot{n}^* = n_a n_b n_c v r_0^5 - n^{*2} v r_0^2 - n^*/\tau \tag{35}$$

where τ represents the radiative lifetime of the exciton. The steady-state solution is then found simply to be

$$n^* = \frac{1}{2\tau v r_0^2}\left[(1 + 4 n_a n_b n_c \tau^2 v^2 r_0^7)^{1/2} - 1\right] \tag{36}$$

where we have selected the physically meaningful root. Since the parameters τ, v, and r_0 are given constants, and since it is physically reasonable to assume that n_a, n_b, and n_c are proportional to the density ρ in a homogeneous system for a wide range of interesting circumstances, expression (36) can be written in the form

$$n^*(\rho) = A_0[(1 + B\rho^3)^{1/2} - 1] \tag{37}$$

with A_0 and B taken as the appropriate constants. Note that for sufficiently high-density ρ, the excited-state density $n^*(\rho)$ goes as $\rho^{3/2}$, which is a weaker dependence than the ρ^2 law governing the collisionally induced absorption. It is also interesting to observe that for constant n_a (a condition which could presumably be approximated by the existence of sufficiently rapid excited-state–excited-state losses in the kinetic chain producing n_a) the exciton density $n^*(\rho)$ scales only as ρ in the high-density limit. With these considerations in mind, we now construct the simple function $Y(\rho)$

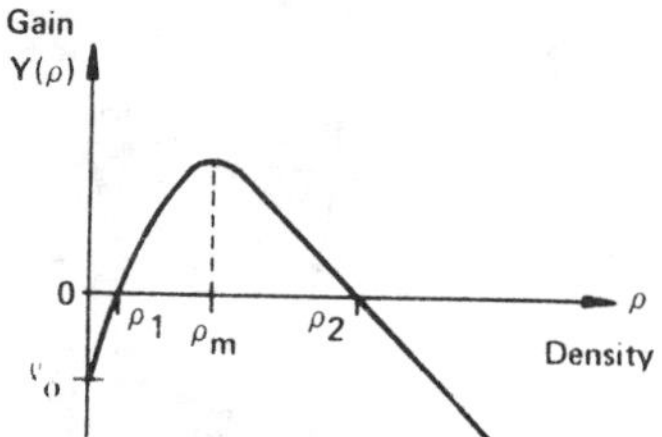

Fig. 22. Net gain parameter $Y(\rho)$ as a function of density r for fixed values of A, B, C, and l_0 such that two thresholds appear at ρ_1 and ρ_2.

$$Y(\rho) = A[(1 + B\rho^3)^{1/2} - 1] - C\rho^2 - l_0 \tag{38}$$

to approximately represent the net optical gain per pass experienced by radiation of wavelength λ in an oscillator configuration with mirror losses described by l_0. The constants A and C depend generally on the optical cross section, the geometry of the excited volume since unexcited gas may occupy a different volume, and the wavelength λ. For the present purpose we do not concern ourselves here with these aspects, but merely regard them as given data. For conditions of interest the parameters A, B, C, and l_0 are all greater than zero. In this connection it is important to note that due to rapid gas heating, as illustrated in Fig. 10, the appropriate value of the parameter C, which is strongly dependent upon the details of the potential curve, corresponds to the *elevated* gas temperature arising from the excitation rather than the initial kinetic temperature. Because of the strong temperature dependence of this quantity, a very large increase in the magnitude of this parameter may result.

The equation

$$Y(\rho) = 0 \tag{39}$$

then defines the thresholds of oscillation and is easily seen to have the possibility of zero, one, or two solutions in the domain $0 \leq \rho < \infty$, depending upon the relative values of A, B, C, and l_0. The situation illustrating the latter alternative is shown in Fig. 22, which, in this very elementary analysis, describes an oscillator exhibiting two oscillation thresholds at densities ρ_1 and ρ_2. This implies the existance of an optimal density at an intermediate density ρ_m such that $\rho_1 < \rho_m < \rho_2$. It should be noted that behavior qualitatively similar to this is observed experimentally in the case of xenon and is shown in Fig. 14. Although it is certainly unwarranted to claim any quantitative significance for this crude description, these simple considerations reinforce the conviction that excited-state–excited-state collisional losses and ground-state absorption must be minimized in order to permit efficient scaling to high densities.[26] The elimination of either or both of

[26] The excited-state–excited-state mechanism imposes a constraint on excimer density, while the collision-induced ground-state absorption is a statement relating essentially to the total density.

these undesirable processes will definitely improve performance. Finally, we note that within the framework of this model it is possible for the oscillator gain and *coherent* output to decrease in the manner indicated by Fig. 14 and Fig. 22, while the spontaneous emission, which follows $n^*(\rho)$ according to (37), increases with added density. Indeed, for xenon it has been experimentally observed in fluorescence studies [101] that the spontaneous emission increases in the range from 200 to 400 psia, while the oscillator output deteriorates under the same conditions.

The basic conclusions of this very simple analysis have been substantiated by more elaborate and refined numerical calculations taking into account the full kinetic model [83], the dynamics of the lower state, and gas heating [102]. Furthermore, comparison of these calculations [102] with the data illustrated in Fig. 14 indicates that the appropriate optical cross section for the xenon dimer transitions is on the order of $\sim 3 \times 10^{-18}$ cm^2. Nevertheless, these findings must be regarded as reasonable preliminary estimates, since the calculated behavior of the oscillator exhibited a greater sensitivity to the details of the molecular potential curves than originally expected. As detailed information concerning these molecular data is currently lacking, it is essential that the appropriate *ab initio* calculations be performed to accurately determine these molecular properties for comparison with experiment. Considerably more work is needed in this area.

Finally, we observe that the demonstration of efficient energy transfer has important implications for laser systems operating on molecular bound–free transitions. It enables a reduction in the required density of the active material, and consequently lowers the collisionally induced absorption, a quantity which may represent a strong limitation on the extractable energy density. In addition, since we have some freedom in selecting the minority acceptor system, the output wavelength is at our disposal. Systems exhibiting efficient energy transfer to Hg or Zn may enable the generation of intense stimulated emission in the near ultraviolet and visible spectral regions.

III. Alternative Sources of Ultraviolet and Shorter Wavelength Radiation

In this section we explore a number of other methods, some demonstrated and others proposed, for the generation of ultraviolet and shorter wavelength radiation. These include harmonic generation and mixing techniques, Raman processes, and proposed extensions into the X-ray region involving the creation of inner shell vacancies.

A. Harmonic Generation and Mixing Techniques

The nonlinear optical response of materials has been used to generate coherent radiation in the ultraviolet spectral region. Nonlinear behavior is a general property of matter under the influence of a sufficiently intense optical wave. For example, a free electron interacting with an electromagnetic wave exhibits nonlinear behavior [103]. The polarization produced in the medium is not linearly related to the driving electric field. Clasically, this leads to currents at harmonic frequencies. The first demonstration of second-harmonic generation of ruby laser radiation at 6943 Å to ultraviolet quanta at 3471 Å was achieved by Franken *et al.* [104] in a quartz crystal. Third-harmonic generation in calcite of ruby radiation was observed by Terhune *et al.* [105] approximately one year later. The basic theory of optical harmonic generation and mixing in nonlinear media has recently been reviewed by Kleinman [106].

Although second-harmonic generation is forbidden in isotropic materials by fundamental considerations [103], third-harmonic generation is allowed and therefore can be accomplished in gaseous media [107]. However, the phase matching required for efficient conversion, which in solid materials was generally achieved by the use of the intrinsic optical anisotropy of the nonlinear medium, must be attained in another way. Phase-matched third harmonic in metal vapor-inert gas mixtures was first discussed by Harris and Miles [108]. At the proper density ratio they showed that the positive and negative dispersive components could be made to balance so that phase matching was achieved. Subsequent results using a variety of gases have been published by the same group [109]. The initial experiments produced tripled 1.064 μ radiation at 3547 Å in a mixture of rubidium and xenon. In mixtures of cadmium and argon this technique was extended further into the ultraviolet with the generation of 1773-, 1520-, and 1182-Å radiation. In order to handle the required metal vapors, the heat-pipe technology was utilized [110]. More recently, 1182-Å radiation has been produced by the same method in Xe/Ar mixtures [111], thus eliminating the need for the heat-pipe oven used in the earlier experiments. These later experiments [111] achieved a conversion efficiency of 2.8 percent at 13-MW input power at an argon/xenon density ratio of 1:430. Although the methods mentioned above [107]–[109], [111] all involve electronic transitions in the active material, a theoretical analysis of optical third-harmonic generation by molecular vibrations has been given by Ueda and Shimoda [112].

Dye lasers [113], both pulsed a continuous wave, have produced ultraviolet radiation with the use of well-established second-harmonic generation techniques [106]. In addition, stimulated emission from organic scintillator molecules has been obtained by Abakumov *et al.* [114] in material pumped by Nd-laser harmonic radiation. Wavelengths as low as 3410 Å have been obtained with paraterphenyl in cyclohexane with a linewidth ~60 Å and a conversion efficiency of 1.3 percent. Also, exciplex laser emission down to 3910 Å has been observed [115] with a 4-methylumbelliferone. Nevertheless, the harmonic generation technique is by far the most widely used. Bradley *et al.* [116] have reported pulsed tunable second-harmonic and sum-frequency generation in the region between 2800–2900 Å with a linewidth of ~20 Å. Tunable power between 2900–3000 Å had been previously demonstrated by Huth *et al.* [117]. Other groups have reported tunable radiation in the regions 2160–2340 Å [118], 2500–3250 Å

[119], and 3500–7300 Å [120]. Tunable continuous-wave operation in the spectral region between 2900–3150 Å has been observed by Gebel and Hercher [121] using a rhodamine 6G oscillator with an intracavity doubling element.

B. X-Ray Lasers

The possibility of coherent X-ray production of Cu $K\alpha$ (1.54 Å) radiation has recently been a topic of extreme interest. Initial reports by Kepros *et al.* [122] advancing the thesis of coherent production based largely on the observation of a collimated X-ray output from a cigar-shaped laser produced plasma of $CuSO_4$-doped gelatin have not been sustained by further experimentation. Although the results of Kepros *et al.* [122] were temporarily supported by evidence obtained by Elton *et al.* [123], more detailed examination of the experimental issues has established that the film exposures originally attributed to X-radiation are produced by other effects [124], [125]. These negative findings are consistent with estimates of the optical gain which indicate for the conditions of the experiment the improbability of sufficient optical gain to produce stimulated emission [124], [126].

An interesting approach for the production of population inversion on inner shell transitions has been given by McCorkle [127]. This method uses the selective excitation of inner shell vacancies which are produced in ion–atom collisions. Large cross sections approaching geometric values ($\sim 10^{-17}$ cm²) for these processes have been reported [128]. It is believed that the primary physical process leading to the selective production of the inner shell vacancies is an electron promotion mechanism that occurs at curve crossings of the diatomic quasimolecule formed transiently during the collision [129].

These processes can be examined within the framework of the familiar molecular-orbital (MO) theory [130]. It has been shown [130], [131] that the principal quantum number of an electron can change when going from the separated atoms to the united atom; viz., to a higher principal quantum number when going to the united system. This effect is easily seen from the fact that the separated two-atom system contains four K-shell electrons, while the united atom clearly has only two because of the Pauli exclusion principle. In the transition between these two limits, two of the original K shell electrons must have been promoted to higher shells of the united atom system. These promoted electrons will often follow steeply rising curves which cross levels corresponding to excited configurations of the separated atoms. Therefore, effects which cause transitions at these curve crossings can lead to the production of inner shell excited atomic states of the separated system as a result of a sufficiently energetic collision. In this way a fraction of the kinetic energy of the colliding particles is converted into internal excitation of the particles. Interactions which cause transitions between the molecular-orbital curves at crossings are [129] electron penetration, nuclear motion, and electron correlation (configuration interaction).

Unfortunately, a practical X-ray laser device built on these principles does not presently appear feasible, given the state of the art of ion-beam technology. Ion currents approximately one hundred times those currently available seem necessary to produce optical gains of sufficient magnitude.

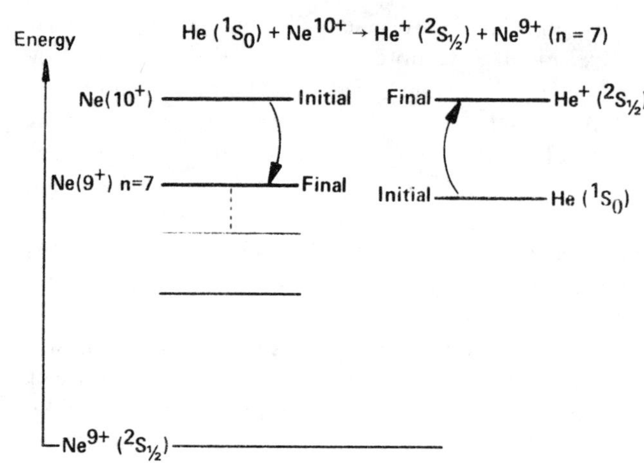

Fig. 23. Energy-level diagrams of He and the hydrogenic Ne^{9+} system illustrating the near resonant charge transfer reaction Ne^{10+} + He (1^1S_0) → Ne^{9+} (n = 7) + He ($1^2S_{1/2}$).

Another imaginative approach to create inversions in the X-ray region using resonant charge exchange has been proposed by Sobel'man [132]. The selective population of certain excited levels of moderate Z materials is produced by near resonant charge exchange of the fully ionized charge Z-ion with neutral helium in the reaction

$$Z + \text{He} \rightarrow (Z - 1)^* + \text{He}^+ \tag{40}$$

producing the excited $(Z - 1)$ charged ion. This then leads to excited ions preferentially populated in one of the higher hydrogenic states with principal quantum number n. The cross sections for these reactions at thermal energies are approximately $\pi a_0^2 Z^2$ so that for Z = 10 a rather substantial rate exists [54]. The situation for Z = 10 is illustrated in Fig. 23. In this case, the value of n = 7 matches the helium ionization potential. Bearing in mind that hydrogenic radiative lifetimes [133] scale as Z^4, it is now possible to consider the production of transient inversions as suitably prepared laser produced plasmas. Sobel'man estimated that a relatively modest laser with an output of only 10 J in 1 ns would be sufficient to demonstrate this effect.

C. Raman Amplifiers

Ultraviolet radiation can be produced by nonlinear optical processes which involve a change in the quantum state of the radiating system. Raman processes from excited systems constitute an example of this mechanism. Radiation at 1090 and 1373 Å has been observed by Bräunlich *et al.* [134] arising from anti-Stokes–Raman scattering and two photon emission from metastable deuterium atoms illuminated with 1.06-μ radiation. In addition, Ducuing *et al.* [135] have experimentally observed anti-Stokes–Raman scattering of 6943-Å radiation from excited Cr^{3+} ions in ruby material.

TABLE I

Material	Wavelength (Å)	Transition	Conditions	References
Hydrogen	1161–1240	$H_2C^1\Pi_u - X^1\Sigma_g^+$ $(v', v'') = (1, 4)$, $(2, 5)$, $(2, 6)$, and $(3, 7)$	pulsed, e-beam excited, 20–100 torr	[43]
	1520–1615	H_2, $B^1\Sigma_g^+ - X^1\Sigma_g^+$ D_2, HD $(v', v'') = (3, 10)$, $(4, 11)$ $(5, 12)$, $(6, 13)$, and $(7, 13)$	pulsed, electric discharge, 100 torr	[38]
Boron	3451 B II	$2p^2\,{}^1D_2 - ({}^2S)2p^1P_1^0$		[139]
Carbon	1548 C IV	$2s^2S_{1/2} - 2p^2P_{3/2}^0$	Traveling wave, transverse discharge (mirrorless)	[149]
	1551	$2s^2S_{1/2} - 2p^2P_{1/2}^0$		
Carbon Monoxide	1811 CO	$A^1\Pi \rightarrow X^1\Sigma^+$ $(v', v'') = (2, 6)$	Traveling wave, transverse discharge (mirrorless)	[45]
	1878	(2–7)		
	1898	(3–8)		
	1950	(2–8)		
	1970	(3–9)		
Nitrogen	3367 N III	$3p^4P_{5/2} \rightarrow 3s^4P_{5/2}^0$		[15]
	3479 N IV	$3p^3P_2^0 \rightarrow 3s^3S_1$	pulsed, electric discharge, 0.05 torr	[14]
	3483 N IV	$3p^3P_1^0 \rightarrow 3s^3S^1$		[15]
	3371–3372	$N_2C^3\Pi_u \rightarrow B^3\Pi_g$ (0, 0)	pulsed, electric discharge, 2 torr	[46]
	3576–3577	(0, 1)		[46]
Oxygen	2984 O III	$3p^1D_2 \rightarrow 3s^1p_1^0$	pulsed, electric discharge, 0.1 torr	[15]
	2985 O III	$4p^5P_2^0 \rightarrow 3d^3D_2$		[137]
	3047 O III	$3p^3P_2 \rightarrow 3s^3P_2^0$		[15]
	3063 O IV	$3p^2p_{3/2}^0 \rightarrow 3s^2S_{1/2}$		[15]
	3381 O IV	$3p^4D_{3/2} \rightarrow 3s^4P_{1/2}^0$		[15]
	3386 O IV	$3p^4D_{7/2} \rightarrow 3s^4P_{5/2}^0$		[15]
	3749 O II	$3p^4S_{3/2}^0 \rightarrow 3s^4P_{5/2}$		[14], [137]
	3755 O III	$3p^3D_2 \rightarrow 3s^3P_1^0$		[14], [137]
	3760 O III	$3p^3D_3 \rightarrow 3s^3P_2^0$		[14], [137]
Fluorine	2760 F III	$3p^2D_{5/2}^0 \rightarrow 3s^2D_{5/2}$	pulsed, electric discharge, 0.002 torr	[16]
	2826 F IV	$3p^3D_3 \rightarrow 3s^3P_2^0$		[16]
	3122 F III	$3p^4D_{7/2}^0 \rightarrow 3s^4P_{5/2}$		[16]
	3174 F III	$3p^2D_{5/2}^0 \rightarrow 3s^2P_{3/2}$		[16]
	3203 F II	$3p'\,{}^1D_2 \rightarrow 3s'\,{}^1D_2^0$		[16]
Neon	2358 Ne IV	$3p^4D_{7/2}^0 \rightarrow 3s^4P_{5/2}$	pulsed, electric discharge, 0.1 torr	[15]
	2473 Ne III			[15]
	2678 Ne III	$3p^3P_2 \rightarrow 3s^3S_1^0$		[138]
	2679 Ne III	$3p^3P_1 \rightarrow 3s^3S_1^0$		[137]
	2778 Ne III	$3p'\,{}^3D_3 \rightarrow 3s'{}^3D_3^0$		[137]
	2867 Ne III			[15]
	3120 Ne III			[15]
	3320 Ne II	$3p'\,{}^2P_{1/2}^0 \rightarrow 3s'\,{}^2D_{3/2}$		[15]
	3324 Ne II	$3p^2P_{3/2}^0 \rightarrow 3s^2P_{3/2}$		[137]
	3327 Ne II	$4p^4D_{3/2}^0 \rightarrow 3s^4P_{3/2}$		[137]
	3329 Ne II	$3d^4D_{7/2} \rightarrow 3p^4D_{7/2}^0$		[138]
	3331 Ne III	$3p^3D_2 \rightarrow 3s'P_1^0$		[138]
	3345 Ne II	$3p'\,{}^2P_{3/2}^0 \rightarrow 3s'\,{}^2D_{5/2}$		[15]
	3378 Ne II	$3p^2P_{1/2}^0 \rightarrow 3s^2p_{1/2}$		[137]
	3393 Ne II	$3p^2P_{3/2}^0 \rightarrow 3s^2P_{1/2}$		[137]
	3393 Ne II	$3d^2D_{3/2} \rightarrow 3p^2D_{5/2}^0$		[138]
Phosphorous	3348 P IV	$4p^3P_2^0 \rightarrow 4s^3S_1$		[16]
Sulphur	2639 S V			[140]
	3325 S III	$({}^2P^0)4p^3P_2 - ({}^2p^0)3d^3P_2^0$		[140]
	3497 S III			[140]
	3709 S III	$({}^2P^0)4p^3D_2 - ({}^2P^0)3d^3P_1^0$		[140]
Chlorine	2633 Cl III	$4p'\,{}^2F_{7/2} \rightarrow 4d'\,{}^2D_{5/2}$	pulsed, electric discharge, 0.002 torr	[16]
	3191 Cl III	$4p'\,{}^4S_1^0 \rightarrow 4s^4P_2$		[16]
	3393 Cl III	$4p'\,{}^2D_1^0 \rightarrow 4s'\,{}^2D_1$		[16]
	3393 Cl III	$4p'\,{}^2D_2^0 \rightarrow 4s'\,{}^2D_2$		[16]
	3530 Cl III	$4p'\,{}^2F_3^0 \rightarrow 4s'\,{}^2D_2$		[16]
	3561 Cl III	$4p'\,{}^2F_2^0 \rightarrow 4s'\,{}^2D_1$		[16]
	3602 Cl III	$4p^4D_3^0 \rightarrow 4s^4P_2$		[16]
	3612 Cl III	$4p^4D_2^0 \rightarrow 4s^4P_1$		[16]
	3623 Cl III	$4p^3D_1^0 \rightarrow 4s^4P_0$		[16]
	3720 Cl III	$4p^2D_2 \rightarrow 4s^2P_1$		[16]
	3749 Cl III	$4p^2D_1^0 \rightarrow 4s^2P_0$		[16]

Finally, we are free to speculate about the possibility of bound–free Raman amplifiers. A synthesis of the bound-free and Raman (or two-photon) concepts unites two extremely attractive features useful in the construction of large, scalable laser systems (i.e., no lower state and no low signal gain). Although information on such systems is not currently in abundant supply, there are indications of the existence of suitable candidates, the study of which will presumably lead to others. As an example, there is evidence that $Hg({}^3P_0)$ combines with N_2 $(X^1\Sigma_g^+)$ to form an excited bound couples $(HgN_2)^*$ which does not spontaneously radiate to the ground state [136]. Such systems may be able to be made to radiate efficiently by the appropriate Raman or two-photon process. Admittedly rough and preliminary estimates of the Raman gain coefficient for a case of this type, assuming an excimer density $\sim 10^{17}$ cm^{-3}, indicate that values $\sim 10^{-9}$ cm/W may be feasible.

TABLE I (*Continued*)

Material	Wavelength (Å)	Transition	Conditions	References
Argon	2625 Ar IV	$4p'\ ^2D_{5/2}^0 \rightarrow 4s'\ ^2D_{5/2}$	pulsed, electric discharge, 0.1 torr	[15]
	2884 Ar III	$4p'\ ^3P_2 \rightarrow 4s'\ ^3D_3^0$		[15]
	2913 Ar IV	$4p^2\ D_{5/2}^0 \rightarrow 4s^2P_{3/2}$		[137]
	2926 Ar IV	$4p^2D_{3/2} \rightarrow 4s^2P_{1/2}$		[137]
	3024 Ar III	$4p''\ ^3D_1 \rightarrow 4s'\ ^3P_2^0$		[137]
	3047 Ar II			[137]
	3055 Ar III	$4p''\ ^3D_2 \rightarrow 4s''\ ^3P_1^0$		[137]
	3336 Ar III	$4p'\ ^3F_4 \rightarrow 4s'\ ^3D_2^0$		[137]
	3344 Ar III	$4p'\ ^3F_3 \rightarrow 4s'\ ^3D_2^0$		[137]
	3358 Ar III	$4p'\ ^3F_2 \rightarrow 4s'\ ^3D_1^0$		[137]
	3511 Ar III	$4p^3P_1 \rightarrow 4s^3S_1^0$		[137]
	3514 Ar III	$4p^3P_1 \rightarrow 4s^3S_1^0$		[137]
	3576 Ar II	$4d^4F_{7/2} \rightarrow 4p^4D_{5/2}$		[137]
	3638 Ar III	$4p'\ F_3 \rightarrow 4s'D_2^0$		[138]
	3795 Ar III	$4p''\ ^3D_3 \rightarrow 3d''\ ^3P_2^0$		[137]
	3858 Ar III	$4p''\ ^3D_2 \rightarrow 3d''\ ^3p_1^0$		[137]
Krypton	1449–1465	$^{1,3}\Sigma_u^+ \rightarrow X^1\Sigma_g^+$	pulsed, *e*-beam pumped, 500 psia	[62]
	2649 Kr II	$(^3P)5f^2D_{3/2}^0 - (^3P)4d^4P_{3/2}$		[15]
	2664 Kr II	$(^1D)5d^2P_{3/2} - (^3P)5p^4D_{1/2}^0$		[15]
	3124 Kr III	$(^2D^0)5p^1D_2 - (^2D^0)5s^1D_2^0$		[15]
	3240 Kr III	$(^2P^0)5p^1D_2 - (^2p^0)5s^1P_1^0$		[15]
	3375 Kr III	$(^2P^0)5p^3D_3 - (^2p^0)5s^3P_2^0$		[141]
	3507 Kr III	$(^4S^0)5p^3P_2 - (^4S^0)5s^3S_1^0$		[134],[141]
	3564 Kr III	$(^4S^0)5p^3P_1 - (^4S^0)5s^3S_1^0$		[15]
	3771 Kr II	$(^3P)5d^4P_{1/2} - (^3P)5p^4P_{3/2}^0$		[135],[142]
Cadmium	3250 Cd II	$5s^2\ ^2D_{3/2} - (^1S)5p^2P_{1/2}^0$		[26]
Xenon	1704–1736	$^{1,3}\Sigma_u^+ \rightarrow X^1\Sigma_g^+$	pulsed, *e*-beam pumped, 250 psia	[61]
	2477 Xe			[15]
	2692 Xe	$(^2P^0)6p^3D_1 - (^2P^0)6s^3P_0^0$		[15]
	2984 Xe III			[141]
	3080 Xe	$(^2P^0)6p^3D_3 - (^2D^0)5d^3D_3^0$		[15]
	3247 Xe III			[15]
	3331 Xe IV			[15]
	3350 Xe			[15]
	3454 Xe III	$(^2D^0)6p^1D_2 - (^2D^0)6s^1D_2^0$		[15]
	3483 Xe			
	3542 Xe III	$(^2D^0)6p^3P_2 - (^2D^0)6s^3D_3^0$		[142]
	3597 Xe III			[143]
	3646 Xe			[15]
	3669 Xe			[15]
	3746 Xe III	$(^2D^0)6p^1D_2 - (^2D^0)5d^1D_2^0$		[15]
	3760 Xe			[141]
	3781 Xe III	$(4S^0)6p^3P_2 - (^4S^0)6s^3S_1^0$		[15]
	3803 Xe			[15]
	3841 Xe III			[144]
	3973 Xe			[15]
	3993 Xe III			[144]
Lead	3640	$6p7s\ ^3P_1^0 - 6p^2\ ^3P_1$	Pb^{208} at 800–900°C with He, Ne, or Ar, pulsed electric discharge	[145]
ZnS	3245–3300		*e*-beam, pulsed	[146]
ZnO	3740–3770		*e*-beam, pulsed	[147]
Gd^{3+}	Glass		77 K, pulsed	[148]

IV. Discussion and Conclusions

Although coherent ultraviolet oscillators have been in existence for nearly a decade, and thus could be regarded as a relatively old development, very little detailed information on their properties exists. Similarly, they have not found broad application. Nevertheless, the recent developments in the bound–free systems such as Xe_2^* and Kr_2^* energized with relativistic electron beams have generated a renewed vitality and interest in the field. Although this research is in its initial stages, we already see the interplay among the several fields of plasma physics, atomic and molecular structure, atomic and molecular collision physics, and laser physics to such an extent that it appears meaningless to differentiate among them. In this sense, the cross fertilization is essentially a synthesis and a fusion of these diverse disciplines.

Historically, events appear to have followed a fairly orderly path from the elementary to the more complex. The first results were obtained with simple ionized atoms under conditions of relatively low density. Following this, additional developments involving light diatomic molecules appeared. Currently, the focus is on relatively complicated heavy diatomic systems in a strongly dynamical high-density environment.

In addition to its rich potential, the ultraviolet region of the spectrum implies a multitude of materials difficulties. These include optical properties such as surface finish and strength. These issues become particularly severe in the vacuum ultraviolet where the choice of materials is quite restricted. These tecnnological materials questions must be thoroughly addressed if the ultraviolet laser systems are to achieve their full potential.

Appendix

Table I contains a list of the transitions, wavelengths, and radiating species known to emit coherent radiation in the ultraviolet spectral region. For molecular transitions where bands are involved the reader should consult the extensive tabulations of Röss [150] and Pressley [151] for the precise data on the individual vibration–rotational transitions.

Acknowledgment

The author wishes to thank the many individuals who helped in the preparation of this manuscript. Notable among these are P. W. Hoff, J. R. Murray, J. C. Swingle, R. R. Jacobs, C. W. Werner, A. M. Karo, and E. V. George. Thanks are also expressed to D. C. Lorents for his comments on the Xe_2^* radiative lifetime.

References

[1] T. H. Maiman, *Nature*, vol. 187, p. 493, 1960.

[2] A. L. Schawlow and C. H. Townes, *Phys. Rev.*, vol. 112, p. 1940, 1958.

[3] V. Weisskopf, *Z. Phys.*, vol. 34, p. 1, 1933.
P. W. Anderson, *Phys. Rev.*, vol. 76, p. 647, 1949.
M. Baranger, *Phys. Rev.*, vol. 111, p. 481, 1958.
——, *Phys. Rev.*, vol. 111, p. 494, 1958.
——, *Phys. Rev.*, vol. 112, p. 855, 1958.
U. Fano, *Phys. Rev.*, vol. 131, p. 259, 1963.
P. R. Berman, *Phys. Rev.*, vol. A6, p. 2157, 1972.
J. R. Fuhr, W. L. Wiese, and L. J. Roszman, "Bibliography on atomic line shapes and shifts" (1889–Mar. 1972), U.S. Dep. Commerce, Washington, D. C., NBS Special Pub. 366, 1972. (Recent comprehensive source of data.)

[4] H. R. Griem, *Plasma Spectroscopy*. New York: McGraw-Hill, 1964.

[5] H. Mark, *The Physics of Electronic and Atomic Collisions* (VII ICPEAC), T. R. Govers and F. J. deHeer, Ed. Amsterdam: North-Holland, 1972, p. 154.

[6] A. H. Wapstra, G. J. Nijgh, and R. Van Lieshout, *Nuclear Spectroscopy Tables*. Amsterdam: North-Holland, 1959.

[7] S. W. Mead, R. E. Kidder, J. E. Swain, F. Rainer, and J. Petruzzi, *Appl. Opt.*, vol. 11, p. 345, 1972.
P. J. Mallozzi, H. M. Epstein, R. G. Jung, D. C. Appelbaum, B. P. Fairand, and W. J. Gallagher, "X-ray emission from laser generated plasmas," Advanced Res. Proj. Agency, Final Rep., Feb. 29, 1972.
(We observe that laser-produced plasmas can be made spatially coherent. The preceding contains a discussion of X-ray generation from laser-produced plasmas.)

[8] R. Haensel, N. Kosuch, U. Nielsen, B. Sonntag, and U. Rössler, "The optical properties of dilute solid rare gas alloys in the extreme ultraviolet," DESY, Rep. SR-72/7, June 1972. (It is useful to note that synchrotron radiation, although incoherent, is polarized. This reference provides an example of the use of synchrotron radiation in solid-state research.)

[9] L. Cohen, U. Feldman, M. Swartz, and J. H. Underwood, *J. Opt. Soc. Amer.*, vol. 58, p. 843, 1968.
I. N. Lie and R. C. Elton, *Phys. Rev.*, vol. A3, p. 865, 1971.
R. C. Elton, *Space Sci. Rev.*, vol. 13, p. 747, 1972.
I. N. Lie and R. C. Elton, *J. Phys. (Paris)*, vol. 32, p. C4-61, 1971.

[10] R. M. Lerner, "M.I.T. Lincoln Laboratory quarterly technical summary," M.I.T. Lincoln Lab., Lexington, June 15, 1972, pp. 11–16.

[11] R. S. Kennedy, "Communication through optical scattering channels: An introduction," *Proc. IEEE*, vol. 58, pp. 1651–1665, Oct. 1970.
N. S. Kopeika and J. Bordogna, "Background noise in optical communication systems," *Proc. IEEE*, vol. 58, pp. 1571–1577, Oct. 1970.

[12] J. F. Holzrichter, C. M. Dozier, and J. M. McMahon, "X-ray point source projection photography with a laser produced source," *Appl. Phys. Lett.*, to be published.

[13] R. E. Kidder, *Physics of High Energy Density*, Caldirda and H. Knoepfel, Ed. New York: Academic, 1971, p. 306.
J. Nuckolls, L. Wood, A. Thiessen, and G. Zimmerman, *Nature*, vol. 239, p. 139, 1972. (Discussion of plasma heating in a laser fusion context.)

[14] R. A. McFarlane, *Appl. Phys. Lett.*, vol. 5, p. 91, 1964.

[15] P. K. Cheo and H. G. Cooper, *J. Appl. Phys.*, vol. 36, p. 1862, 1965.

[16] ——, *Appl. Phys. Lett.*, vol. 7, p. 202, 1965.

[17] W. B. Bridges, A. N. Chester, A. S. Halsted, and J. V. Parker, "Ion laser plasmas," *Proc. IEEE*, vol. 59, pp. 724–737, May 1971.

[18] R. I. Rudko and C. L. Tang, *J. Appl. Phys.*, vol. 38, p. 4731, 1967.

[19] W. B. Bridges, *Appl. Phys. Lett.*, vol. 4, p. 128, 1964.

[20] W. R. Bennett, Jr., J. W. Knutson, Jr., G. N. Mercer, and J. L. Detch, *Appl. Phys. Lett.*, vol. 4, p. 180, 1964.

[21] G. Convert, M. Armand, and P. Martinot-Lagarde, *Compt. Rend.*, vol. 258, p. 4467, 1964.

[22] ——, *Compt. Rend.*, vol. 258, p. 3259, 1964.

[23] W. L. Faust, R. A. McFarlane, C. K. N. Patel, and C. G. B. Garrett, *Phys. Rev.*, vol. 133, p. A1476, 1964.

[24] A. R. Stringanov and N. S. Sventitskii, *Tables of Spectral Lines of Neutral and Ionized Atoms*. New York: Plenum, 1968.

[25] W. T. Silfvast, *Appl. Phys. Lett.*, vol. 13, p. 169, 1968.

[26] J. P. Goldsborough, "Continuous laser oscillation at 3250 Å in cadmium ion," *IEEE J. Quantum Electron.* (Notes and Lines), vol. QE-5, p. 133, Jan. 1969.

[27] C. K. Rhodes and A. Szöke, "Gaseous lasers: Atomic, molecular, and ionic," in *Laser Handbook*, vol. 1, F. T. Arecchi and E. O. Schulz-Dubois, Ed. Amsterdam: North-Holland, 1972, p. 265.
T. G. Giallorenzi and S. A. Ahmed, "Saturation and discharge studies in the He-Cd laser," *IEEE J. Quantum Electron.*, vol. QE-7, pp. 11–17, Jan. 1971.

[28] D. T. Hodges, *Appl. Phys. Lett.*, vol. 17, p. 11, 1970.

[29] L. D. Schearer and F. A. Padovani, *J. Chem. Phys.*, vol. 52, p. 1618, 1970.

[30] G. J. Collins, R. C. Jensen, and W. R. Bennett, Jr., *Appl. Phys. Lett.*, vol. 19, p. 125, 1971.

[31] H. Hotop and A. Niehaus, *Z. Phys.*, vol. 228, p. 68, 1969.
——, *Z. Phys.*, vol. 238, p. 452, 1970.
K. L. Bell, A. Dalgarno, and A. E. Kingston, *J. Phys., Ser. B, Proc. Phys. Soc. London*, vol. I, p. 18, 1968.

[32] L. D. Schearer and L. A. Riseberg, *Phys. Rev. Lett.*, vol. 26, p. 599, 1971.

[33] M. Barrat and J. P. Barrat, *Compt. Rend.*, vol. 257, p. 1463, 1963.

[34] C. H. Corliss and W. R. Bozman, "Experimental transition probabilities for spectral lines of seventy elements," NBS, Washington, D. C., Monogr. 53, 1962.
C. H. Corliss, "Revision of the NBS tables of spectral line intensities below 2450," NBS, Washington, D. C., Monogr. 32 (Supplement), 1967.

[35] V. Čermák, *J. Chem. Phys.*, vol. 44, p. 3774, 1966.
H. K. Holt and R. Krotkov, *Phys. Rev.*, vol. 144, p. 82, 1966.

[36] A. V. Phelps, *Phys. Rev.*, vol. 99, p. 1307, 1955.
A. V. Phelps and J. L. Pack, *Rev. Sci. Instr.*, vol. 26, p. 45, 1955.
J. B. Hasted, *Physics of Atomic Collisions*. New York: Elsevier, 1972.

[37] J. N. Bardsley and M. B. Biondi, *Advances in Atomic and Molecular Physics*, vol. 6, D. R. Bates, Ed. New York: Academic, 1970. (Recombination coefficients greater than 10^{-6} cm^3/s for electronically ground-state ions are not unknown. Electronically excited molecular ions may have even larger recombination rates.)

[38] R. T. Hodgson, *Phys. Rev. Lett.*, vol. 25, p. 494, 1970.

[39] R. W. Waynant, J. D. Shipman, Jr., R. C. Elton, and A. W. Ali, *Appl. Phys. Lett.*, vol. 17, p. 383, 1970.

[40] R. T. Hodgson and R. W. Dreyfus, *Phys. Lett.*, vol. 38A, p. 213, 1972.

[41] R. W. Waynant, J. D. Shipman, Jr., R. C. Elton, and A. W. Ali, "Laser emission in the vacuum ultraviolet from molecular hydrogen," *Proc. IEEE*, vol. 59, pp. 679–684, Apr. 1971.

[42] R. W. Waynant, A. W. Ali, and P. S. Julienne, *J. Appl. Phys.*, vol. 42, p. 3406, 1971.

[43] R. T. Hodgson and R. W. Dreyfus, *Phys. Rev. Lett.*, vol. 28, p. 536, 1972.

[44] R. W. Waynant, *Phys. Rev. Lett.*, vol. 28, p. 553, 1972.

[45] R. T. Hodgson, *J. Chem. Phys.*, vol. 55, p. 5378, 1971.

[46] H. G. Heard, *Nature*, vol. 200, p. 667, 1963.
——, *Bull. Amer. Phys. Soc.*, vol. 9, p. 65, 1964.

[47] J. H. Parks, "High resolution study of the $C^3\Pi \rightarrow B^3\Pi_g$ (0, 0) stimulated transitions in N_2," Ph.D. dissertation, Mass. Inst. Technol., Cambridge, 1968.
J. H. Parks, R. Rao, and A. Javan, *Appl. Phys.*, vol. 13, p. 142, 1968.
R. W. Dreyfus and R. T. Hodgson, *Appl. Phys. Lett.*, vol. 20, p. 195, 1972.
V. M. Kaslin and G. G. Petrash, *JETP Lett.*, vol. 3, p. 55, 1966.
E. L. Patterson, J. B. Gerardo, and A. W. Johnson, *Appl. Phys. Lett.*, vol. 21, p. 293, 1972.

J. D. Shipman, Jr., *Appl. Phys. Lett.*, vol. 10, p. 3, 1967.

[48] A. W. Ali, A. C. Kolb, and A. D. Anderson, *Appl. Opt.*, vol. 6, p. 2115, 1967.

[49] R. C. Elton, R. W. Waynant, R. A. Andrews, and M. H. Reilly, Naval Res. Lab., Rep. 7412, May 1972.

[50] A. W. Ali and P. C. Kepple, *Appl. Opt.*, vol. 11, p. 2591, 1972.

[51] A. W. Ali and A. C. Kolb, *Appl. Phys. Lett.*, vol. 13, p. 259, 1968.

[52] A. P. Bazhulin, I. N. Knyazev, and G. G. Petrash, *Zh. Eksp. Teor. Fiz.*, vol. 48, p. 975, 1965 (transl.: *JETP Lett.*, vol. 23, p. 649, 1965).

——, *Zh. Eksp. Teor. Fiz.*, vol. 47, p. 1590, 1964 (transl.: *JETP Lett.*, vol. 20, p. 1068, 1965). (This discussion is similar to the preceding and relates to the observation of stimulated emission in the infrared from the hydrogen molecule.)

[53] J. Geiger, *Z. Phys.*, vol. 181, p. 413, 1964.

E. N. Lassettre and E. A. Jones, *J. Chem. Phys.*, vol. 40, p. 1222, 1964.

[54] H. Bethe, *Ann. Phys.*, vol. 5, p. 325, 1930.

N. F. Mott and H. S. W. Massey, *The Theory of Atomic Collisions*. London: Oxford, 1965.

H. S. W. Massey and E. H. S. Burhop, *Electronic and Ionic Impact Phenomena*, vol. 2. London: Oxford, 1969.

H. Ehrhardt, K. H. Hesselbacher, K. Jung, and K. Willmann, *Case Studies in Atomic Collision Physics II*, E. W. McDaniel and M. R. C. McDowell, Ed. Amsterdam: North-Holland, 1972, p. 159. (The preceding contains additional data and discussions of electron impact ionization and excitation of atoms and molecules.)

[55] R. J. Spindler, *J. Quant. Spectrosc. Radiat. Transfer*, vol. 9, p. 597, 1969.

[56] G. J. Schulz, *Phys. Rev.*, vol. 125, p. 229, 1962.

[57] G. R. Jepperson, *Phys. Rev.*, vol. 44, p. 165, 1933.

O. W. Richardson, *Molecular Hydrogen and Its Spectrum*. London: Yale Univ. Press, 1934.

G. Herzberg and L. L. Howe, *Can. J. Phys.*, vol. 37, p. 636, 1959. (Contained in the preceding are data on the spectra of H_2.)

[58] J. D. Shipman and A. C. Kolb, "A high power pulsed nitrogen laser," *IEEE J. Quantum Electron.* (Post Deadline Abstracts), vol. QE-2, p. 298, Aug. 1966.

[59] D. C. Cartwright, *Phys. Rev.*, vol. A2, p. 1331, 1970.

[60] F. G. Houtermans, *Helv. Phys. Acta*, vol. 33, p. 933, 1960. (The following contain analyses of the continua of H_2 and Hg_2.)

A. J. Palmer, *J. Appl. Phys.*, vol. 41, p. 438, 1970. (The $H_2 a^3\Sigma_g^+ \rightarrow b^3\Sigma_u^+$ transition.)

C. V. Heer, *J. Appl. Phys.*, vol. 41, p. 1875, 1970. (The $H_2 a^3\Sigma_g^+ \rightarrow b^3\Sigma_u^+$ transition.)

D. A. Leonard, J. C. Keck, and M. M. Litvak, "Population inversion between bound and repulsive molecular electronic states by two-temperature equilibrium," *Proc. IEEE* (Corresp.), vol. 51, pp. 1785–1786, Dec. 1963. (Molecular continuum of Hg_2.)

R. J. Carbonne and M. N. Litvak, *J. Appl. Phys.*, vol. 39, p. 2413, 1968. (Molecular continuum of Hg_2.)

D. C. Lorents, R. M. Hill, and D. J. Eckstrom, "Molecular metal laser," Standford Res. Inst., Menlo Park, Calif., Rep., Nov. 1972. (Molecular continuum of Hg_2.)

W. H. Smith and R. Chevalier, *Astrophys. J.*, vol. 177, p. 835, 1972. (Radiative lifetimes of the emission continua of H_2 and D_2.)

[61] N. G. Basov, V. A. Danilychev, and Yu. M. Popov, *Sov. J. Quantum Electron.*, vol. 1, p. 18, 1971.

H. A. Koehler, L. J. Ferderber, D. L. Redhead, and P. J. Ebert, *Appl. Phys. Lett.*, vol. 21, p. 198, 1972.

P. W. Hoff, J. C. Swingle, and C. K. Rhodes, *Opt. Commun.*, vol. 8, p. 128, 1973.

J. B. Gerardo and A. W. Johnson, "High-pressure xenon laser at 1730 Å," *IEEE J. Quantum Electron.*, vol. QE-9, p. 748–755, July 1973.

A. C. Kolb, N. Rostoker, R. White, K. Boyer, R. Jensen, P. Robinson, and A. Sullivan, *Bull. Amer. Phys. Soc.*, vol. 17, p. 1031, 1972. (Preliminary calorimetric studies.)

R. Jensen, private communication. (Line narrowing with unexplained structure.)

[62] P. W. Hoff, J. C. Swingle, and C. K. Rhodes, "Observations of stimulated emission from high pressure krypton and argon/xenon mixtures," *Appl. Phys. Lett.*, vol. 23, p. 245, 1973.

[63] W. Finkelnburg, *Kontinuierliche Spektren*. Berlin: Springer, 1938. (Data on the continua of Zn_2, Cd_2, and Hg_2, as well as general discussion of the early work on continuous spectra.)

[64] C. A. Slocomb, W. H. Miller, and H. F. Schaefer, III, *J. Chem. Phys.*, vol. 55, p. 926, 1971. (Discussion of HeH.)

[65] V. Bondybey, P. K. Pearson, and H. F. Schaefer, III, *J. Chem. Phys.*, vol. 57, p. 1123, 1972. (Consideration of the potential curves of NeH.)

[66] W. E. Baylis, *J. Chem. Phys.*, vol. 51, p. 2665, 1969. (Discussion of the LiXe molecule.)

[67] M. L. Ginter and R. Battino, *J. Chem. Phys.*, vol. 52, p. 4469, 1970. (Here, as well as in references cited herein, the molecular properties of the He_2 system are discussed.)

W. A. Fitzsimmons, *Atomic Physics 3*, S. J. Smith and G. K. Walters, Ed. New York: Plenum, 1973, p. 477. (Description of recent experimental data on He_2.)

[68] B. Krawetz and C. Rhodes, "Vacuum ultraviolet studies of rare gases and rare gas mixtures excited with pulsed high energy electron beams," in *Proc. Symp. High Power Molecular Lasers* (Quebec City, P.Q., Canada, 1972).

E. V. George and C. K. Rhodes, "M.I.T. quarterly progress report," Mass. Inst. Technol., Cambridge, Rep. 108, Jan. 1973.

[69] R. S. Mulliken, *J. Amer. Chem. Soc.*, vol. 86, p. 3183, 1964.

——, *J. Amer. Chem. Soc.*, vol. 88, p. 1849, 1966.

——, *J. Amer. Chem. Soc.*, vol. 91, p. 4615, 1969.

[70] O. Cheshnovsky, B. Raz, and J. Jortner, in *Proc. 3rd Int. Vacuum Ultraviolet Conf.* (Tokyo, 1971).

J. Jortner, L. Meyer, S. A. Rice, and E. G. Wilson, *J. Chem. Phys.*, vol. 42, p. 4250, 1965.

M. Martin, *J. Chem. Phys.*, vol. 54, p. 3289, 1971.

O. Cheshnovsky, B. Raz, and J. Jortner, *J. Chem. Phys.*, vol. 57, p. 4628, 1972.

[71] M. J. Berger and S. M. Seltzer, "Tables of energy losses and ranges of electrons and positrons," NASA, Washington, D.C., Rep. N65-12506.

L. R. Peterson and J. E. Allen, Jr., *J. Chem. Phys.*, vol. 56, p. 6068, 1972. (Specific treatment concerning the degradation of electrons in argon.)

[72] D. C. Lorents and R. M. Hill, private communication.

S. C. Wallace, R. T. Hodgson, and R. W. Dreyfus, *Appl. Phys. Lett.*, to be published.

[73] C. G. Freeman, M. J. McEwan, R. F. C. Claridge, and L. F. Phillips, *Chem. Phys. Lett.*, vol. 10, p. 530, 1971.

N. Thonnard and G. S. Hurst, *Phys. Rev.*, vol. A5, p. 1110, 1972.

[74] R. Bouciqué and P. Mortier, *J. Phys.*, vol. D3, p. 1905, 1970.

E. Ellis and N. D. Twiddy, *J. Phys.*, vol. B2, p. 1366, 1969. (Rate constants for Ar.)

A. H. Futch and F. A. Grant, *Phys. Rev.*, vol. 104, p. 356, 1956. (Rate constants for Ar.)

R. Turner, *Phys. Rev.*, vol. 158, p. 121, 1967. (Rate constants for Kr.)

[75] A. G. Molchanov, *Sov. Phys.—Usp.*, vol. 15, p. 124, 1972.

[76] A. V. Phelps, *Phys. Rev.*, vol. 114, p. 1011, 1959.

[77] A. B. Callear and R. E. Hedges, *Trans. Faraday Soc.*, vol. 66, p. 2921, 1970.

[78] A. Cohn, *J. Chem. Phys.*, vol. 57, p. 2456, 1972.

[79] R. F. Stebbings, F. B. Dunning, F. K. Tittel, and R. D. Rundel, *Phys. Rev. Lett.*, vol. 30, p. 815, 1973.

[80] G. V. Marr, *Photoionization Processes in Gases*, vol. 28, *Pure and Applied Physics*. New York: Academic, 1967.

[81] K. Wojaczek, *Beitr. Plasmaphys.*, vol. 5, p. 307, 1965.

[82] M. Gryzinski, *Phys. Rev.*, vol. 115, p. 374, 1959.

M. Gryzinski, *Phys. Rev.*, vol. 138, p. A336, 1965.

[83] E. V. George and C. K. Rhodes, *Appl. Phys. Lett.*, vol. 23, p. 139, 1973.

D. C. Lorents and R. E. Olson, "Excimer formation and decay processes in rare cases," Stanford Res. Inst., Menlo Park, Calif., Rep., Dec. 1972.

[84] D. Smith, A. G. Dean, and I. C. Plumb, *J. Phys.*, vol. B5, p. 2134, 1972.

[85] T. R. Conner and M. A. Biondi, *Phys. Rev.*, vol. 140, p. A778, 1965.

[86] L. Frommhold and M. A. Biondi, *Phys. Rev.*, vol. 185, p. 244, 1969.

[87] N. G. Basov, "Opening remarks: Fourth international quantum electronics conference," *IEEE J. Quantum Electron.*, vol. QE-2, pp. 354–357, Sept. 1966.

[88] A. G. Molchanov, I. A. Poluektov, and Yu. M. Popov, *Fiz. Tverd. Tela*, vol. 9, p. 3363, 1967 (transl.: *Sov. Phys.—Solid State*, vol. 9, p. 2655, 1968).

[89] N. G. Basov, E. M. Balashov, O. V. Bogdankevitch, V. A. Danilychev, G. N. Kashnikov, L. P. Lantzov, and D. D. Khodkevitch, *J. Luminescence*, vol. 1/2, p. 834, 1970.

[90] K. J. Swyler and M. Creuzburg, *J. Luminescence*, vol. 1/2, p. 842, 1970.

[91] N. G. Basov, V. A. Danilychev, Yu. M. Popov, and D. D. Khodkevich, *JETP Lett.*, vol. 12, p. 329, 1970.
[92] M. M. Mkrtchyan and V. T. Platonenko, *JETP Lett.*, vol. 17, p. 19, 1973; also see [83].
[93] A. Kogelnik and T. Li, "Laser beams and resonators," *Proc. IEEE*, vol. 54, pp. 1312–1329, Oct. 1966. (A description of mode eigenfunctions and propagation characteristics.)
[94] A. Gedanken, J. Jortner, B. Raz, and A. Szöke, *J. Chem. Phys.* vol. 57, p. 3456, 1972. (In this work the value derived for the cross section was ~2.9 × 10^{-18} cm². Since the xenon $^1P_1$–$^1S_0$ resonance line falls ~ 1296 Å, this process is essentially exactly resonant.)
[95] E. Wigner and E. Witmer, *Z. Phys.*, vol. 51, p. 859, 1928.
[96] H. Margenau and N. R. Kestner, *Theory of Intermolecular Forces*, 2nd ed. New York: Pergamon, 1971.
B. M. Axilrod and E. Teller, *J. Chem. Phys.*, vol. 11, p. 299, 1943.
A. Dalgarno and W. D. Davison, *Advances in Atomic and Molecular Physics*, vol. 2, D. R. Bates and I. Estermann, Ed. New York: Academic, 1966, p. 1.
T. Kihara, *Adv. Chem. Phys.*, vol. 1, p. 267, 1958.
[97] I. V. Kosinskaya and L. P. Polozova, *Opt. Spectrosc. (USSR)*, vol. 30, p. 458, 1971.
[98] A. V. Phelps, "Tunable gas lasers utilizing ground state dissociation," Univ. Colorado, Boulder, JILA Rep. 110, Sept. 1972. (Included are a discussion and references relating to bound–free systems other than the rare gases.)
[99] R. E. M. Hedges, D. L. Drummond, and A. Gallagher, *Phys. Rev.*, vol. A6, p. 1519, 1972.
[100] F. H. Mies, "Stimulated emission and population inversion in diatomic bound-continuum transitions," preprint and private communication through W. Stevens.
[101] P. W. Hoff, private communication.
[102] E. V. George and C. W. Werner, private communication.
[103] N. Bloembergen, *Nonlinear Optics*. New York: W. A. Benjamin, 1965.
[104] P. A. Franken, A. E. Hill, C. W. Peters, and G. Weinreich, *Phys. Rev. Lett.*, vol. 7, p. 118, 1961.
[105] R. W. Terhune, P. D. Maker, and C. M. Savage, *Phys. Rev. Lett.*, vol. 8, p. 404, 1962.
[106] D. A. Kleinman, *Laser Handbook*, vol. 2, F. T. Arecchi and E. O. Schulz-DuBois, Ed. Amsterdam: North-Holland, 1972, p. 1229.
[107] J. F. Ward and G. H. C. New, *Phys. Rev.* vol. 185, p. 57, 1969. (Reported here is the initial observation of third harmonic generation in gases.)
[108] S. E. Harris and R. B. Miles, *Appl. Phys. Lett.*, vol. 19, p. 385, 1971.
[109] J. F. Young, G. C. Bjorklund, A. H. Kung, R. B. Miles, and S. E. Harris, *Phys. Rev. Lett.*, vol. 27, p. 1551, 1971.
A. H. Kung, J. F. Young, G. C. Bjorklund, and S. E. Harris, *Phys. Rev. Lett.*, vol. 29, p. 985, 1972.
[110] C. R. Vidal and J. Cooper, *J. Appl. Phys.*, vol. 40, p. 3370, 1969.
[111] A. H. Kung, J. F. Young, and S. E. Harris, *Appl. Phys. Lett.*, vol. 22, p. 301, 1973.
[112] Y. Ueda and K. Shimoda, *J. Phys. Soc. Jap.*, vol. 28, p. 196, 1970.
[113] B. B. Snavely, "Flashlamp-excited organic dye lasers," *Proc. IEEE*, vol. 57, pp. 1374–1390, Aug. 1969.
F. P. Schäfer, *Laser Handbook*, vol. 1, F. T. Arecchi and E. O. Schulz-DuBois, Ed. Amsterdam: North-Holland, 1972, p. 369. (Recent reviews of dye systems.)
[114] G. A. Abakumov, A. P. Simonov, V. V. Fadeev, L. A. Kharitonov, and R. V. Khokhlov, *JETP Lett.*, vol. 9, p. 9, 1969.
[115] C. V. Shank, A. Dienes, A. M. Trozzolo, and J. A. Meyer, *Appl. Phys. Lett.*, vol. 16, p. 405, 1970.
[116] D. J. Bradley, J. V. Nicholas, and J. R. D. Shaw, *Appl. Phys. Lett.*, vol. 19, p. 172, 1971.
[117] B. G. Huth, G. I. Farmer, L. M. Taylor, and M. R. Kagan, *Spectrosc. Lett.*, vol. 1, p. 425, 1968.
[118] S. G. Dinev, K. V. Stamenov, and I. V. Tomov, *Opt. Commun.*, vol. 5, p. 419, 1972.
[119] F. B. Dunning, E. D. Stokes, and R. F. Stebbings, *Opt. Commun.*, vol. 6, p. 63, 1972.
[120] E. D. Stokes, F. B., Dunning, R. F. Stebbings, G. K. Walters, R. D. Rundel, *Opt. Commun.*, vol. 5, p. 267, 1972.
[121] C. Gaebel and M. Hercher, "A continuous tunable source of coherent UV radiation," *IEEE J. Quantum Electron.* (Corresp.), vol QE-8, pp. 850–851, Nov. 1972.
[122] J. G. Kepros, E. M. Eyring, and F. W. Cagle, Jr., *Proc. Nat. Acad. Sci. U.S.*, vol. 69, p. 1744, 1972.
[123] R. C. Elton, L. J. Palumbo, R. A. Andrews, R. C. Eckardt, and J. N. Bradford, *Appl. Opt.*, vol. 12, p. 155, 1973.
[124] J. N. Bradford, R. C. Elton, T. N. Lee, R. A. Andrews, L. J. Palumbo, and R. C. Eckardt, *Appl. Opt.*, to be published.
[125] T. A. Boster, *Appl. Opt.*, to be published.
[126] B. Lax and A. H. Guenther, *Appl. Phys. Lett.*, vol. 21, p. 361, 1972. (The general feasibility of coherent X-ray generation in laser-produced plasmas excited with picosecond pulses is examined.)
[127] R. A. McCorkle, *Phys. Rev. Lett.*, vol. 29, p. 982, 1972.
——, *Phys. Rev. Lett.* (Erratum), vol. 29, p. 1428, 1972.
[128] R. C. Der, R. J. Fortner, T. M. Kavanagh, and J. M. Khan, *Phys. Rev.*, vol. A4, p. 556, 1971.
J. D. Garcia, R. J. Fortner, T. M. Kavanagh, *Rev. Mod. Phys.*, vol. 45, p. 111, 1973.
[129] U. Fano and W. Lichten, *Phys. Rev. Lett.*, vol. 14, p. 627, 1965.
W. Lichten, *Phys. Rev.*, vol. 164, p. 131, 1967.
[130] R. S. Mulliken, *Phys. Rev.*, vol. 32, p. 186, 1928.
[131] F. Hund, *Z. Phys.*, vol. 40, p. 742, 1927.
[132] I. I. Sobel'man, private communication, Moscow, July 1972.
[133] H. A. Bethe and E. E. Salpeter, *Quantum Mechanics of One- and Two-Electron Atoms*. New York: Academic, 1957.
[134] P. Bräunlich, R. Hall, and P. Lambrupoulos, *Phys. Rev.*, vol. A5, p. 1013, 1972.
[135] J. Ducuing, G. Hauchercorne, A. Mysyrowicz, and F. Padere, *Phys. Lett.*, vol. 28A, p. 746, 1969.
[136] J. M. Campbell, S. Penzes, H. S. Sandhu, and O. P. Strausz, *Int. J. Chem. Kinetics*, vol. 3, p. 175, 1971.
[137] W. B. Bridges and A. N. Chester, "Noble gas ion lasers," *NEREM Rec.*, p. 106, 1964.
[138] W. B. Bridges and A. N. Chester, "Spectroscopy of ion lasers," *IEEE J. Quantum Electron.*, vol. QE-1, pp. 66–84, May 1965.
[139] H. G. Cooper and P. K. Cheo, "Laser transitions in B II, Br II, and Sn," *IEEE J. Quantum Electron.* (Notes and Lines), QE-2, p. 785, Dec. 1966.
[140] ——, *Physics of Quantum Electronics*, P. L. Kelley, B. Lax, and P. E. Tannenwald, Ed. New York: McGraw-Hill, 1966, p. 690.
[141] W. B. Bridges and A. N. Chester, *Appl. Opt.*, vol. 4, p. 573, 1965.
[142] K. G. Ericsson and L. R. Lidholt, "Superradiant transitions in argon, krypton, and xenon," *IEEE J. Quantum Electron.* (Corresp.), vol. QE-3, p. 94, Feb. 1967.
[143] J. R. Fendley, Jr., "Continuous UV lasers," *IEEE J. Quantum Electron.*, vol. QE-4, pp. 627–631, Oct. 1968.
[144] W. B. Bridges and G. N. Mercer, Hughes Res. Labs., Malibu, Calif., Tech. Rep. ECOM-0229-F, 1969.
[145] A. A. Isaev and G. G. Petrash, *JETP Lett.*, vol. 10, p. 119, 1969.
[146] C. E. Hurwitz, *Appl. Phys. Lett.*, vol. 9, p. 116, 1966.
[147] F. H. Nicoll, *Appl. Phys. Lett.*, vol. 9, p. 13, 1966.
[148] H. W. Gandy and M. J. Ginther, *Appl. Phys. Lett.*, vol. 1, p. 25, 1962.
[149] R. W. Waynant, *Appl. Phys. Lett.*, vol. 22, p. 419, 1973.
[150] D. Röss, *Lasers, Light Amplifiers, and Oscillators*. New York: Academic, 1969.
[151] *Handbook of Lasers with Selected Data on Optical Technology*, R. J. Pressley, Ed., Chemical Rubber Co., Cleveland, Ohio, 1971.

Efficient and Practical Hydrogen Vacuum Ultraviolet Laser

I. N. KNYAZEV, V. S. LETOKHOV, AND V. G. MOVSHEV

Abstract—Investigations of the hydrogen vacuum ultraviolet (VUV) laser carried out in the Institute of Spectroscopy of the USSR Academy of Sciences are reviewed. Data for VUV TEA H_2 and D_2 lasers at gas pressure up to 2 atm and for low-pressure high-repetition rate hydrogen lasers are presented. The upper limit quantum system efficiency for both gas discharge and *e*-beam excitation of H_2 lasers is discussed. The possibility of obtaining CW operation of the H_2-VUV laser is also discussed.

I. Introduction

The vacuum ultraviolet (VUV) region is very attractive for many laser applications. The electronic absorption and photoionization bands of most molecules occur in this region. In this wavelength region, the laser frequency becomes comparable with the electron plasma oscillation frequency for plasmas having charged particle concentrations of about 10^{22} cm^{-3}. The nonlinear resonance effects on the short wavelength electron transitions of atoms and molecules are increased sharply in this region. Intensive coherent VUV radiation can be utilized to optically excite tunable lasers which can in turn be utilized to investigate the ultraviolet (UV) region near the VUV cutoff limit. This region is presently unexplored by coherent radiation techniques. The most important laser parameter for the VUV photochemistry applications is the laser's average power output. Molecular excitation rates of the order of 10^{-3} molecules/h can be achieved with a laser having an average power output of 0.1 W. A power density over 1 MW/cm^2 is required for most optical pumping experiments. High power levels and comparatively high coherency are also required for performing nonlinear optical experiments. Lasers having efficiencies greater than 0.1 percent are suitable for most practical applications.

VUV laser action is presently obtained by *e*-beam excitation of condensed inert gases [1] and by frequency multiplying visible high peak power laser pulses [2], [3]. VUV laser action has been obtained by utilizing high current *e*-beam excitation of the bound-free transitions of gaseous xenon, krypton, and argon [4]. Unfortunately, lasers utilizing relativistic *e*-beam excitation present high radiation danger to the operators and the overall efficiency of the frequency multiplying laser systems is too small to be practical.

One of the most attractive VUV laser systems is the hydrogen laser [5]. The low-inductance single-shot self-sustained discharges obtained with solid-state dielectric switches [6] or with the nanosecond pulsed *e* beams [7] are widely used for exciting lasers. The average output power for the solid-state dielectric switch excited laser systems is limited to approximately 1 μW. The low average power is determined by the ratio of the laser pulse energy to the time interval required for the replacement of the dielectric in the switch.

The basic characteristics of the H_2-VUV quantum system are favorable for the conversion of electron excitation energy to the VUV laser emission energy (Table I). Effective electronic excitation cross sections of the upper laser states are comparable with the effective cross section of ionization and the total nonelastic losses of the hydrogen molecule. The ratio of laser radiation quantum energy to the excitation energy is higher than that for a CO_2 laser. The Doppler linewidth of the H_2 spontaneous radiation is four orders of magnitude less than the luminescence bandwidth of rare gas excimers. The parameter $g_{0v'}g_{v'v''}\beta_{v'J'}S_{J'J''}$ in the expression for gain, connected with the splitting of molecular electronic states into a system of vibrational-rotational sublevels, is about 10^{-2} for the H_2 laser transitions.[1]

The molecular hydrogen laser system is, therefore, capable of excellent performance. This performance at the present is far from being realized. The excessively high probability of radiative decay causes the inverted population to have an extremely short lifetime of $\sim$1 ns. Effectively depositing the excitation energy into the active medium during such a short period of time is a rather difficult task. Low-inductance systems utilizing solid-state dielectric switches provide the formation of excitation pulses with appropriate parameters, but these systems are rather inconvenient in practice. The quantitative data on the limiting value of the excitation efficiency of laser states by *e*-beam excitation are still unknown. The operation of VUV lasers at high-repetition rates is important in order for these lasers to be widely utilized.

The main purpose of this paper is to report more precise measurements of the limiting parameters of the H_2 laser. The experimental results obtained with a single-shot TEA H_2-VUV laser and with a high-repetition rate low-pressure hydrogen laser are given. The upper limit of the laser states excitation efficiency for self-sustained discharges and for *e*-beam excitation is presented. The problem of the CW hydrogen VUV laser is also discussed.

II. Single-Shot TEA H_2-VUV Laser

A. Experimental Arrangement

The experimental arrangement of the TEA H_2-VUV laser used in our investigations is shown in Fig. 1. The 0.006 × 1 × 30-cm^3 laser volume was excited by a transverse discharge in the bipolar plane Blumlein line with a varied profile and a dielectric film switch. The probability of the corona discharge

Manuscript received September 30, 1974.
The authors are with the Institute of Spectroscopy, Academy of Sciences, Moscow, USSR.

[1]The characteristic values of Franck–Condon factors for the Lyman band system are $g_{0v'}$ = 0.07, $g_{v'v''}$ = 0.3, the Honle–London factor $S_{J'J''}$ = 0.5, the parameter of rotational population $\beta_{v'J'}$ = 0.5.

TABLE I
CHARACTERISTICS OF THE H_2 LASER QUANTUM SYSTEM

	Wavelength λ (Å)	Linewidth $\Delta\nu$ (cm^{-1})	$h\nu/E_{OK}$	Effective Excitation Cross Section σ_{OK}^{max} (cm^2)	Effective Ionization Cross Section σ_{oi}^{max} (cm^2)
Lyman Bands	1600	0.6	0.65	$5.5.10^{-17}$	10^{-16}
Werner Bands	1200	0.8	0.85	4.10^{-17}	10^{-16}

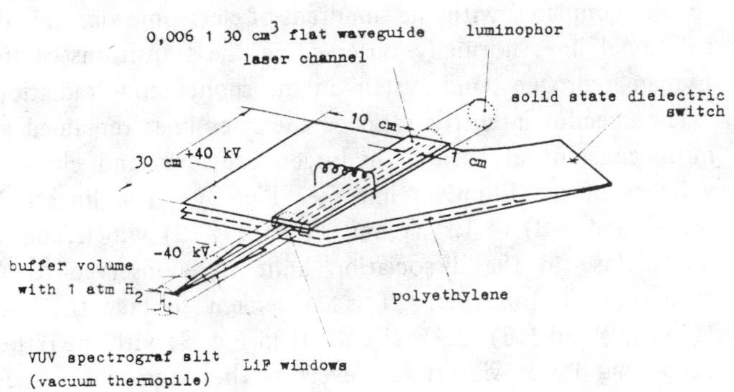

Fig. 1. H_2-VUV laser experimental arrangement.

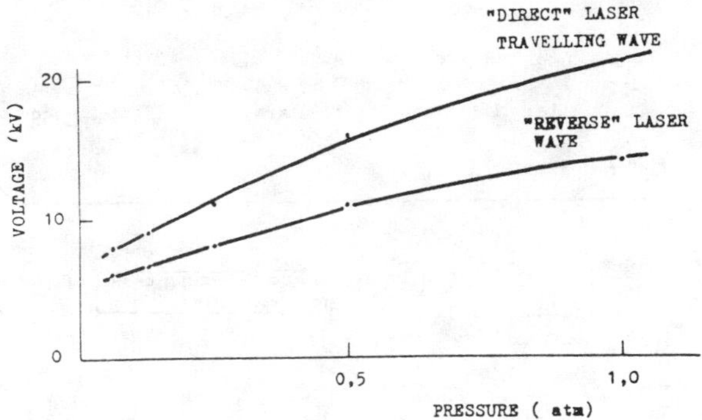

Fig. 2. Threshold voltage versus pressure behavior.

initiation (or surface breakdown) is sharply decreased by using the bipolar charging of the plates to $\pm V/2$. At voltages of $\lesssim 100$ kV, the bipolar charging of the plates is a more convenient solution of the surface breakdown problem compared with the distilled water or oil filled systems approach.

The mechanical initiation of the electrical breakdown of a polyethylene film by an electromagnetic (EM) striker was used. The traveling-wave excitation was provided by designing the pulse forming wing of the Blumlein line at a certain angle to the optical axis of the laser cell. A capacitive voltage divider with a time constant less than ~0.2 ns and the N2-7 oscillograph were used to measure the voltage pulse at the cell. The distinguishing feature of the system was the very narrow laser channel ($h = 60\ \mu$) which provided the high current density and a satisfactory spatial homogeneity of the discharge. The narrow channel also provided a comparatively large effective voltage pulse duration in the discharge gap. As a result, the conditions for laser excitation improved greatly. Copper foil electrodes having a thickness of 50 μ and polished edges were held fixed with epoxy adhesive at a distance $l = 1 \pm 0.05$ cm between polished glass plates. These plates had a rather high reflectivity for beams traveling at a small angle to the laser optical axis and thus formed a peculiar plane waveguide for the short-wave laser radiation. The Fresnel number for the laser volume was 7×10^{-2}.

The laser pulse energy was measured by a calibrated vacuum thermopile connected to the laser cell through a buffer volume (see Fig. 1). The volume was filled with hydrogen at 1 atm in order to prevent electric breakdown to the thermopile. The absence of the false signals was controlled by filling the volume with oxygen. For visual observation of the laser radiation, the rear window of the thermopile was covered by a thin layer of sodium salycilate.

The laser spectrum was measured by means of a VMS-1 spectrograph with an accuracy of 0.1 A. The laser radiation was directed from the cell through the LiF window and the intermediate vacuum tube with a LiF lens to the entrance slit of the spectrograph.

B. *Experimental Results*

For pressures up to 2 atm and with the operating voltage slightly over threshold, the radiation from the laser cell was unidirectional. The intensity ratio of the forwards and backwards beams was more than 10. The radiation divergence in the plane of the laser cell was 2° and about 1° in the direction perpendicular to the cell. For a pressure change of one order of magnitude (i.e., 0.1-1 atm), the threshold voltage V only increases by a factor of 2-2.5 (Fig. 2). Near threshold, laser action was observed as a "reverse" traveling wave towards the commutator. At higher voltages, the unidirectional superluminescence traveling wave in the "forward" direction was observed. For the optimum excitation conditions, $p = 0.1$ atm and $V = 5$ kV, the laser pulse energy was 0.5 mJ. The laser energy remained constant with a diminishing of the wing length to several centimeters. The energy stored by the line for this case was about 0.1 J and the corresponding measured maximum efficiency was 0.5 percent. The formation of the superluminescence traveling wave for a 30-cm active length corresponds to the laser pulse duration of approximately 0.5 ns yielding a peak power of more than 1 MW and a power density of approximately 200 MW/cm^2 at the exit laser opening (Table II).

The densitograms of the H_2 and D_2 superluminescence spectra on the $B'\Sigma_u^+ \rightarrow X'\Sigma_g^+$ transition are given in Figs. 3 and 4. Five new laser lines have been observed in hydrogen, including two lines $P(3)$ (11, 14) and $R(1)$ (8, 14) ending in the last vibrational state $v'' = 14$ of H_2 close to the dissociation limit, as well as five new laser lines in D_2. The measured wavelengths of the new laser lines and their identification are given in Table III.

The laser spectrum differed greatly from the spontaneous

TABLE II

PARAMETERS OF THE TEA SINGLE-SHOT H_2-VUV LASER

λ	1610 Å
Maximum Laser Energy	0.5 mJ
Pulse Duration	0.5 nsec
Peak Power	1 MW
Peak Output Power Density	200 MW/cm^2
Efficiency	0.5%
Maximum H_2 Pressure	2 atm
Timer Interval Between Laser Pulses	10 to 60 sec
Mean Laser Power	$\lesssim$ 10 μW

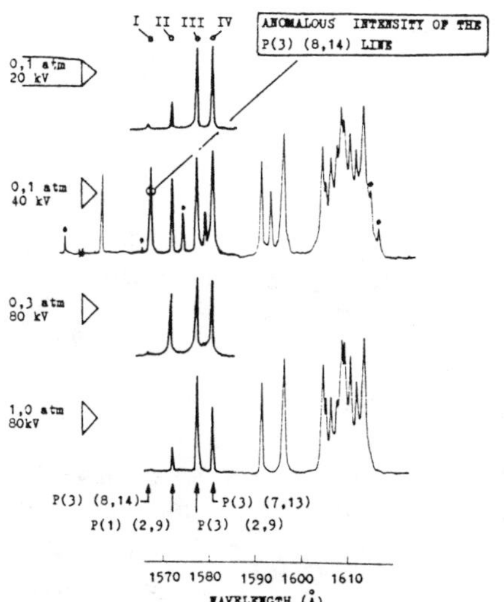

Fig. 3. Densitometer trace of the H_2-VUV laser spectra. The new laser lines are denoted by an asterisk.

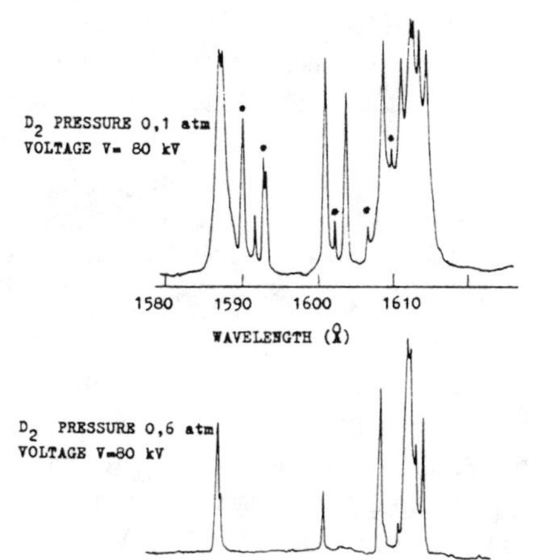

Fig. 4. Densitometer trace of D_2-VUV laser spectra. The new laser lines are denoted by an asterisk.

radiation from the same cell by the line intensity ratio and the number of observed transitions. The 1:0.7 characteristic intensity ratio for *P* and *R* branch lines of spontaneous radiation was not observed for the laser radiation. Luminescence occurs mainly at the *P* branch and there are no lines of the *R* branch in the spectrum, as a rule. The line intensity ratio for ortho- and paramodification of hydrogen was observed to be severely distorted. Radiation was observed on only a relatively few lines. Only 23 lines were observed in the laser cell spectra compared with the hundreds of electronic vibrational-rotational lines normally observed in the transitions of the Lyman hydrogen band system in the spontaneous radiation.

The specific intensity ratio of the laser lines remained almost constant at various hydrogen pressures and charging voltages of the Blumlein line (see Fig. 3). The lines *P*(3) (8,14) and *P*(3) (7,13) (I and IV in Fig. 3) which end at levels close to the dissociation limit were observed to be exceptions to this rule. It is convenient to take the lines *P*(1) (2,9) and *P*(3) (2,9) (II and III in Fig. 3) with the rather deep-lying lower vibrational levels as the comparison lines. The line *P*(3) (8,14) is weaker than the line *P*(1) (2,9) at $p =$ 0.1 atm and at low voltages. At higher voltages, the *P*(3) (8,14) line becomes comparable in intensity with the strongest lines of the spectrum and becomes more intensive than line II. Increasing the gas pressure resulted in decreasing the laser lines' intensities, especially for the *P*(3), (8,14) and the *P*(3) (7,13) lines. The latter becomes weaker than line III. At a low gas pressure, the ratio between intensities of the two last lines become inversed.

The rise time of the voltage pulse applied to the laser cell τ_f is dependent on the width of the forming line (Fig. 5). For a narrow line, τ_f is determined by the commutation time of the solid-state dielectric switch. In our experiment, it was in the range of 0.3-0.6 ns. In a line with variable profile, the voltage transformation illustrated by Fig. 6 was observed.

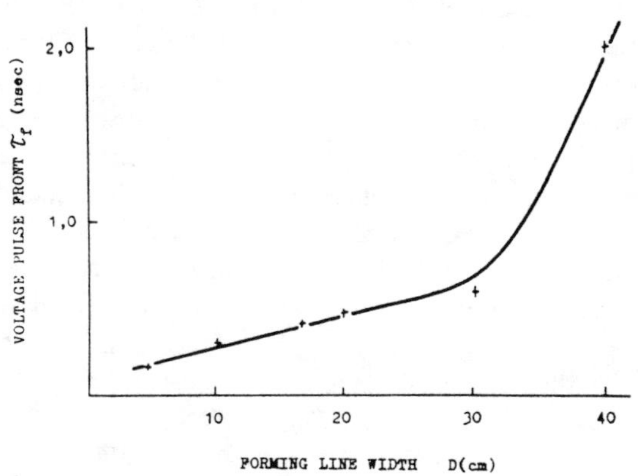

Fig. 5. Voltage pulse rise time applied to the laser cell as a function of Blumlein linewidth.

TABLE III

NEW LASER LINES OF THE H_2 AND D_2 LYMAN LASER

	H_2					D_2				
λ (Å)	1494.2	1565.5	1574.3	1614.8	1616.5	1589.9	1592.3	1602.1	1606.3	1609.5
Transition	P(3)(11,14)	R(1)(8.14)	P(2)(2,9)	P(4)(5,12)	P(5)(5,12)					

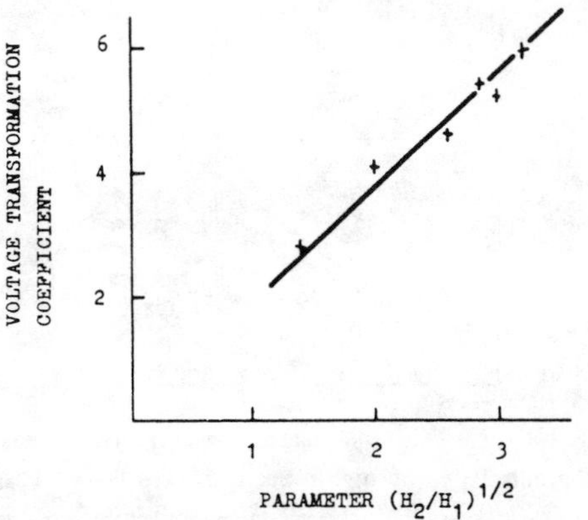

Fig. 6. Peak voltage transformation coefficient versus line thickness ratio near the laser cell and the commutator.

C. Discussion of the Results

Comparatively high operating performance of the single-shot H_2 laser was obtained by using supernarrow laser channels, choosing an optimum width of the line, and operation at a sufficiently high voltage. In the narrow channel, a high current density $j_{max} = V^{max}/\rho^S = 10^5$ A/cm^2 was obtained. For this condition, a rather long effective pulse duration of high electrical field in the discharge, $\tau \sim \gamma_0^{-1} \ln (l/h)$, was achieved; $S = b \cdot h$ is the cross section of the discharge gap perpendicular to current direction; γ_0 is the electron avalanche growth constant; ρ is the wave impedance; and ϵ = 2.2.

The single-channel switch forms in the two-dimensional line a circular wave of voltage having a width b, with variable amplitude, and having a maximum - V at the commutation point. This wave is attenuated as $1/r$ as it propagates down the line. It is reflected from the rear and side edges of the line. The experimental results show that the wave becomes approximately a plane at a distance $2B$. The rise time of this wave depends on the commutation time of the switch and on the formation time of the plane wave. The quantitative analysis of the discharge wave propagation is difficult because of the necessity of solving a two-dimensional wave equation in a limited space. The main conclusion reached from the experimental data is that despite the more complicated process of wave formation in a plane line, the amplitude of the resultant wave at distance $\gtrsim 2b$ is equal to V as in a one-dimensional line. In other words, the line is recharged completely.

The voltage transformation was experimentally observed for the line with a variable profile (Fig. 6). The ratio of transformation for a linear line is $V_2/V_1 = 2(\rho_2/\rho_1)^{1/2}$ where V_1, ρ_1, V_2, ρ_2 are the voltage and wave impedance at the points 1 and 2. The factor of 2 arises due to a reflection at the open end. In accordance with the previously mentioned wave formation, the voltage transformation in a plane line may be described by the same expression with wave impedance ρ_1 averaged over the length of the wave formation. For constant wave impedance $\rho_1 = 377H_1/b(\epsilon)^{1/2}$, where H_1 (centimeters) is the distance between the plates at the beginning of the line. For a constant linewidth, the transformation ratio is

$$K = 2\sqrt{\frac{\rho_2}{\rho_1}} = 2\sqrt{\frac{H_2}{H_1}}$$

where H_2 is the distance between the plates at the end of line. The expression is consistent with the diagram in Fig. 6.

Let us now consider the intensity anomalies of the laser lines terminating near the dissociation limit. Potential curves of some electronic states of molecular hydrogen are illustrated in Fig. 7(a). The radiation lifetimes of the upper laser states are $\tau^B = 0.8$ ns, $\tau^C = 0.6$ ns [9]. The lifetimes of the lower laser states at gas pressures $p \lesssim 0.3$ atm are determined by the wall diffusion with the characteristic time $\tau_d = (h/\pi)^2/D = 10^{-3}$ s ($p = 1$ cm). For pressures $p \gtrsim 0.3$ atm, the lifetimes of the lower laser states are determined by the vibrational-translational relaxation with the corresponding time of the order of the VT relaxation time for the lower molecular levels $\tau_{VT} = 5 \times 10^{-4}$ s · atm [10]. Thus the H_2 laser operates on the typical self-terminated scheme.

The peculiar feature of the hydrogen laser is the decay of the upper laser state $B'\Sigma_u^+$ on the vibrational-rotational levels of the ground state near the dissociation limit [Fig. 7(a) and (b)]. Laser action is observed on the last stable level of the hydrogen molecule $v'' = 14$, $J'' = 3$, located only 48 cm^{-1} below the H_2 dissociation limit. This suggests that the dissociative depletion of the lower laser states is possible with the corresponding interpretation of observed anomalies. The dissociative depletion of laser states has been considered in our paper [12] in connection with the problem of the four-level hydrogen laser.

The intensity of superluminescence is proportional to the excitation rate of the upper laser state. The relative electron excitation rate of vibrational-rotational levels within the laser electronic state does not change sufficiently with the gas pressure and voltage on the discharge gap. Corresponding specific intensity ratio of superluminescence lines should remain constant. An increase in gas pressure results in a relative intensification of intermolecular processes including the molecular dissociation from vibrationally excited states near the dissociation limit.

The depletion of the vibrationally excited molecules is possible due to collisional transitions to the unstable rotational states lying above the dissociation limit and subjected to the rotational predissociation. For laser states lying within kT from the dissociation limit, a direct collisional transition to a continuous state is also possible. The existence of unstable states is connected with the rotational deformation of the potential energy curve of the ground state. The curve of effective potential energy $V_J(r) = V(r) + J(J+1)h^2/2\mu\rho^2$ passes through the maximum [Fig. 7(b)] in the region of large internuclear distances and then approaches gradually the dissociation energy $V(\infty)$; ($V(r)$ is the molecular potential energy without regard to the rotation, and μ is the reduced mass). The rotational levels $J'' = 4,5$, $v'' = 14$ are located above the dissociation limit but below the maximum of the corresponding curve $V_J(r)$. The nonradiative lifetime for these levels due to the tunneling to a repulsive state is of the order $\tau \sim T_{vib}/D^* = 10^{-11}$ s [13] with the corresponding natural linewidth of 0.6 cm^{-1} compared with the Doppler width; T_{vib} is the period of molecular vibration and D^* is the tunneling coefficient. The corresponding comparatively narrow lines have been observed in the spontaneous radiation spectrum [11]. The states $J'' = 6$, $v'' = 14$ overlie the maximum effective potential. The lines terminating on these states have not

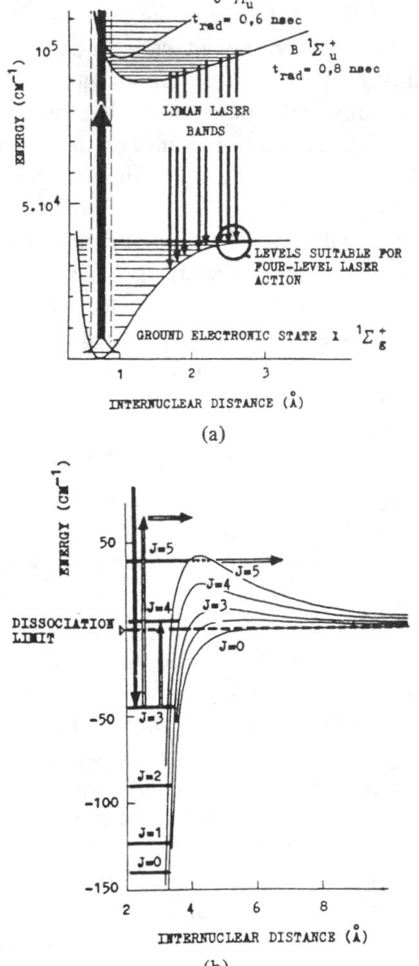

Fig. 7. (a) Potential energy curves of H_2. Lower laser level structure near the dissociation limit (circled) see Fig. 7(b) for details. (b) Energy levels of last excited vibrational state of H_2 $v'' = 14$. Dotted horizontal line denotes dissociation limit of ground state. Downward vertical line corresponds to the observed laser action on the last stable molecular level $v'' = 14, J'' = 3$.

been observed in spontaneous spectra due to the excessive natural width caused by fast molecular dissociation.

The collisional lifetime of the $v'' = 14$, $J'' = 3$ level is approximately equal to $\tau_{14,3}^{\text{coll}} \approx 4.5 \times 10^{-11}$ s · atm. At $p \gtrsim 0.05$ atm $\tau_{14,3}^{\text{coll}}$ becomes less than the radiative lifetime of the upper laser states $\tau^B = 0.8$ ns, and the four-level laser action can take place on the line $P(3)$ (8,14). The lifetime of inversion population on this transition is no longer limited by the value τ^B. Depending on the experimental conditions, at a rather long excitation pulse duration, this lifetime may be much longer than that for the rest of the self-terminated transitions. The corresponding anomalous behavior of the line intensity should show up in the superluminescence spectra. This behavior is determined mainly by the temporal dependence of the excitation rate of the laser electronic states $f_{0K}(t) = N_0 n_e(t) \langle \sigma_{0K} v \rangle\, t$.

The absence of a rather strong superluminescence line $P(3)$ (8,14) at $p \gtrsim 0.3$ atm and a considerable attenuation of the line $P(3)$ (8,13) at $p = 1$ atm indicate that gain is rapidly decreased for transitions terminating on the vibrational-rotational levels $v'' = 13,14$ of the ground state near the dissociation limit. The collisional broadening for these levels is the biggest

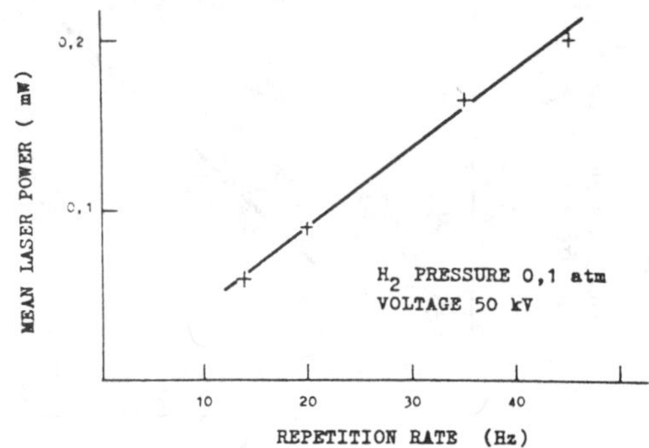

Fig. 8. Characteristics of high-repetition rate H_2-VUV laser. Average power versus repetition rate.

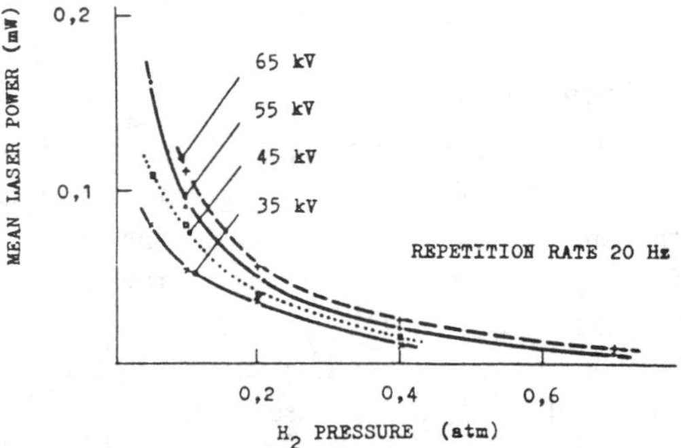

Fig. 9. Average power output versus H_2 pressure.

and accounts for the observed intensity drop for the broadening parameter ~0.3 cm^{-1} atm^{-1}.

The single-shot hydrogen laser with a solid-state dielectric switch is very inconvenient in practice because of the necessity of changing the dielectric film. The mean laser output for a 1-min average time of changing the dielectric switch is about 10 μW. A comparatively high voltage $\gtrsim 40$ kV is needed for laser operation. In this case, the film width should be about 20 cm. For higher voltages, two changeable films are needed. Changing of the films in this case is a rather complicated operation with certain difficulties in mechanization. In this connection, the high-repetition rate H_2-VUV laser with the gas discharge spark-gap commutator is of particular interest.

III. High-Repetition Rate H_2-VUV Laser

A. Experiment

A high-repetition rate pulsed output was obtained by triggering a SF_6 spark gap pressurized at 9 atm. The measured commutation time of the spark gap was slightly longer than 1 ns. The repetition pulse rate was usually operated up to 50 Hz. The mean laser power output was directly proportional to the repetition rate (Fig. 8). The laser power increased with increasing voltage and decreased with increasing gas pressure (Fig. 9). At pressures below 40 mmHg, the system could not be operated because of breakdown. The maximum attained laser power was about 0.4 mW at $f = 45$ Hz and the laser pulse energy was about 10 μJ. The laser output power decreased with increasing dielectric film thickness of the transmission line [Fig. 10(a)]. Decreasing the length of the wings of the transmission line below $l \lesssim 8$ cm [Fig. 10(b)] begins to decrease the laser output power. The efficiency of the system was 0.03 percent (Table IV).

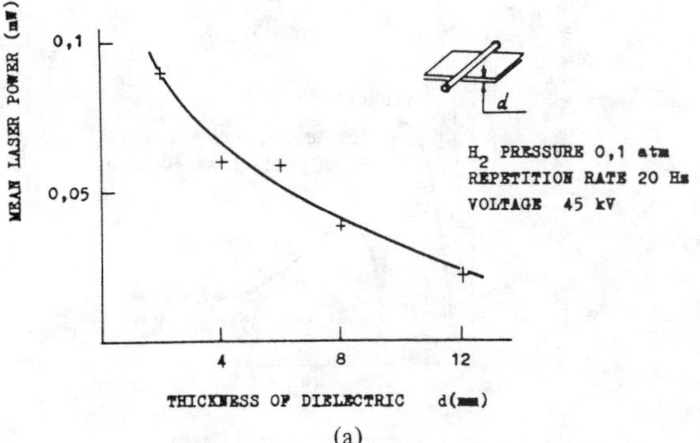

(a)

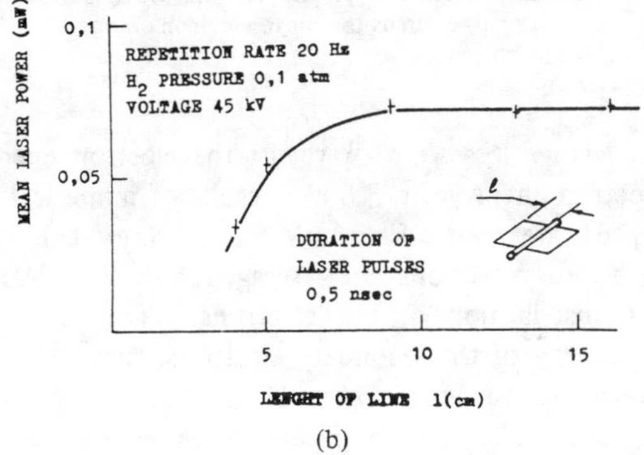

(b)

Fig. 10. (a) Average power output dependence on the Blumlein line thickness. (b) Average power versus Blumlein line length.

TABLE IV
PARAMETERS OF HIGH-REPETITION RATE H_2-VUV LASER

λ	1610 Å
Mean Power	0.4 mW
Repetition Rate	50 Hz
Laser Pulse Duration	0.5 nsec
Peak Power	20 kW
Optimal Pressure	30 torr
Efficiency	0.03%

B. Discussion of the Results

The observed decrease in the laser output power with pressure results from the reduction in the electric field to pressure ratio (E/P) and with the corresponding reduction of the $\langle \sigma v \rangle$ parameter which determines the excitation rate of the laser levels. For fixed (E/P), the laser power increases with increasing laser gas pressure up to a range of approximately 0.1 atm. Beyond this gas pressure, the laser power remains constant. At higher pressures, the molecular quenching of excited electronic states appears to be significant. The probability of quenching is related to the radiative decay probability A at gas pressure p (atmospheres) and to the effective quenching cross section q (square centimeters) by the relationship

$$\sigma_q p = A/2.7 \times 10^{19} vp$$

where $v = 2 \times 10^5$ cm/s is the gas-kinetic velocity of the molecules at room temperature. There is no accurate data available on the value σ_q for B state of molecular hydrogen. This cross section is apparently of the same order of magnitude as for the gas-kinetic cross section [14]. The quenching is substantial in this case at a gas pressure about 0.1 atm.

The region of relatively high pressures $p \gtrsim 0.05$–0.1 atm is unsuitable because of the short time interval τ with respect to the high electrical field existing in the discharge channel where τ is inversely proportional to the rate of electron avalanche growth $\gamma_0 = N_0 \langle \sigma_{01} v \rangle$. Effective excitation of laser states is attained provided the $\langle \sigma v \rangle$ coefficient is a maximum at least during the laser pulse length Δt. This at once sets a limit on the molecular concentration $N_0 \lesssim N_0^*$. For higher molecular concentration, the time interval τ becomes shorter than Δt and the excitation efficiency of the laser states decreases. It should be noted that the same situation may also hold for the nitrogen laser as well as for any other laser excited by a self-sustained discharge.

The laser pulse duration is about 0.5 ns as stated in Fig. 10(b). Laser action in a system having short plates for the transmission line is of particular interest in connection with the ones desired to develop advanced small-size excitation systems for such lasers. As it follows from Fig. 10(a), the wave impedance of the line should be decreased. The limit is set by the electrical strength of available materials.

The laser pulse energy for a discharge system having a spark-gap commutator is approximately one order of magnitude less than for lasers having solid-state switches. This occurs because of two factors. The rise time of the voltage pulse exciting the laser cell is longer for the gas-discharge switch. This is equivalent to considerably decreasing the line charging voltage which, of course, leads to a corresponding decrease in the laser output pulse energy. The wave impedance of the gas discharge switch is comparatively high. As a result, the current density in the active volume is much smaller than when a solid-state switch is utilized. This results in decreasing gain and output laser power.

The average laser power may be substantially increased by pulse charging the line up to a voltage of 150–200 kV. Capacitors of 50–100 pF can be charged to such voltage without much difficulty. The cross section and the active volume of the laser cell can also be increased at the same time in order to obtain higher laser pulse energies. If high-repetition rate high-pressure spark-gap commutators are developed, the average laser output power can be increased by the operation of the laser at higher repetition rates. The repetition rate can be increased up to at least a few kilohertz without physical limitations. Forced cooling of the electrodes and the cell walls can be performed to remove the effects of gas heating on the redistribution of gain on the rotation-vibrational lines of the band, as well as on the tendency to increase the Doppler linewidth. A principal limitation is encountered with the H-atom recombination rate and with the depletion of the long-lived lower laser states. The corresponding characteristic times are of the order of the molecular wall diffusion time $\tau_d = (\Delta/\pi)^2 D^{-1} = 3 \times 10^{-7}$ s, where $\Delta = 10^{-2}$ cm and $D = 10$ cm/s at $p = 0.1$ atm. Thus even with present laser cells, an average power of about 30 mW can be attained at a repetition rate of 5 kHz. This is quite sufficient for many applications for this laser. The major limitation at present is mainly with the commutator. For satisfactory laser operation, the stored electrical energy of a few tenths up to a few joules should be commutated at high-repetition rates. The development of commutators with the required parameters is essentially alleviated due to the smallness of the commutated electrical energy.

The hydrogen laser considered in the preceding operates on a three-level scheme. The main disadvantage of this scheme is an extremely short lifetime for the inversion population of ~1 ns. This short lifetime causes many difficulties. It is difficult to use the resonator effectively. This involves the necessity of having a high gain in the active medium in order to utilize the superluminescence mode of operation. The laser coherence for this mode of operation in this case is comparatively poor. Requirements on pumping power are respectively increased. The consequences are heavy demands on the excitation system. As a result, the alternative four-level laser excitation scheme is of specific interest. The excitation systems for such schemes may have ordinary parameters. Before discussing this scheme, we should consider the limiting efficiency of the H_2 laser quantum-mechanical system.

IV. The Limiting Excitation Efficiency of the Hydrogen Laser Levels

The H_2-VUV laser is excited at present by using nanosecond self-sustained discharge and relativistic electron beams. To choose optimum excitation conditions, it is necessary to have information on the excitation efficiency of the hydrogen laser levels excited by *e* beam or in a gas discharge. The high energy electronic excitation is of interest also in connection with the existence of accelerated electrons in discharges having rather low pressures under high voltages. These electrons may also substantially affect the laser states population.

The excitation efficiency of the *B* and *C* states [Fig. 7(a)] in the electronic energy region $0 \lesssim \epsilon \lesssim 10^2$ eV is considered by using the data on effective cross sections of electron excitation of rotational σ_r [15], [16] and vibrational σ_v [16], [17] levels of the ground state, triplet [18], [19] electronic states $a\,^3\Sigma_g^+$, $b\,^3\Sigma_u^+$, and $c\,^3\Pi_u$ with the total effective cross section σ_d. Excitation of triplet states and a subsequent radiation decay leads to molecular dissociation. We used also the data on the effective excitation cross sections of the laser states σ_{0B}, σ_{0C} [20], the singlet electronic state $E'\Sigma\sigma_{0E}$ [21], ionization with H_2^+ ion formation [22], and the data on the effective elastic collision cross section of electrons with hydrogen molecules σ_e [16].

The energy losses of electrons in nanosecond pulsed discharges occur through collisions of electrons with hydrogen molecules in the ground state. Relative energy losses in the *k*th collisional process are

$$\chi_K^{\rm disch} = \frac{\langle \sigma_{0K} v\rangle \epsilon_{0K}}{\Sigma_J \langle \sigma_{0j} v\rangle \epsilon_{0j} + \left\langle \int_0^{(\epsilon-\epsilon_{0i})/2} \epsilon_s \sigma_{0i}(\epsilon,\epsilon_s)\, d\epsilon_s \cdot v \right\rangle}. \quad (1)$$

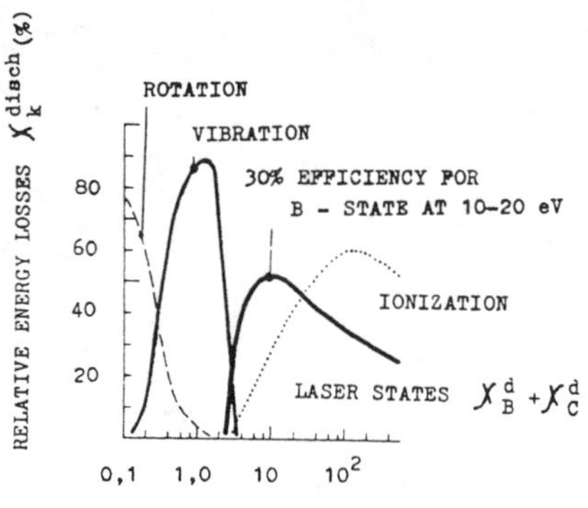

Fig. 11. Excitation efficiency of the H_2 molecular states in the gas discharge versus the mean electron energy.

Fig. 11 shows losses $\chi_K^{\rm disch}$ versus the electron energy. At low electron energy of $\epsilon \lesssim 6$ eV, results of numerical calculations [16] are used. For 6 eV $\lesssim \epsilon \lesssim$ 100-eV energy range, effective cross sections are averaged over the Maxwellian velocity distribution of the electrons. The losses on the kinetic energy of the secondary electrons, given by the right-hand term of the denominator in (1), become substantial at $\epsilon \gtrsim 70$ eV. The maximum excitation efficiency of laser states $\chi_B^d + \chi_C^d = 50$ percent is achieved at the mean electron energy of about 10-20 eV (Fig. 11). Efficiency decreases rapidly with diminishing electric field ϵ, especially in the region $\epsilon < 5$ eV. Electronic energy over 10 eV is attained at $E/p \gtrsim 500$ V $\cdot$ cm^{-1} torr^{-1}. This value of electronic energy is maintained during 0.6 ns at a gas pressure $p = 0.05$ atm for a system having a wave impedance of 1 Ω for the storage line. In the following quasi-CW phase of the discharge, the mean energy $\epsilon \sim$ 2-3 eV is established in accordance with the charged particle balance in the volume. Losses of electrons and positive ions are caused by volume recombination and ambipolar diffusion. The excitation efficiency of the laser states for this phase is insufficient due to comparatively low electron energy.

The excitation efficiency of the H_2 laser states by high energy electron beam is convenient to consider on the basis of a simplified model. The optimal use of the *e*-beam energy is achieved in the case of complete stoppage of the electrons in the laser volume *V*. The corresponding conversion efficiency of the total energy of *e* beam to the *k*th electronic state excitation energy may be considered over all the volume *V* during the current pulse. There is no need in this case for detailed study of the space-time pattern of the electronic energy losses and the approximate analytical analysis becomes possible. The addition of energy losses of the various electrons during the generations process were implicitly used to simplify the analysis. The rather precise set of data on the effective electron cross sections available at present for many atoms and molecules makes it possible to consider the problem using characteristics of particular collisional processes.

Laser states are excited in the process of energy loss of primary and secondary electrons. To determine the total efficiency κ^K, it is convenient to introduce the following value:

$$\kappa^K = \frac{\sigma_{0K}\epsilon_{0K}}{(1/N_0 v)(d\epsilon/dt)} = \frac{\sigma_{0K}\epsilon_{0K}}{(1/N_0)(d\epsilon/dx)}$$

$$\sqrt{\frac{1}{N_0}}\frac{d\epsilon}{dx} = \Sigma_m \sigma_{0m}\epsilon_{0m} + \delta_e + \int_0^{(\epsilon-\epsilon_{0i})/2} \epsilon_s\sigma_{0i}(\epsilon,\epsilon_s)\,d\epsilon_s$$

$$+ \int_0^{\epsilon} \epsilon_b\sigma_b(\epsilon,\epsilon_b)\,d\epsilon_b. \tag{2}$$

The parameter κ^K is the average part of the energy expended by the monoenergetic electrons with the initial energy in the range ϵ, $\epsilon + d\epsilon$ at distance dx on the kth collisional process. The balance equation for the mean electron energy is used in (2). The parameter κ^K does not depend strictly on time and position coordinates and is only a function of energy. Terms in the denominator are, respectively, excitation of quantum states and ionization, elastic losses, losses on the secondary electron kinetic energy, and bremsstrahlung radiation. In (2), v is the velocity of electrons and $d\epsilon/dx$ is the "ionization" losses of the electrons. At comparatively low electronic energies, elastic losses are $\delta_l = 2m\sigma_l\epsilon/M$, where m and M are the mass of the electron and atom/molecule, respectively, and σ_l is the effective cross section of the elastic collisions. The mean energy loss of electrons in elastic collisions with nuclei at energies in the range 10^3-10^5 eV are negligible due to the rapid drop of the corresponding differential scattering cross section with angle.

The parameter κ^K is plotted in Fig. 12 against the electron energy.[2] In the nonrelativistic energy region, approximately up to 0.2-0.4 MeV, the first two terms in the power expansion of the effective cross sections of the optically allowed transitions and ionization, calculated in the Born approximation, may be used (expansion on powers of ϵ^{-1})

$$\sigma_{0K} = \sigma^0_{0K}\frac{\epsilon_K}{\epsilon}\ln\frac{\epsilon}{\epsilon_K}. \tag{3}$$

In (3) $\sigma^0_{0B} = 1.5 \times 10^{-16}$ cm^2, $\sigma^0_{0C} = 1.1 \times 10^{-16}$ cm^2, and $\sigma^0_{0i} = 3.5 \times 10^{-16}$ cm^2. The experimental data on ionization [22] are described by (3) with an accuracy of 20 percent over the entire energy region of $10^2 \lesssim \epsilon \lesssim 10^4$ eV where measurements have been carried out. For the relativistic energy region $\epsilon \gtrsim$ 0.2–0.4 MeV, the following approximation can be used [24]:

$$\sigma^r_{0K} \simeq \sigma^0_{0K}\frac{\epsilon_{0K}}{mv^2}\ln\left[\frac{mv^2}{2\epsilon^2_{0K}}\frac{\epsilon'}{(1-\beta^2)}\right] \tag{4}$$

where m is the rest mass of electron, $\epsilon' = mc^2\,[(1-\beta^2)^{-1/2} - 1]$, and $\beta = v/c$.

General control of used approximations for the effective cross sections of the electronic collisional processes in hydrogen can be carried out by using the known data on energetic losses of electrons $d\epsilon/dx$ [24] according to the relation ($\epsilon \lesssim 60$ MeV)

[2] Index K takes the following values: $r, v, d, B, C, E, i, i^d, b$, and e.

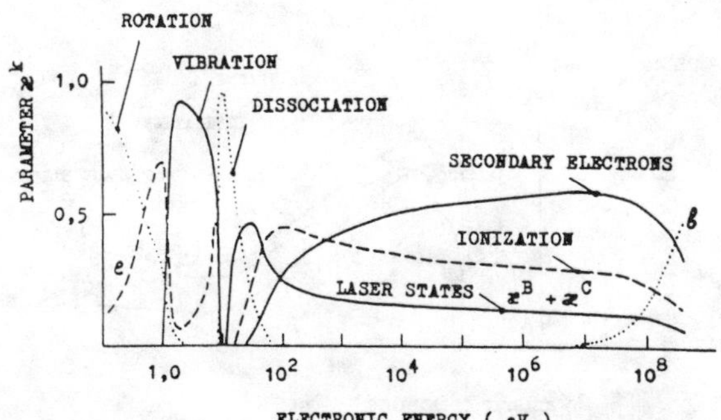

Fig. 12. Parameter κ^K dependence on energy: e—elastic collisions; b—bremsstrahlung radiation.

$$10^6\frac{\rho}{N_0}\frac{d\epsilon}{dx} = \Sigma_m\sigma_{0m}\epsilon_{0m} + \int_0^{(\epsilon-\epsilon_{0i})/2}\epsilon_s\sigma_{0i}$$

$$\cdot(\epsilon,\epsilon_s)\,d\epsilon_s = \delta(\epsilon) \tag{5}$$

where $d\epsilon/dx$ (in MeV/cm^{2}g^{-1}), and $\rho = 9.10^{-5}$g $\cdot$ cm^{-3} is the density of hydrogen. The chosen effective cross sections provide descriptions of the energetic losses of electrons over a wide energy region with an accuracy of <10 percent (Fig. 13). Maximum deviations occur in a relativistic region of $\epsilon \gtrsim 1$ MeV. The energetic dependence of the effective ionization cross section $\sigma_{0i}(\epsilon, \epsilon_s)$ have substantial effect on the curves at high electronic energies. The inverse square dependence increases electronic energy losses at 1 MeV approximately 1.5 times (the curve 1 in Fig. 13). More precise results are obtained with index 2.1 [24].

The maximum excitation efficiency of B and C laser states $\kappa^B + \kappa^C \simeq 50$ percent is achieved at the electronic energy about 30 eV (Fig. 12). The efficiency drops quickly with energy and for 10 keV $\lesssim \epsilon \lesssim$ 10 MeV the efficiency is stabilized at a level $\kappa^B + \kappa^C = 14$ percent. Main energetic losses, up to 55 percent, are accounted for by the kinetic energy of the secondary electrons. In the ultrarelativistic energy region $\epsilon \gtrsim 60$ MeV, the bremsstrahlung radiation becomes a dominating channel of losses, and the excitation efficiency of the laser states drops drastically (Fig. 12). The excitation efficiency of vibration levels and triplet electronic states by the primary electrons is extremely low, of order of the ratio of molecular state energy to the initial electronic energy.

The excitation efficiency of the kth collisional process by completely stopping groups of electrons with initial energy in the interval ϵ, $\epsilon + d\epsilon$ is approximately

$$\kappa^K_0 = \frac{1}{\epsilon}\int_0^t N_0\sigma_{0K}V\epsilon_{0K}dt = \frac{1}{\epsilon}\int_0^{\epsilon}\kappa^K d\epsilon \tag{6}$$

(t_0—time of complete stoppage of electrons). The change of variables $t = t(\epsilon)$ is used here according to the electronic energy balance equation. The electronic energy distribution function is changed for the stopping electrons and the effective width of the function $\Delta\epsilon$ is increased. The effective cross sections of ionization and laser states excitation (allowed optical transitions) at $\epsilon \gtrsim 200$ eV vary rather slowly in

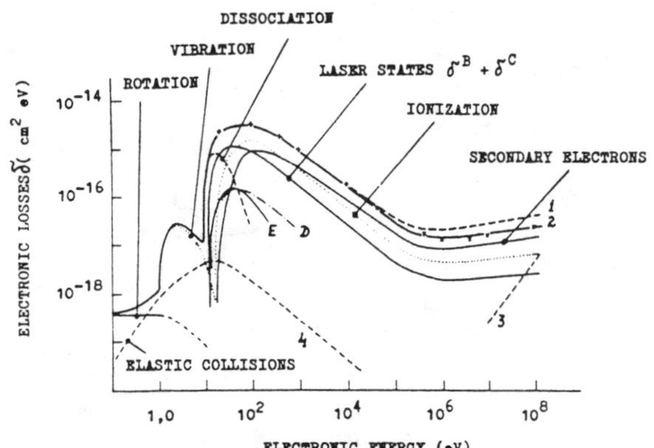

Fig. 13. Energy losses of electrons in H_2. 1–total losses for inverse square dependence of $\sigma_{0i}(\epsilon_1 \epsilon_s)$ from energy. 2–total losses for index 2, 1. 3–bremsstrahlung losses. 4–elastic collisions with nucleus. E, D–singlet electronic states.

the energy range $\Delta\epsilon$. Electrons lose energy by small portions $\sim\epsilon_{0i}$, considerable changes of energy in processes with secondary electrons are unlikely. This fact justifies to some extent the use in (6) of the product $\sigma_{0K}(\epsilon)v(\epsilon)$ at the mean electron energy ϵ instead of the coefficient $\langle\sigma_{0K} V\rangle_t$ averaged over the time-dependent electron velocity distribution.

The interaction of the primary electrons with the gas yields secondary electrons with considerable kinetic energy. These electrons also cause ionization and excitation. Part of the kinetic energy is transmitted to the secondary electrons of the following generations. Overall excitation of the electronic states is determined by the primary electrons and the secondary electrons of all generations.

The basic characteristics of secondary electrons of successive generations are the following: the total number of electrons in jth generation n_j, the energy distribution function of electrons φ_j, the total initial kinetic energy of electrons W_j, the maximum energy of electrons ϵ_j^{max}, and the excitation efficiency of kth process. Table V gives recurrent relations for these parameters, including an approximate expression for the energy distribution function of the electrons. All parameters are integral in time and space for given electron generation.

The total conversion efficiency of energy of the monochromatic electron beam with the energy ϵ_0 to the kth inelastic process, including secondary electrons, is

$$\kappa^K(\epsilon_0) = \frac{1}{W_0} \sum_{j=0} W_j \kappa_j^K = \sum_{j=0} \kappa_j^K \prod_{l=0}^{j-1} \kappa_l^s. \qquad (7)$$

The kinetic energy of the second generation electrons is $\sim$15 percent of that of primary electron beam. The total kinetic energy of the third generation is $\sim$2.0 percent of the initial energy of the electron beam. Fig. 14 shows the energetic dependence of total efficiency κ^K. At energies $\epsilon > 10^3$ eV, the parameters κ^K vary rather slightly. For this energy range, a certain relation between effective cross sections as well as between energetic losses for basic inelastic processes is established. The total efficiency of excitation for laser states of the Lyman and Werner band systems is somewhat less than 30 percent; κ^B = 16 percent, κ^C = 13 percent. Half of the total

TABLE V

TRANSITIONS SUITABLE FOR CW VUV LASER ACTION (LYMAN BANDS)

Band	Parameter $f_{ov'} f_{v'v''} \times 10^2$	Line	Wave Length (Å)
Molecular Hydrogen			
(8,14)	2.02	P(2)	1567.525
		P(3)	1567.249
		P(4)	1566.431
(10,14)	0.83	P(2)	1518.184
		P(3)	1518.005
		P(4)	1517.343
(11,14)	0.89	P(2)	1495.686
		P(3)	1495.565
		P(4)	1495.012
		P(5)	1494.190
Molecular Deuterium			
(11-20)	P(2)	P(2)	1596.249
		P(3)	1596.115
		P(4)	1595.772
(12,21)		P(1)	1580.193

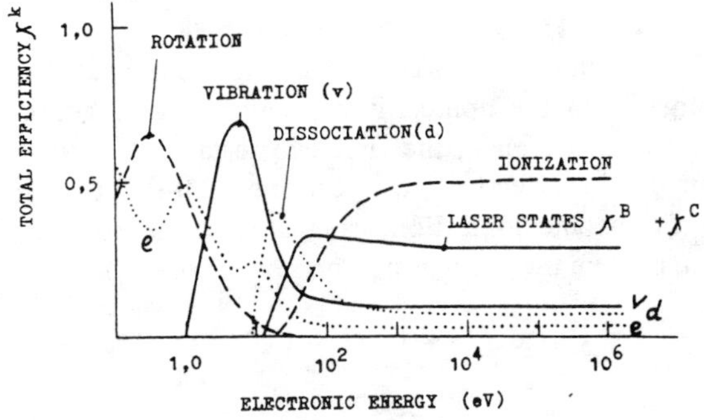

Fig. 14. The total excitation efficiency of molecular states of H_2 by electrons in dependence on the initial electronic energy. e–elastic collisions. For $\epsilon \lesssim 30 \div 50$ eV approximate data are given.

energy is expended on ionization; about 7 percent on excitation of triplet electronic states. Obtained results can be controlled by comparison with the mean energy $\bar{\epsilon}$, needed for ion pair formation. This value is almost constant over wide energy region of primary electrons [23], and for hydrogen it is $\bar{\epsilon}$ = 36.5 eV. For considered scheme $\bar{\epsilon} = \epsilon_0/n = \epsilon_{0i}/\chi^i = 3/\text{eV}$ ($n = \chi^i \epsilon_0/\epsilon_{0i}$ is the total number of secondary electrons produced by the primary electron). The agreement with the approximate calculations is quite satisfactory.

Performed analysis shows that the H_2-VUV laser quantum system converts the energy of e beams into the excitation energy of laser electronic states with the efficiency approximating a limiting value. Complete absorption of electrons in the laser volume is a basic condition for the effective use of electron beam energy in hydrogen. Decreasing the electron path by increasing gas pressure is possible only to a certain limit.

This limit is connected with the quenching of electronic stages and collisional broadening of the amplification lines. The electronic path decreases rapidly with diminishing of electronic energy in proportion to $l \propto \epsilon^{1.8}$. At low electronic energy, the main difficulties are connected with the injection of e beam into the laser volume and with the ability to attain a sufficient value of electronic current. It becomes necessary to use thin separating foils with thickness of 1-10 μ.

For optimal usage of the e-beam energy, the special confining systems of high-speed electrons in the active volume can be used along with methods mentioned in the preceding. Such systems are of particular importance at low gas pressure. In a simple transverse excitation system with magnetic field $H = 1$ kG directed along the active medium the Larmor radius of electrons with energy $\epsilon = 100$ keV, $r = mvc/eH$ is 1 cm. Although the general picture of high energy electron scattering in a rather rarefied gas at $p \sim 0.1$-1.0 atm in a magnetic field is not clearly understood, one should expect from qualitative considerations a sharp reduction of the volume, where electronic energy is absorbed.

It is difficult at present to draw a certain conclusion in favor of self-sustained gas discharge or e-beam excitation methods for H_2-VUV laser. At present, self-sustained discharges are preferred due to the absence of effective e-beam confining systems. In small volumes with narrow laser channels, a higher specific pumping power up to 10 GW/cm^3 is obtained in gas discharges at low-pressure $p \sim 0.1$ atm.

V. On the CW H_2-VUV Laser

A. *Depletion of the Lower Laser Levels*

Four-level laser system of molecular hydrogen and deuterium [12] is one of the most promising for CW laser action in the VUV region due to the rather small spectral width of amplification lines ~0.6 cm^{-1} and to the corresponding comparatively low-threshold pumping energy. The practical realization of this most favorable CW VUV laser scheme is obviously a rather difficult problem. In connection with this difficulty, it is useful to consider the main kinetic processes in the scheme in some detail.

The potential energy curve of the upper state of the Lyman band hydrogen laser is highly displaced about the ground state towards long internuclear distances [Fig. 7(a)]. The result is intensive transitions to the highly excited molecular levels of the ground (lower laser) state located within kT from the dissociation limit. There are three basic mechanisms of effective depletion of these levels. Depletion of H_2 levels $v'' = 14$, $J'' = 4,5$ overlying the dissociation limit has been already considered in the preceding. It occurs due to the rotational predissociation. Dissociation in molecular collisions and depletion due to VT relaxation are also effective. The nonradiative lifetime of the levels at optimum conditions may be much less than the radiative lifetime of the upper laser levels. At moderate pumping power of molecular hydrogen in gas discharge or by CW e beam, the population of the upper laser state is determined mainly by the electronic excitation rate, radiative decay, and molecular quenching. Population of lower laser levels depends on the radiative decay rate of the upper electronic states, dissociation rate, atomic hydrogen recombination, as well as VV and VT relaxation of the vibrational level system of the ground electronic state. The most critical for CW laser action is concentration of atomic hydrogen in the discharge. This concentration is determined by electronic dissociation rate of the molecules and by the atomic recombination rate on chamber walls and during triple molecular collisions in the gas volume.

The probability of predissociation of the levels $v'' = 14$, $J'' = 4,5$, and $W^{pr}_{v''J''} = D_{v''J''}/T_{\text{vib}}$ is about two orders of magnitude more than that of radiative decay of the higher laser states. Calculations of bound-bound and bound-free transitions probabilities for molecular states are the dissociation limit is a rather difficult task of molecular-collision physics [25]. A close bound between vibration and rotation involves certain difficulties in studying the problem. The molecular vibration amplitude is not small compared with the range of intermolecular forces. The Massey parameter $\xi = 4\pi^2\ \Delta\epsilon/\alpha v h \sim 1$ ($\Delta\epsilon$–transition energy, α–constant of exponential interaction potential, v–molecular velocity). The last two circumstances present essential difficulties in using perturbation theory. The exact form of the interaction potential for vibrationally excited molecules and molecules in the ground state is unknown. The corresponding population equations are strongly bound due to rather high transition probability, and it is very difficult to solve them even by numerical methods.

Particular problems, related to dissociation, are usually considered by assuming the coefficients $\langle \sigma_{v''J'',d}\, v\rangle$ for levels $v''J''$ in the immediate vicinity of the dissociation limit to be

$$\langle \sigma_{v''J'',d}\, v\rangle = \kappa \langle \sigma_l v\rangle \exp\left(-\epsilon_{v''J'',d}/kT\right) \tag{8}$$

where σ_l is the effective cross section of elastic collisions, $\epsilon_{v''J'',d}$ is the dissociation energy for the state $v''J''$, and κ is the arbitrary parameter of the order of 1. This corresponds to the dissociation cross section

$$\sigma_{v''J'',d} = \begin{cases} \kappa\sigma_l, & \epsilon \geqslant \epsilon_{v''J'',d} \\ 0, & \epsilon < \epsilon_{v''J'',d} \end{cases} \tag{9}$$

for collisions along the center line.

Levels $v'' = 14$, $J'' = 0, 1, 2, 3$ of H_2, and $v'' = 20, 21$ of D_2 lying within $kT (T \simeq 300$ K) below the dissociation limit are subjected to direct transitions to continuous spectrum during molecular collisions with the probability

$$W^d_{v''J''} = \kappa v/\tau^*_{0vi} = \kappa\sqrt{2}\, N_0 \pi (r_0 + r_{v''})^2\, vp,$$

$$N_0 = 2.7 \times 10^9 \text{ cm}^{-3}$$

where r_0, $r_{v''}$ are effective radii of molecules in ground and excited states, v is the molecular velocity, and parameter $\kappa \simeq 1$ is the dissociation probability of excited molecules during collisions. For $v'' = 14$ of hydrogen, the probability $W^d_{v''J''}$ exceeds the value A_{BX} at gas pressure $p \gtrsim 40$ mmHg.

VT relaxation is an effective depletion mechanism of molecular levels nearby the dissociation limit. The corresponding probability calculated in [26] by using the anharmonic oscillator model is

$$W^{\text{VT}}_{v''J''} \simeq \kappa P/\tau^*_{0v'}, \qquad \kappa \simeq 1.$$

An effective action of the two last mechanisms of collisional depletion is provided at gas pressure $\gtrsim$ 40 mmHg.

B. Population of Laser States

The stationary population of the upper laser state $v'J'$ under amplification mode of operation with excitation by electrons at moderate pumping power depends mainly on the excitation rate of the electronic state $N_0 f_{0B}$, radiative decay, and molecular quenching of level $v'J'$ with probabilities A_{BX} and $W_{B\cdot P}$, respectively (Fig. 15)

$$N_{v'}^{B} = N_0 f_{0B} g_{0v'}^{BX} \beta_{0J'}^{BX} / (A_{BX} + W_{B\cdot P}). \tag{10}$$

Population of lower laser levels is determined mainly by radiative decay of B state, volume recombination of hydrogen atoms with the concentration N_H, and by the total depletion probability

$$W_{v''J''} = W_{v''J''}^{pr} + W_{v''J''}^{d} + W_{v''J''}^{VT}$$

$$N_{v''J''} = \left[\sum_{v'J'} N_{v'J'}^{B} A_{BX} g_{v'v''}^{BX} S_{J'J''}^{BX} / (2J^1 + 1) + \delta N_H^2 N_0 K_{rec}^{vol} \right] W_{v''J''}^{-1} \tag{11}$$

where δ is the relative recombination yield of molecules on level $v''J''$, $K_{rec}^{vol} = 5.10^{-33}$ cm^6 s^{-1} [27]—the volume recombination constant of hydrogen atoms at room temperature. The influence of radiative decay of C state is negligible due to the smallness of the corresponding Franck-Condon factors. The contribution of the highly excited electronic states B', C', d is of no importance due to small value of the oscillator strength of these transitions. For levels near the dissociation limit, the population rate from the underlying vibrational states due to VV exchange is negligible since at gas temperature T = 300-700 K, the probability of VV exchange is small compared with that of VT relaxation.

The H-atom concentration is determined by the molecular dissociation rate connected with excitation of singlet and

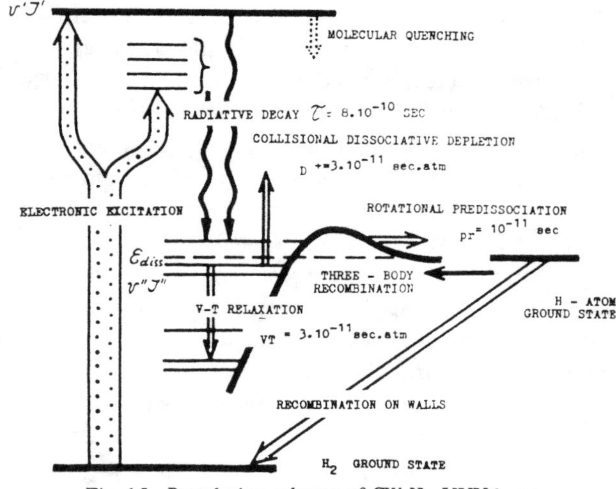

Fig. 15. Population scheme of CW H_2-VUV laser.

concentration. Use of volume recombination with this purpose is inexpedient since this channel leads to increasing the lower laser level population. In the case of surface recombination, the excess energy of the recombined molecules is transferred to the walls and the lower laser levels remain empty. The atomic recombination probability on the walls of the cylindrical cell of radius r_0 is $R_{rec}^{wall} = D(2.4/r_0)^2 \gamma$. The parameter γ is the recombination probability of atoms during collision with the walls. For various wall materials, it ranges from 10^{-2} to 0.5 [29].

There are two criteria which should be fulfilled to obtain CW laser action. The requirements are applied on the excitation rate of the B state (and hence on the absolute intensity of spontaneous radiation of the laser transitions) and on the rate of decreasing the H-atom concentration. The basic condition is excess of gain over losses $K_{v''J''}^{v'J'} \gtrsim \kappa$, where

$$K_{v''J''}^{v'J'} = \mu_{v''J''}^{v'J'} P \cdot f_{0B} \left[1 - (\chi_{v''J''}^{v'J'})^{rad}\, w^{-1} - \chi_{rec} \frac{f_{0B} P^2}{R^2 w} \right] \tag{14}$$

$$\mu_{v''J''}^{v'J'} = \frac{\lambda^2 g_{0v'} g_{v'v''} \beta_{0J'} S_{J'J''} (\pi \ln 2)^{1/2} N_0}{4\pi^2 \Delta\nu_d (1 + \gamma^0 P (\pi \ln 2)^{1/2} / \Delta\nu_d)(2J^1 + 1)[1 + (W_q \cdot P/A_{BX})]} \tag{15}$$

triplet states $\simeq N_0 f_{0D}$, volume and surface recombination as well as by nonrecombination processes which decrease H-atom concentration with the total probability R^*

$$N_H^2 N_0 K_{rec}^{vol} + N_H R = N_0 f_{0D} \tag{12}$$

where $R = R_{rec}^{wall} + R^*$. The molecular dissociation rate is determined by excitation of the repulsion $b\,^3\Sigma_u^+$ state, radiative decay of the $c\,^3\Pi_u$ state, and by the total bound-free radiative decay rate of $B\,^1\Sigma_u^+$ state with emission of the Herzberg continuum [28]

$$N_0 f_{0d} \simeq N_0 f_{0b} + \frac{N_c A_c b}{A_c b + W_c \cdot p} + \frac{N_0 f_{0b}\, \kappa_{cont}}{A_B + W_B P}. \tag{13}$$

Chemical bonding and gas pumping are examples of effective nonrecombination processes resulting in decreasing the H-atom concentration. [sic: continues in right column above]

where p (atmospheres), χ denotes numerical parameters, $w = W_{v''J''}/A_{BX}$, γ_0 is the collisional broadening parameter, $\kappa = l^{-1} \ln(1 - R)$, l is the active medium length, and R is the reflection coefficient.

In the plane of the parameters, (f, R) in logarithmic scale, the region of CW laser action corresponds approximately to a sector limited from below by the straight line $f_{min} = \kappa/\mu_{v''J''}^{v'J'}$ and from above by $f_{max} = wR^2/p^2 \chi_{rec}$ (Fig. 16). The lower line corresponds to the threshold amplification for $N_{v''} = 0$, to the minimum excitation rate f_{0B} and the minimum spontaneous radiation power P_{min} of laser line. For the $P(4)$ (8,14) band line of pure paramodification $P_{min} = K \cdot 1.7 \times 10^3$ W/cm^3. For active medium length l = 1 m and losses of 20 percent, P_{min} = 3.4 W/cm^3. The upper line on the graph corresponds to a decrease of the gain to threshold at high pumping rate due to intense recombination population of the

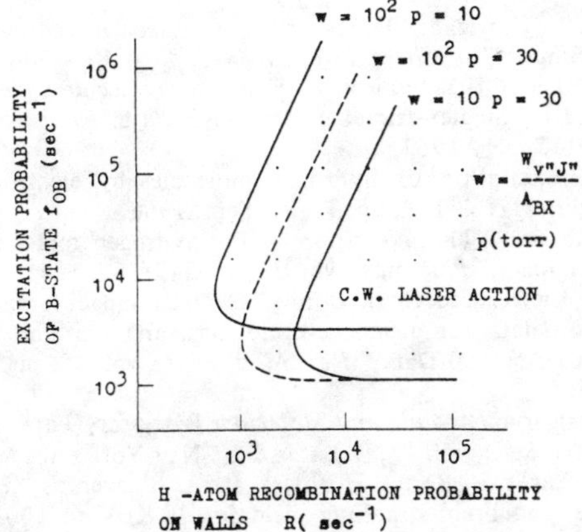

Fig. 16. Criterion of the CW H_2-VUV laser action on the $P(4)$ (8,14) line of pure parahydrogen.

lower laser levels. The minimum value of effective recombination rate

$$R_{\min} = \left(\frac{KW\chi_{\rm rec} P}{\mu_{v''J''}^{v'J'}} \right)^{1/2} \frac{2}{W - \chi_{\rm rad}} \tag{16}$$

is of the order of 5×10^2-5×10^3 s^{-1}.

The most appropriate conditions for attaining the previously mentioned minimum rates of CW excitation and recombination could be created apparently in narrow gas discharge channels. Table V gives the wavelength of transitions suitable for CW VUV laser action in hydrogen and deuterium.

VI. Conclusion[3]

The quantum-mechanical system of the H_2-VUV laser as it is shown in this paper is characterized by rather high limiting operating laser parameters. The problem is to approach these laser parameters in practice.

In gas discharges, the effective excitation of the H_2-VUV laser can be carried out apparently only at comparatively low pressure $p \lesssim 0.05$-0.1 atm. At higher pressures, the electric field and the mean electronic energy in the discharge drop rapidly in a time interval less than the laser pulse duration. The result is low efficiency of excitation.

The main problems in practice are connected with the extremely short lifetime of the inversion population ~1 ns. These problems can be completely removed by using the four-level collisional scheme of excitation. The optimal pressure range for this scheme is rather high $p \gtrsim 0.1$ atm. The most favorable excitation conditions can be attained by using *e*-beam systems with electron trapping. The excitation efficiency in this case, unlike the gas-discharge systems, remains constant during the current pulse irrespective of the pressure. The region of optimum pressure depends on the value of the molecular quenching cross section of excited molecular states of hydrogen. Observed laser action in pure H_2 at 2-atm pressure is certain evidence in favor of rather high optimal pressures. Molecular quenching of laser states may be substantially decreased by the addition of inert gases such as He. In this case, the effective collisional depletion of the lower laser states is provided. The four-level laser action in H_2 could be obtained apparently also on bound-free Lyman transition on Herzberg continuum [28].

The four-level bound-bound transitions of H_2 and D_2 are favorable for achieving the CW VUV laser action on several lines in the region of 1500-1600 Å. The use of supernarrow laser channels yield high probability for wall recombinations and should be used to obtain the needed H-atom recombination rate. Simultaneously, high electronic energy should be provided in the active medium. CW pumping can be carried out by using some sort of gas discharge CW electronic beam. Pure parahydrogen is expedient to use in first experiments.

The wavelength of H_2-VUV laser is near the absolute wavelength limit about 700-1000 Å for neutral atomic and molecular laser systems without photoionization absorption from the ground state. The H_2 electronic transition $D \rightarrow X$ in the region about 900 Å near the photoionization limit remains unstudied. The effective electronic excitation cross section of D state is probably an order of magnitude less than that of the B state. A strong radiative population of the lower levels from B and C states apparently presents some difficulties for obtaining population inversion.

Small-size high-repetition rate gas discharge excited H_2-VUV laser with mean power of even several milliwatts will have wide applications in laboratory experiments. Unlike the *e*-beam excited inert gas excimer systems, this laser is absolutely free of penetrating radiation danger. The laser can be used in investigations of laser VUV photochemistry, including isotopic-selective processes. Dynamic and spectral features of luminescence of the complex molecular systems including biologically active materials can be carried out. Luminescence and photoionization detection of small admixtures in gases, optical pumping of lasers with continuous frequency tuning in the range 1800-3000 Å can also be performed. Applications will be expanded for these lasers in the future in accordance with the growth of the average and the peak laser power and with the simplifcation of the excitation techniques.

[3] After this paper was submitted, similar spectroscopic results were reported by R. W. Dreyfus and R. T. Hodgson, "Molecular-hydrogen laser: 1098-1613 Å," *Phys. Rev.*, vol. 9, pp. 2635-2648, 1974.

References

[1] N. G. Basov, V. A. Danilychev, I. N. Popov, and D. D. Khodkevich, "Laser operating in the vacuum region of the spectrum by excitation of liquid xenon with an electron beam," *JETP Lett.*, vol. 12, pp. 329-331, 1970.

[2] A. G. Akamanov *et al.*, "Generation of coherent radiation at λ = 2120 Å by cascade frequency conversion," *JETP Lett.*, vol. 10, pp. 154-157, 1969.

[3] S. E. Harris and R. B. Miles, "Proposed third-harmonic generation in phase-matched metal vapors," *Appl. Phys. Lett.*, vol. 19, pp. 385-387, Nov. 1971.

[4] a) H. A. Koehler, L. I. Ferderber, D. L. Redhead, and P. I. Ebert, "Stimulated VUV emission in high pressure xenon excited by high-current relativistic electron beams," *Appl. Phys. Lett.*, vol. 21, pp. 198-200, Sept. 1972.
b) P. W. Hoff, I. C. Swingle, and C. K. Rhodes, "Demonstration of temporal coherence, spatial coherence, and threshold effects in the molecular xenon laser," *Opt. Commun.*, vol. 8, pp. 128-131, June 1973.

[5] P. A. Bazhulin, I. N. Knyazev, and G. G. Petrash, "On the possibility of stimulated emission in the far ultraviolet," *Sov. Phys.-JETP*, vol. 23, pp. 649-650, Sept. 1965.

[6] a) R. W. Waynant, J. D. Shipman, R. C. Elton, and A. W. Ali, "Vacuum ultraviolet laser emission from molecular hydrogen," *Appl. Phys. Lett.*, vol. 17, pp. 383-384, Nov. 1970.

b) R. T. Hodgson, "Vacuum-ultraviolet laser action observed in the Lyman bands of molecular hydrogen," *Appl. Phys. Lett.*, vol. 25, pp. 494–497, Aug. 1970.

[7] R. T. Hodgson and R. W. Dreyfus, "Vacuum-UV laser action observed in H_2 Werner bands; 1161–1240 Å," *Phys. Rev. Lett.*, vol. 28, pp. 536–539, Feb. 1972.

[8] V. S. Antonov, I. N. Knyazev, V. S. Letokhov, and V. G. Movshev, "Hydrogen laser in vacuum ultraviolet at atmospheric pressure," *JETP Lett.*, vol. 17, pp. 393-395, 1973.

[9] J. E. Hesser, "Absolute transition probabilities in ultraviolet molecular spectra," *J. Chem. Phys.*, vol. 48, pp. 2518-2535, Mar. 1968.

[10] J. H. Kiefer and R. W. Lutz, "Vibrational and relaxation of hydrogen," *J. Chem. Phys.*, vol. 44, pp. 668-672, Jan. 1966.

[11] G. Herzberg and L. L. Howe, "The Lyman bands of molecular hydrogen," *Can. J. Phys.*, vol. 51, pp. 867-887, May 1973.

[12] I. H. Knyazev, V. S. Letskhov, and V. G. Moushev, "TEA N_2 UV laser with reduced spectra," *Opt. Commun.*, vol. 6, pp. 250–252, Nov. 1972.

[13] I. Tobias and J. Vanderslice, "Potential energy curves for the $X^1\Sigma_g^+$ and $B^1\Sigma_u^+$ states of hydrogen," *J. Chem. Phys.*, vol. 35, pp. 1852–1855, Nov. 1961.

[14] E. H. Fink, D. L. Akins, and C. B. Moore, "Energy transfer in monochromatically-excited hydrogen $(B^1\Sigma_u^+)$. I. Excitation processes, electronic quenching, and vibrational energy transfer," *J. Chem Phys.*, vol. 56, pp. 900–915, Jan. 1972.

[15] A. Dalgarno and R. J. Henry, "The rotational excitation of molecular hydrogen by slow electrons," *Proc. Phys. Soc.* (London), vol. 85, pp. 679–684, 1965.

[16] A. G. Englehardt and A. V. Phelps, "Elastic and inelastic collision cross sections in hydrogen and deuterium from transport coefficients," *Phys. Rev.*, vol. 131, pp. 2115–2128, Sept. 1963.

[17] A. V. Phelps, "Rotational and vibrational excitation of molecules by low-energy electrons," *Rev. Mod. Phys.*, vol. 40, pp. 399–410, Apr. 1968.

[18] S. J. B. Corrigan, "Dissociation of molecular hydrogen by electron impact," *J. Chem. Phys.*, vol. 43, pp. 4381–4386, Dec. 1965.

[19] S. P. Khare, "Excitation of hydrogen molecule by electron impact III. Singlet-triplet excitations," *Phys. Rev.*, vol. 157, pp. 107–112, May 1967.

[20] —, "Excitation of hydrogen molecules by electron impact," *Phys. Rev.*, vol. 149, pp. 33-37, Sept. 1966.

[21] R. Roscoe, "The excitation of the hydrogen molecule by electron impact," *Phil. Mag.*, vol. 31, pp. 349-362, 1941.

[22] L. J. Kieffer and G. H. Dunn, "Electron impact ionization cross-section data for atoms, atomic ions, and diatomic molecules: I. Experimental Data," *Rev. Mod. Phys.*, vol. 38, pp. 1-35, Jan. 1966.

[23] A. Dalgarno, *Atomic and Molecular Processes*, (Pure and Applied Science Ser.), vol. 13, D. Bates, Ed. New York: Academic, 1962.

[24] a) L. Pages, E. Bertel, H. Joffre, and L. Sklavenitis, "Energy loss, range, and bremsstrahlung yield for 10-KEV to 100-MEV electrons in various elements and chemical compounds," *At. Data*, vol. 4, pp. 1-127, Mar. 1972.

b) C. B. Opal, W. K. Peterson, and E. C. Beaty, "Measurements of secondary-electron spectra produced by electron impact ionization of a number of simple gases," *J. Chem. Phys.*, vol. 55, pp. 4100–4106, Oct. 1971.

[25] E. E. Nikitin, "Theory of elementary atomic-molecular processes in gases," in *Chemistry*, Moscow, 1970.

[26] J. H. Kiefer, "Effect of VV transfer on the rate of diatomic dissociation," *J. Chem. Phys.*, vol. 57, pp. 1938–1956, Sept. 1972.

[27] V. H. Shui and J. P. Appleton, "Gas-phase recombination of hydrogen. A comparison between theory and experiment," *J. Chem. Phys.*, vol. 55, pp. 3126–3132, Oct. 1971.

[28] A. Dalgarno, G. Herzberg, and T. L. Stephens, "A new continuous emission spectrum of the hydrogen molecule," *Astrophys. J.*, vol. 162, pp. L49–L53, Oct. 1970.

[29] A. Gelb and S. K. Kim, "Theory of atomic recombination on surfaces," *J. Chem. Phys.*, vol. 55, pp. 4935–4939, Nov. 1971.

Reprinted with the permission of the IEEE from *Proceedings of the IEEE,* Vol. 64(7), pp. 1059-1092 (July 1976).

Review of Short Wavelength Laser Research

RONALD W. WAYNANT, MEMBER, IEEE, AND RAYMOND C. ELTON

Invited Paper

Abstract—A review of the status of research towards achieving lasing action in the vacuum ultraviolet and soft X-ray spectral regions is presented. An analysis of the general problems likely to be encountered is accompanied by numerical results for those approaches currently considered promising. Progress on each approach is detailed and various possible methods of verifying the presence of gain with their relative merits are discussed. Research areas requiring application of short-wavelength lasers also are given.

Manuscript received December 2, 1975. This work was supported in part by the Defense Advanced Research Project Agency under DARPA Order 2694.

The authors are with the U.S. Naval Research Laboratory, Washington, DC 20375.

I. Introduction

HAVING BEEN DORMANT for the first ten years of laser research, the development of short-wavelength lasers emitting in the vacuum region[1] at wavelengths shorter than 2000 Å has advanced rapidly during the last five years. A number of new devices useful as both oscillators and amplifiers have been developed and are finding early applica-

[1]At wavelengths shorter than 2000 Å, oxygen and nitrogen in the atmosphere absorb radiation strongly and vacuum (or helium-purged) paths must be provided to propagate the radiation.

tion as diagnostic probes for materials studies. In addition, techniques have been developed for utilizing nonlinear optical properties of materials to generate laser harmonic frequencies and to mix and add together several lower laser frequencies to produce tunable, coherent emission in the spectral region below 2000 Å. These advances have produced the momentum for research to develop still shorter wavelength X-ray lasers.

Perhaps the most important forerunner of the direct amplifying, self-contained lasers to be developed was the molecular nitrogen discharge laser of Heard [1]. This laser, which emits at 3371 Å from molecular electronic levels, spurred the development of the fast-pumping technology required for shorter wavelength lasers, as well as pointing out the utility of molecular electronic levels for ultraviolet (UV) lasers. This laser has been developed considerably by Leonard [2], Gerry [3], Shipman [4], and numerous others. It is now one of the most important lasers in the near UV and is used extensively as an exciter for dye lasers. French reports claim 50-MW peak power from such N_2 lasers [5]. In addition, there has been success in pumping N_2 with electron beams [6], [7].

Earlier development of N_2 lasers led directly to the realization of the first vacuum ultraviolet (VUV) laser from molecular H_2. The concept of a H_2 laser was advanced by Bazhulin *et al.* [8] in 1965, but the actual realization of the laser awaited application by Shipman [4] of fast-pulsed technology to the N_2 laser. Using the flat plate Blumlein discharge system, both Hodgson [9] and Waynant *et al.* [10], [11] produced lasing on the Lyman band ($B^1\Sigma_u^+ - X^1\Sigma_g^+$) of H_2. Further work produced laser emission from the isotopic molecules, D_2 and HD, and also from para-H_2 [12], [13]. Hodgson also was able to produce stimulated emission on the fourth positive band of CO ($A^1\Pi - X^1\Sigma^+$) giving lines in the 1800–2000-Å region [14].[2]

Continued development of the Shipman technology enabled Waynant to generate lasing in the 1160-Å spectral region on the Werner-band transitions ($C^1\Pi_u - X^1\Sigma_g^+$) from H_2 [15]. Hodgson and Dreyfus switched to a high-current electron beam to generate lasing in N_2 [6], in the H_2 Lyman band [16] and also the Werner band of H_2 [17]. Considerable theoretical [18]–[22] and experimental [23], [24] work has been done on the H_2 laser. In recent reviews of the H_2 laser [25], [26], advances and limitations are detailed for both atmospheric pressure and repetitively discharged operation.

The Soviet scientists were also responsible for another theoretical prediction of a somewhat different VUV laser. In 1968, Molchanov *et al.* proposed that solid crystals of the rare gases could be made to lase [27]. Basov *et al.* conducted a number of experiments using the liquid form of the rare gases, principally Xe, [28]–[33] and report characteristics consistent with stimulated emission. Continuation of this interesting work does not appear forthcoming, probably due to the difficulty of the experiments. Koehler and associates [34]–[35] used high-current electron beams and high-pressure gaseous Xe to form excited Xe molecules (Xe_2^*) called excimers. Lasing was observed at ~1720 Å from these excimers. Extensive theoretical studies [36]–[43] and considerable experimental work [44]–[53] has been devoted to Xe, as reviewed by Rhodes [54]. Other excimers, e.g., Kr_2^* and Ar_2^*, have been made to lase in

[2]Apparently a fiducial calibration mark shown on densitometer traces [9] at 1600.44 Å has been mistakenly listed as an unidentified H_2 laser line in [13].

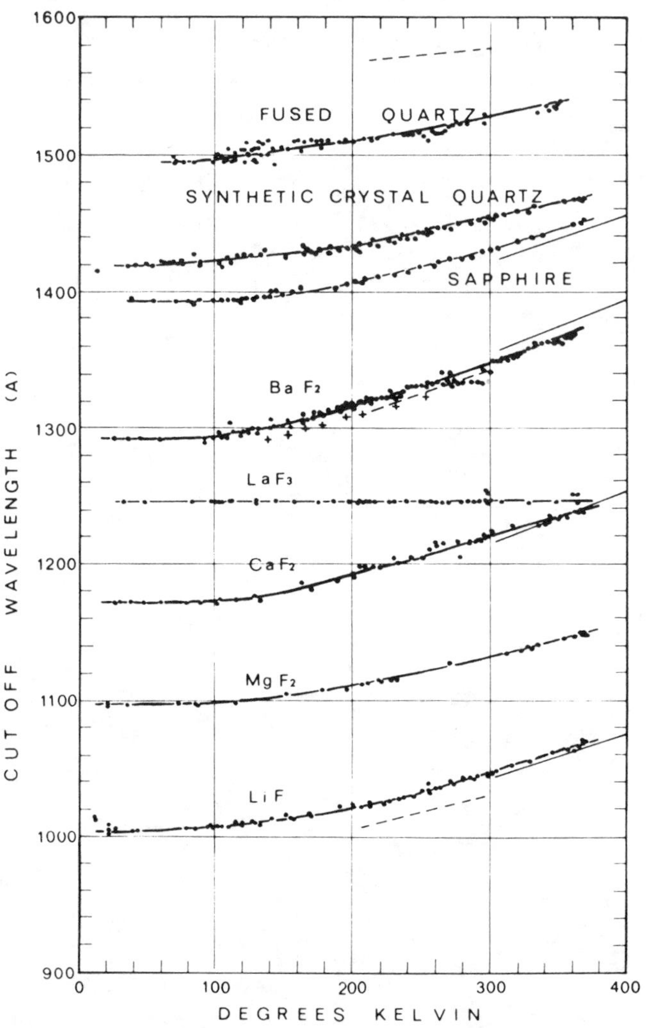

Fig. 1. Short-wavelength transmission cutoff versus temperature for various optical materials [58].

the 1260–1460-Å region [34], [35], [39], [55]–[57]. These lasers appear to have a large potential for both high power and high efficiency.

A. Material Limitations

1) Optical Characteristics: Besides the difficulties of achieving high gain at short wavelengths (which will be explained in Section II), a major impediment for VUV and X-ray lasers has been a lack of suitable materials for both high transmission windows and efficient reflectors for resonators, both of traditional high priority in laser research. The field of optics in the VUV has been surveyed and reviewed recently quite excellently by Hunter [58] and also previously by Tousey [59] and Samson [60]. Fig. 1 from [58] shows the temperature dependence of the short-wavelength transmission limit of various VUV window materials. The cutoff wavelength of all materials drops with temperature, but no material has a cutoff below 1000 Å (LiF). Below 1000 Å the only possibility of building a Fabry–Perot mirrored cavity requires that a hole for output coupling be cut in the mirror. To do this would require sophisticated differential vacuum pumping and gas handling.

For reflection, no material is better than aluminum for wavelengths longer than 1000 Å. In order to use this high reflectance the oxide film which normally develops on its surface must be prevented. This is done by overcoating with magnesium-fluoride or lithium-fluoride films of precisely controlled thickness. Since the overcoating material cuts off at short wavelengths, the reflectance of aluminum cannot be used below 1000 Å. Below 1000 Å no material has very high reflectance. Platinum is usually used, but in some wavelength regions such materials as iridium, osmium, rhenium, and tungsten may have higher reflectance. The reflectance of these materials is given by Hunter as a function of wavelength [58].

Already difficulties have been found in using resonators with the rare-gas molecular lasers. Aluminum coatings are rapidly damaged [45], [61] when used as resonators for high-power Xe lasers and presently limit the output intensity to about 1 MW/cm^2. Intensity inside the resonator is several times higher. The primary reason for this limitation is the power absorbed in the aluminum. The same interband levels responsible for absorption in aluminum are present in other prospective reflector materials. Multilayer dielectric mirrors are a possible choice, but they are difficult to make, would likely still have considerable absorption, and would not be available below 1000 Å.

2) Crystal Resonators:

a) Bragg reflection: Below 1000-Å resonant cavities with high reflectance are difficult to build for the reasons given above, but at very short wavelengths of about 10 Å or less it becomes possible to use Bragg reflection from the crystal planes of solids. Several papers have presented possible X-ray resonators which would be suitable—theoretically at least—for an X-ray laser. The puckered ring design of Bond *et al.* [62] is shown in Fig. 2. This design allows the resonator to be tuned to the laser transition. The losses at each crystal reflection are less than 5 percent, but these losses multiply as crystal elements are added and so does the difficulty of alignment. Single crystals with alignments carefully fabricated might be used as resonators. Such resonators, as proposed by Deslattes [63], are shown in Fig. 3. Cotterill [64] proposes a resonator built using pairs of parallel crystal planes as shown in Fig. 4. In this design the polarization losses are less than the puckered ring, but alignment is likely to be possible only if they are cut from a single crystal. Kolpakov *et al.* [65] consider the proposed resonators and add the idea of using a Borrmann crystal (which has anomalously high X-ray transmission) to insert and extract energy from the cavity. They also suggest that active substances, presumably capable of stimulated emission, might be incorporated in the Borrmann crystal.

In spite of the theoretical work done already on X-ray resonators, they remain an extremely difficult problem. To align and use them in an X-ray laser will certainly be prohibitively difficult in the early stages of laser development.

b) Distributed feedback: Some of the problems of alignment attributed to the previously mentioned resonators may be eliminated if a distributed feedback method, already successful with dye lasers and semiconductor lasers [66]–[71] in the infrared and visible, can be extended to the X-ray region. In these devices the feedback mechanism is distributed through the lasing medium. Feedback is provided by Bragg scattering from a periodic variation of the refractive index of the gain medium or of the gain itself. Kogelnik and Shank [66] solve for the threshold conditions and give results for the case of large gain factors. Chinn and Kelley also analyze distributed feedback lasers [72].

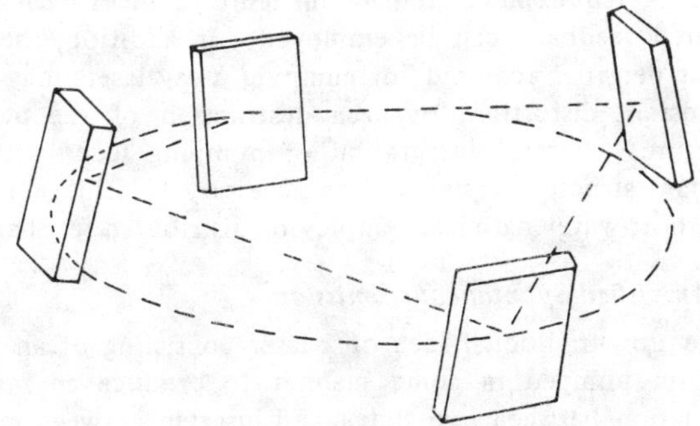

Fig. 2. Simplified drawing of the puckered ring resonator [62].

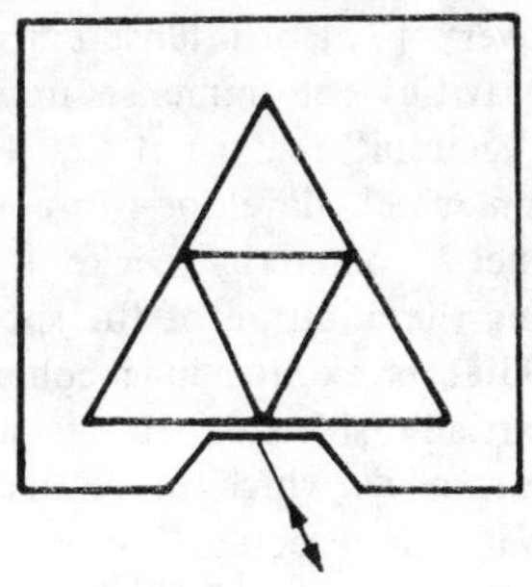

Fig. 3. X-ray resonator cut from a single crystal [63]. The arrows show X-rays entering and exiting the resonator.

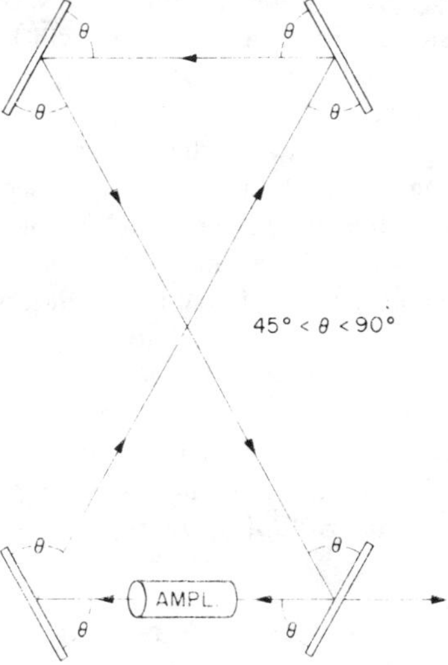

Fig. 4. X-ray resonator and possible amplifier using several Bragg reflections [64].

Several distributed feedback lasers have been built using dyes [66]–[68] and later the principle was transferred to semiconductor lasers [70], [71]. Because of the extremely difficult problem of X-ray resonators, distributed feedback has been suggested as an alternative [73]–[75]. Fisher [73] gives numerous crystals that have the proper lattice spacing to satisfy the requirements for distributed feedback for oxygen $K\alpha$ emission. In addition, the statement is made that standing waves may arise to avoid highly absorbing atoms present in the crystal. This is an interesting possibility which further suggests that traveling waves might experience alternating sites of attenuation and amplification, contradicting the thought that traveling-wave excitation (See Section IV-A-2) would be necessary in order to overcome the short gain lengths dictated by the short excited-state lifetime of X-ray transitions. The pumping requirements remain difficult to meet even if distributed feedback can be employed. In addition, the large power densities required for pumping X-ray lasers may cause expansion, distortion, or even destruction of the periodic structure. Careful integration of pumping techniques and resonant structure design will be necessary to achieve a workable short-wavelength laser employing distributed feedback.

B. Amplified Spontaneous Emission

The now-traditional idea of a laser consisting of an active medium pumped in some manner to produce an inverted population between two states, and inserted between mirrors which form an optical resonant cavity, was formulated by Schawlow and Townes [76] and reinforced by early successful lasers. The discovery [77] of intense emission from systems without optical cavities (of immense importance for lasers operated in the "vacuum" region) at first led to considerable semantic confusion which developed in conjunction with the term "superradiance" coined by Dicke [78], [79] in a hypothesis concerning the addition of the spontaneous emission from quantum radiators excited in a coherent fashion. This confusion was partially side-stepped by substitution of the term "superfluorescence" which more nearly associated the enhanced emission with directed fluorescence. Fortunately, these semantic difficulties were cleared up by Allen and Peters [80] who went on to present a series of papers [81]–[85] to clarify and make respectable the high-gain mirrorless systems which they appropriately termed amplified spontaneous emission (ASE) systems. Since ASE systems will be of major importance in VUV and X-ray lasers, it is appropriate to treat them in some detail.

1) Threshold: By following the arguments of Peters and Allen [81], using nomenclature [86] to be used extensively in Section II and in the three-level model in Fig. 5, a threshold condition can be derived starting with basic principles. Consider a pumped ensemble of excited radiators of length L, cross-sectional area a, and inversion density $\Delta N \equiv [N_2 - (g_2/g_3)N_3]$, for statistical weights g_2 and g_3. A quantity of photons n of frequency ν passing through the cross-sectional area will induce $n\sigma\Delta N/a$ atoms per unit volume to emit at that location. The resonance induced emission cross section is denoted by σ. But $\sigma n/a = B\rho(\nu)$, where

$$B = \frac{c^3}{8\pi h\nu^3} \cdot \frac{1}{\tau_2} \tag{1}$$

is the Einstein coefficient, and

$$\rho(\nu) = \frac{nh\nu}{ac\Delta\nu_D} \tag{2}$$

is the radiation density. Here $\Delta\nu_D$ is the width of the Doppler broadened transition and $\tau_2 \equiv (R_{23} + R_{2n})^{-1}$ is the natural lifetime of state 2. Solving for σ, we obtain

$$\sigma = \frac{c^2}{8\pi\nu^2 \Delta\nu_D \tau_2}. \tag{3}$$

The equation for the rate of change of the number of photons δn due to stimulated emission in the volume La in time δt is given by

$$\delta n/\delta t = n\sigma c\Delta N. \tag{4}$$

If the threshold condition for ASE is defined as the condition when a spontaneously emitted photon at one end of the column ($x = 0$) just induces another photon at the other end ($x = L$), then $\delta n/n = 1$ and $\sigma\Delta NL = 1$. This yields the relation for the critical inversion density ΔN_c to reach threshold [equivalent to unity gain coefficient α; see also (7)]

$$\Delta N_c = \frac{8\pi\Delta\nu_D\tau_2}{L\lambda^2\phi} \tag{5}$$

where ϕ is the branching ratio, i.e., $R_{23}/(R_{2n} + R_{23}) = \tau_2/\tau_{23}$. Alternatively, for a given inversion density (5) will give the critical length L_c required to reach threshold,

$$L_c = \frac{8\pi\Delta\nu_D\tau_2}{\Delta N\lambda^2\phi}. \tag{6}$$

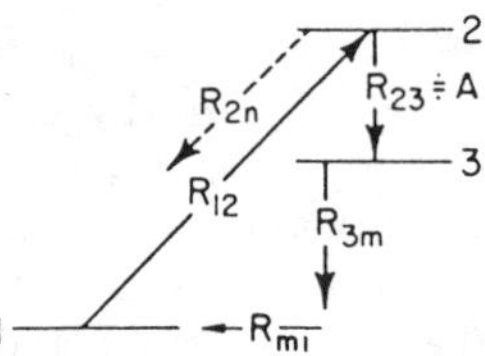

Fig. 5. Schematic defining nomenclature of the simple three-energy-state system referred-to in the text and originally defined in [86]. Pumping occurs from state 1 to 2; lasing from 2 to 3; losses from 2 to n; and lower state depopulation from 3 to m. Replenishment of state 1 can occur for $n = 1$, $m = 1$ or through m to 1 transitions.

Allen and Peters verify their theoretical results by comparison with a series of experiments which they carry out and with the data of others. In a later paper [82] they connect their theory with the semiclassical laser theory of Stenholm and Lamb [87]. The relationship between the critical length L_c for ASE and the minimum length L_T of active discharge at which mirrored laser action takes place is $L_T/L_c = 0.71\delta_l$, where δ_l is the fractional loss per pass in the laser resonator. To test this experimentally the 3.39-μm transition in He–Ne was used, since it would operate both as a laser and a source of ASE [82]. A 125-cm long He–Ne discharge tube was placed between 3-m radius of curvature concave mirrors with mean reflectance $r = 0.98$. The gas was uniformly excited and it was possible to vary the length by removing or adding RF electrodes. Fig. 6 shows the resulting variation of output intensity with length for both modes of operation, and particularly demonstrates the threshold for ASE.

2) Intensity and Saturation: The success of this approach served to spur further investigation by Allen and Peters [82] who solved rate equations for the populations of two levels (from a reservoir level), and the photon transport. Care was taken to include only the radiation that fell into the position-dependent solid angle. The solutions of the rate equations were used for predicting the intensity as a function of length for a constant inversion density and to fit the 3371-Å data of Leonard [2] for N_2 as a test case.

3) Beam Divergence and Spatial Coherence: The general impression of ASE beam divergence is that it is controlled by the geometry of the gain region and would be simply d/L or possibly $d/(L - L_c)$. Peters and Allen point out [84], [85] that each contribution must, however, be weighted by the amount of amplification path through which it passes. When numerical methods are used to weight each element geometrically, the theory fits the divergence data very well. The results show quite convincingly that the simple d/L ratio is not correct and that the "ASE-geometric theory" of Peters and Allen is necessary.

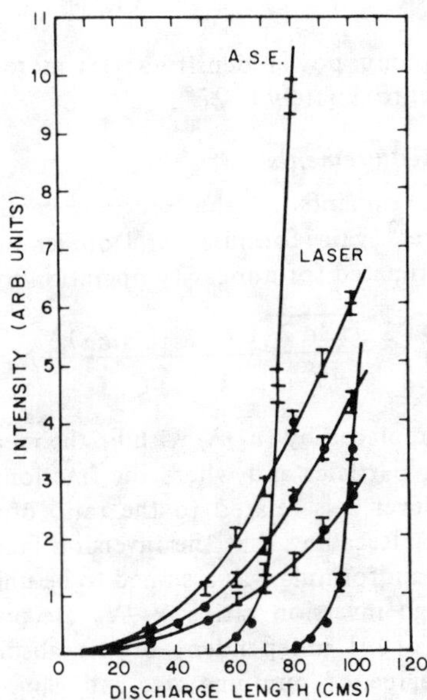

Fig. 6. Output intensity versus length for three different inversion densities when the system is operated with a resonator (laser) and without a resonator (ASE) [85].

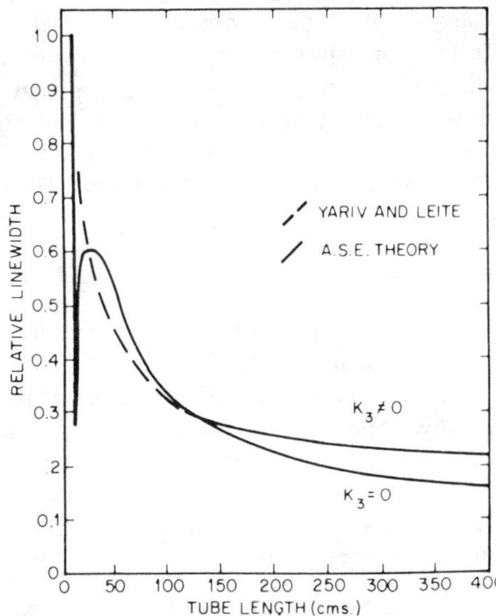

Fig. 7. Spectral distribution versus length as calculated by Allen and Peters for an ASE system. Deviations from the earlier theory of Yariv and Leite are shown for several values of K_3, a term in the numerical calculation. The case of $K_3 = 0$ is that of no saturation whereas $K_3 \neq 0$ is that of some saturation of the amplifier [85].

On the question of spatial coherence, Allen and Peters offer the experimental measurements of fringe visibility versus length. The measurements were made using the 6140-Å pulsed Ne laser line and show that the coherence increases with gain length.

4) Spectral Distribution: The spectral distribution (linewidth) in ASE systems has been somewhat confusing. Early predictions produced a dependency that goes as $\Delta\nu/\Delta\nu_D = 1/(\alpha L)^{1/2}$, i.e., enhanced narrowing at high gain. Allen and Peters have developed a theory in which the linewidth is a rather complicated function of length [84]. They contrast their results with those of Yariv and Leite [88] for He-Ne and N_2 lasers as shown in Fig. 7. The theory predicts a sharp dip in $\Delta\nu$ just above L_c followed by additional broadening as length is increased. The minimum shown is due to competition between narrowing associated with increasing gain and broadening accompanying an increased range of frequencies. The existence of such a sharp minimum could be used as an indicator of stimulated emission. As yet no definitive measurements have been made to resolve the details of the theoretical predictions of Allen and Peters.

It is also important to realize that there are limits to the application of the present ASE theory to likely X-ray and VUV lasers. These devices may be pulsed systems employing traveling-wave excitation. Also, the coupling of ASE amplifiers with a coherent beam produced, for example, by nonlinear mixing with harmonic frequencies may introduce new problems [89]. As yet the theory of ASE has not been extended to cover these cases. In addition, further information may be obtained from more formal and rigorous theoretical techniques such as the semiclassical laser theory of Lamb [90]. It appears that this work is in progress by Lamb [91] and by Hopf [92].

II. Basic Physics Problems

Besides the materials problems described above, the basic physical considerations pertinent to all the general schemes and the specific models tend to demand the very most that the current state-of-the-art can attain in pump power. To produce gain, high inversion densities are called-for and, for most models, very rapidly rising pump pulses are required to achieve inversion and gain prior to equilibration. These problems will be analyzed in this section in a rather general and scalable fashion, with several examples from recently suggested schemes.

A. *Wavelength Dependence of Gain*

Continuing from (3)–(6), the net gain achieved in a single pass through a medium of length L is given by exp (αL), with the small-signal gain coefficient at line center α defined by[3]

$$\alpha = \sigma\Delta N_{23} = \frac{\lambda^2 A_{23}}{8\pi\Delta\nu}\,\xi\Delta N_{23} \tag{7}$$

where the subscripts again refer to the three state system shown in Fig. 5 with pumping from energy state 1 to 2 and lasing from 2 to 3, at rates R_{12}, R_{23}, etc., using nomenclature consistent with [86]. These "states" are not restricted to one atom or ion, i.e., transition 1 to 2 could be by ionization or recombination, for example, providing replenishment of state 1 is present as indicated by R_{m1}. The parameters λ, $\Delta\nu$, and A_{23} are the wavelength [93], linewidth in frequency units, and transition probability, respectively. The factor ξ varies from unity for a Lorentzian line profile to $(\pi \ln 2)^{1/2}$ for a Gaussian-shaped Doppler-broadened line. The net inversion density,[4] ΔN_{23}, is again $[N_2 - (g_2/g_3)N_3]$, with g_2 and g_3 the respective statistical weights, and is approximated by N_2 when a large inversion is achieved. The product $\lambda^2 A_{23} = 0.67(g_3/g_2)f_{32}$ numerically [95], where f_{32} is the absorption oscillator strength. This relation removes the explicit wavelength dependence in (7), since f_{32} is nearly constant along isoelectronic sequences (and approaches unity for intense lines). However, the wavelength enters implicitly in the inversion density

[3] A numerical factor of $1/4\pi^2$ replaces $1/8\pi$ for a power gain relation; the factor-of-$\pi/2$ difference is small.

[4] There is one suggestion for lasing without population inversion [94], based on Doppler recoil line shifts.

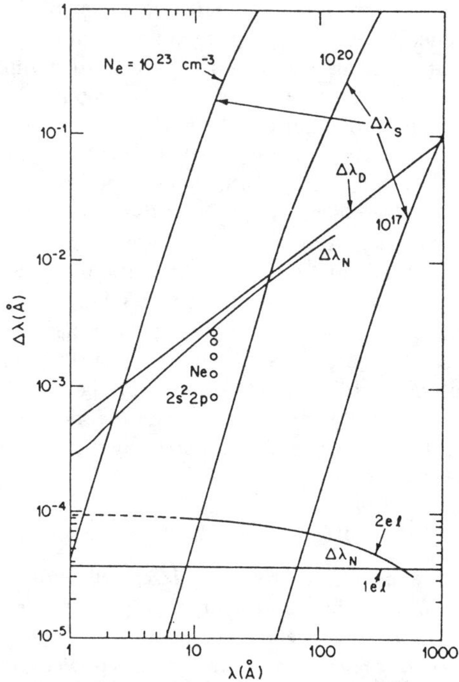

Fig. 8. Estimates of line widths for $K\alpha$ type transitions versus wavelength λ, with natural ($\Delta\lambda_N$), Doppler ($\Delta\lambda_D$), and Stark ($\Delta\lambda_S$) effects included. The decrease in natural broadening with ionization is indicated by circles for neon; and hydrogenic and helium-like ionic species are included [96].

(Section II-B) and also in the expression chosen for the line width $\Delta\nu = (\nu/\lambda)\,\Delta\lambda$ or $= (c/\lambda^2)\,\Delta\lambda$.

Estimations of the linewidth $\Delta\lambda$ as a function of wavelength are summarized in Fig. 8, reproduced from [96] where the appropriate equations and detailed references are given (see also [171]). A Lyman-α model is used. The Doppler width $\Delta\lambda_D$ is dependent upon the particle thermal velocity and is associated with a kinetic temperature of $kT = hc/4\lambda$ (plasma model). The natural width $\Delta\lambda_N$ includes both radiative and Auger decay. A reduction associated with Auger decay (also discussed in Section III-C) for outer-electron stripping is indicated for neon ions. The limits for 1- and 2-electron ions are shown, although these limits are probably not realistically reached compared to the Doppler broadening present when such ions are created at high temperatures. The importance of Stark broadening [97] due to charged particles increases rapidly with density for a specific wavelength, as indicated. In addition to producing a decline in gain at high densities, the onset of significant Stark broadening is associated with an approach of collisional (statistical) equilibrium without population inversion, as discussed in Section II-B. Fortunately, significant gain can be anticipated at densities below the Stark regions with the choice of efficient pumping schemes. However, it is difficult to conceive of reducing the linewidth significantly below the Doppler value $\Delta\nu_D \approx \bar{v}/\lambda$, where $\bar{v}$ is the mean particle velocity.

The inversion density $\Delta N_{23} \lesssim N_2$, in (7) must be maintained against a depopulation rate for level 2 at least as great as A_{23}, i.e., $N_2 \lesssim N_1(R_{12}/A_{23})$, where R_{12} is the pumping rate, and again $A_{23} \propto \lambda^{-2}$. Thus from these general arguments it can be seen that the gain factor depends on a number of parameters, but scales approximately as λ^3. This will be restated from the pump requirement viewpoint in the following section, where it is seen that pump power density scales more strongly with wavelength, approximately as λ^{-4}.

B. Pumping Requirements

From the arguments of the previous section, the high-inversion power[3] gain formula for Doppler broadened lines may be approximated for noncavity operation by

$$\alpha_D \lesssim \frac{\sqrt{\pi \ln 2}}{4\pi^2} \, \frac{0.67 f_{32}(g_3/g_2)\,\lambda}{\bar{v}_1} N_1 \eta_2 \tag{8}$$

where $\Delta\nu_D$ is replaced by $(\bar{v}_1/\lambda)$ with $\bar{v}_1$ the mean velocity for the amplifying particles and where the fractional pumping η_2 achieved for level 2 is related to the ratio of rates R_{12}/A_{23} when $R_{2n} = 0$. Recalling that the inversion factor $(1 - g_2N_3/g_3N_2)$ in the gain formula was assumed to be unity, it is worth noting that high inversion ratios N_2/N_3 are possible and observable [98], [99] independent of the absolute values of density N_1 degree of pumping η_2, and gain. In fact, preliminary experiments towards development of population inversion are sometimes better performed under optically thin conditions at lower densities.

On the other hand, the significant gain ultimately sought at short wavelengths must be accompanied by high densities N_1 and/or large fractional pumping η_2. This is conveniently illustrated with (8) for the case of a laser-produced plasma medium, chosen since at present lasers offer the highest available concentration of pump power. Taking $\alpha L = 5$ as desirable (unity at "threshold" for ASE[5]), $L = 1$ cm,[6] $\bar{v}_1 = 10^7$ cm/s, and $f_{32}(g_3/g_2) \approx 0.5$ for a strong line,

$$\lambda N_1 \eta_2 \gtrsim 10^{18} \tag{9}$$

results for λ in Å and N_1 in cm^{-3}. Thus a 1-percent inversion at 1 Å requires a density of $N_1 \gtrsim 10^{20}$ cm^{-3}. This argument involves a rather arbitrary value for the degree of inversion and does not indicate specific pump requirements to achieve a high inversion density ΔN_{23} at a particular wavelength. By replacing $N_1\eta_2$ by N_1R_{12}/A_{23} in the gain formula and defining $p_{12} \equiv N_1R_{12}$ and $P_{12} \equiv p_{12}(hc/\lambda_p)$ as the volumetric pump rate and pump power, respectively, α_D may be rewritten as

$$\alpha_D \lesssim \frac{\sqrt{\pi \ln 2}}{4\pi^2} \, \frac{\lambda^3}{\bar{v}_1} p_{12} \tag{10}$$

and for the pump wavelength $\lambda_p \approx \lambda/10$,

$$\alpha_D \lesssim \frac{\sqrt{\pi \ln 2}}{40\pi^2 hc} \, \frac{\lambda^4}{\bar{v}_1} P_{12}. \tag{11}$$

These relations demonstrate the strong λ^{-3} and λ^{-4} wavelength dependence of the volumetric pumping parameters for a fixed gain coefficient α_D [100]. With $\alpha_D = 5$ and $\bar{v} = 10^7$ cm/s again, minimum values of p_{12} and P_{12} are calculated and tabulated in Table I for several wavelengths. Note that a closely related parameter of importance is the pump irradiance $P_{12}L$ (W/cm^2), which is fixed by the gain product αL and equivalent to P_{12} in Table I for a laser-produced plasma length $L = 1$ cm.

[5] $1 - r$ with r the reflectivity, where reflecting cavities exist.

[6] Corresponds to sustained inversion for 30 ps, or self-terminating lasing at $\lambda \gtrsim 300$ Å. Shorter wavelengths require reduced lengths or traveling-wave synchronized pumping.

TABLE I
VOLUMETRIC PUMPING REQUIREMENTS

λ[Å]:	1	10	100	1000	2000
p_{12} [$cm^{-3} \cdot s^{-1}$]	10^{33}	10^{30}	10^{27}	10^{24}	10^{23}
P_{12} [$W \cdot cm^{-3}$]	10^{19}	10^{15}	10^{11}	10^{7}	10^{6}

TABLE II
PUMPING RATE COEFFICIENT MAGNITUDES SCALED[a]

Process	$\langle \sigma_p v_p \rangle$ ($cm^3\ s^{-1}$)
Photoionization [96], [101]	$10^{-12}\lambda$
Electron Collisional Excitation [103]	
Plasma	$10^{-13}\lambda^{3/2}$
Beams	$10^{-13}\lambda$
Dielectronic Capture [102]	$10^{-13}\lambda^{3/2}$
Collisional Recombination[b,c] [103]	$10^{-13}\lambda^{5/4}$
Resonance Charge Transfer	
Plasma[d] [100]	$10^{-6}\lambda^{-5/4}$
Ion Beams[e] [104]	$10^{-5}\lambda^{-1}$

[a]Wavelength λ in angstrom units.
[b]Electron density $N_e = N_p = 10^{21}$ cm^{-3}.
[c]Must exceed radiative recombination [103] for which $\langle \sigma_p v_p \rangle \sim 10^{-11}\lambda^{-1/2}$; i.e., $\lambda \gtrsim 15$ Å.
[d]$\bar{v} = 10^7$ cm/s, $\sigma_p = 10^{-16}z^2$, z the net ion charge.
[e]$\bar{v} = 10^8$ cm/s, $\sigma_p = 10^{-16}z^2$, z the net ion charge.

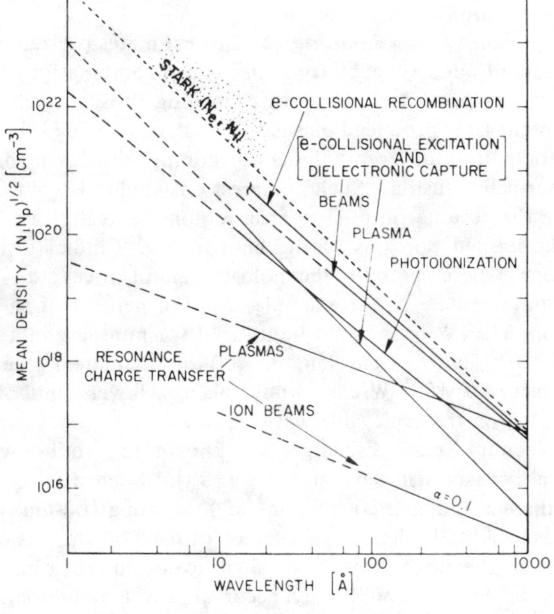

Fig. 9. Mean particle densities (solid and dashed lines) versus wavelength for selected pumping mechanisms and for a gain factor of $\alpha = 5$ ($\alpha = 0.1$ for ion beams). Stark broadening becomes important for large charged particle densities (same scale) in the region above the dotted line, also a region of approaching collisional equilibrium. Collisional recombination is plotted for fixed $N_e = 10^{21}$ cm^{-3} and terminates at ~15 Å due to dominance of radiative recombination to lower levels [106].

1) Wavelength Scaling: The volumetric reaction rate p_{12} can be expressed as $N_p \langle \sigma_p v_p \rangle$ where the subscript p denotes the pumping particle (or photon), σ_p the reaction cross section, and $\langle \sigma_p v_p \rangle$ the rate coefficient, averaged statistically over the distribution of velocities v_p. Estimates of the magnitude of reaction rates for some rather general pumping schemes scaled with wavelength are listed in Table II (collisional ionization is omitted, as it favors outer electron removal).

The rates shown are derived from relations in the indicated references. For photoionization, a peak cross section $\propto Z^{-2}$ was assumed (Z the nuclear charge), multiplied by c, and divided by 100 for ~1-percent absorption in the pumping band. For dielectronic capture, an autoionization (Auger) rate of 10^{14} s^{-1} was used in the detailed balancing formulism. In addition, various approximations were necessary in relating the rate coefficients solely to wavelength, with the emphasis on short wavelengths and a plasma medium. Specifically, the laser wavelength was taken as $\lambda = 1216/z^2$ in angstrom units from Lyman-α scaling, where z is the ion charge. The ionization potential was assumed to be 1.3 times the excitation energy, with the latter taken to be 3 times the plasma electron temperature and also related to wavelength directly by hc/λ.

Returning to Table II, it is first noted that most rate coefficients tend to scale downward with shorter wavelength, which is detrimental for achieving high gain; only the resonance charge transfer process scales in an advantageous manner. A geometric-mean particle density $(N_1N_p)^{1/2}$ can be derived for each of these schemes, using (10) and assuming $\alpha = 5$ cm^{-1} and $\bar{v}_1 = 10^7$ cm/s for plasmas, 10^8 cm/s for ion beams, and c for relativistic electron and photon beams. This parameter, plotted in Fig. 9 is particularly meaningful for plasma pumping schemes, and the reliability of the order of magnitude estimates in Table II is improved by the 0.5 power. From Fig. 9 it is seen that the density requirements are comparable between pumping schemes in the VUV ($\lambda > 100$ Å) within an order-of-magnitude. Electron collisional excitation is somewhat favored and the magnitude at 1000 Å agrees with the H_2 discharge laser conditions [11]; thus the interest in extending proven electron collisionally excited UV ion laser transitions into the VUV region [105]. The resonance charge transfer process with its anticipated (Section III) large cross section appears most favorable for extrapolation to the X-ray region. It requires reasonable densities and gives a wide latitude for increasing the gain coefficient and reducing high-density absorption. Collisional recombination excitation processes limit laser wavelengths to $\gtrsim 15$ Å for $N_e = 10^{21}$ cm^{-3}. This particular limit is found by requiring the collisional recombination rate coefficient ($\sim 10^{-13}\lambda^{5/4}$) to exceed the rate coefficient for radiative recombination into lower states ($\sim 10^{-11}\lambda^{-1/2}$) (See Table II). This wavelength limit also happens to correspond to the assumed density of 10^{21} cm^{-3}, which is an upper limit for present laser-produced plasmas.

Also indicated in Fig. 9 is the region in which plasma Stark-effect line broadening becomes important. Since Stark widths scale approximately as charged particle density in plasmas, the gain factor in the Stark region will tend to scale with N_1 instead of N_1N_p. Approaching the region of Stark broadening importance also implies increased collisional effects on the lasing levels. Indeed, a check of several promising schemes indicates that the dominance of Stark broadening is correlated with an approach to collisional equilibrium with non-inverted statistical population distributions [106]. Thus, densities significantly exceeding the "Stark line" in Fig. 9 would not be particularly advantageous for achieving high gain, and the higher density approaches depicted (e.g., collisional recombination) are the most limited.

2) Pump Power Limitations: The estimates plotted in Fig. 9 are continued (except for collisional recombination) to short wavelengths and to densities exceeding those expected from present laser-produced plasmas ($\sim 10^{21}$ cm^{-3} [107], [108]), in anticipation of eventual inertial compression as planned for laser-pellet fusion. Such compression would also aid in meeting the volumetric pump power requirements indicated above. The dashed portions of the lines in Fig. 9 indicate those regions where present technology cannot meet the density requirements. If, for example, even 10 percent of the power from a 1 TW laser could be utilized for pumping in a volume of 10^{-3} cm^3 (1-cm length, 400-μm diameter), the power density of 10^{14} W/cm^3 would place a lower limit of about $\sim$13 Å on the achievable wavelength.

Vacuum spark discharges are known to produce very-hot dense plasmas in small regions [109]. Such discharges may radiate as much as 10^{15} W/cm^3 of X-rays in a 100-μm spherical plasma [110] where a gain factor of $\alpha = 500$ cm^{-1} is required due to the small dimension. Significant amplification according to Fig. 9 would only occur at wavelengths longer than 700 Å, and with the high densities ($\sim 10^{21}$ cm^{-3}) typical for such a device, collisional domination without inversion is likely at such long wavelengths. Thus this relatively simple and convenient source may be more useful for determining promising population inversion methods at low gain, short wavelength, and under optically thin conditions, for application to extended laser-heated plasmas of similar environment.

Electron beams of power comparable to lasers exist at present; however, the focusing volume achievable so far would be approximately 300 times larger [111] (for a cylindrical geometry) so that a short wavelength limit of $\sim$50 Å is expected for this mode of pumping with present technology, as indicated in Fig. 9.

3) Additional Considerations:

a) Reduced gain factor: High-density limitations can be reduced with a lower gain coefficient α providing the net gain determined by $\exp(\alpha L)$ for a specified degree of amplification is maintained through a correspondingly increased length L and eventually traveling-wave pumping for short wavelength and self-terminating transitions.[6] (An exception to this reduced density option is the collisional recombination scheme where the high electron densities are also required to overcome competitive radiative recombination into lower levels.) Here the pump irradiance $N_1 P_{12} L$ remains the same and must be distributed over a larger volume, which could present a technical problem for laser pumping schemes. However, other extended pumping sources have been suggested, such as traveling-wave transverse electron beams (Section IV) and swept ion beams. For example, by the scaling in Fig. 9 as well as from (10), $\alpha = 0.1$ can be achieved at a wavelength of 300 Å with $(N_1 N_p)^{1/2} \sim 10^{16}$ cm^{-3} obtained in a near-solid target of density $N_1 = 10^{22}$ cm^{-3} and $N_p = 10^{10}$ cm^{-3}. The latter may be obtained from a swept 25-keV 20-mA ion beam focused to a 0.2-cm radius in a resonance charge transfer reaction (see Section III-B). Equation (11) restricts the volume for a beam of this power such that a maximum depth of the order of 10 μm must be maintained. While beam currents in the hundreds of mA are suggested [112], state-of-the-art ion-beam technology appears to limit this approach to the hundreds-of-angstrom region.

b) Competitive decay from state 2: So far it has been assumed that the upper laser state (designated 2 in Fig. 5) decays only through the laser transition to state 3, i.e., alternate decay rates R_{2n} are much less than A_{23}. With this assumption, the pump requirements are independent of line strength (i.e., weak lines are accompanied by an increased pump-state density) and a number of other, often weak, transitions appear to be attractive candidates for lasing at short wavelengths. With R_{2n} included, the degree of pumping, η_2, in (7) becomes $R_{12}/(A_{23} + R_{2n})$ and the volumetric pumping parameters p_{12} and P_{12} as well as the mean density $(N_1 N_p)^{1/2}$ scale up by the ratio $(A_{23} + R_{2n})/A_{23}$, where the line strength again enters through A_{23}^{-1} for R_{2n} large.

One class of schemes for which R_{2n} can be important is when alternate spontaneous decay occurs in an isolated atom or ion. An example is an inner-shell lasing transition (Section III) for which autoionization (Auger) decay is also possible, and highly probable for low-Z elements. Another example would be second-order double electron transitions, where one electron decays in a radiative transition and another changes state so that a shifted line occurs, with reduced reabsorption. In this case R_{2n} represents the "normal" decay mode with a rate much higher (typically $\sim$100 times) than A_{23}.

Another class of schemes applies when R_{2n} is a collisional-depopulation rate. Again, collisional depopulation is expected to be generally important in the high density "Stark region" indicated in Fig. 9, where R_{2n} represents transitions between states 2 and 3. Collisional depopulation to other bound states, with rapid decay, or to other ionic species through ionization or recombination can also be important starting at lower densities, particularly for weak lines and those originating on metastable upper states (see below). Obviously, each case must be treated independently, and knowledge of rates for many important collisional transitions is either very limited or non-existent.

C. Duration of the Inversion

1) Transient to CW Extremes: Using the nomenclature in Fig. 5, a population inversion can be maintained between energy states 2 and 3 as long as the rate R_{3m} of depletion of state 3 to some other state m exceeds the rate R_{23} at which it is filled, with adequate $m \rightarrow 1$ replenishment of the initial state 1. However, if $R_{3m} = 0$ (e.g., with 3 a ground state), population inversion ceases in an equilibration interval. These extremes and the intermediates have been deduced analytically [86] for this three-state model for a pump pulse with both a short risetime $t_r \ll \tau_2$ [$\tau_2 \equiv (R_{23} + R_{2n})^{-1}$, the lifetime of state 2], as well as for a linear-ramp rising pump pulse, i.e., $R_{12} = R_{12} t$. With the inversion density in (7) written with a separate factor $\mathrm{T}(t)$, i.e.,

$$\Delta N_{23} \approx N_1 \mathrm{T} R_{12}/(R_{23} + R_{2n}) = N_1 R_{12} \tau_2 \mathrm{T} \qquad (12)$$

the time dependence of the inversion density is calculated and the results are shown in Fig. 10 versus t/τ_2 for the fast rising pump pulse case. Positive T implies gain, negative values imply net loss. The parameter $G \equiv g_2 R_{23}/g_3(R_{2n} + R_{23})$ is a modified statistical weight ratio. For R_{2n} small, and $g_2 = g_3$, $G \approx 1$ and the inversion time $t_i \approx \tau_{23}$, i.e., inversion ceases in about the radiative lifetime of the upper laser level, as expected. A selection of $g_3 > g_2$ states could extend this time somewhat and also raise the degree of inversion. However, decreasing G by increasing R_{2n} does not extend the inversion

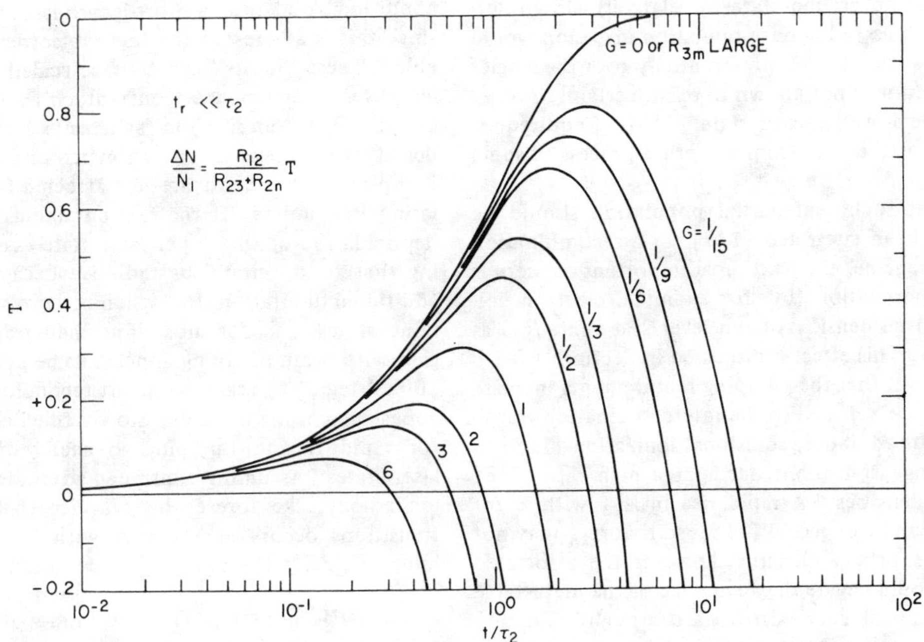

Fig. 10. Time dependence T(t) of inversion density ΔN_{23} for the fast rise pumping case. Positive values indicate net gain; negative values loss. For R_{2n} small, $\tau_2 \approx R_{23}^{-1}$, the laser transition upper-state lifetime. The $G = 0$ case is also the case for self-depleting final laser states where $R_{3m} >> R_{23} + R_{2n}$ [86].

time appreciably, since τ_2 decreases proportionally. An equivalent parameter T(τ_2/t) for the linear-ramp pumping case yields similar results. These $R_{3m} = 0$ examples represent the self-terminating mode of pre-equilibrium population inversion.

Included in Fig. 10 is the $G = 0$ limit which is also equivalent to the case when R_{3m} becomes very large, i.e., the continuous inversion CW mode. Here the time dependent factor T(t) becomes unity and the inversion density is given by $N_1 R_{12} \tau_2$, the coronal-equilibrium value. With high inversion, ΔN_{23} approaches N_2 and $\Delta N_{23}/N_1 \approx R_{12}\tau_2 \equiv \eta$ gives the fractional pumping for the laser medium (Section II-B). This CW mode obviously is the most desirable situation. An intermediate mode of operation is for $R_{3m}\tau_2$ to be finite with values greater or less than unity corresponding to sustained or terminated gain, respectively. The time dependent factor for the fast rising pump pulse case is plotted for $G = 1$ in Fig. 11 and illustrates the approaches to partial equilibrium inversion densities for the intermediate $R_{3m}\tau_2$ cases. Such curves can be used to determine the approximate inversion densities (see Section III-C, for example).

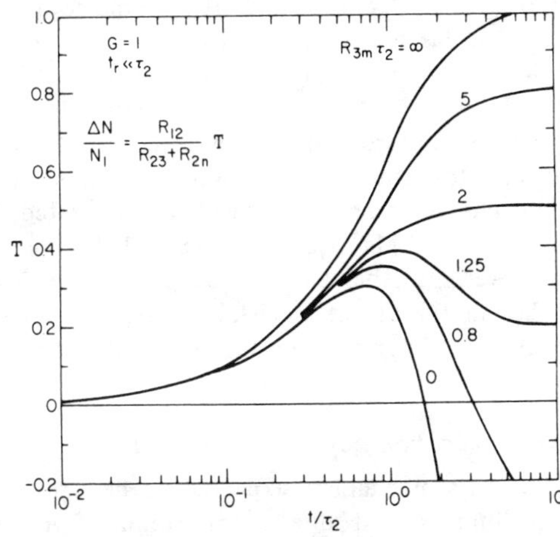

Fig. 11. Time dependence T(t) of the inversion density ΔN_{23}, for the fast-rise pumping case and for $G = 1$ only. Positive values indicate net gain; negative values loss. For R_{2n} small $\tau_2 \approx R_{23}^{-1}$, the laser transition upper state lifetime. The effect of a lower laser state depletion rate R_{3m} exceeding τ_2^{-1} on the steady state inversion density is indicated for long times.

The detailed analytical formulas leading to these graphs can be found in [86]. They are necessarily approximate, but of general usefulness for preliminary analyses. Numerical modeling for specific pump modes and atomic models is essential, particularly for the quasi-CW schemes where the replenishment rates could not be included in the analytical model. Such requirements for replenishment can include both the internal pumping particle (e.g., an energetic plasma electrons or a photon) as well as the amplifying particle. As an example of the latter, the $K\alpha$ quasi-CW scheme discussed in Section III-C generates additional ionization and a sufficient recombination rate is required to sustain the inversion density.

2) Metastable States: The use of metastable states as upper laser states with extended lifetime τ_2 has been suggested as a means of reducing the pump pulse risetime requirements for rapidly terminated population inversions [113], [114]. This is particularly important for lasing at wavelengths shorter than ~30 Å, where subpicosecond risetimes are required. Since both the pump power density and the gain coefficient scale as the product of density and transition probability, the pump power required remains the same for fixed gain whether the laser transition is an allowed dipole or forbidden transition. (However, the densities increase for the longer lived upper laser states.) Unfortunately, it is difficult to find a metastable upper state that terminates in such a high-energy transition on a lower state that does not also accumulate population by a dipole-allowed transition at a higher rate. For example, the well-known $n = 2$ triplet levels of helium-like (and beryllium-like) ions decay to the ground state in relatively slow intercombination transitions [115] but population inversion would require filling of the triplet levels preferentially over the singlet levels. Such a selection is not known to exist, certainly not by excitation from the lower ground state [116]. Required selectivity would have to evolve from a capture process of some sort.

In the event that such preferential population should be discovered, as has been suggested [117] for a recombination radiative trapping scheme, the next most important concern is the competing depopulation (by, for example, electron collisions at the increased densities) from level 2 at a rate R_{2n} as designated in Fig. 5. This effect is discussed in Section II-B-3-b where it is pointed out that the pumping requirements increase as R_{2n}/A_{23} for $R_{2n} >> A_{23}$. For the intercombination transition examples discussed above, collisional ionization [103] as well as spin-exchange transitions occur at a high rate [118] even at moderate densities. A rapid rise in A_{23} with Z for "forbidden" lines can be expected [115], so that R_{2n} may not dominate at very short wavelengths; however the associated short lifetime τ_2 would negate the advantage of the metastable state. Sparse collisional data exist for a thorough evaluation here, but again the first problem is to identify a realistic laser transition.

A somewhat different approach makes use of metastable states for the accumulation of electrons in a majority of the lasant ions (at a relatively low density) and the subsequent transfer of the electrons to a nearby dipole-coupled state by absorption of laser emission [114], [119]-[121]. Singly ionized lithium is a popular example, with 2^1S population (followed by $2^1S \rightarrow 2^1P$ transfer) to be provided either by charge transfer collisions or by photoionization of a 1s electron from neutral lithium atoms. Recently the population and storage by charge transfer has been demonstrated for $(Sr^+)^*$ ions formed by a $Mg^+ + Sr$ reaction [122]. This approach obviously overlaps other areas included in this review, but the novelty lies in the use of metastable states for the accumulation of electrons in an excited state adjacent to the upper laser level.

D. Beam Propagation Losses in the Lasant

The only loss mechanism expected to be significant in the lasant medium is that due to photoionization. Compton scattering as well as inverse bremsstrahlung effects have been considered [123] and shown to be negligible. Photoionization becomes a consideration whenever there are electrons bound with less energy than that of the laser photons. Then the density N_0 of atoms or ions with such bound electrons multiplied by the photoionization cross section σ_{pi} gives the photoionization coefficient α_{pi}, i.e., $\alpha_{pi} \sim 10^{-20} N_0$ for a rather typical value [96] of $\sigma_{pi} \sim 10^{-20}$ cm^2 and N_0 in units of cm^{-3} (σ_{pi} is strongly frequency dependent and varies approximately as ν^{-3} for laser frequencies ν above the absorption edges). Thus it is for innershell transitions at high densities that propagation losses are significant and the gain must be adjusted to overcome such losses [96].

E. Summary of Laser Physics at Short Wavelengths

The achievement of significant gain at short wavelengths is limited to about 10 Å at present by the available power density and, for self-terminating schemes, by the ability to concentrate power into a short-rise-time pumping pulse. The density limits indicated in Fig. 9 are dictated by the $\alpha = 5$ condition based upon a short-length laser-heated plasma model, since this is at present the highest power density source available. These "limits" can thus be scaled down with extended lengths L, keeping αL constant, with the exception of the collisional recombination scheme which depends on high density to achieve an inversion irregardless of absolute gain. Pumping requirements are not affected by the strength of the lasing line unless alternate spontaneous or collision-induced depopulation of the upper laser state occurs at a rate exceeding that for spontaneous radiative decay. This represents an additional limitation for schemes involving weak lines, high lying states, and for most innershell transitions. Significant gain with beam pumping appears to be presently limited to the 100's Å region by state-of-the-art technology. Metastable states appear promising mainly as slowly filled electron-storage states for rapid transfer-pumping to nearby dipole-coupled upper laser states. Assuming continued advancement in pump source technology, the foreseeable wavelength limit for nonnuclear transitions occurs near 0.1 Å with the Lyman-α line for a hydrogenic $Z = 100$ ion.

III. Possible Direct Laser Approaches

A number of approaches have been proposed and/or attempted for achieving sufficient population inversion for lasing in the VUV and X-ray spectral regions. The more attractive and understandable approaches are treated in some detail in the following, as are some experimental observations suggesting short wavelength gain which so far defy reasonable theoretical explanation.

A. Electron Collisional Excitation

1) Electron Collisions with Molecules: Molecular lasers occupy an important place among the types of lasers which have been developed to date. They span the spectrum from the millimeter-wave region to the VUV. They possess characteristics which qualify them for high power CW machining in industry, for pumping dye lasers, for powerful weapons, and for attempting to create thermonuclear fusion. Since the electronic transitions in molecules have been used to generate almost all the VUV lasers developed so far, they must be considered of major importance for the VUV region. Since both the review of Rhodes [54] of UV laser physics and the review by Wood [124] of high-pressure pulsed molecular lasers cover portions of this topic very well, only the fundamental processes will be discussed here from the viewpoint of acquainting the reader unfamiliar with the topic, and for allowing discussions of future lasers to be meaningful.

Fig. 12 shows simplified potential energy diagrams for a) N_2, b) H_2, and c) Xe_2^*. Each of these molecules represents a somewhat different type of laser transition, but N_2 and H_2 have the most in common. These two molecules have stable ground states, and at room temperature only the ground vibrational level is filled. Electron collisions fill the upper states in accordance with Franck–Condon factors and with the energy spectrum of the electrons. In N_2, several triplet levels are heavily populated and lasing is produced on the transition $C^3\Pi_u \rightarrow B^3\Pi_g$ in the near UV and on the transition $B^3\Pi_g \rightarrow A^3\Sigma_u^+$ in the infrared. In both cases the laser emission quickly terminates due to the long lifetime of the lower laser level. This level fills rapidly, destroying the inverted population needed for lasing. Also, these triplet levels cannot make transitions back to the ground electronic level. In

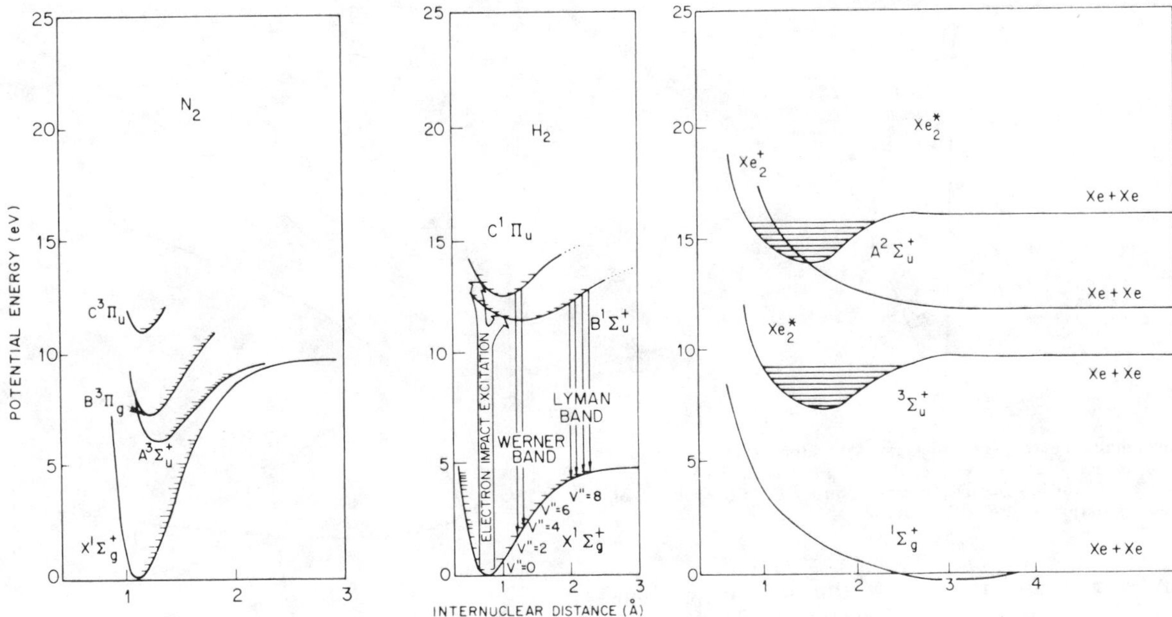

Fig. 12. Simplified potential energy versus internuclear distance of several molecules. Both nitrogen and hydrogen are stable molecules; xenon, however, has no stable ground state and exists as a molecule only in the excited state.

hydrogen, singlet states are populated by electron impact and transitions back to the ground electronic state are possible. Lasing results on the $B^1\Sigma_u^+ \rightarrow X^1\Sigma_g^+$ and $C^1\Pi_u \rightarrow X^1\Sigma_g^+$ transitions producing VUV emission from a number of vibrational-rotational lines. Several studies of possible triplet state lasing have been carried out also [123]-[128].

The energy level diagram for Xe_2^* is considerably different from the other molecules because the ground state is unstable. The molecule exists only in an excited state. When it gives up its excited energy and returns to the ground state, the two atoms rapidly dissociate. This is excellent for lasers because the lower laser level cannot fill and terminate the inversion. As long as the molecules exist some inversion density exists. Production of the excited rare gas molecules is a far more complicated process involving several steps. The molecules are most efficiently produced by excitation or ionization of high-pressure gas volumes. At the high pressures required, the most suitable excitation source is the electron beam. Electron beams have been employed as excitation devices for almost all the rare gas lasers that have been produced (as discussed in Section I), but it seems possible that some less sophisticated method may emerge eventually.

The primary high-energy electrons, the secondary electrons and the return current electrons participate in the excitation process which could go as [54], [129], [130]

$$e^- + Xe \longrightarrow e^- + Xe^* \qquad Xe^* + Xe + Xe \longrightarrow Xe_2^* + Xe \tag{13}$$

or as

$$e^- + Xe \longrightarrow e^- + e^- + Xe^+ \qquad Xe^+ + Xe + Xe \longrightarrow Xe_2^+ + Xe \tag{14}$$

followed by

$$Xe_2^+ + e^- \longrightarrow Xe^* + Xe \qquad Xe^* + Xe + Xe \longrightarrow Xe_2^* + Xe. \tag{15}$$

Here the asterisk and the plus superscripts refer to excited and ionized species, respectively. Typical operating conditions are from 300 keV-2 MeV voltages and at pressures of 100-500 psia. Numerous other molecules have the same characteristic of existing only in the excited state [131], [132].

Certainly additional VUV lasers can be produced using molecular transitions. The bound-free excimer transitions are especially attractive, because the dissociative lower laser level and the high pressures at which the system operates hold out the possibility of high power, high efficiency and possibly even CW operation. The possibility exists of obtaining laser emission in the 600-800-Å region from Ne_2^* and He_2^*. In addition, neutral molecules do exist which have sufficiently spaced electronic energy levels to produce lasing below 1000 Å. For example there exist in N_2 singlet states which couple to high vibrational levels of the ground state. If these states can be excited, emission in the 900-980-Å region appears possible.

2) Electron Collisions with Ions: Lasing in the visible and near UV spectral regions on electron collisionally excited transitions in singly and multiply ionized atoms is well known [54], even though the exact mechanism for population is sometimes debated in particular cases. A favorite lasing transition involves two $n = 3$ levels in light ions where excitation is most easily understood to be from the $n = 2$ ground state, with direct ionization into $n = 3$ excited states from the previous ion species considered a possibility. Electrically excited ion lasers of the discharge variety operate in the CW mode, where excitation presumably takes place in a non-dipole transition followed by lasing on a dipole transition and rapid final state depletion in a second dipole transition.

The success of such ion lasers operated with resonant cavities, particularly the recently developed z-pinch plasma type [133], [134], has encouraged the consideration [105], [135] of extrapolation of such transitions into the VUV region following isoelectronic sequences (for example, ions with the same number of bound electrons). For example, a

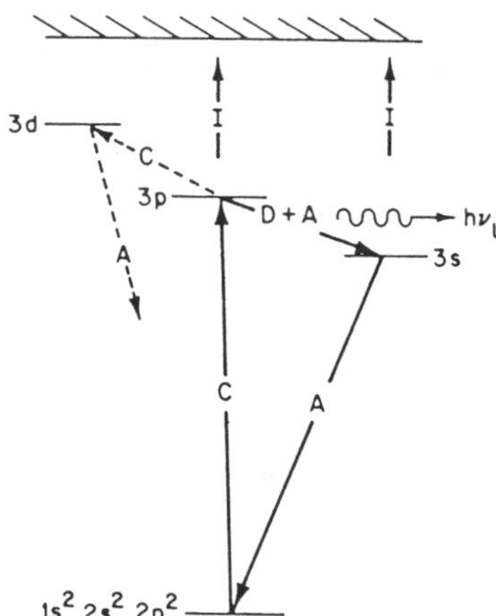

Fig. 13. Schematic energy level diagram for carbon-like ion species. Collisional excitations are designated by C, radiative decays by A, ionization by I, and collisional depopulation by D. Competing collisional depopulation to the $3d$ level is indicated.

successful lasing transition in a six-electron carbon-like N^+ ion might also be expected to prove successful at shorter wavelengths with six-electron ions of higher Z materials. A major obstacle in such an extrapolation arises due to the lack of efficient cavities in the VUV region, so that increases in the required gain coefficient by factors of approximately 100 or more are required. Nevertheless, a simple three-level model was formulated for carbon-like ions which supposed electron-collisional excitation of a $2p$ valence electron into a $3p$ level followed by lasing from $3p$ to $3s$ and finally rapid depletion of the lower laser level $3s$ to the initial $2p$ level, in a quasi-CW scheme [105]. (The terminology quasi-CW is used to indicate that stationary inversion is expected, but most probably is limited to the interval during which proper excitation conditions can be met in a particular plasma, as indeed was found for example in the z-pinch visible ion laser). The basic model is illustrated in the energy level diagram shown in Fig. 13. A gain coefficient of either 1 or 5 cm^{-1} for short noncavity ASE operation can be expected with sufficient $2p$ to $3p$ collisional excitation at high density and/or high temperatures. A high density limit is approached, however, as the electron collisional depopulation rate from the upper $3p$ laser level to the $3d$ and $3s$ levels becomes comparable to the spontaneous decay rate for the laser transition, and this produces values for the upper density limit indicated for various atoms as shown in Fig. 14. A later more complete numerical analysis [136] indicated that electron densities could exceed this limit by as much as a factor-of-ten before population inversion was destroyed by collisional equilibrium; however the losses increase with increasing density above those values shown in Fig. 14. It is to be noted in Fig. 14 that electron temperatures ten times higher than the equilibrium temperatures assumed for the ions are used. This was required in order to attain sufficient gain to reduce the gain length to a length of ~ 1 cm which is considered reasonable for short wavelength lasers such as pumped in laser-produced plasmas. Such high electron temperatures only exist [137] for short times, hence the "quasi" nature of this amplification.

Numerical modeling [136], [138] on the O^{2+} ion has yielded gain coefficients consistent with operation of lasers with this species in the near UV region in cavities, and has also shown that the required temperature differential can be maintained for reasonable times at the low associated densities. However, such modeling only assumes that a certain amount of energy is deposited in the plasmas in a very short time to heat the electrons and that relaxation proceeds from that initial condition. In a practical experiment, the enhanced electron heating in a plasma will probably have to be obtained by a direct electrical process rather than by laser energy deposition [139], since the absorption length for the laser radiation in plasmas at such low density is unreasonably long. For example, proper operation of a 1-m long traveling-wave discharge which has been shown to produce C^{3+} ions [140][7] would seem to be a possibility at gain coefficients $\gtrsim 0.01$ cm^{-1}. Gain lengths ≈ 100 cm are possible without enhanced electron heating as shown in Fig. 15.

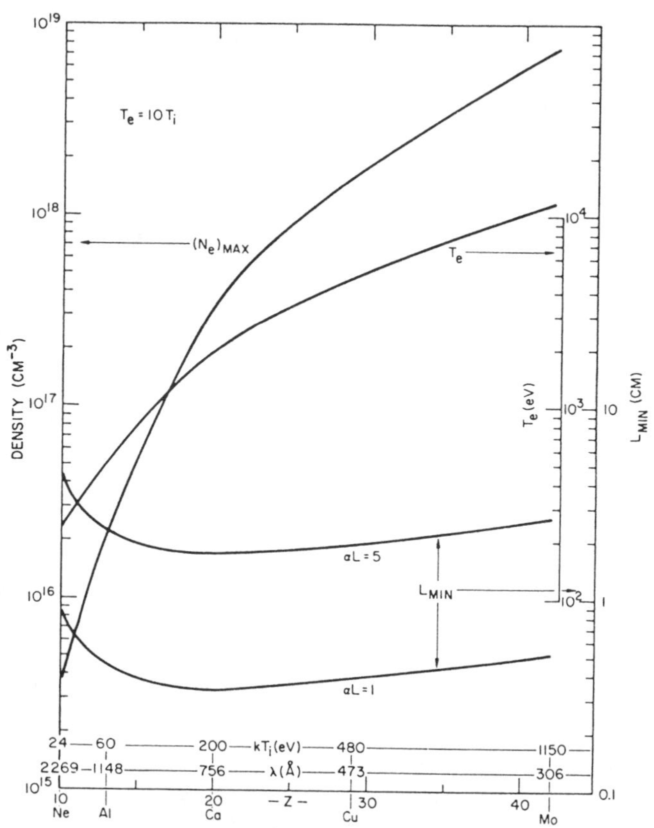

Fig. 14. Minimum length L_{min} for amplification in carbon-like ions with a gain of exp (αL) versus atomic number Z, wavelength λ, and ion kinetic temperature kT_i. The electron temperature T_e is assumed equal to 10 T_i and is plotted. The electron density $(N_e)_{max}$ at which collisional mixing becomes important is also plotted [105].

As noticed from Figs. 14 and 15, $3p \rightarrow 3s$ transitions are limited as far as reaching short wavelengths. Transitions involving $n = 4$ states are less desirable, both because of the more rapid collisional coupling between $n = 4$ levels and the associated lower density limits and longer lasing wavelengths. For shorter wavelengths it is more interesting to consider lasing on $n = 3$ to $n = 2$ transitions where, for example, again quasi-CW inversion can be expected in helium-like two-electron ions with electron collisional pumping from the 1^1S ground state to the 3^1S state, followed by lasing between 3^1S and 2^1P and rapid lower state depletion from 2^1P to 1^1S. The situation is not dissimilar to the $3p \rightarrow 3s$ scheme

[7] The mechanism for $2p$-$2s$ population inversion in C^{3+} is not well understood; perhaps a dynamic mechanism as suggested by Norton and Wooding [141] for similar ions is applicable.

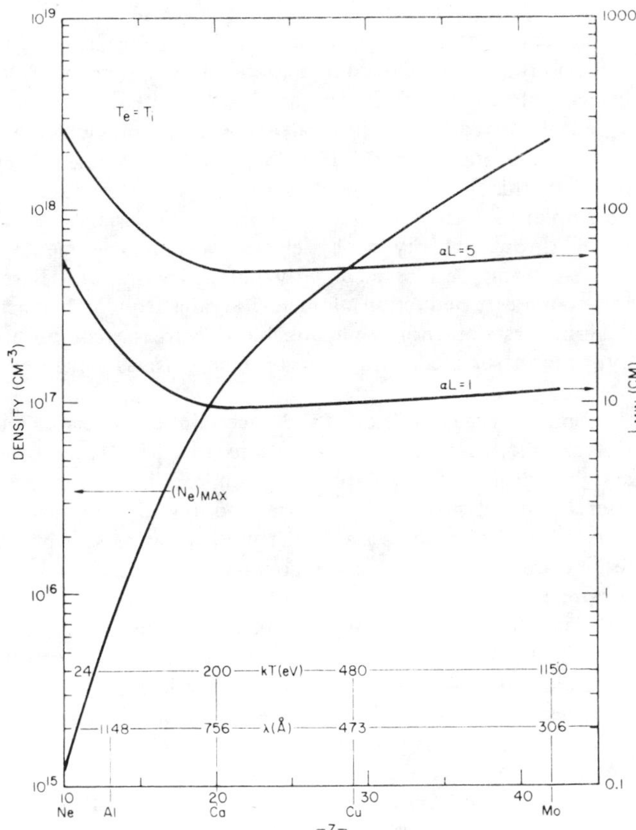

Fig. 15. Minimum length L_{min} for amplification in carbon-like ions with a gain of exp (αL) versus atomic number Z, wavelength λ, and ion kinetic temperature kT_i. The electron temperature T_e is assumed equal to T_i. The electron density $(N_e)_{max}$ at which collisional mixing becomes important is also plotted [105].

in that collisional coupling between $n = 3$ levels enter at some density. However, final collisional destruction of the population inversion between the $n = 3$ and $n = 2$ levels occurs at a much higher density, so that high gains can be expected at shorter wavelengths. An initial analysis by Palumbo [136] again indicates that electron temperatures exceeding ion temperatures are required to accomplish the necessary pumping over the large $1s \rightarrow 3s$ energy gap in He-like ions. In this case it is reasonable to consider as a lasant the critical absorption layer in a plasma produced by a $\lambda = 1$-μm laser at an electron density of 10^{21} cm^{-3}. Assuming a density of this magnitude, electron kinetic temperature kT_e varying from 1 to 5 keV, and an ion kinetic temperature of $kT_i = kT_e/2$ (prior to complete equipartition of energy), gain coefficients have been calculated for He-like ions of various elements and are plotted versus Z in Fig. 16 [136]. The computations show a peak gain coefficient of less than 7 cm^{-1} and an optimum atomic number Z in the range 11 to 15 for these temperatures and densities. The ion temperature T_i affects the calculated results only through Doppler broadening of the lasing line; and a higher T_e/T_i ratio results in increased α according to $T_i^{-1/2}$. Higher electron temperatures have little effect on α, because kT_e becomes comparable to the pump energy and exponential factors are less effective. Electron temperatures >1 keV at present are mainly produced in condensed spark plasmas [109], [110] of dimensions on the order of 0.01 cm or less, resulting in low values of the product αL. Such high electron temperatures in laser-

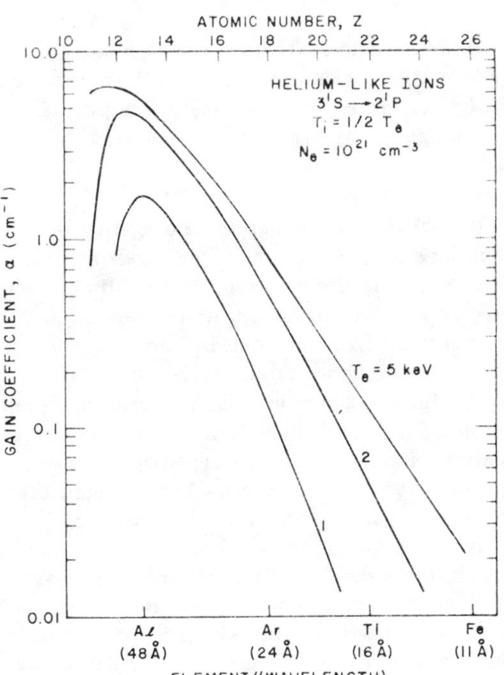

Fig. 16. Gain coefficient in cm^{-1} calculated from a steady state model for the $3^1S \rightarrow 2^1P$ transition in helium-like ions. The electron density N_e was chosen to be 10^{21} cm^{-3} for efficient plasma heating by 1.06-μm lasing radiation. Curves are shown for the highest temperature range expected for state-of-the-art laser-produced plasmas. At values of $Z < 11$, the calculational results show a negative inversion density ΔN due to collisional mixing of the upper and lower laser levels; the decrease in gain at higher Z is caused by a small ΔN resulting from a larger energy gap for pumping from the ground state [136]. These results are preliminary and likely to vary as further effects are added, such as radiative trapping.

produced plasmas will probably depend upon compression in pellet experiments.

Prior to direct amplification experiments, it may be possible to measure population inversions at low net gain, as outlined in Section II-B. This is true for either the $3p \rightarrow 3s$ or the $3s \rightarrow 2p$ schemes described above. For example, in the latter case a relative intensity measurement of the $3^1S \rightarrow 2^1P$ and the $2^1P \rightarrow 1^1S$ lines would yield the relative upper and lower laser state populations using known oscillator strengths. The wavelength difference (approximately a factor-of-ten) could be spanned with corresponding $3^1P \rightarrow 2^1S$ and $3^1P \rightarrow 1^1S$ lines in a branching ratio approach, since both originate on the same level. Typical population deviations from "normal" may be only a factor-of-two [136], so that available overall experimental precision must be carefully assessed.

Another experiment also involving the pumping of helium-like O^{6+} ions in a laser-produced plasmas has been proposed [142], where electron-collisional pumping from the 1^1S ground state to the 3^1P state would be followed by lasing from $3^1P \rightarrow 2^1S$. This would be a self-terminating (pre-equilibrium) scheme and also requires that electron collisional population of the lower laser 2^1S level from the ground state occur at a lower rate than the upper 3^1P level population. Indeed, at very high electron energies it is expected that the $1^1S \rightarrow 3^1P$ electron collisional excitation rate exceed the non-dipole $1^1S \rightarrow 2^1S$ rate. In this experiment it is proposed that a transient nonthermal electron energy distribution be obtained, featuring a very strong high-energy component to provide the preferential 3^1P excitation at a sufficiently large

$1^1S \rightarrow 3^1P$ excitation rate, in a situation somewhat similar to that above where high electron temperatures were discussed. An experiment to test this scheme using a plasma produced by a focused high-power laser beam is underway.

B. Electron Attachment

1) Collisional Recombination: Population of upper laser states in ions by the capture of free electrons appears to be an efficient pumping process compared to direct excitation, although sufficient energy to produce and maintain the necessary density of free electrons in a plasma must still be attained. Free-electron capture with the release of radiant energy (radiative recombination) proceeds preferentially into tightly bound states which is not desirable for achieving a population inversion. At high densities, however, three-body (collisional) recombination can become significant, wherein the excess capture-energy is carried away by an additional electron. In contrast to radiative recombination, collisional recombination strongly favors capture into states with lower binding energy, i.e., potential upper laser states. Such capture is followed by cascading, for which radiative rates are highest for the low-lying states; this supports population inversion.

There are a number of published suggestions for short wavelength lasers based upon this idea [123], [143]-[154], starting with the 1965 paper by Gudzenko and Shelepin [143]. Most are for hydrogen or hydrogenic ions with $3 \rightarrow 2$ lasing transitions, although some have suggested inversion with the ground state, i.e., $2 \rightarrow 1$ Lyman-α lasing. There have been both semiquantitative, analytical and, more recently, numerical treatments of the concept, some predicting very high gain coefficients for optimum conditions.

A rather basic requirement of such collisional recombination schemes is a high pumping rate, achievable at high densities, prior to reaching a non-inverted state of equilibrium. This has led to an increasing recognition of the demand for extremely rapid cooling following the creation of the stripped ions. In fact, most of the high gains predicted numerically assume a very low temperature compared to that necessary to create the ions in an equilibrium plasma. Free expansion of, for example, a laser-produced target plasma has been proposed, but this alone may not provide a sufficient rate of cooling, and a density decrease accompanies the expansion. In one proposed experiment [145] with lasing on the Lyman-α line of neutral hydrogen at 1216 Å, cold electrons would be produced by multiphoton ionization followed by recombination and lasing in times shorter than the collisional heating times for the electrons. This approach seems limited to neutral hydrogen, but is still interesting for the VUV region. Most proposals involve transient phenomena, although there is one proposal [149] for a stationary inversion between $n = 3 \rightarrow n = 2$ in an expanding arc-heated plasma. No gain factors are given for the relatively low densities involved here and radiation trapping, which adds to the population rate for the lower state in particular, is neglected.

A fundamental difficulty in any modeling of the recombination laser is the lack of reliable collisional rate coefficient data. Collisions are of vital importance in the pumping process, in the redistribution of population between bound and free states, and in the electron cooling/heating processes. While most excitation (and deexcitation) rates are known or can be calculated, collisional ionization rates, particularly from excited states, are relatively difficult to obtain theoretically and experimental data are nonexistent. Since the critical three-body collisional-recombination pumping process is the inverse of collisional ionization from excited states, it is usually deduced by detailed balancing arguments, which adds further importance to the collisional ionization rate. Therefore, at this point it seems appropriate to emphasize the obtainment of such fundamental and critical data, perhaps either through theory or by electron beam experiments on excited atoms or ions resonantly pumped with tuned lasers, for examples. Deduction of such vital rates from high-density experiments does not seem possible due to the complicated dynamics associated with most of such plasmas generated at present.

In spite of the complexities and uncertainties associated with this scheme, some direct observations [98], [99], indicate a marginal degree of population inversion existing in expanding laser produced plasmas at densities too low for demonstrable gain. The uncertainties are admittedly large at present but the results are encouraging, since population inversion is indeed the prerequisite for eventual useful gain devices.

It may be recalled from Section I that this approach has some basic short wavelength limitations due to the eventual dominance of radiative recombination into lower states and to densities approaching the solid level. The actual limits again vary with formulas chosen, but this certainly appears to be most promising as a VUV and perhaps soft X-ray laser scheme.

2) Dielectronic Capture: As the name implies, dielectronic capture is an interaction involving a double transition. It occurs when a free electron interacts with an ion and is first "captured" into an excited state with the associated excitation of a bound electron. Thus, a metastable complex is formed, and the associated excitation has been suggested as an X-ray laser pumping mechanism. Since the free electron can have a kinetic energy less than the threshold value for collisional excitation of the bound electron (by the amount of its final binding energy), the process is sometimes considered as a subthreshold resonance in the overall scattering process. The captured electron may exist in quasi-discrete levels prior to stabilization. Following capture, stabilization can occur through several possible channels, one of which is autoionization (a radiationless "Auger" transition) which is the inverse process and effectively results in an elastic scattering resonance. Relaxation of both electrons into stable bound states can also occur in an overall rearrangement collision with radiative recombination. In addition, a radiative-Auger stabilization mode is possible, causing the release of both the captured electron and a photon of variable energy due to an overall rearrangement collision with "bremsstrahlung"-type emission [155]. It is the recombination mode that would be most attractive for achieving population inversion, and this can only be expected to dominate over autoionization for high Z ($\gtrsim$ 40) elements (see, e.g., [156]).

Nevertheless, assuming that all captured electrons produce candidate ions for amplification, a pumping rate coefficient $\langle \sigma v \rangle_{\text{diel}}$ can be estimated from the capture rate. This rate, which is easily obtained from detailed balancing arguments for free electron capture into a specific state, is [102], [157]

$$\langle \sigma v \rangle_{\text{diel}} = \frac{h^3 \, \Gamma}{2(2\pi m \, kT_e)^{3/2}} \frac{g_f}{g_i} \exp\left[\frac{-\Delta E_{if}}{kT_e}\right]. \tag{16}$$

Here g_i and g_f are the statistical weights of the initial and final bound states, respectively, ΔE_{if} is the absolute energy difference between these states, and $\Gamma(\lesssim 10^{15}\ s^{-1})$ is the (inverse) autoionization rate. This can be summed over the few ($\lesssim$ 10) bound states expected at the high densities involved in short-wavelength laser media. Numerically the rate is at best comparable to direct electron collisional excitation, which is not unexpected [158]. This conclusion is supported by the observation of somewhat weaker satellite lines to He-like resonance lines observed in a number of laboratory plasmas and associated with dielectronic recombination [157].

It might be remarked that the large relative importance [158], [159] of this process to overall recombination rates in stellar atmospheres at low densities, as well as the associate large population of high-lying states [160], comes about because of the multitude of very high discrete quantum states present and does not carry over to densities found in laboratory plasmas [160], [161]. Therefore, dielectronic recombination appears at best to be a supplement to direct electron collisional excitation, under the conditions where the lasing ion is formed by recombination from a higher ionic species.

3) Atom-Ion Resonance Charge Transfer: As pointed out in Section II, a pumping process which has a large cross section for preferential population of specific excited states in ions is most desirable for achieving population inversion at short wavelengths. The resonance charge transfer collisional interaction

$$I^{z+} + A \longrightarrow I^{(z-1)+}(n^*) + A^+ + \Delta E \tag{17}$$

between a neutral atom A and an ion I^{z+} of net charge z with a cross section of approximately $10^{-16}\ z^2\,\text{cm}^2$, is a very promising candidate [100], since this cross section is several orders-of-magnitude higher than other excited-state population cross sections. The energy defect here is designated ΔE and the final ion excited state quantum number is shown as n^*.

Resonance charge transfer occurs spontaneously only in an exothermic reaction, where classical level crossings are expected at some distance of separation R_x according to the simple classical Landau–Zener theory [162], [163]. In this theory, cross section peaks occur at a relative particle velocity $(V_{\text{rel}})_{\max}$ which increases with an increasing exothermic energy defect ΔE_{exo} as shown in Fig. 17. Thus this process is level-selective by its near-resonance nature. The resonance is associated with a near-coincidence between the binding energies of the initial atom's electronic state and the final ion's electronic state into which this electron is transferred. For initial ions of light elements, the coincidence may occur for low-lying (e.g., n = 3 or 4) states (Fig. 18) resulting in direct pumping of a population inversion with a lower ($n \geqslant 2$) state [164]. For heavier ions, possibly leading to shorter wavelength lasing, near-coincidence occurs with higher lying final-ion states, and population inversion through cascading is expected; this is similar to the collisional recombination schemes (Section III-B) except for the much higher cross section ($\sim 10^4$ times) with this process. This latter approach was originally proposed by Vinogradov and Sobel'man [100] for an expanding z = 10 plasma ion source experiment.

Assuming that ions expand with thermal velocities determined from $kT = \chi^{(z-1)+}/4$ where $\chi^{(z-1)+}$ is the ionization potential of the preceding ion state, direct upper laser level population in light elements (Fig. 18) should be possible according to the theoretical curves shown in Fig. 17, including the mean velocity estimates indicated for stripped and hydrogenic initial-ionic species [164]. An inversion of these data for various charge states is plotted in Fig. 19 which yields the optimum energy defects ΔE_{exo}. For background atoms of hydrogen, helium, and neon, the principle quantum numbers

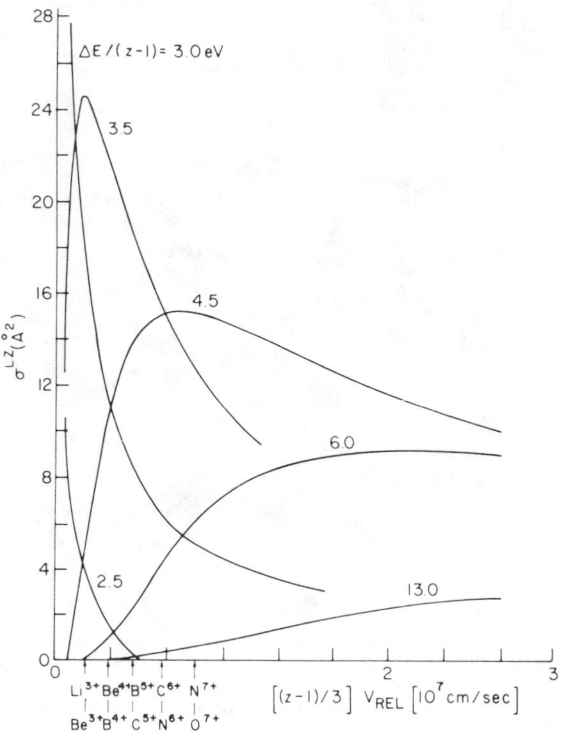

Fig. 17. Resonance charge transfer cross section from *s-s* Landau–Zener theory versus scaled relative velocity V_{rel} for the atom-ion combination (data adapted from [162]). ΔE represents the energy defect in eV for the exothermic reaction z the effective charge of the ion. Velocities for the ions designated are assumed thermal and the kinetic temperature was chosen as one-fourth of the ionization potential for creating the ion [106].

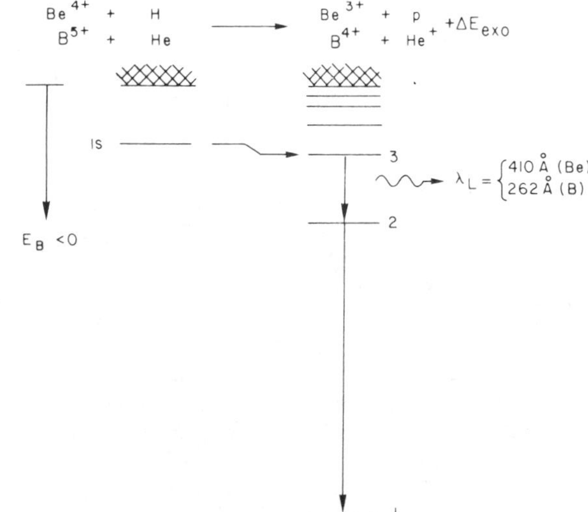

Fig. 18. Schematic diagram of exothermic *s-s* resonance charge transfer reaction leading to a quasi-stationary population inversion between n = 3 and n = 2 levels in certain helium-like or hydrogenic ions [106]. Refer to Fig. 19 for other possible ion/atom combinations. E_B is the binding energy.

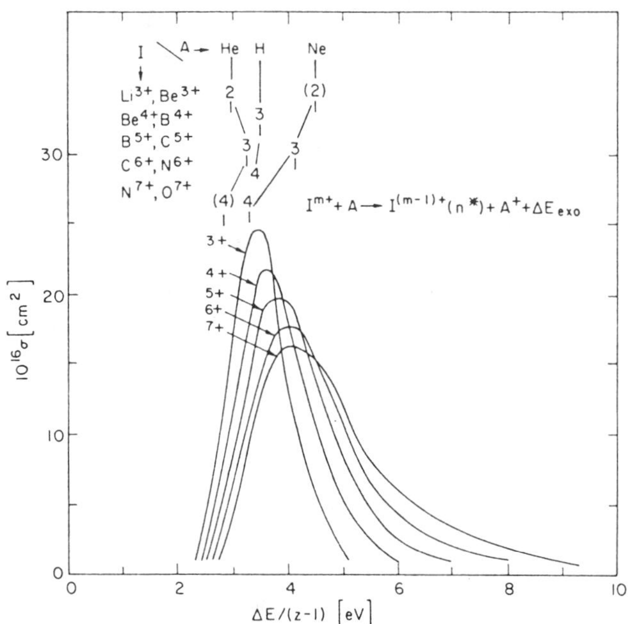

Fig. 19. Resonance charge transfer cross section obtained by inversion of Fig. 17 data [106]. Final quantum states n of high capture probability for each ion I^{m+} and atom A combination are indicated by numerals, with parentheses to indicate less probably transitions. ΔE is the exothermic energy defect and z is the effective ion charge.

n^* of the final excited states which are expected to be preferentially populated are indicated.

The classical theory behind these estimates is rather inexact but illuminating. As recently emphasized by Presnykov and Ulantzev [165], improved theory is available giving a typical peak cross section of $\sigma_{rct} \equiv \pi a_0^2 z^2 (I_H/I_A)$, where I_H and I_A are the ionization potentials of hydrogen and the atomic gas, respectively. These calculated cross sections are in agreement with measurements obtained from crossed beam experiments for low degrees of ionization. They point out that both double-electron transfer, when two equivalent outershell electrons exist (e.g., helium atoms) and also innershell electron transfer are possible, at reduced cross sections. In addition, they suggest that ion–ion resonance charge transfer might be possible when a large difference in net charge exists between the interacting particles, although no quantitative results are derived.

Experiments with laser-produced plasmas expanding into neutral atom gaseous atmospheres are underway at the U.S. Naval Research Laboratory, with space-resolved grazing incidence spectroscopy of resonance lines used in an initial search for anomalous populations in C^{5+} and C^{6+} ion excited states [106], [166]. Absorption of the laser radiation by the neutral atmosphere is minimized by the lower density possible with the large cross section, by confined regions, and by the high photon energy of the laser line relative to the neutral atom absorption edge energy.

Presnyakov and Shevel'ko [167] have pointed out the advantage for Lyman-α inversion of the large proton-cesium resonance charge transfer cross section at low energies. (The general difficulty with inverting a ground state is again to be recognized [100].) Two experiments have recently been proposed for investigating this scheme [120], [168], using a rapidly advancing plasma from a plasma gun or a duoplasmatron injected into a neutral cesium atmosphere. Cavity operation at Lyman-α at a reduced gain coefficient has been suggested [120], [167], and extension to helium (584-Å amplification) without a cavity is proposed for both experiments. Also, electron storing in 2^1S states of helium has been considered [120], [121].

A second maximum in the cross-section distribution is expected to occur at high (10's of keV) particle energies [162], and one proposal is to use a high energy ion source in a traveling-wave mode to invert ionized helium. No experiments are planned unless ion beam sources of greatly increased current become available (see Section IV).

C. Photoabsorption

1) Innershell Photoionization: The terminology "innershell transitions" is meant here to designate those transitions that occur as the result of a vacancy being created in a closed shell (all n-orbitals filled) of an atom or ion for which at least one electron exists in a shell of larger principle quantum number. The vacancy can be created by, for example, collisions of electrons, ions or photons. Subsequent stabilization can occur by numerous channels including radiative, Auger, and radiative-Auger double electron transitions. Shake-off and shake-up transitions are also well known to occur during the vacancy-production phase. Activity in this area has been well summarized in the four volume proceedings of the 1972 International Conference on Inner Shell Ionization Phenomena [169], which includes some papers on X-ray lasers as future applications.

Innershell transitions for lasing are inherently more complicated than the so-called "optical" transitions of valence electrons simply because of the multitude of possible decay channels, particularly the radiationless Auger channel which cannot contribute directly to lasing but does consume pumping energy. In addition, the pumping source energy must be concentrated in a restricted energy band in order to preferentially remove the innershell electrons when outershell electrons exist. The initial attractiveness of innershell transitions is somewhat traditional for X-ray generation and does appear to offer short wavelengths in a low temperature medium, if indeed Doppler broadening were to be the dominant mechanism. However, as shown in Section I, natural broadening with Auger decay included is comparable to Doppler broadening even at the elevated temperatures where one and two-electron ions are created with optical transitions in the traditionally K region. Thus there would not appear to be any clear advantage to innershell transitions for short wavelength self-terminating lasers, although there have been a number of published suggestions with different pumping schemes. Innershell pumping by collisions of plasma electrons has been proposed only once in a brief note [170] without apparent regard to the effect on outer electrons of the broad energy distribution of free electrons. Selective innershell pumping by collisions of ion beams with atoms (forming quasi-molecules) has been suggested [112], [171]; however, the beam current required is formidable (Section II), particularly when all possible states and decay channels are considered. Greater consideration seems to have been given to photoionization pumping schemes [96], [113], [172]–[176] both because of the ability to concentrate the pump energy and the likelihood of being able to tune the pump source to a spectral region of preferential innershell photoionization.

In the simplest self-terminating schemes an innershell hole is created by photon impact and lasing occurs on a radiative transition. Population inversion terminates in a time approximately equal to the lifetime of the vacancy state (see Section II). Both $K\alpha$ transitions with many outer electrons and transitions to first full-shell vacancies in alkalis (e.g., L-shell Na) have been studied. In the latter only one outershell electron exists and Auger effects are not present; however the wavelengths are typically 30 times longer than for $K\alpha$ transitions. A variation on the photoionized-Na scheme which has recently been proposed by McGuire [177] involves the production of K-shell vacancies in Na^+ ions followed by K-LL vacancy Auger transitions producing Na^{3+} ions with electrons in various (n = 2) L-subshells. Lasing is predicted in the 400-Å region on $2p \rightarrow 2s$ transitions instead of $3s \rightarrow 2p$ in the neutral sodium pumped scheme. Pumping by X-rays from laser-produced plasmas has been proposed [178]. In this proposal the laser plasmas are arranged to produce a traveling wave pumping configuration on the material to be pumped. Both sodium schemes require that photoionization losses in the medium be overcome. The principle difference is whether an n = 2 vacancy is produced directly by L-electron photoionization or indirectly by K-electron photoionization followed by an Auger decay. The selective pumping spectrum required will fall into obviously different energy ranges. This could be a deciding factor in designing an experiment, and it is pointed out [177] that it is easier to produce a filtered hard X-ray spectrum for K-shell pumping.

It is interesting that one of the major objections to photon-pumped $K\alpha$ lasers, namely the Auger decay channels that consume pumping energy, could conceivably be utilized to alleviate a more formidable problem common to most short wavelength lasers, i.e., the extremely fast pump pulse risetime (see Section II). It was first suggested by Stankevich [173] in 1970 that L-shell vacancies created by $K\alpha$ transitions could be filled by Auger transitions at a higher rate than that at which they are created, so that a population inversion could be sustained for as long as the particular species exists. Hence, a quasi-CW laser is conceivable along with resonance cavity operation. Stankevich's analysis was based upon some very rough approximations for the relevant rates. When reanalyzed [96] in 1974 with new calculations published in the interim, the net gain coefficient on his simple model remained positive but became small. However, Stankevich also ignored the fact that the further-stripped ions created by Auger transitions possess shifted $K\alpha$ absorption lines and, therefore, decreased laser beam reabsorption. The requirement for sustained inversion then becomes one of exceeding only the K-L radiative rate, which is considerably less than the K-LL Auger rate for light elements [179]. When the analysis [96] is extended to this situation, the ratio of rates and hence the approximate ratio of population densities becomes significant for elements in the range of Z = 20 as shown in Fig. 20. Indeed, a gain coefficient of 70 is predicted in a 30 μm by 300 μm medium of silicon atoms at a wavelength of 7.1 Å and with a currently realistic photon pumping source of 4 TW power. However, actually making and maintaining a medium having the rather idealized conditions assumed is another matter. For example, a high density of a specific atomic or ionic species must be maintained against continuing ionization with delicately balanced recombination into the proper states. This approach should be pursued further with both numerical modeling and experiments, the first experimental efforts probably being directed towards developing suitable pump sources with sufficient power concentrated in the required spectral region. Such a source may be a laser-produced plasma, an exploded wire, or even a more simple heavy-element spark discharge.

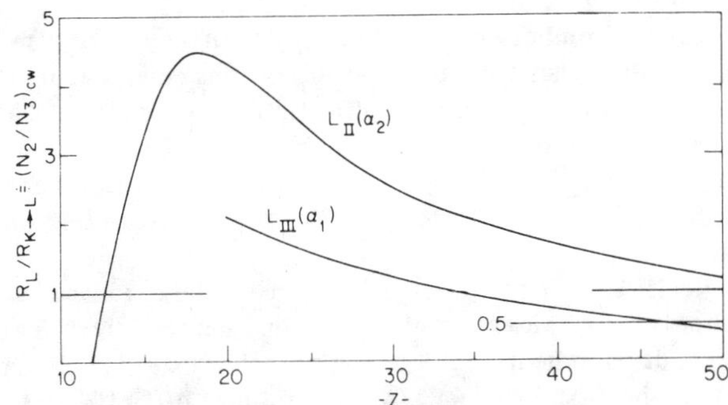

Fig. 20. Ratio of rates $R_L/R_{K\rightarrow L}$ for total transitions out of an L vacancy state and radiative decay out of a K vacancy state versus atomic number Z. This ratio is equivalent to N_2/N_3 for equilibrium conditions reached after long times in CW operation. Values exceeding unity and one-half indicate gain for the $K\alpha_2$ and $K\alpha_1$ transitions, respectively. The model used assumes that only radiative transitions produce absorbers and that Auger transitions generate shifted ion lines. Both the $K \rightarrow L_{II}$ (α_2) and $K \rightarrow L_{III}$ (α_1) transitions are shown [96].

2) Photoexcitation: Absorption of discrete emission such as from a spectral line leading to excitation to a specific upper laser level is an intriguing possibility for selective pumping by photons. Generally two species are required[8] with overlapping intense lines. Considerations so far [180], [181] have centered around the intense resonance lines of hydrogenic and He-like ions which can become "opacity broadened" for the desired frequency overlap. A typical example is absorption of the C^{5+} Lyman-α line at 33.74 Å by a C^{4+} ion in a 1^1S-4^1P transition, with the 4^1P level becoming overpopulated relative to lower 3^1S and 2^1S levels and possible lasing in the 700-Å and 200-Å regions, respectively. Considerable thought must go into a practical experiment for efficient coupling of the pumping line emission to the absorber. In this respect the practical problems are not unlike those encountered in photoionization-pumping experiments. A coaxial design utilizing an expanding cylindrical plasma from a specially tailored laser-irradiated target may prove most efficient. Obviously, many combinations of ions and elements may be considered as long as overlapping intense lines are present.

D. Ion-Atom Collisions

Another method of producing inner shell inversions for lasers is based on the promotion of electrons to higher levels during the collisions of atoms or ions with other atoms. These promotions of the inner shell electrons occur when violent inelastic atomic collisions take place with deep interpenetration of electron shells. During the collision the innershell electrons are forced into energy levels in accord with molecular orbital theory. After the collision the atoms are left in narrow, discrete states with several electrons simultaneously highly excited [183].

McCorkle and Joyce [112], [171] have proposed that the above method of excitation might be suitable for the produc-

[8] Single species pumping of isotope shifted lines has been proposed [182].

tion of gain by stimulated emission in the X-ray region. They propose the bombardment of thin foils with an ion beam in such a manner that the excited atoms or ions emerge from the other side of the foil where amplification can take place. They propose to use long gain-lengths, in spite of the short excited-state lifetimes, by deflection of the ion beam in the manner described by Louisell *et al.* [104] to produce traveling-wave excitation.

Difficulties with this approach lie in the large ion currents required and in the extremely short time before Auger decay. Recent developments in ion beam technology [184] may assist in the first problem. Auger lifetimes of $\lesssim 10^{-14}$ s severely limit the cross-sectional width of excited plasma and force close tolerances on traveling-wave deflection and focusing. If the planarity of the wave varies by only 10^{-3} cm, then the traveling-wave will not be of uniformly correct velocity for amplification. In addition, diffraction losses from such regions of gain may be extremely high. Coherence brightening and laser lethargy effects for this approach have also been considered [185].

E. Nuclear Transitions

The use of nuclear transitions to produce lasing in the X-ray and γ-ray spectral regions was considered as early as 1961 in laser history [186]-[189]. The conclusions at that time were that the difficulties were so great that no practical experiments could be started. The recent success in the vacuum UV and the anticipated success in the X-ray region has inspired a new look at the more penetrating γ-ray lasers. Much of the revived interest in γ-ray lasers has originated in the Soviet Union and emerged at the 1973 Vavilov Conference on Nonlinear Optics. Soviet scientists Khokhlov [190], Letokhov [191], Dmitriev and Shuryak [192], and Goldanskii [193] have contributed significant new ideas or proposals on the γ-ray laser. In England, Byrne *et al.* [194] have considered the γ-ray laser and in the U.S.A., Baldwin at Rensselaer Polytechnic Institute [195], [196], Wood and Chapline [197] at the Lawrence Livermore Laboratory, and a group at the Naval Research Laboratory [198] have examined the problem. No one claims that development of the γ-ray laser will be easy, but some aspects of the problem appear no more difficult than those for hard X-ray lasers. Some of the fundamental problems of γ-ray lasers and some of the rather elaborate schemes for producing them will be discussed below.

From (6), the threshold inversion density ΔN for mirrorless systems varies as

$$\Delta N \geqslant \frac{8\pi \Delta \nu \tau}{\lambda^2 L \phi}. \tag{18}$$

For practical systems, of course, the inversion density must be much higher, as Wood and Chapline point out, but this equation illustrates the basic problem of γ-ray lasers. An attraction of γ-ray lasers is the availability of long-lived excited nuclear states (measured in years versus femtoseconds). These metastable lifetimes would enable the population inversion to be assembled slowly using low power level pumping sources. Such long lifetimes, however, greatly increase the inversion density required for lasing. To use these long-lived transitions, the linewidth $\Delta\nu$ must be reduced to the point where ΔN is below the density of solid material. This implies that $\Delta\nu$ cannot exceed τ^{-1} by more than a few orders-of-magnitude. Recoilless Mössbauer transitions are a starting point for narrow linewidth. These transitions may be narrowed even further by growing more perfect crystals, by placing the crystals in a uniform temperature, uniform field environment, or by using special RF field techniques to narrow the resonance lines [199].

It should be clear that resonators would not be practical for a γ-ray laser. No material is known to be reflective at these wavelengths and the high energy flux expected from the laser would destroy most materials placed in the beam. Therefore, in most cases γ-ray lasers will be ASE devices of length as great as practical (an exception is proposed in [192] for long lifetime transitions pumped by γ-rays) and with diameter $d \ll L$ to avoid radial amplification losses, but large enough to avoid diffraction losses. Absorption losses must be taken into account within the laser material. These losses may vary considerably depending upon the orientation of the crystal axes with respect to the direction of laser propagation. The gain coefficient per unit length α must exceed the absorption coefficient per unit length μ in order to have a useful laser. In addition, the gain equation must be multiplied by the fraction f of excited nuclei that undergo recoilless transitions, by the branching ratio β for the isomeric transition, and by $(1+x)^{-1}$ where x is the internal conversion coefficient (in this process excitation energy is lost to the nucleus in a radiationless manner). The gain coefficient condition becomes

$$\alpha = \Delta N \frac{\lambda^2}{2\pi} \frac{f}{\tau \Delta \nu_T} \frac{\beta}{1+x} > \mu \tag{19}$$

where $\Delta\nu_T$ is now the full linewidth. Khokhlov [190] estimates that the absorption coefficient μ is no greater than 1 cm^{-1} and that it is possible to obtain gain coefficients of

$$\alpha = (10^3 - 10^4)/\tau \Delta \nu_T \text{ cm}^{-1} \tag{20}$$

Transitions in which the $\tau \Delta \nu_T$ product is near unity have been observed for short lifetime transitions (10^{-7}-10^{-9} s), but when longer-lived transitions are considered there are little data available. One measurement of Ag^{107}, which has a 44-s lifetime, showed a $\tau \Delta \nu_T$ of 10^6.

Obviously more work is needed to investigate the linewidth of long-lived transitions. It may be that narrower bandwidth transitions exist for some long-lived isomers. If not, then techniques for reducing the linewidth must be developed if long-lived transitions are to be used for γ-ray lasers.

The alternative to reducing the linewidth of long-lived transitions is to accept the breadth of short-lived transitions and to try to overcome this factor by increased pumping intensity. In doing this one finds that inversion densities greater than that of solids are required and that the pumping power required to achieve the required inversion densities (10^{24} cm^{-3}) is overwhelmingly high. To reach such inversion densities, it has been proposed that laser compression techniques similar to those proposed for pellet fusion might be used. One concept consists of a cylindrical thread of beryllium as the γ-ray laser host material. Added to the beryllium thread is a small amount of parent isotopic material [193]. The Mössbauer effect will be preserved in the impurity material. Surrounding the beryllium host with its impurity is a concentric cylinder of fissile material which will be driven to criticality by a series of laser beams aimed at the cylinder from all sides and timed to produce a wave of excitation moving at the velocity of light down the length of the cylinder.

The laser beam compresses the fissile material causing a miniaturized explosion and the release of many pumping neutrons. These neutrons pass through the beryllium exciting the impurity nuclei quite rapidly and providing a gain medium for those γ-ray photons that are emitted in the axial direction of the cylinder [195].

If pumping a γ-ray laser is difficult when lifetimes are short, and if linewidths are too great when isomer lifetimes are long, perhaps a compromise is to use intermediate lifetimes and assemble the laser as fast as possible. One idea [191] proposes that pumped nuclear material be quickly vaporized with a laser beam and that the excited nuclei be separated isotopically, ionized and electrostatically deposited on a host substrate. The rapidly assembled laser would emit as soon as sufficient excited nuclei reached the substrate. This approach is quite complicated, and considerable research would be required to attempt it. It would be necessary to study the isotope separation process in detail as well as the excitation-vaporization process, but it appears that this technique might work where others do not.

The question of coherent emission of Fermions (neutrons, protons, alpha particles) has come up in some discussions [200]. Byrne *et al.* [194] have given further consideration to α particle emission. Their conclusions are that alpha particle capture and emission processes are incoherent with no phase relationship. An α particle with megaelectronvolt energy has a wavelength of $\sim 10^{-12}$ cm. The frequency spread associated with the Doppler motion is $\sim 10^{16}$ Hz at room temperature for a heavy element ($A \sim 240$). The resulting cross section for stimulated emission is 10^{-35}–10^{-57} cm^2 for lifetimes in the range of 10^{-6} to 10^{16} s. Absorption cross sections are many orders of magnitude larger and seem to preclude the possibility of stimulated α particles.

On the other hand, Rivlin, the Soviet scientist who filed an early patent disclosure on the γ-ray laser, has proposed that antimatter might serve as an amplifying medium [201]. In discussing some aspects of the problem he chose to consider positrons. Positrons, of course, are quickly annihilated by the close presence of an electron with the resulting emission of two photons. The minimum energy for the created photon is 0.51 MeV which results in a wavelength of 0.024 Å. Rivlin's idea is to inject a pulse of positrons into an electron-rich target and observe the emission upon annihilation of the positrons. He calculates that he needs a positron density of 10^{18} cm^{-3} in a time of 10^{-10} s. While this may be difficult to achieve in practice, there appears to be no problem with coherence, since the process is one of *stimulated* annihilation of antimatter.

F. Stimulated Compton Scattering

The idea of using stimulated Compton scattering to produce short wavelength lasers has been considered by numerous authors [202]–[205]. The attraction of such a laser is that photons injected into a relativistic electron beam can be scattered back at much higher energies. Hence it may be possible to build a laser based on stimulated Compton scattering and reach well into the X-ray region. In addition, the output wavelength would be tunable over wide frequency ranges by varying the acceleration voltage of the electron beam.

Pantell *et al.* [204] have outlined the problem of stimulated Compton scattering. For a colinear geometry with the electron beam and photon beam of frequency ν_1 pointed toward one another, the frequency of the backscattered wave ν_2 is given by

$$\nu_2 = 4\nu_1 (E/E_0)^2 \tag{21}$$

where E is the electron energy and E_0 is the electron rest mass (0.5 MeV). For 5-MeV electrons the emitted frequency is 400 times the input signal frequency. Therefore, 1000-Å input photons would emerge as 2.5-Å hard X-ray photons. Both linear and synchronous accelerators are capable of producing electrons with more than 1 GeV of energy so that even shorter wavelengths can be reached.

Of course, there are important questions which must be answered such as the net power out of such a laser, given state-of-the-art input intensities of electron beams and lasers. Pantell has determined that the net power scattered into a single mode, for an electron velocity v, is

$$P = \frac{c^2 r_0^2 (1 + v/c)}{4h\nu_1^2 \nu_2^2} I_1 I_2 E h\nu_2 \frac{d^2 N_e}{dE^2} \tag{22}$$

where r_0 is the classical electron radius (2.8×10^{-13} cm), I_1 and I_2 are the intensities of incident and stimulating radiation, E is the electron energy, and N_e is the electron density. The gain coefficient in per centimeter can be determined using the expression

$$\alpha = 0.7 r_0^2 \frac{E h\nu_2}{(\Delta E)^2} \lambda_1 \lambda_2^2 N_\nu N_e \tag{23}$$

where λ_2 is the wavelength of the emitted signal, N_ν is the photon density in the incident beam, and ΔE is the linewidth of the energy scatter of the electrons. Calculations by Molchanov [205] for a neodymium laser beam at 1.06 μm with a photon density N_ν of 1.8×10^{22} cm^{-3}, an electron voltage of 2 MeV, a $E/\Delta E$ of 10^5, and N_e of 2×10^{13} cm^{-3} (current density of 10^5 A/cm^2) indicate a gain of 2.2 cm^{-1} at a wavelength of about 220 Å. This is a relatively large gain and it is in the soft X-ray region. Shorter wavelengths could be generated by increasing the electron energy. If similar $E/\Delta E$ and N_e could be produced at 20 MeV, wavelengths of 2.2 Å would be produced but the gain would drop due to the λ_2^2 dependence. Hence the ability to go to short wavelengths by increasing the electron energy must be accompanied by the ability to produce greater electron or photon densities to generate significant gain.

G. Unresolved Experiments

1) Gain Experiments at University of Paris, Orsay: A group at the University of Paris at Orsay led by Jaeglé have recently reported [206] a measured net gain of 17 percent and a gain coefficient of 10 cm^{-1} in the dense portion of an expanding laser-produced aluminum plasma. The spectral line on which this gain was observed arises from a $2p^5 4d\ ^3P_1 \rightarrow 2p^6\ ^1S_0$ intercombination transition in the Al^{3+} neon-like ion. Two identical plasmas are created by splitting a single laser beam and the transmission of the second plasma to radiation (in a region assumed to be uniform) from the first is used to ascertain absorption and the reported gain. This last paper follows approximately four years of effort with progress documented in the references listed in [206]. Other supporting evidences given are the narrowness of this particular line and a significantly shorter duration of the emission from time-resolved spectral measurements. Net gain on other lines in this particular ion or in other ions has not been reported. No explanation for how the population inversion is achieved is offered in this paper, although it was previously suggested that a series of autoionizing transitions may be responsible [207].

An attempt to reproduce this experiment has been made by Valero [208] in a similar experiment but with a somewhat more powerful ruby laser. Valero reports results in essential agreement with Jaeglé *et al.*, but concludes from a comparison of relative intensities of Al^{3+} lines from various series members as well as lines from more highly stripped Al ions that the anomalies observed are due to high absorption of the "allowed" lines which have large absorption oscillator strengths, rather than net gain on the single line. Valero also disputes evidence [207] of autoionizing transitions and presents evidence of lines from different ions as an alternative explanation of some of the observed structure.

McGuire [177] has also challenged the Jaeglé *et al.* results and suggests that the $4d\,^3P$ upper level may be overpopulated in the second plasma by Auger transitions, following inner-shell vacancies created by X-radiation from the first plasma (See Section III-C). Most recently, Silfvast *et al.* [209] have criticized the conclusions of the Orsay group and the two plasma technique of gain measurement in general. They also explain the reported results with an opacity model.

2) Experiments at Texas Tech University: In recent articles, Das Gupta at Texas Tech University has presented a number of observations which could possibly imply an association with coherent X-ray emission [210], [211]. These experimental observations include a nonlinear increase in intensity with excitation current, and a narrowing of X-ray lines from a microfocus X-ray tube [210]. However, any interpretation of these results as an indication of lasing would appear to contradict the basic requirements for X-ray lasers as presently understood. More recent experiments using a Van de Graff accelerator with cylindrical bore targets yielded nondivergent discrete X-ray emission [211]. Das Gupta's model of parametric coupling between photons and electrons, suggested as an explanation, has been scrutinized very carefully by two groups [212], [213], who conclude that Das Gupta's observations can be explained on the basis of instrumental effects. In repeated experiments [213], [214], the discrete frequencies reported by Das Gupta are not observed. It appears that there is little reason for X-ray laser enthusiasm in the results reported by Das Gupta unless a more substantial understanding and support of these results is offered.

3) $CuSO_4$ Experiment at University of Utah: The existence of coherent hard X-rays from a laser-heated gelatin doped with $CuSO_4$ was reported by Kepros *et al.* at the University of Utah in 1972 [215]. The report generated a flurry of interest and activity. The main evidence on which the conclusion was drawn was the observation of clustered small (~100 μm) spots on X-ray films placed at distances of 30 to 110 cm along the axis of the 10 mm by 0.1-mm portion of the gelatin that was irradiated. Ionization chamber (electrometer) results indicated a preferred axial emission of up to 10^5 photons per burst. These findings, which supported the film data, were reported in private conversations [216], [217] and added to the interest in the effect. No wavelengths were measured, but the association with X-ray emission was inferred by the apparent transmission through aluminum and paper shielding surrounding the film.

An attempt to reproduce the results at the U.S. Naval Research Laboratory, where a similar laser was available, indicated at first that indeed such spots with some degree of localization could be present in coincidence on multiple films on about 10 percent of the shots [218]. However, in continued experiments with the use of "active" X-ray detectors (capable of counting photons) did not produce any X-rays, and thus disassociated the film anomalies with X-ray emission [219]. No other source of X-rays associated with the laser or the experiment was found. A more recent report [220] from the University of Sofia also describes the observation of 90–130-μm film spots with up to 90 percent reproducibility; however no attempt at auxiliary X-ray detection is reported. Other attempts [221] at corroborating the X-ray emission reported by the Utah group proved negative, including one so-far unpublished study [222] by an independent team assembled by the University of Utah using the original apparatus. The original researchers have not extended their measurements and the electrometer results have never been published.

Following a visit to the University of Utah during which he exposed a number of multiple-film film packs to the "X-ray laser," Boster reported [223] the presence of a number of small features on the films and associated these with a triboelectric effect caused by improper handling of the films, i.e., independent of the laser/gelatin experiment. Boster's explanation is not entirely satisfactory, because the effects have not been duplicated at the U.S. Naval Research Laboratory or elsewhere [224] even when Boster's prescription for "mishandling" was followed exactly.

Developing a theoretical mechanism to explain population inversion in this experiment proved extremely difficult from the beginning and required complete absorption and concentration of the available laser energy (by some unknown mechanism) into a filament of about 1-μm diameter. (Indeed, the amount of absorption was found [219] to be ~30 percent and, furthermore, independent of the presence of $CuSO_4$ in the gelatin.) Kepros [225] recently attempted to explain his original results with a partially stripped model and higher peak powers. Billman and Mark [217] offered a nonlasing explanation for the presence of any collimated X-rays that may have been observed at the University of Utah. Their explanation is based upon a model of a transmitting and collimating channel created in the gelatin by the incident laser beam.

To summarize this experiment, it must be concluded that, whatever may have been the cause of the observed film effects, the absence of any further evidence of X-ray emission with the most sensitive detectors available precludes further credibility to the original claim of coherent hard X-ray emission. Credit should be given to the originality demonstrated in the approach which may someday prove interesting, particularly with more powerful lasers.

IV. Production and Detection of Gain

A. Pumping Sources

At present, two sources are given serious consideration for pumping X-ray transitions: 1) laser beams, particularly the very short pulsewidth, mode-locked picosecond beams; and 2) high energy electron beams and recently associated ion beams. All of these sources have their advantages and weaknesses. By mode-locking, Nd^{3+} laser beams can be made to have pulsewidths of $\sim 10^{-12}$ s and they can be focused to small volumes with high irradiance. However, the photon energy is too small to pump X-ray transitions directly, and they must be used either to transfer electrons from an excited metastable level, to heat electrons in a plasma with subsequent electron-collisional pumping, or to produce X-rays (again from a laser-heated plasma) which will in turn pump an X-ray laser transition. Short pulse lasers have low overall efficiency (not a primary problem for initial X-ray laser research), are power and energy limited, and are somewhat difficult to adapt to a traveling-wave pumping geometry (Section IV-A-2-b). Gain lengths tend to be restricted to about one centimeter and the ramifications of this are analyzed below. More efficient CO_2 lasers do exist having comparable energy, but the pulse widths are limited to $\sim 10^{-9}$ s at present and the photon energy is lower by a factor-of-ten. High current electron (and ion) beams are also limited to pulsewidths of about 10^{-9} s; they have high efficiency, high energy, and appear adaptable to a traveling-wave transverse pumping geometry. They produce large fluxes of high energy particles which can be converted to photons by colliding the particles with a target. A very severe additional limitation for charged particle beams comes in focusing against space-charge effects to produce a high flux in a very small volume.

1) Short Pulsed Lasers: The process of mode-locking to produce extremely short optical pulses has been reviewed thoroughly by both DeMaria *et al.* [226] and Smith [227]. Pulses with a length of 10^{-12} s can be generated at 1.06 μm using the broad bandwidth of Nd^{3+} in glass or yttrium aluminum garnet (YAG). When amplified, these narrow pulses can reach peak powers of more than 10^{12} W. Except when used for transfer pumping from an excited metastable level (Lebedev Institute, Moscow), the low photon energy of these pulses prevents direct pumping of X-ray transitions; however, several indirect methods are being actively pursued.

a) Electron heating and relaxation: This concept utilizes a high power laser pulse to generate a highly ionized plasma and either directly produces a population inversion by preferential excitation of an X-ray transition by a high energy electron component of the plasma (being done at the University of Rochester) or generate an inversion during the relaxation and expansion period following either electron-ion recombination (being done at Lawrence Livermore Laboratory, University of Rochester, Culham Laboratory, University of Hull) or ion–atom charge transfer (being done at U.S. Naval Research Laboratory).

b) Synchronized double pulse excitation: If a highly ionized plasma can be prepared just in advance of the arrival of an intense picosecond laser pulse, then the picosecond pulse may be useful in quickly heating plasma electrons which in turn will excite the already existing ions to large population inversions prior to equilibration. Lasing would occur when sufficient ions become excited for the ASE conditions to be met. The density must be sufficient for the laser beam to be absorbed, but not so high that collisional rates dominate.

c) Laser-plasma X-rays: An alternative method of pumping X-ray transitions is to use the high-power laser pulse to vaporize and heat a target material to generate plasma X-rays. These X-rays fall onto a nearby material and optically pump energy levels to inverted populations. Silfvast and Wood [228] have demonstrated this technique at longer wavelengths by using the plasma generated by a CO_2 laser to pump a near-UV dye laser. There has been considerable work done to study the radiation emitted from laser plasmas in the X-ray region, and the conversion of laser radiation to X radiation has good efficiency. With this background it may be possible to pick target materials that have sufficient emission in either the rather narrow photoionization or the discrete line photoexcitation absorption bands of the X-ray transition selected for lasing. Photoionization pumping is pursued at Battelle and Sandia Laboratories.

d) Laser Compression Techniques: Because the power densities required to produce X-ray lasers are similar to those required for laser fusion, there is a strong technology overlap between these programs. Therefore, there is activity in X-ray lasers at such laser-fusion laboratories as Lawrence Livermore Laboratory, the U.S. Naval Research Laboratory, the University of Rochester, and Battelle. For example, Chapline and Wood [123] at Lawrence Livermore Laboratories have proposed to conduct X-ray laser experiments which make use of the compressive force of numerous laser beams aimed to uniformly irradiate a cylinder and to attain inversion densities greater than the density of solids. This traveling-wave compression concept is an extremely complex one. Not only must the irradiation be radially uniform for high compression, but there is the added difficulty that the amplified X-ray pulse velocity will be gain dependent. This added dependency will require uniform inversion density in the axial direction in order to maintain the velocity matching of the X-ray pulse and the excitational compression wave. In short, this method may encounter severe practical difficulties in addition to those common to laser-fusion compression.

2) Electric Discharge Lasers:

a) Advantages: Electric discharge lasers are conceptually simple and have the advantage that electrically stored pumping energy is transferred directly and efficiently to gases at relatively low pressures in short path lengths, due to the short mean free path Λ_{ci} for collisional ionization processes of cross section σ_{ci}, i.e., $\Lambda_{ci} = (\sigma_{ci} N_0)^{-1} \sim 10^{13}/N_0$ for N_0 in cm^{-3}. Low densities are an advantage for lasers pumped by electron collisions (Section III), but longer lengths are required for gain coefficients exceeding threshold [105]. When the required lasant length exceeds $c\tau_p$ where τ_p is the laser pump time, the pumping of the lasant must be axially synchronized with the growth of the beam; hence the need for traveling-wave pumping. Such pumping is most appropriate for transverse electrical discharge devices and has been successfully applied to molecular (see Section I) as well as ionic C^{3+} [140] lasants. Hence its present use at the U.S. Naval Research Laboratory for the investigation of electron-collisionally excited ionic lasers.

b) Traveling-wave pumping: The short lifetimes of X-ray transitions usually places a restriction on the amount of amplification that can be produced by a given population inversion density. For example in a material in which gain lasts only 10^{-15} s a pulse can only be amplified for a distance of 3×10^{-5} cm. Also, the inversion density required to reach threshold approaches the density of a solid. Producing such densities is very difficult; they might occur only in compressed laser plasmas. These inversion density problems can be eased considerably if the region of gain can be made to travel in synchronism with the pulse to be amplified. This scheme is called traveling-wave pumping and it contains several advantages. First, the entire volume does not have to be pumped at one instant; the pumping energy delivered to the material can be spread over time and space. Secondly, a unidirectional output beam is acquired with no mirrors, so that the intensity within the laser material is not higher than the output emission. Thirdly, this method of excitation is suitable for the production of long gain paths, so that the critical length for ASE can be met, at least in principle, for low inversion densities. Traveling-wave discharge techniques have already been used successfully to produce high-power unidirectional emission from nitrogen [4] and hydrogen [15], [10]–[12], [229] molecules. The traveling wave was produced in a flat-plate transmission line by a series of synchronous fast-closing dielectric switches. This resulted in a fast-rising high voltage transverse traveling-wave discharge which excited the molecules. Since the closing interval of the dielectric switches can be varied, the velocity of the traveling-wave can be adjusted to match the velocity of the optical pulse.

The value of the traveling-wave approach for X-ray lasers has been appreciated, but it has somewhat simplistically been assumed that synchronous traveling-wave excitation could be produced with optical or electron beams by simply phasing several beams or by inclining the material at an appropriate angle to the beam. This approach must be taken with extreme caution. Casperson and Yariv [230] have shown that the velocity of a pulse being amplified is a function of the gain and less than c. If the gain is uniform, then a simple inclination of the target can produce a traveling-wave excitation that stays in phase with the pulse being amplified. If the gain is not uniform, the problem becomes far more difficult and at least some of the gain will not be usable. Consider a pumping laser beam of circular cross section with a Gaussian radial intensity distribution, focused by a cylindrical lens to irradiate and excite a linear length of material. The focal line could have a hot spot in the center with a continuous fall off toward each end. Since the gain would vary in direct relation to the intensity distribution, the propagation velocity would vary greatly also and no one angle would produce amplification over the entire length. Even if the beam had radial uniformity of intensity, the focusing of the cylindrical lens may not produce uniform gain. The idea of phasing many laser beams on a cylinder [231] to compress a material to the necessary inversion density will be plagued by the nonuniform gain that these focused beams will produce. For gain at very short wavelengths the excitation wave and the pulse being amplified must not separate more than 3×10^{-5} cm. The focusing of many high power laser beams onto a cylinder to maintain uniformity on such small spatial dimensions is an extremely difficult practical problem.

In spite of the cautions pointed out above, it may indeed be possible to use traveling-wave pumping with laser excitation sources. To do so will require careful experimental design, where the parameters of the lasing medium must be known and uniform and where the intensity of the line focus of the laser has also been designed to be uniform. These conditions are not trival for lasers. It may even be easier to adapt electron beams or discharges to the traveling-wave configuration as described below.

3) Electron Beam Systems: During the last ten years electron-beam technology has made dramatic strides forward [232]. From machines which previously emitted beams of only a few amperes, progress now places current capabilities at megamperes and voltages as high as 12 MeV for pulses in the 100-ns range. The energy storage to produce these intense beams is in the megajoule region. It is difficult to ignore these new machines for the production of shorter wavelength lasers. Already electron beams with pulses as short as 1 ns have been used to produce VUV lasers in the rare gases at high pressures and also in hydrogen (See Sections I and III). Electron beams have also been used to initiate the reactions which have led to high-power chemical lasers and to semiconductor lasers of small size. In addition, focused electron beams are being considered for use in the beam-pellet approach to fusion.

For short-wavelength laser research, electron beams coupled into lasants through boundaries such as thin foils offer the potential advantage of a shorter electron pump pulse risetime not limited by the collisional ionization time for discharge devices. To further implement this concept, a traveling-wave electron-beam adaptation of the discharge device described above was proposed [233] and a prototype of such a system is presently being tested on N_2 and H_2 at the U.S. Naval Research Laboratory. Once feasibility has been established, it is expected to be scalable to higher energies and more rapid operation than at present.

4) High Current Ion Beams: Recently new work in the generation of high current ion beams has been proposed and initial work carried out [184], [234]. Based on a rather simple modification to the relativistic electron beam machines already discussed above, the possibility of 10^5-A pulsed ion beams with energies of 0.5–10 MeV has been suggested by Sudan and Lovelace [184]. While the pulsewidth and focusing limitations remain, they discuss the usefulness of such beams for heating plasmas to fusion temperatures and in nuclear studies. It is also useful to speculate on the application of such beams to short-wavelength lasers. Some charge exchange experiments discussed previously consider the use of ion beams to produce excited populations. The primary difficulty in these charge exchange lasers, i.e., a lack of intense ion sources, may be eliminated when these new pulsed high-current ion beams are developed. It may be possible to develop high-intensity traveling-wave ion beams for lasers by applying the same diode modifications used above to the traveling-wave electron beam mentioned above [233]. High current ion beams should find numerous uses in the development of short wavelength lasers (see Section III-B).

5) Exploding Wires: High intensity X-ray emission can be produced when the diodes of electron-beam machines are shorted by very fine short wires. The wire is vaporized early in the discharge and its atoms reach extreme stages of ionization ($\lesssim 51$ times) over finite volumes, resulting in a copious flux of X-rays which could be used for pumping X-ray lasers. Making the assumption that the average temperature of the exploding wire plasma is the same as a 100-eV blackbody, Jones and Ali [175], [176] calculate that it may be possible to pump Na vapor (Section III-C) using exploding wires. One remaining question in assessing the practicality of exploding wire pumping is the risetime of the X-ray radiation. If it is as short as 0.1 ns (one tenth the electron beam machine's risetime), then the Jones and Ali calculations show that the gain would be sufficient for ASE operation. If the risetime is longer, then a more complicated experiment with some form of resonant cavity may be needed. The practical problem of designing this experiment is not one to be taken lightly. It is difficult to get lasing material close to the high-voltage wire, and equally as difficult to focus the X-rays at some distance. In another numerical analysis of this scheme, Bey considers what might happen if the pumping were accomplished in a traveling-wave fashion [174]. This model assumes that the risetime of the soft X-rays follows the risetime of the current and concludes that ASE would not occur unless the risetime were reduced to about 2.5 ns or that the intensity were increased by a factor-of-ten. Considering the difficulties of building an X-ray laser, these requirements for a 370-Å laser are not far beyond present capabilities.

B. Detection of Gain

1) Concepts: The importance of this subject can be underscored by pointing to a number of experiments already claiming the existence of very-short-wavelength laser emission and the even more numerous alternative explanations of these experiments without the existence of gain. The confusion already demonstrated over short wavelength lasers serves to demand that experimenters give irrefutable evidence of the existence of gain in the future. It is often necessary but *not* sufficient to infer lasing from small spots on film, narrowed lines, anomalously small absorption in a second medium, or nonlinear intensity effects alone. A definitive test for gain must be performed. In the belief that early X-ray lasers will likely be ASE devices, a significant portion of this paper has been devoted to the theory of these systems. This can now be drawn upon to give some guidelines for determining the presence of gain.

In many experiments the detection of gain is complicated by the fact that its existence lasts for a very short period of time—as short as 10^{-15} s! This short burst of radiation may come somewhere early in a plasma radiation process lasting nanoseconds or longer, and may not be resolvable with present techniques. In addition, many of the characteristics of lasers with resonant cavities will not exist for noncavity ASE lasers. If gain exists however, it will amplify a signal exponentially as a function of its length unless it has saturated due to the intensity of the signal. Therefore, a good test for gain is to vary the length and observe the intensity of the line in question. If the strength of the signal is such that saturation is occurring, then the length should be reduced until an exponential dependence is observed. The gain coefficient is obtained in this manner, of course. This method for determining gain requires that the amplifying region is defined, of finite length, homogeneous, and controllable. In some experiments that have been proposed it may be difficult to determine where the amplifying region may be located, as well as the extent and uniformity, and it may be impossible to vary only the length of the gain region. If this is the case, then experimental verification of laser action becomes very difficult.

The comparison of axial and transverse emission is a valid test for axial stimulated amplification, providing again that sufficient time resolution is available to discriminate against spontaneous emission of longer duration.

Other methods of verifying gain are difficult to use with ASE systems. Line width and beam divergence are sometimes considered good indicators of gain, but their behavior is somewhat complicated as shown in Section I-B. If length can be varied, then the intricacies of the line width can be used as support for claims of gain. For example, Jaeglé *et al.* [206] claim that several soft X-ray lines are narrowed due to amplification in a two-laser-plasma experiment. While the calculations of Allen and Peters support the existence of a line width minimum just above threshold [85], additional data, both with more amplifying plasma and without a second plasma, would put this claim of line narrowing in better perspective.

D. Detectors

There are numerous techniques for detection of X-ray emission. Photographic film is available for both the vacuum ultraviolet and X-ray regions and is invaluable for recording images and large quantities of spectral data with limited ($\gtrsim$ 1-μs shuttered) time resolution. Electronic photodetectors such as photomultipliers, photodiodes, ionization chamber tubes, and semiconductor tubes are all responsive to X-ray radiation either directly or through the use of fluorescent scintillators, but the time response of these detectors is limited to no better than a few tenths of a nanosecond. In addition, no oscilloscopes are available with risetime much faster than a few tenths of a nanosecond, so that conventional methods of observation are not available if very short X-ray laser pulses are produced. While some sampling techniques exist [235], a more useful device, a picosecond X-ray streak camera, has recently been developed [236]. The operation of this streak camera is sufficiently important for further discussion.

In general, the X-ray streak camera utilizes the image converter tube in which photons incident on a photocathode liberate electrons which in turn are focused onto a phosphor to reproduce the image falling on the photocathode. While the electrons are in transit, they can be deflected to move the image across the output phosphor producing a streaked image. This image can be increased in brightness by using stages of image intensifier tubes behind the streak tube until sufficient brightness for photographic recording exists. Actually these techniques have been used for some time to make picosecond cameras for infrared laser pulse measurement. The important development which allowed X-ray operation was the construction of a stable X-ray-sensitive photocathode. In one design, the cathode is made by depositing 100 Å of gold on the back of an 8-μm thick beryllium vacuum window [236]. X-ray photons in the 1–10-keV (12–1.2-Å) range are able to penetrate the beryllium foil and liberate electrons. The maximum time resolution, limited by the transit time dispersion, is presently about 50 ps. Other cameras, designed to be operated entirely in a vacuum environment, use only a gold cathode without a window and are usually attached directly to a vacuum spectrograph for VUV and soft X-ray detection purposes.

V. Nonlinear Short-Wavelength Techniques

While most of this paper deals with techniques for the direct production of VUV and X-ray emission, it would not be complete without the inclusion of the new and promising techniques for converting high-power infrared and visible signals into the VUV and X-ray regions by using nonlinear optical techniques. Some of the attractive features of pulses obtained by the nonlinear techniques are that the pulses maintain the temporal and spatial characteristics of the original infrared pulses and that tunability is sometimes possible. An infrared pulse at 1.06 μm having a width of 30 ps and a good beam divergence can emerge after the nonlinear stages as a 1773, 1182, or 887-Å pulse still possessing good beam quality and still 30 ps wide. In addition to the discrete frequencies avail-

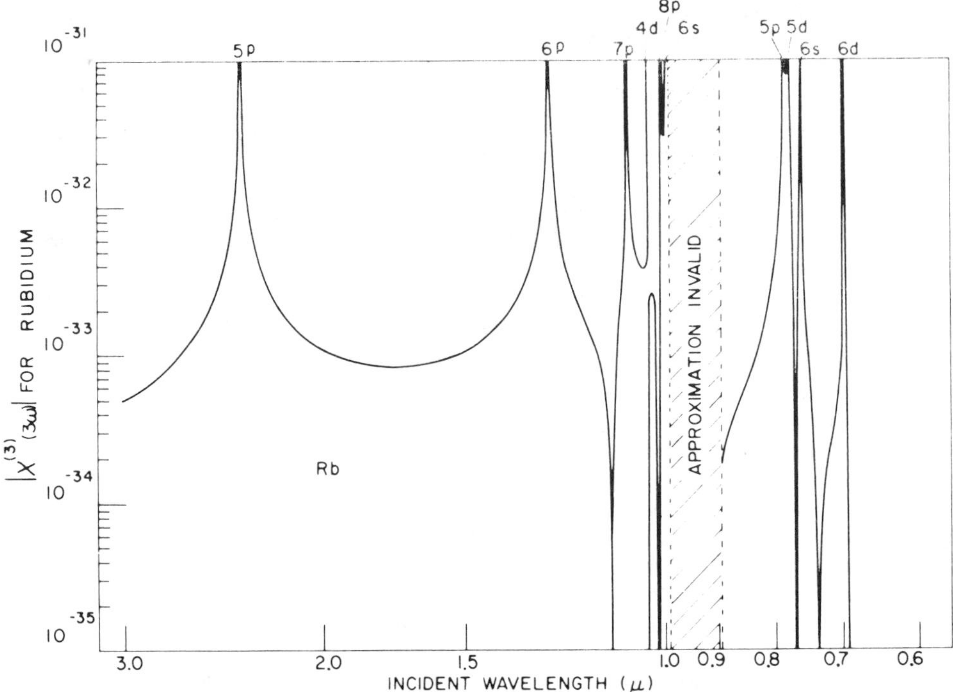

Fig. 21. Nonlinear susceptibility of rubidium as a function of wavelength [240].

able from harmonic generation, other non-linear mixing techniques are also available which allow the mixing and summing of tunable laser frequencies to produce tunable output signals in the VUV. The possibility of extending these techniques to produce soft X-rays appears real and the fundamental concepts have already been explored.

A. Third Harmonic Generation

Under the influence of extremely intense optical fields the polarization of a material becomes a nonlinear function of the electric field, i.e.,

$$P = \epsilon_0(\chi^{(1)}E + \chi^{(2)}E^2 + \chi^{(3)}E^3 + \cdots) \tag{24}$$

where ϵ_0 is the permittivity of free space and $\chi^{(1)}$ is the linear, and $\chi^{(2)}$, $\chi^{(3)}$ are the nonlinear components of the susceptibility. The polarization becomes a source term in the wave equation and the nonlinear components give rise to harmonic frequencies. The amplitude of the harmonics depends upon the magnitude of the nonlinear susceptibility terms. Second harmonic generation is possible in crystals which possess no inversion symmetry, but for the generation of short wavelengths, such crystals with useful VUV transmission are difficult to find. The transmission problem is even more severe in liquids. Gases possess the required transmission and have the added advantage of being self-repairable at damaging laser intensities, but the lack of asymmetry requires the generation of third (or higher odd) harmonic frequencies [237].

Harris and Miles [238] were the first to propose third harmonic generation in metal vapors. The third harmonic susceptibility term as given by Armstrong *et al.* [239] is given as

$$\chi(3\omega,\omega,\omega,\omega) = (e^4/\hbar^3)\sum_{ijk} A_{ijk} Z_{gi} Z_{ij} Z_{jk} Z_{kg} \text{ (ESU)} \tag{25}$$

where the A_{ijk} are frequency-dependent coefficients with resonant denominators at $(\omega_{gp} - \omega)$, $(\omega_{gp} - 2\omega)$, and $(\omega_{gp} - 3\omega)$, where ω is the fundamental laser frequency, ω_{gp} corresponds to atomic transition frequencies to ground, and the Z terms are the dipole matrix elements. Harris and Miles recognized that by operating near the atomic resonances the susceptibility could be significantly increased. Calculations of third-order susceptibility for the alkali metal vapors have been carried out by Miles and Harris [240] as a function of wavelength. A typical graph for Rb is shown in Fig. 21.

Miles and Harris also calculate the conversion efficiency, the ratio of third $P^{(3)}$ to first $P^{(1)}$ harmonic power, in terms of a factor I which accounts for focusing and dispersion, the alkali atom density N in atoms/cm^3, the nonlinear coefficient $\chi^{(3)}$ in ESU, and the incident wavelength λ in centimeters. The conversion efficiency becomes

$$\frac{P^{(3)}}{P^{(1)}} = \frac{8.215 \times 10^{-2}}{\lambda^4} N^2 [\chi^{(3)}]^2 |I|^2 [P^{(1)}]^2. \tag{26}$$

Under the focusing conditions where the confocal beam parameter b, is much greater than the length L of the vapor cell, the I^2 term reduces to $(4L^2/b^2)\,\text{sinc}^2(\Delta kL/2)$ where the wave vector mismatch $\Delta k = (6\pi/\lambda)(n_3 - n_1)$. In order to take advantage of the length of the cell, the index of refraction n_3 at 3ω must equal the index of refraction n_1 at ω. This is the condition of phase matching. Phase matching in gas vapors can be accomplished by adding an additional gas with opposite dispersion to the metal vapor. This technique is similar to the technique demonstrated by Bey *et al.* [241] in liquids. The addition of Xe to the alkali atoms would enable phase matching to be achieved according to the calculations of Harris and Miles [238].

The experimental verification of the proposed third harmonic generation in Rb vapor was reported by Young *et al.* [242]. This experiment was performed with 100-kW Q-switched pulses at 1.064 μm. At a Rb temperature of 262°C and a Xe : Rb ratio of 412 : 1, phase matching was accomplished

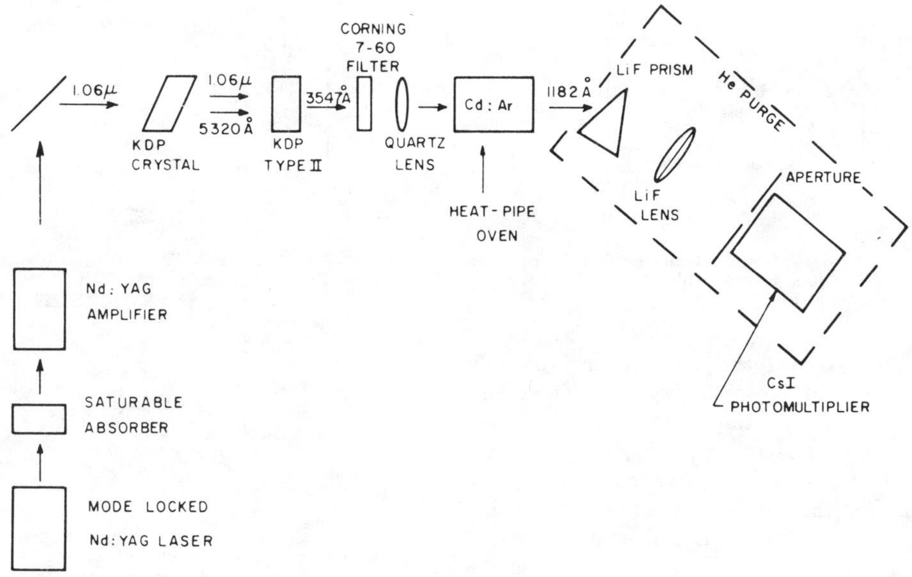

Fig. 22. The experimental apparatus used by Kung *et al.* to generate VUV wavelengths by up-conversion [243].

TABLE III

SUMMARY OF VUV HARMONIC GENERATION EXPERIMENTS VIA CD VAPOR [243]

Input Wavelengths (Å)	Generated Wavelength (Å)	Coherence Length at 10^{17} atom/cm^3 (cm)	Phase-Matching Ratio $N_{Cd}:N_{Ar}$	Energy Conversion Efficiency	$\chi^{(3)}$ (ESU/atom)
5320	1773	−0.57	1:25	10^{-4}	2×10^{-34}
2 × 3547 + 10640	1520	−0.23	1:15	10^{-6}	2×10^{-33}
3547	1182	. . .	1:2.5	10^{-7}	. . .

in the 19-cm long Rb cell, resulting in an improved power of 33 times the non-phase-matched case or an output power of 0.1 mW at 3547 Å. Having demonstrated the process of phase-matched third harmonic generation, the technique was refined and extended into the VUV [243]. Cd vapor was employed for its negative dispersion and strong nonlinear susceptibility at VUV wavelengths. The experimental apparatus is shown in Fig. 22. This experiment uses the increased power of a mode-locked laser and amplifier which produced 50-ps pulses with a total peak power of 20 MW. A KDP crystal is used to double the frequency to 5320 Å with an efficiency of up to 80 percent. For portions of the experiment requiring 3547-Å radiation, a second type II phase-matched KDP crystal was used to sum the 1.064 μm with a 5320-Å radiation yielding 3547-Å radiation with an overall efficiency of about 10 percent. For tripling, the Cd vapor was contained in a heat-pipe to which argon was added in order to phase-match with the fundamental frequency.

Table III summarizes the three experiments which were performed. Energy conversion efficiency varies from 10^{-4} to 10^{-7}, but higher efficiencies may be expected from longer vapor cells and higher power densities, provided metal vapor absorption does not cause the process to saturate.

In more recent work, improved efficiencies were indeed accomplished by using a concentric double heat pipe to obtain higher vapor pressures, and longer cell length and by using greater power density [244], [245]. By using a 30-ps pulse of about 300 MW focused into the 40-cm double vapor heat pipe to produce power densities of 10^9–10^{10} W/cm^2 in a Rb:Xe mixture, a conversion efficiency of 10% has been achieved in the conversion of 1.064 μm to 3547-Å radiation. As yet there is no indication whether comparable improvements can be expected in the VUV up-conversion. Some improvement in the generation of 1182-Å radiation has been reported by Kung *et al.* [246] by using the negative dispersion and decreased absorption found in Xe by operating slightly above the frequency of the strong 1192-Å transition. By replacing the metal vapor cell of Fig. 22 with a Xe:Ar gas cell and by very tight focusing into the gas mixture to attain power densities of about 6.3×10^{12} W/cm^2, an optimum conversion efficiency of about 0.1 percent is obtained for the conversion of 3547-Å radiation to 1182-Å radiation. Further improvement to as much as 20-percent efficiency is predicted at higher input power levels if the theoretical model does not break down. The shortest wavelength (887 Å) was generated by these techniques by tripling the 2660-Å radiation obtained from twice doubling 1.064-μm radiation. The 887-Å radiation is obtained without phase matching in Ar gas and with an efficiency of only about 10^{-7}.

B. Tunable Coherent VUV Generation

Tunable VUV signals can be obtained by utilizing the general case of resonance enhancement of the nonlinear susceptibility. Since only two photons are necessary to achieve resonance in (25), the third photon has no constraint on its frequency and can be tunable. This was exploited by Hodgson

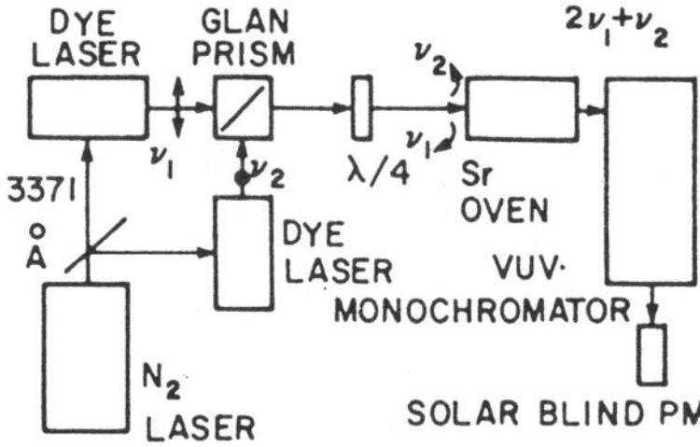

Fig. 23. Schematic of the apparatus used by Hodgson *et al.* to produce tunable VUV emission using Sr vapor [247].

et al. [247], who used two tunable dye lasers synchronously pumped by one N_2 laser as shown in Fig. 23. These two laser frequencies, ν_1 and ν_2, were tuned so that $2\nu_1$ coincided with a double-quantum allowed transition in Sr vapor. With ν_1 then fixed on the Sr resonance, ν_2 can be varied over a wide frequency range and the output of the Sr cell is the sum frequency, $2\nu_1 + \nu_2$. For the lasers used in this experiment the conversion efficiency from visible to VUV was on the order of 10^{-5}. Xe was added to the Sr vapor to phase match. Studies of the autoionizing levels of Sr were also conducted [248].

A very similar idea was also proposed by Harris and Bloom [249] using a dye laser and a parametric oscillator. The experiment was carried out by Bloom *et al.* [250] for the generation of near UV radiation and by Kung [251] for the generation of tunable picosecond VUV radiation. In the latter experiment, a 30-ps 1.064-μm pulse is doubled twice to produce the 2660-Å fourth-harmonic frequency. This radiation serves as an input to an ADP crystal with a controlled temperature which generates signal and idler frequencies. These signals are amplified further in a second ADP crystal and then tightly focused into a Xe cell. Using a combination of such third-order processes as sum generation, difference generation or third-harmonic generation, along with the different combinations of pump (2660 Å), and tunable signal idler frequencies, tunable radiation over the region from 1180 to 1946 Å can be observed. Sum generation is particularly sensitive to the conditions of focusing. These conditions have been treated in detail by Bjorklund [252]. Fig. 24 shows all the ranges over which tunability has been obtained.

To summarize, there are several closely related experimental techniques which have the potential of producing tunable VUV emission from 2000 Å to at least 1100 Å and probably much lower. In both the experiment of Hodgson *et al.* and Kung the conversion efficiency was low (10^{-7}) and the output power on the order of 1 W. It is likely that improvement in these figures will result in the future.

C. Possible Shorter Wavelengths

Because the nonlinear up-conversion process preserves the coherence of the original driving wavelength, there is an attractiveness to use the nonlinear process in generating soft X-rays. Two processes have been considered: 1) using higher harmonics, and 2) amplifying and using third-harmonic processes. Harris [253], [254] has proposed experimental processes using 5th, 7th, and 15th harmonics to reach as low as 169 Å. Li ions are proposed for the nonlinear generation in the soft X-ray region and tight focusing will be required. Table IV shows the proposed processes, the limiting power flux, and the theoretical efficiencies.

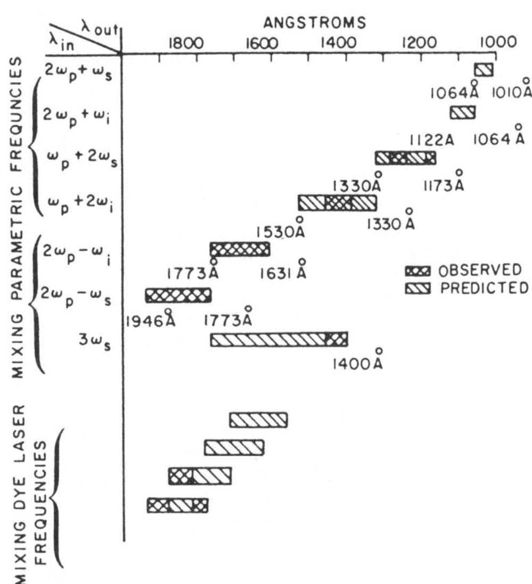

Fig. 24. The ranges of wavelength covered by the tuning methods described by Kung [243] using parametrically generated frequencies and by Hodgson *et al.* [247] using tunable dye laser frequencies.

TABLE IV
LIMITING POWER DENSITY AND CONVERSION EFFICIENCY FOR SOME HIGHER ORDER NONLINEAR PROCESSES [254]

Process	Specie	$(P/A)_{max}$ (W/cm^2)	Efficiency (percent)
5320 Å ÷ 3 → 1773 Å	Xe	1.9×10^{12}	0.08
5320 Å ÷ 5 → 1064 Å	Xe	1.9×10^{12}	0.05
1182 Å ÷ 5 → 236 Å	Li^+	1.7×10^{15}	0.002
1182 Å ÷ 7 → 169 Å	Li^+	1.7×10^{15}	0.004
2660 Å ÷ 15 → 177 Å	Li^+	3.5×10^{15}	4×10^{-7}

The second approach proposes the use of those existing VUV lasers as amplifiers for the up-converted pulses so that other stages of nonlinear generation can be used. For example, if a tunable picosecond pulse at 1161 Å could be amplified by the hydrogen laser, the tripling process could generate 387-Å radiation. The rare-gas molecule lasers could also be used as amplifiers. Nonlinear optical processes are likely to play a very important part in further short-wavelength laser development.

D. Nonlinear Techniques at X-Ray Frequencies

In anticipation of the development of X-ray lasers, Eisenberger and McCall [255], [256] worked out the theoretical details of the mixing of optical and X-ray photons and have observed X-ray parametric conversion using spontaneous X-ray photons. These techniques can be used to tune the frequency of X-ray lasers just as they are presently used for tuning in the visible. If sufficient X-ray laser intensity can be generated, efficient generation of tunable X-ray laser photons can be produced. It must be realized that the addition of optical photons and X-rays would not produce a very large change in the X-ray frequency. Other techniques which may be possible are the frequency down-conversion of two X-ray beams to produce visible radiation or the addition of two visible photons with one X-ray photon. Under ideal conditions it may even be possible to use these mixing techniques to assist in the detection of an X-ray laser pulse.

E. *Nonlinear Optics with Inelastic Collison Resonances*

In a recent paper [257], Harris and Lidow propose resonant energy coupling between atoms which is induced by photons and in which energy is conserved by optical photons instead of kinetic properties. In essence, resonant multiphoton absorption in one atom is followed by resonant coupling absorption for a second atom, with the associated transfer of excitation energy. Large effective cross sections are derived and examples are given.

VI. Applications

In most of the papers referenced to this point, there is only a sentence or two devoted to potential applications of VUV or X-ray laser beams (two exceptions are [186] and [258]). This reflects the general attitude in the scientific community that probably the most important applications of an X-ray laser beam will develop after a useful device has arrived and will depend to a significant extent upon the characteristic of the particular device that proves most feasible. For examples, a subpicosecond device could open up new areas in stop-motion radiography, while a highly coherent device will offer more promise for interferometric techniques. This attitude of invent-it-now apply-it-later is neither unreasonable nor unprecedented in the laser field, or for that matter in other fields such as solid state physics. Indeed, it would seem most unwise at this point to attempt to narrowly channel approaches toward very specific applications while many basic physical approaches to pumping of meaningful populations inversions are still being explored on a rather fundamental scale.

Nevertheless, it is helpful and useful to periodically assess the long range applications foreseen. An excellent example is the 1973 "pre CLEA" symposium and the summaries [178] which brought to focus the near term applications for materials analyses. Those applications requiring greater laser penetration (e.g., weapons) were placed in the more distant future with later-generation devices.

Some features associated with short-wavelength radiation from a source with laser characteristics are indicated in Fig. 25 as a function of wavelength λ and corresponding photon energy $h\nu$. The wavelength scale is also labeled with existing laser progress. It is interesting to note that progress in the last three years has mainly advanced by the optical mixing techniques (see Section V) from 1182 Å to 887 Å; this emphasizes the long road ahead if the X-ray region is to be reached systematically, as would seem most likely at present. The nuclear (γ-ray)/atomic (X-ray) interface at approximately 0.1 Å is anticipated by the short-wavelength Lyman-α limit for ionized heavy atoms. It will be recalled from Section II that the 10^4-times wavelength step indicated corresponds approximately to 10^{12} in gain and 10^{16} in pump power. Thus the quite natural turn to high power laser and electron beams under current development in other research areas (such as pellet fusion) for concentrated pump power sources. The interaction is expected to be bilateral; i.e., short-wavelength lasers may be necessary for both efficient heating and for diagnostics of the extremely high density ($\sim 10^{26}$ cm^{-3}) compressed plasmas associated with pellet fusion approaches, simply because of the more penetrating character of the radiation. This is illustrated at the top in Fig. 25, where the critical electron plasma densities are indicated; only shorter wavelengths will penetrate at each of these densities. Thus it becomes doubly clear why so much

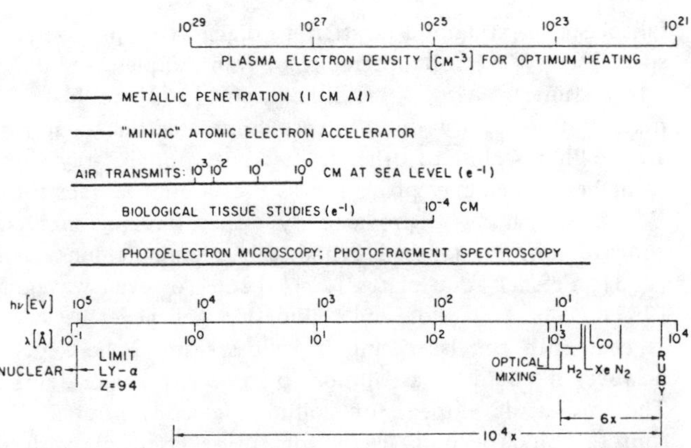

Fig. 25. Useful characteristics of a collimated and coherent laser beam at short wavelengths.

activity in short-wavelength laser research is done at laboratories also active in pellet-fusion programs.

A. *Propagation*

The long-wavelength applications indicated in Fig. 25 involve surface-photon-produced effects requiring low penetration [259]. Spectroscopy from surfaces can illuminate features without the damage of penetrating beams. Cancer research may benefit here, for example. Penetration of thin biological membranes begins on a useful scale at about 100 Å. A short burst of intense directional soft radiation could advance this area of research where higher photon energy radiation would neither provide contrast in thin samples nor time resolution for stop-motion studies.

Between 1 and 10 Å the atmosphere transmits at the $1/e$ level for various distances as indicated in Fig. 25. Here one can begin to consider X-ray microscopy on living tissue without a vacuum environment. At 1 Å, absorption (mainly due to photoionization) takes place in about 10. m of path, unless burn-through at high flux levels by nonlinear effects can be invoked to enhance the transmission [260]. For the near term then, it is indeed appropriate to consider applications that either require short paths or else can function in a laboratory vacuum or extraterrestrial environment of low absorption.

At the shorter wavelengths in Fig. 25, penetration of solid materials will become possible with more selectivity and with a more specific interaction than an electron beam, thereby creating a lower background level. The fascinating "miniac" [261] miniature electron accelerator, operating in crystals on discrete impulses from metastable atomic states and on atomic-length scales, would deserve more serious consideration. This has been proposed as a 1-cm version of the two mile Stanford linear accelerator (SLAC) in the rather far-off world of microminiaturization. A coherent pump source of penetrating radiation, such as afforded by the X-ray laser, is required. Also, the generation and manipulation of damaging dislocations in crystals can be considered [178].

B. *Collimation*

Many of these applications, given very broad-brush treatment here, require the intense, collimated characteristics of an ASE device. This will be the most likely first generation "laser" produced in the soft X-ray region. Into this category fall plasma heating and (scattering) diagnostics, photoelectron spectroscopy, microphotography of thin samples, and damage effect studies. Also, X-ray lithography [262] could become much more useful with an intense collimated beam. It can be argued that scaling of other more conventional X-ray sources to higher power may prove just as useful and perhaps sooner. Collimation may be provided by either (grazing incidence) concave mirrors, tapered cylindrical grazing-incidence lenses [263], Fresnel zone plates [264]-[266] or even waveguides [267]. The collection and collimation will never be as great as that with the laser, and huge losses are to be expected; however it could be a solution to some immediate demands. The optics developed for collimating conventional X-ray sources could become useful for future laser cavity designs when the requirements are better formulated for the most promising laser approaches.

C. Short Pulse

An X-ray laser operating in the subnanosecond (to femtosecond) region could immediately surpass the time-resolving capabilities of any conventional X-ray source foreseen. This would come about by the rapid self-terminating nature of the laser. A time resolution on such scales is not even envisioned as a need at present, except in the pellet fusion area where measurements of changes in plasma parameters on picosecond time scales are desired. Flash radiography of crystal motions under shocked conditions is another application [178]. Also relaxation and fluorescence studies could be extended.

D. Coherence

One of the most important characteristics of any laser is the coherence quality of the beam. Without resonant cavities ASE devices may indeed be limited in coherence. Thus the nonlinear optical frequency multiplication techniques are important for transferring coherence to the short wavelength region and can be used in parallel with efforts to develop amplifiers to recover the power lost in the nonlinear mixing devices. Coherence will be vital to the miniature accelerator idea. Furthermore, it may allow stop-motion holographic microscopy and image projection with sufficient penetration for pellet fusion plasmas, biological specimens, large and complex molecules and other materials. While there is some debate at present as to the degree of resolution possible, already Fraunhofer far-field holography of <1.0-μm spheres (approaching virus size [178]) with a single beam of 12-ps duration has been accomplished at 1182 Å with a frequency up-converted beam. Also, a holographic grating with 826-Å spacings has been produced and analyzed (Fig. 26) [254], [268]. Holograms obtained with VUV wavelengths and reconstructed with visible laser light offer the promise of enlargement according to the wavelength ratio of the two beams [268]. Phase contrast microscopy, though difficult, could improve contrast for objects with slight variations in index of refraction ($n \lesssim 1$) for radiation [178]. Such advanced investigations are most appropriate as coherent beams become available at decreasing wavelengths, even though the power available will be low at the outset.

E. Monochromaticity

Most "conventional" high emittance X-ray sources such as produced by pulsed relativistic electron beams, vacuum sparks, exploding wires, etc., radiate as continuum and/or multiline sources. Discrete-line sources or the ultilization of dispersing elements result in greatly reduced emission levels. An X-ray laser would emit intense monochromatic emission which could be well focused for good resolution without chromatic aberrations (e.g., with a Fresnel lens). Also, such applications as crystal topography which depend on Bragg diffraction could benefit by a monochromatic beam of short duration for dislocation tracing on a temporal basis.

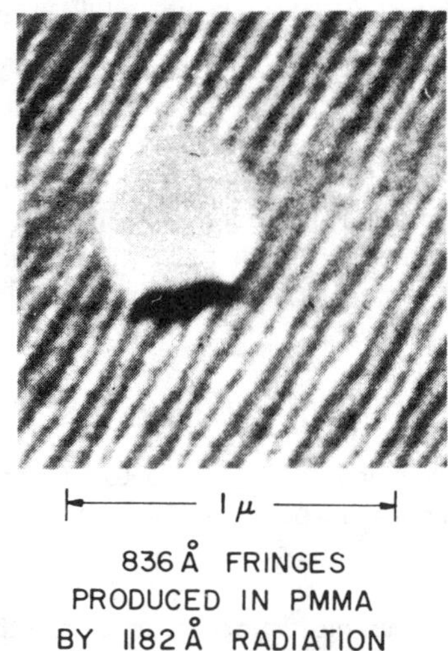

1 μ
836 Å FRINGES
PRODUCED IN PMMA
BY 1182 Å RADIATION

Fig. 26. Fringes produced in polymethyl methacrylate (PMMA) at 836-Å spacing and analyzed with a scanning electron microscope. The round object is a 0.5-μm latex sphere placed after development for magnification calibration [268].

VII. Prognosis and Summary

The recent interest and activity in short-wavelength laser research is chronologically illustrated in Fig. 27, compiled from those references in the present article pertaining directly to X-ray laser schemes. A rather sudden upturn in activity beginning in 1970 can be associated with a number of factors, including the attention given to high-intensity pump source development for the pellet fusion programs. This pumping requirement was already identified in the 1960's as a prerequisite for serious X-ray laser research, but could be justified only on the scale required by the potential payoff of fusion power. Added to this is the impetus given by the apparent quick success at the University of Utah [215]; the momentum generated by the controversy surrounding this experiment still can be felt. Much of the activity during the period immediately following the Utah activity could be considered a positive contribution of the bold efforts of this group. The period of peak activity around 1973-1974 may be largely attributed to an abundance of activity and advancements in specific areas (such as the recombination and molecular excimer approaches) which will probably level off as various groups pursue these approaches to further development. At this point the most promising schemes are identified, in general terms at least, and advances in the near future will be more methodical. Some areas, such as the efficient use of metastable levels for the temporary storage of populations at excited energies and the efficient coupling of strong line radiation for preferential pumping of specific levels will probably be advanced soon for more efficient pumping with available power sources. Large cross-section reactions such as resonance charge transfer will continue to attract the attention deserved

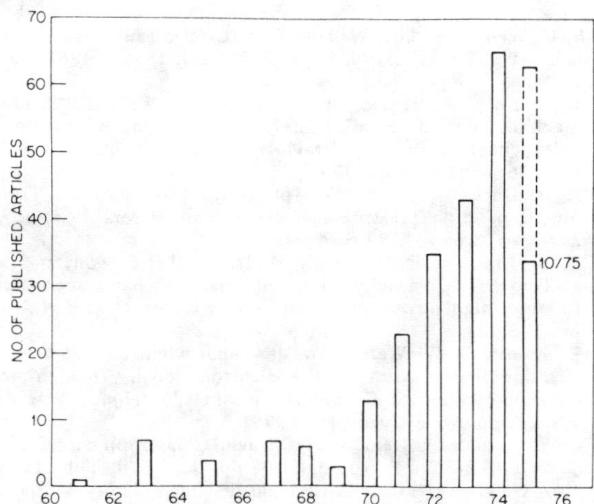

Fig. 27. Record of activity in short-wavelength laser research as compiled from the reference on this topic in the present review. The data for 1975 are as of October and still incomplete, particularly for those articles not yet translated.

for promising high pumping efficiency. Coherence is recognized as a necessary characteristic of an X-ray laser beam, and efforts to extend frequency up-conversion of coherent beams using nonlinear mixing in vapors and plasmas will undoubtedly be vigorously pursued since these processes are independent of the development of high-power pump sources. The necessary power at short wavelengths for stimulating additional nonlinear processes may come either through amplification by ASE devices or through increased initial energy and pulse compression techniques. Coherence with cavities at short wavelengths may also be advanced by the development of X-ray optics for other more immediate sources.

It is important to further develop the tunable nature of VUV and X-ray lasers both for reaching atomic resonances in nonlinear devices and for providing the transfer lasers required for pumping (over relatively narrow energy gaps) of metastable "storage" levels. For example, it may be necessary to couple a tunable VUV laser in the 1700-Å region with a Xe excimer amplifier to provide sufficient power to transfer-pump a He-like ion, such as O^{6+} from a metastable state to an allowed decay state. This could then lead to ASE amplification of another up-converted beam in the soft X-ray region. This example illustrates one way in which the interplay of the various presently considered approaches could work together in the not-too-distant future to produce a useful coherent soft X-ray laser beam.

In summary, progress in short-wavelength laser research has been most impressive in identifying reasonable approaches to follow consistent with the development of increasingly powerful pumping sources. Advancements in nonlinear mixing and their initial application are impressive. Population inversions in plasmas following recombination have been reported by two groups [98], [99]. We can look forward in the next few years to advancements in both the generation of coherent beams at shorter wavelengths by up-conversion and the achievment of population inversion by direct methods in experiments leading to significant amplification at short VUV and soft X-ray wavelengths. The advances will result from clever and diligent pursuit of experiments using refined pump sources and further careful analysis of the fundamental ideas given here.

Acknowledgment

It is a pleasure to acknowledge the initial encouragement and organizational efforts of R. A. Andrews; only the obligations associated with his leave from the Naval Research Laboratory during the period of preparation prevented his valuable contribution to this review. We are also indebted to L. J. Palumbo for permission to present his unpublished data on electron collisional pumping.

References

[1] H. G. Heard, "Ultraviolet gas laser at room temperature," *Nature*, vol. 200, p. 667, 16 Nov. 1963.

[2] D. A. Leonard, "Saturation of the molecular nitrogen second positive laser transition," *Appl. Phys. Lett.*, vol. 7, pp. 4-6, 1 July 1965.

[3] E. T. Gerry, "Pulsed-molecular-nitrogen laser theory," *Appl. Phys. Lett.*, vol. 7, pp. 6-8, 1 July 1965.

[4] J. D. Shipman, Jr., "Traveling wave excitation of high power gas lasers," *Appl. Phys. Lett.*, vol. 10, pp. 3-4, Jan. 1967.

[5] J. P. Girardeau-Montaut, M. Roumy, J. Hamelin, and L. Avan, "Realisation d'un amplificateur laser d'une puissance atteignant 50 MW a 3371 Å dans l'azote moléculaire," *C. R. Acad. Sc. Paris*, t. 274, pp. 607-610, 28 Feb. 1972.

[6] R. W. Dreyfus and R. T. Hodgson, "Electron-beam excitation of the nitrogen laser," *Appl. Phys. Lett.*, vol. 20, pp. 195-197, Mar. 1972. See also M. Clerc and M. Schmidt, "Emissions stimulées des systémes premier et deuxième postifs de N_2, produites par radiolyse impulsionnelle," *C. R. Acad. Sci. B.*, t. 272, pp. 668-671, Mar. 15, 1971.

[7] E. L. Patterson, J. B. Gerardo, and A. W. Johnson, "Intense-electron-beam excitation of the 3371 Å N_2 laser system," *Appl. Phys. Lett.*, vol. 21, pp. 293-295, 15 Sept. 1972.

[8] P. A. Bazhulin, I. N. Knyazev, and G. G. Petrash, "On the possibility of stimulated emission in the far ultraviolet," *Sov. Phys.–JETP*, vol. 23, pp. 649-650, Sept. 1965.

[9] R. T. Hodgson, "Vacuum-ultraviolet laser action observed in the Lyman bands of molecular hydrogen," *Phys. Rev. Lett.*, vol. 25, pp. 494-497, Aug. 1970.

[10] R. W. Waynant, J. D. Shipman, Jr., R. C. Elton, and A. W. Ali, "Vacuum ultraviolet laser emission from molecular hydrogen," *Appl. Phys. Letts.*, vol. 17, pp. 383-384, Nov. 1970.

[11] R. W. Waynant, J. D. Shipman, Jr., R. C. Elton, and A. W. Ali, "Laser emission in the vacuum ultraviolet from molecular hydrogen," *Proc. IEEE*, vol. 59, pp. 679-684, Apr. 1971.

[12] R. W. Waynant, A. W. Ali, and P. S. Julienne, "Experimental observations and calculated band strengths for the D_2 Lyman band laser," *J. Appl. Phys.*, vol. 42, pp. 3406-3408, Aug. 1971.

[13] —, *Handbook of Lasers with Selected Data on Optical Technology*, R. J. Pressley, Ed. Cleveland: The Chemical Rubber Co., 1971, pp. 319-322.

[14] R. T. Hodgson, "Vacuum-ultraviolet lasing action observed in CO: 1800-2000 Å," *J. Chem. Phys.*, vol. 55, pp. 5378-5379, Dec. 1971.

[15] R. W. Waynant, "Observations of gain by stimulated emission in the Werner band of molecular hydrogen," *Phys. Rev. Lett.*, vol. 28, pp. 533-535, Feb. 1972.

[16] R. T. Hodgson and R. W. Dreyfus, "Electron-beam excitation of vacuum ultraviolet hydrogen laser," *Phys. Lett.*, vol. 38A, pp. 213-214, Jan. 1972.

[17] —, "Vacuum UV laser action in H_2 Werner Bands: 1161-1240 Å," *Phys. Rev. Lett.*, vol. 28, pp. 536-539, Feb. 1972.

[18] A. W. Ali and A. C. Kolb, "Hydrogen molecular vacuum ultraviolet laser theory," *Appl. Phys. Lett.*, vol. 13, pp. 259-261, Oct. 1968.

[19] A. W. Ali and P. C. Kepple, "H_2 Lyman and Werner bands laser theory," *Appl. Opt.*, vol. 11, pp. 2591-2596, Nov. 1972.

[20] I. N. Knyazev, V. S. Letokov, and V. G. Movshev, "On the collisional four level H_2 VUV laser," *Opt. Commun.*, vol. 6, pp. 424-426, Dec. 1972.

[21] M. Gallardo, C. A. Massone, and M. Garavagil, "On the inversion mechanism of the molecular hydrogen vacuum ultraviolet laser," *IEEE J. Quantum Electron.*, vol. QE-10, pp. 525-526, June 1974.

[22] I. N. Knyazev, "Efficiency of fast-electron-beam excitation of molecular electronic states of hydrogen in a hydrogen laser," *Sov. J. Quantum Electron.*, vol. 4, pp. 1197-1203, Apr. 1975.

[23] V. S. Antonov, I. N. Knyazev, V. S. Letokhov, and V. G. Movshev, "Hydrogen laser in vacuum ultraviolet at atmospheric pressure," *JETP Lett.*, vol. 17, pp. 393-395, May 20, 1973.

[24] S. A. Borgstrom, "A simple low-divergence H_2 laser at 160 nm," *Opt. Commun.*, vol. 11, pp. 105-108, June 1974.

[25] R. W. Dreyfus and R. T. Hodgson, "Molecular-hydrogen laser: 1098-1613 Å," *Phys. Rev. A.*, vol. 9, pp. 2635-2648, June 1974.
[26] I. N. Knyazev, V. S. Letokhov, and V. G. Movshev, "Efficient and practical vacuum ultraviolet laser," *IEEE J. Quantum Electron.*, vol. QE-11, pp. 805-817, Oct. 1975.
[27] A. G. Molchanov, I. A. Poluektov, and Yu. M. Popov, "The possibility of the generation of vacuum ultraviolet radiation by electron excitation of inert-gas crystals," *Sov. Phys.–Solid State*, vol. 9, pp. 2655-2656, May 1968.
[28] N. G. Basov, E. M. Balashov, O. V. Bogdankevitch, V. A. Danilychev, G. N. Kashnikov, N. P. Lantzov, and D. D. Khodkevitch, "Luminescence of condensed Xe, Kr, Ar and their mixtures in vacuum region of spectrum under excitation by fast electrons," *J. Lumin.*, vol. 1-2, pp. 834-841, 1970.
[29] N. G. Basov, V. A. Danilychev, and Yu. M. Popov, "Stimulated emission in the vacuum ultraviolet region," *Proc. Int. Quantum Electronics Conf.* (Kyoto, Japan) 1970.
[30] N. G. Basov, V. A. Danilychev, Yu. M. Popov, and D. D. Khodkevich, "Laser operating in the vacuum region of the spectrum by excitation of liquid xenon with an electron beam," *JETP Lett.*, vol. 12, pp. 329-331, Nov. 20, 1970.
[31] N. G. Basov, V. A. Danilychev, and Yu. M. Popov, "Stimulated emission in the vacuum ultraviolet region," *Sov. J. Quantum Electron.*, vol. 1, pp. 18-22, July-Aug. 1971.
[32] N. G. Basov, "Soviet approach to e-beam pumping," *Laser Focus*, vol. 8, pp. 45-47, Sept. 1972.
[33] N. G. Basov, E. M. Belenov, V. A. Danilychev, O. M. Kerimov, I. B. Kovsh, A. S. Podsosonnyi, and A. F. Suchkov, "Electric ionization lasers," *Sov. Phys.–JETP*, vol. 37, pp. 58-64, July 1973.
[34] H. A. Koehler, L. J. Ferderber, D. L. Redhead, and P. J. Ebert, "Stimulated VUV emission in high-pressure xenon excited by high-current relativistic electron beams," *Appl. Phys. Lett.*, vol. 21, pp. 198-200, Sept. 1972.
[35] H. A. Koehler, L. J. Ferderber, D. L. Redhead, and P. J. Ebert, "Vacuum-ultraviolet emission from high-pressure xenon and argon excited by high-current relativistic electron beams," *Phys. Rev. A*, vol. 9, pp. 768-781, Feb. 1974.
[36] B. L. Borovich, V. S. Zuev, and D. B. Stavrovsky, "Pressure-induced ultraviolet absorption in rare gases: absorption coefficients for mixtures of Xe and Ar at pressures up to 40 atm in the vicinity of 147 nm," *J. Quant. Spectros. Radiat. Transfer*, vol. 13, pp. 1241-1249, Mar. 1973.
[37] M. M. Mkrtchyan and V. T. Platonenko, "Feasibility of high-pressure noble-gas lasers," *JETP Lett.*, vol. 17, pp. 19-21, Jan. 5, 1973.
[38] V. M. Andriyakhin, V. V. Vasil'tsov, S. S. Krasil'nikov, and V. D. Pis'mennyi, "Nuclear pumping of molecular gas lasers," *Sov. Phys.–JETP*, vol. 36, pp. 865-869, May 1973.
[39] A. W. Johnson and J. B. Gerardo, "Model of the VUV molecular-xenon laser," Sandia Lab., Albuquerque, NM, SLA-73-5872A, Oct. 1973.
[40] E. V. George and C. K. Rhodes, "Kinetic model of ultraviolet inversions in high-pressure rare-gas plasmas," *Appl. Phys. Lett.*, vol. 23, pp. 139-141, Aug. 1973.
[41] A. W. Ali, "Towards shorter wavelength lasers and breaking the 1000 angstrom barrier (II) (Bound-continuum emission)," U.S. Naval Research Lab., Washington, DC, Memo Rep. 2863, Aug. 1974.
[42] A. G. Molchanov and Yu. M. Popov, "Possibility of electric-ionization excitation of the stimulated emission of vacuum ultraviolet radiation in compressed xenon," *Sov. J. Quantum Electron.*, vol. 4, pp. 613-615, Nov. 1974.
[43] G. R. Fournier, "A model for electron-beam excited VUV fluorescence from xenon," *Opt. Commun.*, vol. 13, pp. 385-389, Apr. 1975.
[44] S. C. Wallace, R. T. Hodgson, and R. W. Dreyfus, "Excitation of vacuum ultraviolet emission from high-pressure xenon by relativistic electron beams," *Appl. Phys. Lett.*, vol. 23, pp. 22-24, July 1973.
[45] E. R. Ault, M. L. Bhaumik, W. M. Hughes, R. J. Jensen, C. P. Robinson, A. C. Kolb, and J. Shannon, "Xenon molecular laser in the vacuum ultraviolet," *IEEE J. Quantum Electron.*, vol. QE-9, pp. 1031-1032, Oct. 1973.
[46] D. A. Emmons, "Xenon photo-absorption in the vacuum ultraviolet," *Opt. Commun.*, vol. 11, pp. 247-260, July 1974.
[47] D. J. Bradley, D. R. Hull, M. H. R. Hutchinson, and M. W. McGeoch, "Megawatt VUV xenon laser employing coaxial electron-beam excitation," *Opt. Commun.*, vol. 11, pp. 335-338, Aug. 1974.
[48] Z. Ophir, B. Raz, and J. Jortner, "Exciton-enhanced photo-emission from doped solid rare gases," *Phys. Rev. Lett.*, vol. 33, pp. 415-418, Aug. 1974.
[49] S. C. Wallace and R. W. Dreyfus, "Continuously tunable xenon laser at 1720 Å," *Appl. Phys. Lett.*, vol. 25, pp. 498-500, Nov. 1974.
[50] J. W. Keto, R. E. Gleason, Jr., and G. K. Walters, "Production mechanisms and radiative lifetimes of argon and xenon molecules emitting in the ultraviolet," *Phys. Rev. Lett.*, vol. 33, pp. 1365-1368, Dec. 1974.
[51] J. B. Gerardo and A. W. Johnson, "Comment on 'Dynamic model of high pressure rare-gas excimer lasers'," *Appl. Phys. Lett.*, vol. 26, pp. 582-584, May 15, 1975.
[52] D. J. Bradley, D. R. Hull, M. H. R. Hutchinson, and M. W. McGeoch, "Co-axially pumped, narrow band, continuously tunable, high power VUV xenon laser," *Opt. Commun.*, vol. 14, pp. 1-3, May 1975.
[53] E. Zamir, C. W. Werner, W. P. Lapatovich, and E. V. George, "Temporal evolution of the electron density in high-pressure electron-beam-excited xenon plasmas," *Appl. Phys. Lett.*, vol. 27, pp. 56-58, July 15, 1975.
[54] C. K. Rhodes, "Review of ultraviolet laser physics," *IEEE J. Quantum Electron.*, vol. QE-10, pp. 153-174, Feb. 1974; see also G. G. Petrash, "Pulsed gas-discharge lasers," *Sov. Phys. Usp.*, vol. 14, pp. 747-765 May-June 1972.
[55] P. W. Hoff, J. C. Swingle, and C. K. Rhodes, "Demonstration of temporal coherence, spatial coherence, and threshold effects in the molecular xenon laser," *Opt. Commun.*, vol. 8, pp. 128-131, June 1973.
[56] J. B. Gerardo, and A. W. Johnson, "High pressure xenon laser at 1730 Å," *IEEE J. Quantum Electron.*, vol. QE-9, pp. 748-755, July 1973.
[57] P. W. Hoff, J. C. Swingle, and C. K. Rhodes, "Observations of stimulated emission from high-pressure krypton and argon/xenon mixtures," *Appl. Phys. Lett.*, vol. 23, pp. 245-246, Sept. 1973.
[58] W. R. Hunter, "Optics in the vacuum ultraviolet," *Electro-Optical Systems Design*, vol. 5, pp. 16-23, Nov. 1973. (Very recent narrow-band, high-reflectance vacuum ultraviolet mirrors have been made using multi-layer dielectric coatings by L. Stelmack and B. Flint at Acton Research Corp., Acton, Mass.)
[59] R. Tousey, "The extreme ultraviolet-past and future," *Appl. Opt.*, vol. 1, pp. 679-693, Nov. 1962.
[60] J. A. R. Samson, *Techniques of Vacuum Ultraviolet Spectroscopy*. New York: Wiley, 1967.
[61] R. W. Dreyfus, R. J. von Gutfeld, and S. C. Wallace, "Aluminum mirror degradation in a VUV laser," *Opt. Commun.*, vol. 9, pp. 342-345, Dec. 1973.
[62] W. L. Bond, M. A. Duguay, and P. M. Rentzepis, "Proposed resonator for an X-ray laser," *Appl. Phys. Lett.*, vol. 10, pp. 216-218, Apr. 15, 1967.
[63] R. D. Delattes, "X-ray monochromators and resonators from single crystals," *Appl. Phys. Lett.*, vol. 12, pp. 133-135, Feb. 15, 1968.
[64] R. M. J. Cotterill, "A universal planar X-ray resonator," *Appl. Phys. Lett.*, vol. 12, pp. 403-404, June 1968.
[65] A. V. Kolpakov, R. N. Kuzmin, and V. M. Ryaboy, "Some characteristics of the resonators for X-ray frequencies," *J. Appl. Phys.*, vol. 41, pp. 3549-3550, July 1970.
[66] H. Kogelnik and C. V. Shank, "Stimulated emission in a periodic structure," *Appl. Phys. Lett.*, vol. 18, pp. 152-154, Feb. 1971.
[67] C. V. Shank, J. E. Bjorkholm, and H. Kogelnik, "Tunable distributed-feedback dye laser," *Appl. Phys. Lett.*, vol. 18, pp. 395-396, May 1971.
[68] I. P. Kaminow, H. P. Weber, and E. A. Chandross, "Poly (methyl methacrylate) dye laser with internal diffraction grating resonator," *Appl. Phys. Lett.*, vol. 18, pp. 497-501, June 1971.
[69] H. Kogelnik and C. V. Shank, "Coupled-wave theory of distributed feedback lasers," *J. Appl. Phys.*, vol. 43, pp. 2327-2338, May 1972.
[70] C. V. Shank, R. V. Schmidt, and B. I. Miller, "Double-heterostructure GaAs distributed-feedback laser," *Appl. Phys. Lett.*, vol. 25, pp. 200-201, Aug. 1974.
[71] D. R. Scifres, R. D. Burnham, and W. Streifer, "Distributed-feedback single heterojunction GaAs diode laser," *Appl. Phys. Lett.*, vol. 25, pp. 203-206, Aug. 1974.
[72] S. R. Chinn and P. L. Kelley, "Analysis of the transmission, reflection and noise properties of distributed feedback laser amplifiers," *Opt. Commun.*, vol. 10, pp. 123-126, Feb. 1974.
[73] R. A. Fisher, "Possibility of a distributed-feedback X-ray laser," *Appl. Phys. Lett.*, vol. 24, pp. 598-599, June 1974.
[74] A. Yariv, "Analytical considerations of Bragg coupling coefficients and distributed-feedback X-ray lasers in single crystals," *Appl. Phys. Lett.*, vol. 25, pp. 105-107, July 1974.
[75] C. Elachi, G. Evans, and F. Grunthaner, "Proposed distributed feedback crystal cavities for X-ray lasers," *Appl. Opt.*, vol. 14, pp. 14-15, Jan. 1975.

[76] A. L. Schawlow and C. H. Townes, "Infrared and optical masers," *Phys. Rev.*, vol. 112, pp. 1940–1949, Dec. 15, 1958.
[77] A. L. Bloom, W. E. Bell, and R. E. Rempel, "Laser operation at 3.39 μ in a helium-neon mixture," *Appl. Opt.*, vol. 2, pp. 317-318, Mar. 1963.
[78] R. H. Dicke, "Coherence in spontaneous radiation processes," *Phys. Rev.*, vol. 93, pp. 99–111, Jan. 1954.
[79] R. H. Dicke, "The coherence brightened laser," *Quantum Electronics, Proceedings of the Third International Conference on Quantum Electronics* Vol. I, Grivet and Bloembergen, Eds. New York: Columbia Univ. Press, 1964, pp. 35–53.
[80] L. Allen and G. I. Peters, "Superradiance, coherence brightening and amplified spontaneous emission," *Phys. Lett.*, vol. 31A, pp. 95–96, Feb. 1970.
[81] G. I. Peters and L. Allen, "Amplified spontaneous emission I. The threshold condition," *J. Phys. A*, vol. 4, pp. 238-243, Mar. 1971.
[82] L. Allen and G. I. Peters, "Amplified spontaneous emission II. The connection with laser theory," *J. Phys. A.*, vol. 4, pp. 377–381, May 1971.
[83] —, "Amplified spontaneous emission III. Intensity and saturation," *J. Phys. A*, vol. 4, pp. 564–573, July 1971.
[84] G. I. Peters and L. Allen, "Amplified spontaneous emission IV. Beam divergence and spatial coherence," *J. Phys. A*, vol. 5, pp. 546-554, Apr. 1972.
[85] L. Allen, "Amplified spontaneous emission," in *Coherence and Quantum Optics*, L. Mandel and E. Wolf, Eds. New York: Plenum, 1973, pp. 467–490; see also L. Allen and G. I. Peters, "Spectral distribution of amplified spontaneous emission," *J. Phys. A*, vol. 5, pp. 695–704, May 1972.
[86] R. C. Elton, R. W. Waynant, R. A. Andrews and M. H. Reilly, "X-ray and vacuum-UV lasers (Current status and prognosis)," U.S. Naval Research Lab., Washington, DC, Rep. No. 7412, May 1972.
[87] S. Stenholm and W. E. Lamb, Jr., "Semiclassical theory of a high-intensity laser," *Phys. Rev.*, vol. 181, pp. 618–635, May 10, 1969.
[88] A. Yariv and R. C. C. Leite, "Super radiant narrowing in fluorescence radiation of inverted populations," *J. Appl. Phys.*, vol. 34, pp. 3410-3411, Nov. 1963.
[89] L. Allen and G. I. Peters, "Amplified spontaneous emission and external signal amplification in an inverted medium," *Phys. Rev. A*, vol. 8, pp. 2031-2047, Oct. 1973.
[90] W. E. Lamb, Jr., "Theory of an optical maser," *Phys. Rev.*, vol. 134, pp. A1429–A1450, June 15, 1964.
[91] W. E. Lamb, Jr., "Amplification of incoherent radiation," *1974 IEEE Int. Quantum Electron. Conf. Dig. Tech. Papers*, p. 41.
[92] F. A. Hopf, "Statistical changes in amplified thermal light," *1974 IEEE Int. Quantum Electron. Conf. Dig. Tech. Papers*, p. 41.
[93] R. L. Kelly with L. J. Palumbo, *Atomic and Ionic Emission Lines Below 2000 Ångstroms*, U.S. Naval Research Lab. Rep. 7599, Washington, DC: U.S. Government Printing Office, 1973.
[94] D. Marcuse, "Maser action without population inversion," *Proc. IEEE*, vol. 51, pp. 849–850, May 1963.
[95] W. L. Wiese, M. W. Smith, and B. M. Glennon, "Atomic transitions Probabilities, Vol. 1, Hydrogen through Neon," Nat. Bur. Stand., Boulder, CO, Rep. NSRDS-NBS-4, May 1966.
[96] R. C. Elton, "Quasistationary population inversion on $K\alpha$ transitions," *Appl. Opt.*, vol. 14, pp. 2243–2249, Sept. 1975.
[97] H. R. Griem, *Spectral Line Broadening by Plasmas*. New York: Academic Press, 1974.
[98] F. E. Irons, and N. J. Peacock, "Experimental evidence for population inversion in C^{5+} in an expanding laser-produced plasmas," *J. Phys. B*, vol. 7, pp. 1109–1112, June 21, 1974.
[99] R. J. Dewhurst, D. Jacoby, G. J. Pert, and S. A. Ramsden, "Ionization, recombination and population inversion in laser produced plasmas," Univ. Hull, Hull, England, Rep. LPI-74-2, 1974.
[100] A. V. Vinogradov, and I. I. Sobel'man, "The problem of laser radiation sources in the far ultraviolet and X-ray regions," *Sov. Phys.-JETP*, vol. 36, pp. 1115–1119, June 1973.
[101] W. D. Barfield, G. D. Koontz, and W. F. Huebner, "Fits to new calculations of photoionization cross sections for low-Z elements," *J. Quant. Spectrosc. Radiat. Transfer*, vol. 12, pp. 1409–1433, Oct. 1972.
[102] S. M. R. Ansari, G. Elwert, and P. Mücklich, "On dielectronic recombination," *Z. Naturforsch.*, vol. 25a, pp. 1781–1797, Dec. 1970.
[103] R. C. Elton, "Atomic processes," in *Methods of Experimental Physics, Plasma Physics*, vol. 9A, H. R. Griem and R. H. Lovberg, Eds. New York: Academic Press, 1970, pp. 115–168.
[104] W. H. Louisell, M. O. Scully, and W. B. McKnight, "Analysis of a soft X-ray laser with charge exchange excitation," *Phys. Rev. A*, vol. 11, pp. 989–1000, Mar. 1975.
[105] R. C. Elton, "Extension of 3p-3s ion lasers into the vacuum ultraviolet region," *Appl. Opt.*, vol. 14, pp. 97–101, Jan. 1975.
[106] R. C. Elton and R. H. Dixon, "X-Ray laser research: guidelines and progress at NRL," *Ann New York Acad Sci.*, vol. 267, pp. 3–14, 1976.
[107] M. Galanti, N. J. Peacock, B. A. Norton, and J. Puric, "Light absorption and energy balance at the surface of a laser-irradiated solid target," in *Proc. 5th IAEA Conf. Plasma Physics and Controlled Nuclear Fusion Research* (Tokyo, Japan), Nov. 1974.
[108] A. M. Malvezzi, E. Jannitti, and G. Tondello, "Observations of the Stark broadening of the resonance lines in a beryllium laser produced plasma," (to be published).
[109] T. N. Lie (Lee) and R. C. Elton, "X-radiation from optical and inner-shell transitions in a highly ionized dense plasma," *Phys. Rev.*, vol. 3, pp. 865–871, Mar. 1971.
[110] T. N. Lee, "High density ionization with an intense linear focus discharge," *Ann. New York Acad. Sci.*, vol. 251, pp. 112–125, May 1975.
[111] G. Cooperstein, *private commun.*, Feb. 1975.
[112] R. A. McCorkle, "Praticable X-ray amplifier," *Phys. Rev. Lett.*, vol. 29, pp. 982–985, Oct. 1972.
[113] V. B. Rozanov, "Feasibility of producing an inverted medium by photoionization of the inner electrons in atoms," *JETP Lett.*, vol. 12, pp. 340–342, Nov. 20, 1970.
[114] I. Freund, "Optically stimulated X-ray laser," *Appl. Phys. Lett.*, vol. 24, pp. 13–15, Jan. 1974. The gain estimates seem overly optimistic in this paper for reasonable line broadening.
[115] R. C. Elton, "Intercombination line oscillator strengths in the helium isoelectronic sequence," *Astrophys. J.*, vol. 148, pp. 573–578, May 1967.
[116] R. C. Elton and W. W. Köppendörfer, "Measured collisional excitation rate coefficients for oxygen VII," *Phys. Rev.*, vol. 160, pp. 194–201, Aug. 1967.
[117] L. I. Gudzenko, V. V. Evstigneev, and S. I. Yakovlenko, "Amplification of X-ray radiation in a decaying plasma using transitions in helium-like ions," *Sov. J. Quantum Electron.*, vol. 4, p. 1148, Mar. 1975; see also L. I. Gudzenko, Yu. K. Zemtsov, and S. I. Yakovlenko, "Amplification of vacuum-ultraviolet radiation in a decaying dense helium plasma," *JETP Lett.*, vol. 12, pp. 167–169, Sept. 1970.
[118] H. J. Kunze, A. H. Gabriel, and H. R. Griem, "Measurement of collisional rate coefficients for helium-like carbon ions in a plasma," *Phys. Rev.*, vol. 165, pp. 267–276, Jan. 1968.
[119] R. H. Pantell, *Reports on Contract N00014-67-A-0112-0033 (1–3)*, Arlington, VA, 22217: Office of Naval Research; see also [86, p. 18].
[120] H. Mahr and U. Roeder, "Use of metastable ions for a soft X-ray laser," *Opt. Commun.*, vol. 10, pp. 227–228, Mar. 1974.
[121] A. A. Vekhov, V. N. Makhov, F. A. Nikolaev, and V. B. Rozanov, "Possibility of using metastable heliumlike ions in generation of ultrashort X-ray stimulated radiation," *Sov. J. Quantum Electron.*, vol. 5, pp. 718–720, June 1975.
[122] S. E. Harris *et al.* (to be published).
[123] L. Wood and G. Chapline, "Conditions for X-ray laser action," Lawrence Livermore Lab., Livermore, CA, Rep. UCRL-75184 (Rev. 2), June 1974. See also [171].
[124] O. R. Wood, II, "High-pressure pulsed molecular lasers," *Proc. IEEE*, vol. 62, pp. 355–397, Mar. 1974.
[125] C. V. Heer, "Broadband gain with naturally inverted stable to continuum molecular transitions," *J. Appl. Phys.*, vol. 41, pp. 1875–1876, Mar. 15, 1970.
[126] A. J. Palmer, "Stimulated emission of the H_2 continuum," *J. Appl. Phys.*, vol. 41, pp. 438–439, Jan. 1970.
[127] S. Metz, "Enhanced light emission from a pulsed discharge in hydrogen," *Phys. Lett.*, vol. 34A, pp. 315–316, Apr. 1971.
[128] A. Cohn, A. G. Rubin, and A. L. Besse, "The hydrogen dissociation laser," AFCRL, Cambridge, MA, TR-74-0110, Apr. 5, 1974.
[129] F. H. Mies, "Stimulated emission and population inversion in diatomic bound-continuum transition," *Mol. Phys.*, vol. 26, pp. 1233–1246, Nov. 1973.
[130] D. C. Lorents, "A model of rare-gas excimer formation and decay and its application to VUV lasers," *Radiation Res.*, vol. 59, pp. 438–440, 1974.
[131] A. V. Phelps, *Tunable Gas Lasers Utilizing Ground State Dissociation*, Univ. Colorado, Boulder, JILA Rep. 110, Sept. 15, 1972.
[132] H. T. Powell, J. R. Murray, and C. K. Rhodes, "Laser oscillation on the green bands of XeO and KrO," *Appl. Phys. Lett.*, vol. 25, pp. 730–732, Dec. 15, 1974.
[133] Y. Hashino, Y. Katsuyama, and K. Fukuda, "Laser oscillation of multiply ionized Ne, Ar, and N ions in a z-pinch discharge," *Jap. J. Appl. Phys.*, vol. 11, p. 907, June 1972.

[134] Y. Hashino, Y. Katsuyama, and K. Fukuda, "Laser oscillation of OV in z-pinch discharge," *Jap. J. Appl. Phys.*, vol. 12, p. 470, Apr. 1973.

[135] R. A. Andrews, "Soft X-ray lasers via electron-collisional pumping," in *Progress in Lasers and Laser Fusion*, A. Perlmutter and S. M. Widmayer, Eds. New York: Plenum Press, 1975, pp. 235–268.

[136] L. J. Palumbo (to be published).

[137] K. G. Whitney and J. Davis, "The use of intense relativistic electron beams to pump VUV lasers," *J. Appl. Phys.*, vol. 46, pp. 4103–4105, Sept. 1975.

[138] R. C. Elton, T. N. Lee, J. Davis, J. F. Reintjes, R. H. Dixon, R. C. Eckardt, K. Whitney, J. L. DeRosa, L. J. Palumbo, and R. A. Andrews, "Towards X-ray lasers with VUV amplification on 3p-3s transitions," *Physica Fennica*, vol. 9, Suppl. Sl, pp. 400–402, July 1974.

[139] I. N. Knyazev and V. S. Letokhov, "Excitation of far vacuum uv lasers by fast heating of plasma electrons in ultrashort pulsed optical fields," *Opt. Commun.*, vol. 3, pp. 332–334, July 1971.

[140] R. W. Waynant, "Vacuum ultraviolet laser emission from C IV," *Appl. Phys. Lett.*, vol. 22, pp. 419–420, Apr. 1973.

[141] B. A. Norton and E. R. Wooding, "Proposed method for obtaining population inversion for vacuum ultraviolet and X-ray transitions," *Phys. Rev. A*, vol. 11, pp. 1689–1691, May 1975.

[142] T. C. Bristow, M. J. Lubin, J. M. Forsyth, E. B. Goldman, and J. M. Soures, "High-intensity X-ray spectra and stimulated emission from laser plasmas," *Opt. Commun.*, vol. 5, pp. 315–318, Aug. 1972.

[143] L. I. Gudzenko and L. A. Shelepin, "Radiation enhancement in a recombining plasma," *Sov. Phys. Doklady*, vol. 10, pp. 147–149, Aug. 1965.

[144] B. F. Gordiets, L. I. Gudzenko, and L. A. Shelepin, "Relaxation processes and amplification of radiation in a dense plasma," *Sov. Phys.–JETP*, vol. 28, pp. 489–493, Mar. 1969.

[145] J. Peyraud and N. Peyraud, "Population inversion in laser plasmas," *J. Appl. Phys.*, vol. 43, pp. 2993–2996, July 1972.

[146] B. Lax and A. H. Guenther, "Quantitative aspects of a soft X-ray laser," *Appl. Phys. Lett.*, vol. 21, pp. 361–363, Oct. 1972.

[147] L. Ya. Efremenkova and B. M. Smirnov, "Ultraviolet laser using the Lyman transition," *Sov. Phys. Doklady*, vol. 17, pp. 336–338, Oct. 1972.

[148] G. I. Gudzenko, M. V. Nezlin and S. I. Yakovlenko, "Recombination laser with a supercooled plasma generated by an electron beam," *Sov. Phys.–Tech. Phys.*, vol. 18, pp. 1218–1221, Mar. 1974.

[149] W. L. Bohn, "Possible population inversions for VUV and soft X-ray transitions in hydrogen-like ions," *Appl. Phys. Lett.*, vol. 24, pp. 15–17, Jan. 1974.

[150] G. J. Pert and S. A. Ramsden, "Population inversion in plasmas produced by picosecond laser pulses," *Opt. Commun.*, vol. 11, pp. 270–273, July 1974.

[151] W. W. Jones and A. W. Ali, "Theory of short-wavelength lasers from recombining plasmas," *Appl. Phys. Lett.*, vol. 26, pp. 450–451, Apr. 15, 1975.

[152] E. Ya. Kononov and K. N. Koshelev, "Inverse population of levels of multiply charged ions," *Sov. J. Quantum Electron.*, vol. 4, pp. 1340–1343, May 1975.

[153] G. Chapline and L. Wood, "X-ray and γ-ray lasers," in *Progress in Lasers and Laser Fusion*, A. Perlmutter and S. M. Widmayer, Eds. New York: Plenum Press, 1975, pp. 269–279.

[154] E. Kononov, "On the level population of A1 XI in a laser plasma," in *Proc. 4th Int. Conf. Beam Foil Spectroscopy*, to be published, 1976.

[155] R. C. Elton and L. J. Palumbo, "Radiative-Auger transitions in soft X-ray plasma emission," *Phys. Rev.*, vol. 9, pp. 1873–1884, May 1974.

[156] D. L. Walters and C. P. Bhalla, "Nonrelativisitic Auger rates, X-ray rates, and fluorescence yields for the K shell," *Phys. Rev. A*, vol. 3, pp. 1919–1927, June 1971.

[157] A. H. Gabriel and T. M. Paget, "Measurement and interpretation of dielectronic recombination satellite line intensities," *J. Phys. B.*, vol. 5, pp. 673–685, Mar. 1972.

[158] A. Burgess, "A general formula for the estimation of dielectronic recombination coefficients in low-density plasmas," *Astrophys. J.*, vol. 141, pp. 1588–1590, May 1965.

[159] A. Burgess, "Dielectronic recombination and the temperature of the solar corona," *Astrophys. J.*, vol. 139, pp. 776–780, Mar. 1964.

[160] A. Burgess, and H. P. Summers, "The effects of electron and radiation density on dielectronic recombination," *Astrophys. J.*, vol. 157, pp. 1007–1021, Aug. 1969.

[161] H. P. Summers, "The ionization equilibrium of hydrogen-like to argon-like ions of elements," *Mon. Not. R. Astron. Soc.*, vol. 169, pp. 663–680, Dec. 1974.

[162] H. J. Zwally and D. W. Koopman, "Single-electron capture by C^{4+} in helium, neon, and argon below 40 keV," *Phys. Rev. A.*, vol. 2, pp. 1851–1861, Nov. 1970.

[163] H. J. Zwally, "Single-electron capture by multiply-charged carbon ions at energies below 40 keV," Ph.D. dissertation, Univ. Maryland, College Park, 1968.

[164] R. C. Elton, "Three quasi-CW approaches to short wavelength lasers," in *Progress in Lasers and Laser Fusion*, A. Perlmutter and S. M. Widmayer, Eds. New York: Plenum Press, 1975, pp. 117–145.

[165] L. P. Presnyakov and A. D. Ulantsev, "Charge exchange between multiply charged ions and atoms," *Sov. J. Quantum Electron.*, vol. 4, pp. 1320–1324, May 1975.

[166] R. C. Elton and R. H. Dixon, "Spectroscopy of plasmas for short wavelength lasers," in *Proc. 4th Int. Conf. on Beam Foil Spectroscopy*, to be published, 1976.

[167] L. P. Presnyakov and V. P. Shevel'ko, "Possibility of producing inverted population in atomic beams by charge exchange of protons with atoms," *JETP Lett.*, vol. 13, pp. 203–204, Mar. 20, 1971.

[168] C. D. Cantrell and M. O. Scully, "Review of soft X-ray lasers using charge exchange," in *Progress in Lasers and Laser Fusion*, A. Perlmutter and S. M. Widmayer, Eds. New York: Plenum Press, 1975, pp. 147–234.

[169] ——, *Proc. Int. Conf. on Inner Shell Ionization Phenomena and Future Applications*, USAEC Rep. CONF-720404, vols. 1–4, R. W. Fink, S. T. Manson, J. M. Palms, and P. V. Rao, Eds., 1973.

[170] V. V. Kokorin and V. F. Los, "The pumping of an X-ray laser by means of an optical laser," *Phys. Lett.*, vol. 45A, pp. 487–488, Nov. 5, 1973.

[171] R. A. McCorkle and J. M. Joyce, "Threshold conditions for amplified spontaneous emission of X-radiation," *Phys. Rev. A*, vol. 10, pp. 903–912, Sept. 1974.

[172] M. A. Duguay and P. M. Rentzepis, "Some approaches to vacuum UV and X-ray lasers," *Appl. Phys. Lett.*, vol. 10, pp. 350–352, June 1967.

[173] Yu. L. Stankevich, "The possibility of induced intensification of characteristic X-radiation," *Sov. Phys. Doklady*, vol. 15, pp. 356–357, Oct. 1970.

[174] P. P. Bey, "Analysis of VUV and X-ray lasers pumped by a traveling-wave source," U.S. Naval Research Lab., Washington, DC, Rep. 2847, July 1974.

[175] W. W. Jones and A. W. Ali, "Calculations for a VUV laser from sodium vapor pumped by radiation from an exploding wire," U.S. Naval Research Lab., Washington, DC, Memo Rep. 2807, June 1974.

[176] W. W. Jones and A. W. Ali, "Sodium vapor laser (372 Å) calculations using exploding wire radiation," *Phys. Lett.*, vol. 50A, pp. 101–102, Nov. 1974.

[177] E. J. McGuire, "Soft X-ray amplified spontaneous emission via the Auger effect," *Phys. Rev. Lett.*, vol. 35, pp. 844–848, Sept. 29, 1975; also "Auger cascades in aluminum," *Phys. Rev. A*, vol. 11, pp. 1889–1898, June 1975.

[178] R. A. Andrews, "X-ray lasers–Current thinking," U.S. Naval Research Lab., Washington, DC, Memo Rep. 2677, Oct. 1973; also summarized in *Laser Focus*, vol. 9, pp. 41–46, Nov. 1973.

[179] F. T. Arecchi, G. P. Banfi, and A. M. Malvezzi, "Threshold evaluations for an X-ray laser," *Opt. Commun.*, vol. 10, pp. 214–218, Mar. 1974.

[180] A. V. Vinogradov, I. I. Sobel'man, and E. A. Yukov, "Possibility of construction of a far-ultraviolet laser utilizing transitions in multiply charged ions in an inhomogeneous plasma," *Sov. J. Quantum Electron.*, vol. 5, pp. 59–63, July 1975.

[181] B. A. Norton and N. J. Peacock, "Population inversion in laser-produced plasmas by pumping with opacity-broadened lines," *J. Phys. B*, vol. 8, pp. 989–996, Apr. 1975.

[182] G. Moruzzi and F. Strumia, "A technique for optical pumping in vacuum ultraviolet," *Opt. Commun.*, vol. 2, pp. 279–281, Nov. 1970.

[183] W. Lichten, "Molecular wave functions and inelastic atomic collisions," *Phys. Rev.*, vol. 164, pp. 131–142, Dec. 5, 1967.

[184] R. N. Sudan and R. V. Lovelace, "Generation of intense ion beams in pulsed diodes," *Phys. Rev. Lett.*, vol. 31, pp. 1174–1177, Nov. 1973.

[185] F. A. Hopf, P. Meystre, M. O. Scully, and J. F. Seely, "Coherence brightening and laser lethargy in X-ray laser amplifiers," *Phys. Rev. Lett.*, vol. 35, pp. 511–513, Aug. 25, 1975.

[186] L. A. Rivlin, Soviet Invention Disclosures 709414 of January 1961 and 710508 of 1 April 1961.

[187] V. Vali and W. Vali, "Induced γ-ray emission," *Proc. IEEE*, vol. 51, pp. 182–184, Jan. 1963.

[188] G. C. Baldwin, J. P. Neissel, and L. Tonks, "Induced gamma-ray emission," *Proc. IEEE*, vol. 51, pp. 1247–1248, Sept. 1963.

[189] B. V. Chirikov, "The kinetics of induced Mossbauer radiation," *Sov. Phys.–JETP*, vol. 17, pp. 1355–1359, Dec. 1963.
[190] R. V. Khokhlov, "Concerning the feasibility of a γ laser based on radioactive crystals," *JETP Lett.*, vol. 15, pp. 414–416, May 5, 1972.
[191] V. S. Letokhov, "Pumping of nuclear levels by X-ray radiation of a laser plasma," *Sov. J. Quantum Electron.*, vol. 3, pp. 360–361, Jan.–Feb. 1974; see also V. S. Letokhov, "On the problem of the nuclear-transition γ-laser," *Sov. Phys.–JETP*, vol. 37, pp. 787–793, Nov. 1973.
[192] V. F. Dmitriev and É. V. Shuryak, "The possibilities of producing a γ laser," *Sov. Phys.–JETP*, vol. 40, pp. 244–248, Feb. 1975.
[193] V. I. Gol'danskii and Yu. Kagan, "The possibility of creating a nuclear γ laser," *Sov. Phys.–JETP*, vol. 37, pp. 49–52, July 1973. See also V. I. Vorontsov and V. I. Vysotskii, "Concerning the kinetics of stimulated gamma radiation in the transient regime," *Sov. Phys.–JETP*, vol. 39, pp. 748–751, Nov. 1974.
[194] J. Byrne, G. I. Peters, and L. Allen, "Stimulated emission from nuclei," *Appl. Opt.*, vol. 13, pp. 2499–2504, Nov. 1974.
[195] G. C. Baldwin and R. V. Khokhlov, "Prospects for a gamma-ray laser," *Phys. Today*, vol. 28, pp. 33–39, Feb. 1975.
[196] G. C. Baldwin, *Problems of the Gamma Ray Laser*, Aberdeen, MD: BRL-CR-179, Contract DA-ARO-D-31-124-73-G162, Aug. 1974.
[197] L. Wood and G. Chapline, "Towards gamma-ray lasers," *Nature (Lond.)*, vol. 252, pp. 447–450, Dec. 6, 1974.
[198] L. Cohen (chairman), J. B. Aviles, Jr., C. Bond, L. Cox, I. Manning, K. W. Marlow, and D. J. Nagel, "Gamma-ray lasers (grasers) a status report," U.S. Naval Research Lab., Washington, DC, Memo Rep. 2947, Dec. 1974.
[199] Y. A. Il'inskii and R. V. Khokhlov, "Narrowing of γ-resonance lines in crystals by radio-frequency fields," *Sov. Phys.–JETP*, vol. 38, pp. 809–812, April 1974.
[200] ——, *Fund. and Appl. Laser Phys.* (*Proc. Esfahan Symposium 29 Aug. to 5 Sept. 1971*), M. S. Feld, A. Javan, and N. A. Kurnit, Eds. New York: Wiley, 1973, p. 17.
[201] L. A. Rivlin, "Antimatter as a source of negative-temperature states," *Sov. J. Quantum Electron.*, vol. 4, p. 1151, Mar. 1975.
[202] R. H. Milburn, "Electron scattering by an intense polarized photon field," *Phys. Rev. Lett.*, vol. 10, pp. 75–77, Feb. 1, 1963.
[203] F. R. Arutyunian and V. A. Tumanian, "The Compton effect on relativistic electrons and the possibility of obtaining high energy beams," *Phys. Lett.*, vol. 4, pp. 176–178, Apr. 1, 1963.
[204] R. H. Pantell, G. Soncini, and H. E. Putoff, "Stimulated photoelectron scattering," *IEEE J. Quantum Electron.*, vol. QE-4, pp. 905–907, Nov. 1968.
[205] A. G. Molchanov, "Lasers in the vacuum ultraviolet and in the X-ray regions of the spectrum," *Sov. Phys. Usp.*, vol. 15, pp. 124–129, July–Aug. 1972.
[206] P. Jaeglé, G. Jamelot, A. Carillon, A. Sureau, and P. Dhez, "Super radiant line in the soft X-ray range," *Phys. Rev. Lett.*, vol. 33, pp. 1070–1073, Oct. 1974.
[207] A. Carillon, G. Jamelot, A. Sureau, and P. Jaeglé, "Autoionizing series in the Al^{3+} ion spectrum of a laser-produced plasma," *Phys. Lett.*, vol. 38A, pp. 91–92, Jan. 17, 1972.
[208] F. P. J. Valero, "Intensity anomalies in the extreme VUV spectrum of Al^{3+} obtained in a laser-produced plasma, " *Appl. Phys. Lett.*, vol. 25, pp. 64–66, July 1, 1974; see also, K. N. Koshelev and S. S. Churilov, "A possible interpretation of the observed superradiance in the spectra of Al IV ions in the plasma of laser jet," *Sov. J. Quantum Electron.*, vol. 5, pp. 400–402, Apr. 1975.
[209] W. T. Silfvast, J. M. Green, and O. R. Wood, II, "Population inversions and the measurement of gain in laser-produced plasmas," *Phys. Rev. Lett.*, vol. 35, pp. 435–438, Aug. 1975.
[210] K. Das Gupta, "Non-linear increase in Bragg peak and narrowing of X-ray lines," *Phys. Lett.*, vol. 46A, pp. 179–180, Dec. 1973.
[211] K. Das Gupta, "Nondivergent radiation of discrete frequencies in continuous X-ray spectrum," *Phys. Rev. Lett.*, vol. 33, pp. 1415–1418, Dec. 1974.
[212] P. J. Ebert, "Comments on 'Nondivergent radiation of discrete frequencies in continuous X-ray spectrum,'" *Bull. Amer. Phys. Soc.*, vol. 20, p. 549, Apr. 1975.
[213] H. Aiginger, E. Unfried, and P. Wobrauschek, "Interpretation of 'Nondivergent radiation of discrete frequencies in continuous X-ray spectrum,'" *Phys. Rev. Lett.*, vol. 35, pp. 815–816, Sept. 22, 1975.
[214] P. J. Ebert and C. E. Dick, "Comments on the observation of non-divergent radiation of discrete frequencies," *Phys. Rev. Lett.*, vol. 34, pp. 1537–1539, June 16, 1975.
[215] J. G. Kepros, E. M. Eyring, and F. W. Cagle, Jr., "Experimental evidence of an X-ray laser," *Proc. Nat. Acad. Sci., USA*, vol. 69, pp. 62–63, July 1972.
[216] J. G. Kepros, private communication, 1972.
[217] K. W. Billman and H. Mark, "Cautionary note concerning the $CuSO_4$ X-ray laser," *Appl. Opt.*, vol. 12, pp. 2529–2531, Nov. 1973.
[218] R. C. Elton, L. J. Palumbo, R. A. Andrews, R. C. Eckardt, and J. N. Bradford, "Further evidence of collimated X-ray emission from $CuSO_4$ doped gelatin," *Appl. Opt.*, vol. 12, p. 155, Jan. 1973.
[219] J. N. Bradford, R. C. Elton, T. N. Lee, R. A. Andrews, L. J. Palumbo, and R. C. Eckardt, "Further comments on collimated X-ray emission from laser-heated $CuSO_4$-doped gelatin," *Appl. Opt.*, vol. 12, pp. 1095–1096, June 1973.
[220] S. G. Dinev and I. V. Tomov, "Further results concerning X-ray collimated emission from $CuSO_4$ doped targets," *Opto-Electronics*, vol. 6, pp. 197–198, Mar. 1974.
[221] P. D. Rowley and K. W. Billman, "Experimental attempts to confirm X-ray lasing from $CuSO_4$," *Appl. Opt.*, vol. 13, pp. 453–455, Mar. 1974.
[222] J. Rasmussen, Technical University of Denmark, private communication, 1973; see also [225].
[223] T. A. Boster, "Some questions on the evidence of laser X-ray emission from $CuSO_4$ doped gelatin," *Appl. Opt.*, vol. 12, pp. 433–434, Feb. 1973.
[224] K. E. Siegenthaler, H. Weichel, A. C. Saxman, R. D. Wick, and A. H. Guenther, "Further observations relating to X-ray laser emission from $CuSO_4$ doped gelatin," *Appl. Opt.*, vol. 12, pp. 2005–2006, Sept. 1973.
[225] J. G. Kepros, "Theoretical model explaining some aspects of the Utah X-ray laser experiments," *Appl. Opt.*, vol. 13, pp. 695–696, Apr. 1974.
[226] A. J. DeMaria, W. H. Glenn, Jr., M. J. Brienza, and M. E. Mack, "Picosecond laser pulses," *Proc. IEEE*, vol. 57, pp. 2–25, Jan. 1969.
[227] P. W. Smith, "Mode-locking of lasers," *Proc. IEEE*, vol. 58, pp. 1342–1357, Sept. 1970.
[228] W. T. Silfvast and O. R. Wood, II, "A 3400 Å p-terphenyl dye laser pumped by a CO_2-laser-produced plasma," *Appl. Phys. Lett.*, vol. 26, pp. 447–449, Apr. 15, 1975.
[229] R. W. Waynant, "A traveling wave vacuum ultraviolet laser," *Proc. Electro-Optical Systems Design Conference*, Anaheim, CA, 1971, pp. 1–5.
[230] L. Casperson and A. Yariv, "Pulse propagation in a high-gain medium," *Phys. Rev. Lett.*, vol. 26, pp. 293–295, Feb. 8, 1971.
[231] G. Chapline and L. Wood, "X-ray lasers," *Phys. Today*, vol. 28, pp. 40–48, June 1975.
[232] H. H. Fleischmann, "High-current electron beams," *Phys. Today*, vol. 28, pp. 34–43, May 1975.
[233] R. W. Waynant, "A transverse traveling-wave electron beam pump for short wavelength lasers," in *Conf. Laser Engr. Applic. Digest* (Washington, DC), 1973, p. 28.
[234] S. Humphries, J. J. Lee, and R. N. Sudan, "Generation of intense pulsed ion beams," *Appl. Phys. Lett.*, vol. 25, pp. 20–22, July 1, 1974.
[235] M. A. Duguay and A. Savage, "Picosecond optical sampling oscilloscope," *Opt. Commun.*, vol. 9, pp. 212–215, Oct. 1973.
[236] C. F. McConaghy and L. W. Coleman, "Picosecond X-ray streak camera," *Appl. Phys. Lett.*, vol. 25, pp. 268–270, Sept. 1, 1974.
[237] J. F. Ward and G. H. C. New, "Optical third harmonic generation in gases by a focused laser beam," *Phys. Rev.*, vol. 185, pp. 57–72, Sept. 5, 1969.
[238] S. E. Harris and R. B. Miles, "Proposed third-harmonic generation in phase-matched metal vapors," *Appl. Phys. Lett.*, vol. 19, pp. 385–387, Nov. 1971.
[239] J. A. Armstrong, N. Bloembergen, J. Ducuing and P. S. Pershan, "Interactions between light waves in a nonlinear dielectric," *Phys. Rev.*, vol. 127, pp. 1918–1939, Sept. 15, 1962.
[240] R. B. Miles and S. E. Harris, "Optical third-harmonic generation in alkali metal vapors," *IEEE J. Quantum Electron.*, vol. QE-9, pp. 470–484, Apr. 1973.
[241] P. P. Bey, J. F. Giuliani, and H. Rabin, "Generation of a phase-matched optical third harmonic by introduction of anomalous dispersion into a liquid medium," *Phys. Rev. Lett.*, vol. 19, pp. 819–821, Oct. 9, 1967.
[242] J. F. Young, G. C. Bjorklund, A. H. Kung, R. B. Miles, and S. E. Harris, "Third-harmonic generation in phase-matched Rb vapor," *Phys. Rev. Lett.*, vol. 27, pp. 1551–1553, Dec. 1971.
[243] A. H. Kung, J. F. Young, G. C. Bjorklund, and S. E. Harris, "Generation of vacuum ultraviolet radiation in phase-matched Cd vapor," *Phys. Rev. Lett.*, vol. 29, pp. 985–988, Oct. 9, 1972.
[244] D. M. Bloom, G. W. Bekkers, J. F. Young, and S. E. Harris, "Third harmonic generation in phase-matched alkali metal vapors," *Appl. Phys. Lett.*, vol. 26, pp. 687–689, June 15, 1975.
[245] D. M. Bloom, J. F. Young, and S. E. Harris, "Mixed metal vapor

phase matching for third-harmonic generation," *Appl. Phys. Lett.*, vol. 27, pp. 390–392, Oct. 1, 1975.

[246] A. H. Kung, J. F. Young, and S. E. Harris, "Generation of 1182 Å radiation in phase-matched mixtures of inert gases," *Appl. Phys. Lett.*, vol. 22, pp. 301–302, Mar. 15, 1973. See also errata, *Appl. Phys. Lett.*, vol. 28, p. 294, Mar. 1, 1976.

[247] R. T. Hodgson, P. P. Sorokin, and J. J. Wynne, "Tunable coherent vacuum-ultraviolet generation in atomic vapors," *Phys. Rev. Lett.*, vol. 32, pp. 343–346, Feb. 1974.

[248] J. A. Armstrong and J. J. Wynne, "Autoionizing states of Sr studied by the generation of tunable vacuum uv radiation," *Phys. Rev. Lett.*, vol. 33, pp. 1183–1185, Nov. 11, 1974.

[249] S. E. Harris and D. M. Bloom, "Resonantly two-photon pumped frequency converter," *Appl. Phys. Lett.*, vol. 24, pp. 229–230, Mar. 1, 1974.

[250] D. M. Bloom, J. T. Yardley, J. F. Young, and S. E. Harris, "Infrared up-conversion with resonantly two-photon pumped metal vapors," *Appl. Phys. Lett.*, vol. 24, pp. 427–428, May 1, 1974.

[251] A. H. Kung, "Generation of tunable picosecond VUV radiation," *Appl. Phys. Lett.*, vol. 25, pp. 653–654, Dec. 1, 1974.

[252] G. C. Bjorklund, "Effects of focusing on third-order nonlinear processes in isotropic media," *IEEE J. Quantum Electron.*, vol. QE-11, pp. 287–296, June 1975.

[253] S. E. Harris, "Generation of vacuum-ultraviolet and soft-X-ray radiation using high-order nonlinear optical polarizabilities," *Phys. Rev. Lett.*, vol. 31, pp. 341–344, Aug. 6, 1973.

[254] S. E. Harris, J. F. Young, A. H. Kung, D. M. Bloom, and G. C. Bjorklund, "Generation of ultraviolet and vacuum ultraviolet radiation," in *Laser Applications to Optics and Spectroscopy*, S. F. Jacobs, M. Sargent, III, J. F. Scott, and M. O. Scully, Eds. Reading, Mass: Addison Wesley, 1975, vol. 2, pp. 181–197. See also E. A. Stappaerts, "Harmonic generation at high field strengths. Frequency shifts and saturation phenomena," *Phys. Rev. A.*, vol. 11, pp. 1664–1667, May 1975.

[255] P. Eisenberger and S. L. McCall, "X-ray parametric conversion," *Phys. Rev. Lett.*, vol. 26, pp. 684–688, Mar. 22, 1971.

[256] P. M. Eisenberger and S. L. McCall, "Mixing of X-ray and optical photons," *Phys. Rev. A*, vol. 3, pp. 1145–1151, Mar. 1971.

[257] S. E. Harris and D. B. Lidow, "Nonlinear optical processes by Van der Waals interaction during collision," *Phys. Rev. Lett.*, vol. 33, pp. 674–676, Sept. 16, 1974.

[258] A. Ferguson, "How to make an X-ray laser," *New Scientist*, vol. 67, pp. 207–209, Oct. 23, 1975.

[259] D. E. Eastman and M. I. Nathan, "Photoelectron spectroscopy," *Phys. Today*, vol. 28, pp. 44–51, Apr. 1975.

[260] H. D. Jones, D. Eccleshell, and J. K. Temperley, "Propagation Characteristics of narrow X-ray pulses," U.S. Army Ballistic Research Lab., Rep. no. 1781, May 1975.

[261] R. Hofstadter, "The Atomic Accelerator," Stanford Univ. High Energy Physics Lab., Stanford, CA, Rep. 560, Apr. 23, 1968.

[262] P. V. Lenzo and E. G. Spencer, "High-speed low-power X-ray lithography," *Appl. Phys. Lett.*, vol. 24, pp. 289–291, Mar. 15, 1974.

[263] T. Zehnpfennig, R. Giacconi, R. Haggerty, W. Reidy and G. Vaiana, "A laboratory program to develop improved grazing incidence X-ray optics," National Aeronautics and Space Administration, Rep. NASA-CR-717, Feb. 1967.

[264] A. V. Baez, "Fresnel zone plate for optical image formation using extreme ultraviolet and soft X-radiation," *J. Opt. Soc. Amer.*, vol. 51, pp. 405–412, Apr. 1961.

[265] C. D. Pfeifer, L. D. Ferris, and W. M. Yen, "Optical image formation with a Fresnel zone plate using vacuum-ultraviolet radiation," *J. Opt. Soc. Amer.*, vol. 63, pp. 91–95, Jan. 1973.

[266] B. Niemann, D. Rudolph and G. Schmahl, "Soft X-ray imaging zone plates with large zone numbers for microscopic and spectroscopic applications," *Opt. Commun.*, vol. 12, pp. 160–163, Oct. 1974.

[267] E. Spiller and A. Segmüller, "Propagation of X-rays in waveguides," *Appl. Phys. Lett.*, vol. 24, pp. 60–61, Jan. 15, 1974.

[268] G. C. Bjorklund, S. E. Harris, and J. F. Young, "Vacuum ultraviolet holography," *Appl. Phys. Lett.*, vol. 25, pp. 451–452, Oct. 15, 1974.

Recombination lasers utilizing vapors of chemical elements. II. Laser action due to transitions in metal ions

V. V. Zhukov, V. S. Kucherov, E. L. Latush, and M. F. Sém

State University, Rostov-on-Don
(Submitted July 21, 1976)
Kvantovaya Elektron. (Moscow) 4, 1257–1267 (June 1977)

General requirements specifying the distribution of energy levels and discharge conditions are used as the basis of a discussion of the stimulated emission mechanisms in ionic recombination lasers utilizing strontium, calcium, beryllium, aluminum, tin, and lead vapors. The attention is concentrated on the strontium vapor laser. The population inversion which results in the emission of $\lambda = 430.5$ nm radiation from Sr II is calculated allowing for radiative and collisional transitions between the levels. The role of deexciting collisions with slow electrons in the depopulation of the lower laser level is demonstrated. The results are given of theoretical and experimental determination of the electron temperature in the afterglow of gas discharges in mixtures of metal vapors with inert gases. The electron temperature is found to rise with the metal vapor pressure and this effect is explained. Average powers of 0.5 W at $\lambda = 373.7$ nm from Ca II and 1 W at $\lambda = 430.5$ nm from Sr II at the pulse repetition frequency 5 kHz and efficiencies of 0.1–0.14% are reported. The distributions of the active levels of new recombination laser transitions are considered briefly for beryllium, aluminum, tin, and lead ions.

PACS numbers: 42.55.Hg

Up to now, the generation of coherent radiation in the recombination regime has been achieved mainly as a result of transitions in metal ions.[1–4] We shall consider the mechanisms of stimulated emission due to such transitions on the basis of the conditions for obtaining a population inversion during the plasma recombination stage which are deduced in the preceding paper.[5]

1. IONIC STRONTIUM VAPOR LASER

The ionic strontium vapor laser is the system in which a population inversion is achieved most completely as a result of the recombination-collision kinetics.[1] Therefore, we shall consider first the stimulated emission mechanism of this laser.

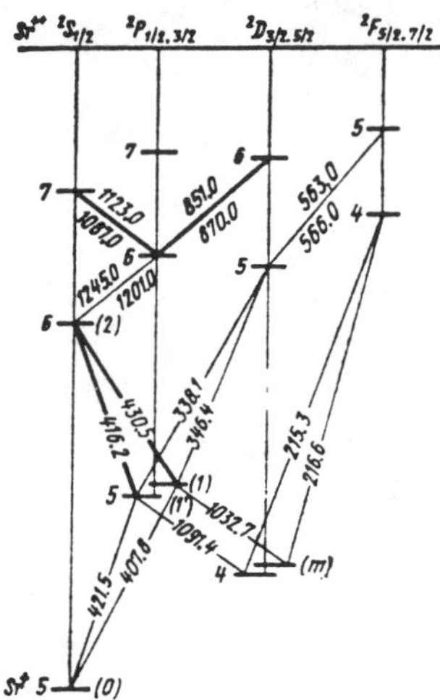

FIG. 1. Energy level scheme of the strontium ion. The thick lines represent the recombination laser transitions.

1. The energy level system of the strontium ion is shown in Fig. 1 together with the laser transitions achieved by us. The most interesting is the stimulated emission as a result of the $6^2S_{1/2}-5^2P_{3/2,1/2}$ transitions in Sr II resulting in the emission of the $\lambda = 430.5$ and 416.2 nm lines which lie in the short-wavelength part of the spectrum and are characterized by high output powers and gains. Stimulated emission as a result of these transitions is observed under optimal conditions during a brief peak in the discharge afterglow stage (Fig. 2b). When the discharge current exceeds the optimal value, the infrared transitions tend to be displaced toward the slow afterglow stage (Fig. 2e).

In an earlier paper[1] we demonstrated that the cause of the appearance of the ionic strontium lines during the afterglow stage is the impact-radiative recombination of doubly charged Sr^{++} ions and that the initial brief peak in the afterglow of the ionic strontium lines (Fig. 2c) is due to the recombination of the Sr^{++} ions created during a current pulse and the slow afterglow is due to the recombination of the Sr^{++} ions created after this pulse[6] by the reaction

$$He^{+} + Sr \rightarrow He + Sr^{++} + e. \quad (1)$$

We shall now consider the mechanism of population inversion in the Sr II ion. It is clear from Fig. 1 that the distribution of the laser levels of Sr II satisfies largely the general requirements postulated in Ref. 5. Thus, the 7S and 6D levels are the lowest in the group comprising 7S, 7P, 6D, 5F, and 4G and the 6P level is one of the higher levels in the group comprising 6S, 6P, 5D, and 4F. Similarly, the upper active level 6S of the strongest laser transitions ($\lambda = 430.5$ nm and $\lambda = 416.2$ nm) is the lowest in the group comprising 6S, 6P, 5D, and 4F and the lower active level 5P is the higher of the group of two levels 5P and 4D. Therefore, electron deexcitation concentrates the recombination pumping on the upper active levels and reduces the populations at the lower active levels.

The distribution of the active levels shows that a population inversion in the S–P transitions is unlikely to occur because of the optical excitation, particularly when the self-absorption is allowed for. This conclusion is in agreement with our calculations of the optical probability which we carried out by the Bates and Damgaard method in Ref. 1.

On the other hand, the presence of the 4D level located close to (~1 eV) the 5P level provides an efficient depopulation channel for the latter level (by electron deexcitation) in a low-temperature recombining plasma, which is a decisive factor in the establishment of a population inversion of 6S–5P transitions in the strontium ion under recombination conditions.

2. We shall illustrate this point by a simplified calculation of a population inversion of the strongest laser transition $6^2S_{1/2}-5^2P_{3/2}$ which occurs in Sr II and produces the $\lambda = 430.5$ nm line. We shall allow for the self-absorption of the $\lambda = 407.8$ nm radiation from the lower active level, electron deexcitation of all the levels, and excitation of the $5^2P_{3/2}$ level by electron impact from the metastable level $4^2D_{5/2}$. It is assumed that under optimal conditions the concentration of the strontium ions in the ground state is $N_0 = 0.5n_e$ and the pump energy W is supplied only to the upper level $6^2S_{1/2}$. Then, the system of equations for quasisteady conditions (the designations of the levels are given in Fig. 1 in parentheses) has the following form

$$W-(A_{21}+A_{21}'+F_{21}n_e+F_{21}n_e)N_2=0; \quad (2)$$

$$(A_{21}+F_{21}n_e)N_2+F_{01}n_eN_0+F_{m1}n_eN_m -(A_{10}g+A_{1m}+F_{1m}n_e+F_{10}n_e)N_1=0; \quad (3)$$

$$(A_{1m}+F_{1m}n_e)N_1-(F_{m0}n_e+F_{m1}n_e)N_m=0, \quad (4)$$

where A_{ik} and F_{ik} are the probabilities of radiative and collisional transitions from the i-th to the k-th level, respectively; N_i is the population of the i-th level; n_e is the electron density; g is the self-absorption factor.

The optical probabilities are calculated in the Coulomb approximation and the collisional probabilities by the method described in Refs. 7 and 8.

The results of the calculations (Fig. 3a) show that a population inversion capable of producing the $\lambda = 430.5$ nm line does not occur at low electron densities up to

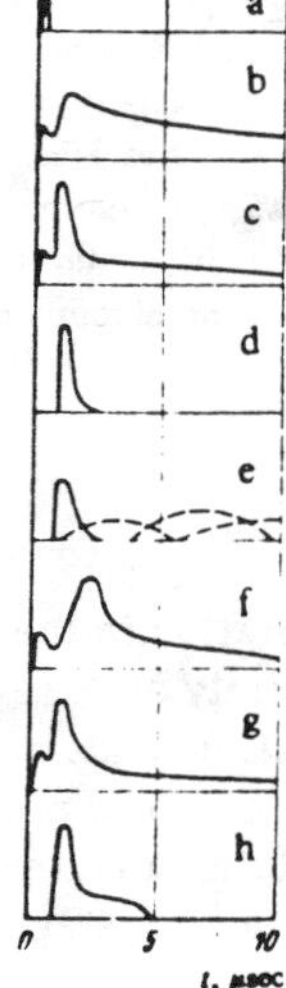

FIG. 2. Oscillograms of the spontaneous emission and coherent radiation: a) current pulse; b) afterglow emission of He I and Sr I lines; c) afterglow emission of Sr II lines in an Sr–He mixture; d) stimulated emission at $\lambda = 430.5$ nm from Sr II in an Sr–He mixture; e) stimulated emission due to infrared transitions in Sr II in an Sr–He mixture (the dashed curves show the positions of the stimulated emission pulses obtained when the current is increased); f) afterglow emission at $\lambda = 430.5$ nm from Sr II in an Sr–Ne mixture; g) afterglow emission at $\lambda = 430.5$ nm from Sr II in an Sr–Ne–H_2 mixture; h) stimulated emission at $\lambda = 430.5$ nm from Sr II in an Sr–Ne–H_2 mixture.

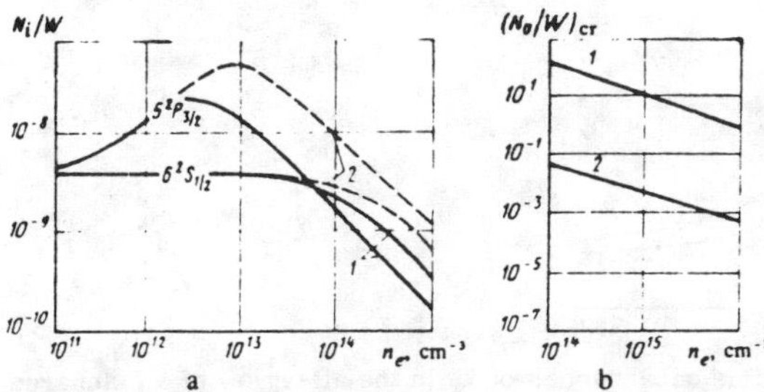

FIG. 3. Results of calculations of the populations of the $5^2P_{3/2}$ and $6^2S_{1/2}$ levels of Sr II (a) and of the quantity $(N_0/W)_{cr}$ (b) for electron temperatures corresponding to $kT_e = 10^3$ cm^{-1} (1) and $kT_e = 10^4$ cm^{-1} (2).

$n_e \sim 5\times10^{13}$ cm^{-3} because of the unfavorable ratio of the radiative lifetimes and the occurrence of self-absorption from the lower level. However, in spite of the fact that the self-absorption increases strongly with rising n_e (because of increase in N_0) and that the emission of radiation is highly unlikely in the range $n_e > 10^{13}$ cm^{-3}, it is found that when the electron density becomes $n_e > 5\times10^{13}$ cm^{-3} a considerable inversion of the $6^2S_{1/2}-5^2P_{3/2}$ transition takes place because at high electron densities the lower level is depopulated by electron de-excitation to the metastable D term and to the ground S state of the strontium ion.

An increase in the electron temperature T_e destroys this inversion because of a reduction in the rate of electron deexcitation and particularly because of an increase in the excitation of the lower laser level by electron impact from the metastable D term. The reported calculations do not allow for the excitation of levels by electron impact from the ground state of the ion, i.e., it is assumed that the terms containing N_0 in Eqs. (2)–(4) all vanish.

If allowance is made for the terms containing N_0, it is found that the population inversion is influenced also by the parameter N_0/W and for each electron temperature T_e there is a critical value of this parameter $(N_0/W)_{cr}$ above which there is no population inversion. Figure 3b gives the results of a calculation of this critical value for different temperatures T_e, which shows that $(N_0/W)_{cr}$ rises rapidly when T_e is reduced.

The existence of $(N_0/W)_{cr}$ explains why in most cases there is no stimulated emission of the violet lines of Sr II during the slow afterglow stage. In fact, during this stage the value of W falls steeply whereas N_0 changes only slightly and the parameter N_0/W becomes higher than the critical value. On the other hand, the rate of pumping in the case of generation of the infrared lines is governed mainly by the gain because there are no long-lived metastable levels in the lower group of terms. Therefore, stimulated emission as a result of the infrared transitions is shifted most readily in the direction of slow afterglow and the inversion is less sensitive to the value of T_e.

3. The dominant factor which governs the inversion of ionic transitions in strontium is the low value of the electron temperature T_e. Therefore, it is of interest to follow the behavior of T_e after the end of a current pulse. We shall begin by writing down the electron energy in an inert gas:

$$d/dt(3/2kT_e n_e) = -\delta\nu_{eff} 3/2\, k(T_e - T)n_e + \varepsilon_m\langle\sigma v_e\rangle N_m n_e + \Delta\varepsilon_r \alpha n_e^3, \quad (5)$$

where $\delta = 2m_e/M$ is the fraction of the energy given up in an elastic electron collision; ν_{eff} is the elastic collision frequency; ε_m is the energy of metastable atoms; N_m is the concentration of metastable atoms; $\langle\sigma v_e\rangle$ is the rate of quenching of these atoms by electrons; $\Delta\varepsilon_r$ is the energy evolved as a result of recombination; α is the recombination coefficient; T is the gas temperature.

An exact analytic solution of this equation is difficult to obtain because the recombination coefficient depends in a complex manner on T_e. We shall find the time during which the initial fast cooling of the electron gas take place. For $T_e \gg T$, the second and third terms in Eq. (5) can be ignored and the solution becomes

$$T_e \approx T_e^0 \exp(-t/\tau); \quad (6)$$

$$\tau \quad (\delta\nu_{eff})^{-1} = (\delta_a\nu_{ea} + \delta_i\nu_{ei})^{-1}, \quad (7)$$

where ν_{ea} and ν_{ei} are the frequencies of collisions of electrons with atoms and ions, respectively.

We shall now find T_e after the initial rapid fall, when quasisteady conditions are established and the right-hand side of Eq. (5) can be equated to zero. Bearing in mind that at high values of n_e

$$N_m = \frac{\alpha n_e^3}{\langle\sigma v_e\rangle n_e}, \quad (8)$$

we obtain

$$T_e - T = \frac{(\varepsilon_m + \Delta\varepsilon_r)\,\alpha n_e^2}{3/2k\delta\nu_{eff}}. \quad (9)$$

The frequency of elastic collisions of electrons with helium atoms can be taken from Ref. 9:

$$\delta\nu_{eff} = \frac{2m_e}{M}\,\sigma_{ae} N_{He}\left(\frac{8kT_e}{\pi m}\right)^{1/2} = 3.0\cdot10^3 P_{He} T_e^{1/2} = BP_{He} T_e^{1/2}, \quad (10)$$

where N_{He} is the concentration of the helium atoms; P_{He} is the helium pressure; B is a constant.

The recombination coefficient can be represented in the form[5]

$$\alpha = c(z)\, T_e^{-9/2}. \quad (11)$$

Substituting Eqs. (10) and (11) into Eq. (9), we find that

$$T_e^6 \approx \frac{(\varepsilon_m + \Delta\varepsilon_r)\, c(1)\, n_e^2}{3/2 kBP_{He}}. \quad (12)$$

Under our conditions, the expression $\varepsilon_m + \Delta\varepsilon_r$ is near equal to the ionization potential of helium which is ~20 eV; $n_e \approx 5\times10^{14}$ cm^{-3} and $P_{He} = 300$ Torr. We then find from Eq. (12) that the electron temperature T_e is ~2500 °K, i.e., after the initial rapid fall the temperature T_e is still fairly high and we have to allow for the deexcitation processes and the reverse processes involving the excitation of levels by electron impact.

We shall now find the expression for the duration τ_r of a recombination peak producing ionic lines on condition that T_e is given by Eq. (12). It follows from Eqs. (11) and (12) that τ_r is described by

$$\tau_r = \frac{1}{\alpha n_e^2} = \left[\frac{(\varepsilon_m + \Delta\varepsilon_r)\, c(1)}{{}^3/_2 kBP_{\text{He}}}\right]^{3/4} \frac{n_e^{-1/2}}{c(2)}. \tag{13}$$

When the concentration of charged particles in a plasma is high, the value of T_e may be affected not only by elastic collisions of electrons with neutral atoms but also with ions and the frequency of the latter can be represented in the form[9]

$$\delta_i \nu_{ei} = \frac{4e^4 N_{\text{He}^+}}{3(kT_e)^{3/2}} \frac{(2\pi m_e)^{1/2}}{M} L, \tag{14}$$

where e is the electron charge; N^+_{He} is the concentration of the singly charged helium ions; L is the Coulomb logarithm.

When allowance is made for these collisions, Eq. (9) can be rewritten in the form

$$T_e - T = \frac{(\varepsilon_m + \Delta\varepsilon_r)\, \alpha n_e^2}{{}^3/_2 k (\delta_a \nu_{ea} + \delta_i \nu_{ei})}. \tag{15}$$

Estimates based on Eqs. (10) and (14) show that in the case of discharges in helium the frequencies of elastic collisions with atoms and ions become comparable for $n_e \sim 10^{14}$ cm^{-3}, $T_e = 3000$ °K, and $P_{\text{He}} = 10$ Torr.

Thus, it follows from the above analysis that a current pulse is followed by a rapid fall of T_e to a value in the range 2000–4000 °K and this changes to a monotonic slow decay of the electron temperature. The time of the initial fall and the quasisteady value of T_e during the slow decay are governed primarily by the frequencies of elastic collisions of electrons with atoms and ions.

4. We shall use the results of the above analysis of the behavior of T_e during the discharge afterglow stage in considering the behavior of the characteristics of stimulated emission from an Sr–He laser when the discharge conditions are varied.

The experimental evidence shows that an increase in the strontium vapor pressure (P_{Sr}) increases the amplitude and duration of a recombination peak representing the ionic strontium lines; the stimulated emission power rises with P_{Sr} and, as τ_r increases, this power begins

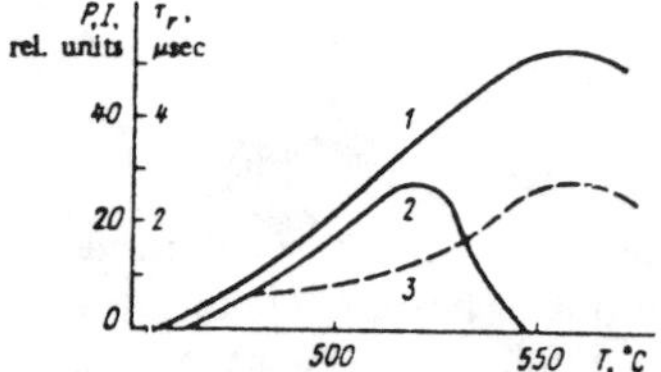

FIG. 4. Dependences of the amplitude of the recombination peak I (curve 1), stimulated output power P (curve 2), and duration of recombination peak τ_r (curve 3) at the $\lambda = 430.5$ nm wavelength of Sr II on the laser tube temperature; the helium pressure was 70 Torr.

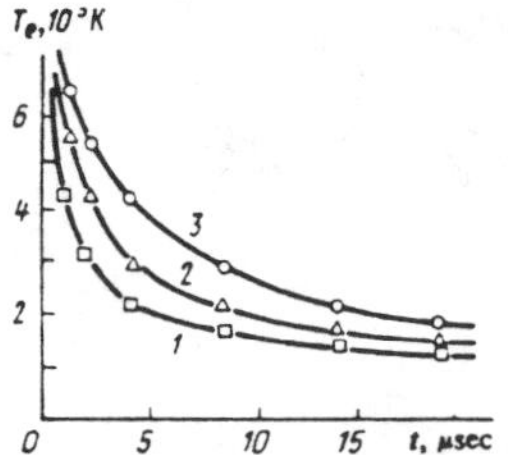

FIG. 5. Time dependences of T_e in the afterglow of a discharge in pure helium (curve 1) and of the strontium vapor pressures 3×10^{-3} Torr (curve 2) and 2×10^{-2} Torr (curve 3). The helium pressure was 10 Torr, the tube diameter was 8 mm, and the current in the pulse was 50 A.

to decrease and disappears completely in spite of the continuing rise of the amplitude of the recombination peak (Fig. 4). This increase in the duration of recombination can be explained only by the rise of T_e because introduction of an easily ionizable component (strontium vapor) into the discharge does not reduce the electron density but probably increases it. This conclusion is confirmed by our probe measurements of T_e in the discharge afterglow (Fig. 5).

The increase in T_e and in the duration of recombination of the Sr^{++} ions with increasing P_{Sr} can be understood if we bear in mind that the introduction of the vapor of the easily ionizable component results in the replacement of the helium ions with the much heavier strontium ions for which δ is over an order of magnitude smaller than for helium. Consequently, it follows from Eqs. (7) and (15) that the duration of the initial fall of the electron temperature and the value of T_e increase. Moreover, at temperatures $T_e \geq 3000$ °K the impact recombination coefficients of various singly charged ions may differ.[10] For example, in the case of atoms with a relatively uniform density of levels in the spectrum (alkali and alkaline earth metals), the $T_e^{-9/2}$ law is obeyed up to high temperatures [$(8–10)\times10^3$ °K]. In the case of atoms with a nonuniform spectrum (inert gases), the recombination coefficient falls much more rapidly with rising T_e. For example, at $T_e \approx 6000$ °K, we have $\alpha(K^+) \approx 50\alpha(He^+)$. Thus, the strong recombination of singly charged strontium ions causes recombination heating of the electron gas during the afterglow stage and, therefore, the process of recombination of the doubly charged strontium ions slows down. It follows from the above discussion that these two factors should increase T_e during the afterglow stage and quench the laser action. Moreover, as P_{Sr} increases, so does the concentration of the strontium ions in the ground state, which facilitates (under the conditions of rising T_e) the quenching because of the filling of the lower active levels by electron impact from the ground state of the strontium ion.

5. In view of the condition that T_e should be low, the pressure and nature of the buffer gas become particularly important. In this sense, helium has unique properties. Helium is the lightest inert gas and, therefore, in the case of elastic collisions with atoms or helium ions the electrons give up a relatively large part of their energy. Moreover, the cross section for the elastic collisions of electrons with helium in the range $kT_e < 1$ eV is

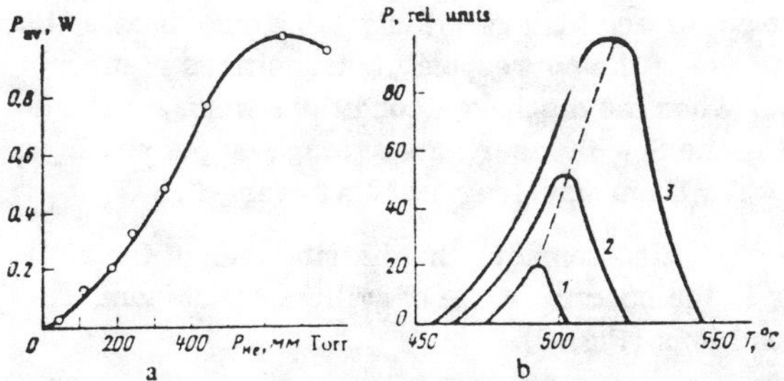

FIG. 6. Dependences of the average stimulated emission power at the λ = 430.5 nm wavelength of Sr II on the helium pressure (a) and the temperature of the laser tube (b) at helium pressures of 5, 20, and 70 Torr (curves 1, 2, and 3, respectively). The tube diameter was 11 mm, the active length was 50 cm, and the pulse repetition frequency was 5 kHz.

$\sim 5\times 10^{-16}$ cm^2, which is considerably greater than in the case of collisions of electrons with neon and other inert gases. These factors may result in rapid initiation and effective continuation of the processes responsible for the pumping of the levels and creation of a population inversion of the investigated transitions. This is supported by, for example, the much shorter duration of the recombination peak of the Sr II lines for a discharge in an Sr–He mixture, compared with that in an Sr–He mixture (see Figs. 2c and 2f). Another important factor is the high ionization potential of helium which does not prevent the creation of a high concentration of the doubly charged strontium ions during a current pulse and attainment of high rates of pumping because of their recombination. Therefore, stimulated emission of the violet lines of Sr II is observed in a mixture with helium, and when the helium pressure is increased right up to 600–700 Torr, the stimulated emission power (Figs. 6a) and the optimal strontium vapor pressure (Fig. 6b) both increase; this enhances the recombination pumping because of an increase in the concentration of the Sr^{++} ions. One of the reasons for the increase in the stimulated emission power with rising helium pressure may also be a greater energy deposition per unit length of the discharge.

The use of the light helium isotope (He^3) as the buffer gas made it possible to obtain stimulated emission at lower helium pressures (~1–2 Torr) and to increase the stimulated emission power by 15–20% at high helium pressures.

It seemed to interest to investigate hydrogen as the buffer gas because it is even lighter than helium. As in Ref. 11, we were unable to achieve stimulated emission of the violet lines of Sr II in an $Sr–H_2$ mixture. This could be explained by the existence of the parameter $(N_0/W)_{cr}$ and the general principles for obtaining a population inversion during the plasma recombination stage.[5] In fact, the low ionization potential of H_2 in the $Sr–H_2$ plasma made it impossible to create a high concentration of the doubly charged Sr^{++} ions and, consequently, the rate of pumping W of the upper active levels because of the recombination of Sr^{++} was less than in the case of the Sr–He mixtures. Moreover, at high strontium vapor pressures $[N_0/W > (N_0/W)_{cr}]$ the population could not be inverted because of the predominant repopulation of the lower active levels by electron impact from the ground and metastable states of the strontium ion.

However, the addition of a small amount of hydrogen to an Sr–He mixture so that the concentration of the doubly charged strontium ions and rate of pumping were not affected, reduced the duration of recombination of Sr^{++} (see Fig. 2g), i.e., it reduced T_e and gave rise to stimulated emission. Moreover, the addition of H_2 to Sr–He and Sr–Ne mixtures produced stimulated emission during the slow afterglow stage and such emission lasted 6–7 μsec (Fig. 2h).

The maximum pulse repetition frequency was determined for an Sr–He mixture excited by pairs of current pulses. As expected, the stimulated emission pulses could be shifted until they were separated by ~1 μsec without a reduction in the power of the second pulse, i.e., under these conditions the second current pulse was not superimposed on the initial recombination peak of the spontaneous radiation after the first pulse.

6. We optimized the laser characteristics on the basis of the above discussion of the pumping mechanism and population inversion. A ceramic tube with nickel electrodes and uniformly distributed pieces of metallic strontium was the active part of the strontium laser. Stimulated emission was usually observed under self-heating conditions.

The power supply unit of the Sr–He laser included a thyratron and had the circuit suggested in Ref. 12. This excitation circuit generated voltage pulses up to 20 kV and current pulses up to 300 A of duration in the range 100–300 nsec, and it ensured stable operation at high helium pressures.

Stimulated emission was observed mainly at the λ = 430.5 nm wavelength. In a conventional resonator the λ = 416.2 nm line was greatly weakened because of the competition for the shared upper active level. When the stimulated emission at λ = 430.5 nm was suppressed by introducing a dispersive element (prism), the λ = 416.2 nm line increased up to 60% of the power of the λ = 430.5 nm emission.

When a tube with an internal diameter of 11 mm and an active length of 50 cm was excited by current pulses of 5 kHz repetition frequency and 150 nsec duration, the stimulated emission at the λ = 430.5 nm wavelength was characterized by an average output power of 1 W and the efficiency was 0.1–0.14%. The pulse power was ~0.4 kW and the duration of the stimulated emission pulses was 0.5 μsec. The gain reached 30 dB/m and the laser tube could be operated in the superradiance regime with one mirror but the optimal transmission coefficient of the exit mirror was 30–50%.

These stimulated emission parameters were far from optimal. An increase in the volume of the active medium, improvement of the characteristics of the excitation pulses, and modification of the discharge tube construction should increase greatly the output power and efficiency (a particularly promising modification would

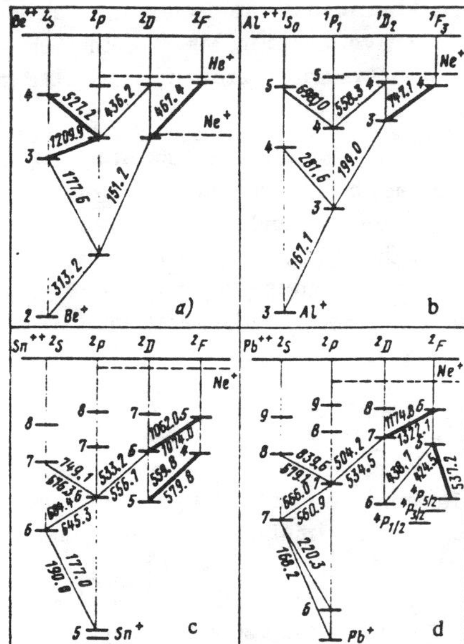

FIG. 7. Energy level schemes of the beryllium, aluminum, tin, and lead ions. The thick lines are the laser transitions.

be the adoption of a transverse discharge configuration). A simple increase of the pulse repetition frequency to 10–20 kHz without any change in the remaining parameters of the discharge could increase the average power to a few watts.

An increase in the pulse repetition frequency would also increase the efficiency. If the repetition frequency were such that the concentrations of the Sr^+ and He^+ ions during the time interval between the pulses did not fall significantly, a greater proportion of the pulse energy would be used to create the Sr^{++} ions and the Sr^+ ions would be created by multistage ionization from the ground state. Estimates indicate that in this case the efficiency could reach 0.5–1%.

Thus, the general principles of the recombination-collision kinetics and an analysis of the behavior of T_e during the discharge afterglow stage make it possible to understand the basic features of the appearance of a population inversion of the ionic transitions in Sr II and to explain the influence of the discharge parameters on the stimulated emission from the Sr–He laser.

2. LASER TRANSITIONS IN IONIC SPECTRA OF OTHER METALS

Some laser transitions observed by us in vapors of other chemical elements will now be considered from the point of view of the recombination-collision principles.

We shall begin by considering the ionic calcium vapor laser. The distributions of the Ca II and Sr II levels are almost identical and, therefore, stimulated emission from calcium should occur as a result of similar laser transitions, should have similar characteristics, and the above discussion should apply also to the calcium vapor laser. The greatest interest lies in the stimulated emission of the $\lambda = 373.7$ and $\lambda = 370.6$ nm lines of Ca II because these lines are characterized by a fairly high output power and high gain (only 1.5 times smaller than in the case of the corresponding transitions in strontium). When the discharge conditions were similar to those in the Sr–He laser, the average output power at the $\lambda = 373.7$ nm wavelength of Ca II was ~0.5 W.

We shall also consider the distributions of the active levels in the spectra of the beryllium, aluminum, tin, and lead ions (Fig. 7).

The distribution of the levels active in the $\lambda = 467.3$ nm transition in Be II (Fig. 7a) is not quite appropriate for stimulated emission during the plasma recombination stage because although the lower active level $3D$ is the highest in the $n = 3$ group, the upper active level $4F$ is the highest in the $n = 4$ group. Therefore, stimulated emission of this line occurs mainly because of the favorable ratio of the optical lifetimes of the levels and it disappears at high discharge currents because of the electron de-excitation of the upper level. Consequently, stimulated emission occurs at low discharge currents because of the charge exchange with helium ions and when the current is increased, the stimulated emission pulse moves further on the time scale into the afterglow stage where the electron density is lower and the conditions for a stimulated emission are again favorable. The distribution of the levels for the $4S$–$3P$ transition ($\lambda = 527.1$ nm) is more convenient for stimulated emission in the recombination regime and, therefore, in spite of the lower rate of pumping of the upper active level, stimulated emission does occur as a result of this transition during the recombination of the doubly charged Be^{++} ions at high discharge currents. The $3P$–$3S$ transition becomes inverted because of the favorable ratio of the level lifetimes, as a result of which stimulated emission is obtained at low discharge currents because of the pumping in the course of charge exchange between the Be atoms and Ne^+ ions.

As pointed out in Ref. 13, the transition producing the $\lambda = 177.6$ nm line of Be II is a potential laser transition: the upper level is the lowest in the group $3S$, $3P$, and $3D$ and the lower level is fairly close to the ground state of the beryllium ions so that one may expect the latter level to be depopulated by superelastic electron impact. In this connection it is worth mentioning the possibility of a population inversion in the recombination regime as a result of S–P and D–P transitions in doubly ionized scandium, which should give rise to short-wavelength radiation ($\lambda \sim 200$ nm).

The distribution of the levels involved in the 4^1F_3–3^1D_2 transition ($\lambda = 747.1$ nm) in Al II is also favorable for a population inversion in the recombination-collision regime (Fig. 7b). The upper active level is one of the lowest in the group of closely spaced levels $5S$, $5P$, $4D$, and $4F$, and the lower active level is the highest in the group $3D$, $4P$, and $4S$. Moreover, the upper level is characterized by a high statistical weight. Therefore, this transition produces a fairly high stimulated emission power and is characterized by a high coefficient when the discharge current is large during the recombination peak of the spontaneous radiation.

For the same reason the recombination regime can

give rise to stimulated emission of the $\lambda = 579.9$ and 558.8 nm lines of Sn II (Fig. 7c). The nonoptimal positions of the lower levels of these transitions is to some extent compensated by the higher optical probability of the depopulation of the lower level and, therefore, the stimulated emission is optimal at lower discharge currents and it is not as strong as in the case of aluminum. The upper laser levels involved in the infrared transitions in Sn II are situated conveniently. This is not quite true of the lower levels of these transitions and since the gap between the active levels involved in the infrared transitions is small, the saturation of the population because of electron de-excitation occurs at lower electron densities and this results in the saturation of the stimulated emission at low currents when the pumping is due to charge exchange with He^+ [in accordance with the reaction of the (1) type] or with Ne^+.

Stimulated emission as a result of the $5F-6D$ transitions in the lead vapor (Fig. 7d) does not occur because of the inappropriate distribution of the lower levels (they lie fairly low in the group $7S$, $7P$, and $6D$). At low currents the inversion is prevented by the less favorable (than for other elements) ratio of the optical lifetimes of the upper and lower active levels.

The levels involved in the infrared transitions in Pb II are more favorably distributed and this provides suitable conditions for a population inversion (at relatively low currents).

Stimulated emission of the $\lambda = 537.2$ nm line of Pb II occurs as a result of transitions between levels of different configurations. In this case the distribution of the active levels is more favorable. True optical transitions from the lower active levels are forbidden within this configuration and this reduces the probability of electron de-excitation of the lower level. Moreover, the $6^4P_{1/2,3/2,5/2}$ levels are semimetastable. These factors mean that low values of T_e are needed for a population inversion and, therefore, stimulated emission is not observed immediately after the current pulse but later during the afterglow when levels are pumped by the recombination of doubly charged Pb^{++} ions formed as a result of thermal collisions of the Pb atoms with the He^+ ions [this is analogous to the reaction (1)].

In addition to those discussed above, recombination laser transitions occur also in the ionic spectra of barium,[1] thallium,[2] magnesium,[6] mercury, cadmium, zinc,[14] and etc. The distribution of the laser levels of these elements is quite similar to the distribution of the levels of the elements analyzed above and it satisfies the general requirements to a greater or smaller extent. Therefore, we shall not consider them here.

Our investigation has made clear the special characteristics of stimulated emission in recombination lasers. It is shown that the strontium and calcium vapor lasers can be very efficient and are among the most promising ionic vapor lasers.

The observed characteristics of stimulated emission from the existing recombination lasers are in good agreement with the general requirements formulated in Ref. 5 and, therefore, these requirements can be used in the search for new recombination laser transitions.

[1]E. L. Latush and M. F. Sém, Kvantovaya Elektron. (Moscow) No. 3(15), 66 (1973) [Sov. J Quantum Electron. 3, 216 (1973)].

[2]I. G. Ivanov and M. F. Sém, Zh. Prikl. Spektrosk. 19, 358 (1973).

[3]V. V. Zhukov, V. G. Il'yushko, E. L. Latush, and M. F. Sém, Kvantovaya Elektron. (Moscow) 2, 1409 (1975) [Sov. J. Quantum Electron. 5, 757 (1975)].

[4]V. V. Zhukov, E. L. Latush, V. S. Mikhalevskiĭ, and M F. Sém, Kvantovaya Elektron. (Moscow) 2, 842 (1975) [Sov. J. Quantum Electron. 5, 468 (1975)].

[5]V. V. Zhukov, E. L. Latush, V. S. Mikhalevskiĭ, and M. F. Sém, Kvantovaya Elektron. (Moscow) 4, 1249 (1977) [Sov. J. Quantum Electron. 7, 704 (1977)].

[6]E. L. Latush and M. F. Sém, Pis'ma Zh. Eksp. Teor. Fiz. 15, 645 (1972) [JETP Lett. 15, 457 (1972)].

[7]E. L. Latush, V. S. Mikhalevskiĭ, and M. F. Sém, Opt. Spektrosk. 34, 214 (1973) [Opt. Spectrosc. (USSR) 34, 120 (1973)].

[8]L. A. Vaĭnshtein, I. I. Sobel'man and E. A. Yukov, Electron-Excitation Cross Sections of Atoms and Ions [in Russian], Nauka, Moscow (1973).

[9]I. Ya. Fugol', O. N. Grigorashchenko, and D. A. Myshkis, Zh. Eksp. Teor. Fiz. 60, 423 (1971) [Sov. Phys. JETP 33, 227 (1971)].

[10]L. M. Biberman, V. S. Vorob'ev, and I. G. Yakubov, Usp. Fiz. Nauk 107, 353 (1972) [Sov. Phys. Usp. 15, 375 (1973)].

[11]É. K. Karabut, V. F. Kravchenko, V. S. Mikhalevskiĭ, and A. P. Shelepo, Kvantovaya Elektron. (Moscow) 2, 2514 (1975 [Sov. J. Quantum Electron. 5, 1371 (1975)].

[12]P. A. Bokhan, V. N. Nikolaev, and V. I. Solomonov, Kvantovaya Elektron. (Moscow) 2, 159 (1975) [Sov. J. Quantum Electron. 5, 96 (1975)].

[13]L. I. Gudzenko and S. I. Yakovlenko, Kratk. Soobshch. Fiz. No. 7, 3 (1970).

[14]V. S. Aleĭnikov, Opt. Spektrosk. 28, 31 (1970) [Opt. Spectrosc. (USSR) 28, 15 (1970)].

Translated by A. Tybulewicz

Reprinted with permission from *Applied Physics Letters,* Vol. 31(3), pp. 181-184 (August 1, 1977). ©1977 American Institute of Physics.

Vacuum ultraviolet lasing from highly ionized noble gases[a)]

Jack B. Marling and Daniel B. Lang[b)]

University of California Lawrence Livermore Laboratory, Livermore, California 94550
(Received 11 April 1977; accepted for publication 17 May 1977)

Vacuum ultraviolet laser emission was obtained from highly ionized noble gases using a simple longitudinal discharge device. Electric discharge excitation pulses with 500 ns duration and peak current density up to 14000 A/cm^2 produced lasing on five argon and krypton ion transitions below 200 nm. The two strongest emissions exhibited 0.1–1 kW peak power from Kr IV at 195.027 nm and 175.641 nm.

PACS numbers: 42.55.Fn, 42.72.+h, 33.20.Ni

This investigation evaluates ionized noble gases for use as a simple and reliable high-repetition-rate vacuum ultraviolet laser. A number of different types of laser systems have exhibited laser emission in the vacuum ultraviolet. Large single-shot electron-beam-pumped devices yielded strong laser emission from the excimer ArF at 193 nm [1] and from the noble-gas dimers Xe_2 at 172 nm,[2] Kr_2 at 146 nm,[3] and Ar_2 at 126 nm.[4] Molecular laser emission has also been observed from CO at 190 nm.[5] Vacuum ultraviolet superfluorescence has been obtained from the molecular hydrogen Lyman bands for H_2, HD, and D_2 in the range 152–161 nm [6] and also from the Werner bands in the range 116–124 nm.[7] A traveling wave electric discharge device has yielded superfluorescent emission at 155 nm [8] from C IV present as impurities, and most recently from the excimer ArCl at 175 nm.[9] Other sources of coherent ultraviolet light have been reviewed.[10] These sources of direct VUV laser emission are essentially single-shot or low-repetition-rate devices but they do provide very high peak powers in the range 10^5–10^9 W. This present paper reports the successful extension of simple Z-pinch ion laser technology[11] into the vacuum ultraviolet, so that the convenience of all day hands-off operation at multihertz repetition rate can be available in a relatively inexpensive, simple, and small device. This approach has already been successful in opening the chemical ultraviolet to dozens of ion laser emission lines spanning the range 200–300 nm,[11,12] in addition to the five vacuum ultraviolet laser emission lines observed in this present study. Of particular interest is the very strong laser emission observed from Kr IV at 195.027 nm and 175.641 nm which exhibit relatively low threshold, high gain, and usefully high peak power in the 0.1–1-kW range.

A straightforward extension of simple Z-pinch longitudinal discharge ion laser technology into the vacuum ultraviolet can be achieved by increasing discharge current density to above 10 000 A/cm^2 and using high-reflectivity dielectric mirrors to permit lasing even on low-gain transitions. Multilayer dielectric coating technology is fairly well developed for the region above 200 nm, so that ~98% R coatings are easily available. However, coating technology for the region below 200 nm is not well developed, primarily because very few commercial organizations have the instrumentation for vacuum ultraviolet transmission and reflectance measurements. Nevertheless, the need for vacuum ultraviolet dielectric mirrors for the noble-gas dimer lasers has stimulated development in this area, so that a dielectric mirror reflectivity of about 95% can be

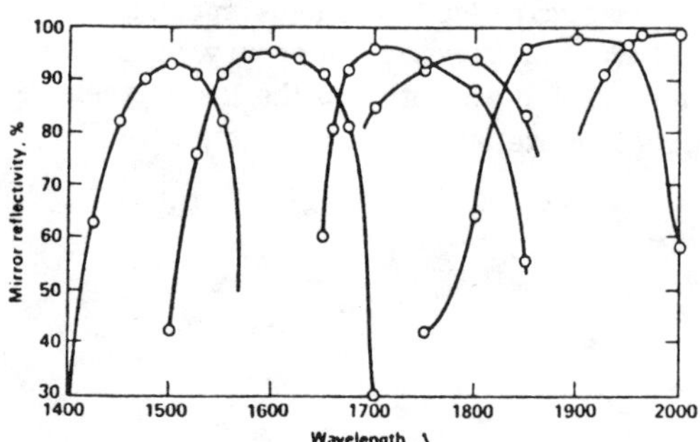

FIG. 1. Measured dielectric mirror reflectivity achievable in the vacuum ultraviolet from 145 to 200 nm for the six typical mirrors used in this study.

[a)]Work performed under the auspices of the U.S. Energy Research and Development Administration under Contract No. 7405-Eng-48.

[b)]Present address: California Institute of Technology Pasadena, Calif.

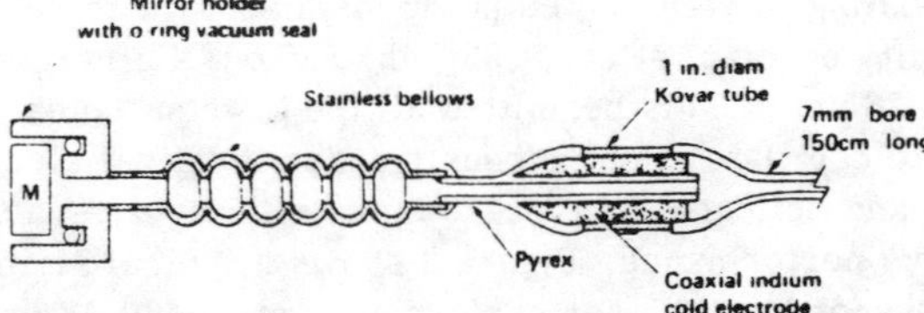

FIG. 2. Schematic diagram of mirror holder connected to the ion laser by a flexible metal bellows. The electrode is coaxial cold indium with electrical connection by the outer Kovar tube.

obtained for any wavelength in the range 145–200 nm.[13] Figure 1 shows the reflectance curves of six sets of dielectric mirrors used to cover the range 145–205 nm reported in this investigation. It can be seen that reflectivity generally exceeded 90% throughout this range, reaching a maximum of about 96% at 160 nm and 98% at 190 nm. Each mirror was exposed directly to the plasma discharge to avoid losses from Brewster windows, used in the investigation above 200 nm.[11] Figure 2 shows the experimental configuration with the mirror sealed by an O-ring and connected to the laser tube by means of a stainless-steel bellows. This permits mirror adjustment while maintaining a vacuum-tight connection. The mirror concave radius of curvature was 10 m. Gas flowed continuously from anode to cathode at an operating pressure of 5–30 μ, depending on the gas.

The electrical configuration is identical to the configuration described earlier,[11] except that the energy storage capacitor was increased from 0.03 to 0.12 μF in the present investigation. An all coaxial low-inductance electrical discharge geometry permitted a discharge rise time of less than 200 ns, even with the 150-cm-long discharge length. The electrodes were all coaxial and made from indium to form a cold cathode and anode. Figure 2 shows the electrode configuration, which has been extremely successful in maintaining low inductance from its coaxial geometry and perhaps more importantly in preventing mirror contamination by sputtered material. All sputtered material is directed away from the mirrors, as shown in Fig. 2, and toward the discharge bore. Such an arrangement permits pulsed operation for of the order of 10^9 shots without difficulty. Capacitor energy is switched by means of a hydrogen thyratron to permit high repetition rates, details of which are shown in Figs. 1 and 2 of Ref. 11; the electrical and mechanical layout is detailed in Fig. 3 of Ref. 11. The discharge length is 150 cm with a 7-mm-bore inside diameter.

TABLE I. Vacuum ultraviolet ion laser emission from noble gases.

Measured wavelength vacuum nm ± 0.003 nm	Spectrum	Threshold[b] (A/cm^2)	Relative[c] performance
206.530[a]	Ne IV ?	4000	~50
202.219[a]	Ne IV	4500	~50
184.343	Ar V ?	11 000	~10
219.192[a]	Kr IV	6200	600
205.108[a]	Kr IV	7500	3
196.808	Kr IV	8000	~4
195.027	Kr IV	7000	440
183.243	Kr V ?	9600	10
175.641	Kr IV	7800	1000
231.536[a]	Xe IV ?	3000	1400

[a] Wavelengths measured in air. These lines are included from Ref. 11 for comparison.
[b] Threshold at pressure for optimum output. Threshold can be up to half this value at lower pressure.
[c] Performance measured at 11 000 A/cm^2 discharge current density. Pressure was 6 μ for the krypton and 10 μ for the argon VUV transitions. The transitions from Ref. 11 are given in watts.

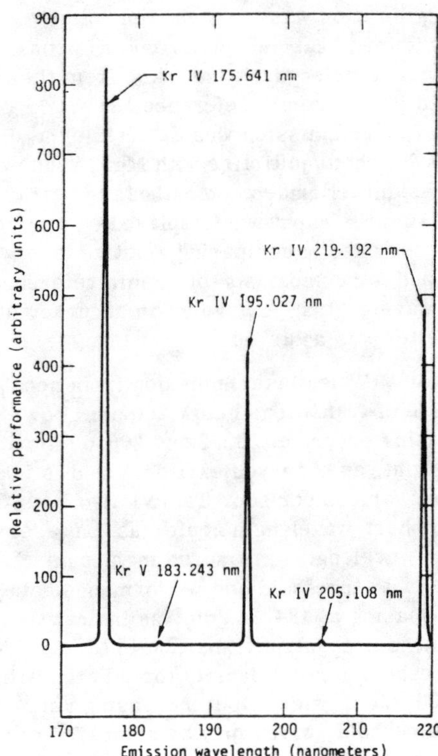

FIG. 3. Laser performance of krypton at 11 400 A/cm^2 discharge current density, as displayed on a strip-chart recording of photomultiplier output from the scanning vacuum monochromator. The transitions at 183 and 205 nm are about 100 times weaker than the three main laser lines at 176, 195 and 219 nm. Wavelengths below 200 nm are given in vacuum nanometers.

Spectroscopy of the new ion laser lines was performed by a 0.3-m vacuum scanning monochromator, generally in the second to fourth order of the 1200-line/

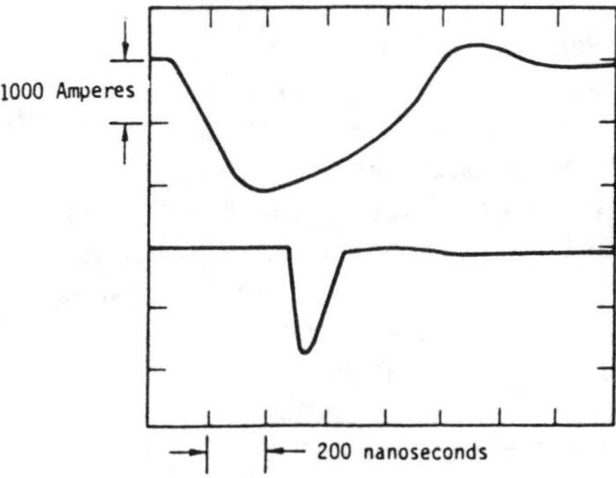

FIG. 4. Discharge current in amperes (upper trace) compared to laser emission at 195 nm. Laser emission at 176 nm is similar. Vertical scale of lower trace is uncalibrated.

mm grating. Calibration was from an iron hollow-cathode lamp with neon carrier gas. Iron and neon vacuum reference wavelengths were taken from the recently published list of atomic reference lines.[14] Spontaneous and laser emission was detected by a vacuum ultraviolet photomultiplier with MgF_2 window material and cesium telluride photocathode to permit sensitivity to 110 nm. Output was displayed on a strip-chart recorder for ease in comparing relative laser performance, and for comparison of atomic reference line and laser wavelengths. A wavelength accuracy of 0.003 nm or better was achieved.

The search for VUV ion laser emission from neon was unproductive of transitions below 200 nm. However, strong lasing occurs at 202.2 and 206.5 nm with quite low threshold, as observed earlier,[11] and is included in Table I for comparison. Table I also lists the other observed short-wavelength noble-gas ion laser transitions with wavelengths measured in vacuum nanometers and with threshold and performance data. Argon exhibited lasing at 184.343 nm, as indicated in Table I, on what is probably a transition in the Ar V spectrum. Threshold current density for this transition was about 11 000 A/cm^2 with output increasing very rapidly above threshold, which may be compared to the Ar IV laser lines,[11] which were also seen in this study and exhibited threshold at about 3000–6000 A/cm^2.

Krypton was most productive of vacuum ultraviolet ion laser emission of the noble gases and exhibited lasing at 196.8, 195.0, 183.2, and 175.6 nm as shown in Table I. The emission at 195.027 nm was observed earlier,[11] but is actually much stronger than first indicated.[11] Peak output of several hundred watts is available for this line with low-loss dielectric mirrors, which makes this one of the strongest ion laser lines in krypton and similar in performance to the strong Kr IV line at 219.2 nm, also included in Table I for comparison. Very strong and high gain lasing was observed at 175.641 nm, apparently from the Kr IV spectrum since threshold and performance was similar to the krypton lines at 195 nm and 219 nm. However, the line at 175.6 nm was the strongest of all krypton ion laser lines with a peak power of about 1000 W available with low-loss dielectric mirrors (for example, $R_1 = 95\%$, $R_2 = 75\%$). The krypton line at 176 nm is, thus, unique in exhibiting both the shortest wavelength and highest peak power of any VUV line yet observed in the noble gases.

Lasing observed at 183.243 nm appears to belong to the Kr V spectrum, since lasing threshold occurred at about 10 000 A/cm^2, well above that of the other Kr IV ion lines. Output was about 100 times weaker than the other VUV laser lines in krypton, but this line may well be strong at higher discharge current densities than attempted in this investigation, since output was increasing very rapidly above 11 000 A/cm^2. Xenon was unproductive of vacuum ultraviolet laser emission below 200 nm, but very strong lasing at 231.5 nm is included in Table I for comparison.

In order to assess the relative performance of the new krypton VUV ion laser transitions, the dielectric mirrors were replaced by aluminum mirrors with MgF_2 overcoating to yield 3% output transmission with reflectivity constant at about 83% throughout the range 170–220 nm.[13] This permitted all the krypton laser lines to oscillate simultaneously under identical electrical and optical conditions to more effectively evaluate relative performance. Figure 3 shows a typical strip-chart recording of laser performance at 11 400 A/cm^2 excitation current density as the vacuum spectrometer scanned from 170 to 220 nm. Figure 3 shows that the three transitions at 176, 195, and 219 nm are of nearly equal strength, and perhaps two orders of magnitude stronger than the transitions at 183 and 205 nm. Actual linewidth is much narrower than Fig. 3 indicates and is of order 0.002 nm. Because the photomultiplier in use had a rise time of about 15–20 ns, it was sufficiently fast to measure both pulse shape and peak power. Figure 4 shows a typical trace of laser output at 195 nm compared to discharge current. Figure 4 shows a pulse duration of 80 ns FWHM which occurs well after the current peak. The pulse shape of the Kr IV 175.6-nm transition was nearly identical, but the Kr IV 219-nm pulse duration was about two times longer. Figure 5 compares peak output of these same three krypton ion laser transitions as excitation current density is varied between 6000 and 14 000 A/cm^2. Figure 5 shows that relative performance was similar throughout the range of investigated current densities. Furthermore, there is no evidence of peak output power saturation at the highest current densities. Data for Fig. 5 were taken at 6.6 μ krypton pressure. At a pressure of 5 μ the Kr IV 176-nm threshold drops to about 5000 A/cm^2 using lower-loss dielectric mirrors, compared to the 9000 A/cm^2 threshold indicated in Fig. 5 using mirrors with 35% round-trip loss and slightly higher pressure.

The search for vacuum ultraviolet ion laser emission from a simple longitudinal discharge has been successful. Lasing has been seen in argon at 1843 Å, and krypton at 1968, 1950, 1832, and 1756 Å.[15] Lasing was

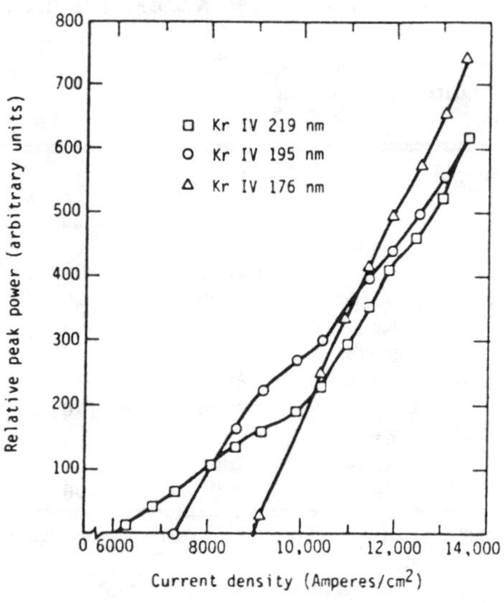

FIG. 5. Relative peak pwer of the Kr IV laser transitions at 176, 195, and 219 nm as peak excitation current density is varied between 6000 and 14 000 A/cm^2. No saturation is apparent.

observed even with aluminized mirrors overcoated with MgF_2 with a reflectivity of only 81 and 84% (i.e., 35% round-trip cavity loss). This type of ion laser can serve as a convenient probe for noble-gas excimer and dimer laser gain or loss. KrF can be probed using the Ne IV line at 247.3 nm,[11] KrBr probed using the Ne IV line at 206.5 nm, ArF probed using the Kr IV line at 195.0 nm, and both Xe_2 or ArCl probed using the Kr IV line at 175.6 nm. Ion laser transitions near 200 nm have already found biological use as illumination sources in photoelectron emission microscopy.[16] Additional applications for this simple source of vacuum ultraviolet laser emission are apparent, such as in photochemistry and kinetics.

[1]J.M. Hoffman, A.K. Hays, and G.C. Tisone, Appl. Phys. Lett. 28, 538 (1976).

[2]See, for example, J.B. Gerardo and A.W. Johnson, IEEE J. Quantum Electron. QE-9, 748 (1973).

[3]P.W. Hoff, J.C. Swingle, and C.K. Rhodes, Appl. Phys. Lett. 23, 245 (1973).

[4]W. Hughes, J. Shannon, and R. Hunter, Appl. Phys. Lett. 24, 488 (1974).

[5]R.T. Hodgson, J. Chem. Phys. 55, 5378 (1971).

[6]See, for example, R.W. Waynant, J.D. Shipman, Jr., R.C. Elton, and A.W. Ali, Proc. IEEE 59, 679 (1971).

[7]R.T. Hodgson and R.W. Dreyfus, Phys. Rev. Lett. 28, 536 (1972); R.W. Waynant, Phys. Rev. Lett. 28, 553 (1972).

[8]R.W. Waynant, Appl. Phys. Lett. 22, 419 (1973).

[9]R.W. Waynant, Appl. Phys. Lett. 30, 234 (1977).

[10]C.K. Rhodes, IEEE J. Quantum Electron. QE-10, 153 (1974).

[11]J.B. Marling, IEEE J. Quantum Electron. QE-11, 822 (1975).

[12]P.K. Cheo and H.G. Cooper, J. Appl. Phys. 36, 1862 (1965).

[13]L.A. Stelmack, Laser Focus 12 (No. 9), 41 (1976).

[14]V. Kaufman and B. Edlen, J. Phys. Chem. Ref. Data 3, 825 (1974).

[15]Preliminary results were presented at the Third Colloquium on Electronic Transition Lasers, Snowmass-in-Aspen, Colo., 1976 (unpublished).

[16]G.A. Massey and J.C. Johnson, Optical Society of America Conference, Tucson, Ariz., paper WF 15 (unpublished).

Reprinted with permission from *Applied Physics Letters,* Vol. 43(9), pp. 823-825 (November 1, 1983). ©1983 American Institute of Physics.

High-power transverse-discharge Ca^+ recombination laser

M. S. Butler and J. A. Piper
School of Mathematics and Physics, Macquarie University, North Ryde, New South Wales 2113, Australia

(Received 12 July 1983; accepted for publication 16 August 1983)

Operation of a transverse-discharge-excited Ca^+ recombination laser at high He buffer gas pressures (1200 Torr) and high discharge current densities (10^3 A/cm^2) is reported. Single laser pulse energies at λ 373.7 nm exceeding 0.7 mJ have been obtained corresponding to specific energy densities over 35 μJ/cm^3. There appear to be no fundamental limitations to attainment of pulse repetition rates in the megahertz range.

PACS numbers: 42.55.Hq, 42.60.By

Operation has been reported recently of transversely excited (TE) discharge Sr^+ recombination lasers giving extraction energy densities over 50 μJ/cm^3 at λ 430.5 nm.[1-3] The high current densities ($\sim 10^3$ A/cm^2) and high He buffer gas pressures (> 1000 Torr) which can be achieved with TE discharge devices are favorable for efficient recombination pumping which requires both generation of high ion and electron densities during the discharge pulse and rapid plasma cooling in the afterglow.

Earlier experiments by Zhukov *et al.*[4] with longitudinally excited discharge tubes at low buffer gas pressures (< 500 Torr) have shown the λ 430.5 nm Sr^+ and the λ 373.7 nm Ca^+ recombination lasers, which both operate on the $^2S_{1/2}$–$^2P_{3/2}$ transition, are closely analogous. Mean powers approaching 1 W have been obtained on the UV line of Ca^+ at pulse repetition rates 5–10 kHz corresponding to single pulse energies ~ 100 μJ and extraction energy densities 3–4 μJ/cm^3.[5] We report an extension of our current investigation of TE discharge recombination lasers to the Ca^+ system. Single pulse energies at λ 373.7 nm as high as 750 μJ corresponding to extraction energy densities over 35 μJ/cm^3 have been achieved.

The TE discharge tube employed is identical to that used in the earlier Sr^+ recombination laser studies.[1] The active volume of 30 cm^3 is defined by four pairs of opposing (5 mm diameter $\times$ 60 mm long) cylindrical stainless-steel electrode segments separated by 25 mm. The silica discharge vessel is externally heated and can operate at temperatures up to 850 °C. A period of several hours passivation at high temperatures is necessary following introduction of metallic calcium (purity > 99%) to the tube before adequate Ca vapor pressures can be achieved.

For the present experiments the discharge was excited by a spark-gap-switched pulse-charging circuit with the storage and peaking capacitances 20–70 nF and 10–35 nF, respectively. Charging voltages were 10–25 kV giving discharge current densities $2-8\times10^2$ A/cm^2. As for the Sr^+ laser tuning of the excitation circuit to produce a zero field null in the ringing current waveform immediately after the first forward current pulse is critical to good laser performance. Laser emission is observed for the full duration of this null, typically 200 ns (Fig. 1). Under optimum excitation conditions gain on the λ 373.7 nm Ca^+ transition is sufficiently high for observation of superfluorescence using one high-reflectance mirror only. However, the optimum output coupling lies in the range 30–50% for the present device; a 50% coupling mirror was used for all the data presented here. The aperture of the optical cavity was restricted by the diameter of the mirrors (19 mm) rather than the electrode separation so that the extraction volume was reduced to approximately two-thirds of the active discharge volume (i.e., 20 cm^3).

Laser pulse energy (λ 373.7 nm) as a function of operating temperature is shown in Fig. 2(a) for a range of He buffer gas pressures. A clear optimum in temperature is evident at each pressure, rising from 760 °C at 570 Torr to 805 °C at 1140 Torr, and corresponding to an increase in Ca vapor pressure from 0.25 to 0.6 Torr. In common with the Sr^+ laser there is also a clear optimum value of peak discharge current density in the first forward pulse for each set of conditions of the gas mixture, rising from 3×10^2 to 7×10^2 A/cm^2 from the lower to upper limits of the pressure range investigated. Note it is necessary to modify the tuning of the excitation circuit to maintain appropriate excitation conditions as the discharge impedance alters with changing gas pressure.

The dependence of laser pulse energy on the buffer gas pressure for optimum conditions of Ca vapor pressure and discharge current density is illustrated in Fig. 2(b). The pulse energy rises from only 50 μJ at 400 Torr to 750 μJ at 1200 Torr, the latter corresponding to a peak power of 7.5 kW and an extraction energy density approximately 35 μJ/cm^3. Laser efficiency based on energy deposited in the first forward current pulse (calculated from experimental current and voltage curves and taking account of circuit inductance) is also shown as a function of pressure in Fig. 2(b). Although the deposited energy increases towards higher pressures as the excitation circuit becomes better matched to the discharge, the laser efficiency itself increases, apparently due to the increased ion densities and more rapid plasma cooling. Since only about one-tenth to one-fifth of the stored energy is deposited in the laser volume in the first forward current pulse, overall efficiencies achieved in these experiments are correspondingly less than the values of Fig. 2(b).

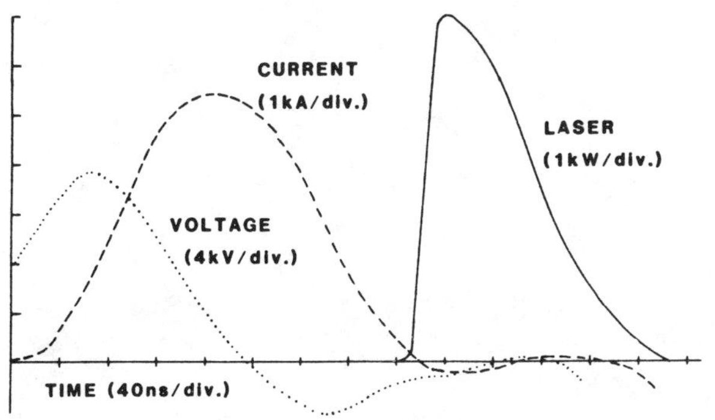

FIG. 1. Oscillograph of the applied voltage, discharge current, and laser emission pulses.

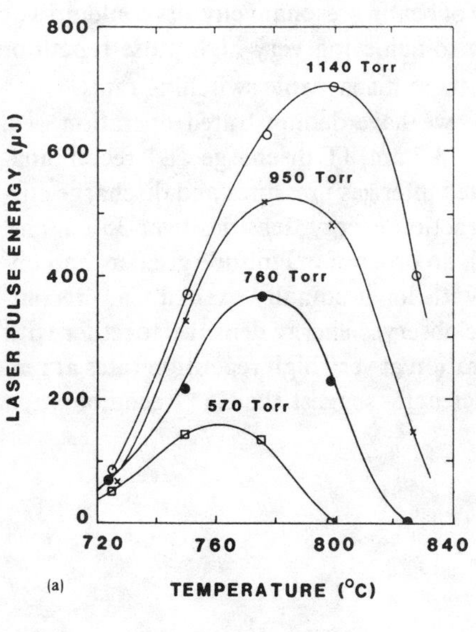

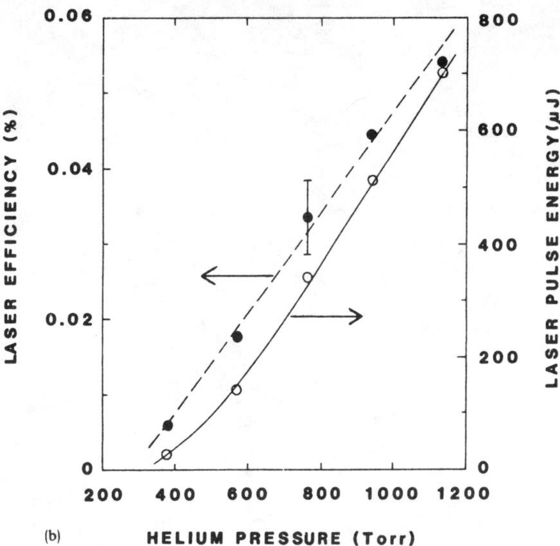

FIG. 2. Operating characteristics of the λ 373.7 nm TE Ca^+ laser: (a) laser pulse energy as a function of temperature at various He buffer gas pressures for optimum peak current densities. (b) laser pulse energy and efficiency (dashed curve) as functions of buffer gas pressure for optimum peak current densities and temperatures.

Tuning the excitation circuit to achieve two successive zero field nulls in the current waveform results in emission of two laser pulses of approximately equal intensity (as described previously for the Sr^+ laser[3]). In this manner we have observed successive laser pulses at λ 373.7 nm with energies over 400 μJ each and separated by less than 300 ns, indicating there are no fundamental barriers to achieving megahertz pulse repetition rates. This observation also suggests that overall laser efficiencies at high-repetition rates would approach those efficiences based on deposited energy in the first forward pulse presented in Fig. 2(b). Indeed synchronous pumping of beating resonant circuits could prove a practical approach to achieving very high pulse repetition rates with these lasers at manageable switching rates.

In conclusion, we have demonstrated operation of a high-power UV (λ 373.7 nm) TE discharge Ca^+ recombination laser at high He buffer gas pressures and discharge current densities. Extraction energy densities over 35 $\mu J/cm^3$ have been achieved, an order of magnitude greater than obtained previously with longitudinally excited Ca^+ recombination lasers. The observed energy densities together with the promise of operation at very high repetition rates at reasonable overall efficiencies suggest the Ca^+ recombination laser may become a high-mean-power near-UV source of some practical importance.

The authors gratefully acknowledge the support of the Australian Research Grants Scheme for this work.

[1]M. S. Butler and J. A. Piper, *Proc. Lasers* '82 (STS, McLean, VA, in press).
[2]M. Brandt, Appl. Phys. Lett. **42**, 127 (1983).
[3]M. S. Butler and J. A. Piper, Appl. Phys. Lett. **42**, 1008 (1983).
[4]V. V. Zhukov, V. S. Kucherov, E. L. Latush, and M. F. Sem, Sov. J. Quantum Electron. 7, 708 (1977).
[5]E. L. Latush, V. V. Zhukov, V. S. Mikhalevski, and M. F. Sem, *Proc. Lasers* '81 (STS, McLean, VA 1982), p. 1121.

Reprinted with permission from *Physical Review Letters,* Vol. 66(24), pp. 3136-3139
(June 17, 1991).

116-nm H_2 Laser Pumped by a Traveling-Wave Photoionization Electron Source

S. J. Benerofe, Guang-Yu Yin, C. P. J. Barty, J. F. Young,[a] and S. E. Harris
Edward L. Ginzton Laboratory, Stanford University, Stanford, California 94305
(Received 4 October 1990)

We report the use of a photoionization electron source to pump a 116-nm laser in the Werner band ($C\,^1\Pi_u \rightarrow X\,^1\Sigma_g^+$) of molecular hydrogen. The laser is pumped by free electrons which are created by photoionizing molecular hydrogen with soft x rays from a traveling-wave laser plasma. We show that even though the free electrons have an average temperature of ~10 eV, the lasing hydrogen molecules retain an ambient temperature of ~0.01 eV. This allows an extrapolated small-signal gain of exp(43), with a 1064-nm pumping energy of 580 mJ in 200 psec.

We describe the use of a traveling-wave photoionization electron source[1] (PES) to pump a 116-nm laser in the Werner band of H_2. The PES is constructed by using a grazing-incidence, traveling-wave laser plasma[2] to make soft x rays which in turn photoionize ambient hydrogen molecules (Fig. 1). The electrons have an average energy which corresponds to the difference in energy of the pumping x rays and the ionization potential of H_2, and at sufficient pumping intensity may have a density which corresponds to a discharge current in excess of MA/cm^2. The rise time of the electron density is equal to that of the x-ray source, and may be picoseconds or shorter in duration, making PES an ideal source for pumping short-wavelength lasers.[3]

In this Letter we quantitatively demonstrate the advantages of PES over conventional electron pumping sources by generating saturated laser emission at 116 nm in the Werner band of H_2. We emphasize a special feature of this type of excitation, which is its ability to produce hot electrons while at the same time retaining an ambient (lasing medium) temperature which is comparatively cold. This is confirmed by measurements of the 116-nm gain as a function of the ambient H_2 temperature. In this work the free electrons have an average temperature of 10 eV while the lasing hydrogen molecules retain an ambient temperature of ~0.01 eV. This allows very high gain at modest pumping energy; here we obtain an extrapolated small-signal gain of exp(43), with a 1064-nm pumping energy of 580 mJ in a pulse width of 200 psec.

Before proceeding we note that previous short-wavelength lasers have operated in the focus of the incident laser and under conditions where the exciting electrons and target ions are relatively thermalized.[4] H_2 lasers have been constructed by using a Blumlein discharge (Waynant)[5] and by using a field-emission diode (Hodgson and Dreyfus).[6] In this work we obtain a gain coefficient which is over an order of magnitude larger than that previously obtained, demonstrating quantitatively one of the advantages of PES over conventional electron pumping sources.

Using a simple model for the PES excitation mechanism we will verify that in the present experiment the H_2 laser is pumped by electrons and is not directly photopumped. We will then proceed to describe the experimental setup and results. The calculation of the gain for the 116-nm laser pumped by a PES proceeds as follows: The 580-mJ, 200-psec, 1064-nm pump laser pulse creates a plasma on the target surface. Following Ref. 1 the spectral distribution of the soft x rays from the laser-produced plasma is modeled as a blackbody [see Fig. 1(a)] which has a characteristic temperature determined by the conversion efficiency of the pump laser to soft x rays and a pulse width comparable to that of the pump laser. From previous measurements of conversion efficiency done under similar experimental conditions,[7] we estimate the conversion efficiency of our laser to be approximately 2% into the energy range of interest. This implies a blackbody temperature of 12 eV. The soft x rays photoionize some of the hydrogen molecules surrounding the target, creating free electrons. In Fig. 1(b) we show the photoionization cross section for H_2.[8] Combining the blackbody-flux spectral distribution and the photoionization cross section, we calculate an electron density of 3×10^{15} cm^{-3} in the lasing region, and an average electron energy of 10 eV [Fig. 1(c)]. This is equivalent to a discharge current of about 9×10^4 A/cm^2. The cross section for electron excitation of the Werner band has been calculated by Gerhart[9] and is shown in Fig. 1(d). The cross section for pumping the 116-nm line is then calculated using Refs. 10 and 11. By multiplying the electron distribution by the electron pumping cross section for the upper laser level, and integrating, we estimate an upper-state ($C\,^1\Pi_u$, $v'=1$, $J'=1$) density of approximately 6×10^{12} cm^{-3} at room temperature [note that the upper laser level has a lifetime of approximately 600 psec (Ref. 12)]. This yields a calculated gain on the 116-nm transition of 0.35 cm^{-1} at room temperature (293 K).

This PES gain calculation is to be compared to the gain calculated for direct photopumping of the upper laser level. For this calculation we use the 12-eV black-

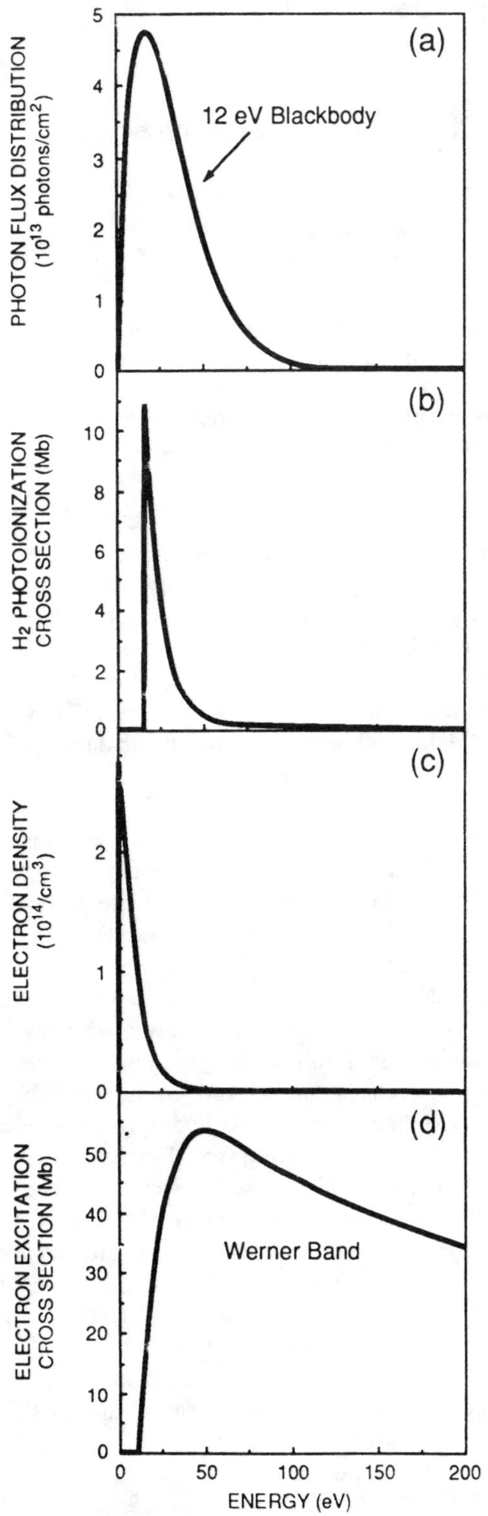

FIG. 1. (a) Photon flux vs energy for a 12-eV blackbody. (b) H_2 photoionization cross section vs energy. (c) Calculated electron-density energy distribution; the average electron energy is 10 eV. (d) Werner-band electron-excitation cross section vs energy.

body spectral density and the cross section for optical pumping of the upper laser level calculated using the oscillator strengths from Allison and Dalgarno.[13] We obtain a calculated gain due to optical pumping of 0.0014 cm^{-1} at room temperature, a factor of 250 lower than that calculated for electron pumping. Thus, it is clear that this laser is PES pumped.

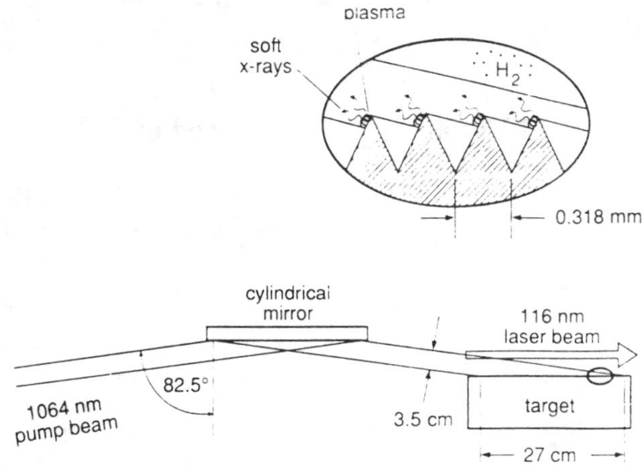

FIG. 2. Schematic of geometry used to pump H_2 laser.

The above calculation helps to point out some qualitatively important features of a PES which makes it an ideal pumping source for short-wavelength lasers. In Fig. 1 we see that by choosing a source of the photoelectrons with an appropriate ionization potential and photoionization cross section (as compared to the blackbody spectral distribution) an electron density distribution can be set up which will overlap well with the pumping cross section for the upper laser level. Also, as we can see from Fig. 1(d) electron pumping cross sections can be very large, allowing a large acceptance bandwidth in energy to make efficient use of the pumping source. Furthermore, the fast rise time of the electron density distribution combined with the traveling-wave excitation of the experimental setup allows most of the energy put in the upper laser level to be stored until it is extracted by the stimulated emission of the laser. We also note that the rapid rise of the electron density allows the lasing medium to be excited into the upper laser level and lase before the lasing medium has been significantly heated by the surrounding high-energy electrons. The maintenance of a low temperature for the lasing medium allows the ambient temperature of the lasing medium to set the Doppler width of the transition.

Our experimental setup is shown in Fig. 2. The geometry is the 82.5°-angle-of-incidence version of the traveling-wave laser-produced-plasma geometry described in detail in Ref. 14. For this experiment, the 580-mJ, 200-psec, 1064-nm pump pulse, initially a 3.5-cm × 1.2-cm oval beam, is reflected off of an aluminum-coated cylindrical mirror at 82.5° from normal incidence with the 3.5-cm axis of the beam in the plane of incidence. The mirror focuses the beam to a line on the target with a transverse spot size of 100 μm and a length of 27 cm, yielding an intensity on the target of 8×10^{10} W/cm^2. The target is a stainless-steel tube threaded at

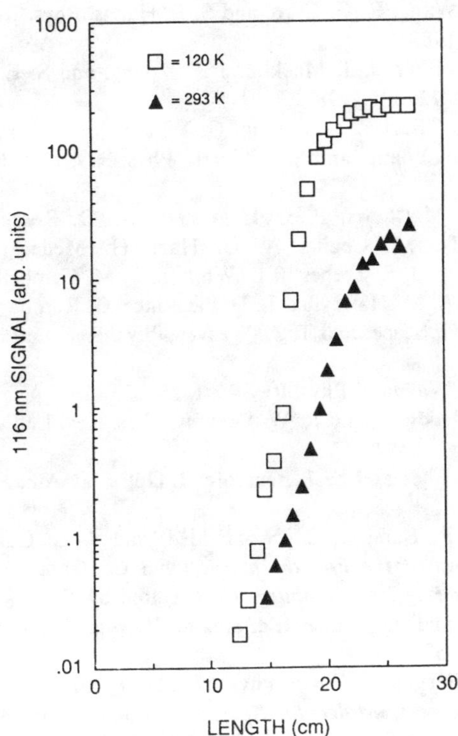

FIG. 3. Representative gain measurements. Signal vs plasma length for 116.1-nm line in the Werner band of H_2. Each data point represents the average of about 10 measurements.

31.5 grooves per cm; the density of the hydrogen molecules surrounding the target was fixed for all temperatures at 6×10^{17} molecules/cm^3. The temperature of the H_2 gas inside the cell was measured using two separate methods: (1) A *K*-type thermocouple gauge was suspended inside the cell, and (2) we measured the pressure of the H_2 gas inside the cell, which for a fixed density and volume determines the temperature. Both of these methods agreed to within 10 K. The output signal of the H_2 laser was detected using a microchannel-plate detector mounted on a 1-m normal-incidence McPherson VUV spectrometer (model number 225). The entrance slits of the spectrometer were 75 cm away from the end of the plasma. The spectrometer and the experiment cell were separated by a 1-mm-thick LiF window. All gain coefficients were obtained by varying the plasma length, measuring the output signal, and fitting the data with an exponential curve.

We observed saturated emission in both the Lyman and Werner bands. In Fig. 3 we show two representative gain measurements on the 116-nm line, one at an ambient H_2 temperature of 293 K and the other at 120 K. The average gain coefficient on the 116-nm line was measured to be 0.9 cm^{-1} at an ambient H_2 temperature of 293 K and 1.6 cm^{-1} at 120 K. In Fig. 4 we have an x-ray streak-camera trace of the 116-nm line at 296 K. For this trace the laser-produced plasma is at its full length, and therefore the 116-nm signal is a result of

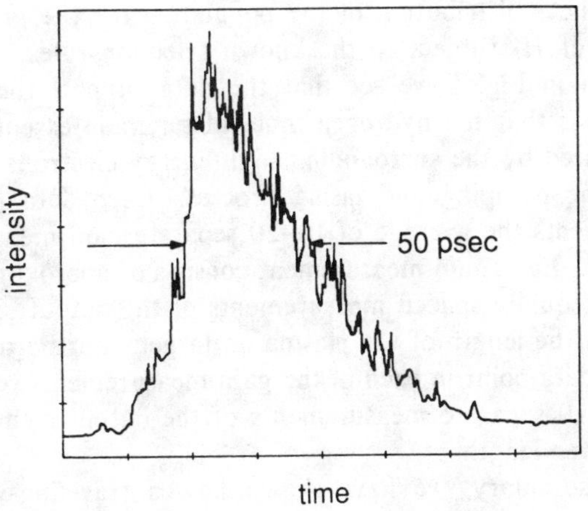

FIG. 4. Streak-camera trace of the saturated 116-nm output signal.

saturated output. From the trace we see the clear indications of saturation: the sharp rising edge of the 116-nm output and the shortening of the output pulse relative to the pump pulse.

We have also shown quantitatively that by cooling the ambient H_2 gas we can increase the gain cross section of the 116-nm laser. The experiment cell, which contained the threaded target and the H_2 gas, was cooled to two different temperatures by either surrounding the cell with dry ice or with liquid nitrogen. Given the measured gain coefficient of the 116-nm laser at room temperature, if we assume Doppler broadening of the lasing transition, we can calculate the gain expected at other temperatures due to the change in the linewidth of the laser transition

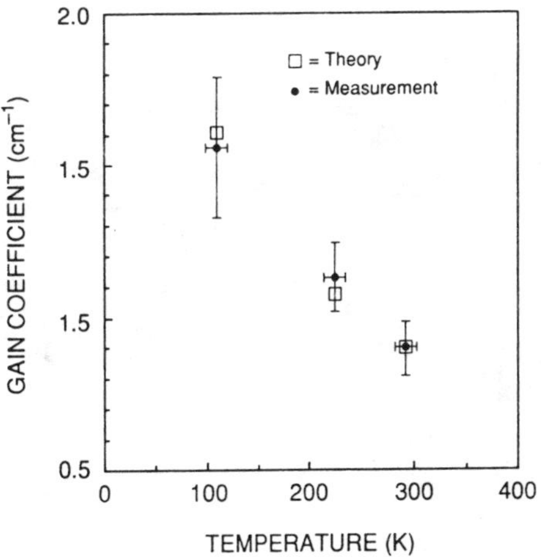

FIG. 5. 116-nm gain coefficient vs ambient H_2 pressure. □ denotes the calculated gain; ● denotes the average of gain. The error bars in gain on the graph are the standard deviation of the measured gain for the given temperature. The error bars in temperature represent the 10-K uncertainty in the temperature measurement of the ambient hydrogen gas because of the discrepancy between the two temperature measurement methods used.

and the redistribution of the population for the ground state of H_2 subject to the known selection rules.[11] As shown in Fig. 5 we see that the data support the hypothesis that the hydrogen molecules remain essentially unheated by the surrounding high-energy electrons during the pumping and lasing process. Each data point represents the average of 10–20 separate gain measurements. Each gain measurement consists of approximately 15 equally spaced measurements of the output signal versus the length of the plasma on target. Furthermore, each data point in each of the gain measurements represents 10 separate measurements of the output signal at the given length.

In summary, we have shown how a traveling-wave source of laser-produced x rays may be used to produce an electron source of high average energy, high equivalent current, and very fast rise time. This source allows laser operation with atoms at a kinetic temperature less than 1/1000th of the pumping electrons, thereby allowing high gain at modest pumping energy.

This work was jointly supported by the Strategic Defense Initiative Organization, the U.S. Office of Naval Research, the U.S. Air Force Office of Scientific Research, and the U.S. Army Research Office.

---

[a]Present address: Electrical and Computer Engineering, Rice University, Houston, TX 77251.

[1]J. C. Wang, R. G. Caro, and S. E. Harris, Phys. Rev. Lett. **51**, 767 (1983).

[2]M. H. Sher, J. J. Macklin, J. F. Young, and S. E. Harris, Opt. Lett. **12**, 891 (1987).

[3]C. P. J. Barty, D. A. King, G. Y. Yin, K. H. Hahn, J. E. Field, J. F. Young, and S. E. Harris, Phys. Rev. Lett. **61**, 2201 (1988).

[4]D. L. Matthews, P. L. Hagelstein, M. D. Rosen, M. J. Eckart, N. M. Ceglio, A. U. Hazi, H. Medecki, B. J. MacGowan, J. E. Trebes, B L. Whitten, E. M. Cambell, C. W. Hatcher, A. M. Hawryluk, L. D. Pleasance, G. Rambach, J. H. Scofield, G. Stone, and T. A. Weaver, Phys. Rev. Lett. **54**, 110 (1985).

[5]R. W. Waynant, Phys. Rev. Lett. **28**, 533 (1972).

[6]R. T. Hodgson and R. W. Dreyfus, Phys. Rev. Lett. **28**, 536 (1972).

[7]M. H. Sher and S. J. Benerofe, J. Opt. Soc. Am. B (to be published).

[8]J. A. R. Samson, G. N. Hadded, and J. L. Garder, in *Proceedings of the Fourth International Conference on VUV Radiation Physics, Hamburg, 1974,* edited by E. E. Koch, R. Haensel, and C. Kunz (Pergamon, Viewig, Braunschweig, 1974), p. 157.

[9]D. E. Gerhart, J. Chem. Phys. **62**, 821 (1975).

[10]G. Herzberg, *Molecular Spectra and Molecular Structure* (Van Nostrand Reinhold, New York, 1950), Vol. 1.

[11]R. J. Spindler, Jr., J. Quant. Spectrosc. Radiat. Transfer. **9**, 627 (1969).

[12]J. E. Hesser, J. Chem. Phys. **48**, 2518 (1968).

[13]A. C. Allison and A. Dalgarno, At. Data **1**, 289 (1970).

[14]M. H. Sher, S. J. Benerofe, J. F. Young, and S. E. Harris, J. Opt. Soc. Am. B **8**, 114 (1991).

Section Two

VUV Excimer Lasers—Rare Gas Molecules

The Soviets also contributed the idea of the diatomic excited rare gas molecule (excimer) laser. Early reports of success with solid xenon in the USSR triggered efforts to pump the rare gas molecules, which led to early success at Lawrence Livermore National Laboratory by Koehler et al., who used a pulsed electron beam and high pressure gaseous xenon. Other workers published results before Koehler's group finally released their results. These workers quickly produced very high energy output limited by mirror damage and the difficulty of pumping larger volumes of very high pressure gas.

Mirror damage problems, coupled with the difficulty and expense of working with high voltage excitation systems, has kept rare gas molecule excimers from reaching their full potential. Recent efforts have focused on attempts to discharge pump these molecules by exciting and forming them in a gas expansion nozzle. These efforts have not yet been successful. However, the potential of these rare gas excimer molecules for producing strong laser sources in the VUV remains and awaits new excitation methods and better resonator mirrors to become extremely useful for many applications.

Reprinted with permission from *Soviet Physics Solid State,* Vol. 9(11), pp. 2655-2656 (May 1968).

THE POSSIBILITY OF THE GENERATION OF VACUUM ULTRAVIOLET RADIATION BY ELECTRON EXCITATION OF INERT-GAS CRYSTALS

A. G. Molchanov, I. A. Poluéktov, and Yu. M. Popov

P. N. Lebedev Physics Institute, Academy of Sciences of the USSR, Moscow
Translated from Fizika Tverdogo Tela, Vol. 9, No. 11,
pp. 3363-3364, November, 1967
Original article submitted June 5, 1967;
revision submitted July 4, 1967

1. The generation of short-wavelength radiation in solids requires the use of substances with a wide forbidden band. It is of interest, therefore, to consider the crystals of the inert gases He, Ne, Ar, Kr, Xe [1] which are known to have very wide forbidden bands [2, 3]: $\Delta_{Ar} = 14$ eV, $\Delta_{Kr} = 12$ eV, $\Delta_{Xe} = 9.3$ eV, etc., corresponding to emission wavelengths in the vacuum ultraviolet region. With the exception of He and Ne, the basic properties of these crystals have been studied sufficiently thoroughly [2-6]. The most extensively studied is Ar and, therefore, actual calculations will be carried out for this crystal. The bottom of the conduction band and the top of the valence band of Ar are in the center of the Brillouin zone so that direct interband radiative transitions are allowed.

During electron excitation of a crystal, the nonequilibrium carriers generated in the bands emit phonons and thus slow down, with a characteristic time τ_S, to thermal energies. If τ_S is less than the lifetime of nonequilibrium carriers in a band, these carriers can either concentrate at the bottom of a band or can form exciton states [7]. Furthermore, if the characteristic time of the interband radiative recombination of carriers τ_R is shorter than the time for binding them into exciton states τ_B, we may expect to obtain a population inversion between the conduction and valence bands. In the opposite case, when $\tau_R > \tau_B$, such an inversion is possible in relation to the exciton states if, at the moment of formation, these states deform the lattice or are localized at impurity centers. We shall calculate the electron beam density J_0 and the density of nonequilibrium carriers N_0, which are necessary for laser emission in the two cases indicated: direct band-band transitions and transitions from exciton states, which deform the crystal lattice.

2. a) <u>Interband transitions ($\tau_R < \tau_B$).</u> The intraband energy relaxation time τ_S for intrinsic semiconductors is [7]

$$\tau_S = \frac{3\sqrt{\pi}}{4}\frac{wkT}{eu^2} \leqslant 3.4 \cdot 10^{-11} \text{ sec}, \quad (1)$$

since for Ar the mobility is $w \leqslant 100$ cm$^2 \cdot$ V$^{-1} \cdot$ sec^{-1} [8] and the velocity of sound is $u = 1.6 \cdot 10^5$ cm $\cdot$ sec^{-1} [9]. The radiative recombination time of electron-hole pairs τ_R is easily calculated:

$$\tau_R = \frac{2\hbar^2 c^3 m^*}{ne^2\Delta^2 f_h}, \quad (2)$$

and for Ar, $m^* = 3.6 \cdot 10^{-28}$ g, $n = 1.3$, $\Delta = 14$ eV; at the band edge the hole distribution function is $f_h \leqslant 1/2$; $\tau_R \geqslant 2.8 \cdot 10^{-10}$ sec so that $\tau_R \gg \tau_S$. The laser threshold condition for intrinsic semiconductors (Eq. (11) in [10]) with a resonator of length L = 1 cm, a reflection coefficient for the mirrors R = 0.2, and an absorption coefficient for the interband transitions $\alpha = 2 \cdot 10^5$ cm$^{-1} \cdot$ eV$^{-1/2}$, temperature T = 77°K, gives a threshold density $N_0 = 2.8 \cdot 10^{18}$ cm^{-3}. Next, we shall write the relationship between N_0 and $\mathcal{J}_0$ in the form

$$N_0 = \frac{\tau_R}{e\varepsilon}\frac{dE}{dx}\mathcal{J}_0, \quad (3)$$

where $\varepsilon = 26$ eV is the energy needed to form one carrier pair [11], and dE/dx = 25 MeV/cm is the stopping power of the substance associated with the ionization losses ($\bar{E}$ = 10 keV), so that $\mathcal{J}_0 \simeq 1600$ A/cm^2; this value is considerably larger than the values of $\mathcal{J}_0$ for semiconductors with a narrow forbidden band (for example, for GaAs with Δ = 1.35 eV, $\mathcal{J}_0 \simeq 1$ A/cm^2). The threshold currents for Kr and Xe are obviously considerably smaller.

b) Transitions from exciton states ($\tau_R > \tau_B$). In order to obtain the threshold density, we shall use the general threshold condition for laser generation [7]:

$$R^2 e^{2(\gamma-\beta)L} = 1, \tag{4}$$

where γ is the amplification factor and β is the absorption coefficient which takes into account the losses due to the photoionization of a localized exciton. If we substitute in Eq. (4) the known values of γ and β, which depend on N_0, and calculate the photoionization cross section using Eq. (34.64) in [12], we then obtain $N_0 \simeq 10^{16}$ cm^{-3}, which leads to $\mathcal{J}_0 \simeq 6$ A/cm^2. It should be noted that in order to avoid overheating of a crystal the duration of a current pulse must not exceed $\Delta t = eC_v\Delta T\left(\mathcal{J}_0 \frac{dE}{dx}\right)^{-1} \simeq 10^{-7}$ sec, where C_V is the specific heat, ΔT = 5°K, $\mathcal{J}_0$ = 6 A/cm^2. The wavelength of the generated radiation should be λ = 1260 Å [13].

3. The recombination radiation spectra of liquid and solid inert gases excited with a beam of fast α particles have been investigated before [13]. The nature of the radiation spectra obtained is to a considerable degree in agreement with the assumption that excitons deform a crystal and create localized complexes of the excited diatomic molecule type, while 10-100% of the total energy of α particles is converted into radiation. If similar conditions arise also during excitation with an electron beam, then the conditions necessary for the laser generation (case "b") should be easily attainable. Localization of excitons may occur also in ArKr, KrXe, ArH and other solid solutions whose thermodynamic properties are known [6, 14, 15]. In these substances the excitons may be localized at Kr, Xe, H, and other impurity atoms. In this case inversion appears if more than half the impurity atoms are excited.

In conclusion, we note that the above results apply qualitatively to the threshold of laser generation in inert-gas liquids and their mixtures.

The authors are grateful to N. G. Basov for his useful discussions and for his constant interest in the investigation.

LITERATURE CITED

1. N. G. Basov, IEEE, JQE-2, No. 9, 354 (1966).
2. G. Baldini, Phys. Rev., 128, 1562 (1962).
3. J. C. Phillips, Phys. Rev., 136, A1714 (1964).
4. K. Moorjani, Phys. Letters, 23, 652 (1966).
5. O. Bostanjoglo and L. Schmidt, Phys. Rev., 22, 130 (1966).
6. E. R. Dobbs and G. O. Jones, Rep. Prog. Phys., 20, 516 (1957).
7. Yu. M. Popov, Tr. FIAN, 31, 3 (1965).
8. H. Schnyders, S. A. Rice, and L. Meyer, Phys. Rev. Letters, 15, 187 (1965).
9. H. R. Moeller and C. F. Squire, Phys. Rev., 151, 689 (1966).
10. O. N. Krokhin, Fiz. Tverd. Tela, 7, 2612 (1965) [Sov. Phys. – Solid State, 7, 2114 (1966)].
11. S. V. Starodubtsev and A. M. Romanov, Passage of Charged Particles through Matter [in Russian], Izd. AN UzbekSSR, Tashkent (1962).
12. I. I. Sobel'man, Introduction to the Theory of Atomic Spectra [in Russian], FM (1963).
13. J. Jortner, L. Meyer, S. A. Rice, and E. G. Wilson, J. Chem. Phys., 42, 4250 (1965).
14. G. Baldini and R. S. Knox, Phys. Rev. Letters, 11, 127 (1963).
15. G. Baldini, Phys. Rev., 136, A248 (1964).

CATHODOLUMINESCENCE OF SOLID XENON IN THE ULTRAVIOLET REGION OF THE SPECTRUM

N. G. Basov, O. V. Bogdankevich, V. A. Danilychev, A. G. Devyatkov, G. N. Kashnikov, and N. P. Lantsov
P. N. Lebedev Physics Institute, USSR Academy of Sciences
Submitted 22 February 1968; resubmitted 20 March 1968
ZhETF Pis'ma 7, No. 11, 404-405 (5 June 1968)

In view of the fact that the effective temperature of an electron beam used as a laser-pump source is very high, this method can be used to excite practically all energy levels. We observed the luminescence of solid xenon grown from the gas phase and bombarded with fast electrons. The luminescence spectrum (see the figure) consists of two lines. 1735 and 1620 Å. The width of the more intense line is ~70 Å and the distance between lines is ~115 Å. The spectra were recorded with a vacuum spectrometer with a diffraction grating; the spectrum shown in the figure was recorded at a spectrometer resolution ~ 2.5 Å. The electron energy was 300 - 400 keV, the electron-current pulse duration was 50 nsec, and the pulse repetition frequency was 10 Hz. The initial xenon was ~99.5% pure. The crystal temperature was maintained within the range 60 - 70°K. The total power of one emission pulse reached several hundred watts.

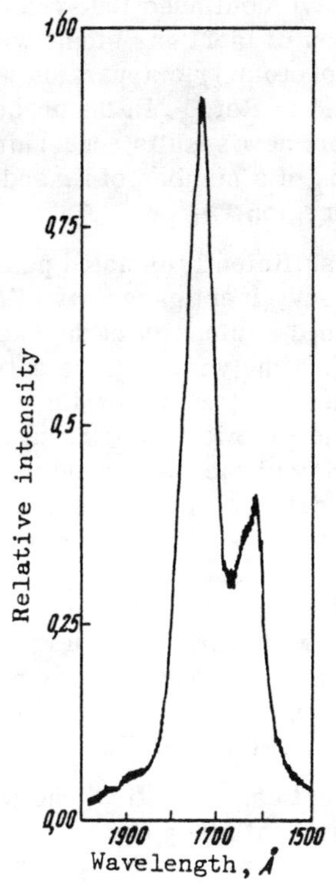

Luminescence spectrum of solid xenon subject to electron excitation.

The observed luminescence is apparently connected with the emission of localized excitons. The Stokes shift of the emission line is 2 eV. A Stokes shift of like magnitude was observed in [1], where measurements were made of the luminescence spectra of solid xenon excited by α particles from a radioactive source (5 mCi and Po^{210}). The luminescence spectrum in the cited investigation consisted of one line near 1730 Å of width ~100 - 120 Å. The excitation intensity was much lower in [1] than in our investigation. The high luminescence efficiency of solid xenon, the absence of absorption in the region of the emission line, and the realistic values of the threshold pump power (according to estimates given in [2]) point to the possibility of attaining laser action in solid xenon excited by electrons.

[1] J. Hortner, L. Meyer, S. A. Rice, and E. G. Wilson, J. Chem. Phys. 42, 4250 (1965).
[2] A. G. Molchanov, A. I. Poluektov, and Yu. M. Popov, Fiz. Tverd. Tela 9, 3363 (1967) Sov. Phys.-Solid State 9, 2655 (1968)].

Reprinted with the permission of the Optical Society of America from *Optics and Spectroscopy,* Vol. 34(4), pp. 475-476 (April 1973).

Electronic excitation of some Kr and Xe lines in the vacuum ultraviolet

I. G. Zhukov, I. P. Zapesochnyi, and P. V. Feltsan

(Received 14 July 1972)
Opt. Spektrosk. **34**, 820-821 (April 1973)

We have continued the systematic investigation of the excitation of inert gas atoms with the vacuum ultraviolet spectrophotometric apparatus whose first results were published in Ref. 1. In the present short communication we report new results concerning the optical excitation functions of a number of Kr and Xe lines in the 900–1300 Å region.

The sufficiently isolated position of the spectral lines of the heavy inert gases has allowed us to substantially increase the intensity of the vacuum monochromator by increasing the widths of the entrance and the exit slits to 2 mm (spectral slit-width ~ 15 Å). This in turn, permitted us to lower the current density of the electron beam without increasing the pressure of the excited gas at spectral line intensities adequate for their reliable recording. The electron gun with a circular cross-section for the electron beam was replaced by a 127 degree electron selector of the Yuz-Rozhansky type or an electron gun with a flat beam (cross-section of the beam 0.4×7 mm^2, current density ~ 10^{-4} A/cm^2). These changes resulted in an improvement of the conditions of excitation relative to Ref. 1.

The optical excitation functions of Kr and Xe obtained in the present study can be subdivided, according to their physical nature, into two groups. The first is related with the process of direct ejection of an ns electron from the outer electron shell of the inert gas atom,

$$\mathrm{AI}\ ns^2np^6\,{}^1S_0 + e \rightarrow \mathrm{A^*II}\ nsnp^6\,{}^2S_{1/2} + 2e,$$

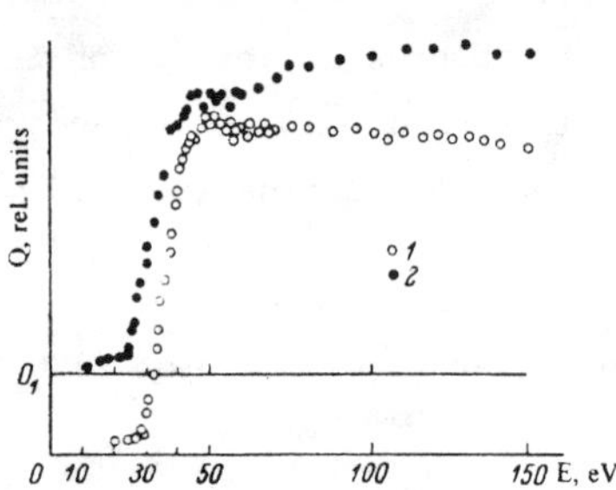

FIG. 1. Functions of excitation of the Kr II and Xe II spectral lines. 1–Kr II λ 965Å, 2–Xe II λ 1100Å.

accompanied by the decay of the nsnp^6 $^2S_{1/2}$ level in the optical channel,

$$\mathrm{A^*II}\ nsnp^6\,{}^2S_{1/2} \rightarrow \mathrm{AII}\ ns^2np^5\,{}^2P^0_{1/2,\,3/2} + h\nu.$$

The optical excitation function of these spectral lines reflect the dependence of the ionization cross-section of the inert gas atom on the energy of the colliding electron including the radiation and autoionization contributions.

We measured the following optical excitation functions of this type of transitions: Kr II λ 965 Å $4s^24p^5\ ^2P^0_{1/2}$–$4s4p^6\ ^2S_{1/2}$ and Xe II λ 1100 Å $5s^25p^5\ ^2P^0_{3/2}$–$5s5p^6\ ^2S_{1/2}$, which are shown in Fig. 1. At the threshold energy these functions are different from zero, which is explained by the presence within the spectral slit-width of the monochromator of weak lines of the atomic spectrum: Kr I λ 963 Å ($4p^6\ ^1S_0$–$5d\ [^1/_2]^0_1$) or Xe I λ 1089 and 1100 Å, respectively.

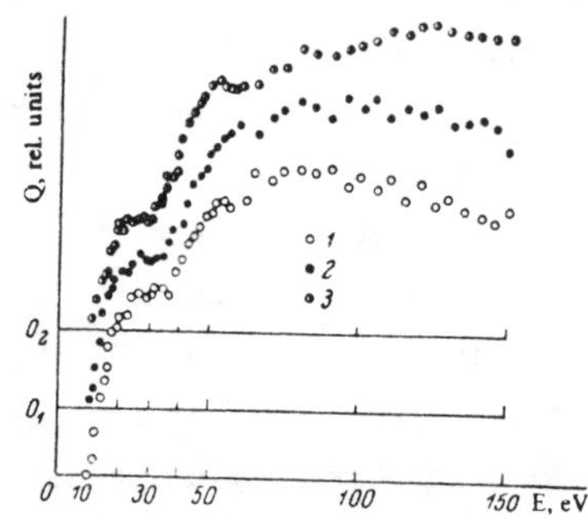

FIG. 2. Functions of excitation of the Kr I and Xe I resonance lines. 1–1165Å (Kr I), 2–1236Å (Kr I), 3–1192Å (Xe I).

The second group consists of the resonance lines of the Kr atom: λ 1165 Å $4p^6\ ^1S_0$–$5s'\ [^1/_2]^0_1$ and λ 1236 Å $4p^6\ ^1S_0$–$5s\ [^3/_2]^0_1$, and also of one of the lines of the Xe atomic spectrum λ 1192 Å $5p^6\ ^1S_0$–$5d\ [^3/_2]^0_1$, which are shown in Fig. 2.

The optical excitation functions of the Kr I resonance lines at electron energies of 20–30 eV exhibit inflections corresponding to the ones observed by Yakhontova,[2] employing a gas-filled excitation glass tube with a LiF window (distance from beam to window 12–14 mm, current 500 μA at a diameter of 5 mm).

The practically identical behavior of the optical excitation functions of both resonance lines of KrI indicates that, in this case, the (J, *l*) coupling manifests itself in an almost pure form.

[1]I. G. Zhukov, I. P. Zapesochnyi, and P. V. Feltsan, Opt. Spektrosk., **32**, 1049 (1972) [Opt. Spectrosc. **32**, 569 (1972)].
[2]V. E. Yakhontova, Opt. Spektrosk., **28**, 176 (1970) [Opt. Spectrosc. **28**, 90 (1970)].

Reprinted with permission from *Optics Communications,* Vol. 8(2), pp. 128-131 (June 1973).

DEMONSTRATION OF TEMPORAL COHERENCE, SPATIAL COHERENCE, AND THRESHOLD EFFECTS IN THE MOLECULAR XENON LASER†

Paul W. HOFF, James C. SWINGLE and Charles K. RHODES

Lawrence Livermore Laboratory, University of California, Livermore, California 94550, USA

Received 2 April 1973

Stimulated emission has been observed at 1722 ± 1 Å in high-pressure xenon gas originating from the bound–free continuum of the Xe_2^* molecule. This emission exhibits strong line narrowing, spatial coherence corresponding to a few times the diffraction limit, a sharp oscillation threshold, and an output time dependence radically different from the spontaneous emission observed without an optical cavity or below threshold. The confluence of all these observations is an explicit and unequivocal demonstration of a coherent stimulated emission process. Specific data detailing the pressure dependence of the stimulated output and results with rare-gas mixtures are given.

Considerable interest has recently centered on the possibility of a xenon laser operating on the 1700 Å bound–free continuum of the Xe_2^* dimer‡ because of its projected high efficiency≠, large energy storage per unit volume, and short wavelength‡. Spectral line narrowing of the 1700 Å transition in xenon has been reported in electron beam excited liquid xenon [4] and high-pressure gaseous xenon [5, 6]. The kinetic details of these rare-gas plasmas have been treated elsewhere [7].

In relativistic electron beam excited gas, we observe a conclusive demonstration of a coherent stimulated process giving rise to laser emission at 1722 ± 1 Å over a range of gas pressures near 200 psia. Since the excited xenon dimers are strong spontaneous radiators, great care must be taken to ensure that the radiation from this system truly represents a coherent process‡.

† This work was supported under the auspices of the United States Atomic Energy Commission.

‡ For details of the molecular energy levels, see ref. [1].

≠ Efficiencies between 10% and 100% have been reported for alpha particle excited xenon in ref. [2].

‡ A short wavelength is particularly useful in the heating of high density plasmas for controlled fusion applications since the inverse Bremsstrahlung heating rate scales very nearly as λ^{-2}. For a discussion of this and related topics, see ref. [3].

In our case, the conclusion asserting the presence of a coherent stimulated process is founded not only on the measurement of spectral line narrowing (a necessary but insufficient condition), but also on the observation of spatial coherence and the resulting spatially directed beam, the existence of a sharp oscillation threshold, a time dependence of the directed output radiation radically different from the spontaneous emission observed below threshold, and a dip in the spontaneous emission viewed perpendicular to the laser axis. The confluence of these observations unequivocally demonstrates the presence of a genuine coherent stimulated process.

A schematic of the apparatus is illustrated in fig. 1. A high-pressure gas cell with internal mirrors and mode-limiting optical apertures was attached to a Febetron 705 relativistic electron beam generator which emits a 40 nsec pulse in a 10 kA beam with a nominal energy of 1.5 MeV over a 2 cm diameter apreture. The optical cavity consisted of two one-meter radius of curvature mirrors separated by 5 cm. The mirrors were fabricated from highly polished MgF_2 substrates which were Al coated and MgF_2

‡ This problem was alluded to very early in the development of optical masers. See the section entitled Summary and High-Frequency Limits, in ref. [8].

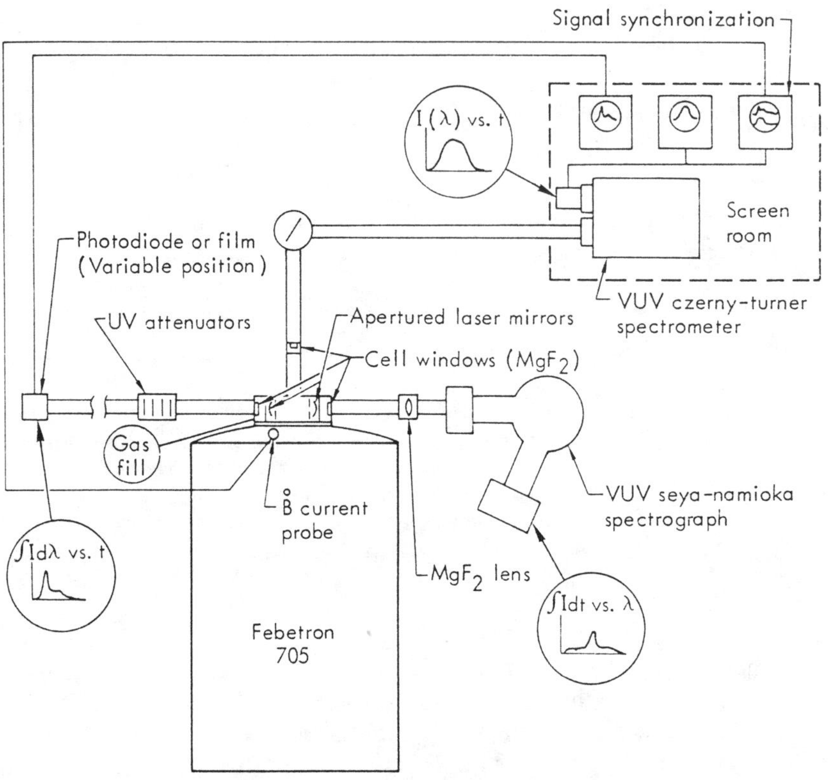

Fig. 1. Schematic of the experimental apparatus illustrating the three diagnostic systems; Seya–Namioka spectrograph, photodiode, and Czerny–Turner spectrometer viewing the side light.

overcoated. The reflectance and transmittance of the mirrors at 1700 Å were measured to be 80% and 8%, respectively†. The 2 mm diameter intra-cavity apertures limited the field of view of the diagnostic systems essentially to the volume contained in the cylinder defined by the apertures. Research grade xenon and high-vacuum turbomolecular pumps were used in the fill system. The spectral composition of the radiation along the optical axis was detected by a 0.75 m Seya–Namioka spectrograph using Kodak SWR film and capable of spectral resolution of 0.1 Å. The temporal characteristics were observed using an ITT 4115 photodiode with a 2 nsec risetime. Spatial propagation studies were performed by replacing the photodiode with SWR film mounted on a variable length line-of-sight pipe, and attenuation in this pipe was accomplished with calibrated sapphire attenuators. The spontaneous radiation emitted perpendicular to the cavity axis was monitored using a 0.82 m Czerny–Turner spectrometer with a typical bandpass of 5 Å about a center wavelength of 1715 Å.

† The mirrors, fabricated by Acton Research Corp., withstood over 50 shots before deteriorating. Some mirrors of poorer optical polish deteriorated with one shot.

Our conclusion of stimulated emission derives from the following five observations.

(1) The spectral linewidth (measured photographically) narrowed from ≈160 Å (as observed without mirrors) to a half-width of ≈15 Å with the optical cavity. Fig. 2a illustrates the typical spectral output of the laser for conditions above and below threshold along with a calibration spectrum.

(2) Marked changes in the time dependence of the directed output radiation were observed for conditions above and below the oscillation threshold. This dramatic change in the temporal pulse shape is seen as an intense ≈10 nsec pulse as shown in fig. 2b. Spectral

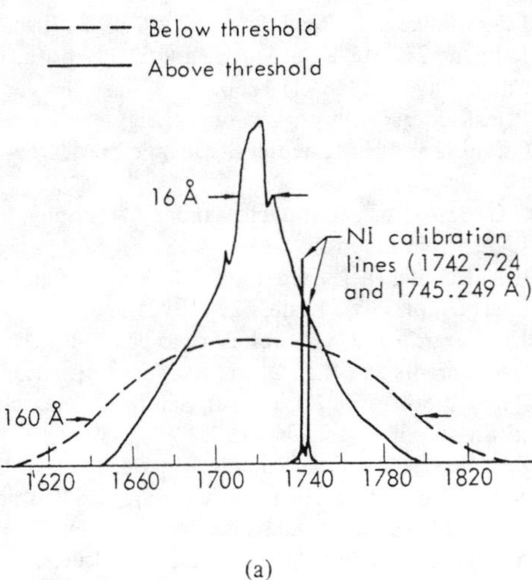

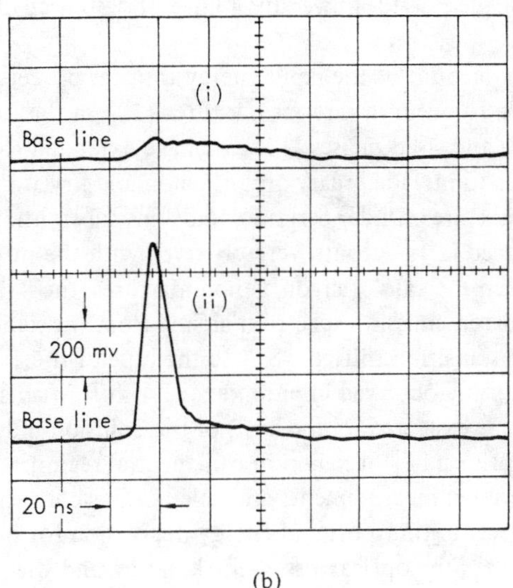

Fig. 2. (a) Time integrated spectral output (logarithmic densitometer trace) from spectrograph for (i) conditions below threshold and (ii) conditions above threshold showing NI calibration lines. Two unidentified absorption lines appear at 1708 and 1726 Å. (b) Spectrally integrated photodiode output as a function of time for (i) conditions below threshold and (ii) conditions above threshold.

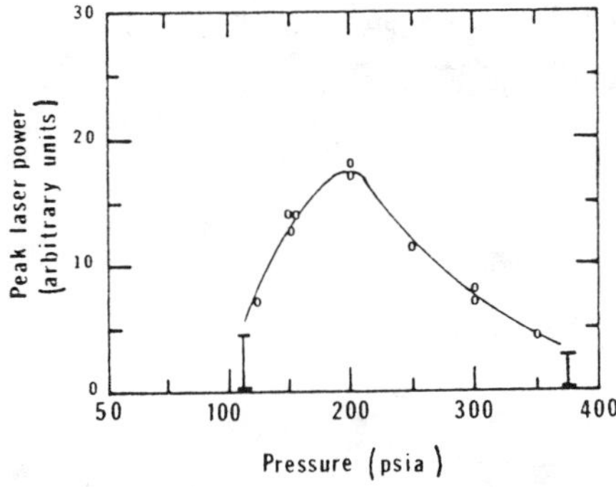

Fig. 3. Laser peak power versus xenon pressure. Note the existence of thresholds at ≈110 and ≈375 psia. The maximum standard deviation of the data points was 0.612.

line narrowing was observed only in conjunction with this fast pulse.

(3) The radiation was spatially coherent as observed photographically by positioning film at various distances from the laser cavity. The half-angle of divergence so determined was 5 mrad, which is a factor of nine larger than the divergence of the fundamental mode (0.6 mrad). Since the ratio of the diameter of a higher-order mode to the fundamental mode is a constant†, the divergence of the higher-order mode is larger by this constant factor. In our case, the diameter of the fundamental mode at the 2 mm aperture is 0.186 mm. Assuming that the highest-order mode is the size of the aperture, the diameter ratio is 10.7, which agrees well with observation.

(4) A definite oscillation threshold depending on xenon gas pressure existed. Fig. 3 illustrates the dependence of the peak laser output power on xenon pressure. Sharp threshold phenomena are observed at 125 psia and 375 psia.

(5) A dip in the sidelight spontaneous emission at 1715 Å occurred simultaneously with the 10 nsec pulse observed on the photodiode.

The direct observation of spatial coherence and threshold effects reinforces the earlier reports of spectral narrowing [5] and conclusively demonstrates the existence of optical gain on the 1700 Å xenon dimer transition. Furthermore, it was observed that the oscillation was concurrent with the pump pulse and that the laser behaved as a gain-switched oscillator. Temporally, three types of pulses were observed: a single pulse of 10–20 nsec duration, a double pulse,

† A description of mode patterns is found in ref. [9].

or a single pulse followed by a knee of ≈30 nsec duration.

On account of the rapid energy transfer processes known to occur in rare-gas mixtures [10] in the gas, liquid, and solid phases [11], we have extended these studies to include binary argon/xenon and krypton/xenon mixtures. Under certain conditions substantially enhanced laser outputs were observed with the mixtures. In the case of argon/xenon mixtures, the stimulated emission spectrum arising from the xenon dimer transition shifted ≈8 Å to the blue of the 1722 ± 1 Å value observed in pure xenon. A shift of this nature is expected on the basis of the collision-induced absorption [12] of xenon in this spectral region.

Detailed measurements and calculations concerning the electron transport and energy deposition for our geometry, the optical losses, the kinetics, and the overall efficiency of these systems will be reported in forthcoming correspondence.

The authors acknowledge many helpful conversations with P. Ebert, H. Koehler, L. Ferderber, and D. Redhead in addition to the patient and expert technical assistance of D. Rea and J. Wengert.

References

[1] R.S. Mulliken, J. Chem. Phys. 52 (1970) 5170.

[2] J. Jortner, L. Meyer, S.A. Rice and E.G. Wilson, J. Chem. Phys. 42 (1965) 4250.

[3] R.E. Kidder, in: Physics of high-energy density, eds. P. Caldirola and H. Knoepfel (Academic Press, New York, 1971) p. 306.

[4] N.G. Basov, V.A. Danilychev and Yu.M. Popov, Soviet J. Quantum Electron. 1 (1971) 18.

[5] H.A. Koehler, L.J. Ferderber, D.L. Redhead and P.J. Ebert, Appl. Phys. Letters 21 (1972) 198.

[6] J.B. Gerardo and A.W. Johnson, to be published.

[7] D.C. Lorents and R.E. Olson, Excimer Formation and Decay Processes in Rare Gases, Stanford Research Institute Report, December 1972;
E.V. George and C.K. Rhodes, Kinetic Model of Ultraviolet Inversions in High Pressure Rare Gas Plasmas, UCRL-74516, to be published.

[8] A.L. Schawlow and C.H. Townes, Phys. Rev. 112 (1958) 1940.

[9] A. Kogelnik and T. Li, Proc. IEEE 54 (1966) 1312.

[10] A. Gedanken, J. Jortner, B. Raz and A. Szöke, J. Chem. Phys. 57 (1972) 3456.

[11] A. Cheshnovsky, B. Raz and J. Jortner, Proceedings of the Third International Vacuum Ultraviolet Conference, Tokyo (1971).

[12] A.V. Phelps, Tunable Gas Lasers Utilizing Ground State Dissociation, JILA Report #110, University of Colorado, September 5, 1972.

Reprinted with permission from *IEEE Journal of Quantum Electronics,* Vol. QE-9(7), pp. 748-755 (July 1973). ©1973 IEEE.

High-Pressure Xenon Laser at 1730 Å

J. B. GERARDO AND A. WAYNE JOHNSON

***Abstract*—Experimental measurements are reported of optical gain due to stimulated transitions between the lowest-bound diatomic states of xenon (Xe) and the repulsive ground state. The optical gain was greatest at a wavelength of (1730 ± 10) Å, where the effective gain cross section is estimated to be 7×10^{-19} cm².**

Manuscript received December 12, 1972; revised March 5, 1973. This work was supported by the U. S. Atomic Energy Commission.

The authors are with Sandia Laboratories, Albuquerque, N. Mex. 87115

I. INTRODUCTION

AS HAS BEEN recognized for many years, a laser system that is attractive for many reasons utilizes excited diatomic molecules that radiate to repulsive states [1]. Appropriate sets of states can be found in many molecules. The noble gases are particularly attractive because they offer the possibility of high quantum efficiency, high net efficiency, wavelength tunability, and high power in the vacuum–ultraviolet (VUV). Many articles have been published that report the results of experiments aimed at achieving net gain in dissociating systems of the type considered here [2]–[10]. These previous studies were performed in gases, liquids, and solids. While some of the published results were negative, others definitely indicated narrowing of the spectral continuum band and the effect of stimulated emission. However, none of these studies conclusively demonstrated that net gain had been achieved.

We report here the results of a study of VUV radiation from high-pressure xenon (Xe) (1.3×10^3–2×10^4 torr) during and following its excitation with a pulsed beam of relativistic electrons (1.5-MV, about 250-A, and 50-ns pulsewidth). The experimental system was similar in many respects to the system that was used by Koehler *et al.* [10]. Our results distinctly demonstrate that the cross section for stimulated transitions from the lowest-bound diatomic states of Xe to the repulsive ground state is larger than the photoionization cross section of these excited states, and an experimental estimate of the optical gain cross section is made.

The spontaneous-emission continuum spectrum was (205 ± 20) Å wide [full width at half maximum (FWHM)] and was centered at (1730 ± 15) Å. The effective gain cross section at 1730 Å was estimated from experimental measurements to be 7×10^{-19} cm^2. This cross section is the difference between the stimulated-emission cross section and the photoionization cross section. When the medium was located in an optical resonator, the spectral width of the radiation that was coupled out of the resonator narrowed to (30 ± 4) Å (FWHM) centered at (1730 ± 10) Å and the temporal width narrowed to less than 30 percent of the temporal width of the spontaneous emission.

The measured peak laser intensity coupled out of the resonator by means of a hole in one of the mirrors was about 10^5 W, which corresponds to a power flux inside the optical resonator of greater than 10^7 W/cm^2. No attempt was made to optimize the coupling of the energy out of the resonator.

II. Experimental Apparatus

The experimental apparatus is illustrated in Fig. 1. The electron beam from a Febetron 705[1] was injected through a 75-μ-thick titanium (Ti) diaphragm into the high-pressure cell. The Ti window was 38 mm by 6.3 mm with the larger dimension parallel to the optical axis of the two mirrors. Each mirror was 16 mm in diameter with a 1.6-mm-diam hole drilled through the Pyrex substrate at its center. The reflection coefficient of the Al–MgF_2-coated mirrors at a wavelength of 1700 Å was (85 ± 1) percent. The two mirrors were separated by 15.2 cm. The distance between the Ti window and the optical axis of the resonator was adjustable to distances up to 1.3 cm (unless

[1] Febetron 705 is manufactured by Field Emission Corp., McMinnville, Ore. 97128.

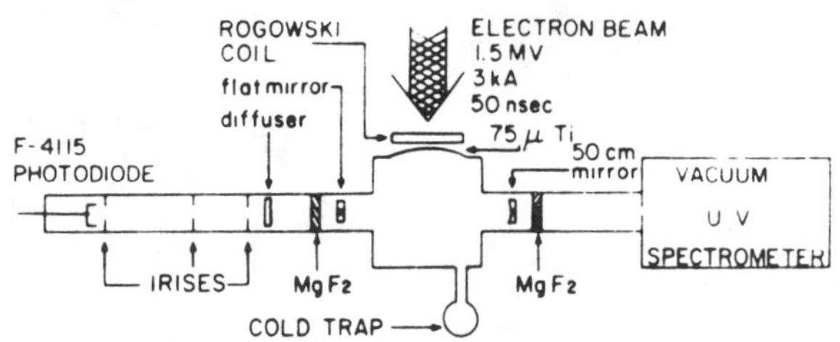

Fig. 1. Experimental apparatus.

otherwise noted, the distance was 1.3 cm). Two side pipes that connected the high-pressure cell to the spectrometer and the photodiode were evacuated to less than 10^{-6} torr. The VUV spectrometer was a 1-m McPherson model 225 with a 1200-line/mm curved grating blazed at 1200 Å and a dispersion of 8.3 Å/mm. The spectra were recorded on Kodak type SWR film. The diffuser was a piece of ground MgF_2; the attenuation of the radiation by the diffuser was calibrated and was used to attenuate the radiation to an acceptably low level so that the photodiode was not saturated by the intense radiation. The diffuser was used only when the laser output was being detected. Spontaneous emission was observed by removing the two mirrors and placing a small iris between the high-pressure cell and the photodiode. The iris reduced the radiation to an acceptable level and defined the volume from which the detected radiation originated. The high-pressure cell was evacuated and filled with reagent-grade Xe to pressures up to 2×10^4 torr. The reagent-grade Xe was distilled before it was injected into the high-pressure cell and re-distilled after each pulse of the electron beam. The distillation process reduced the photoabsorption coefficient of 1730-Å photons by minority impurity gases to about $5 \times 10^{-7} p$ cm^{-1}, where p is the total gas pressure in torrs.

The net current of the electron beam that was incident on the high-pressure cell was measured with a Rogowski coil (rise time less than 3 ns). Since the diameter of the electron beam incident on the window was larger than the width (6.3 mm) of the Ti window, only a small fraction of the current incident on the high-pressure cell was injected into it. The value of the current that passed through the Ti window was determined by filling the high-pressure cell with air at a few-torr pressure and measuring the current that traversed the cell. This measurement was made with a Faraday cup (rise time about 3 ns) that was located on the high-pressure cell opposite the Ti window; at this pressure, the electron beam is almost totally transported across the high-pressure cell. The Faraday cup, Rogowski coil, and photodiode signals were correlated in time to an accuracy of ±2 ns with the aid of a fiducial time mark, which was added to each signal.

The ITT F-4115 photodiode is sensitive to radiation between 1550 and 3300 Å, has a rise time of about 0.5 ns, and has a negligible additional time delay. When uniformly illuminated, the photodiode response was linear to within 15 percent for output voltages up to 50 V. The power measurements reported here were made by using the individual tube calibration supplied by the manufacturer at a wavelength of 2300 Å; the assumption was made that the quantum efficiency is the same in the wavelength range from 1600 to 1800 Å as it is at 2300 Å.

The current density through the Ti window on the high-pressure cell was nearly uniform over the central 22 mm and essentially zero outside of the central 25 mm. In all calculations in this paper it will be assumed that a slab of gas 6.3 mm by 25 mm in cross section is excited by the electron beam.

III. The Atomic System

The upper-energy laser states are excited diatomic states Xe_2^*, which spontaneously radiate a continuous spectrum and diffuse bands in transitions between the stable excited states and the repulsive ground state. Some work has been directed toward obtaining an understanding of the important physical processes [11]-[14] and the potential energy curve [15]. Although no general quantitative reliance can be placed on the available potential curves, they do serve as a qualitative guide. The process by which the excited diatomic states are formed is at least qualitatively understood. They are formed mainly by associative combination of an excited and a ground-state Xe atom in a three-body collision, direct electron excitation of van der Waals' molecules of Xe_2, and electronic recombination of molecular Xe ions. The frequency for the conversion of excited atoms to excited diatomic molecules, Xe_2^*, has been measured to be $26p^2$ s^{-1} by Boucique and Mortier [16] where p is the Xe pressure in torrs. The results of [10] indicate that in high-pressure Xe excited with a pulsed electron beam, the formation of Xe_2^* by all processes may yield an effective formation frequency as large as $100p^2$ s^{-1}. No experimental study of a high-pressure Xe plasma has satisfactorily determined the relative importance of the multitude of reactions that are responsible for the formation of Xe_2^*.

The spontaneous-emission lifetime of the excited diatomic molecules that radiate the continuum spectrum is $(50 \pm 20) \times 10^{-9}$ s [17], and the collisional deactivation cross section by atomic Xe is (3.3 ± 1.3) 10^{-18} cm^2 [17]. The excited molecules are also deactivated by mutual ionizing collision, at a rate of (3.5 ± 1.4) 10^{-10} $cm^3 \cdot s^{-1}$ [17]. In the mutual ionizing collision, two excited molecules react and form a free electron, an ion (atomic or molecular), and two or three ground-state atoms [18]. The spontaneous-emission lifetime of 50 ns is larger than the value arrived at in [10], because the authors did not take into account the other two deactivation processes.

At the high gas pressure considered here, it is conceivable that photoabsorption by unbound ground-state Xe molecules in a direct transition to an excited diatomic molecule could be appreciable [19]. We attempted to measure this absorption coefficient for 1730-Å photons in 300K Xe, but the photoabsorption was dominated by impurity gases in the Xe gas that was used in this study. We estimate that the photoabsorption coefficient attributable to Xe is less than $5 \times 10^{-12}p^2$ cm^{-1}, where p is the total gas pressure in torrs, and thus is not a factor in this study. The photoabsorption coefficient by impurity gases was typically $5 \times 10^{-7}p$ cm^{-1} and was a factor in some of the studies.

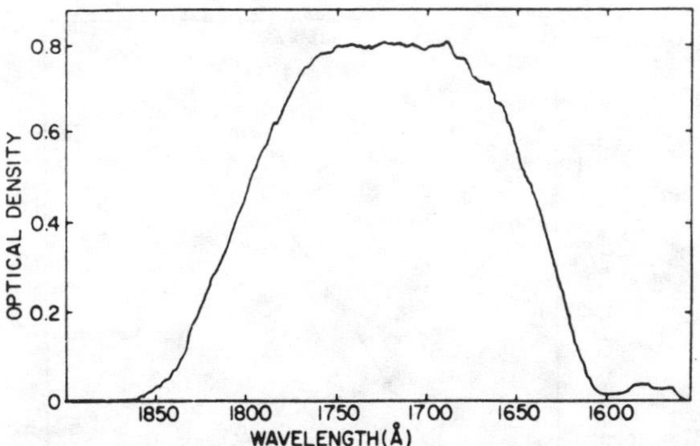

Fig. 2. Densitometer tracing of the time-integrated spontaneous-emission spectrum at a Xe pressure of 10^4 torr. The spectral resolution is about 20 Å. The vertical axis is the difference between the optical density of the exposed film and the background optical density after development of the film.

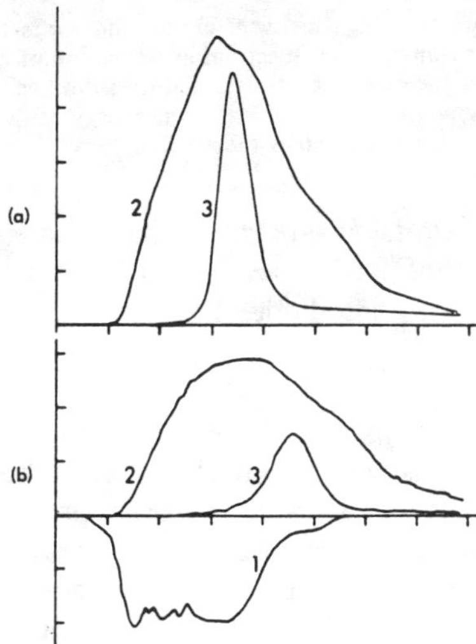

Fig. 3. Typical time-resolved recordings of 1—the electron-beam current injected into the high-pressure cell at 140 A/div, 2—the spontaneous emission $V_s = 0.91 \times 10^{-17}$ $[Xe_2^*]$ at 0.5 V/div, and 3—the laser output. (a) 13 000 torr with signal 3 at 10 V/div. (b) 8250 torr with signal 3 at 5 V/div. The oscilloscope sweep speed is 20 ns/div. The slowly decaying tail on the laser output is believed to be due to fluorescence of the MgF_2 windows. The current trace shown in (b) is also applicable to (a).

A typical densitometer tracing of the time-integrated spontaneous-emission spectrum in the VUV is illustrated in Fig. 2. For all conditions studied, the spectral width of the spontaneous-emission continuum spectrum was (205 ± 20) Å (FWHM) centered at (1730 ± 15) Å. The general film characteristics supplied by Kodak for their type SWR film were used to estimate the spectral width from the densitometer tracings of the exposed film.

The temporal behavior of the VUV spontaneous-emission continuum radiation is illustrated in Fig. 3. The number density of excited molecules, $[Xe_2^*]$, that radiate the VUV continuum can be related to the amplitude of the photodiode signal by considering the light-collection geometry, the quantum efficiency of the photodiode, and the radiative lifetime of $[Xe_2^*]$. If photoabsorption and

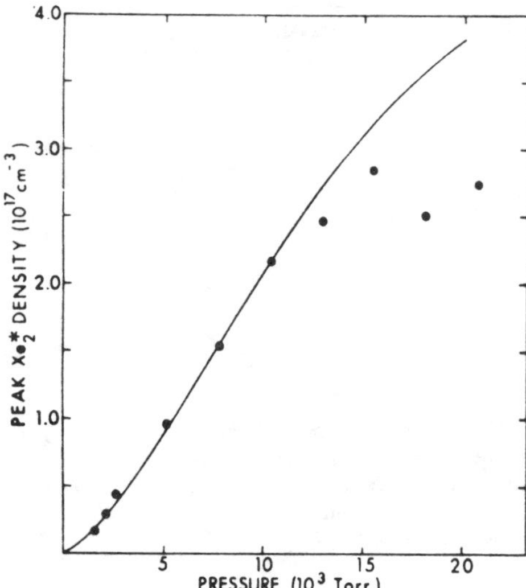

Fig. 4. Measured peak density of excited molecules that radiate the VUV continuum-emission spectrum as a function of Xe gas pressure. The dots are the experimental data and the solid line is the calculated density assuming that 6.2 percent of the energy of the electron beam that is deposited in the gas is radiated in the VUV.

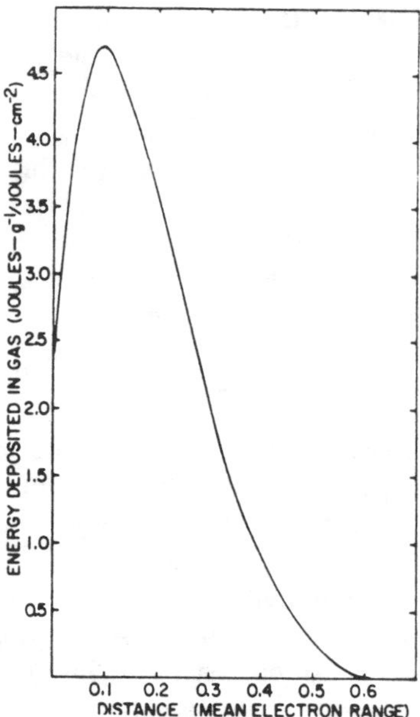

Fig. 5. Calculated energy-deposition profile for 1.5-MeV electrons in Xe. The abscissa is distance into the medium in units of the mean range of the 1.5-MeV electrons, which in Xe is $1.6 \times 10^6 \times p^{-1}$ cm, where p is the gas pressure in torrs.

stimulated emission are negligible, and if collisional deactivation of Xe_2^* does not yield a photon that is detected by the photodiode, then

$$[Xe_2^*] = 1.1 \times 10^{17} V_s \text{ cm}^{-3} \quad (1)$$

where V_s is the amplitude of the photodiode signal in volts.

The peak density of Xe_2^* during an excitation pulse is illustrated in Fig. 4 as a function of Xe gas pressure. The solid line in Fig. 4 is the calculated density of Xe_2^* when 6.2 percent of the energy deposited in the gas by the electron beam is radiated in the VUV. This calculation was performed by using a Monte Carlo technique that was developed by Halbleib [20].[2] The energy of the relativistic electron beam is deposited in the gas as excitation, ionization, and thermal energy. The calculated deposition profile is shown in Fig. 5 for a 1.5-MeV electron beam. The ordinate is the energy deposited in the Xe in units of joules/gram for a 1.5-MeV electron beam of intensity 1 J/cm^2. The abscissa is the distance from the injection plane in units of the mean range of 1.5-MeV electrons in Xe which is $1.6 \times 10^6 p^{-1}$ cm, where p is pressure in torrs. Approximately 75 percent of the electron-beam energy is deposited in the gas, and the remainder is radiated as bremsstrahlung. The energy-deposition calculation is one dimensional, so it does not account for scattering of electrons out of the finite cross section of the electron beam. Since the beam will spread because of coulomb collisions, the actual energy deposited in the gas per unit volume will be somewhat less than the calculated value [21].

The data illustrated in Fig. 4 demonstrate that the efficiency of conversion from deposited energy to the energy radiated in the VUV is about 6 percent at gas pressures less than 10^4 torr. This estimated efficiency is in reasonable agreement with the value arrived at in [10]. At gas pressures slightly above 10^4 torr, the ratio of the power radiated in the VUV to the calculated value of the power deposited in the gas by the electron beam is less than 6 percent. The apparent smaller efficiency for conversion of electron-beam energy to VUV radiation at higher pressures is evidently due to one or a combination of the following effects: collisional quenching of Xe_2^* by Xe [17], inaccuracy of the energy-deposition calculation, effects of impurity gases, photoabsorption by two Xe atoms [19], or collisional deexcitation of Xe_2^* states in an ionizing collision between two Xe_2^* molecules [17]. The shape of the experimental curve shown in Fig. 4 is difficult to predict because of the variety of physical processes that must be considered. There is also the added complication of gas heating by the electron beam, since all of the above-mentioned effects are gas-temperature dependent. Thus it is difficult to project our results to those which may be obtained by using more-energetic electron beams. The measured efficiency of conversion from electron-beam energy to VUV radiation was close to 10 percent when the optical axis was at a distance of 0.63 cm from the Ti window. This difference in efficiency at the two locations is attributed to the same effects that are discussed above.

Prior to this time, both Koehler *et al.* [10] and Basov *et al.* [7]–[9] have reported narrowing of the continuum-emission spectrum of Xe at a wavelength near 1700 Å. While spectral narrowing is evidence that stimulated emission contributed greatly to the total radiation, it does not necessarily imply that the medium can supply net gain [22], because the 1700-Å photons have sufficient energy to photoionize the excited diatomic molecules. Photoionization cross sections generally do not vary rapidly with energy above threshold, but the stimulated-emission cross section is strongly peaked at line center. Thus the spectral width could narrow because of stimulated emission even if the net gain coefficient at line

[2] The energy-deposition profile for an electron beam through Xe was not actually reported in [20], but the same numerical program was used.

center was negative because of photoionization. This is easily demonstrated by considering the radiation emitted from a volume along an optical path of length l from a uniform medium with a gain coefficient $\gamma(\nu)$ and a loss coefficient $\alpha(\nu)$, which are functions of frequency ν. If the gain is not saturated, the radiation intensity is

$$I_\nu = I_\nu^0 \frac{1}{[\gamma(\nu) - \alpha(\nu)]l} \{\exp[\gamma(\nu) - \alpha(\nu)]l - 1\} \quad (2)$$

where I_ν^0 is the radiation intensity in the limit of zero net gain (i.e., $[\gamma(\nu) - \alpha(\nu)]l \to 0$). This equation is approximately applicable to unsaturated radiating mediums that are located in resonators if l is interpreted as the effective length of the medium and I_ν is the envelope of the amplitudes of the resonator modes. Both γ and α are proportional to [Xe_2*]. The contribution to α due to photoionization is nearly independent of wavelength in the range (1730 ± 100) Å, while $\gamma(\nu)$ has a dependence with ν that is the same as that of I_ν^0. If γ_0 is the gain coefficient at line center, it is clear that when γ_0 is greater than zero, the spectral shape of I_ν is narrower than that of I_ν^0 regardless of whether the quantity $(\gamma_0 - \alpha)$ is less than or greater than zero.

The small-signal gain coefficient can be estimated by using the standard expression [23]

$$\gamma(\nu) = \frac{c^2}{8\pi\nu^2\tau} g(\nu)(N_2 - N_1) \quad (3)$$

where τ is the spontaneous-emission lifetime, N_2 and N_1 are the densities of molecules in the upper- and lower-energy levels, respectively, and $g(\nu)$ is the normalized line-shape function $\int_{-\infty}^{\infty} g(\nu)\, d\nu = 1$. The justification for lumping the multitude of collisionally coupled states into one state with density N_2 = [Xe_2*] and with spontaneous-emission lifetime τ is the very rapid collisional mixing of the levels at the high gas pressure considered here. For all gas pressures studied in this experiment, $N_1 \approx 0$. For the line shape observed here (Fig. 2), the line-shape function at line center is $g_0 \approx \lambda_0^2/(c\Delta\lambda)$, where $\Delta\lambda$ is the width of the line (FWHM). For λ_0 = 1730 Å, $\Delta\lambda$ = 200 Å, and τ = 50 ns, the gain at line center is $\gamma_0 = 1.2 \times 10^{-18}$ [Xe_2*] cm^{-1}, where [Xe_2*] is in units of cm^{-3}.

IV. Gain Measurements

The optical gain of the excited Xe at wavelengths corresponding to the VUV continuum spectrum was measured by removing the spherical mirror from the apparatus illustrated in Fig. 1, locating a photodiode in place of the spectrometer, and placing a small iris between each photodiode and the high-pressure cell. The photodiode on the left-hand side of the illustration viewed the excited medium through the 1.6-mm-diam hole in the flat mirror. The relation between the amplitude of V_s, the signal by the photodiode on the left-hand side, to the density of Xe_2* is given by (1). The amplitude of V_m, the signal by the photodiode that is located on the right-hand side of the illustration, is proportional to Xe_2* plus a term due to reflection of the radiation off the flat mirror, through the active medium, and onto the photodiode. When the ratio of V_m/V_s increases with increased values of V_s, the medium has net optical gain, if photoionization of Xe_2* is the only photon loss process.

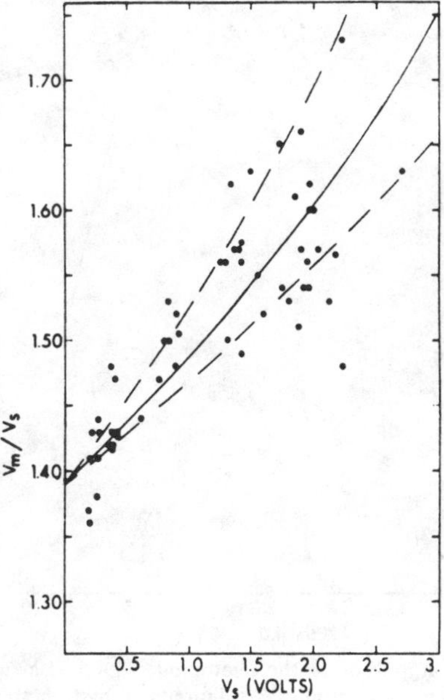

Fig. 6. Experimental measured ratio V_m/V_s as a function of $V_s = 9.1 \times 10^{-18}$ [Xe_2*]. The slope of the data points is a measure of the optical gain at a wavelength of 1730 Å. The solid line represents the shape that would be obtained for a gain coefficient of $\gamma_0 = 7.7 \times 10^{-2} V_s\ cm^{-1}$. The intercept with the ordinate is not 1.8 because the photodiode sensitivities are not the same.

In Fig. 6 is plotted the ratio of the two photodiode signals as a function of V_s. While the scatter is large, the data definitely indicate net gain. The solid and dashed lines drawn in Fig. 6 are calculated curves that were obtained by setting V_s proportional to $\int_0^{\infty} I_\nu\, d_\nu$, where I_ν is given by (2). The amplitude of V_m was calculated in this same manner with due consideration being given to the radiation that is reflected by the flat mirror, and subsequently through the active medium and onto the photodiode. The calculated curves are for a mirror reflectivity of 80 percent and a line shape of approximately the shape that is illustrated in Fig. 2. In determining the calculated curves, we have set $\alpha(\nu) = 0$ and thus have neglected photoionization effects. The solid curve in Fig. 6 is for an assumed value of $\gamma_0 = 7.7 \times 10^{-2} V_s\ cm^{-1}$. Using the relation between V_s and [Xe_2*] as given by (1), we estimate the gain coefficient at line center to be

$$\gamma_0 = 7 \times 10^{-19} [Xe_2^*]\ cm^{-1}.$$

This value is approximately one half as large as the value derived by using (3). The difference may be due to photoionization, but could just as well be due to experimental inaccuracy.

Data are included in Fig. 6 for pressures less than 1.3×10^4 torr. At a higher gas pressure, the measured ratio V_m/V_s was smaller at a given V_s due to photoabsorption by the gas.

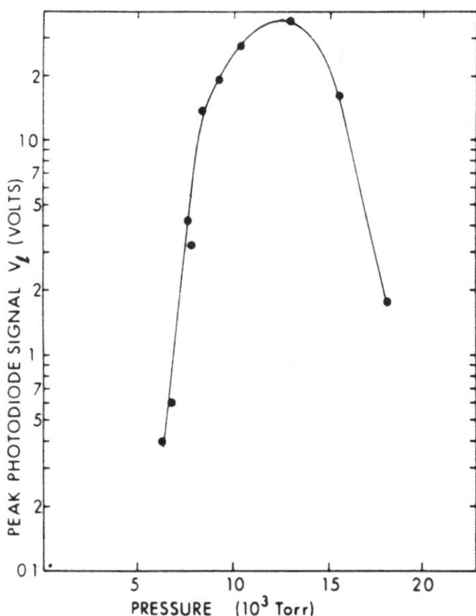

Fig. 7. Peak amplitude of the photodiode signal as a function of gas pressure when the photodiode is illuminated by the radiation coupled out of the optical resonator.

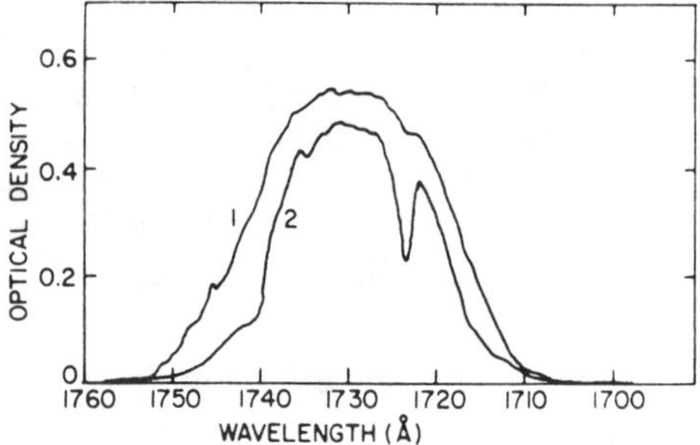

Fig. 8. Densitometer tracings of the time-integrated spectra of the radiation coupled out of the optical resonator at a Xe pressure of 9800 torr. Spectral resolution is about 1 Å. 1—First pulse of the electron beam into the gas. 2—Fourth pulse of the electron beam into the gas. The cold trap was maintained at about −50°C. The sharp absorption line in 2 is due to absorption by an impurity gas. Weaker absorption lines are also observed in both 1 and 2.

V. Experiments with the Resonator

The gain coefficient estimated in the previous section and the measured value of [Xe_2^*] indicate that at 10^4 torr, the optical gain per pass through the excited medium is about 40 percent. This gain should be sufficient to establish laser oscillation when the medium is located in the optical resonator. Some typical signals that were recorded by the photodiode when illuminated by the radiation through the hole in the flat mirror are illustrated in Fig. 3. The amplitude of this signal, V_l in volts, is related to the power coupled out of the 0.02-cm² hole by

$$P_l = 10^3 V_l \text{ W}.$$

This corresponds to a one-way power flux, on axis and inside the resonator, of $5 \times 10^4 \cdot V_l$ W/cm². The peak power flux inside the resonator is surely larger than the value on axis because the holes in the mirrors will tend to establish a mode in the resonator with a relative minimum in intensity on axis. The largest laser output observed in this study was 10^6 W, which corresponds to a two-way flux inside the cavity of greater than 10^7 W/cm².

The peak power coupled out of the resonator as a function of gas pressure is illustrated in Fig. 7, and the spectrum of this radiation is illustrated in Fig. 8. Comparison of the data in Fig. 7 to the excited-state density given in Fig. 4 demonstrates the strong nonlinear relationship between the excited-state density and the amplitude of the radiation inside the resonator. This behavior is suggestive of a pulsed laser with a small-signal gain that is just slightly above oscillation threshold. The decrease in laser output with increase in pressure above 1.3×10^4 torr is evidently due to an increase in resonator loss by photoabsorption in the gas.

When studying the laser output, either the Xe was distilled after each pulse of the electron beam into the gas or a slightly cold trap (about −50°C) was used to condense impurities. When neither of these procedures was followed, the laser output decreased on each successive electron-beam pulse—by as much as a factor of 100 after about 4 pulses. If the distillation procedure was not followed, there was a marked increase in the measured photoabsorption coefficient at a wavelength of 1730 Å in the gas that had several electron-beam pulses into it. The effect of an impurity gas that was not condensed out by the distillation process is evident in the spectra shown in Fig. 8. The impurity gases had little, if any, affect on the atomic reactions.

Spectra similar to those shown in Fig. 8 were analyzed by using the general film characteristics suggested by Kodak. The densitometer tracings illustrated in Fig. 8 are for film exposures in the most linear region of the film characteristics; thus the vertical deflection is nearly proportional to the $\log_{10}$ of the spectral intensity. The wide variation in film exposure made it difficult to quantitatively correlate the width of the optical density curve with the width of the spectra for all observed spectra. However, a semiquantitative correlation was made by using the SWR film characteristic supplied by Kodak. When this was done, it was found that the half-intensity widths of all the observed laser spectra were (30 ± 4) Å (FWHM), with no consistent change in width for different experimental conditions or peak intensity of the laser radiation. Only for the weakest observed laser-output intensities was there a trend to more narrow widths, and this trend may have been entirely due to the threshold behavior of the film that was used to record the spectra.

The temporal growth of the radiation intensity in the resonator as seen by an observer traveling with the wave velocity is given by [23]

$$\frac{dI_\nu}{dt} = \frac{c}{L}\left[(\gamma(\nu)l - \mathcal{L})\right]I_\nu + S_\nu(t) \tag{4}$$

where L is the distance between the mirrors, l is the length of the active medium, and $\mathcal{L}$ is the loss per pass by the wave. In (4), both the loss and the gain are assumed to be uniformly distributed between the mirrors. The quantity $S_\nu(t)$ is a source of radiation by spontaneous emission into the mode that is relevant to I_ν. For a nonsaturated medium, $\gamma(\nu)$ is proportional to $S_\nu(t)$. The solution of this equation was obtained for various values of the ratio $\gamma_0/\mathcal{L}$ and for the measured temporal behavior of normalized $S_\nu(t)$ and the resonator parameters. Comparison of the shape of the calculated $I_\nu(t)$ to the experimentally measured $V_l(t)$ showed that the calculated behavior of $I_\nu(t)$ was very similar to that of $V_l(t)$ for low levels of laser output. For example, a good fit to the 8.25×10^3-torr data illustrated in Fig. 3 was obtained by using $\mathcal{L} = 0.2$ and $\gamma_0 l = 0.3$—values which are consistent with the resonator parameters and the measured gain. For experimental conditions that gave a much larger peak value of V_l, comparison of the shape of the measured and calculated waveforms was not successful, which we attribute to either gain saturation [23] or a time-dependent loss mechanism. It is estimated that gain saturation would occur if the average flux inside the resonator is about a factor of ten larger than the flux passing through the hole in the mirror—a condition that is within the realm of possibility. A time-dependent loss could be introduced, for example, by a time-dependent mirror reflectivity.

In the context of (4), temporal narrowing will occur only if γ is positive, unless the resonator losses are time dependent. Therefore, the observed temporal narrowing and measured temporal delay between the peak radiation and the peak spontaneous emission are an independent demonstration that the stimulated-emission cross section is larger than the photoionization cross section of the lowest-bound diatomic states of Xe.

Koehler *et al.* [10] mention in their paper that the temporal width of the radiation narrowed to about 3 ns when the excited Xe was located in an optical resonator. This is probably evidence that they also observed laser action. We have not been able to assess why the temporal width we observed is about five times larger than was observed in [10]; in no instance did we observe such a narrow pulse of radiation. Perhaps the different pulsewidth is due to differences in the properties of the optical resonator.

VI. Conclusion

We have conclusively demonstrated that the cross section for stimulated transitions from the lowest-bound diatomic states of Xe to the repulsive ground state is larger than the photoionization cross section of these excited states. This result was demonstrated in two ways: direct measurement of net optical gain at wavelengths near 1730 Å and temporal narrowing of the radiation intensity when the excited Xe was located in an optical resonator. The observed narrowing of the spectrum further supports the conclusion that the atomic system had net gain, but, as discussed in the text, this is not a conclusive observation by itself.

The optical gain is greatest at a wavelength of (1730 ± 10) Å. The effective gain cross section at 1730 Å is estimated to be 7×10^{-19} cm². This cross section is the difference between the stimulated-emission and photoionization cross sections.

Note Added in Proof: Recent studies have demonstrated that the spectral width of the spontaneous-emission continuum spectrum is about 70 percent of the value arrived at from the densitometer tracings of the film. It probably follows that the spectral width of the laser output is also about 70 percent of the value reported here. This difference in the spectral width affects the theoretically predicted value of gain, but it does not affect the experimentally derived value.

Acknowledgment

The authors wish to thank their colleagues for many helpful discussions. They also wish to thank F. W. Bingham for much constructive criticism and H. A. Koehler, P. J. Ebert, and L. J. Ferderber, all of Lawrence Livermore Laboratory, for the time they spent in discussing their experiment and experimental results.

References

[1] F. G. Houtermans, "Über Maser-Wirkung im Optischen Spektralgebiet und die Möglichkeit absoluten Negativer Absorption für einige Fälle von Molekulspektren (Licht-Lawine)," *Helv. Phys. Acta.*, vol. 33, p. 933, 1960.

[2] D. A. Leonard, J. C. Keck, and M. M. Litvak, "Population inversion between bound and repulsive molecular electronic states by two-temperature equilibrium," *Proc. IEEE* (Corresp.), vol. 51, pp. 1785–1786, 1963.

[3] R. J. Carbone and M. M. Litvak, "Intense mercury-vapor green-band emission," *J. Appl. Phys.*, vol. 39, pp. 2413–2416, 1968.

[4] N. G. Basov *et al.*, "Cathodoluminescence of solid xenon in the ultraviolet region of the spectrum," *Pis'ma Zh. Eksp. Teor. Fiz.*, vol. 7, pp. 404–405, 1968.

[5] C. V. Heer, "A broadband ultraviolet molecular hydrogen laser," *Phys. Lett.*, vol. 31A, pp. 160–161, 1970.

[6] A. J. Palmer, "Stimulated emission of the H_2 continuum," *J. Appl. Phys.*, vol. 41, pp. 438–439, 1970.

[7] N. G. Basov *et al.*, "Luminescence of condensed Xe, Kr, Ar and their mixtures in vacuum region of spectrum under excitation by fast electron," *J. Lumin.*, vol. 12, pp. 834–841, 1970.

[8] N. G. Basov, V. A. Danilychev, Yu. M. Popov, and D. D. Khodkevich, "Laser operating in the vacuum region of the spectrum by excitation of liquid xenon with an electron beam," *Pis'ma Zh. Eksp. Teor. Fiz.*, vol. 10, pp. 473–474, 1970.

[9] N. G. Basov, V. A. Danilychev, and Yu. M. Popov, "Stimulated emission in the vacuum ultraviolet region," *Sov. J. Quantum Electron.*, vol. 1, pp. 18–22, 1971.

[10] H. A. Koehler, L. J. Ferderber, D. L. Redhead, and P. J. Ebert, "Stimulated VUV emission in high pressure xenon excited by high current relativistic electron beams," *Appl. Phys. Lett.*, vol. 21, pp. 198–200, 1972.

[11] P. G. Wilkinson and E. T. Byram, "Rare gas light sources for the vacuum ultraviolet," *Appl. Opt.*, vol. 4, pp. 581–588, 1965.

[12] R. E. Huffman, J. C. Larrabee, and Y. Tanaka, "Rare gas continuum light sources for photoelectric scanning in the vacuum ultraviolet," *Appl. Opt.*, vol. 4, pp. 1581–1588, 1965.

[13] T. E. Steward *et al.*, "Proton excitation of continuous emission in the noble gases," *J. Opt. Soc. Am.*, vol. 60, pp. 1290–1297, 1970.

[14] O. Cheshnovsky, B. Raz, and J. Jortner, "Temperature dependence of rare gas molecular emission in the vacuum ultraviolet," *Chem. Phys. Lett.*, vol. 15, pp. 475–479, 1972.

[15] Robert S. Mulliken, "Potential curves of diatomic rare-gas molecules and their ions, with particular reference to Xe_2," *J. Chem. Phys.*, vol. 52, pp. 5170–5180, 1970.

[16] R. Boucique and P. Mortier, "On the production and the decay of

delayed molecular ultraviolet radiation in rare gas Townsend discharges," *J. Phys. D: Appl. Phys.*, vol. 3, pp. 1905–1911, 1970.
[17] A. W. Johnson and J. B. Gerardo, "Deexcitation of diatomic xenon molecules by mutual ionizing collisions, spontaneous emission, and collisional deactivation," to be published.
[18] ——, "Ionizing collisions of two metastable helium atoms (2^3S)," *Phys. Rev.*, vol. 7, Mar. 1973.
[19] I. V. Kosinskaya and L. P. Polozova, "Molecular absorption of xenon in the vacuum ultraviolet," *Opt. Spectrosc.* (USSR), vol. 30, pp. 458–460, 1971.
[20] J. A. Halbleib, "Parametric study of pulsed electron beam environments," Sandia Lab., Albuquerque, N. Mex., Res. Rep. SC-RR-72 9435, 1972.
[21] P. A. Miller and J. B. Gerardo, "Relativistic electron beam propagation in high-pressure gases," *J. Appl. Phys.*, vol. 43, pp. 3008–3013, 1972.
[22] E. I. Gordon, "Optical maser oscillators and noise," *Bell Syst. Tech. J.*, vol. 43, pp. 507–539, 1964.
[23] A. Yariv, *Introduction to Optical Electronics.* New York: Holt, Rinehart and Winston, 1971.

Excitation of vacuum ultraviolet emission from high-pressure xenon by relativistic electron beams*

Stephen C. Wallace, R. T. Hodgson, and R. W. Dreyfus

IBM Thomas J. Watson Research Center, Yorktown Heights, New York 10598

This letter reports an investigation of the vacuum ultraviolet emission from gaseous xenon excited with a 4-nsec 10-kA cm^{-2} electron beam. The observed decrease in the emission lifetime at 171.5 nm for high xenon number density is due to a quenching process intrinsic to xenon. Treatment of the quenching data yields a radiative lifetime of 130 ± 20 nsec for the excited xenon diatomic, and a quenching constant of 5.1×10^{-13} cm^3 $atom^{-1}$ sec^{-1}. Thus, the theoretical threshold for laser action in excited diatomic xenon molecules is $\sim$ 26 times higher than had been previously anticipated from the 5-nsec lifetime observed in liquid xenon.

The development of short-wavelength molecular dissociation lasers by using the vacuum ultraviolet emission from excited rare-gas diatomic molecules has centered on xenon in the liquid[1,2] and gas phases.[3] Very efficient pumping (>10% energy conversion) of the second continuum of xenon by both relativistic electrons[3] and protons[4] has been observed. Therefore, taking the fluorescent lifetime for this excited xenon diatomic molecule to be a few nanoseconds[2] the lasing threshold in ~30 atm of xenon should be attainable with presently available kiloampere electron accelerators of the field emission type. A recent publication[3] has reported evidence for stimulated emission in high-pressure xenon, pumped in a transverse geometry by a 50-nsec 0.5-kA cm^{-2} 2-MeV electron beam. The evidence of laser action was the observation of spectral and temporal narrowing of the fluorescence at 171.8 nm when aluminized mirrors (overcoated with MgF_2) were used to form an optical cavity.

The following letter describes a study of the emission from the xenon diatomic molecule excited by a 4-nsec 10-kA cm^{-2} 300-keV (mean energy) electron beam. Because the Febetron 706 electron accelerator used is a simple, reliable, and relatively inexpensive laboratory instrument, development of a vacuum ultraviolet laser using it for a power source would be very desirable. In addition, the short pulse duration permits the direct observation of energy transfer and the formation and decay of excited molecular species in rare gases.

A transverse pumping scheme was used in all experiments. A portion of the 1-cm-diam beam from the Febetron 706 (5516 electron tube) was shaped into a rectangular patter, 1.4×0.4 cm, by using self-focusing effects in a beam transport tube tapered in one dimension and filled with 15 Torr of nitrogen. The electron window (0.0025-cm stainless steel) of the high-pressure cell was supported by a honeycombed plate on which the foil had been hydrogen brazed. This plate contained four holes (0.315 cm in diameter and separated by 0.036 cm) giving an effective excitation region ~1.2 cm long. In this configuration the incident electron flux was 10 kA cm^{-2}, of which 75% was transmitted by the electron window. By taking the mean electron energy to be 300 keV, the estimated energy input into the cell was 1.5 J. This agrees well with the value of 1.4 J, which was determined using the method of adiabatic calorimetry.[5] The peak power input was thus 3×10^9 W cm^{-2}. A plane parallel cavity was used, consisting of a high-reflectivity aluminum back reflector overcoated with Al/MgF_2 ($R > 0.8$ at 170 nm) and a thin sapphire output mirror (0.025 cm thick, $R > 0.35$ at 170 nm [6]).

Light emission was studied by using a McPherson Model 225 vacuum spectrograph with a 1200-line/mm grating, blazed at 150 nm. Spectra were recorded photographically either on Kodak SWR or Kodak Pathé SC7 film or photometrically by an ITT biplanar photodiode (S20) with a sapphire window, in conjunction with a Tektronix 519 or 7904 oscilloscope.

Research-grade xenon from Matheson was used throughout. The vacuum system and high-pressure lines were stainless steel, and ion pumps were generally employed for clean pumping.

Spectrographic measurements (see Fig. 1) at low xenon pressures (4.3 atm) show a broad-band emission centered at a wavelength $\lambda = 170$ nm with a fullwidth at half-maximum $\Delta\lambda_{1/2} \approx 10$ nm and a lifetime $\tau_1 = 20$ nsec. As the pressure of xenon is increased (keeping the incident electron flux constant), this emission spectrum narrows, shifts to slightly longer wavelengths, and its lifetime is markedly decreased. A comparison of the temporal and spectral data for pressures of 4.3 and 34 atm is given in Fig. 1. Over this pressure range the peak of the emission shifts to 171.5 nm, narrows to $\Delta\lambda_{1/2} \approx 6$ nm, and the decay of the luminescence develops into two fast components: an initial very rapid decay $\tau_1 < 1$ nsec, whose measurement is limited by the duration of the electron pulse (4 nsec), and a slower tail $\tau_2 \approx 5$ nsec. Time-resolved spectra show that this tail has a spectrum similar to that obtained at low pressures (4.3 atm). Spectrographic measurements detected no other emissions for $155 < \lambda < 185$ nm.

At pressures >10 atm (2.6×10^{22} atom cm^{-3}) the formation time of the excited xenon molecule is <1 nsec (using the three-body collision rate of 1.5×10^{-32} cm^6 $atom^{-2}$ sec^{-1}[7]), so that the peak height of the emission should be proportional to the energy absorbed by the xenon and hence the xenon number density. Instead, as is shown in Fig. 2, it is observed that for pressures greater than 27 atm (8×10^{20} atom cm^{-3}) there is a dramatic decrease in the light output. In contrast, when the number density of excited zenon diatomic molecules is varied by decreasing the input power (over an eightfold

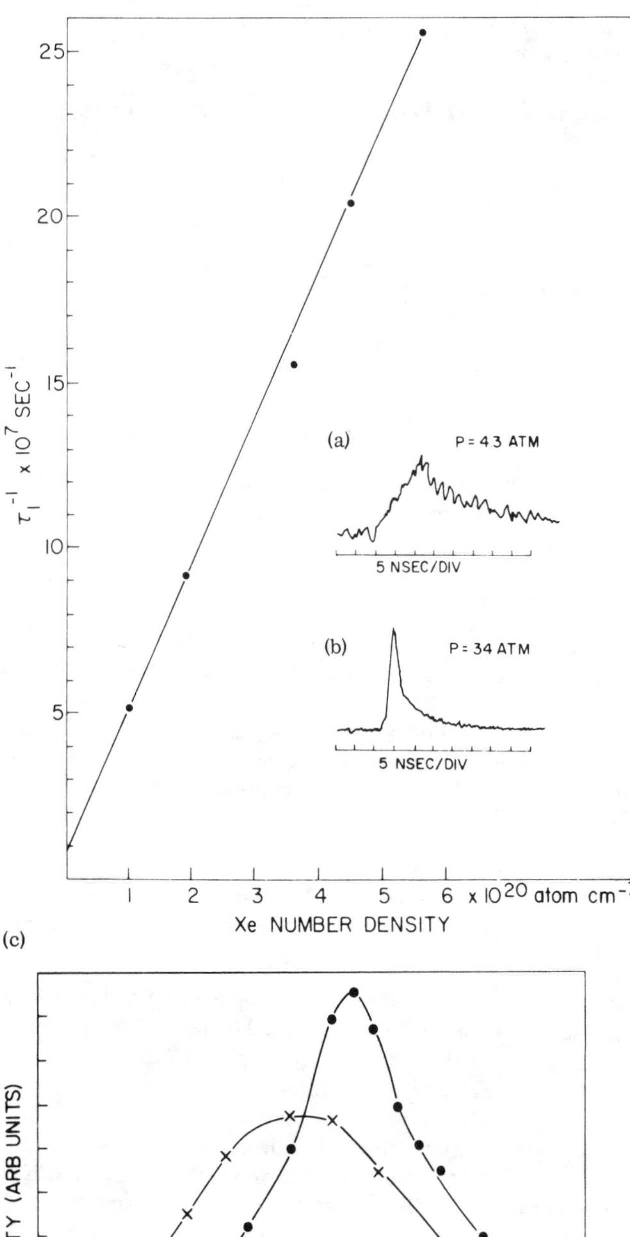

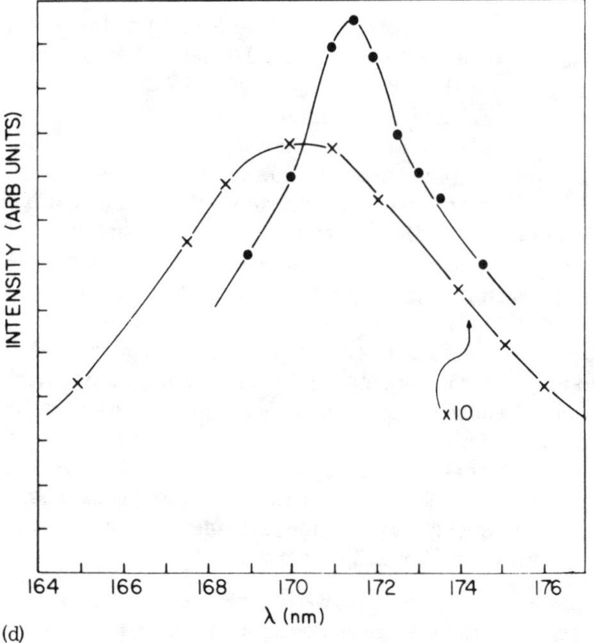

FIG. 1. (a) and (b), oscilloscope traces showing the decay of the Xe_2 fluorescence at $\lambda = 171.5$ nm for low and high pressures. (c) Inverse lifetime of the principal decay component τ_1 as a function of xenon number density. (d) Emission spectra at 4.3 (×) and 34 (●) atm.

range from its maximum value) at a constant xenon pressure, the emission is directly proportional to the energy absorbed. Furthermore, the unusual time dependence observed at high pressures, given by τ_1 and τ_2, is independent of the energy absorbed.

The observed decrease in the lifetime and linewidth of the luminescence, as the number density of xenon is increased so that more energy is absorbed in the gas and hence more excited states are produced, is similar to the behavior of amplified spontaneous emissions as threshold is approached. However, the fact that τ_1 and τ_2 are independent of energy absorbed at a constant pressure excludes such an explanation. Quenching must therefore determine the lifetime of the excited xenon diatomic molecules at high pressures. Treatment of the lifetime data by plotting the inverse of the principal decay component τ_1 as a function of xenon number density gives the straight line shown in Fig. 1. The two-body quenching constant, $k_q = 5.1 \times 10^{-13}$ cm^3 atom^{-1} sec^{-1}, is given by the slope and the radiative lifetime, $\tau_1 = 130 \pm 20$ nsec, is obtained by extrapolation to zero pressure. We do not believe that this quenching is due to impurities, because no changes were observed in emission lifetimes when extra purification procedures such as treatment with activated titanium or distillation over an activated molecular sieve at dry-ice temperature were used. Furthermore, sufficient impurities to account for this quenching would be easily detectable, as shown by the fact that addition of 500 ppm of oxygen was necessary to lower the emission lifetime by a factor of 2 at a pressure of 4.3 atm.

It is instructive to compute the theoretical gain due to stimulated emission from the xenon diatomic molecule by using the pumping parameters of this work. Taking the band shape of the excited xenon diatomic molecule emission to be Lorentzian, the gain per unit length, α, at band center is

$$\alpha = \sigma N = (c^2/8\pi^2)(N/\nu_0^2 \Delta\nu\tau), \tag{1}$$

where ν_0 and $\Delta\nu$ are the frequency and linewidth, τ is the radiative lifetime, and N is the number density of emitting species. By using the radiative lifetime ($\tau_1 = 130$ nsec) obtained from this work, the cross section for stimulated emission from the excited xenon diatomic at 171.5 nm is $\sigma = 6 \times 10^{-19}$ cm^2. In order to calculate the number density of the excited states and thus the gain, one must take into account the pressure-dependent lifetime in xenon, because at number densities high enough to absorb the incident electron beam a significant fraction of the excited xenon molecules will have decayed during the pulse, for pulse durations longer than 4 nsec (cf. $\tau_1 \approx 4$ nsec at a pressure of ~20 atm). Finally, by using an energy efficiency of 10% for the converson of absorbed dose to light emission in the second continuum at ~170 nm, the calculated gain at a xenon pressure of 17 atm is $\alpha = 0.12$ cm^{-1}. The gain in this system is not a linear function of xenon number density because raising the number density so that more energy is absorbed per unit volume has the additional effect of increasing the rate of quenching of the excited xenon diatomic molecule, thus decreasing the energy efficiency for light emission. Because of this quenching, the maximum theoretical gain in this work was $\alpha = 0.23$ at a xenon pres-

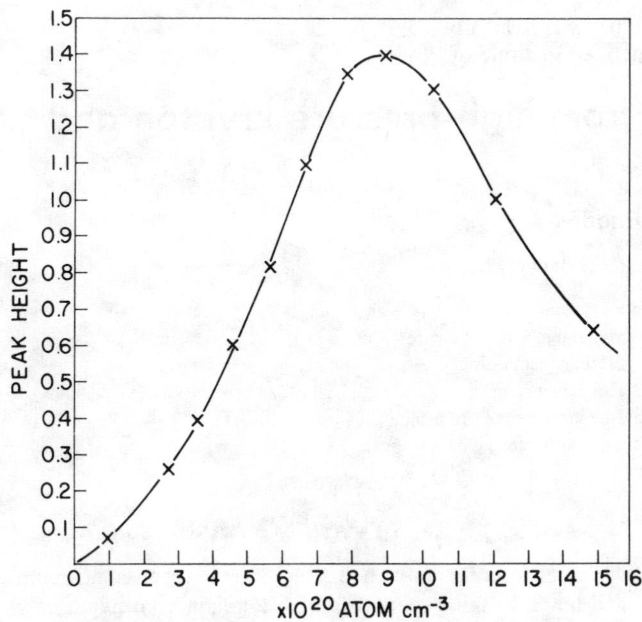

FIG. 2. Emission peak height at λ = 171.5 nm as a function of xenon number density.

sure of 38 atm. These values are to be compared with the theoretical threshold gain for laser action, $\alpha = 0.5$, estimated from the equation $(R_1R_2)^{1/2}\exp(\alpha l) = 1$, where R_1 and R_2 are the mirror reflectivities and l is the length of the excitation volume.

Further work is in progress, using a new type of electron tube which produces a rectangular beam, 0.8×2.2 cm, and is therefore more suited to transverse pumping. It is estimated that by using a high-reflectivity output mirror gains of up to five times the theoretical thres-threshold gain will be possible.

Stimulating discussions with J.A. Armstrong and C. Bradley Moore and the technical assistance of R. Linn are gratefully acknowledged.

---

*Research supported in part by the U.S. Army Research Office, Durham, and by the Advanced Research Projects Agency of the Dept. of Defense, and was monitored by the Office of Naval Research under Contract No. N00014-73-C-0072.

[1]N. G. Basov, V. A. Danilychev, Yu. M. Popov, and D. D. Khodevich, JETP Lett. **9**, 329 (1970).
[2]A. G. Molchanov, Sov. Phys.-Usp. **15**, 124 (1972).
[3]H. A. Koehler, L. J. Ferderber, D. L. Redhead, and P. J. Ebert, Appl. Phys. Lett. **21**, 198 (1972).
[4]G. S. Hurst, T. E. Stewart, and J. E. Parks, Phys. Rev. A **2**, 1717 (1970).
[5]S. C. Wallace and D. C. Walker, J. Phys. Chem. **76**, 3780 (1972).
[6]D. F. Heath and P. A. Sacher, Appl. Opt. **5**, 397 (1966).
[7]G. C. Freeman, M. J. McEwan, R. F. C. Claridge, and L. F. Phillips, Chem. Phys. Lett. **10**, 530 (1971).

Reprinted with permission from *Applied Physics Letters,* Vol. 23(5), pp. 245-246 (September 1, 1973). ©1973 American Institute of Physics.

Observations of stimulated emission from high-pressure krypton and argon/xenon mixtures*

Paul W. Hoff, James C. Swingle, and Charles K. Rhodes

Lawrence Livermore Laboratory, University of California/Livermore, California 94550

Experimental data demonstrating coherent oscillation in high-pressure krypton at 1457 ± 1 Å with an 8-Å linewidth are reported. Observations of stimulated emission from argon/xenon mixtures arising from the operation of efficient energy transfer processes and resulting in a twofold enhancement of the xenon laser output at ∾ 1720 Å are also given. The influence of collisional-induced absorption on the oscillator output is indicated by the measurement of a blue shift in the spectrum of the stimulated output for argon/xenon mixtures relative to the case of pure xenon.

In this letter, we report initial experimental findings concerning the observations of stimulated emission from high-pressure krypton and argon/xenon mixtures excited with a pulsed relativistic electron beam. Kinetic analyses of these electron-beam-excited plasmas appear in earlier publications.[1,2] The details of the experimental apparatus, which allows the simultaneous measurement of (a) the spectrally integrated time dependence of the spatially directed oscillator output, (b) the temporally integrated spectrum of the emitted radiation (photographed spectrum), and (c) the behavior of the spontaneous emission of the excited material viewed perpendicular to the oscillator axis, are described elsewhere.[3]

The molecular continuum of krypton arising from bound-free transitions of the excited krypton dimer Kr_2^* and centered at ~1500 Å is analogous to the corresponding spectral feature in xenon at ~1700 Å. As a first approximation, the level structure of the Kr_2 system can be understood *mutatis mutandis* from the published data[4] on Xe_2. We have observed strong stimulated emission on this transition in krypton at 1457 ± 1 Å with a linewidth of 8 Å as shown by the spectrum in Fig. 1(a). This emission occurred in an ~10-nsec pulse as observed on the photodiode. Due to a small but unavoidable impurity of xenon in the krypton sample, the xenon 1470-Å resonance line is a prominent absorptive feature in the spectrum. Moreover, our observations indicate that this absorptive loss dominates the optical losses of the system and easily prevents oscillation unless considerable care is taken to limit contamination from xenon. Furthermore since the 1470-Å xenon resonance line absorption has a strong wavelength dependence in the region which overlaps the wavelength of the observed stimulated emission, we expect that the precise values of the krypton stimulated emission center frequency and bandwidth will be dependent on the xenon impurity level. The pressure dependence of the peak power (detected with an ITT 4115 photodiode) is illustrated in Fig. 1(b). A threshold[5] for oscillation was observed at ~250 psia; pressure cell limitations prevented an examination of the region above 500 psia.

On account of the rapid energy transfer processes known to occur between certain rare-gas atoms and molecules in the gas,[6] liquid,[7] and solid[7] phases, we have extended these studies to include rare-gas mixtures. Of particular interest is the resonant energy transfer process[6]

$$Ar_2(^{1,3}\Sigma_u^+) + Xe(^1S_0) \rightarrow Ar(^1S_0) + Ar(^1S_0) + Xe(^1P_1), \qquad (1)$$

which efficiently quenches the 1300-Å argon continuum and leads to the generation of the xenon continuum at ~1700 Å through a strong coupling of the argon and xenon kinetic chains in argon/xenon mixtures. We report below a substantial enhancement of the stimulated emission from Xe_2^* at ~1720 Å in argon/xenon mixtures along with the observation of a blue shift of the mixture spectrum in comparison to the case of pure xenon.[3]

Figure 2(a) displays both the output peak power and energy for pure xenon and argon/xenon mixtures. The mixture data refer to a fixed xenon pressure of 100 psia. In this case, the enhancement is measured by the relative peaks of the two pairs of curves. Note that for pure xenon the maximum output energy occurs at a xenon

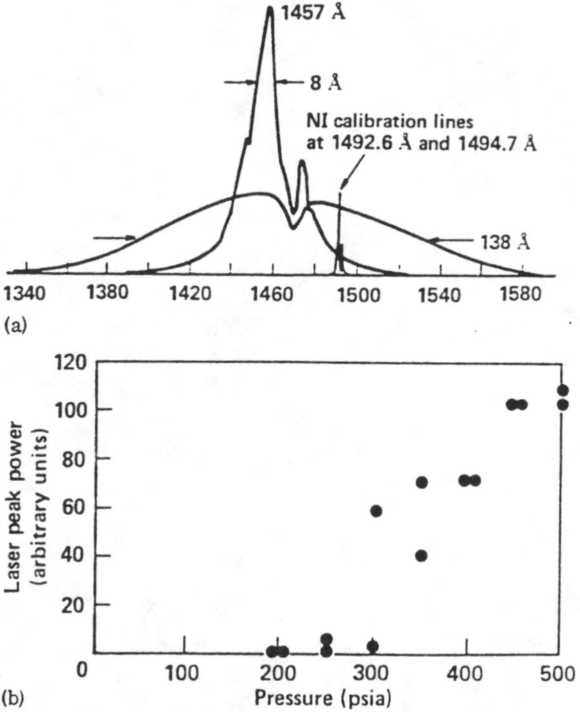

FIG. 1(a). Time-integrated spectral output (logarithmic densitometer trace) showing NI calibration lines. Minor absorption bands tentatively attributed to the $X^1\Sigma_g^+ - a'^1\Sigma_u^-(\Delta v = 0, 1)$ transition of N_2 are observed in addition to the xenon resonance absorption at 1470 Å. [See M. Ogawa and Y. Tanaka, J. Chem. Phys. 32, 754 (1960).] (b) Pressure dependence of the krypton oscillator output. Note the threshold at ~250 psia.

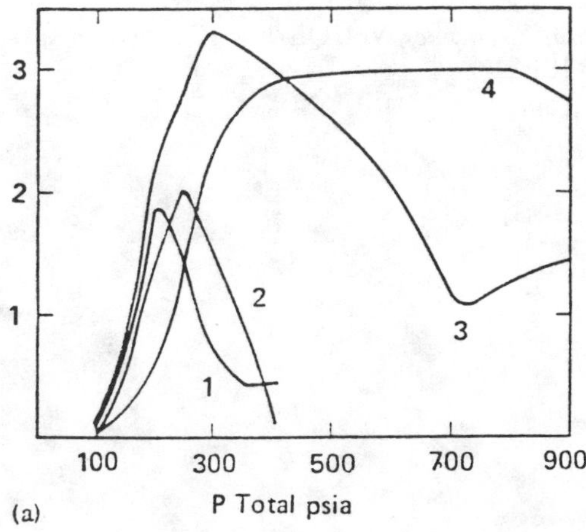

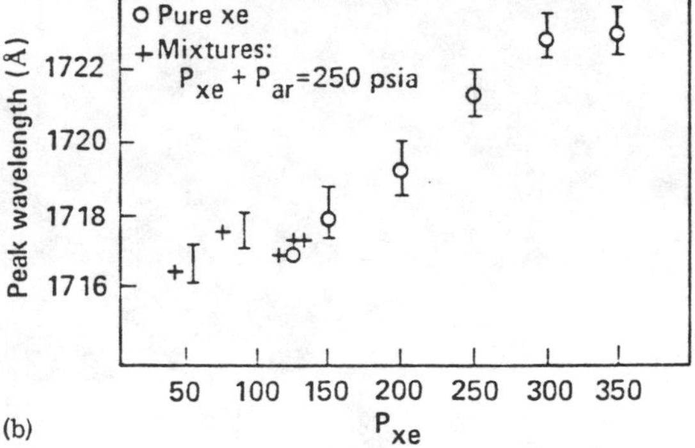

FIG. 2(a). Dependence of pulse energy and pulse peak power vs total pressure for the xenon laser at ~1720 Å operating on pure xenon and argon/xenon mixtures. Curve 1, pulse energy for pure xenon; curve 2, peak power for pure xenon; curve 3, pulse energy for 100-psia xenon with added argon; curve 4, peak power for 100-psia xenon with added argon. (b) Dependence of the laser peak wavelength on xenon partial pressure.

pressure of ~200 psia, while the corresponding maximum of the mixture falls at 100-psia xenon and ~200-psia argon. For these conditions, the output is essentially doubled although the stopping power of the mixture is somewhat lower than the pure xenon case. This indicates an improvement in the efficiency as well. In addition, the use of argon-xenon mixtures results in a reduction of the oscillation threshold in terms of xenon partial pressure. Oscillation on the xenon molecular transition has been observed in mixtures of 50-psia xenon and 400-psia argon where the xenon is truly the minority constituent.

We note, however, that these data pertain to an oscillator configuration which contained no provision for control of the mode volume. Calibrated sapphire attenuators were used to prevent detector saturation over the full dynamic range of the measurements. Among the several factors which may contribute to the increased oscillator output are the following: (i) the possibility of lower excited state-excited state collisional loss rates in the argon kinetic chain as compared to the corresponding xenon kinetic processes. For fixed Xe_2^* excimer density, the excited state losses will be the same; therefore, for this process to be operative, the differential losses would have to occur higher in the kinetic chain[1] presumably involving the argon system. (ii) Lower collisional-induced absorption arising from xenon-xenon encounters (at fixed temperature and wavelength, this effect scales as the square of the xenon density). (iii) Oscillation over a larger effective mode volume due to the decrease in the optical losses noted in (ii) above, or due to a more beneficial electron energy deposition in the gas. Internal apertures are necessary to limit the mode volume in order to separate these geometrical averaging effects from increases in localized inversion density.[1]

An indication that collisional-induced absorption[8] originating from xenon-xenon collisions[9] is an important factor in the increased output is given by the observation of a blue shift in the stimulated emission spectrum of the argon/xenon mixtures. Figure 2(b) illustrates the dependence of the laser peak wavelength on xenon partial pressure. Blue shifts as large as 7 Å are observed, and the shift is independent of argon pressure. Since the collisional-induced absorption increases toward shorter wavelengths, a blue shift as observed in the experiment is anticipated when these losses are diminished. Refined experiments and calculations are in progress to more precisely determine the relative contributions to the enhanced output of points (i), (ii), and (iii) noted above.

Finally, we observe that the demonstration of efficient energy transfer has important implications for laser systems operating on molecular bound-free transitions. It enables a reduction in the required density of the active material, and consequently lowers the collisional-induced absorption, a quantity which represents a strong limitation on the extractable energy density. In addition, since we have some freedom in selecting the minority acceptor system, the output wavelength is at our disposal. Systems exhibiting efficient energy transfer to Hg or Zn may enable the generation of intense stimulated emission in the near-ultraviolet and visible spectral regions.

The authors gratefully acknowledge the technical assistance of H. Rien, D. Rea, and J. Wengert in the completion of these experiments.

*Work performed under the auspices of the U. S. Atomic Energy Commission.

[1]E. V. George and C. K. Rhodes, Appl. Phys. Lett. 23, 139 (1973).
[2]D. C. Lorents and R. E. Olson, Stanford Research Institute Report, 1972 (unpublished).
[3]Paul W. Hoff, James C. Swingle, and Charles K. Rhodes, Opt. Commun. (to be published).
[4]R. S. Mulliken, J. Chem. Phys. 52, 5170 (1970). For these larger diatomics, Hund's coupling case *c* is appropriate.
[5]The cavity was bounded by curved 1-m-radius mirrors with measured transmittances and reflectances of ~ 5% and ~ 80%, respectively.
[6]Aharon Gedanken, Joshua Jortner, Baruch Raz, and Abraham Szöke, J. Chem. Phys. 57, 3456 (1972).
[7]A. Cheshnovsky, B. Raz, and J. Jortner, Proceedings of the Third International Vacuum Ultraviolet Conference, Tokyo, 1971 (unpublished).
[8]A. V. Phelps, University of Colorado JILA Report No. 110, 1972 (unpublished); I. V. Kosinskaya and L. P. Polozova, Opt. Spectrosc. 30, 458 (1971).
[9]At ~ 1700 Å there is also the possibility of a component due to argon-xenon collisions which would scale like the product of the argon and xenon densities. The importance of this quality depends upon the details of the molecular potential curves of the ArXe system. Measurements are currently in progress for the evaluation of these losses.

Reprinted with permission from *IEEE Journal of Quantum Electronics*, Vol. QE-9, pp. 1031-1032 (October 1973). ©1973 IEEE.

Xenon Molecular Laser in the Vacuum Ultraviolet

E. R. AULT, M. L. BHAUMIK, W. M. HUGHES, R. J. JENSEN, C. P. ROBINSON, A. C. KOLB, AND J. SHANNON

***Abstract*—Vacuum ultraviolet emission from high-pressure Xe gas under excitation by a pulsed electron beam has been investigated. When cavity mirrors were provided, significant line narrowing and a thousandfold increase in spectral intensity occurred at 1730 ± 10 Å. This was accompanied by severe mirror burning and provides strong evidence that an associative molecular Xe laser has been achieved.**

Evidence of laser emission in the vacuum ultraviolet from molecular Xe was first reported by Basov *et al.* [1] using *E*-beam excitation of liquid xenon. Recently, Koehler *et al.* [2] and Ault *et al.* [3] have presented evidence of stimulated emission from gaseous Xe, including spectral line narrowing. We wish to report the observation of stimulated emission from gaseous Xe with increased line narrowing and with thousandfold enhancement in spectral intensity relative to the fluorescence emission. The optical emission inside the cavity was sufficiently intense to evaporate ~1-cm^2 area of the mirror coating providing a symmetric burn pattern on the mirrors which only occurred in coincidence with line narrowing and the increase in spectral intensity.

Manuscript received May 3, 1973; revised June 9, 1973.

E. R. Ault and M. L. Bhaumik are with the Northrop Research and Technology Center, Hawthorne, Calif. Their research was supported in part by the Advanced Research Projects Agency of the Department of Defense and monitored by the Office of Naval Research under Contract N00014-72-C-0456.

W. M. Hughes, R. L. Jensen, and C. P. Robinson are with the Los Alamos Scientific Laboratory, University of California, Los Alamos, N. Mex. Their work was supported by the U.S. Atomic Energy Commission.

A. C. Kolb and J. Shannon are with Maxwell Laboratories, Inc., San Diego, Calif. Their work was supported by the Defense Nuclear Agency.

The experimental arrangement consisted of an optical cavity inside a high-pressure gas cell excited transversely by an *E* beam. The optical resonator was comprised of a 5-m total reflector on a Pyrex substrate and a plane output mirror on a MgF_2 substrate. The mirrors were spaced 12 cm apart, and were prepared by Al coating followed by a MgF_2 overcoat. Each mirror was mounted on adjustable mirror mounts and the alignment was accomplished by a He–Ne laser. The optical cavity was housed within the pressure cell so that the static pressure on both sides of the cavity mirrors would be the same. This greatly reduced the mechanical requirements on the optical components and their mounts. The *E* beam was supplied by a Maxwell Laboratories POCO electron accelerator delivering ~150 kA at 0.5 MeV. The circular beam was shaped in a 15-kG magnetic field into a rectangular cross section of 9 × 3.5 cm. The average current density inside the high-pressure gas cell was estimated to be ~1000 A/cm^2 providing about 1200 J of input energy to the gas.

Diagnostics were primarily accomplished by spectral measurements to observe line narrowing. The spectral measurements were performed with a SPEX 3/4-m VUV spectrograph model 1500 provided with a 1200-lines/mm grating blazed at 1500 Å. The dispersion of the spectrograph near 1700 Å was ~10 Å/mm with a maximum resolution of 0.1 Å. Radiation from the laser cell was directed by a 45° mirror through an evacuated chamber to the spectrograph and was recorded on Kodak 101-01 special UV film. In most of the spontaneous emission experiments the spectrograph slit width was kept at 200 μ, limiting the resolution to 2 Å. The target chamber was evacuated by a LN_2-trapped oil-diffusion pump before filling with Xe gas. The spectrograph camera was shielded to reduce any possible fogging due to X-rays.

The densitometer trace of the spectrum obtained from 12-atm Xe gas inside the optical cavity is shown in Fig. 1(a). The cor-

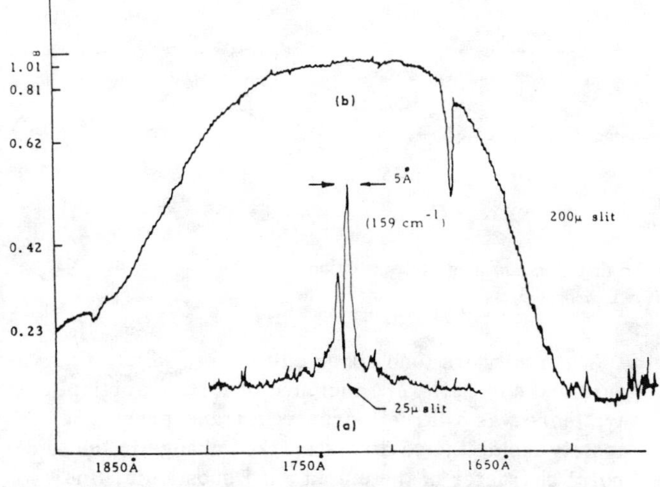

Fig. 1. (a) Laser spectrum [attenuated by ~ 1000 compared to (b)]. Spectrometer slit width 25 μ–0.25-Å resolution. Output coupling ~ 1 percent. Absorption losses 35 and 27 percent for the flat and spherical mirrors, respectively. (Photographic density on vertical axis.) (b) Typical fluorescence spectrum for Xe gas at ~12 atm without optics (200-μ slit–2-Å resolution).

responding spontaneous-emission spectrum obtained without the mirrors is shown in Fig. 1(b). The intensity of the spectrum in Fig. 1(a) was larger by over a factor of 1000 compared to that in Fig. 1(b). Such an enormous increase in spectral intensity can only occur by laser emission. The densitometer traces show that the laser spectrum exhibits two peaks of ~2.5-Å width separated by ~5 Å. The spectrometer resolution for the laser traces was ~0.25 Å. Each trace represents the time-integrated spectrum of a single shot.

The cross-sectional area of the excited volume, which demonstrated strong lasing as indicated by the symmetric burn pattern on both mirrors, is shown in Fig. 2. The mirror burn spot became smaller and moved towards the *E*-beam entrance window when the pressure was raised to 15 atm, causing a reduction in electron range and consequently the excitation volume.

The mirror burn spot attendant with line narrowing and increase in spectral intensity was repeatable each time in a series of seven shots. When the mirrors were misaligned or the total reflector was taken out, there was neither a burn spot on the mirror nor any significant line narrowing. This indicates that the

Fig. 2. Photographs of the output mirror (MgF_2) on the left and the spherical (5-m radius) total reflector on the right. The electron-beam direction is from top to bottom in this picture.

observed mirror burn spot is not due to damage by scattered *E* beam, pressure wave, or superradiant emission.

Since an energy measurement was not available for these experiments, an attempt was made to estimate the laser energy from the mirror burn spots. This was on the assumption that the mirror burning occurred by heating due to laser energy absorption and as such constitutes merely a first-order estimate. The mass of the removed 1.25-cm^2 × 800-Å coating on the semitransparent window is 2.7×10^{-5} g. The amount of energy required to evaporate this mass of Al is ~0.38 J. Considering the evaporation of the Al coatings from both the mirrors along with the protective MgF_2 coating, the total laser energy absorbed by the mirrors was estimated to be approximately 1 J. This corresponds to an energy extraction of ~0.1 J/cm^3.

The results presented here leave little doubt that laser emission has been observed from molecular Xe in the VUV region. Since the emitted photon has enough energy to ionize an excited Xe molecule, it is not obvious that laser emission in the VUV could actually be achieved with this type of laser medium. These results demonstrate that sufficient net gain for laser emission from molecular Xe is possible in spite of the competition with photoionization.

References

[1] N. G. Basov, V. A. Danilychev, and Yu. M. Popov, "Stimulated emission in the vacuum ultraviolet region," *Sov. J. Quantum Electron.*, vol. 1, pp. 18–22, 1971.

[2] H. A. Koehler, L. J. Ferderber, D. L. Redhead, and P. J. Ebert, "Stimulated VUV emission in high-pressure xenon excited by high-current relativistic electron beams," *Appl. Phys. Lett.*, vol. 21, pp. 198–200, 1972.

[3] E. R. Ault and M. L. Bhaumik, "UV gas laser studies," Northrop Rep. NRTC 72-14R.

126.1-nm molecular argon laser

William M. Hughes*

Los Alamos Scientific Laboratory, University of California, Los Alamos, New Mexico 87544

John Shannon and Robert Hunter†

Maxwell Laboratories, Incorporated, San Diego, California 92123

Electron beam excitation of high-pressure argon has resulted in the first demonstration of laser action from molecular argon at 126.1±0.3 nm. Strong laser action was achieved at pressures up to 6.89 MPa (1000 psia).

Net positive gain has been demonstrated for the dissociative transition to the repulsive ground state in molecular Xe [1-3] and Kr.[4] In the experiment discussed here, spectral, temporal, and calorimetric diagnostics were performed simultaneously and provide conclusive proof of laser action from molecular argon. This is a clear demonstration that for argon the stimulated emission cross section is larger than the photoionization cross section in the 126-nm region and the transition occurs to a favorable position on the ground-state potential curve.

A schematic of the experimental apparatus is shown in Fig. 1. Electrons from a Maxwell POCO facility were emitted by a rectangularly shaped diode and propagated through a short (~2-cm) pressure-controlled drift region and entered a high-pressure target chamber through a 0.01-cm-thick titanium foil. Approximately 600 J were delivered to the gas by 800-keV electrons in a 60-ns pulse. The current density at the foil was ~1.2 kA/cm^2. The average excitation density and current density were roughly estimated to be 6 J/cm^3 and 300 A/cm^2, respectively, at 4 MPa (~600 psia) in the experimental region.

The temporal and calorimetric diagnostics were performed by photodiodes and a compensated conical thermopile. Kodak Type 101-01 film was used in the vacuum spectrograph to determine the output spectrum. Nitrogen and hydrogen output from a dc discharge were used to wavelength calibrate the photographic plate.

The target chamber-gas handling system could be operated to pressures of ~7 MPa (~1000 psia). A fresh charge of research-grade gas was used for each shot. Optical output was through 3-mm-thick supported MgF_2 circular windows. For laser experiments, partially transmitting Al-MgF_2 mirrors were used on both sides of the optical cavity. The mirrors, which were 12 cm apart, were mounted internally to the chamber and supported no static pressure gradient (approximately 10 cm of this dimension was excited). Typical mirror reflectivity and transmission were 75% and 1%, respectively.

Fluorescence data taken as a function of argon pressure are shown in Fig. 2. Estimates show an ~10% conversion efficiency of electron beam energy into fluorescence output. The fluorescence linewidth was observed to be ~8 nm, and it did not vary substantially as a function of argon pressure. A considerable number of absorption lines were readily observed in the fluorescence spectrum; hydrogen (121.5 nm) and xenon (129.6 nm) lines have been identified.

When mirrors (one spherical – 4-m radius of curvature and one flat) were included to form an optical cavity, there was a large increase in transverse light intensity inside the cavity, a marked change in the temporal character of the output, and substantial line narrowing. Laser action was achieved over the full range of pressures tested, 2.07–6.89 MPa (300–1000 psia).

Figures 3 and 4 show the peak laser signal and the time delay, respectively, for laser initiation as a function of argon pressure. The light intensity in the transverse direction increased as much as 150 times and can only be explained by stimulated emission. The laser pulse duration varied from ~4 to 15 ns. Severe mirror damage with an obvious mode pattern structure was observed for each laser shot. Assuming that mirror damage is caused by evaporation of the Al-MgF_2 film, then ~$\frac{1}{2}$ J/cm^2 of absorbed energy would be required, which indicates that argon does lase quite strongly. No calorimetric measurement could be made, because of the small output coupling of the mirror. The laser linewidth was ~1.4 nm and did not vary in any consistent way with argon pressure. The laser wavelength line center, which was calibrated by using a Lyman-α, occurred at 126.1±0.3 nm and exhibited a very slight dependence on argon pressure of $-(1.4\pm2.9)\times10^{-5}$ nm/kPa [$-(1\pm2)\times10^{-3}$ Å/psia]. This is in marked contrast to Xe, which exhibits a $+2.9\times10^{-4}$-nm/kPa ($+2\times10^{-2}$-Å/psia) laser wavelength dependence on pressure.[1] If the wavelength-dependent optical losses in the 126-nm region for this experiment are dominated by impurities, then the observed effect could be explained by laser action between two impurity absorption lines. Absorption due to ground-state psuedomolecules formed by thermal collisions has been advanced as one possible

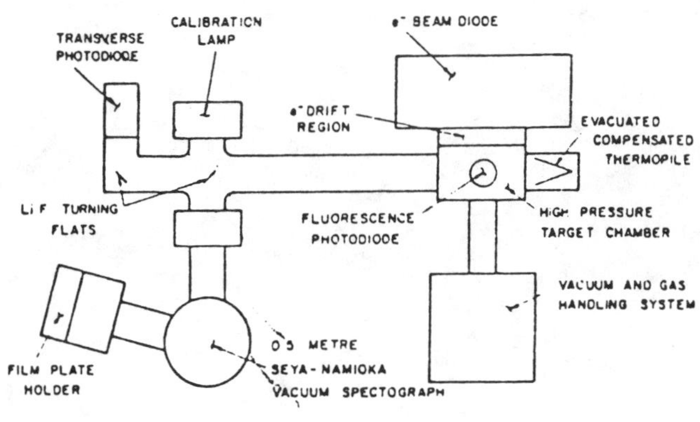

FIG. 1. Schematic diagram of apparatus.

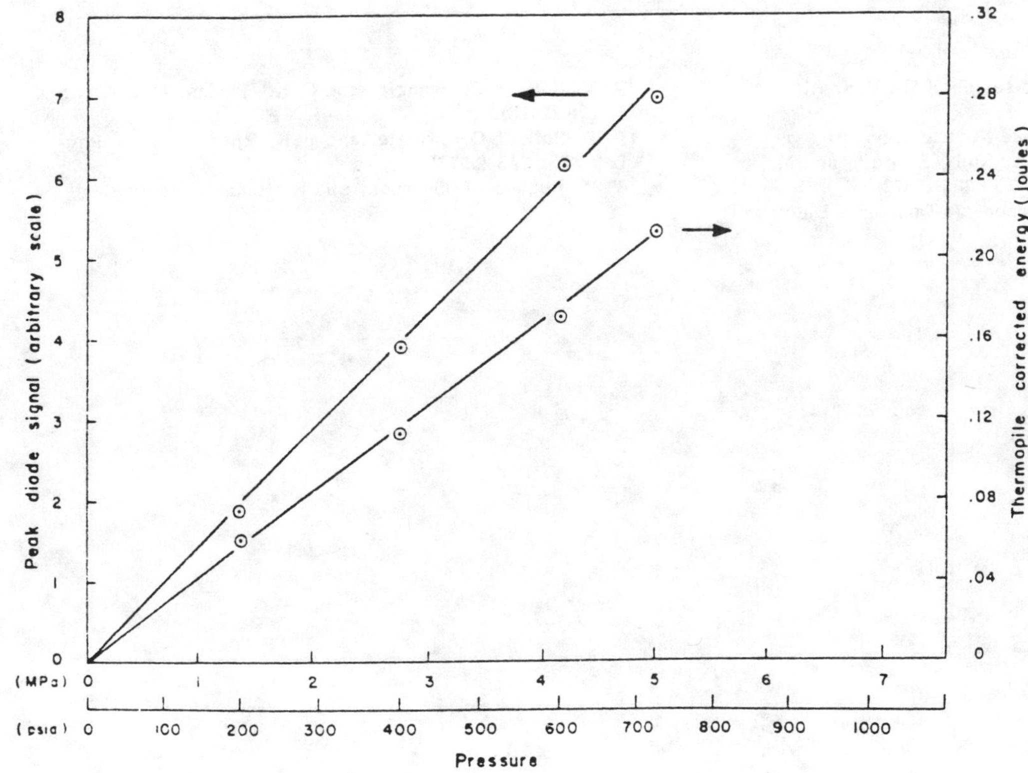

FIG. 2. Fluorescence output versus Ar pressure, with the thermopile energy corrected for MgF_2 window transmission.

reason for the pressure-dependent wavelength shift in xenon.[1,4] Two possible reasons for less absorption in argon are (1) that the temperature rise for argon is approximately three times less than that for Xe with the use of the same experimental apparatus because of the larger heat capacity of Ar and (2) that the argon laser transition may occur to a higher energy on the ground-state potential curve.

Results of these experiments point to gas purity as a problem. The increase in transverse light intensity when using mirrors, although large, is ~10 times smaller when compared with Xe with exactly the same experimental apparatus being used.[5] The many absorption lines in the fluorescence spectrum and the slight laser wavelength dependence on pressure also support this conclusion. The Ar used in these experiments was transferred to an evacuated (~10^{-6}-Torr) stainless steel cylinder held at liquid-nitrogen temperature from a commercial cylinder which was slightly above liquid-nitrogen temperature. This indicates that a significant amount of noncondensible impurities were contained in the commercial gas.

In any event, laser action at 126.1 nm from high-pressure argon gas has been clearly demonstrated for the first time. The fluorescence output is efficient, and strong laser action was obtained.

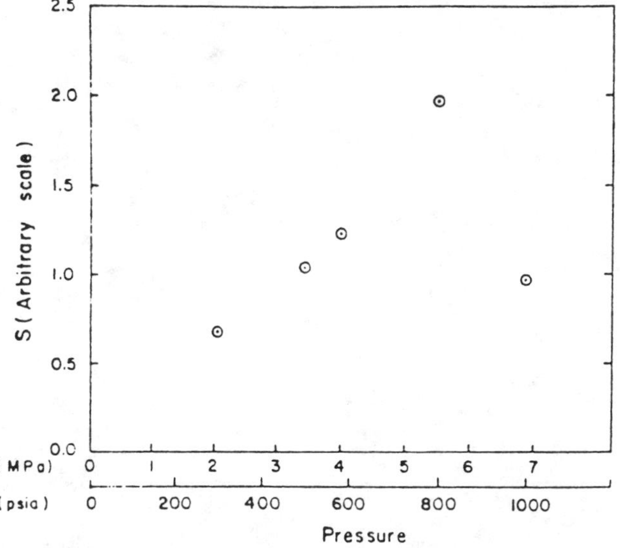

FIG. 3. Peak laser signal S versus Ar pressure.

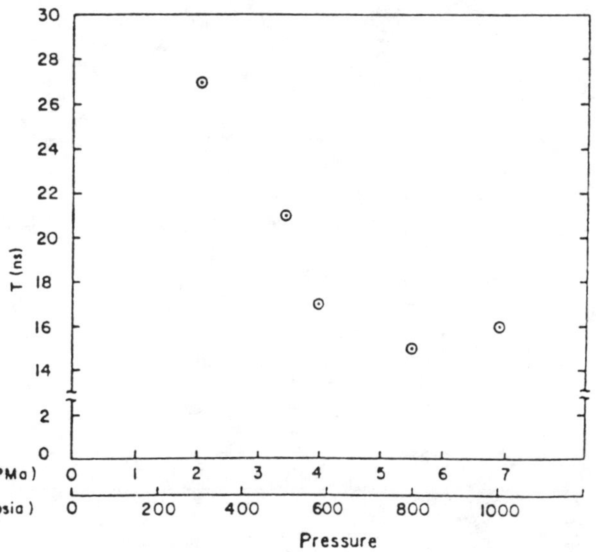

FIG. 4. Laser initiation time delay T versus Ar pressure.

*Work performed under the auspices of the U.S. Atomic Energy Commission.

†Work supported by the Defense Nuclear Agency.

[1]W.M. Hughes, J. Shannon, A. Kolb, E. Ault, and M. Bhaumik, Appl. Phys. Lett. 23, 385 (1973).

[2]J.B. Gerardo and A.W. Johnson, J. Quantum. Electron. QE-9, 748 (1973).

[3]P.W. Hoff, J.C. Swingle, and C.K. Rhodes, Opt. Commun. 8, 128 (1973).

[4]P.W. Hoff, J.C. Swingle, and C.K. Rhodes, Appl. Phys. Lett. 23, 245 (1973).

[5]W.M. Hughes, J. Shannon, and R. Hunter (unpublished).

Reprinted with permission from *Optics Communications,* Vol. 11(4), pp. 335-338 (August 1974).

MEGAWATT VUV XENON LASER EMPLOYING COAXIAL ELECTRON-BEAM EXCITATION

D.J. BRADLEY, D.R. HULL. M.H.R. HUTCHINSON and M.W. McGEOCH

Optics Section, Physics Department, Imperial College, London SW7 2BZ, UK

Received 11 June 1974

3 nsec laser pulses, of bandwidth 1.3 nm, are obtained from a 10 J, 600 keV coaxial diode electron-beam pumping arrangement. Uniform pumping, with a well defined cylindrical geometry, facilitates experimental investigation of the laser parameters. Gas heating limits the laser repetition rate. While mirror damage at present limits the peak power to ~ 1 MW, higher powers seem available. The addition of helium results in a drastic reduction of peak molecular xenon fluorescence.

To date quasi-molecular vacuum ultraviolet lasers have employed transverse pumping of high-pressure xenon [1–5], krypton [6], argon [7] or noble gas mixture [6,8] by relativistic electron beams. Apart from the work described in [5], the electron-beam sources employed for laser pumping delivered several hundreds of joules in pulses of duration ~ 50 nsec, or longer. With such long pulse excitation premature termination of laser action occurs [2,3] and the overall laser efficiency is $\ll 1\%$ despite a potential fluorescence efficiency of ~ 10% [1,9]. To obtain an efficient and convenient laser system with short duration, low energy pumping and capable of peak powers exceeding 1 MW, we have designed and constructed a coaxial diode, electron-beam arrangement. Also with uniform pumping of a well-defined cylindrical geometry, investigations of the laser parameters are more easily carried out than in the case of transverse pumping systems, In particular, because the pumping pulse duration (2.5 nsec) is shorter than the fluorescence lifetime of the xenon molecular dimer, at the gas pressures employed [9], laser and fluorescence kinetics can be studied.

The experimental arrangement is shown in fig. 1. The coaxial field emission diode consists of a thin-walled (~ 70 μm) stainless steel tubular anode, of ~ 4 mm internal diameter, maintained at earth potential. The anode, which is also the container for the high pressure laser gas, is concentric with a cylindrical field emission cathode. 10 J, 600 keV, 2.5 nsec pulses are produced by a Marx bank and Blumlein switch circuit. Both electrodes are contained in a glass envelope, which is evacuated by continuous pumping to a pressure of $\sim 2 \times 10^{-5}$ torr. One laser mirror is sealed into the unsupported end of the anode tube and the output mirror, on a kinematic mount, is supported inside the xenon reservoir. The output beam is transmitted through a BaF_2 window into a vacuum for intensity and spectral measurements.

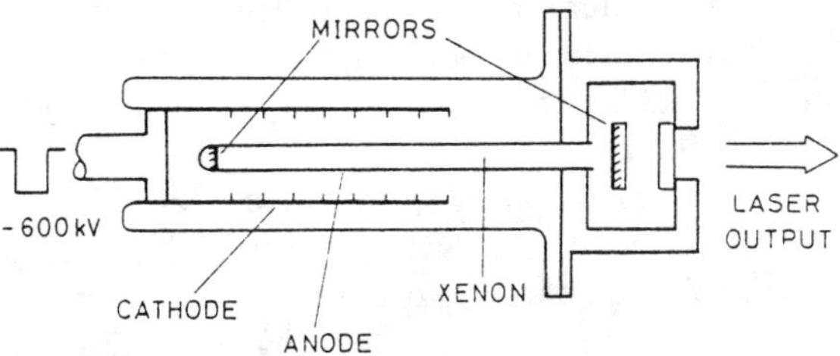

Fig. 1. Details of coaxial diode construction.

The diode was designed for use with a Febetron 706 pulse generator (Field Emission Corp) which has a load impedance of 60 Ω (10 kA, 600 kV). The tube radius is determined by the range of the electrons and hence by the gas pressure. For 600 keV electrons at

10 ktorr, a tube of ~ 4 mm diameter gives uniform pumping. The cathode which has a diameter of ~ 3 cm and a length of 7 cm, was constructed from titanium sheet, perforated to produce an array of spikes. The distribution of pumping energy over the inner surface of the anode tube was measured using cellophane dye dosimetry [10]. The microdensitometer trace of fig. 2 shows a variation of less than 10% in dose along the tube. Because of end effects, the pumped length exceeds the physical length of the cathode. The energy entering the gas was measured calorimetrically with a thermopile and found to be ~ 5 J.

The anode tube was evacuated to 10^{-4} torr by a mercury diffusion pump. Liquid-nitrogen cold traps were used on both the diffusion pump and the rotary backing pump. The xenon (B.O.C. Research Grade) was frozen in a high-pressure bomb by liquid nitrogen and pumped to $< 10^{-4}$ torr to ensure that impurity concentrations were < 1 ppm. The bomb temperature was maintained < 0°C while the tube was filled to the working pressure of 10 ktorr. This helped to reduce the water vapour partial pressure. With these procedures stimulated emission intensity measurements could be reproduced to ± 5% and laser output was maximum.

Two combinations of mirrors were employed in the optical cavity. Megawatt powers were obtained with a spherical mirror of one metre radius of curvature and a plane mirror with a 1.4 mm diameter hole for output coupling. Both mirrors had Al:MgF_2 maximum reflectivity coatings. Better results were obtained with two plane mirrors, one of which had a transmission of ~ 8%. In both cases the mirror separation was 22.5 cm. Mirror damage at present limits the peak power to ~ 1 MW. By employing multilayer dielectric mirror coatings [11] or prisms, higher working powers should be possible.

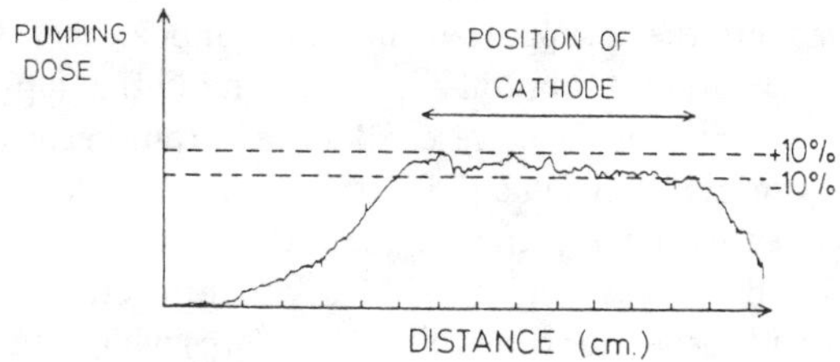

Fig. 2. Microdensitometer trace of cellophane recording of electron energy deposition, showing uniformity along anode.

The laser spectrum was recorded in a 1 metre normal incidence vacuum spectrograph, with a 600 lines/mm grating. The microdensitometer traces of fig. 3 clearly show the considerable spectral narrowing produced by the mirrors. The laser linewidth is ~ 13 Å when account is taken of the absorption lines on either side of the peak. The full height of the spectro-

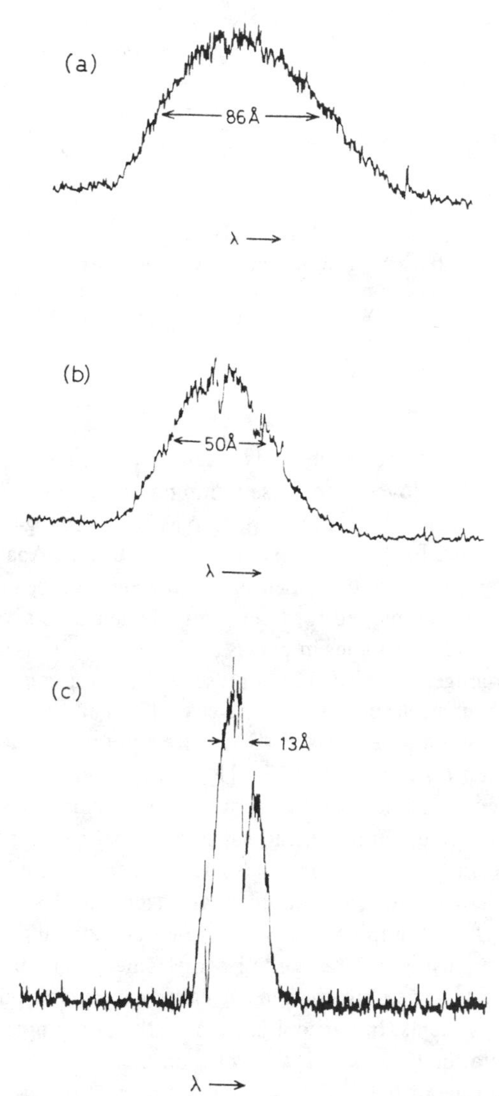

Fig. 2. Microdensitometer traces of spectra (1 metre normal incidence spectrograph) recorded with (a) no mirrors, (b) single high reflectivity plane mirror (double transit), and (c) 1 metre radius of curvature mirror and output plane mirror with 1.4 mm diameter coupling aperture (both mirrors high reflectivity). Spectral resolution of (c) is < 1 Å.

graph slit is illuminated when only one mirror is employed or when the output mirror of the laser resonator is misaligned but only a 1 mm length of the slit (placed 35 cm from the output mirror) is illuminated by the laser beam. The beam cross section was recorded on SC7 film (Kodak–Pathe) at a distance of 1 metre. With the hole-coupled resonator an annular beam of 6 mm diameter was obtained, corresponding to a beam divergence of ~ 5 mrad. As expected, a circular beam of slightly better divergence was produced with the semi-transparent mirror.

Pulse duration and output power were measured using a solar-blind ITT FW 4115 photodiode and a Tektronix 519 oscilloscope. A typical oscillogram obtained at a xenon gas pressure of 10 ktorr is shown in fig. 4. The pulse duration is 3.5 nsec. At this pressure the fluorescence lifetime is ~ 7 nsec [9]. Output powers in excess of 1 MW were measured using the manufacturer's calibration of the diode, assuming that the quantum efficiency is constant at wavelengths shorter than 230 nm. These powers corresponded with the output energies obtained from a thermopile (Laser Instrumentation Ltd) enclosed in a vacuum chamber. To eliminate errors arising from electrical noise, the thermopile readings were compared with those recorded when the vacuum chamber was at atmospheric pressure. To prevent saturation of the photodiode, the laser radiation was attenuated by a known pressure of oxygen contained in a 14 cm long cell. Since at megawatt powers saturation is beginning to occur and could influence the observed laser intensity profile, we confirmed that the oscillograms did not change in shape with a variation of X 10 in laser power.

To maintain high laser powers it was necessary to allow ~ 20 minutes to elapse between firings. We have investigated possible reasons for this effect. Fig.

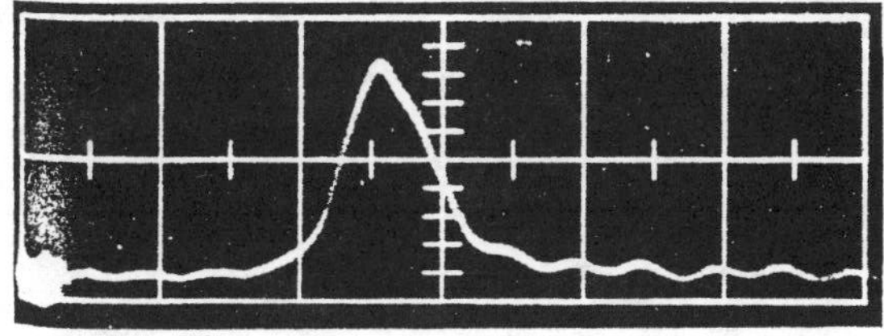

Fig. 4. Oscillogram of laser output. Time-scale 5 nsec per major division.

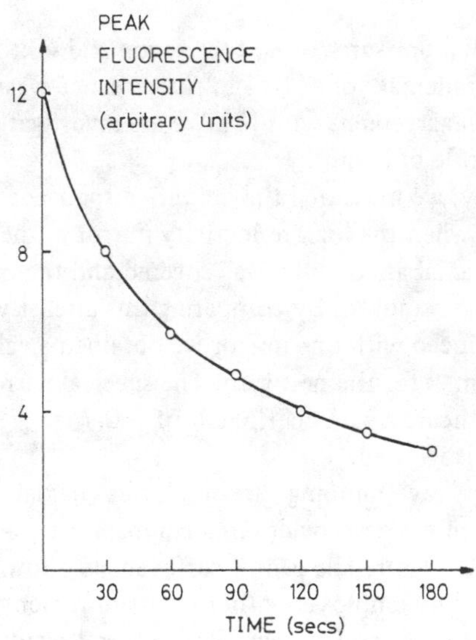

Fig. 5. Variation of fluorescence intensity from coaxially excited xenon at 6 ktorr pressure. Points on graph represent consecutive firings of the electron beam source.

5 shows how the fluorescence intensity changes with repetitive pumping at the maximum rate (permitted by the power supply) of 2 pulses per minute. If the delay between the first and second firings was increased to 5 minutes, the intensity reduction was ~ 10%. We have calculated that the instantaneous rise in temperature of the xenon is ~ 700°C and that the steel tube temperature increases by ~ 30°C after thermalization with the xenon gas which occurs after a few seconds. Absorption by unbound ground-state xenon molecules increases rapidly with increasing temperature [12], and consequently gas heating would be expected to strongly affect both fluorescence and laser intensities. The thermal time constant of the anode tube is estimated to be ~ 10 minutes, which would explain the long recovery time of the laser.

An increase in xenon fluorescence efficiency by the addition of helium was attributed to cooling effects, by the authors of [8]. However, adding partial pressures of 4 ktorr and 8 ktorr of helium (B.O.C. Research Grade) to 5 ktorr of xenon in our system, resulted in both cases in a reduction of peak fluorescence by an order of magnitude. Since the results quoted in [8] were obtained with a Febetron 705 which produces a 50 nsec pulse, we repeated our measurements with the same type of electron beam source. In this case, with partial pressures of 5 ktorr xenon and 4 ktorr helium, and increase of ~ 10% in fluorescence was recorded, in agreement with [8]. We are investigating further the role of helium.

Finally, we measured the amplified spontaneous emission when the high reflectivity mirror at the end of the coaxial anode tube was covered and the output mirror was removed. By comparing this intensity with that produced with one mirror we obtained a value of ~ 0.25 cm^{-1} for the nett gain. The spectral narrowing would indicate a gain coefficient of ~ 0.7 cm^{-1}, if absorption is ignored.

With its low pumping threshold, this coaxial electron–beam design provides in a compact form a high power VUV laser. The gain is sufficient to allow prism tuning and by employing other gases convenient tunable lasers covering the near VUV spectral region should be possible. Because of its well defined geometry the system has advantages for studying kinetics, and the atomic and molecular processes involved in quasi-molecular dissociative ground-state lasers.

Financial support from the Science Research Council and UK AEA Culham Laboratory is also acknowledged.

References

[1] H.A. Koehler, L.J. Ferderber, R.L. Redhead and P.J. Ebert, Appl. Phys. Letters 21 (1972) 198.
[2] W.M. Hughes, J. Shannon, A. Kolb, E. Ault and M. Bhaumik, Appl. Phys. Letters 23 (1973) 385.
[3] J.B. Gerardo and A. Wayne Johnson, IEEE J. Quantum Electron. QE-9 (1973) 748.
[4] P.W. Hoff, J.C. Swingle and C.K. Rhodes, Opt. Commun. 8 (1973) 128.
[5] S.C. Wallace, R.T. Hodgson and R.W. Dreyfus, Appl. Phys. Letters 23 (1973) 672.
[6] P.W. Hoff, J.C. Swingle and C.K. Rhodes, Appl. Phys. Letters 23 (1973) 245.
[7] W.M. Hughes, J. Shannon and R. Hunter, Appl. Phys. Letters 24 (1974) 488.
[8] A. Wayne Johnson and J.B. Gerardo, J. Appl. Phys. 45 (1974) 867.
[9] D.J. Bradley, M.H.R. Hutchinson and H. Koetser, Opt. Commun. 7 (1973) 187.
[10] E.J. Henley and D. Richman, Analytical Chemistry 28 (1956) 1850.
[11] A. Malherbe, Applied Optics 13 (1974) 1276.
[12] I.V. Kosinskaya and L.P. Polozova, Opt. Spectrosc. (USSR) 30 (1971) 458.

Reprinted with permission from *Physical Review Letters*, Vol. 33(7), pp. 415-418 (August 12, 1974). ©1974 American Physical Society.

Exciton-Enhanced Photoemission from Doped Solid Rare Gases*

Zohar Ophir, Baruch Raz, and Joshua Jortner
Department of Chemistry, Tel-Aviv University, Tel-Aviv, Israel
(Received 9 April 1974)

We report the observation of exciton-induced photoemission resulting from electronic energy transfer from "free" exciton levels to impurity states in solid Xe and Kr. A diffusion length of $l_0 \simeq 75$ Å for Wannier excitons in solid Xe was deduced, corresponding to a diffusion coefficient of $D = 0.5$ cm^2 sec^{-1}. The energy of the bottom of the conduction band is $V_0 = -0.46 \pm 0.1$ eV for Xe and $V_0 = -0.23 \pm 0.1$ eV for Kr.

The physical information available concerning exciton dynamics in simple insulators such as solid rare gases is rather meager. The vacuum-ultraviolet luminescence spectra of pure solid Ar, Kr, and Xe exhibit the emission from rare-gas diatomic molecules, which results from an efficient exciton-trapping process.[1] No emission could be detected from exciton states in these solids.[2,3] Thus, from the exciton radiative lifetime $\tau_r \simeq 10^{-9}$ sec, we infer that exciton trapping occurs within $\tau_0 < \tau_r/100 \simeq 10^{-11}$ sec. Relevant information regarding exciton dynamics can be obtained from experimental studies of photoemission resulting from electronic energy transfer to impurity states in solid rare gases. The impurity energy gap $E_G{}^i$ in these simple solids is $E_G{}^i = I_g{}^i + P_+{}^i + V_0$, where $I_g{}^i$ is the impurity gas-phase ionization potential, $P_+{}^i$ is the medium polarization energy by the impurity positive ion, and V_0 represents the energy of the matrix conduction band (relative to the vacuum level).[4] The photoemission threshold from the impurity is $E_T{}^i = E_G{}^i - V_0$. The lowest Wannier exciton states of the matrix, characterized by the energy levels E_n $(n = 1, 2, \ldots)$, can be located either above or below $E_T{}^i$. In the former case, i.e., $E_n > E_T{}^i$, one will observe direct photoemission from impurity states in the energy range $E_T{}^i \leq E \leq E_1$. In the latter case, when $E_1 \leq E_T{}^i$, one can expect photoemission due to energy transfer from free exciton states, E_n $(n \geq 1)$, of the solid to the impurity. This Auger-type impurity ionization process can result only from the "collision" of a free exciton with the impurity. The electronic energy E_M of the trapped diatomic molecule[1-3] is too low, i.e., $E_M \leq E_T{}^i$, to induce impurity ionization. We have observed a dramatic enhancement of the photoemission yield of lightly doped solid rare gases (doping level <1%) when excited into the exciton manifold of the host crystal. Exciton-induced photoemission was reported twenty years ago in alkali halides containing F centers.[5] The present experiments on solid rare gases provide information regarding free-exciton dynamics on the time scale $\tau_0 \approx 1$ psec,[5] prior to exciton trapping.

The systems studied were C_3H_6/Xe ($E_G{}^i = 7.75$ ev[7] and $E_1 = 8.40$ eV[8]), and Xe/Kr [$E_G{}^i = 10.4$ eV and $E_1(^3P_1) = 10.17$ eV].[9] Photoemission studies were carried out in the energy range 6–11.5 eV. The vacuum-ultraviolet light source consisted of a high-pressure (2–5 atm), high-intensity, gas pulsed discharge lamp.[10] The light was passed through a 0.3-m Czerny-Turner monochromator employing a spectral resolution of 5 Å (~0.025 eV). The monochromator was separated from the sample chamber by a LiF window. The optical arrangement allowed for a simultaneous measurement of optical absorption and photoemission yield. The emitter electrode consisted of a 3-mm-wide gold strip evaporated on a LiF window. The collector electrode was a gold ring 15 mm in diameter, located 30 mm from the emitter. The signal was amplified in two stages and integrated by a boxcar integrator. A noise level of 5×10^{-18} A was achieved. The samples were prepared by deposition of a gaseous mixture on the emitter electrode mounted on a variable-temperature helium-flow cryostat at 30–40°K. The gaseous mixtures were prepared and handled in an ultrahigh-vacuum system previously pumped down to less than 10^{-9} Torr. The sample chamber was pumped by an ion pump and a cryogenic pump down to less than 10^{-9} Torr.

The curve of photoemission yield,[11] for pure Xe, Fig. 1, agrees with previous work.[12,13] A square-root extrapolation of the yield versus energy (see Fig. 1) results in $E_T = 9.74 \pm 0.05$ eV which together with the spectroscopic value $E_G = 9.28 \pm 0.05$ eV results in $V_0 = -0.46 \pm 0.10$ eV for pure Xe. At energies lower than the threshold a structure is observed (photoemission yield ~1%) at 1380 Å, which coincides with the E_2 exciton states of Xe. Several possible interpretations of this effect are as follows: (1) Impurity ioniza-

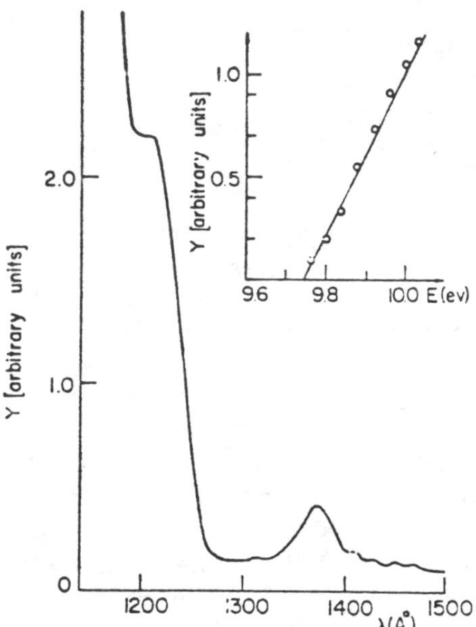

FIG. 1. Photoemission yield from solid Xe at 40°K. Upper inset: square-root extrapolation of the yield versus energy.

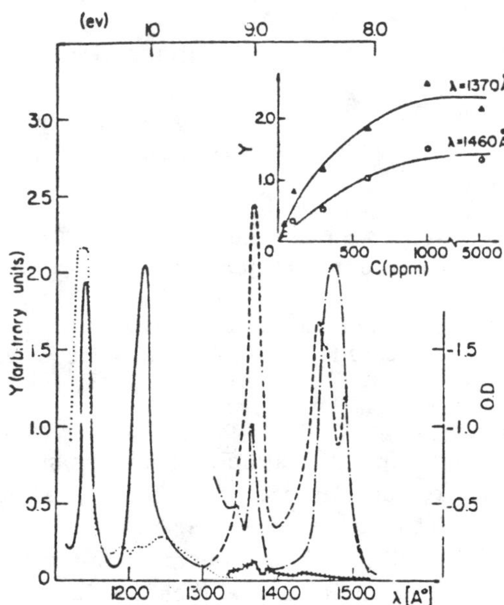

FIG. 2. Photoemission-yield curves in dilute (1%) impurity states in solid Xe and solid Kr measured at 30 K. Dashed curve, photoemission from benzene/Xe; dotted curve, photoemission from Xe/Kr. A photoemission-yield curve (hatched) for pure Xe is presented in the same arbitrary units as that for C_6H_6/Xe. The photoemission-yield curves are compared with the absorption spectra of pure Xe (dot-dashed curve) and of pure Kr (solid curve). Upper inset: the dependence of the photoemission yield on the benzene concentration C in C_6H_6/Xe solid films.

tion.[12] On the basis of our data for the C_6H_6/Xe we infer *inter alia* that the (unidentified) impurity concentration should exceed 5 ppm, which is rather high under our experimental conditions. (2) Nonlinear processes such as exciton-exciton collisions[14] or exciton photoionization,[14] which can be ruled out for the low light intensity employed in these experiments and in view of our observations that Y is independent of the light intensity. (3) Exciton diffusion to the gold substrate followed by electron ejection from the electrode. A preliminary result indicating that the 1380-Å photoemission peak decreases with increasing the sample thickness tends to support this mechanism.

In Fig. 2 we display the photoemission-yield curves for C_6H_6/Xe and for Xe/Kr. The emission onset for C_6H_6/Xe occurs at $E_x{}^i = 8.15 \pm 0.05$ eV which together with the spectroscopic value[7] $E_G{}^i = 7.75$ eV results in $V_0 = -0.4 \pm 0.1$ eV for solid Xe in good agreement with the result for the pure solid. For Xe/Kr the onset $E_x{}^i = 10.68 \pm 0.1$ eV together with $E_G{}^i = 10.40$ eV results in $V_0 = -0.28 \pm 0.1$ eV for solid Kr.

The most prominent feature of these results involves the large photoemission yield in the energy range where light absorption occurs predominantly into the host-matrix exciton states below the photoemission threshold for the pure solids. The absolute quantum yields for photoemission from C_6H_6/Xe are estimated[15] to be approximately $Y \approx 20\%$ at 1455 Å and $Y \approx 30\%$ at 1380 Å. The photoemission originates from exciton-induced Auger-type impurity ionization.

The line shapes of the emission curves are expected to provide pertinent information regarding exciton dynamics. The C_6H_6/Xe system exhibits a minimum in the Y curve at 1480 Å which coincides with the maximum of the $n = 1$ exciton state. The photoemission peaks at 1380 and 1350 Å practically coincide with the exciton energies E_2 (1380 Å) and E_3 (1345 Å). The dip in the photoemission curve at 1480 Å cannot be adequately explained in terms of the "dead-layer" theory,[16] which results in $L \simeq 150$ Å for the electron escape length and in the unphysically large value $h > 70$ Å for the width of the dead layer.

An attractive alternative approach to this problem involves a kinetic picture where competition between exciton trapping and energy transfer from excitons to homogeneously distributed impurities is considered. The number density $n(x, t)$ of "free" excitons at the distance x from the surface is governed by the diffusion equation

$$\frac{\partial n(x,t)}{\partial t}=D\frac{\partial^2 n(x,t)}{\partial x^2}+kI_0\exp(-kx)$$

$$-\frac{n(x,t)}{\tau_0}-S[X]n(x,t), \qquad (1)$$

where D is the exciton diffusion coefficient, k the absorption coefficient, I_0 the incident light intensity, S the rate constant for impurity ionization, and $[X]$ the impurity concentration. Under steady-state conditions, $n(x,t)=n(x)$, and Eq. (1) is readily solved using the appropriate boundary conditions $n(0)=n(\infty)=0$. The photoemission quantum yield Y can be expressed in the form

$$Y=\frac{S[X]\tau}{1-(kl)^2}\left[\frac{kL}{kL+1}-\frac{kl}{(l/L)+1}\right], \qquad (2)$$

where the effective exciton lifetime is $\tau=(1/\tau_0+S[X])^{-1}$ and $l=[D(1/\tau_0+S[X])^{-1}]^{1/2}$ is the exciton diffusion length in the doped crystal, which is related to the diffusion length $l_0=(D\tau_0)^{1/2}$ in the pure crystal via $l=l_0(1+S\tau_0[X])^{-1/2}$.

In the limit $l\to 0$, $Y\propto kL(kL+1)^{-1}$ and a monotonic increase of Y with k is exhibited. Thus our observation of the splitting of the Y curve about the $n=1$ exciton state implies that l is finite. Numerical calculations of $Y=Y(k)$ were performed utilizing the experimental absorption spectrum of solid Xe and employing a wide range of parameters $k_{max}^{(1)}L$ and l/L. These calculations result in the following conclusions: (1) For $k_{max}^{(1)}L>2$ and $l/L>0.03$ the Y curve around the $n=1$ exciton band exhibits a symmetric splitting revealing a minimum at E_1^{max}. (2) The Y curve around the $n=2$ exciton band peaking at E_2^{max}, which is characterized by a lower absorption coefficient $k_{max}^{(2)}\simeq 0.25k_{max}^{(1)}$, is unsplit, its maximum coinciding with E_2^{max} for $k_{max}^{(1)}L<8$. (3) The Y value at $E_{max}^{(2)}$ and the maximum value of Y around $n=1$ are practically identical for the range of parameters mentioned in point (1). Our experimental results are in qualitative agreement with these features. The asymmetric splitting observed around E_1^{max} results from the energy dependence of L about the threshold, while the ratio Y(1370 Å)/Y(1450 Å)$\simeq 1.5$ which is larger than the expected value of unity may originate from the inefficient electronic relaxation of the $n=2$ state to the $n=1$ state on the time scale of $\tau_0\simeq 10^{-12}$ sec, whereupon the parameters l_0 and L for the two electronic states may be somewhat different.

A semiquantitative fit of the Y line shape, the concentration dependence of Y, and the absolute Y values was accomplished using Eq. (2) with the parameters $k_{max}^{(1)}L=2.5$, $l_0/L=0.2$, and $S\tau_0=5\times 10^{-19}$ cm^{-3}, all of which are reliable within a numerical factor of 2. The parameters l_0 and $S\tau_0$ for the $n=1$ excitons and for the $n=2$ excitons are identical within this margin of uncertainty. From $k_{max}^{(1)}=6\times 10^5$ cm^{-1}, we estimate a mean value of $L\simeq 380$ Å, which is reasonable for solid rare gases at sufficiently high energies. The "free" exciton diffusion length is $l_0\simeq 75$ Å.

The diffusion length of excitons in solid Xe is lower than the corresponding values in organic crystals, i.e., $l_0=150$ Å for singlet excitons[17] ($\tau_0=25\times 10^{-9}$ sec) and $l_0=10^5$ Å for triplet excitons[18] ($\tau_0=25\times 10^{-3}$ sec) in crystalline anthracene. However, the exciton diffusion process in the solid rare gas occurs on an extremely short time scale, $\tau_0\simeq 10^{-12}$ sec, which implies that $D\simeq 0.5$ cm^2 sec^{-1} in this system. The rate constant $S\simeq 5\times 10^{-7}$ cm^{-3} sec^{-1} is consistent with this high D value. We now focus our attention on the interesting question of whether the excited motion is coherent or diffusive. Setting $S=\pi R^2\langle V^2\rangle^{1/2}$ and $D=\Lambda\langle V^2\rangle^{1/2}$, where R is the reaction radius, $\langle V^2\rangle^{1/2}$ the rms exciton group velocity, and Λ the exciton mean free path, we get $\Lambda=(D/S)\pi R^2$, which with $R=10$ Å results in $\Lambda\simeq 3$ Å. Thus Λ is of the order of the lattice spacing and the exciton motion is diffusive (at least above ~20°K).

Complementary information concerning dynamics of free excitons is obtained from optical line-shape studies.[19,20] The Wannier exciton results in an $n=1$ exciton optical linewidth $\hbar\Gamma=3.19\times 10^{-4}m^{3/2}E_d^{\,2}$ (eV) for weak exciton-phonon coupling.[19] Taking the experimental value $m=0.5$ for the effective mass[8,9] and $E_d=1-3$ eV[20,21] for the deformation potential, we estimate $\hbar\Gamma\simeq 10^{-4}$–$10^{-3}$ eV which is appreciably lower than the experimental value $\hbar\Gamma=0.075$ eV for the $n=1$ ($^3P_1$) state. Thus the solid-rare-gas exciton states are close to the limit of strong exciton-phonon coupling which together with the low value of Λ provides *a posteriori* justification for the diffusion model adopted herein.

The photoemission yield of Xe/Kr (1% xenon), portrayed in Fig. 2, reveals that light absorption into the low-energy $n=1$ ($^3P_1$) exciton state of solid Kr does not lead to impurity photoemission. The $n=1$ ($^1P_1$) state of solid Kr is active in Auger-type energy transfer to the Xe impurity state. Thus the nonradiative $n=1(^1P_1)-n=1(^3P_1)$ multiphonon relaxation process in solid Kr is slow on the time scale of energy transfer from the mobile "free" excitons to the Xe impurity.

---

*Work supported by the National Council for Research and Development, Israel.

[1]J. Jortner, L. Meyer, S. A. Rice, and E. G. Wilson, J. Chem. Phys. 42, 4250 (1965).

[2]A. Gedanken, B. Raz, and J. Jortner, J. Chem. Phys. 58, 1178 (1973).

[3]O. Cheshnovsky, B. Raz, and J. Jortner, J. Chem. Phys. 59, 3301 (1973).

[4]B. Raz and J. Jortner, Proc. Roy. Soc., Ser. A 317, 113 (1970).

[5]L. Apker and E. Taft, Phys. Rev. 79, 964 (1950), and 81, 698 (1951).

[6]M. Martin, J. Chem. Phys. 54, 3289 (1971).

[7]Gedanken, Raz, and Jortner, Ref. 2.

[8]G. Baldini, Phys. Rev. 128, 1562 (1962).

[9]G. Baldini, Phys. Rev. 137, A508 (1965).

[10]Z. Ophir, U. Even, B. Raz, and J. Jortner, "Pulsed High Pressure Lamp for the Vacuum Ultraviolet" (to be published).

[11]The photon current was normalized to the total photon flux hitting the sample. A small (10%) correction due to reflection of the pure matrix was neglected.

[12]J. F. O'Brien and K. J. Teegarden, Phys. Rev. Lett. 17, 919 (1966).

[13]N. Schwentner, M. Skibowski, and W. Steinmann, to be published.

[14]S. I. Choi and S. A. Rice, J. Chem. Phys. 38, 366 (1963).

[15]This estimate is based upon taking the absolute value $Y = 13$% for solid Xe at 10.3 eV, obtained by Schwentner (private communication).

[16]M. Hebb, Phys. Rev. 81, 702 (1951).

[17]O. Simpson, Proc. Roy. Soc., Ser. A 238, 402 (1957)

[18]P. Avakian, V. Ern, R. E. Merrifield, and A. Suna, Phys. Rev. 165, 974 (1968).

[19]Y. Toyozawa, Progr. Theor. Phys. 20, 53 (1958).

[20]A. Gold and R. S. Knox, J. Chem. Phys. 36, 2805 (1962).

[21]S. D. Druger, J. Chem. Phys. 54, 2339 (1971).

Reprinted with permission from *Physical Review A*, Vol. 12(3), pp. 968-973 (September 1975). ©1975 American Physical Society.

Vacuum-ultraviolet emission from high-pressure krypton*

H. A. Koehler, L. J. Ferderber, D. L. Redhead, and P. J. Ebert
Lawrence Livermore Laboratory, University of California, Livermore, California 94550
(Received 8 August 1974; revised manuscript received 12 May 1975)

Krypton gas was excited by high-current relativistic electron bursts, and spectral and temporal characteristics of the uv continuum peaked at 1460 Å were measured as functions of pressure. Gas pressure ranged from 0.14 to 68 atm. The spectral full width at half-maximum of 90 ± 6 Å was virtually independent of pressure from 3.4 to 68 atm. Exponential time constants for the buildup and decay of the uv intensity obeyed a $P^{-1.5}$ pressure dependence for $P < 4$ atm. Three pressure-independent intensity decay constants of 9 ± 1.5, 32 ± 6, and 350 ± 70 nsec were obtained for $P > 6$ atm. The efficiency for conversion of electron kinetic energy to uv energy was (4 ± 1.6)%.

I. INTRODUCTION

Experimental evidence of lasing in high-pressure noble gases excited by high-current relativistic electron beams[1-3] has stimulated much of the current interest in the characteristics of the spontaneous uv emission from these gases. Such measurements for high-pressure Ar and Xe excited by relativistic electrons were previously reported.[4] No spontaneous emission measurements for Kr under excitation conditions where uv lasing is obtained[2] have been reported. An investigation of Kr that parallels our earlier work with Ar and Xe is the subject of this report. Preliminary results were given previously.[5]

II. EXPERIMENT

The experimental apparatus and procedure for this experiment were previously described in detail.[4] For completeness, a brief description of these follows. The electron sources were a Febetron 705 and a Febetron 706. The peak current of the Febetron 705 is 7×10^3 A at 2-MV peak potential. The full width at half-maximum (FWHM) is 50 nsec. The average electron excitation energy is 1.3 MeV. The Febetron 705 was used to obtain spectra, peak power and efficiency data. The peak current of the Febetron 706 is 7×10^3 A at 0.6-MV peak potential. The pulse FWHM is 2.5 nsec (5 nsec at the base).[6] Upon entering the gas cell, the average electron energy was approximately 0.2 MeV. Time constants for the buildup and decay of the uv intensity and efficiency data were obtained with the Febetron 706.

The stainless-steel excitation cell was pressurized with He to 100 atm and did not leak. Electrons entered the cell through a stainless-steel foil 0.13 mm thick. The excited gas was viewed perpendicular to the electron beam axis through 2-mm-thick LiF windows, each having uv transmittance of 0.74 at 1470 Å.

High-purity Kr was admitted to the evacuated excitation cell after passing through a molecular sieve cooled in a solid-CO_2-freon bath. Impurity concentrations, measured with a gas chromatograph were: O_2, 1 ppm; N_2, 3 ppm; H_2O, 1 ppm; Ar, <2 ppm; CH_4, <0.2 ppm; H_2, <1 ppm; Xe, <10 ppm. The temperature of the gas before excitation was 22 °C. After each electron burst the Kr was reclaimed in a liquid N_2 cooled vessel for impurity analysis. Impurity concentrations were unchanged.

Time-integrated spectra were recorded on Kodak 101-01 uv-sensitive film located at the focal plane of a 0.5-m Saya-Namayoka-type vacuum monochromator. A 1200-line/mm grating blazed at 1500 Å was used. Density of the exposed film was measured with a Joyce-Loebl scanning microdensitometer.

At each pressure the continuum output intensity as a function of time was measured with ITT F4115 planar photodiodes of known uv sensitivity. A pinhole placed in the line-of-sight between the gas cell and the photodiode limited the output current to 5 A, well within the linear operating region of the photodiode. Tektronix 519 and 581 oscilloscopes recorded the photodiode signals. For measuring the buildup and decay time constants, two type 519 oscilloscopes were used in series. One had high vertical sensitivity and a relatively slow horizontal sweep speed to measure long-term decay. The other had lower sensitivity and a fast horizontal sweep to record the uv buildup and fast initial decay. The photodiode output connector was directly inserted in the first oscilloscope. The unattenuated signal passed through the first oscilloscope and through appropriate attenuators to the second. This minimized signal distortion due to cable dispersion.

III. EXPERIMENTAL RESULTS

A. Spectra

Time-integrated spectra of the 1460-Å continuum were obtained for pressures ranging from 3.4 to 68 atm. Figure 1(a) shows a spectrum taken at 7 atm. The emission peaked at 1460 Å and did not change with gas pressure. The spectral FWHM of 90 ± 6 Å was virtually independent of pressure. This behavior is shown in Fig. 1(b). No other emission was observed with film between 1100 and 2000 Å. The absorption line at 1470 Å results from resonance absorption by Xe.

B. Time constants

Time constants for the buildup and decay of the 1460-Å continuum were determined for pressures ranging from 0.14 to 68 atm. Photodiode oscilloscope traces taken at 20 atm are shown in Fig. 2. At each pressure, the traces were spliced absolutely in both time and amplitude to obtain the composite intensity curve. Each curve was fit with a sum of exponentials. A minimum of exponential terms was used to fit each curve to within the experimental error. All fits extended over a time of > 500 nsec and over a dynamic voltage range of > 200.

Table I lists the time constants and the relative amplitudes at several gas pressures. Figure 3 is a plot of the time constants as a function of pressure.

Below 1 atm, one buildup and one decay term accurately fit each oscilloscope trace. Near 1 atm, it was necessary to introduce an additional decay term. The faster of the two decays had a $P^{-1.5}$ pressure dependence. The slower decay was pressure independent, with a value near 350 nsec. At 6 atm, the buildup time constant could not be measured accurately because the buildup time was comparable to the duration of the excitation pulse and was obscured by a precursor pulse. At this pressure three decay components were needed to fit each trace. The slowest of these components had a 350-nsec time constant. The other two decay constants approached pressure-independent values of approximately 32 and 9 nsec. Above 10 atm, the amplitude ratio of the fast-decay components was approximately 3.5:1.

Similar to our observations in Ar and Xe,[4] a very fast precursor coinciding with the excitation pulse was also evident in Kr at low pressure. This precursor was not used in the curve fitting since it was of longer wavelength than the 1460-Å continuum. By using optical filters (Corning 0-54, 90-30, 3-138 and air), the wavelength of the precursor was determined to be 2400 ± 200 Å. The amplitude of this emission increased linearly as the pressure was raised from 0.14 to 4 atm.

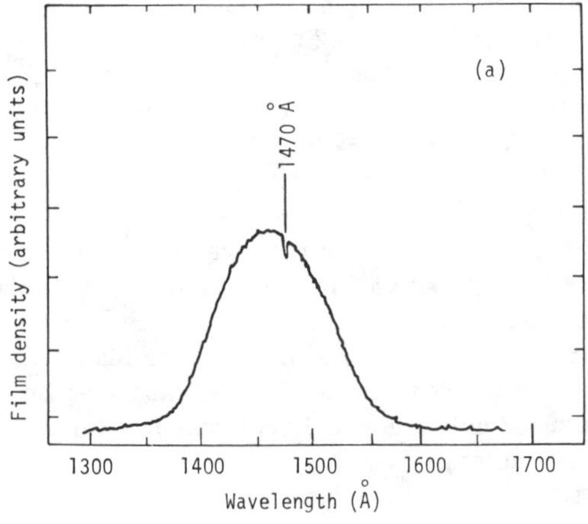

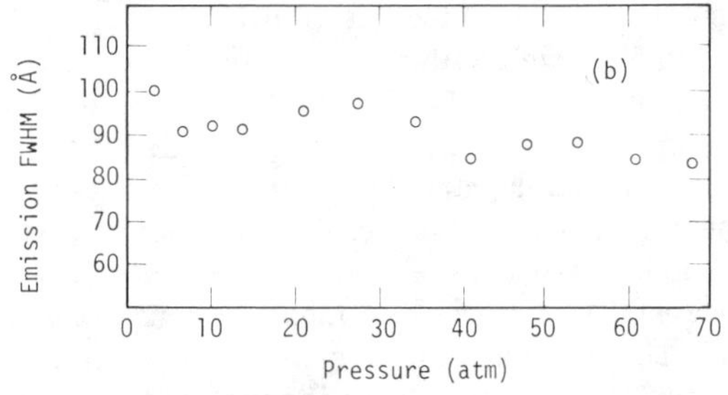

FIG. 1. (a) Time-integrated emission spectrum at 7 atm. (b) Pressure dependence of emission spectrum FWHM of Kr. Background was subtracted from photodensitometer recordings used in obtaining FWHM values. 1.3-MeV electrons excited the gas. Wavelength values are uncorrected for grating reflectivity and LiF transmittance.

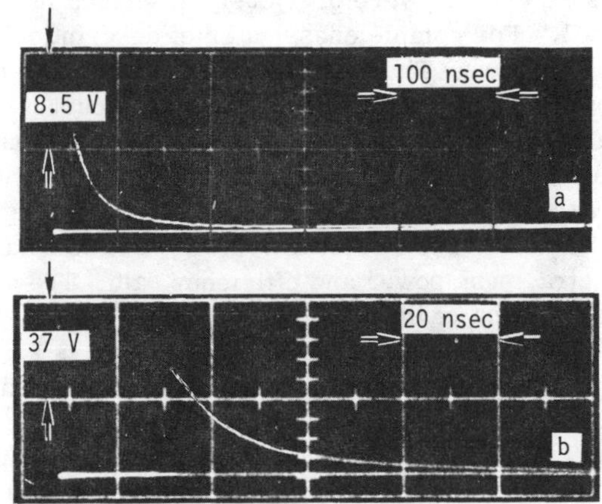

FIG. 2. Traces from (a) slow-sensitive and (b) fast-insensitive oscilloscopes showing photodiode output at $P = 20$ atm. The gas was excited with a 2.5-nsec-FWHM electron burst. Baselines were obtained with zero-volt signal prior to gas excitation.

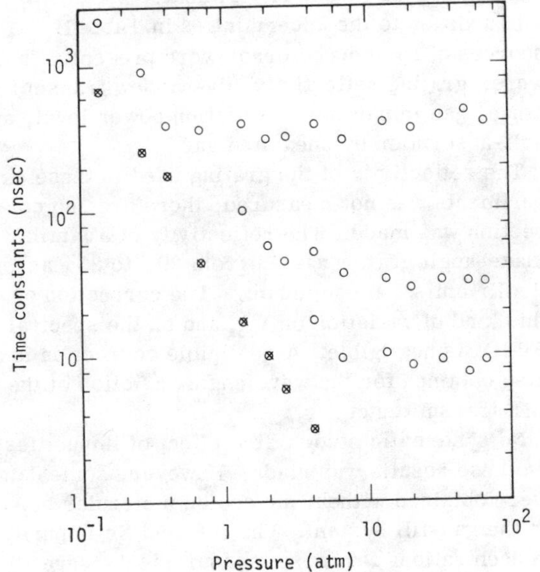

FIG. 3. Time constants for Kr buildup and decay as a function of pressure. Gas was excited with a 2.5-nsec-FWHM electron burst.

C. Peak power and efficiency

Figure 4 shows the peak power emitted by approximately 1.3 cm^3 of excited Kr as a function of pressure. The power values were calculated from the peak output voltage of the oscilloscope traces, knowing the detector geometry and sensitivity. Isotropic gas emission was assumed. Correction was made for LiF window transmission. No correction was made for uv transmission through 4 cm of unexcited Kr gas. The peak power increased with pressure, reaching a maximum of 3.1×10^7 W at 54 atm. At this pressure, the emission energy, obtained by measuring the area under the oscilloscope trace, was 1.5 J. To assure that no energy was lost in unobservable, long decay components, the photodiode output current was also integrated ($RC = 35$ μsec) and displayed on an oscilloscope. An identical result was obtained.

To obtain the efficiency for conversion of electron kinetic energy to uv energy, the electron energy absorbed per unit volume was calculated from the expression $W_e = jF\gamma(dE/dx)\rho$, where j is the electron current density (1700 A/cm^2), F is the geometrical transmission of the plate supporting the electron entrance window (0.6), γ is the FWHM of the electron burst (50 nsec), dE/dx is the effective collision energy-loss rate determined by a Monte Carlo calculation[7] (~3.3 MeV/g cm^{-2}), and ρ is the gas density.[8] For these experimental conditions, $W_e \cong 170\rho$ J/cm^3. This approximation is valid if the variation in the energy-loss rate is small throughout the observed gas volume. On the basis of the Monte Carlo calculation, this is reasonable up to approximately 34 atm.

The uv energy density was divided by the electron-energy density at several gas pressures <34 atm. The efficiency was $(4\pm 1.6)\%$.

IV. ERROR

Sources of error in the emission spectra, the time constants and their corresponding amplitudes, and the output power and efficiency have been discussed in detail previously.[4] Table II lists the

TABLE I. Time constants and amplitudes for Kr buildup and decay obtained by fitting oscilloscope traces to $[I(t)=\sum_i A_i e^{-t/\tau_i}]$. Amplitudes were obtained with peak current density of 500 A/cm^2 and an initial energy of approximately 0.2 MeV.

Pressure (atm)	Amplitude (arbitrary units) $-A_1$	A_2	A_3	A_4	Time constants (nsec) τ_1	τ_2	τ_3	τ_4
0.13	0.014			0.014	650			2000
0.27	0.074			0.074	260			900
0.54	0.71			0.71	175			390
0.68	1.2			1.2	45			360
1.3	4.7		2.7	1.3	17		100	400
2.0	30.0		10.0	1.7	10		57	310
2.7	34.0		16.0	2.2	6		45	330
4.4	32.0	21	17.0	1.8	3	17.0	52	390
6.8		42	42.0	2.7		9.5	37	300
13.0		140	50.0	2.5		10.5	34	400
20.0		150	70.0	2.5		8.5	29	370
34.0		200	47.0	2.1		9.5	33	440
52.0		180	33.0	1.3		7.5	32	480
68.0		90	14.0	0.47		9.0	32	400

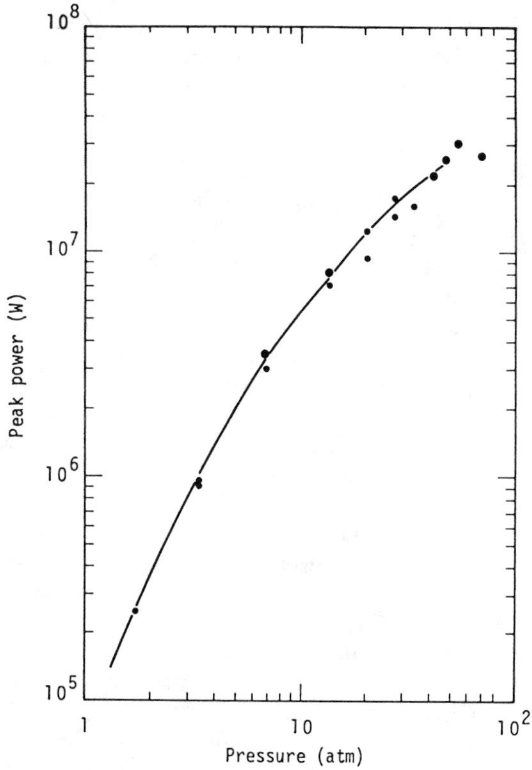

FIG. 4. Peak power of Kr emission from 1.3 cm^3 of gas as a function of pressure. The points were corrected for transmittance of the LiF window, but not for unknown absorption by unexcited gas. 1.3-MeV electrons excited the gas.

random errors in this experiment.

In addition to the uncertainties in Table II, sources of systematic error were present. These were: grating reflectivity, uv-window transmittance, gas impurities, excitation power level, and self-absorption by unexcited gas.

The reflectivity of the grating used in these experiments was not measured; therefore, no correction was made. The reflectivity of a similar blaze-angle grating varied from 20% to 23% across the Kr emission continuum.[9] The correction of this kind of variation on λ_{max} and on the spectral FWHM is negligible. A negligible correction is also obtained for the wavelength variation of the LiF transmittance.

No systematic study of the effect of impurities on these results was made. However, some data were obtained without the cooled molecular sieve in the gas-fill system. The H_2O and Xe impurity concentrations for these measurements were 10 ppm and 50 ppm, respectively. Identical oscilloscope traces were obtained with and without the molecular sieve. The Xe absorption line in the continuum was the only obvious evidence of an impurity.

To determine if the time constants were influenced by the high excitation current, some data were obtained with less than one-tenth the usual current density. The relative amplitude of the 350-nsec decay component increased with decreasing current. The time constants and other

TABLE II. Summary of random experimental errors.

Error sources		Estimated error
Emission peak	± 0.5 mm	± 8.5 Å
Half-intensity location (FWHM)	± 0.15 mm	± 6 Å
Decay and buildup time constants		± 20%
Oscilloscope trace reading		
(0.5) trace width	± 0.2 mm	
Amplitude of decay components		± 50% (9 nsec)
		± 25% (32 nsec)
		± 20% (350 nsec)
Decay time constants	± 20%	
Breakout of uv emission pulse	± 0.3 nsec	
Amplitude of buildup component		± 25%
uv output energy		± 22%
Photodiode sensitivity	± 20%	
Oscilloscope attenuators	± 5%	
Oscilloscope dc-calibration	± 2%	
Oscilloscope trace reading	± 3%	
Optical geometry factor	± 6%	
LiF window transmission	± 5%	
Conversion efficiency		± 41%
uv output energy	± 22%	
Excited gas volume	± 20%	
Electron current density	± 20%	
dE/dx	± 20%	

relative amplitudes were unchanged.

No corrections were made for self-absorption by unexcited gas.

V. DISCUSSION

The behavior of Kr under intense electron excitation is very similar to that of Ar and Xe. Potential curves for Ar [10] and Xe,[11] together with kinetic models[10,12] for the formation and decay of excited molecules, serve as guides to discuss qualitatively some of our observations.

A. Spectra

Nearly all of the radiant energy emitted was in the uv continuum peaked at 1460 Å. This is very close to the 1457-Å wavelength at which oscillation occurs,[2] but is in marked disagreement with 1440 Å obtained for proton excitation[13] and 1425 Å obtained for low-intensity electron excitation.[14] These differences could be the consequence of different grating reflectivities. The continuum is attributed to radiative transitions from the $^1\Sigma_u^+$ and $^3\Sigma_u^+$ states to the $^1\Sigma_g^+$ molecular ground state. These transitions are spectrally unresolvable. No emission was detected at shorter wavelengths. This indicates resonance trapping of photons from atomic transitions and the absence of photons from radiative decay of higher-energy molecular states to the molecular ground state. A spectral FWHM of 90 ± 6 Å is consistent with spectral widths reported by Leichner and Ericson[14] and Stewart *et al.*[13] Weak emission observed at 2400 ± 200 Å was associated with the very fast precursor and may be evidence of radiative recombination of electrons with atomic ions.[15] The lack of strong, longer wavelength uv indicates rapid collisional deexcitation of the large initial atomic and molecular ion population to lower excited atomic states. Infrared radiation arising from molecular transitions to the $^1\Sigma_u^+$ and $^3\Sigma_u^+$ states was suggested by Mulliken[11] and was observed in Ar by Arai and Firestone.[16] Our experiments did not cover this spectral region.

B. Time constants

Time constants at low pressure ($P<4$ atm) have a $P^{-1.5}$ pressure dependence that is evidently associated with the formation of radiative molecules. Above 6 atm, excellent fits to the oscilloscope traces were obtained with three pressure-independent, exponential decay constants. These results, together with spectral data, suggest that two spectrally unresolvable molecular states ($^1\Sigma_u^+$, $^3\Sigma_u^+$) decay independently to the molecular ground state ($^1\Sigma_u^+$). Since singlet-singlet transitions are more probable than triplet-singlet transitions, it is reasonable to assign the 9-nsec decay to the $^1\Sigma_u^+$ state and the 32-nsec decay to the $^3\Sigma_u^+$ state. The 350-nsec decay could result from undetected infrared transitions from higher excited molecular levels to the $^1\Sigma_u^+$ and $^3\Sigma_u^+$ molecular states.[11] The ratio of the amplitudes of the 9- and 32-nsec decay components was approximately 3.5 to 1. This implies that the initial concentrations of the singlet and triplet radiative molecules were approximately equal.

The $P^{-1.5}$ pressure dependence of the time constants obtained here for $P<4$ atm agrees with that reported by Boucique and Mortier[17] and by Leichner and Ericson[14] for Kr at $P<1$ atm. The pressure-dependent buildup time constant and the 350-nsec pressure-independent decay constant are in excellent agreement with those reported by Leichner and Ericson. The longer decay constant observed by Boucique and Mortier (1.7 μsec) was not found. Our results indicated that the excitation current density affected only the relative amplitude of the 350-nsec time constant. An even longer decay component might have been effectively suppressed because of the high excitation levels used in these experiments.

C. Output power and efficiency

The maximum power density observed for the Kr continuum under 1.3-MeV electron excitation was 2.4×10^7 W/cm^3 at 54 atm. The efficiency of approximately $(4 \pm 1.6)\%$ does not agree with the value of 12% reported by Stewart *et al.*[13]

ACKNOWLEDGMENTS

The authors thank D. Jones, G. Clough, S. Stribling, and V. Gregory for the help in the mechanical aspects of these experiments.

---

*Work performed under the auspices of the USERDA.

[1]H. A. Koehler, L. J. Ferderber, D. L. Redhead, and P. J. Ebert, Appl. Phys. Lett. 21, 198 (1972).

[2]P. W. Hoff, J. C. Swingle, and C. K. Rhodes, Appl. Phys. Lett. 23, 245 (1973).

[3]W. M. Hughes, J. Shannon, and R. Hunter, Appl. Phys. Lett. 24, 488 (1974).

[4]H. A. Koehler, L. J. Ferderber, D. L. Redhead, and

P. J. Ebert, Phys. Rev. A 9, 768 (1974).
[5]H. A. Koehler, L. J. Ferderber, and P. J. Ebert, Bull. Am. Phys. Soc. 19, 157 (1974).
[6]A different electron tube was used in these experiments. The excitation pulse width depends on tube characteristics. A 1.6-nsec-FWHM pulse was measured with the tube used in Ref. 4.
[7]M. J. Berger and S. M. Seltzer, NASA Report No. SP-169, 1968 (unpublished). Calculations were carried out with program ETRAN-15.
[8]G. A. Cook, *Argon, Helium and the Rare Gases* (Interscience, New York, 1961), p. 268. The Ottawa virial coefficients were used.
[9]G. S. Hurst, T. E. Bortner, and T. D. Strickler, Phys. Rev. 178, 4 (1969).
[10]D. C. Lorents and R. E. Olson, Stanford Research Institute Semi-Annual Technical Report No. 1, 1972 (unpublished).
[11]R. S. Mulliken, J. Chem. Phys. 52, 5170 (1970).
[12]C. W. Werner, E. V. George, P. W. Hoff, and C. K. Rhodes, Appl. Phys. Lett. 25, 235 (1974).
[13]T. E. Stewart, G. S. Hurst, T. E. Bortner, J. E. Parks, F. W. Martin, and H. L. Weidner, J. Opt. Soc. Am. 60, 1290 (1970).
[14]P. K. Leichner and R. J. Ericson, Phys. Rev. A 9, 251 (1974).
[15]J. A. Viecelli, LLL Report No. UCRL-51374, 1973 (unpublished).
[16]S. Arai and R. F. Firestone, J. Chem. Phys. 50, 4575 (1969).
[17]R. Boucique and P. Mortier, J. Phys. D 3, 1905 (1970).

Reprinted with permission from *Applied Physics Letters,* Vol. 33(6), pp. 525-527 (September 15, 1978).

Time-resolved spectroscopy of the Ar_2^*-excimer emission

M. Diegelmann,[a] W. G. Wrobel,[b] and K. Hohla[c]

Max-Planck-Gesellschaft, D-8046 Garching bei München, Germany
(Received 8 June 1978; accepted for publication 11 July 1978)

High-pressure argon was excited by a 2-ns 600-keV e-beam pulse, and time integrated as well as time resolved fluorescence spectra were measured. No significant dependence of line center (126.2±0.1 nm) or spectral width (80±10 nm) of the Ar_2^* continuum on gas pressure was found in the range 0.5–20 bar. From the buildup time constant of fluorescence we calculated the three-body rate constant for Ar_2^* formation to be 5×10^{-33} cm^6/sec. The fluorescence decay was found to consist of two exponentials with time constants 8.6 and 39.2 ns at 20 bar and 12.6 and 73.9 ns at 10 bar, respectively. We attribute this behavior to the fluorescence originating from the singlet and triplet upper state. From the spectral shift between the two components we determined the singlet-triplet splitting in the excited Ar_2 molecule to be 12 Å corresponding to 760 cm^{-1}.

PACS numbers: 78.60.Fi, 79.20.Kz

The Ar excimer laser is the shortest-wavelength laser[1,2] in the class of rare-gas excimer high-power lasers. Tunable laser action has been achieved with the Xe_2^* system[3,4] and single-line operation with the Kr_2^* system.[5,6] Although considerable work has been done on the Xe_2 molecule, there is far less known about Ar_2.

A tunable Ar_2^* laser would be interesting as a direct source of intense coherent radiation at the wavelength of Lyman α (121.6 nm). This lies within the gain profile of the Ar excimer. As a first step, we have investigated the kinetics and spectroscopy of the Ar_2 molecule.

We have excited a sample of argon (impurity level below 1 ppm) with a short-pulse e-beam. For the experimental setup see Fig. 1. Our coaxial e-beam diode, which has been described elsewhere,[3] delivered a short 2-ns pulse of 600-keV peak energy electrons to the gas contained in a 70-μm thin-walled stainless-steel cell. The latter, which could be pressurized up to 20 bar, served as the anode foil. Fluorescence light could be observed in the axial direction of the tubular gas cell through two 5-mm-thick LiF windows either directly with a fast solar blind vacuum photodiode (ITT F 4115) or through a 1-m normal incidence VUV spectrograph (McPherson 225). We would record time-integrated spectra on film (Kodak 101-01) or alternatively take time-resolved spectra with another photodiode of the same type scanning the wavelength setting from shot to shot. This photodiode and the solid-state preamplifier immediately following this detector needed lead shielding against hard x rays produced in the e-beam gun. We have monitored both this x-ray burst, with a fast PIN diode, as well as the current, with a coaxial Faraday cup. The signals exhibited identical temporal shapes, ensuring that we had a clean 2–2.5-ns FWHM e-beam pulse without any prepulses postpulses affecting our time resolution. All electrical signals were recorded on a Tektronix 7912 transient digitizer. The overall system risetime was measured to be 1 ns.

By initially taking film spectra (see Fig. 2), we studied the influence of gas pressure, pumping energy, and pumping density upon the emission. In the pressure range 1–20 bar, and with a variation of pumping density over two orders of magnitude, no significant dependence of the wavelength or spectral width of the fluorescence band was found. This confirms our assumption that at these pressures vibrational relaxation in the upper state is fast enough (about 10 ps) for thermal equilibrium to be established. Moreover, no line narrowing was observed with increasing pumping density. This indicates that our spectra are not strongly affected by the onset of stimulated emission in the axial direction.

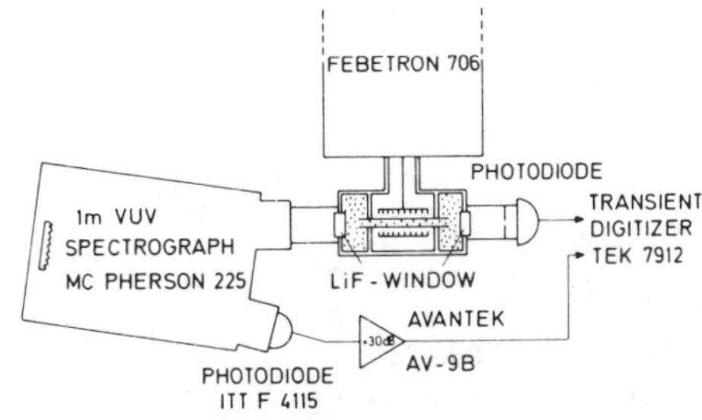

FIG. 1. Schematic diagram of the experimental setup.

[a]Projektgruppe für Laserforschung.
[b]Institut für Plasmaphysik.
[c]Projektgruppe für Laser forschung.

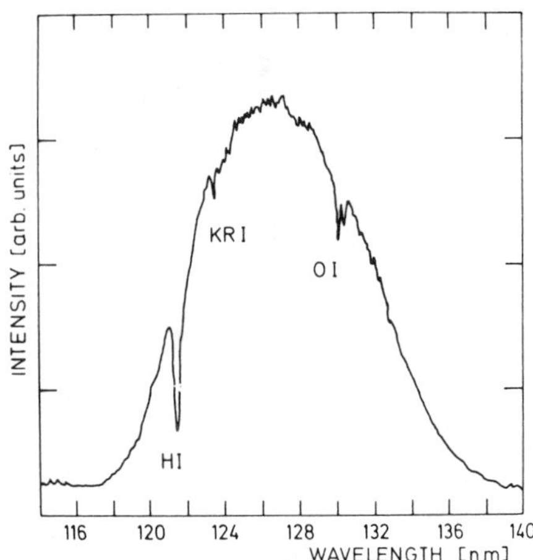

FIG. 2. Time-integrated emission spectrum of Ar at 20 bar excited by 0.6-MeV electrons. The densitometer tracing is uncorrected for wavelength dependence of window transmission, grating reflectivity, and absorption in the gas.

From a time-resolved measurement of the fluorescence buildup following short-pulse e-beam excitation as a function of Ar pressure we have determined the three-body rate constant for the formation of Ar_2 to be 5×10^{-33} cm^6/s. This number agrees quite well with the value reported by other authors.[7,8]

By electronically integrating the output of the photodiode directly mounted to the cell and correcting for window transmission, solid angle, and detector response we have determined the number density of Ar_2^* molecules decaying radiatively to be 1.5×10^{17} cm^{-3} (with maximum pumping). This lower limit of the total excimer concentration corresponds to approximately 100 mJ of fluorescence energy. For comparison, the total energy deposited in the gas was 2–3 J. This value is an extrapolation from the numbers, given by Bradley for his nearly identical e-beam system.[3]

The most interesting result of our investigation was found in our spectrally resolved time-dependent measurements. A computer fit of the experimental data showed that the fluorescence decay was a sum of two exponentials with time constants $\tau_1 = 8.6\pm1.1$ ns and $\tau_2 = 39.2\pm6.1$ ns at $P_{Ar} = 20$ bar independent of

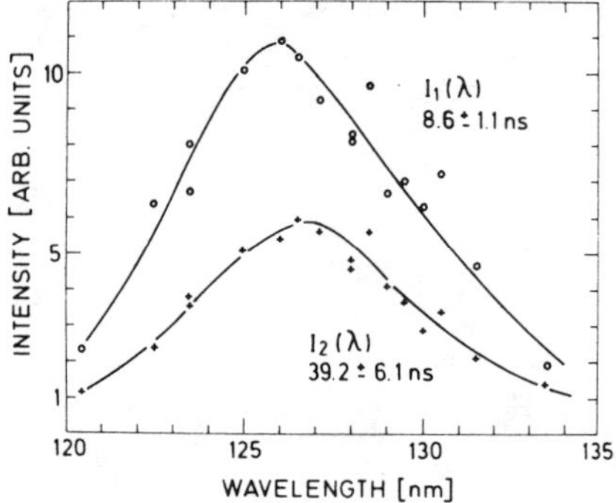

FIG. 3. Amplitude functions $I_{1,2}(\lambda)$ of the fast and slowly decaying components of the Ar_2^* emission. Note the 12-Å shift between the two spectra.

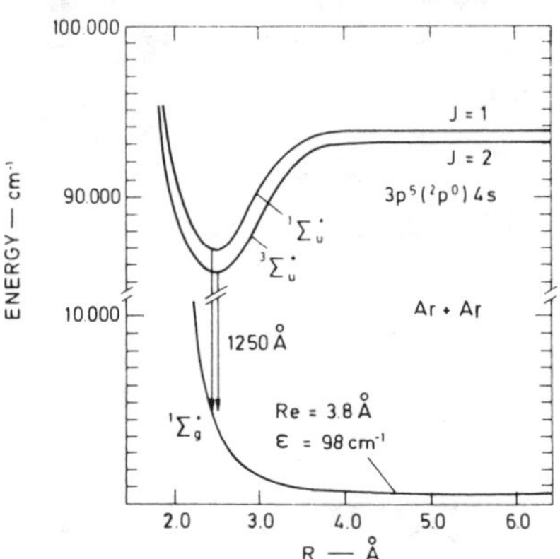

FIG. 4. Potential curves of Ar_2 after Lorents (Ref. 11). High-lying levels are omitted.

wavelength:

$$I(\lambda, t) = I_1(\lambda)\exp(-t/\tau_1) + I_2(\lambda)\exp(-t/\tau_2).$$

At 10 bar the lifetimes are 12.6 ± 1.6 and 73.9 ± 18 ns, respectively.

Therefore the upper state must consist of two different radiating species. Different vibrational levels can be ruled out because of the above-mentioned fast VV relaxation. Following Koehler,[9] we assume the emission originates from the $^1\Sigma_u^+$ and $^3\Sigma_u^+$ excited states of Ar_2. Mixing of the two upper states via electron collisions can be excluded after the termination of the e-beam because we observed an additional continuum centered around 195 nm which precisely followed the 2-ns pumping pulse in its temporal behavior. According to Viecelli[10] this band results from radiative recombination of electrons and argon ions. Hence the electron density drastically drops as soon as the e-beam is off.

The amplitude functions $I_{1,2}(\lambda)$ are obviously spectrally shifted with respect to one another (see Fig. 3). We thereby have first spectroscopically determined the singlet-triplet splitting in the Ar_2 molecule. Our value of 12 Å is in reasonable agreement with the number 1040 cm^{-1} ($\simeq$16 Å) given by Lorents[11] (see Fig. 4). Recently, the singlet-triplet splitting was measured by time-resolved fluorescence spectroscopy after optical excitation of a solid noble-gas sample with 100-ps synchrotron radiation pulses at the Ar resonance line. Again this yielded a value similar to ours.[12]

At 121.6 nm the gain of the Ar_2^* excimer is still about one-third of its peak value. The possibility of generating Ar_2^* laser emission at the Lyman α wavelength therefore seems promising. Work along these lines is in progress.

Work supported by the Bundesministerium für Forschung und Technologie and Euratom.

[1]W.M. Hughes, J. Shannon, and R. Hunter, Appl. Phys. Lett. **24**, 488 (1974).
[2]P.W. Hoff (private communication).
[3]D.J. Bradley, D.R. Hull, M.H.R. Hutchinson, and M.W. McGeoch, Opt. Commun. **14**, 1 (1975).

[4]S.C. Wallace and R.W. Dreyfus, Appl. Phys. Lett. **25**, 498 (1974).
[5]P.W. Hoff, J.C. Swingle, and C.K. Rhodes, Appl. Phys. Lett. **23**, 245 (1973).
[6]C.W. Werner, E.V. George, P.W. Hoff, and C.K. Rhodes, J. Quantum Electron. **QE-13**, 769 (1977).
[7]J.W. Keto, R.E. Gleason, and G.K. Walters, Phys. Rev. Lett. **33**, 1365 (1974).
[8]N. Thonnard and G.S. Hurst, Phys. Rev. A **5**, 1110 (1972).
[9]H.A. Koehler, L.J. Ferderber, D.L. Redhead, and P.J. Ebert; Phys. Rev. A **9**, 768 (1974).
[10]J.A. Viecelli, UCRL Report No. UCRL 51374, 1973 (unpublished).
[11]D.C. Lorents and R.E. Olson, Research Inst. Semiannual Technical Report No. 1, 1972 (unpublished).
[12]G. Zimmerer (private communication).

Section Three

Excimer UV Lasers—Rare Gas Halide

While rare gas excimers produced high energy, the high pressure of the gas made them excitable only with e-beams. The inconvenience and high cost limited the development of rare gas excimers. Renewed interest in excimer lasers was sparked by work by Setser and others that showed spectra from the halides of xenon. This work was seized by Searles and Hart and by Ewing and Brau to develop rare gas halide lasers in the mid- and near-UV with xenon and krypton halides and into the VUV with argon fluoride. These lasers, which work at only a few atmospheres pressure, were discharge pumped by Djeu and Burnham. Discharge pumping gave the economy and simplicity that allowed them to become widely useful commercial products. Further research results have led to other new wavelengths, new pumping methods, and a wide variety of applications.

Reprinted with permission from *Journal of Chemical Physics,* Vol. 62(5), pp. 1990-1991 (March 1, 1975).

Bound-free emission spectra of diatomic xenon halides

J. E. Velazco and D. W. Setser

Chemistry Department, Kansas State University, Manhattan, Kansas 66506
(Received 17 December 1974)

Certain physical properties, such as polarizability[1] and elastic scattering,[2] of the metastable states of the heavy rare gas atoms, which arise from the first excited configuration, $np^5(n+1)s^1$, are known to resemble those of the corresponding alkali metal atoms. We wish to report a similarity between the chemical properties of the metastable $Xe(^3P_2)$ atoms and alkali metal atoms; namely, direct reaction[3-6] with halogen-containing molecules to produce XeX^* which subsequently radiates to the dissociative $Xe(^1S)+X(^2P)$ ground state. Since the cross sections for formation of XeX^* from several reagents are large, these bound-free emissions have considerable potential as ultraviolet laser systems for excitation[7-9] of mixtures of xenon (or other rare gases) and halogen-containing compounds.

Xenon metastable atoms were generated in a flowing afterglow apparatus by passing a ~0.1% Xe mixture in argon through a cold cathode discharge.[10,11] Metered flows of reagents were added downstream from the discharge. The experiments consist of observing the emission spectra from the interaction of $Xe(^3P_2)$ atoms with the added reagents and of measuring the total quenching rate constants. The spectra were recorded by a 0.75 m Jarrell–Ash monochromator fitted with an EMI 9558QB photomultiplier tube. The quenching rate constants were measured by monitoring the concentration of $Xe(^3P_2)$ atoms by absorption spectroscopy along the flow reactor in the presence of added reagent, as previously described.[10,11]

The emission spectra assigned to $XeCl^*$ and $XeBr^*$ are shown in Fig. 1. The identity of these spectra was confirmed by obtaining very similar spectra from several reagents, i.e., the $XeCl^*$ spectrum was obtained from $Xe(^3P_2)+Cl_2$, NOCl, and $SOCl_2$; the $XeBr^*$ spectrum was obtained from $Xe(^3P_2)+Br_2$ and PBr_3. Reaction of $Xe(^3P_2)$ with F_2, NOF, and CF_3OF gave spectra similar in nature to that of Fig. 1, which was assigned to XeF^*. Spectra for XeI^* were obtained from reaction with I_2 and CF_3I. The spectrum from XeI^* shows evidence of the large spin–orbit splitting in the lower state. All of the spectra are somewhat sensitive to total pressure and above ~5 torr the undulations on both the long and short wavelength side of the peak intensities are re-

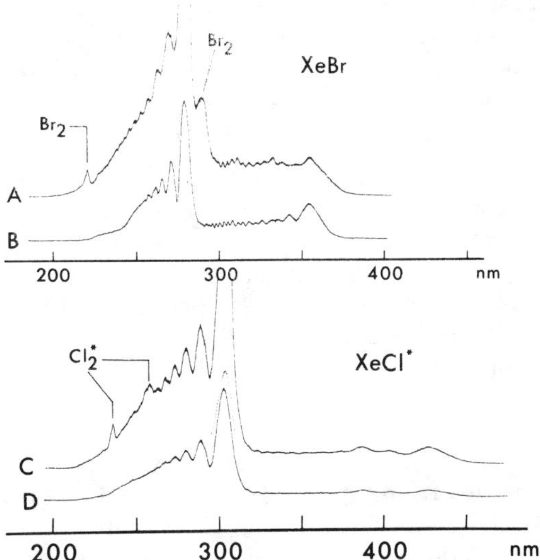

FIG. 1. Emission spectra for Xe^*+Br_2(A), Xe^*+PBr_3(B), Xe^*+Cl_2(C), and Xe^*+SOCl_2(D). Experimental conditions were identical for all the runs: pressure, 1.2 torr; slits 250 μ; scan speed, 12.5 nm·min^{-1}. Also the Xe* and reagent concentrations were the same, except for PBr_3 which had a reduced (unknown) flow rate because of the low vapor pressure. Dashed curves indicate the position of the peaks for spectra A and C, respectively for attenuation by a factor of 1/3. The weak molecular emissions for Br_2^* and Cl_2^* are also labeled on A and C. The maximum in intensity occurs at 304.3 nm for $XeCl^*$ and 278.2 nm for $XeBr^*$ as shown. For XeI^* and XeF^* (not shown) the maximum occurs at 251.8 and 346.0 nm, respectively. The features to the long wavelength side of the main peak is significantly more structured for XeI^*; whereas, for XeF^* the emission to the red side is similar to $XeCl^*$ but extends so far to the red that it appears to overlap the shorter wavelength emission in the second order. The features to the red of the main emission appear to belong to a separate system; a possible explanation is that the emission originates from *two* upper bound states, which correlate with $Xe^+(^2P_{3/2})$ and $Xe^+(^2P_{1/2})$.

TABLE I. Quenching cross sections[a] and relative XeX^* emission intensity.[b]

Reagent	Cross section (Å^2)	Relative intensity
Cl_2	176	100
$SOCl_2$	224	44
Br_2	210	122
CF_3I	184	49
CF_3OF	144	24[c]

[a]The estimated uncertainty in the measurements is ±15%, see Refs. 10 and 11.

[b]These values are based upon a simple scan of one mixture, the uncertainty, thus, could be ±20%. All measurements were done with dilute mixtures of Ar and the reagent being studied.

[c]The integration measurement of the XeF^* emission intensity was arbitrarily stopped at 550 nm, because beyond this point, second order emission contributes to the signal (see caption to Fig. 1).

duced. The wavelength of the transitions are consistent with essentially Coulombic XeX^* states, which are expected to lie ~3 eV below the $Xe(^3P_2)+X_2$ entrance channel. The wavelength for the maxima of the emission intensity increase for the XeI^*, $XeBr^*$, $XeCl^*$, and XeF^* series, as would be expected based upon the anticipated bond energies. Very recent interpretations[12] of the McLennan bands of I_2 support assignment of the transitions of Fig. 1 as being of the bound-free type.

The total quenching cross section of $Xe(^3P_2)$ for several of the reagent molecules are summarized in Table I along with the relative XeX^* emission intensities obtained for a common $[Xe(^3P_2)]$ and the same flow rate of reagent. This latter column, hence, is proportional to the relative cross sections for formation of XeX^*. These have been normalized to the $XeCl^*$ emission intensity from Cl_2 because an estimate could be obtained for the absolute value of this quenching channel in the following way. A comparison was made between the emission intensities from Cl_2^* and Kr^* states excited by reaction of $Ar(^3P_{0,2})$ with Cl_2 and Kr, respectively. Since the cross sections for formation of the Kr^* states are known,[13] the cross section for formation of the Cl_2^* state, which gives the 260 nm continuum, could be assigned. Xenon then was added to the argon flow to convert the $Ar(^3P_2)$ atoms to $Xe(^3P_2)$ atoms; the Cl_2 flow was unchanged. Based on 50% conversion of $Ar(^3P_{0,2})$ to $Xe(^3P_2)$[10] and a Cl_2^* 260 nm cross section of 9 Å^2, the relative areas of the $XeCl^*$ and 260 nm Cl_2^* emissions gave a cross section for formation of $XeCl^*$ of 210 Å^2. This very rough estimate is consistent with only very minor Cl_2^* and Br_2^* emissions from the $Xe(^3P_2)+Cl_2$ or Br_2 reactions (see figure caption), and formation of $XeCl^*$ and $XeBr^*$ certainly is the main quenching channel for Cl_2 and Br_2. As shown in Table I the cross sections for formation of XeX^* from the other halogen compounds is less than for X_2, which suggests competition with other exit channels.

Golde and Thrush[14] were the first to discover that reaction of $Ar(^3P_{0,2})$ with molecules containing chlorine gives emission in the vacuum ultraviolet region, which can be assigned as the bound-free transition of $ArCl^*$. However, the cross sections for formation of $ArCl^*$ are lower than for $XeCl^*$, even for $Ar(^3P_2)+Cl_2$, because of competitions by other exit channels.[15] Golde and Thrush[14] also have identified the bound-free emission from ArO^* and KrO^* and reassigned the emission peaking at 237 nm[16] from the $Xe(^3P_2)+N_2O$ reaction to XeO^*. We have compared the $XeCl^*$ and XeO^* emission intensities from $Xe(^3P_2)$ reacting with Cl_2 and N_2O; the cross section for formation of XeO^* is, at least, a factor of 10 below that for formation of $XeCl^*$ even though the total quenching cross section of $Xe(^3P_2)$ by N_2O is large.[10]

In addition to being possible candidates for laser systems, the XeX^* bound-free emission spectra should be valuable for characterization of the XeX potential curves[17] and for further elucidation of reaction dynamics for this class of reactions.[3-6] The formation of bound diatomic products from quenching of excited atomic states that are within a few eV of the ionization limit by halogen-containing molecules with sizeable electron affinities may be a general quenching mechanism.

This work was supported by U. S. Army Research Office—Durham under grant DAHCO4-75-G0018. We also wish to acknowledge discussions with Dr. L. Gundel and Dr. D. King of this laboratory. We thank Dr. Golde and Dr. Thrush for a preprint of Ref. 14.

[1](a) E. J. Robinson, J. Levine, and B. Bederson, Phys. Rev. 146, 95 (1966). (b) R. W. Molof, H. L. Schwartz, T. M. Miller, and B. Bederson, Phys. Rev. A 10, 1131 (1974).
[2](a) D. H. Winicur, J. L. Fraites, and F. A. Stackhouse, Chem. Phys. Lett. 23, 123 (1973). (b) D. H. Winicur and J. L. Fraites, J. Chem. Phys. 61, 1548 (1974).
[3]D. R. Herschbach, Adv. Chem. Phys. 10, 319 (1966).
[4]J. L. Kinsey, MTP Int. Rev. Sci., Phys. Chem. Ser. One 9, 173 (1972).
[5]K. T. Gillen, A. M. Rulis, and R. B. Bernstein, J. Chem. Phys. 54, 2831 (1971).
[6](a) S. A. Edelstein and P. Davidovits, J. Chem. Phys. 55, 5164 (1971). (b) J. Maya and P. Davidovits, *ibid.* 59, 3143 (1973). (c) J. Maya and P. Davidovits, *ibid.* 61, 1082 (1974).
[7]P. W. Hoff, J. C. Swingle, and C.K. Rhodes, Appl. Phys. Lett. 23, 245 (1973).
[8]H. A. Koehler, L. J. Ferderber, D. L. Redhead, and P. J. Ebert, Phys. Rev. A 9, 768 (1974).
[9]S. K. Searles and G. A. Hart, Appl. Phys. Lett. 25, 79 (1974).
[10]J. E. Velazco and D. W. Setser, Chem. Phys. Lett. 25, 197 (1974).
[11]L. G. Piper, J. E. Velazco, and D. W. Setser, J. Chem. Phys. 59, 3323 (1973).
[12]J. Tellinghuisen, Chem. Phys. Lett. 29, 359 (1974).
[13]L. G. Piper, D. W. Setser, and M. A. A. Clyne, J. Chem. Phys. (to be submitted).
[14]M. G. Golde and B. A. Thrush, Chem. Phys. Lett. 29, 486 (1974).
[15]L. A. Gundel, M. A. A. Clyne, J. A. Coxon, and D. W. Setser, Chem. Phys. Lett. (to be submitted).
[16]D. H. Stedman and D. W. Setser, J. Chem. Phys. 52, 3957 (1970).
[17]J. Tellinghuisen, J. A. Coxon, and D. W. Setser (to be published).

Reprinted with the permission of the American Institute of Physics from *Applied Physics Letters,* Vol. 27(4), pp. 243-245 (August 15, 1975).

Stimulated emission at 281.8 nm from XeBr†

S. K. Searles and G. A. Hart*

Laser Physics Branch, Optical Sciences Division, Naval Research Laboratory, Washington, D. C. 20375
(Received 19 May 1975)

Xenon with 0.10–4% Br_2 was excited by an e-beam device over the range 10–3000 Torr. Stimulated emission was observed on the transition $XeBr^* \rightarrow Xe + Br + h\nu$ (281.8 nm). Proof of laser emission and mechanistic details are discussed.

PACS numbers: 42.60.C, 82.20.M

Previous excimer lasers have been confined to stimulated emission from Xe_2^*, Kr_2^*, Ar_2^*, XeO^*, and KrO^*. Recent studies[1–3] confirmed the existence of a new class of excimers RX^*, where R is a rare gas atom, X is a halogen atom, and $*$ denotes the first excited electronic state of the molecule. We wish to report the first rare gas halide excimer laser. The kinetics of this laser are described by a three-step mechanism:

$$\vec{e} + Xe \rightarrow Xe^* + \vec{e}, \quad (1)$$

$$Xe^* + Br_2 \rightarrow XeBr^* + Br, \quad (2)$$

$$XeBr^* \rightarrow Xe + Br + h\nu \text{ (281.8 nm)}. \quad (3)$$

Xe^* generated by a high-energy electron beam device reacts with Br_2 at a gas kinetic rate (4.6×10^{-10}, Ref. 1; $2.0\pm0.4\times10^{-9}$ cm^3/sec, Ref. 4) to produce $XeBr^*$ which undergoes a bound-free transition with a lifetime of 17.5 ± 2.5 ns.[4]

The experimental facility was essentially the same apparatus as was used in earlier laser studies.[5,6] Figure 1 shows a schematic drawing of the diode and laser cell. The diode injected a 50-ns-long pulse of 433-kV electrons into the laser cell through a 37.5-μ-thick Inconel 750-X foil[7] supported by a foil holder with fourteen 0.95-cm-diam holes as the open area. The total beam energy measured in the cell with this foil—foil-support configuration was 36 J. An ITT F-4018-S5 photodiode was used to monitor side emission while an ITT F-4115 photodiode was used to monitor laser emission.

99.995% pure Xe was condensed directly into a cold

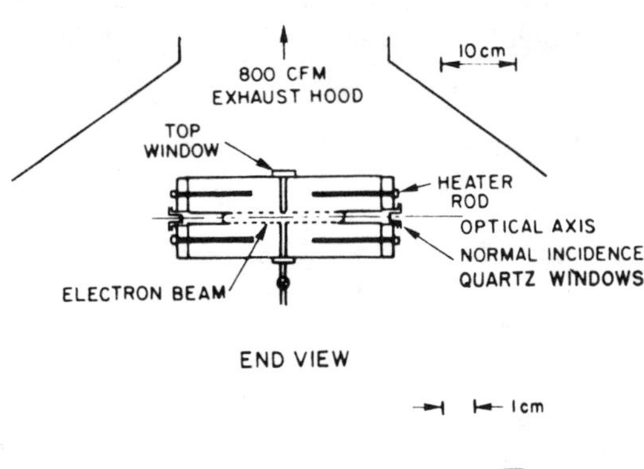

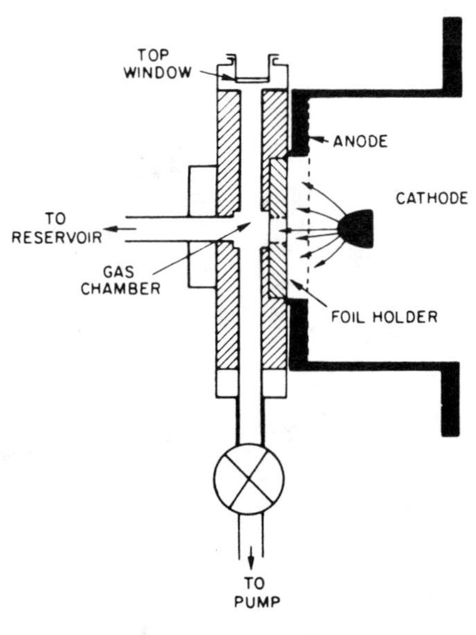

FIG. 1. Diode and laser cell drawn to scale. An *LC* generator connected to a water-filled folded Blumlein transmission line was used to energize the carbon cathode.

finger from the supplier's tank. The Xe pressure required for the experiments was controlled cryogenically. Analytical reagent-grade Br_2 was placed in a separate cold finger and thoroughly degassed. The Br_2 pressure was also temperature controlled. The two gases were mixed turbulently and then admitted to the laser cell.

Initially, a series of experiments were performed with 1–4% Br_2. This relatively high percentage of bromine was chosen to allow the desired energy transfer process of step (2) to effectively compete with the dimerization loss step

$$Xe^* + 2Xe \rightarrow Xe_2^* + Xe, \quad (4)$$

which becomes increasingly important at high xenon pressures. High pressures of xenon were investigated because of pumping and efficiency considerations. As the total gas pressure is increased the fraction of the incident e-beam energy absorbed becomes larger. A pressure of approximately 5000 Torr is required to attenuate the 433-kV primary beam by a factor of 2. High-pressure operation is thus more likely to provide the intense pumping needed to produce adequate gain on a bound-free transition. In addition the largest over-all laser efficiency is achieved at high pressure even though the laser efficiency for such e-beam-pumped systems is often calculated on the basis of the e-beam energy absorbed.

The result of these experiments was that the integrated fluorescence peaked in the region 500–1500 Torr with the intensity inversely proportional to the bromine concentration. Since Br_2 was clearly quenching $XeBr^*$, further experiments were carried out with only 0.1–1.0% Br_2. An optical gain of 4% per pass (15 cm of active length) was calculated from the peak fluorescence.

In order to increase the pumping, the e-beam foil holder was changed from a linear array of fourteen 0.95-cm holes to a slot 1.27×15 cm. Normal incidence flat quartz windows were installed on the optical axis and carefully aligned to minimize the loss due to the 4% reflection per window surface. Dielectric mirrors (> 99.5%, 3.12-m radius of curvature, 2.54-cm diameter) spaced 34.3 cm apart were used. The mirror separation distance is significant since it determines the number of amplifying passes which can occur during the brief time for which optical gain is present.

With a 760 Torr Xe–3.8 Torr Br_2 mixture laser emission was observed as evidenced by the following: (i) Laser emission disappeared when the far mirror was blocked. (ii) The laser spectrum was less than 0.75 nm wide at 281.8 nm while the fluorescence is a banded continuum over the range 230–360 nm. A comparison is presented in Fig. 2. (iii) As indicated in Fig. 3, the laser FWHM is much less than the fluorescence FWHM. (iv) The laser emission showed typical near-laser-threshold behavior displaying a highly nonlinear dependence on the side emission.

In conclusion laser emission was initially sought in xenon with 1–4% Br_2 because these mixtures allow high-pressure pumping where the e beam is strongly absorbed. Since Br_2 quenched $XeBr^*$ as evidenced by the decreasing fluorescence yields at high pressure, xenon with 0.1–1% Br_2 was subsequently investigated. The mixture and pressure with the greatest fluorescence was found to give stimulated emission. It is expected that the power of this new laser can be significantly in-

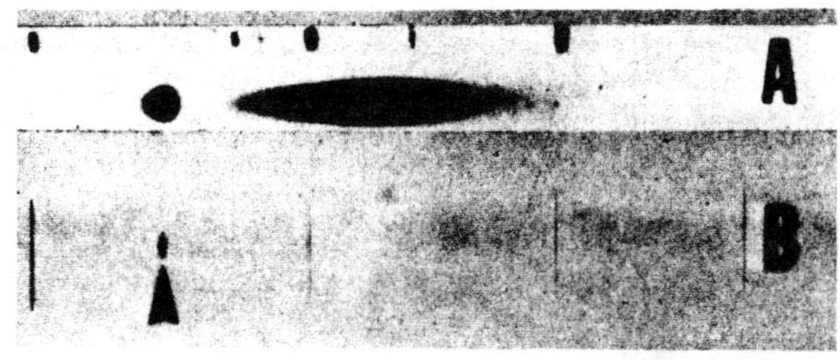

FIG. 2. Laser line narrowing. (a) Low-resolution fluorescence spectrum with Hg calibration lines. Extreme left Hg line is 253.652 nm and extreme right line is 365.015 nm. Filtered photodiode measurements showed the uv band to be more intense than the long-wavelength band in agreement with a previously published densitometer trace (Ref. 1). (b) High-resolution spectrum of Hg lines and laser emission which is denoted with an arrowhead.

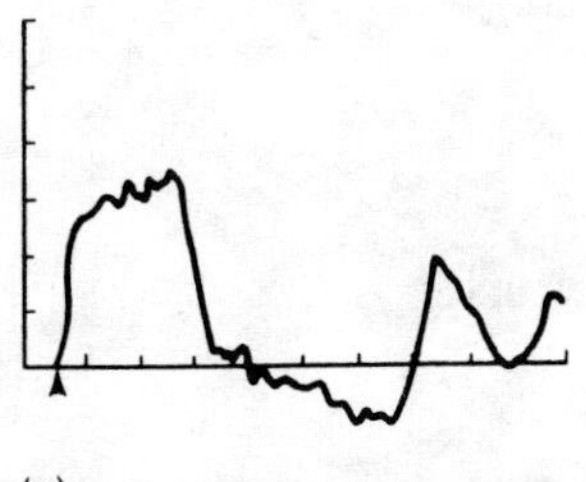

(a)

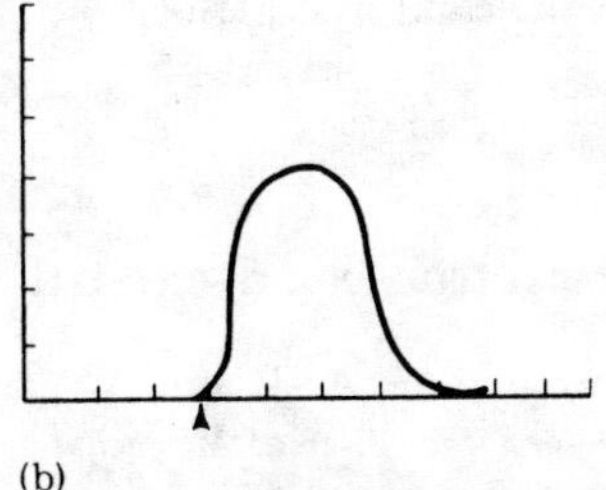

(b)

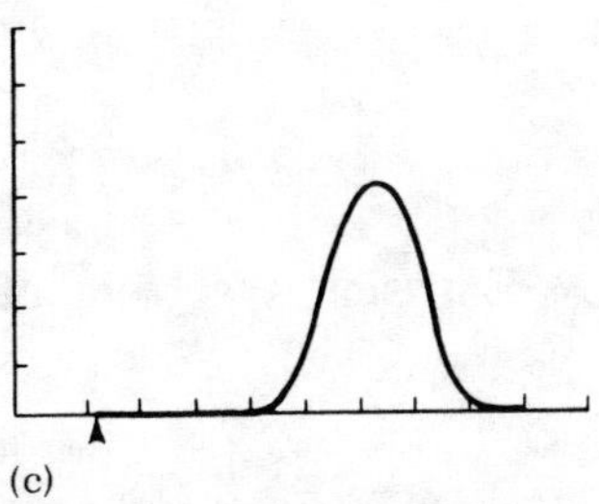

(c)

FIG. 3. Temporal comparison of the e-beam excitation, side fluorescence, and laser emission. The arrowheads mark the zero time point and baseline: (a) e-beam current. Events after the main 50-ns pulse do not cause excitation in the laser cell, 20 ns/div. (b) Fluorescence viewed through a Corning 250—390-nm bandpass filter, 20 ns/div. (c) Laser emission. Peak of 200 W occurs after peak fluorescence due to the low optical gain, 10 ns/div.

creased and that it can also be made to operate as a tunable high-power laser in this wavelength region of photochemical interest.

†Work supported in part by DARPA.

*NRC-NRL Postdoctoral Research Associate.

[1]J. E. Velazco and D. W. Setser, J. Chem. Phys. 62, 1990 (1975).

[2]M. F. Golde and B. A. Thrush, Chem. Phys. Lett. 29, 486 (1974).

[3]J. J. Ewing and C. A. Brau, Phys. Rev. A (to be published).

[4]G. A. Hart and S. K. Searles (unpublished).

[5]S. K. Searles and G. A. Hart, Appl. Phys. Lett. 25, 79 (1974).

[6]S. K. Searles, Appl. Phys. Lett. 25, 735 (1974).

[7]Warning: Bromine rapidly attacks titanium foil.

Reprinted with permission from *Physical Review A,* Vol. 12(1), pp. 129-132 (July 1975). ©1975 American Physical Society.

Emission spectrum of XeI* in electron-beam–excited Xe/I_2 mixtures*

J. J. Ewing and C. A. Brau
Avco Everett Research Laboratory, Inc., Everett, Massachusetts 02178
(Received 2 January 1975)

Emission spectra observed from electron-beam–excited atmospheric-pressure gas mixtures of Xe and I_2 are reported and analyzed in terms of an ionic alkali-halide-like excited state Xe^+I^-. A simple theory is given to analyze the observed spectra, and predictions of the uv spectra of other inert-gas monohalides are made. This class of molecules appears to offer interesting possibilities for production of new uv lasers.

INTRODUCTION

This paper describes the continuum emission spectrum of XeI* which is produced when mixtures of Ar/Xe/I_2 are irradiated with a high-intensity electron beam. A narrow band near 2535 Å is observed and assigned to the transition $(XeI)^*(^2\Sigma_{1/2}) \to XeI(^2\Sigma_{1/2})$. XeI is an unstable species which rapidly decays into Xe and I. Broader bands are observed at longer wavelengths, 3190 and 3610 Å, and are assigned to transitions which terminate on the $^2\Pi_{3/2}$ and $^2\Pi_{1/2}$ states of XeI. XeI* is a prototype of a set of inert-gas monohalides which should show similar emission continua in the ultraviolet region.[1]

A simple ionic-bonding model is used to predict that the primarily ionic molecule, Xe^+I^-, an excited state of XeI, is bound with respect to Xe and electronically excited $I(6s\,^4P)$. This "ionic" xenon halide, formed in our high-pressure experiments by rapid energy transfer and three-body processes, can radiate to the repulsive ground-state potentials of XeI. The ionic model can be used to estimate the binding energy of XeI* as well as the wavelengths of the emission bands which terminate on the repulsive lower-lying states. The diabatic Coulomb potential curve of Xe^+I^- crosses the Xe $+I^*$ potential curve at fairly large internuclear separations as shown in Fig. 1. This is not surprising since Xe* has an ionization energy comparable to the ionization energy of Cs, which forms ionic molecules with halogens. The large Coulomb binding energy leads to very large shifts in the molecular XeI spectra from the free-atom spectra. Such molecular emission bands could be ideal for an "excimer" or "molecular association" laser. XeI is not unique in this respect, and we make predictions of the approximate wavelengths for similar emission bands for other inert-gas halides.

EXPERIMENTAL DETAILS

Room-temperature mixtures of I_2 with Ar containing 8.5% Xe (total impurity limits ~5 ppm) and also I_2 with pure Xe (50-ppm impurities) were irradiated with a 0.4-MeV electron beam. The $1\times15\text{-cm}^2$ beam was produced by pulse charging a carbon cathode with a Marx generator (Ion Physics Corp.). The energy incident on the test gas is roughly 1 J/cm^2. The pulse time is 100 nsec. The primary electrons ionize and excite the Ar and Xe. This excitation eventually resides in the most bound excited electronic state which then radiates or is quenched. The kinetics of the latter is not yet known for Xe-I_2 mixtures, but three-body processes will be rapid at the pressures used and recombination into bound excited states occurs on a time scale of nanoseconds. Emission spectra were recorded on film (Kodak 103-O) using an $f/3.5$ Hilger quartz prism spectrograph with an entrance slit width of 100 μm; one to three shots gave sufficient film blackening. Time-resolved emission was observed with a 1P28 photomultiplier viewing the exit slit of a Spex 100-mm Micromate monochromator with a bandpass of typically 40 Å.

Figure 2 shows the emission spectrum of 25 lb/in.^{2} (absolute) of 8.5% Xe/Ar inert gas mixed with room temperature I_2 (density ~10^{16} cm^{-3}). These continuum bands do not appear when Ar/I_2 mixes are excited with the electron beam. Similarly, when mixtures of Xe and Ar or pure Xe without I_2 are irradiated, the continua are not observed.[2] Finally when pure Xe is mixed with I_2, the continuum bands are recovered. No evidence has been found on film or by photomultiplier of I_2 emission in the visible or uv. Since the continua require both I_2 and Xe but do not appear in Ar/I_2 mixtures, we conclude that they must arise from a xenon-iodine atom complex. Finally under the conditions of our experiment we do not anticipate that the I_2 will exist for very long during the electron-beam pulse. I_2 will be removed by the processes of energy transfer from Xe* and Xe_2^*, dissociative attachment by the slow electrons and photodissociation in the visible and most especially in the vacuum uv, where the Xe_2^* excimer band overlaps the I_2 (X $\to$ I) band.[3] Experimental study and detailed computer modeling of the kinetics of

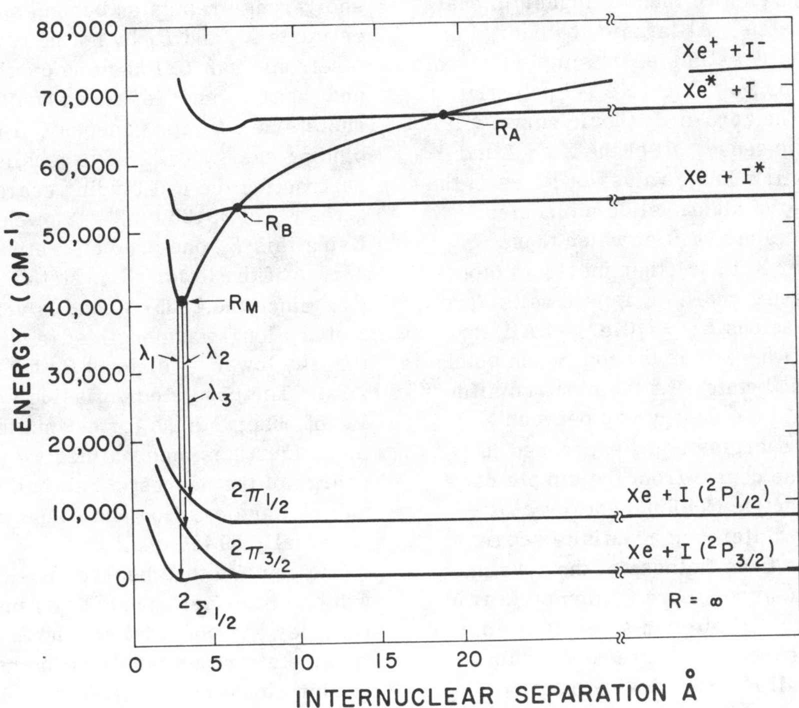

FIG. 1. Estimated potential curves for XeI.

these processes are currently under way.

The emission band at 2535 Å has a fairly sharp edge at ~2549 Å, and about 95% of the emission is found between about 2510 and 2549 Å. This band is noticeably asymmetric and shades off into the blue, indicating that the lower-state potential energy curve for this bound-to-free transition is not changing rapidly with internuclear separation. The 3190 and 3610-Å bands are broad and fairly symmetric, being ~1500 and 4120 cm^{-1} wide, respectively, probably terminating on strongly repulsive lower-state potentials.

IONIC MODEL FOR XeI*

The spectrum observed can be interpreted by the potential energy diagram shown in Fig. 1.

At infinite internuclear separation one has Xe $+I(^2P_{3/2})$ at zero energy, Xe $+I(^2P_{1/2})$ at 7819 cm^{-1}, Xe $+I(^4P)$ at 54633 cm^{-1} (labeled as Xe $+$I*), $Xe(^3P_2)+I(^2P_{3/2})$ at 67078 cm^{-1} (labeled as Xe* $+$I), and $Xe^+ + I^-$ at 73128 cm^{-1}. $Xe^+ + I^-$ is lower in energy than $Xe^+ + e + I$ by an amount equal to the electron affinity of iodine.[4] For simplicity, only the lowest-lying excited states are shown. As R decreases the low-lying ^2P states are split into $^2\Sigma_{1/2}$, $^2\Pi_{3/2}$, and $^2\Pi_{1/2}$ states.[3] These molecular potentials should be repulsive at small R. The $^2\Sigma_{1/2}$ state lies lowest since the p orbital hole on the I atom points directly at the electron-rich Xe atom. The $^2\Pi$ states, however, put two p electrons in the immediate vicinity of Xe and hence should be considerably more repulsive than the $^2\Sigma_{1/2}$ state.

Similarly the ^2P Xe^+ and the ^1S I^- ions will produce $^2\Sigma_{1/2}$ and $^2\Pi_{1/2,3/2}$ states having the same order as the lower states for similar reasons. At

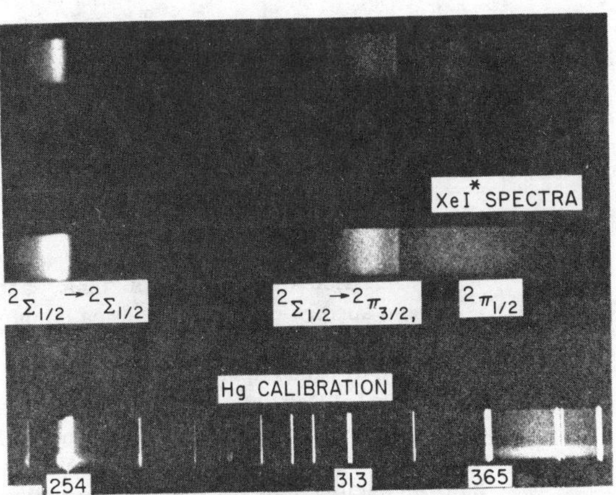

FIG. 2. Emission spectra of Ar/Xe/I_2 mixes. Top, 1 shot; middle, 3 shots; bottom, Hg calibration.

the minimum of the ionic curve, the $^2\Pi$ states of XeI^* will probably be more than kT higher in energy than the $^2\Sigma$ ion state. At large R the energy of the ion pair is readily estimated by simple Coulomb attraction, while the $Xe+I^*$ and Xe^*+I potential curves are flat. The zero-order ionic curve will cross, in a diabatic sense, all of the Xe^*+I and I^*+Xe curves at fairly large values of R, as in the more familiar case of alkali halide molecules.[5]

Table I lists the values of R at which these crossings occur for XeI and other inert gas monohalides. The crossing radii, in atomic units, are given by the expressions $R_A^{-1} = V_I(Xe^*) - EA(I)$ and $R_B^{-1} = V_I - EA + E_D$, where V_I is the ionization potential of the Xe excited state, EA the electron affinity of iodine, and E_D the energy gap between Xe^*+I and $Xe+I^*$, all energies being expressed in atomic units. These derive from the simple condition that the attractive Coulomb energy e^2/R be equal to the energy difference at infinite separation. Any deviation from flatness of the covalent potential or deviation from pure Coulombic attraction for the ion pair will alter this result of course. Deviations can be expected for crossings which would occur at small R. The closer crossing, R_B, may never occur for some of the inert-gas monohalides such as ArI. For XeI^*, R_A and R_B are sufficiently large that the lowest excited state potential will be predominantly ionic in nature.

The ionic curve drops in energy to R_M, where short-range repulsion becomes important. We estimate R_M and E_M by noting that the nearly isoelectronic salt CsI has comparable ionic binding, and that Cs^+ and Xe^+ ions should have about the same size. R_M for gaseous CsI is 3.32 Å,[6] and the binding energy relative to ions is 97.4 kcal/mole.[7] Subtracting the CsI binding energy from $E(Xe^+ + I^-)$ gives E_M of 39135 cm^{-1}. E_M would be 39135 cm^{-1}. Using this E_M one predicts emission to occur at 2555 Å if the lower $^2\Sigma_{1/2}$ state has zero energy at R_M. Since the 2535-Å band is very narrow and has a sharp long-wavelength edge, the presumption that the lower $^2\Sigma$ state is flat at R_M is probably good. The predicted emission wavelength is within 1% of observed; so for estimating the spectra of other inert gas monohalides we will use the binding energy of the nearest alkali halide. The observed $^2\Sigma \rightarrow {}^2\Sigma$ band position and shape implies E_M (XeI^*) is actually 39 450 cm^{-1}.

One can use the observed positions and spectral widths of the XeI^* bands to estimate the lower-state energies and potential gradients at R_M. In the upper state roughly 95% of the molecules will be in vibrational states. $v = 0, \ldots, 4$, assuming a vibrational temperature of 300°K. Using the molecular constants of CsI, we estimate the spread in R accessible to the XeI^* molecules from the rms value of $(R - R_M)/R_M$ for a harmonic oscillator,

TABLE I. Estimated features of inert-gas monohalides.

Molecule	R_A (Å)	R_B (Å)	R_M (Å)	E_M (cm^{-1})	λ_1 (nm)	λ_2 (nm)	λ_3 (nm)
XeI	19.2	6.3	3.3	39 135	256	302	342
XeBr	32.0	15.9	3.1	34 272	292	354	407
XeCl	71.9	a	2.9	30 860	324	402	417
XeF	39.6	a	2.35	25 895	386	503	512
KrI[b]	14.1	3.5	3.2	54 000	185	208	247
KrBr	19.9	5.2	2.9	49 353	203	231	252
KrCl	30.5	9.8	2.8	45 592	219	253	258
KrF	22.7	a	2.27	39 229	256	301	305
ArBr[c,b]	17.0	3.2	2.8	62 152	161	178	190
ArCl[c,d]	24.1	4.5	2.7	58 042	172	192	195
ArF[c]	18.9	a	2.17	37 484	267	318	322
NeF[c,b,e]	9.6	2.6	1.93	93 266	107	115	115

[a]These species have halogen excited-state levels only above the inert-gas excitation levels. Hence no R_B crossing occurs.

[b]These species will not be as "ionic" as those with large R_B.

[c]These spectra could be complicated due to multiple excited states because of the smaller spin orbit splitting in Ar^+ and Ne^+.

[d]The ArCl bands appear at 170 nm (λ_1) and 175 nm (λ_2, λ_3) in low-pressure discharge flow experiments, Ref. 9; λ_1 apparently is predicted within 1% while λ_2, λ_3 are within 10%.

[e]For ArI, NeI, NeBr, NeCl, and the helium halides the inert-gas ionization potential is so large that the Coulomb curve does not make up sufficient energy to approach the low-lying halogen excited states. These compounds should only have small well depths and the molecular continua should be near the free atom lines. Possibly ionic states of the opposite polarity, viz. $Ne^- + I^+$, could enter into the binding.

$[2B\omega^{-1}(v+\frac{1}{2})]^{1/2}$, apparently an adequate estimate for the alkali halides.[8] We calculate a total R width of 0.3 Å for $v = 4$. From the plates, we estimate the 95% widths to be 650 cm^{-1}, 1500 cm^{-1}, and 4120 cm^{-1}. The width of the bands in excess of $2kT$ is attributable to a slope in the lower-state potential curve. For $^2\Sigma_{1/2}$ the slope is about 670 cm^{-1} Å^{-1}, again indicating that this state is not in the region of strong repulsion at R_M. The $^2\Pi_{3/2}$ slope is estimated to be 5000 cm^{-1} Å^{-1}, $^2\Pi_{1/2}$ is 13 700 cm^{-1} Å^{-1}. We do not understand why the $^2\Pi_{1/2}$ band is broader.

The center of the $^2\Pi$ bands locates the energies of these repulsive states at R_M. $^2\Pi_{3/2}$ is at about 8100 cm^{-1}, while $^2\Pi_{1/2}$ is ~4150 cm^{-1} above its separated-atom limit of $^2P_{1/2}$.

These pieces of information then can be used to make crude estimates of the emission spectra of the other inert-gas monohalides as given in Table I. The rules for obtaining Table I are: E_M is determined by subtracting the bond energy of the nearest alkali halide from the infinite-R ion pair energy (CsBr is used for XeBr*, etc.); R_A and R_B are obtained by assuming the covalent potentials are flat for all R; the $^2\Sigma \to {}^2\Sigma$ band position is estimated by assuming the $^2\Sigma_{1/2}$ ground state has zero energy at R_M; the $^2\Pi$ states energies at R_M are estimated to be 6000 cm^{-1} (the average of our $^2\Pi_{3/2}$ and $^2\Pi_{1/2}$ XeI repulsions) above their respective infinite-separation values. We feel these estimates will predict the emission wavelengths to within 10%, and future measurements should give better estimates of the potentials of other inert-gas halides.

Note added. Since the submission of this paper a communication by Velazco and Setser[10] has appeared substantially confirming the predictions for the $\Sigma \to \Sigma$ bands of XeCl, XeBr, and XeF. Peak wavelengths appear at: XeI, 252 nm; XeBr, 278 nm; XeCl, 304 nm; and XeF, 346 nm. The spectra they observe are broader since their work is done at low pressures and they observe emission from species which do not have time to vibrationally relax before emitting uv photons. The peak wavelengths are in agreement with recent data on these species obtained in our high-pressure experiments. Also a paper by Golde and Thrush[11] on ArCl emission has appeared making many of the same arguments about the ionic binding in this molecule. As pointed out in the table, the wavelength for ArCl emission is in good agreement with our prediction for the $\Sigma \to \Sigma$ transition.

---

*This work was supported by Advanced Research Projects Agency, Department of Defense, and monitored by Office of Naval Research under Contract No. N00014-75-C-0063.

[1]D. L. King and D. W. Setser, in Fourth Conference on Chemical and Molecular Lasers, St. Louis, 1974, Paper WA1 (unpublished).

[2]We do see the XeO "auroral line" continua in the green, and an unidentified band near 3290 Å when "pure" Ar/Xe or Xe is excited with the electron beam.

[3]G. Herzberg, *Spectra of Diatomic Molecules* (Van Nostrand, Princeton, N. J., 1963); R. S. Mulliken, J. Chem. Phys. 55, 288 (1971); J. A. Myer and J. A. R. Samson, *ibid.* 52, 716 (1970).

[4]C. E. Moore, *Atomic Energy Levels*, Natl. Bur. Stds. Circ. 467 (U. S. GPO, Washington, D. C., 1962); R. S. Berry and C. W. Reimann, J. Chem. Phys. 38, 1540 (1963).

[5]J. L. Magee, J. Chem. Phys. 8, 6817 (1940); R. S. Mulliken, Phys. Rev. 50, 1017 (1963); 50, 1028 (1963).

[6]C. H. Townes and A. L. Schawlow, *Microwave Spectroscopy* (McGraw-Hill, New York, 1955).

[7]Y. P. Varshni and R. C. Shukla, J. Mol. Spectrosc. 16, 63 (1965).

[8]S. A. Rice and W. Klemperer, J. Chem. Phys. 27, 573 (1957).

[9]D. H. Stedman and D. W. Setser, Prog. React. Kinet. 6, 193 (1971).

[10]J. E. Velazco and D. W. Setser, J. Chem. Phys. 62, 1990 (1975).

[11]M. G. Golde and B. A. Thrush, Chem. Phys. Lett. 29, 486 (1974).

Reprinted with permission from *Applied Physics Letters,* Vol. 27(8), pp. 435-437 (October 15, 1975).

354-nm laser action on XeF†

C. A. Brau and J. J. Ewing

Avco Everett Research Laboratory, Inc., Everett, Massachusetts 02149

This letter reports laser action on the xenon monofluoride $^2\Sigma_{1/2} \rightarrow {}^2\Sigma_{1/2}$ band at 354 nm. Lasing on discrete vibrational bands has been achieved by pulse excitation of high-pressure mixtures of F_2/Xe/Ar with an electron beam. XeF is a member of a new class of diatmoic molecules, the noble gas monohalides, which all exhibit similar molecular structure and spectra, and laser action should be attainable on the various bands of other members of this class of molecules. The kinetics and loss mechanisms of these laser candidates are briefly discussed.

We have recently been studying the spectroscopy,[1] kinetics, and laser potential of a new class of molecules, the noble-gas monohalides. The possibility of laser action on bound-free transitions in molecules of this type was first suggested by Setser and co-workers.[2,3] Recently, Searles and Hart demonstrated laser action on the 282-nm transition in XeBr.[4] This letter reports e-beam—excited laser action on XeF at 354 nm. The laser transition originates on an excited state formed directly by chemical reactions in e-beam—excited Xe/F_2 mixtures. It terminates on a high vibrational level of the slightly bound XeF ground state. XeF is the one member of this class of molecules which, theoretically, should have both the highest intrinsic grain and the lowest intrinsic loss of this class of molecules.

The salient features of these diatomic molecules can be understood in terms of the approximate XeF potential-energy curves shown in Fig. 1. The lowest states of XeF and the other inert-gas halides are covalent in nature and have molecular symmetry $^2\Sigma_{1/2}$, $^2\pi_{3/2}$, and $^2\pi_{1/2}$. The covalent $^2\Sigma$ state is slightly bound while the $^2\pi$ states are repulsive. The binding energy of the $^2\Sigma$ state of XeF is probably of the order of 8000 cm^{-1}.[5] Transitions from the higher-lying excited states can be either bound to bound, as in the $^2\Sigma_{1/2} \rightarrow {}^2\Sigma_{1/2}$ 354-nm XeF lasing transition, or bound to free, as in the $^2\Sigma_{1/2} \rightarrow {}^2\pi_{1/2,3/2}$ transitions.

The higher-lying excited states of XeF, and the other noble-gas monohalides, are predominantly ionic in nature, having the polarity Xe^+F^-.[1] This ion pair is entirely analogous to an alkali halide both in binding energy and in gross structural properties. The ionic excited states have molecular symmetry $^2\Sigma_{1/2}$, $^2\pi_{3/2}$, or $^2\pi_{1/2}$, with the $^2\Sigma_{1/2}$ ionic state lying lowest.

The possibility of laser action on these species is apparently enhanced by a large reactive cross section for producing excited species by chemical reactions of the type

$$Xe^* + F_2 \rightarrow XeF^* + F. \tag{1}$$

The measured rates for the analogous reactions of Xe* + Cl_2 or Br_2 are quite large.[3] Apparently these chemical reactions, which start on an excited potential-energy surface of the Xe + X_2 triatomic system, have a high probability of staying on an excited potential surface, producing the electronically excited species with a large rate constant.

The estimated stimulated emission coefficient for the $^2\Sigma_{1/2} \rightarrow {}^2\Sigma_{1/2}$ band in XeF is about 2×10^{-16} cm^2. This estimate is based on the measured spontaneous emission spectrum and the radiative lifetime, whose measurement will be described in a separate article. We have studied the spontaneous emission spectrum of XeF as a function of pressure and find that at pressures above about one-half atmosphere the upper state remains in vibrational equilibrium. The laser transition evidently originates from the lowest vibrational level of the excited state. Since the equilibrium bond length of the excited state[1] is apparently larger than that of the ground state,[5] it is believed that the laser transition terminates on a high vibrational level of the lower state, as shown in Fig. 1. The bandwidths of the $^2\Sigma \rightarrow {}^2\Sigma$ transitions in the other xenon halides are somewhat larger. This is due to the fact that the other xenon halides have more closely spaced vibrational levels in both lower and upper states, and the spectra appear more like continua. The $^2\Sigma \rightarrow {}^2\pi$ transitions in both XeF and the other xenon halides are considerably broader since these transitions are truly bound to free. Stimulated emission coefficients of the order of 10^{-18} cm^2 are calculated for these broad bands.

The lasing experiments were carried out in a high-vacuum high-pressure cell constructed of aluminum. Quartz optical windows, sealed to the cell with Viton o

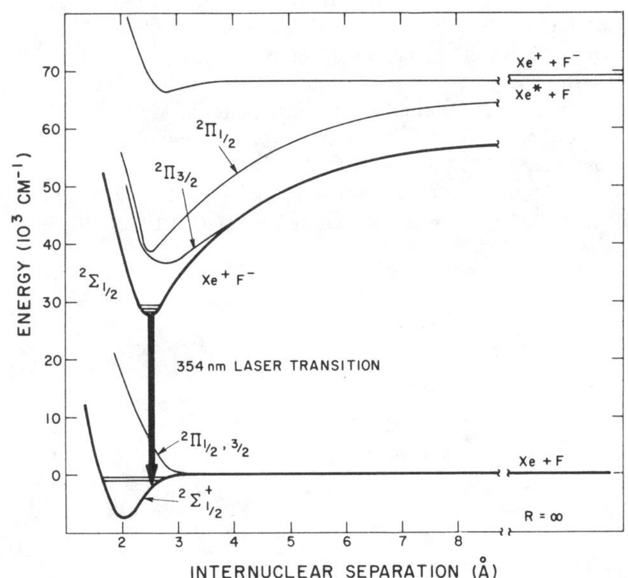

FIG. 1. Potential-energy curves for xenon fluoride.

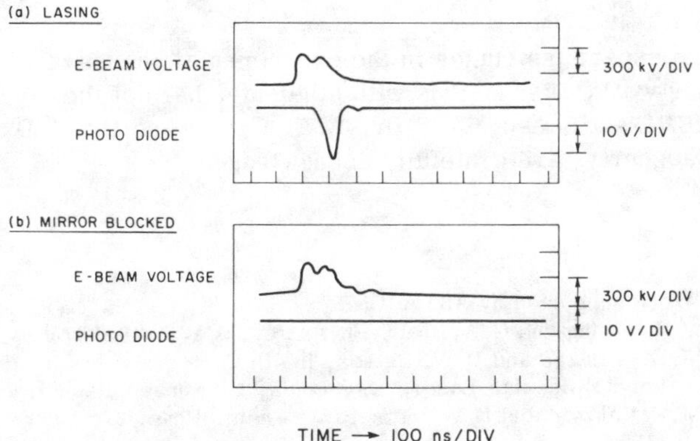

FIG. 2. XeF laser time history.

rings and a support structure, were located at the opposite ends of the cell. The optical aperture was about 1.2 cm in diameter. The volume between the windows was irradiated by a 100-ns pulsed e beam. The e beam, roughly 1×15 cm in area, was injected into the gas transverse to the laser cavity optical axis through a 2-mil aluminized kapton foil. The foil was supported by high-transparency aluminum-foil support. Pressures in the cell could be varied from high vacuum to pressures in excess of 5 atm. Since high pressure caused a measurable movement of the optical windows, as well as more frequent foil ruptures, most lasing experiments were performed at pressures under 4 atm. Gas mixtures were made up in a fully fluorine passivated stainless-steel system. The final gas mixes were placed in high-purity passivated stainless-steel sample bottles and allowed to stand for several hours before use.

During the mixing period, at room temperature, there is very little conversion of the Xe/F_2 mixtures into XeF_2. This has been determined by spectrophotometric measurements of the F_2 absorption in the uv. Irradiation of a sample with the e beam, however, converts a large fraction of the irradiated mixture into stable species such as XeF_2.[5] Thus, gas samples were discarded after being excited by the e beam. Typical mixture mole fractions were 0.001 F_2/0.003 Xe/0.996 Ar. Use of such Xe/Ar mixtures minimizes the amount of Xe_2^* and Ar_2^* that can be present during the e-beam pulse.

The e beam was formed between a cold-cathode electron-gun pulse charged to over 300 kV by an eight-stage Marx generator (Ion Physics Corporation). With an anode-cathode spacing of 1.3 cm, the current density impinging on the foil support structure was roughly 200 A/cm^2. Because of resistive and inductive voltage drops in the Marx generator, the beam voltage dropped by about 20% during the 100-ns pulse duration. The high voltage applied across the diode and the e beam formed therein was terminated after 100 ns by a spark-gap crowbar.

The optical cavity was formed by two curved mirrors (1 m in radius) having 99.97% reflectivity and 97.50% reflectivity at the wavelength of the XeF emission. The mirrors were external to the cell and separated by 30 cm. By carefully aligning the quartz optical windows, losses due to these surfaces could be minimized. Because of the proximity in wavelength of the Ar/N_2 $(C \rightarrow B)$ 358-nm laser transition, alignment could be readily and independently checked by producing laser action on this well studied molecular band.[6,7] Laser action on XeF could also be achieved using an 8% output coupling mirror. However, the laser power output and the gas-mixture pressure range over which one could achieve laser action was much more limited than was the case with the lower output coupling mirrors.

The output of the laser was directed onto a photodiode (ITT FW 128) and onto a spectrograph for temporal and spectral analysis of the laser-beam pulse. The laser beam was attenuated by a factor of 500 by passing through two 11% transmitting screens and a 350-nm filter ($\Delta\lambda = 35$ nm) before reaching the photodiode. The beam emerging from the other mirror was attenuated by a factor of 5 before reaching the entrance slit of an $f/10$ Hilger medium-resolution quartz spectrograph. Spectrograph slit widths of 20 μ were utilized, giving a resolution of about 0.1 nm at 354 nm. Spectra were recorded on Kodak 103-O plates.

Figure 2 shows typical photodiode and e-beam voltage signals obtained in lasing and nonlasing experiments. The stimulated emission intensity was a factor of 100 times brighter than the spontaneous emission intensity in the same band as measured by the photodiode signals. The stimulated emission typically started about 50 ns after the beginning of the e-beam pulse and lasted about 50 ns, at which time the electron beam was turned off. Peak powers of the order of 6 kW were attained. The intensity of the XeF laser beam was comparable to that from a mixture of 5% N_2 in Ar at the same pressure. A complete parametric optimization of the XeF system remains to be done. The spontaneous emission spectrum is considerably different from the stimulated emission spectrum. A comparison of the spectral plates and their microdensitometer tracings shows that the spontaneous emission band contains many vibrational bands while the laser spectrum shows two very pronounced and two weak vibrational bands. The strongest lines in the laser are also the strongest lines in the spontaneous emission spectrum. The integrated photodiode signal corresponds to a laser efficiency of the order of 0.01%. This efficiency is based on the energy deposited in the gas by the e beam, which is estimated from the incident e-beam current density using the stopping power tables of Berger and Seltzer.[8] Optimization of the laser mixtures, pumping power, and output coupling should increase this number.

The population inversion on XeF is caused by reactions of two kinds. First, F_2 can react with electronically excited xenon, Xe*, reaction (1). The Xe* is formed by rapid energy transfer[9] from Ar* and Ar_2^* which are produced by the electron beam.

The XeF* ionic excited state can also be formed by the rapid termolecular recombination of Xe^+ ions with F^- ions:

$$Xe^+ + F^- + M \rightarrow XeF^* + M. \quad (2)$$

These ion neutralization processes can have huge three-body rates.[10] The F^- is formed by dissociative attachment of electrons to the F_2 in the gas:

$$e^- + F_2 \rightarrow F + F^-. \quad (3)$$

Detailed modelling of the kinetics of this new laser needs to be completed however.

It is possible that the inversion can be sustained in this laser transition by the vibrational relaxation of the high-lying vibrational levels which are the lower laser levels in this transition. We do not yet know if this is possible.

Of this class of molecules, XeF stands out as having the potential for the highest gain and the lowest loss. It has higher gain than other species such as XeI because of its longer wavelength and distinctly structured spectrum. More important, however, this band in XeF is not overlapped by self-absorption by the XeF* to higher-lying states, it does not have halogen-molecule absorption, as does the $XeCl/Cl_2$ system, and it is below the threshold for photoionization of both Ar* and Xe* metastables. Although laser action on the $^2\Sigma - {}^2\Sigma$ bands of other xenon halides is apparently possible, we anticipate that XeF will have the lowest intrinsic loss of this family of molecules.

The authors wish to thank James Dodge for invaluable and expert assistance in the experimental phases of this work. Discussions with other members of the AERL staff, especially Dr. R. E. Center and Dr. J. D. Daugherty, are gratefully acknowledged.

†Work supported by ARPA/ONR.

[1]J. J. Ewing and C. A. Brau, Phys. Rev. A **12**, 129 (1975).
[2]J. E. Velazco and D. W. Setser, in 4th Conference in Chemical and Molecular Lasers, St. Louis, 1974 (unpublished).
[3]J. E. Velazco and D. W. Setser, J. Chem. Phys. **62**, 1990 (1975).
[4]S. K. Searles and G. A. Hart (private communication).
[5]N. Bartlett and F. U. Sladky, *The Chemistry of Krypton, Xenon and Radon in Comprehensive Inorganic Chemistry*, edited by J. C. Bailar (Pergamon, London, 1973).
[6]E. R. Ault, M. L. Bhaumik, and N. Thomas Olson, IEEE J. Quantum Electron **10**, 624 (1974).
[7]S. Searles and G. A. Hart, Appl. Phys. Lett. **25**, 79 (1974).
[8]M. J. Berger and S. M. Seltzer, National Academy of Science Report No. 1133 (1964) (unpublished).
[9]O. Cheshnovsky, B. Raz, and J. Jortner, J. Chem. Phys. **59**, 337 (1973).
[10]J. J. Thompson, Philos. Mag. **47**, 337 (1924).

Laser action on the $^2\Sigma^+_{1/2} \rightarrow {}^2\Sigma^+_{1/2}$ bands of KrF and XeCl[†]

J. J. Ewing and C. A. Brau

Avco Everett Research Laboratory, Incorporated, Everett, Massachusetts 02149
(Received 17 June 1975)

This letter describes two new lasers operating on the $^2\Sigma^+_{1/2} \rightarrow {}^2\Sigma^+_{1/2}$ bands of XeCl (at 308 nm) and KrF (at 249 nm). Pumping was achieved by high-intensity electron beam excitation of high-pressure Ar containing small amounts of Xe and Cl_2 or Kr and F_2. An efficiency of about 0.4% was observed in the initial experiments on KrF, and higher efficiencies appear possible.

PACS numbers: 51.70., 42.60.C

Recently we reported stimulated emission on the $^2\Sigma^+_{1/2} \rightarrow {}^2\Sigma^+_{1/2}$ band of XeF at 353 nm.[1] Searles and Hart have also reported laser action on the comparable band of XeBr at 282 nm.[2] This letter reports laser action on corresponding bands of two other members of this class of new molecular lasers, namely, XeCl (at 308 nm) and KrF (at 248 nm).

The experimental apparatus has been described previously.[1] A Marx generator is used to impulse charge a cold-cathode electron beam gun to about 350 kV for about 100 ns. This produces a pulsed electron beam having a current density of roughly 150 A/cm^2 into the gas over an area 15×1 cm. At an Ar pressure of 50 psia, the power deposited in the gas is about 1.3 MW/cm^3, corresponding to a total energy of about 2 J in the 15-cm^3 laser volume. The laser optical cavity was formed by two reflectors positioned outside the cell and separated by about 30 cm. uv-grade quartz flats were used for the cell windows, and were optically aligned normal to the laser axis to minimize reflection losses. Absorption by the windows at 250 nm was about 1% per window. The output of the laser cavity was viewed at one end with a planar photodiode [ITT F4000(S5)], and at the other end of the cavity by either a $\frac{1}{2}$-m Hilger quartz spectrograph or a Scientech model 360203 energy meter.

Laser action from XeCl was obtained with a mixture of Ar, Xe, and Cl_2 in the ratio 89.9:10:0.1. The cavity output coupling was 0.5% out of each mirror, for a total output coupling of 1%. Lasing could be achieved only at pressures in excess of 30 psia. Laser action could not be achieved with a mixture containing substantially more Cl_2, viz., 89:10:1. This is not surprising since the XeCl band is overlapped by Cl_2 absorption.[3] This introduces a loss of about 6% per pass in the 0.1% Cl_2 lasing mixture. However, this loss might be avoided by using a different chlorine-bearing compound in place of Cl_2. Figure 1 shows an oscillogram of the photodiode signal from the XeCl laser. The laser intensity was attenuated by a factor of 100 before reach-

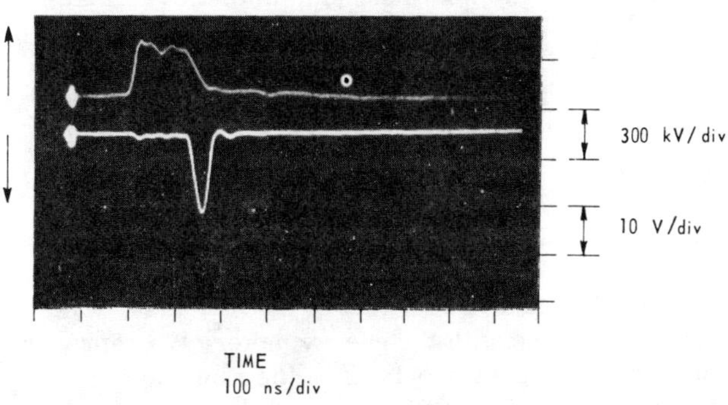

FIG. 1. Oscillogram of XeCl laser emission intensity. Upper trace, e-beam voltage. Lower trace, photodiode signal. Laser intensity attenuated by 10^2.

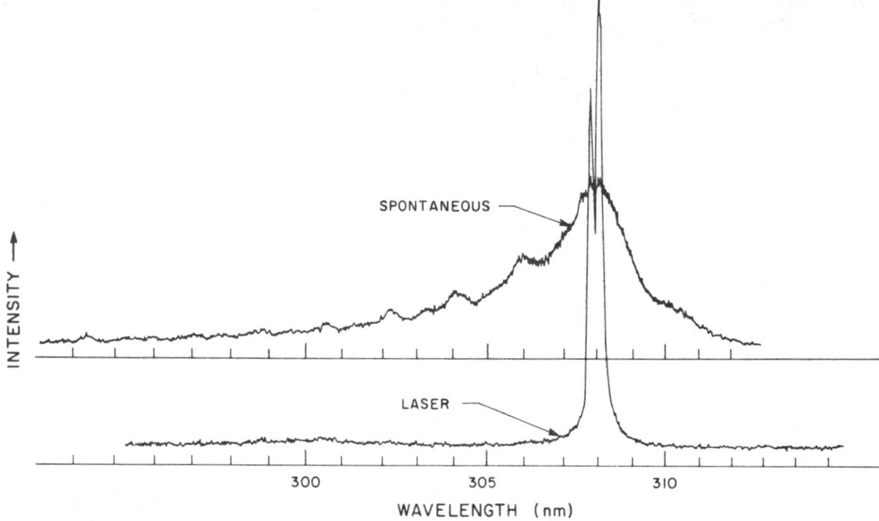

FIG. 2. Comparison of spontaneous and laser emission spectra from XeCl.

ing the photodiode. Note that the e-beam is on for about 100 ns before laser oscillation begins. The small photodiode signal appearing before the laser pulse is spontaneous emission leaking through the 0.5% transmitting laser reflector at wavelengths where the mirrors have larger transmission, $\lambda < 300$ nm, $\lambda > 350$ nm. The peak laser power as measured by the photodiode was roughly 3 kW. Measurements of the total energy output were difficult because they were small, of the order of 50 μJ or less. Laser action could not be achieved with one mirror blocked. Figure 2 shows a comparison of the XeCl spontaneous and stimulated emission spectra. We do not yet understand the origin of the two peaks in the laser spectrum. The spectroscopy of these molecules at high pressure is discussed in a lengthier paper.[4]

In contrast to XeCl, KrF laser action was easily achieved over a broad pressure range from 15 psia to 60 psia with laser reflectors having $\lesssim \frac{1}{2}$% output coupling. As in the XeF and XeCl lasers, the power output increased with increasing pressure. The most intense laser emission was obtained from mixtures of Ar, Kr, and F_2 in the ratio 98.9:1:0.1. Figure 3 shows a typical oscillogram of the KrF laser intensity as monitored by the photodiode. The laser turns on very soon after the e-beam has reached full voltage, and stays on for the duration of the e-beam pulse. The KrF laser pulse durations are longer than those observed from XeF, and show no sign of bottlenecking in the lower laser level. In comparing the weak XeCl laser signal shown in Fig. 1 to the KrF signal shown in Fig. 3, it should be noted that the KrF laser beam intensity has been attenuated by a factor of 2×10^4 before reaching the photodiode. The KrF laser intensity is 5000 times brighter than the unattenuated spontaneous emission intensity as measured both with the photodiode and on film. Laser action could not be achieved with one laser reflector blocked. The output of the KrF laser was easily measured with the energy meter. We reproducibly measured energy outputs in the range 3–4 mJ from one end. Since both reflectors had the same nominal output coupling, the total energy output was of the order of 6–8 mJ. This corresponds to a laser efficiency of about 0.4%, based on the energy deposited into the gas in the optical cavity. This efficiency can probably be increased with greater output coupling, since the transition appears to be saturated and the window losses exceed the output coupling. Figure 4 shows a comparison of the spntaneous and stimulated emission spectra of KrF. To our knowledge, this is the first published spectrum of this molecule, and the band position agrees well with predictions.[4,5]

The potential efficiency of the rare-gas halide lasers may be much higher than we have obtained in these preliminary experiments. Initially, the electron beam ionizes and excites the argon buffer. However, the ions rapidly recombine to form excited states[6] which transfer their energy to the krypton or xenon.[7] The excited rare-gas halides are then formed by reactions of the type

$$Kr^* + F_2 \rightarrow KrF^* + F. \tag{1}$$

Additional excited rare-gas halides may be formed by dissociative attachment of electrons to the F_2, followed by three-body Thompson recombination of the F^- ions with Kr^+ ions. The ultimate efficiency will depend on the efficiency of reaction (1) for producing excited states. Since the energy required to form an argon ion or excited state with an electron beam is roughly 20.6 eV,[6] the effective quantum efficiency of a KrF laser, for example, is 24%. If a discharge were used to pump the krypton metastable levels directly, the effective

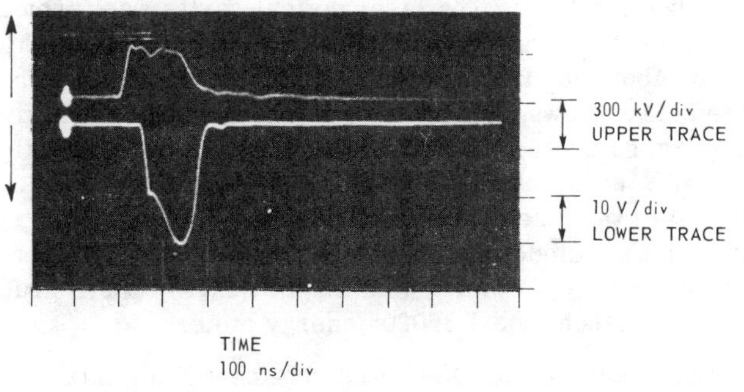

FIG. 3. Oscillogram of KrF laser emission intensity.

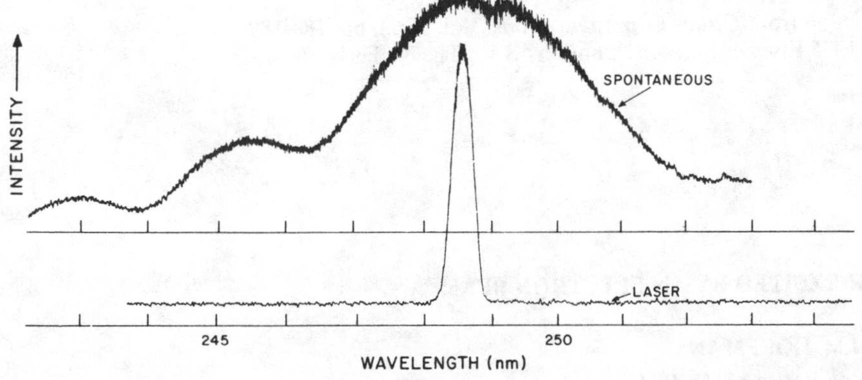

FIG. 4. Comparison of spontaneous and laser emission spectra from KrF.

quantum efficiency is roughly 50%. The ultimate efficiency of these lasers depends on the details of the molecular kinetics.

To provide an experimental indication of the possible efficiency, we have made relative fluorescence efficiency measurements in mixtures of Ar with N_2 (97:3), Ar with Xe and F_2 (99.6:0.3:1), Ar with Xe and Cl_2 (89.9:10:0.1), and Ar with Kr and F_2 (98.9:1:0.1). All the measurements were made at a total pressure of 40 psia. Taking into account the relative transmission of the broad-band interference filters used to isolate the bands of interest and the photodiode response, the peak fluorescence intensities relative to the 358-nm band of N_2 were found to be in the ratio 2:3:16 for XeCl, XeF, and KrF, respectively. These may be converted to rough estimates of the absolute fluorescence efficiencies by using the known kinetics of the Ar/N_2 system, [8] and the Franck-Condon factors for the N_2 $C \rightarrow B$ bands.[9] In the Ar/N_2 system, the energy is deposited in the form of Ar* and Ar^+ ions. The latter rapidly recombine to form Ar*. Over-all, 20.6 eV must be deposited to form one Ar*.[6] Under our conditions, 40% of this energy is transferred to N_2, the remainder being lost to Ar_2^*. Of the energy transferred to the N_2, approximately 40% goes to the $N_2(C)$ state either directly or through $N_2(E)$. Of the energy in $N_2(C)$ approximately 25% is radiated, the remainder being quenched by Ar and N_2. Of the $N_2(C)$ fluorescence approximately 33% appears within the bandpass of the interference filter utilized. Thus, in steady state the Ar/N_2 fluorescence efficiency for the mixture cited above is about 0.2%. From this the fluorescence efficiencies are estimated to be 0.4, 0.6, and 3% for the XeF, XeCl, and KrF mixtures, respectively. The difference between the observed fluorescence efficiency and the effective quantum efficiency may be due to the branching ratio for reaction (1), and part may be due to quenching of the excited rare-gas halide molecules by the parent halogens. For example, preliminary data indicate that the XeF* radiative lifetime is 50 ns and that the rate of quenching of XeF* by F_2 is 8×10^{-10} cm^3/s. Thus, under the conditions described above, approximately 73% of the XeF* molecules are quenched before they fluoresce. In a laser, most of this wasted excitation may be recovered by making the stimulated emission time short compared with the quenching time. Thus, these lasers show promise for higher efficiencies than has been heretofore achieved in the visible and uv.

†Work supported by ARPA/ONR under Contract No. N00014-75-C-0062.

[1]C.A. Brau and J.J. Ewing, Appl. Phys. Lett. (to be published).
[2]S.K. Searles and G.A. Hart, Appl. Phys. Lett. **27**, 243 (1975).
[3]D.J. Seery and D. Britton, J. Phys. Chem. **68**, 2263 (1964).
[4]C.A. Brau and J.J. Ewing (unpublished).
[5]J.J. Ewing and C.A. Brau, Phys. Rev. A **12**, 129 (1975).
[6]D. C. Lorents and R. E. Olson, Stanford Research Institute Project PYU-2018, Semiannual Report, 1972 (unpublished).
[7]A. Gedanken, J. Jortner, B. Raz, and A. Szoke, J. Chem. Phys. **57**, 3456 (1972).
[8]R.M. Hill, R.A. Gutcheck, D.L. Huestis, Stanford Research Institute Report MP 74-39, 1974 (unpublished).
[9]R.N. Zare, E.O. Larsson, and R.A. Berg, J. Mol. Spectrosc. **15**, 117 (1965).

Reprinted with permission from *Optics Communications*, Vol. 15(2), pp. 188-189 (October 1975).

100 MW, 248.4 nm, KrF LASER EXCITED BY AN ELECTRON BEAM *

G.C. TISONE, A.K. HAYS and J.M. HOFFMAN
Sandia Laboratories, Albuquerque, New Mexico 87115, USA

Received 7 July 1975

Laser oscillations have been observed at 248.4 nm from excited KrF molecules. The excited KrF molecules were produced by injecting an intense electron beam into mixtures of Ar, Kr and F_2. A peak power of 1.15×10^8 W with a total energy of 5.6 J has been observed. Up to 3% of the deposited e-beam energy was converted to laser-energy.

Emission from rare-gas–halogen molecules has recently been reported [1–3] and the use of these molecules in laser systems has been suggested. Laser action for some of the Xe–halogen molecules has been reported [4]. The observed emission in these molecules is due to a transition from an upper state of the rare-gas–halogen molecules that correlates with a deeply bound ionic state of the molecule. The lower state of the transition can be one of three repulsive or slightly bound states that correlate to the rare-gas ($^1S_0$) ground state and the lower states of the halogen atom ($^2P_{3/2}$ and $^2P_{1/2}$). In the rare-gas–halogen molecules that we have studied, the transition to the lowest repulsive states is observed. The emission from many of the rare-gas–halogens is in the near uv and blue, giving the possibility of tunable lasers in this spectral region. In this note we want to report the results of some preliminary studies of the rare-gas–halogen KrF as a laser system.

Laser oscillation with the KrF molecule was observed when mixtures of Ar, Kr and F_2 were irradiated with an intense electron beam. The electron beam was transverse to the optical axis. The excitation region was 40 cm long. The electron beam had a peak current of 142 kA and an initial electron energy of 1.2 MeV. The pulse width of the electron beam was 50 ns (fwhm). The reaction cell was constructed from stainless steel, and the electron beam entered the excitation region through a 80 μ stainless steel window. The optical cavity mirrors were placed inside the cell but outside of the excitation region. The initial experiments were done with two 6-m-radius mirrors, that were 2.54 cm in diameter. Two different sets of mirrors were used: 1) 99.9% reflection on both ends, and 2) 99.9 and 97% on the ends of the laser cavity. Laser-output energies of up to 10 mJ were obtained with the high-reflectance mirrors. In a later experiment, in order to extract larger energies, a 5-cm-diameter aluminum flat and a 5-cm-diameter quartz flat (uncoated) were used as a cavity.

Ultra-high-purity argon and krypton were used along with F_2. The laser emission from the cavity was detected with a photodiode after attenuation by neutral-density filters. The wavelength dependence of the spontaneous emission and the laser emission were recorded on Kodak Tri X film with a one-meter spectrometer operating in third order. The total laser energy was measured with a calorimeter.

In fig. 1 the fluorescence spectrum is compared with the laser spectrum that was obtained with high-reflectance mirrors. The gas mixtures were the same for both spectra. The KrF fluorescence spectrum has not been fully analyzed, but the two broad maxima appear to be typical of a bound-free transition to the lowest repulsive state. The two maxima at 248.4 nm and at 249.1 nm in fig. 1 are most likely due to transitions from two different vibrational levels of the $^2\Sigma_{1/2}$ bound upper state to the $^2\Sigma_{1/2}$ repulsive ground state. The more intense peak at 248.4 nm has a width of

* This work was supported by the United States Energy Research and Development Administration.

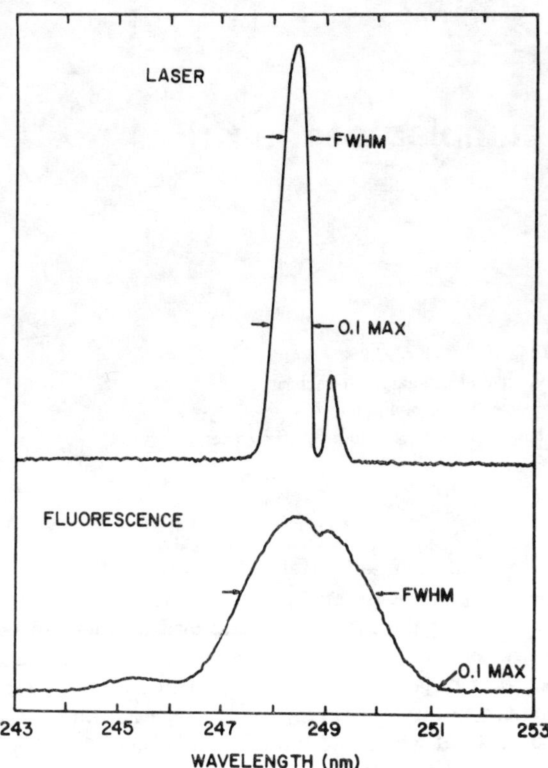

Fig. 1. Densitometer tracings of the fluorescence of KrF compared with the laser emission of KrF. The intensities, relative to the peak emission, are shown by the arrows at 0.5 of the maximum intensity (fwhm) and at 0.1 of the maximum intensity (0.1 max).

0.4 nm (fwhm) and is 18 times more intense than the peak at 249.1 nm. Mixtures of Ar–Kr and Ar–F_2 were also studied to verify that the observed emission was from KrF and not ArF or ArKr. The time history of the laser pulse at the high pressures, when the gain was very high, was identical to the electron-beam excitation pulse. The start of the laser emission coincided with the start of the electron beam and the emission ended with the excitation.

The maximum energy that was measured with the calorimeter was 5.6 J. This energy was obtained with the 5-cm-diameter mirrors as a cavity. A mixture of 3000 torr of Ar, 150 torr of Kr and 6 torr of F_2 was found to give the maximum energy. The gas mixtures were not critical as long as the Ar pressure was greater than 3000 torr.

Using measurements of the electron-beam dimensions in the excitation region and estimates of the electron-beam energy deposited in the gas, the efficiency of the laser (defined as laser energy extracted divided by energy deposited) was 2 to 3%. The maximum energy of 5.6 J corresponded to a power of 1.15×10^8 W. Several Xe–halogen molecules have been observed to lase in the above apparatus but with much less energy.

From these preliminary studies it appears that the efficiency of the KrF laser is reasonable. However, the transverse excitation that was used in these experiments does not effectively utilize the high-energy electron beam (1.2 MeV). Only a small fraction of the electron-beam energy is deposited in the gas. In order to deposit most of the electron-beam energy, axial excitation of the laser could be used [5]. It appears that if the electron beam machine used in these experiments was used with axial excitation, KrF laser energies of up to 200 J and peak powers of up to 5×10^9 W could be obtained.

We gratefully acknowledge the invaluable assistance of J.C. Bagg, D.L. Bolton, R.A. Klein and M.A. Palmer.

References

[1] M.F. Gold and B.A. Thrush, Chem. Phys. Lett. 62 (1975) 1990.
[2] J.E. Velasco and D.W. Setser, J. Chem. Phys. 62 (1975) 1990.
[3] C.A. Brau and J.J. Ewing, Paper TE8 given at the Thirtieth Symp. on Molecular Structure and Spectroscopy, June 1975, Ohio State Univ.
[4] Post deadline papers given at the 1975 IEEE/OSA Conf. on Laser Engineering and Applications by S.K. Searles and G.A. Hart and by J.J. Ewing and C.A. Brau.
[5] E.L. Patterson and R.A. Gerber, IEEE J. Quantum Electron., to be published.

Reprinted with permission from *Applied Physics Letters,* Vol. 27(9), pp. 495-498 (November 1, 1975).

Electron-beam-controlled discharge pumping of the KrF laser*

J. A. Mangano and J. H. Jacob

Avco Everett Research Laboratory, Everett, Massachusetts 02149
(Received 7 July 1975)

Laser action has been obtained in atmospheric-pressure mixtures of 0.1% F_2/2% Kr/97.9% Ar at 248.5 and 249.5 nm with electron-beam-controlled discharge pumping. The laser and discharge characteristics are explored as a function of discharge electric field and total mixture pressure. These preliminary measurements indicate laser output energies up to 6 mJ with a pulse length of 90 nsec. Limiting efficiencies for this laser system are discussed.

PACS numbers: 42.60.C

Recently, lasing action in the rare-gas-monohalide systems has been predicted[1,2] and observed.[3-5] To date these lasers have been pumped by high-energy electron beams only. In this letter we wish to report lasing action of KrF* in an atmospheric-pressure electron-beam-controlled discharge.

Discharge pumping of these laser systems can lead ultimately to increased average laser power and efficiency over that achievable with electron-beam pumping.[6] For electron-beam pumping, the principal limitation on average laser power achievable can be calculated from the average power that can be put through the foil separating the electron gun vacuum chamber from the laser cavity. The limitations on the average power through this foil can be calculated from a consideration of the self-magnetic-field of the electron beam, foil heating, and beam energy. Pinching of the electron beam under the influence of its own magnetic field limits one dimension of the volume which can be pumped and therefore the single pulse energy (for a given beam energy and laser length). Foil heating limits the repetition rate at which the laser can operate. The repetition rate together with the single pulse energy determines the average laser power. For fixed input power densities, e-beam-controlled discharge pumping requires electron-beam current densities ≤ 0.1 of that required by pure electron-beam pumping. Therefore, the limitations on average laser power discussed above are greatly reduced for a fixed pumping power density. This argument assumes, of course, comparable laser electrical efficiencies for both pumping methods. In fact,

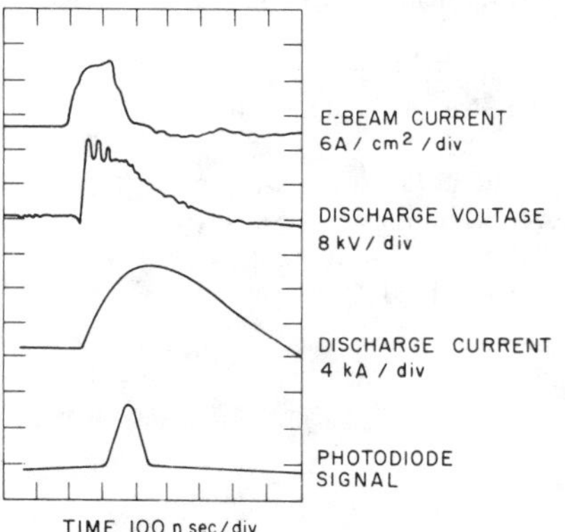

FIG. 1. Oscillograms showing temporal variation of e-beam current, discharge voltage, discharge current, and laser pulse.

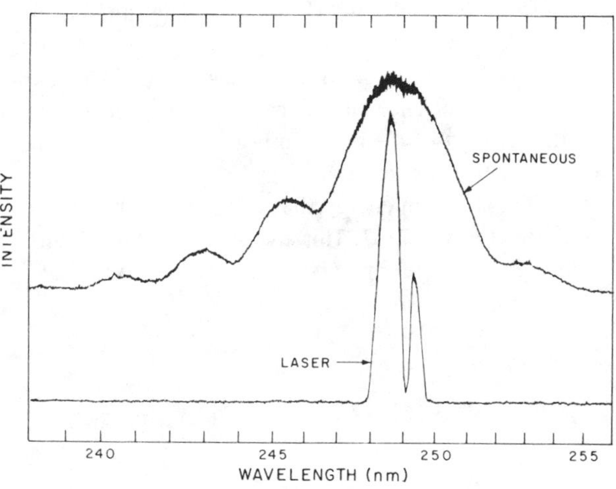

FIG. 2. Spontaneous and laser spectra of KrF*.

discharge pumping may be more efficient for the rare-gas-monohalide systems for three reasons:

(i) Beam energy losses in the foil and its support structure are less. (ii) Energy losses due to scattering of the electron beam in the foil and gas are reduced. (iii) Rare-gas metastable production efficiencies may be larger, 40—50% with electron-beam pumping[7] against a possible 70% with discharge pumping.[8]

The laser experiments were carried out in a high-vacuum high-pressure discharge cavity constructed of Lucite and stainless steel. In the experiments, the beam from a cold cathode electron gun (150 keV, 8 A/cm^2, 135 nsec, 2×20 cm) was used to preionized atmospheric-pressure mixtures containing Ar, Kr, and F_2. The beam, which was generated in a vacuum chamber, entered the discharge cavity ($2\times2\times 20$ cm^3) through an 80% transparent foil support structure, a 2-mil aluminized Kapton foil, and a 70% transparent wire screen. The wire screen served as a grounded discharge cathode. A stainless steel Rogowski-shaped discharge anode was placed 2 cm from this cathode. Approximately 35 nsec after the start of the electron-beam pulse, a spark gap was triggered which switched a 0.1-μF capacitor across the discharge electrodes. A series 2-Ω water resistor was used to absorb most of the capacitor energy if arcing occurred, thereby preventing damage to the laser cavity.

Prior to filling, the discharge cavity was typically evacuated to $\leq 10^{-4}$ Torr with a LN_2-baffled diffusion pump system. The entire discharge cavity was passivated with a 1% F_2/99% Ar mixture for 2 h prior to the laser experiments. Gas mixtures were prepared in passivated stainless steel sample cylinders (1 liter) at pressures up to 10^3 psia and were allowed to stand for several hours before use to ensure complete mixing.

Optical access to the discharge cavity was provided by uv-grade quartz windows spaced 60 cm apart and aligned at Brewster's angle to the long (20 cm) dimension of the cavity. A stable 2.3-cm-diam optical resonator was formed by aligning flat and spherical (radius of curvature = 2 m) mirrors each having an output coupling of 1.3% at the KrF* laser wavelength. The mirrors were placed 80 cm apart.

In Table I, the laser and discharge performance is summarized for six values of the mean discharge electric field. The input power by the electron beam was about 0.03 MW/cm^3. The laser mixture contained F_2/Kr/Ar at a total pressure of 1 atm. The mixture mole fractions were chosen to be 0.001/0.02/0.979, respectively, to minimize the formation of Kr dimers.[4] The first column in the table lists the observed total laser pulse energies as measured with a Scientech calorimeter (model 360203). From these data it can be seen that the laser pulse energy increases monotonically with increasing discharge electric field and therefore power input.

The laser electrical efficiency is defined here as the laser output energy divided by the discharge energy put into the laser cavity during the stable portion of the discharge pulse.[9] The measured laser efficiencies rise rapidly after laser threshold is reached, peak, and then decrease rapidly with increasing discharge power input. A possible explanation for the decrease in laser efficiency at higher input power is increased losses caused by metastable excitation and ionization as the metastable population becomes large. Energetic plasma electrons can, of course, readily excite and ionize the Kr and Ar metastables while 248.5-nm photons can ionize them.

The onset lag is defined as the time between discharge and laser turn on. As expected, this time lag is maximum near threshold and decreases to approximately 100 nsec with increasing pumping power. The magnitude of the onset lag is determined by the relevant kinetic transfer times and reaction rates as well as the discharge current rise time. Finally, the last column in Table I gives the duration of the stable portion of the discharge pulse before the onset of discharge arcing. At the larger electric field values, discharge arcing occurred simultaneously with e-beam turn off. Rapid e-beam turn off is accompanied by a large increase in plasma resistivity: F_2 attaches the discharge electrons. The subsequent increase in discharge voltage, induced by the circuit inductance and the rapid change in discharge current, results in immediate discharge arcing.

Laser and discharge performances were also investigated for six values of the laser mixture pressure between 0.75 and 3 atm. The F_2/Kr/Ar mole fractions were held fixed at 0.001/0.02/0.979, respectively. The capacitor charge voltage in these experiments was 60 kV. It was found that laser action at 0.5 atm could not be achieved with discharge electric fields up to 5.6 kV/cm. For pressures ≥ 0.75 atm, laser action was achieved. The mean power input remained approximately constant at 1 MW/cm^3 and the input energy was about 0.1 J/cm^3 over the pressure range studied. The laser efficiency was found to vary between 0.05 and 0.08% and the laser output energy between 3.2 and 5.8 mJ. The onset lag and laser pulse width (FWHM) steadily decreased with increasing pressure: the former from 140 to 60 nsec and the latter from 90 to 40 nsec.

TABLE I. Laser and discharge performance for different values of the discharge electric field.

Laser pulse energy (mJ)	Pulse width (nsec)	Onset lag (nsec)	Efficiency (%)	Electric field (kV/cm)	Mean power input (MW/cm^3)	Discharge pulse duration (nsec)
1.1	70	180	0.085	1.7	0.090	250
2.5	100	160	0.12	3.0	0.22	150
3.9	90	130	0.19	3.0	0.22	160
4.4	90	110	0.08	4.8	0.70	130
5.4	90	100	0.06	7.2	1.25	120
6.0	90	100	0.06	8.0	1.6	110

In Fig. 1 oscillograms are presented which show the time variation of the electron gun cathode current, discharge voltage and current, and the laser pulse. These oscillograms were obtained under conditions similar to those described above. Note that the discharge voltage remains nearly constant for ~100 nsec and abruptly begins to decay. This discontinuity in discharge voltage slope marks the transition from a stable discharge to discharge arcing. No noticeable effect on total discharge current is observed because the plasma impedance was much less than the circuit impedance before discharge arcing occurred. The laser output pulse was attenuated by a factor of $\approx 10^4$ and viewed with a photodiode (ITT F4000 S5). Laser action was not observed with the mirror opposite the photodiode blocked. Peak laser powers in excess of 100 kW have been observed. However, in the laser experiments performed to date, the laser output always peaked after the termination of the stable portion of the discharge pumping pulse. Hence, no evidence of bottlenecking has been seen, indicating an unbound or very weakly bound lower laser level.[4] The spontaneous emission spectrum of KrF* is shown in Fig. 2. This spectrum was obtained on a $\frac{1}{2}$-m Hilger quartz spectrograph by removing one of the mirrors from the laser cavity and attenuating the spontaneous emission signal by a factor of 10. The vibrational band structure is clearly visible in the spectrum.[10] The lower trace shows the line narrowing characterizing laser action on these bands. Laser action is shown on two lines: the stronger at 248.5 nm and the weaker at 249.5 nm. The reason for the double line emission is presently not known.

Although the maximum efficiency observed in the discharge cavity was 0.2%, it is felt that much higher efficiencies are possible if most of the following cavity losses are eliminated: (i) Loss of 1.4% per pass per Brewster window. (ii) Loss of 2% per pass per atmosphere of the laser mixture through the 60 cm between windows because of F_2 absorption.[11] (iii) Loss of 0.4% per pass because of photoionization of Kr*.[12] The output coupling was 1.3% per mirror. So the total loss per round trip was about 13% of which only 2.6% was output coupling. Therefore, the efficiency can probably be increased to about 1% by increasing the output coupling and eliminating the F_2 absorption regions at both ends of the cavity.

Threshold lasing by e-beam pumping alone was achieved in the laser cavity with an input power of 0.04 MW/cm^3. The total mixture pressure was 1.5 atm. From the considerations discussed above, the optical cavity loss was about 17%. Assuming that KrF* is produced by the following reaction:

$$Kr^* + F_2 = KrF^* + F$$

and the lifetime of KrF* is 10 or 20 nsec, a branching ratio of 0.15–0.3 is estimated. The branching ratio is < 1 because $Kr^* + F_2$ can form other products. If Kr* can be produced with a 75% efficiency in a discharge, the possible efficiency of the KrF laser is 5–10%.

The authors wish to thank Dr. C. A. Brau, Dr. J. J. Ewing, Dr. R. E. Center, and Dr. J. D. Daugherty for useful discussions during the course of this work.

*Research supported by the Advanced Research Projects Agency of the Department of Defense and monitored by the Office of Naval Research.

[1]J. J. Ewing and C. A. Brau, Phys. Rev. A **12**, 129 (1975).
[2]J. E. Velazco and D. W. Setser, J. Chem. Phys. **62**, 1990 (1975).
[3]C. A. Brau and J. J. Ewing, Appl. Phys. Lett. 27, 435 (1975).
[4]J. J. Ewing and C. A. Brau, Appl. Phys. Lett. **27**, 350 (1975).
[5]S. K. Searles and G. A. Hart, Appl. Phys. Lett. **27**, 243 (1975).
[6]J. A. Mangano and J. H. Jacob (unpublished).
[7]R. M. Hill, R. A. Gutcheck, D. L. Huestis, D. Mukherjee, and D. C. Lorents, Stanford Research Institute Report No. MP74-39, 1974 (unpublished).
[8]In pure Ar, for example, the AERL Boltzmann code predicts a metastable production efficiency of 71% for electric fields of 2 kV/cm atm.
[9]Obtaining the efficiency in this manner is valid because discharge experiments performed with no e-beam preionization of the atmospheric-pressure laser mixture resulted in immediate discharge arcing. No laser action was observed under these operating conditions.
[10]C. A. Brau and J. J. Ewing, J. Chem. Phys. (to be published).
[11]Jack G. Calvert and James N. Pitts, Jr., *Photochemistry* (Wiley, New York, 1966), p. 184.
[12]In computing the loss due to photoionization we have assumed a cross section of 10^{-19} cm^2. This is just the photoionization cross section of Rb at 2485 Å.
[13]J. J. Ewing and C. A. Brau (private communication).

Reprinted with permission from *Applied Physics Letters,* Vol. 28(2), pp. 86-87 (January 15, 1976).

Xenon fluoride laser excitation by transverse electric discharge

R. Burnham*

Science Applications Incorporated, Alexandria, Virginia 22202

N. W. Harris and N. Djeu

Naval Research Laboratory, Washington, D. C. 20375

Stimulated emission has been produced in mixtures of He, NF_3, and Xe at total pressures between 300 and 1000 Torr. Laser emission was on lines at 3511 and 3531 Å which have been associated with the excited XeF molecule. Excitation of the gas mixture was by a transverse electric discharge which produced pulses with peak currents of approximately 10^4 A and rise times of 20 ns. A maximum laser energy of 7 mJ was obtained from a gas mixture with a ratio of He:Xe:NF_3 of 98.0:1.5:0.5 at a total pressure of 300 Torr.

Recent studies[1,2] of the new class of excimers, the rare-gas monohalides, have led to the very rapid development of high-power lasers operating in the near ultraviolet in at least four of the species.[3,4] To date, lasers in KrF and XeF have produced the highest powers and efficiencies.[5,6] Heretofore, however, these lasers have been obtained only under excitation by electron beams or in electron-beam-sustained discharges.[7] We report here the demonstration of laser action at 3511 and 3531 Å in XeF excited in a transverse electric discharge.

Stimulated emission was obtained in mixtures of He or Ne, Xe, and NF_3 at total pressures between 300 and 1000 Torr excited in a pulsed transverse discharge device similar in design to those commonly used for excitation of lasers on the second positive transitions of N_2.[8] The discharge cell had an active length of 1 m with electrodes made of two band saw blades separated by approximately $\frac{1}{2}$ in. The device was powered by a fast capacitor-dumping circuit which had a storage capacity of up to 10 J. The maximum electric current through the discharge was of the order of 10 kA and the rise time of the discharge pulse was 20 ns. Spectra of the laser pulses showed two components, a stronger line at 3511 Å and a weaker line at 3531 Å. Laser emission was not observed when either NF_3 or Xe was omitted from the gas mixture in the discharge.

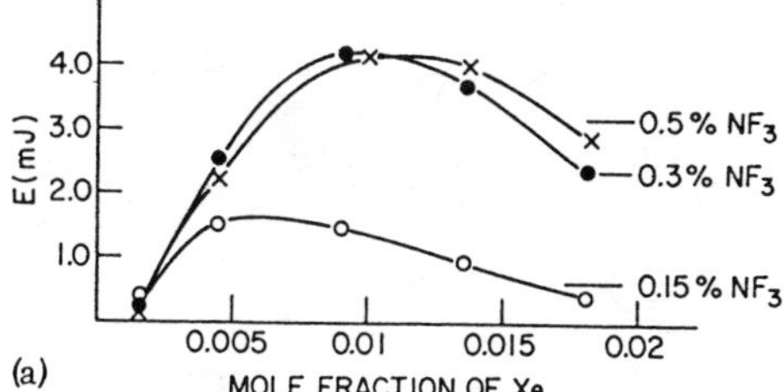

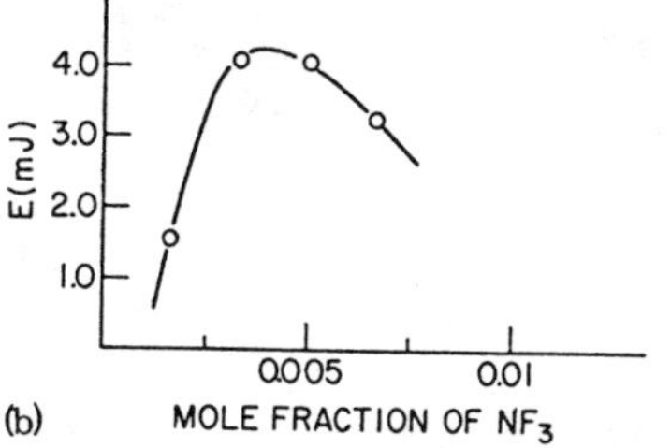

FIG. 1. (a) Pulse energy from the XeF laser at 3511 and 3531 Å vs concentration of Xe in the gas mixtures for several concentrations of NF_3. The major constituent of the gas mixtures was He. (b) Laser energy vs concentration of NF_3 for a constant ratio of the concentrations of He to NF_3 of 2.5 :1.

Figure 1 shows the performance of the laser for a variety of gas mixtures. The data shown were all taken with He as the major constituent of the mixtures. Comparable performance was obtained when Ne was substituted for He. The use of argon in the discharge led to severe arcing and laser emission was never observed. Figure 1(a) shows the laser output energy as a function of the mole fraction of Xe in the gas mixture for several concentrations of NF_3. These data show that the maximum laser energy was generally obtained with gas mixtures containing two to three parts Xe to one part NF_3. The decrease in laser energy at higher concentrations of Xe may have been due either to the increase in importance of reaction channels which compete with the formation of the excited molecular state, XeF* (e.g., production of Xe_2^*) or to the effect of higher concentrations of Xe on the conditions of the discharge. It is felt that the latter effect was more important since arcing in the discharge was observed visually for concentrations of Xe above 10%.

Figure 1(b) shows the pulse energy of the laser as a function of the mole fraction of NF_3. These data were taken with a constant ratio of the concentrations of Xe to NF_3 of 2.5 to 1. The decrease in the laser energy for concentrations of NF_3 beyond 0.5% may be attributable to either of the processes mentioned above or to collisional deactivation of XeF* by NF_3. Further studies

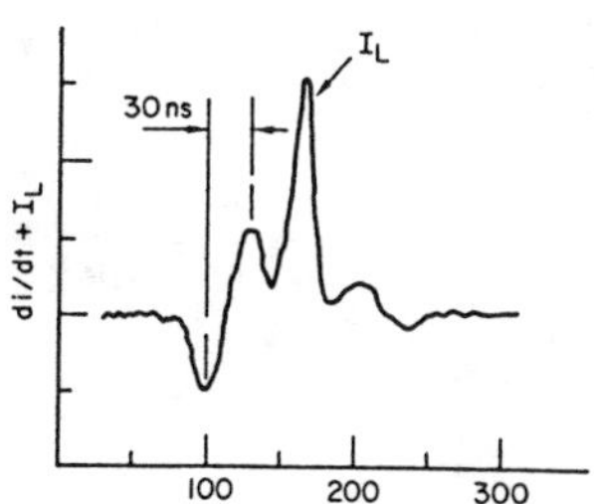

FIG. 2. Discharge current derivative (*di/dt*) and laser power (I_L) vs time.

of the kinetics of formation of the excited molecular state in the discharge as well as studies of the performance of the transverse discharge in the gas mixtures used here are planned.

The total pressure in the discharge at which maximum energy was obtained from the laser varied between 300 and 600 Torr, and depended on the mole fraction of NF_3 in the mixture. However, it was found that the partial pressure of NF_3 in the discharge cell at which the maximum laser energy was obtained remained constant at about 1 Torr. The most stable operation of the laser was obtained with a pulse repetition rate of about 1 Hz with the gas mixture flowing slowly through the discharge cell. The average pulse energy from the laser was found, however, to decrease rapidly if the pulse repetition rate was increased while the gas flow rate was held constant. Increasing the gas flow rate allowed the pulse repetition rate to be raised from 1 to 10 Hz with no decrease in the average pulse energy. With the discharge cell sealed, the laser energy was found to diminish after about ten shots. We have, however, under conditions of low flow rates produced double and triple laser pulses of equal energy separated by time intervals of 1 ms. It is felt that the decrease in the output of the laser with high repetition rates resulted from depletion of the NF_3 in the gas mixture due to reaction of free fluorine produced in the discharge with materials in the cell.

The time development of a typical laser pulse is shown in Fig. 2. Plotted is the sum of the laser signal from a vacuum photodiode and a voltage proportional to the time derivative of the current in the discharge. The time interval between the maximum and minimum of the current derivative gives the pulse width of the discharge current. The laser pulse may be seen to have a half-width of about 20 ns and to arise only near the end of the current pulse. The delay in the onset of the laser emission indicates that the laser was near threshold for superradiant emission. The limiting process which delays the onset of laser oscillation has not been identified, but may be either the rate of production of Xe metastables in the discharge, or the rate of reaction of the Xe metastables with NF_3 to form XeF*. The maximum energy was obtained from the laser with an optical cavity composed of a total reflector and an output mirror having a reflectivity of approximately 35% at 3530 Å. Although superradiance was occasionally observed with only the total reflector in place, use of the output coupler increased the laser power by an order of magnitude and decreased the divergence of the beam. The maximum pulse energy obtained from the laser was 7 mJ which corresponded to a peak pulse power of 700 kW. The over-all efficiency of the laser based on the energy stored in the charging capacitors was about 0.1%.

An estimate of the ultimate performance which should be obtainable from the XeF laser using excitation by transverse electric discharge may be made from a comparison of the energy emitted by the XeF laser to the energy emitted by an N_2 laser at 3371 Å produced in the same apparatus. Using the discharge device described above we have obtained laser pulses of 2.0 mJ at 3371 Å in N_2 and energies up to 3.5 mJ from N_2 with approximately 1% additive of SF_6. It appears, therefore, that the efficiency obtainable from the XeF laser should be significantly higher than that of the N_2 laser. The results of the present study indicate the feasibility of developing in XeF, and other rare-gas monohalides, lasers of higher efficiency and average power than are presently available in the visible or ultraviolet regions of the spectrum.

*Work performed in the Laser Physics Branch, Naval Research Laboratory, Washington, D.C. 20375.

[1]J. E. Valazco and D.W. Setser, J. Chem. Phys. **62**, 1991 (1975).
[2]J. J. Ewing and C. A. Brau, Phys. Rev. A **12**, 129 (1975).
[3]S. K. Searles and G. A. Hart, Appl. Phys. Lett. **27**, 243 (1975).
[4]J. J. Ewing and C. A. Brau, Appl. Phys. Lett. **27**, 350 (1975).
[5]G. C. Tisone, A. K. Hays, and J. M. Hoffman, Proceedings of the Second Annual Conference on Electronic State Lasers (unpublished).
[6]E. R. Ault, R. S. Bradford, and M. L. Bhaumik, Appl. Phys. Lett. **27**, 413 (1975).
[7]J. A. Mangano and J. H. Jacob (unpublished).
[8]Peter Schenck and Harold Metcalf, Appl. Opt. **12**, 94 (1973).

Reprinted with permission from *Applied Physics Letters,* Vol. 28(9), pp. 530-531 (May 1, 1976). ©1976 American Institute of Physics.

Laser oscillation on the 292-nm band system of Br_2†

J. R. Murray, J. C. Swingle, and C. E. Turner, Jr.

University of California, Lawrence Livermore Laboratory, Livermore, California 94550

Laser oscillation has been observed on numerous rotational transitions of the most intense bands of the Br_2 emission system near 292 nm. The laser is electron-beam excited in an Ar-Br_2 mixture. Quenching of the lower level by Br_2 is inferred.

Laser oscillation[1,2] and efficient fluorescence[3] have recently been studied on the 342-nm "high-pressure" bands of I_2 excited by an electron beam in the presence of several atmospheres of argon. Evidence of gain on the analogous Br_2 292-nm bands has also been reported.[4] We confirm that these bands are inverted and can be made to oscillate in an argon-bromine mixture under such conditions.

The laser medium consisting of 2 atm of argon plus a few Torr of Br_2 is transversely excited by a 235-keV electron beam over a 10×100 cm^2 area. The e-beam excitation pulse observed by Faraday cup and current probe measurements in the gas cell is approximately trapezoidal with a FWHM of 1.1 μsec and ~150 nsec rise and fall times. On the laser axis (3 cm from the beam window) the mean current density is 5 A/cm^2, and the energy deposited is 50 mJ/cm^3 at an argon pressure of 2 atm. The stainless steel cell is protected from bromine attack by a polyethylene coating, and the 40-μm titanium foil electron window is protected by a 20-μm Kapton® polyamide film. The cell and e-beam machine as well as the method of determining current density and energy deposition have been discussed in more detail elsewhere.[5,6] Fused silica Brewster-angle windows separated by 111-cm- and 10-m-radius dielectric mirrors of ~99% reflectivity at 292 nm separated by 2 m were used for the laser experiments reported here. Fluorescence and laser signals are detected by biplanar photodiodes, with appropriate narrow-band interference filters, or a thermopile calorimeter. Photographic spectra are obtained with a 1-m grating spectrograph.

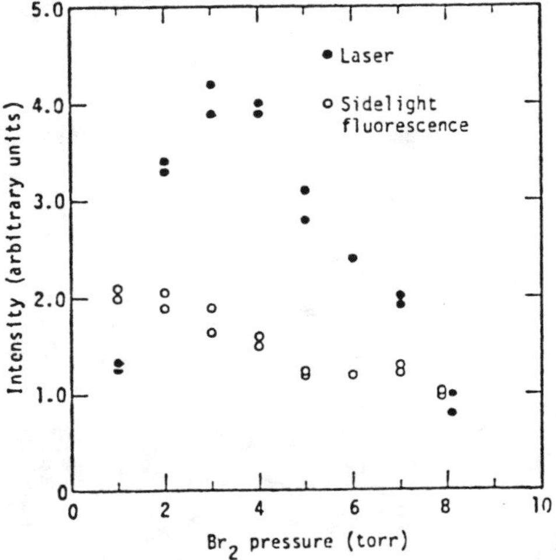

FIG. 1. Pressure dependence of Br_2 laser peak power and fluorescence.

Figure 1 shows the peak intensity of laser and fluorescence signals as a function of Br_2 pressure at constant argon pressure and excitation conditions. Note that above 1 Torr the fluorescence decreases monotonically with increasing Br_2 pressure, whereas the laser output maximizes for 3 Torr at a value corresponding to a cavity circulating power of 100 kW/cm^2. Figure 2 shows the time dependence of laser and fluorescence intensities for four Br_2 pressures covering the operating range of the laser. At 3 Torr of Br_2 and below, there are two distinct time-resolved features in the laser emission. As the Br_2 pressure is increased to 3 Torr, the first and more energetic laser peak maintains constant delay to oscillation but increases in width and amplitude to follow the excitation pulse in spite of the decreasing fluorescence intensity. A likely explanation of this behavior is electronic or vibrational quenching of the lower laser level by Br_2. As the Br_2 pressure is further increased, the fluorescence intensity continues to decrease and the delay to lasing steadily increases until eventually the gain goes below threshold. We observe some contamination of the Brewster windows at higher Br_2 pressures which may contribute to the decline in laser performance. The second laser feature contains an increasingly smaller portion of the total emission as the bromine pressure is raised. At 1 Torr of Br_2 it lies in the tail of the fluorescence and shifts toward the fall of the excitation pulse as the Br_2 pressure is increased. Above 3 Torr it can no longer be resolved. It appears clear from the behavior of the first laser pulse at low Br_2 pressure that lower-level population effects are important in this laser. One might suspect, therefore, that the second pulse is governed by the kinetics of production and quenching of the lower laser level as the excitation terminates.

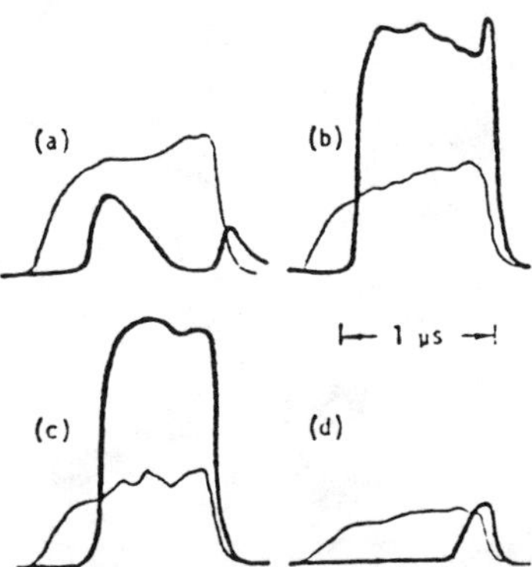

FIG. 2. Oscilloscope traces of fluorescence (thin line) and laser signals (thick line) at (a) 1 Torr, (b) 3 Torr, (c) 4 Torr, and (d) 8 Torr.

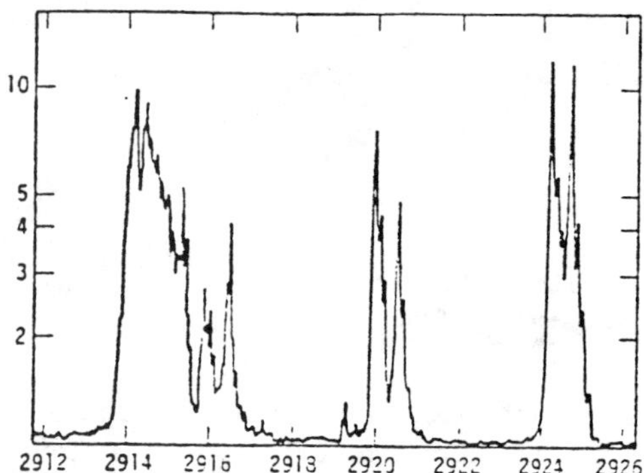

FIG. 3. Logarithmic densitometer trace of the Br_2 laser spectrum.

Some variation of output coupling was performed with available mirrors for the 3-Torr Br_2 plus 2-atm argon mixture. The laser small-signal gain is estimated to be about 20–25% per meter from the observation of substantial output with a 70% reflector. The pulse energies transmitted by mirrors having reflectivities of 0.96, 0.92, and 0.70 were 5, 17, and 10 mJ, respectively from a 3-cm^2 aperture. Although we have not fully optimized the output coupling, the energy available to be coupled out is clearly a few tens of millijoules, which is a very small fraction of the 15 J deposited in the 300-cm^3 volume accessible to the laser field. A Br_2 laser is, therefore, not likely to be exceptionally efficient under the present conditions. The laser output energy may be limited by lower-level bottlenecking since the laser self-termination at low Br_2 pressures implies that the lower-level population is important.

Figure 3 shows the laser output spectrum at 3-Torr Br_2 plus 2-atm Ar with 99% mirrors, and Fig. 4 shows a fluorescence spectrum. Numerous rotational transitions of the most intense Br_2 emission bands are oscillating under these conditions, some more closely spaced than the 0.005-nm spectrograph resolution. Venkateswarlu and Verma[7] have identified the bands between 291 and 293 nm as transitions from the 0-4 vibrational levels of an 0_g^+ state with ω_0 of 149 cm^{-1} to the 11-16 vibrational levels of an 0_u^+ state with ω_0 of 166 cm^{-1}.

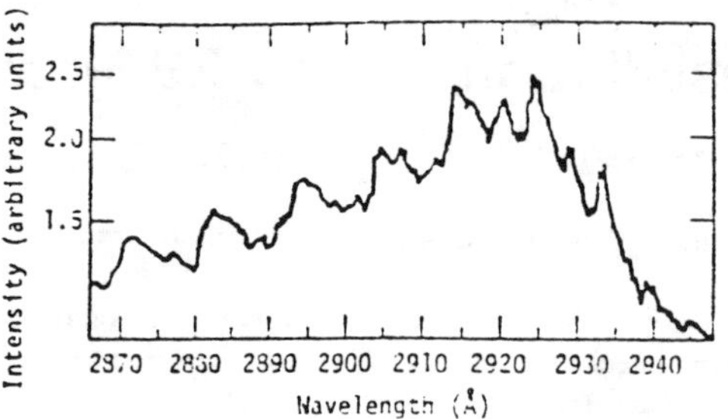

FIG. 4. Logarithmic densitometer trace of the Br_2 fluorescence.

The lower level has constants similar to the $B^3\pi_u(0_u^+)$ state which is the upper level of the visible absorption in Br_2 and may be that state. If the lower level is the B state, the laser upper level is at 51 802 cm^{-1} or 6.4 eV above the bottom of the Br_2 ground-state well. Energy transfer from more energetic species, such as Ar_2^* or Ar^*, might be expected to populate this state by processes analogous to those discussed elsewhere for I_2 [1-3] and for rare-gas halides.

The authors are very grateful to L. Rhodes for expert technical assistance and to Dr. J. Marling for the loan of several laser mirrors.

†Work performed under the auspices of the U.S. Energy Research and Development Administration.

[1]J.J. Ewing and C.A. Brau, Appl. Phys. Lett. 27, 557 (1975).
[2]R.S. Bradford, Jr., E.R. Ault, and M.L. Bhaumik, Appl. Phys. Lett. 27, 546 (1975).
[3]M.V. McCusker, R.M. Hill, D.L. Huestis, D.C. Lorents, R.A. Gutcheck, and H.H. Nakano, Appl. Phys. Lett. 27, 363 (1975).
[4]R.O. Hunter, ARPA Review Meeting, Stanford Research Institute, Menlo Park, Calif., 1975 (unpublished).
[5]C.E. Turner, Jr., P.W. Hoff, and J. Taska, Proceedings of the International Topical Conference on Electron Beam Research and Technology, Report No. SAND 76-5122, Albuquerque, N.M., 1975 (unpublished).
[6]J.C. Swingle, C.E. Turner, Jr., J.R. Murray, E.V. George, and W.F. Krupke, Appl. Phys. Lett. 28, 387 (1976).
[7]P. Venkateswarlu and R.D. Verma, Proc. Ind. Acad. Sci. 46, 251 (1957).

Reprinted with permission from *Applied Physics Letters,* Vol. 29(4), pp. 252-253 (August 15, 1976). ©1976 American Institute of Physics.

KrCl laser oscillation at 222 nm*

J. R. Murray and H. T. Powell

Lawrence Livermore Laboratory, University of California, Livermore, California 94550

Laser oscillation has been observed on the $^2\Sigma^+_{1/2}$-$^2\Sigma^+_{1/2}$ band of KrCl at 222 nm in an electron-beam-excited mixture of argon, krypton, and chlorine. The laser performance and spectral features of KrCl and KrF are compared.

Laser oscillation has been observed on ultraviolet transitions of XeF,[1-3] XeCl,[4] XeBr,[5] KrF,[3,4,6] and ArF[3] in electron-beam-excited argon gas containing small concentrations of xenon or krypton and halogen-bearing molecules. We have demonstrated that KrCl can also be made to oscillate under such conditions.

Argon gas at several atmospheres pressure containing a small concentration of krypton and chlorine is excited by a pulsed electron-beam source through a 0.1-mm-thick stainless steel foil. The 2×10-cm electron beam indicent on the gas contains 760 J of ≈600 keV electrons in a 50-nsec pulse with rise and fall times of 10 nsec. The energy deposition on the laser axis 1.5 cm from the foil is estimated to be ≈0.5 J cm^{-3} when the cell contains 4.4 atm of argon gas. The electron-beam energy incident on the gas may be decreased from this value by inserting attenuators into a beam drift chamber which is between the electron-beam source and the stainless steel foil. These attenuators are carbon plates drilled with patterns of holes which transmit a fraction of the electron-beam current without changing the beam voltage. They are calibrated for fractional transmission with a carbon calorimeter placed in the laser cell. After passing through the attenuator, there is sufficient transverse expansion of the beam in the 7-cm drift space at 10 Torr air pressure to give uniform illumination of the stainless steel foil, as verified by 4-chlorostyrene film dosimetry.

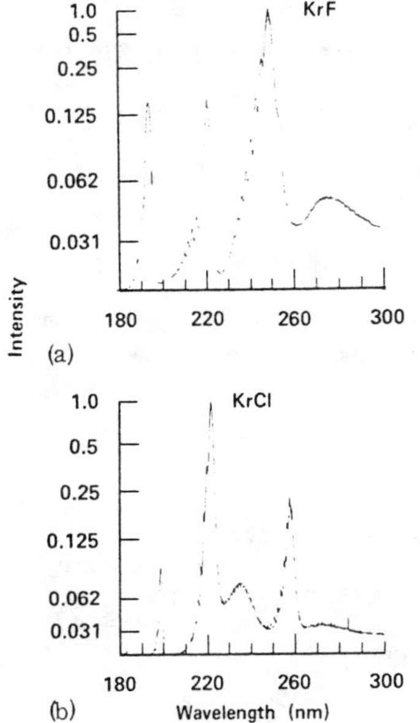

FIG. 1. Density scans of film spectra produced by electron-beam-excited mixtures of Ar, Kr, and NF_3 (a) or Cl_2 (b).

Internal multilayer dielectric laser mirrors with a clear aperture of 2 cm separated by 20 cm are mounted such that the laser cavity axis is parallel to the 10-cm dimension of the electron beam and is 1.5 cm from the foil. The mirrors degrade rapidly with e-beam excitation of gas containing Cl_2. All reflectances stated below are determined with a Cary 14 spectrophotometer with reflectance attachment standardized at 266 nm directly after the measurements quoted, and are typically 6—12% less than the initial mirror reflectance.

Figure 1 shows a spectrum of KrCl fluorescence from a gas mixture of 4.4 atm Ar, 100 Torr Kr, and 5 Torr Cl_2 at maximum beam current. A KrF fluorescence spectrum at the same rare-gas pressures with NF_3 substituted for Cl_2 and excited by $\frac{1}{4}$ of the maximum current is also shown in Fig. 1. The spectra are recorded on a $\frac{1}{2}$-m grating spectrograph with 0.1-nm resolution using Kodak 101-01 film. The intensity calibration is determined by overlaying two fluorescence spectra of equal intensity to determine the film density increment corresponding to a factor-of-2 increase in exposure, and is uncorrected for wavelength variation of film and grating response, and intermittency effects on the exposure. The wavelength scale is determined by reference to several HgI lines lying between 184 and 254 nm. The main bands of KrF at 249 nm and KrCl at 222 nm have been identified[7] as $^2\Sigma^+_{1/2}$–$^2\Sigma^+_{1/2}$ transitions between an ionic upper state, Kr^+F^- or Kr^+Cl^-, and a nearly flat lower curve. *Ab initio* calculations of KrF potentials[8] have predicted a $^2\pi_{1/2}$ ionic state lying above this state at an energy given by the $^2p_{1/2}$-$^2p_{3/2}$ spin-orbit splitting of the krypton ion. The energy splitting of the secondary transitions at 199 nm in KrCl and 220 nm in KrF from their main bands, 5210 and 5290 cm^{-1}, respectively, compare well with the spin-orbit splitting of Kr^+, 5371 cm^{-1}. Hence, these transitions are identified as $^2\pi_{1/2}$-$^2\Sigma^+_{1/2}$, with the same lower state as the main bands. Such secondary transitions appear to be quite general in the rare-gas halides occurring at 264 nm in XeF[9] and 236 nm in XeCl with energy splitting from the main band appropriate to Xe^+. These secondary transitions are also laser candidates although their gain is greatly reduced from the main bands.

Other experimenters have also identified the $^2\pi_{1/2}$-$^2\Sigma^+_{1/2}$ bands.[10,11] The $^2\pi_{1/2}$ state appears to be collisionally quenched under electron-free conditions.[10] Its appearance in our spectra suggests that there may be a strong coupling of the ionic states via inelastic electron processes, tending to equilibrate their populations to the electron temperature. The upper and lower states of the broad-band transitions at 275 nm in KrF and

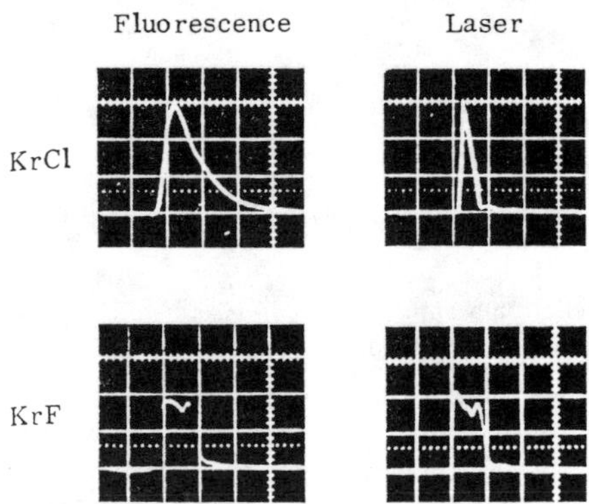

FIG. 2. Time dependence of KrF and KrCl fluorescence and laser emission. Time: 50 nsec/div.

235 and 272 nm in KrCl have not been firmly established. The transition at 193 nm in Fig. 1 is the ArF $^2\Sigma^+_{1/2}$-$^2\Sigma^+_{1/2}$ band, and the transition at 257 nm is a Cl_2 band.[12]

The KrCl laser output with the gas mixture stated above using mirrors of 42% and 99% reflectance at 222 nm is a single peak centered at 222.1 ± 0.1 nm with a resolvable width of ≈ 0.3 nm. Figure 2 shows the time dependence of KrCl laser output and fluorescence for these conditions. The detector is an ITT F 4115 CsTe photodiode with a 230 ± 10 nm bandpass filter, and the laser pulse energy transmitted by the 42% mirror is 50 mJ as detected by a thermopile calorimeter. The laser is delayed by ≈ 20 nsec from the rise of the fluorescence and terminates before the end of the fluorescence pulse. The 4115 photodiode, located 75 cm from the laser cell, has a geometric collection efficiency ≈ 10^{-4} of the total fluorescence power. Laser threshold was presumed when the stimulated emission into this solid angle exceeded the fluorescence transmitted through the high-reflectivity mirror. With mirrors of 92% and 78% reflectivity, the KrCl laser threshold was at slightly less than $\frac{3}{8}$ of the maximum current. The KrCl fluorescence rises coincident with the excitation pulse and falls before the end of the excitation pulse at maximum beam current. The peak fluorescence intensity is proportional to the electron-beam current over the range from $\frac{1}{16}$ to full current. The fluorescence tracks the excitation pulse more closely at lower beam currents but always shows an extended tail. The dependence of laser and fluorescence intensities on gas partial pressures has not been fully explored but is similar to that reported for other rare-gas halides.[1-6]

The performance of the KrCl laser may be compared to the performance of KrF under similar conditions, also shown in Fig. 2. For a gas mixture of 4.4 atm Ar, 100 Torr Kr, and 5 Torr NF_3 and mirrors of 90% and 54% reflectance at 249 nm, the laser pulse energy transmitted by the 54% mirror is 600 mJ at maximum beam current. The laser pulse tracks the fluorescence with a short delay. Laser threshold occurs at $\frac{3}{16}$ of the maximum beam current using two mirrors of 90% reflectance. The fluorescence from the 249-nm KrF band is approximately a factor of 2 more intense than that from the 222-nm KrCl band, which agrees with the ratio of laser thresholds. The 249-nm KrF fluorescence intensity is linear with beam current from $\frac{1}{16}$ to $\frac{1}{2}$ current and shows some superfluorescence along the long axis of the cell at maximum current. The KrF fluorescence tracks the excitation pulse unlike the KrCl fluorescence.

It is not clear from measurements made to date whether the lower output energy in KrCl compared to KrF reflects less favorable kinetics for KrCl formation, more serious intrinsic optical losses in the KrCl system, or an insufficient gain-time product to reach an intensity which can saturate the laser output and overcome nonradiative losses. The delay of the KrCl laser with respect to fluorescence and the failure of KrCl laser output to track the fluorescence suggests that the laser may not be fully saturated. The difference in KrCl and KrF fluorescence time dependence also suggests differences in either radiative lifetimes or formation kinetics. Several models for rare-gas halide kinetics have been proposed.[1-6]

The authors are very grateful to D. Roberts for technical assistance and to E. Jerbic for measuring the mirror reflectances.

*Work performed under the auspices of the U.S. Energy Research and Development Administration under Contract No. W-7405-Eng-48.

[1]C.A. Brau and J.J. Ewing, Appl. Phys. Lett. 27, 435 (1975).

[2]E.R. Ault, R.S. Bradford, Jr., and M.L. Bhaumik, Appl. Phys. Lett. 27, 413 (1975).

[3]J.M. Hoffman, A.K. Hays, and G.C. Tisone, Appl. Phys. Lett. 28, 558 (1976).

[4]J.J. Ewing and C.A. Brau, Appl. Phys. Lett. 27, 350 (1975).

[5]S.K. Searles and G.A. Hart, Appl. Phys. Lett. 27, 243 (1975).

[6]M.L. Bhaumik, R.S. Bradford, Jr., and E.R. Ault, Appl. Phys. Lett. 28, 23 (1976).

[7]J.J. Ewing and C.A. Brau, Phys. Rev. A 12, 129 (1975).

[8]T.H. Dunning, Jr. and P.J. Hay, Appl. Phys. Lett. 28, 649 (1976).

[9]C.A. Brau and J.J. Ewing, J. Chem. Phys. 63, 4640 (1975).

[10]J.E. Velazco, J.H. Holts, and D.W. Setser, J. Chem. Phys. (to be published).

[11]S.K. Searles (private communications). Dr. Searles has also communicated independent observation of KrCl laser oscillation.

[12]C.H. Chen and M.G. Payne, Appl. Phys. Lett. 28, 219 (1976). We have been unable to observe laser oscillation on this transition using mirrors of nominal 98% reflectivity and a gas mixture of 2—10 Torr Cl_2 and 3—8 atm Ar.

vuv emissions from mixtures of F_2 and the noble gases—A molecular F_2 laser at 1575 Å[a)]

James K. Rice, A. Kay Hays, and Joseph R. Woodworth

Sandia Laboratories, Albuquerque, New Mexico 87115
(Received 7 April 1977; accepted for publication 22 April 1977)

We have observed two new emission features in electron-beam-excited mixtures of molecular fluorine with either neon or helium. One feature is a continuum centered at 1080 Å which we attribute to NeF*. The other emission feature is a band system extending from 1500–1600 Å which we attribute to a transition of molecular fluorine. This transition lased near 1575 Å.

PACS numbers: 42.55.Hq, 42.72.+h

Within the past few years, a variety of fluorescing and lasing species have been obtained by electron-beam excitation of mixtures of noble gases and halogen-bearing compounds. These species include the rare-gas–halogen excimers (ArF*, KrF*, etc.)[1–4] and halogen molecules (I_2^*, Br_2^*).[5–9] We report here the observation of two new emission features following electron-beam excitation of He/F_2 and Ne/F_2 gas mixtures. First, we have obtained both spontaneous and stimulated emission from a previously unreported band system between 1500 and 1600 Å that we attribute to transitions in molecular fluorine. Second, we have observed, for the first time, spontaneous emission from a continuous band centered at 1080 Å which we attribute to NeF*.

Previously, both the 3460–3015-Å band system of I_2 [5–7] and the 2950–2410-Å band system of Br_2 [8,9] have been observed to lase following electron-beam excitation of a mixture of rare gases and suitable halogen-containing compounds. The 3460–3015-Å band system of I_2 has been assigned[10] as a $^3\Pi_{2g} \rightarrow {}^3\Pi_{2u}$ transition. Analysis[11,12] of spectra obtained using naturally occurring Br_2 have attributed the 2950–2410-Å band system of Br_2 to a $^3\Pi_{0g} \rightarrow {}^3\Pi_{0u}$ transition. A more recent investigation[13] of the Br_2 spectrum using isotopically pure Br_2 indicates that this band system may be assigned as a $^3\Pi_{2g} \rightarrow {}^3\Pi_{2u}$ transition, analogous to the I_2 3460–3015-Å band system. The 1500–1600-Å band observed in the present work is possibly the corresponding $^3\Pi_{2g} \rightarrow {}^3\Pi_{2u}$ transition in molecular fluorine.

Although NeF* radiation has not been observed before, a simple calculation based on the dissociation energy of ground-state sodium fluoride,[14] the ionization potential of Ne, and the electron affinity of F predicts that, assuming a flat ground-state potential, NeF* should emit near 1070 Å. More refined calculations[15] predict that NeF* should emit in a 15-Å-wide band centered at 1130 Å.

A diagram of the apparatus used in the present experiments is shown in Fig. 1. The electron beam had a peak current of 20 kA, a beam area of 45 cm^2, a pulse width of ~300 nsec (FWHM), and an electron energy of 850 keV. The electron beam, confined by an externally

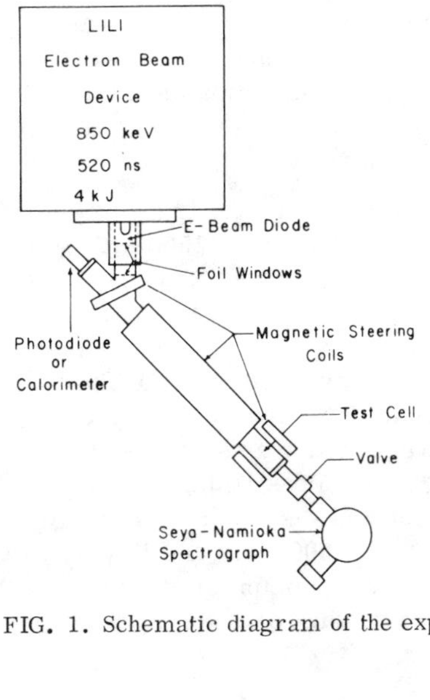

FIG. 1. Schematic diagram of the experimental apparatus.

a)Work supported by the Energy Research and Development Administration.

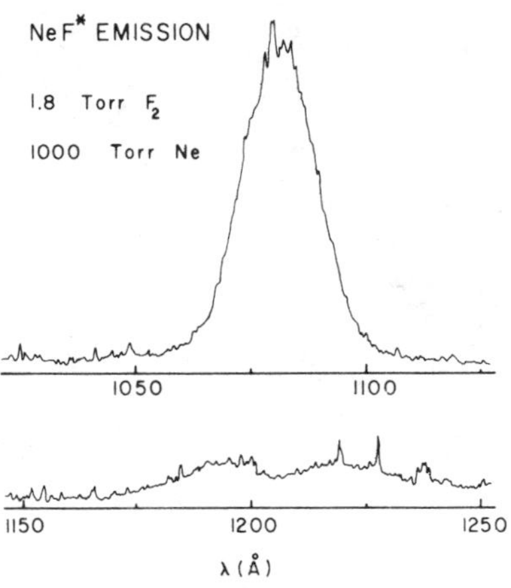

FIG. 2. Microdensitometer trace of the emission spectrum in the spectral region from 1050 to 1250 Å for electron-beam-excited Ne/F_2 mixtures. The vertical scale is linear in optical density.

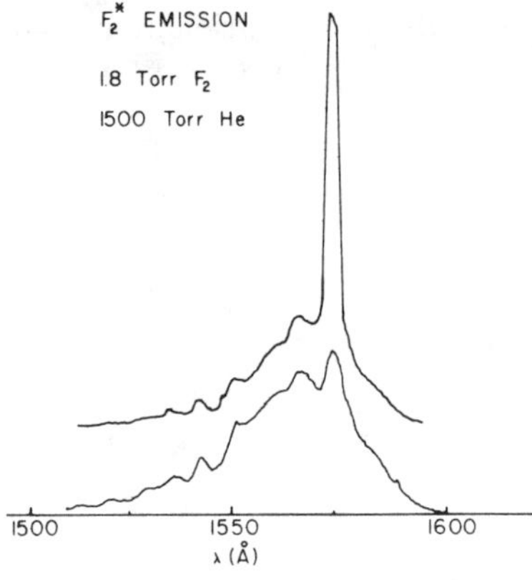

FIG. 3. Microdensitometer trace of the emission spectrum in the spectral region from 1500 to 1600 Å for electron-beam-excited He/F_2 mixtures showing the spontaneous emission (lower trace) and lasing emission (upper trace). The vertical scale is linear in optical density. The base line for the lasing spectrum is vertically displaced, and the film is saturated at the peak of this spectrum.

applied 3-kG axial magnetic field, passed through the anode and entered a low-pressure drift region. After drifting 61 cm, the electron beam entered the high-pressure region through a 32-μm-thick stainless-steel foil. The magnetic field then turned the beam 45° into the laser excitation region. The length of this region was 210 cm; the diameter was 7.5 cm. The temporal behavior of the 1080-Å radiation was recorded using a windowless photodiode[16] containing a tantalum cathode. An ITT 4115 photodiode was used to observed the time history of the 1500–1600-Å radiation. Spectra of these two emission features were taken on Kodak SWR film using a Seya-Namioka 0.5-m spectrograph in first order with 200-μ slits. While taking spectra near 1080 Å the window on the cell was replaced with a gate valve. The spectrometer was then filled with Ne to a pressure matching the total pressure in the cell, and the gate valve was open during the time of the shot.

A microdensitometer trace of the exposed film showing the NeF* spontaneous spectrum is presented in Fig. 2. The peak of the emission is centered at 1080 Å. Two much weaker features are seen at 1195 and 1220 Å. The NeF* signal was monitored as a function of fluorine pressure from 0.8 to 6 Torr and Ne pressure from 500 to 1500 Torr. The maximum NeF* signal was observed at an F_2 pressure of 1.8 Torr and a Ne pressure of 1000 Torr. The 1080-Å-emission feature is not present when the electron beam is used to excite neon alone or helium/fluorine mixtures.

Figure 3 shows a microdensitometer trace of the spontaneous-emission spectrum of the 1500–1600-Å molecular fluorine band (lower trace). This band is observed in electron-beam-excited Ne/F_2 and He/F_2 mixtures but not in Ar/F_2 mixtures. No other emission features were observed at wavelengths up to 3200 Å in He/F_2 mixtures. Figure 3 also shows a microdensitometer trace of a stimulated-emission spectrum (upper trace) of the F_2^* band. Peak lasing occurs at 1575 Å. This laser spectrum was observed in He/F_2 mixtures at He pressures ≥ 1500 Torr and F_2 pressures between 1 and 4 Torr. The maximum pressure the test cell could withstand was ≈1750 Torr. Ne/F_2 mixtures did not lase in the pressure range investigated. The F_2^* laser was investigated using a ~90% reflecting aluminum mirror at one end of the cell and a 1.5-cm-diam flat MgF_2 output coupling window at the other end. The F_2^* laser energy was measured using an evacuable calorimeter assembly that consisted of a 125-μm-thick titanium foil coated with carbon black and spot welded to a chromel-constantan thermocouple. The maximum laser energy output of 22 mJ was obtained at an F_2 pressure of ~2 Torr and a He pressure of 1500 Torr.

The temporal behavior of the spontaneous emission from NeF* and F_2^* followed the electron-beam current pulse. Under conditions for which F_2^* lased, the photodiode signal exhibited a sharp onset, delayed from the start of the current pulse, and followed the current pulse thereafter.

These new emission sources show promise as efficient photolytic drivers for a group-VI ^1S atomic laser.[17] The radiation from NeF* at 1080 Å is the appropriate wavelength to dissociate CO_2 to form O(^1S) with high quantum efficiency.[18] Likewise, the F_2^* emission can be used to dissociate COS to form S(^1S).[19]

We gratefully acknowledge the technical assistance of W. D. Curtis in maintaining the apparatus and M. A. Palmer in processing the film.

[1]S. K. Searles and G. A. Hart, Appl. Phys. Lett. 27, 243 (1975).
[2]J. J. Ewing and C. A. Brau, Appl. Phys. Lett. 27, 350 (1975).
[3]C. A. Brau and J. J. Ewing, Appl. Phys. Lett. 27, 435 (1975).
[4]J. M. Hoffman, A. K. Hays, and G. C. Tisone, Appl. Phys. Lett. 28, 538 (1976).
[5]A. K. Hays, J. M. Hoffman, and G. C. Tisone, Chem. Phys. Lett. 39, 353 (1976).
[6]R. S. Bradford, Jr., E. R. Ault, and M. L. Bhaumik, Appl. Phys. Lett. 27, 546 (1975).
[7]J. J. Ewing and C. A. Brau, Appl. Phys. Lett. 27, 557 (1975).

[8]R. O. Hunter, ARPA Review Meeting, Stanford Research Institute, Menlo Park, Calif., 1975 (unpublished).
[9]J. R. Murray, J. C. Swingle, and C. E. Turner, Jr., Appl. Phys. Lett. **28**, 530 (1976).
[10]J. B Tellinghuisen, Ph. D. thesis (University of California, Berkeley, 1969) (unpublished).
[11]P. Venkateswarlu and R. D. Verma, Proc. Indian Acad. Sci. **46**, 251 (1957).
[12]K. Wieland, J. B. Tellinghuisen, and A. Nobs, J. Mol. Spectrosc. **41**, 69 (1972).
[13]J. B. Tellinghuisen (private communication).
[14]P. Brumer and M. Karplus, J. Chem. Phys. **58**, 3903 (1973).
[15]N. W. Winter, C. F. Bender, and T. N. Rescigno (unpublished).
[16]J. A. R. Sampson, *Techniques of Vacuum-Ultraviolet Spectroscopy* (Wiley, New York, 1967), p. 226.
[17]J. R. Murray and C. K. Rhodes, J. Appl. Phys. **47**, 5041
[18]G. M. Lawrence, J. Chem. Phys. **57**, 5616 (1972).
[19]G. Black, R. L. Sharpless, T. G. Slanger, and D. C. Lorents, J. Chem. Phys. **62**, 4274 (1975).

Reprinted with the permission of the American Institute of Physics from *Applied Physics Letters,* Vol. 30(3), pp. 160-161 (February 1, 1977).

1-μs laser pulses from XeF†

L. F. Champagne, J. G. Eden,* N. W. Harris, N. Djeu, and S. K. Searles

Naval Research Laboratory, Washington, D. C. 20375
(Received 27 August 1976; in final form 29 November 1976)

Long-pulse operation of the XeF laser has been achieved utilizing electron beam excitation of $Ar/Xe/NF_3$ gas mixtures. For a total mixture pressure of 2.5 atm, ~0.30 J of 350-nm radiation was obtained in a 1-μs FWHM pulse.

PACS numbers: 42.55.Fn

The performance of rare-gas halide lasers has been considerably improved since their discovery less than two years ago.[1] Advances in laser peak power and efficiency have been demonstrated. However, laser pulse duration has been restricted to less than 220 nsec (KrF).[2] For some applications long-duration pulses are required. We report observation of long essentially cw laser pulses from XeF with electron beam (e-beam) pumping. These pulses, up to 1.5 μs, are a factor of 15 longer than previously reported for XeF.[3]

A diagram of the laser cell is shown in Fig. 1. A Maxwell cold-cathode electron gun[4] was used to generate 300-keV electrons. The current density at the 25-μ-thick Ti foil was 14 A/cm^2 for a 1.2-μs FWHM pulse, 8 A/cm^2 for 1.5 μs, and 5.2 A/cm^2 for 2 μs. The reduction in current density results from the greater anode-cathode spacing required for the longer pulse lengths. The electron beam entered the laser cell with a rectangular cross section of 2.6 cm × 100 cm.

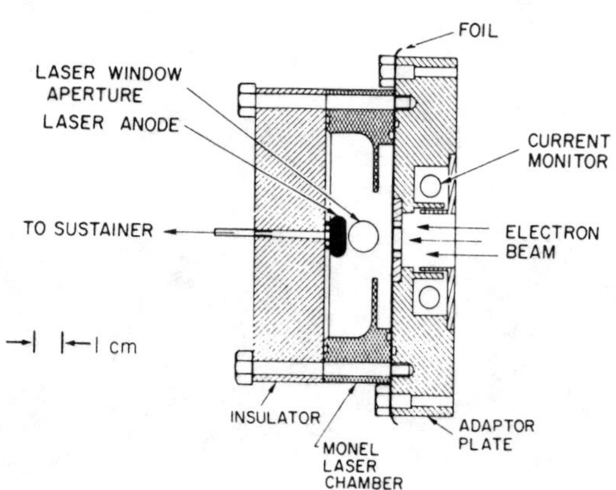

FIG. 1. Schematic diagram of the laser cell. The sustainer electrode was grounded in these experiments.

Laser energy was extracted from a cylindrical volume 100 cm long and 2.22 cm in diameter. Optical-quality CaF_2 or fused silica windows were installed at Brewster's angle. Dielectric-coated mirrors of 3 m radius of curvature separated by 2 m formed the laser cavity. One mirror was > 99% reflecting. The reflectance of the output mirror or quartz flat can be read from the abscissa of Fig. 3. Laser energy coupled out of the laser resonator was measured by a Gen-Tec ED-500 pyroelectric detector. Laser power was mea-

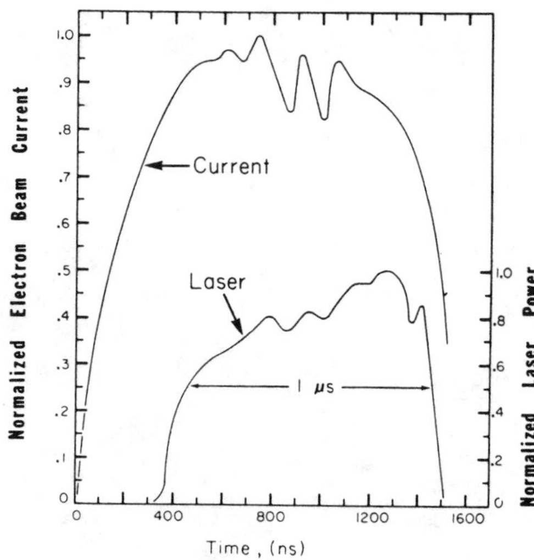

FIG. 2. Electron beam current and laser waveforms. Peak current corresponds to 11 A/cm^2 at the foil. Total pressure 1 atm.

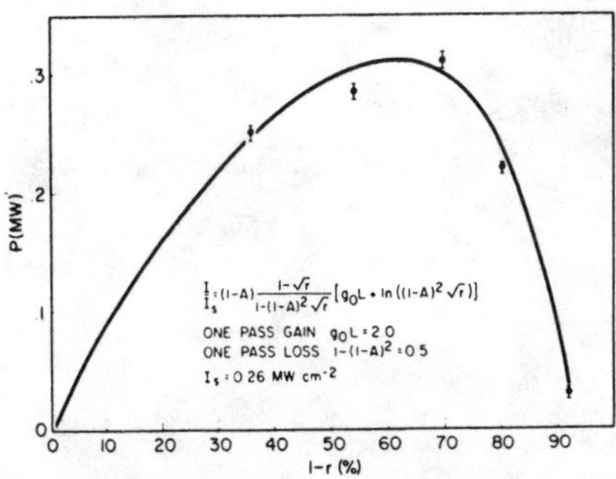

FIG. 3. Output laser power versus output mirror reflectance. Line shows best fit of Eq. (1) to the data.

sured by directing 10% of the power output to an S-5 F4018 photodiode detector. The Ar and Xe were research grade, while the NF_3 was commercial quality, 98% pure. In a few experiments F_2 (98% pure) was substituted for NF_3. As expected NF_3 gave better laser performance than F_2.

The partial pressures of Ar, Xe, and NF_3 were varied to get optimum laser efficiency with 1.2–1.4-μs e-beam excitation pulses. A mixture of Ar (99.5%), Xe (0.38%), and NF_3 (0.12%) gave the highest energy, 300 mJ at 2.5 atm total pressure. The optimum gas composition did not change with pressure. At the lowest pressure (1 atm) the energy dropped to 200 mJ and at the highest pressure (5 atm) the energy was 36 mJ. Over most of this range the pulse was 1 μs long.

Figure 2 shows typical oscilloscope traces of the laser and e-beam current waveforms. The beam current has been normalized, unity corresponding to a current density of 11 A/cm^2. It can be seen that laser emission occurred as long as the current density exceeded 8.5 A/cm^2. With a pumping pulse of 8.0 A/cm^2 (peak current density with 1.6 μs FWHM), laser action with a low-loss cavity was observed for 1.5 μs but was so close to threshold that the laser energy was only 10 mJ.

The laser experiments were repeated with various output couplings. Figure 3 shows the effect of the coupling on laser power. From Eq. (1), the saturation intensity, gain, and loss were calculated using the data points shown in Fig. 3.

$$\frac{I}{I_s} = (1-A)\frac{1-(r)^{1/2}}{1-(1-A)^2(r)^{1/2}}\{g_0 L + \ln[(1-A)^2(r)^{1/2}]\}. \quad (1)$$

This equation is a modified version of the one given by Rigrod[5] for high-gain lasers. In the derivation here, we have included a lumped loss just in front of each mirror (as an approximation to loss in the laser medium itself) which absorbs a fraction A of the power incident upon it. Since the laser beam passes each lumped loss twice in a round trip, the single-pass loss represented by each is $1-(1-A)^2$. The other symbols have their usual meanings: g_0 is the small-signal gain coefficient, L is the length of the excitation region, r is the reflectivity of the output mirror, and I_s is the saturation intensity. The best fit of the data gave $g_0 L = 2.0$, $1-(1-A)^2 = 0.5$, and $I_s = 0.26$ MW cm^{-2}. The value for the single-pass loss is unexpectedly high. However, recent probe measurements suggest that F^- absorption could account for the high loss.[6]

The principal purpose of this work was to demonstrate long-pulse (cw) operation. Inspection of Fig. 2 indicates that even longer laser pulses than 1 μs are possible. Note that the laser intensity is increasing as long as the pumping level is above 8.5 A/cm^2. This implies that longer laser pulses at this pumping level would be more efficient. Also we believe depopulation of the lower level which is bound by 1100 cm^{-1} [7] and gas heating are not problems at these power levels. In fact the calculated temperature rise of 110 °C may enhance the power output by improving the rate of dissociation of the lower level.

The energy deposited in the gas was calculated[8] to be 60 J at 2.5 atm which gives an efficiency of 0.5%. This value is to be compared with the 3% figure reported earlier for short-pulse operation.[3] Much of the difference between these two values is due to the different method of calculating e-beam energy deposition.

Efficiencies ~1% are of interest for practical devices. We note that the use of a higher-voltage gun allows longer powerful pumping pulses and that greater net efficiency will result.

†Work supported in part by DARPA.
*NRC-NRL Postdoctoral Research Associate 1975—present.
[1]S.K. Searles and G.A. Hart, Appl. Phys. Lett. 27, 243 (1975); C.A. Brau and J.J. Ewing, Appl. Phys. Lett. 27, 435 (1975).
[2]R.S. Bradford, Jr., W.B. Lacina, E.R. Ault, and M.L. Bhaumik, Inter. Quantum Elec. Conf., Amsterdam, 1976, Postdeadline paper (unpublished).
[3]E.R. Ault, R.S. Bradford, Jr., and M.L. Bhaumik, Appl. Phys. Lett. 27, 413 (1975).
[4]J. Jansen, Soc. Photo-Opt. Inst. Eng., 17th Tech. Meeting, San Diego, 1973 (unpublished).
[5]W.W. Rigrod, J. Appl. Phys. 36, 2487 (1965).
[6]J. Mangano and J. Jacobs, 3rd Annual Conf. on Electronic State Transition Lasers, Aspen, Colo., 1976 (unpublished).
[7]J. Tellinghuisen, G.C. Tisone, J.M. Hoffman, and A.K. Hays, J. Chem. Phys. 64, 4796 (1976).
[8]S.K. Searles and G.A. Hart, Appl. Phys. Lett. 28, 384 (1976).

Reprinted with permission from *IEEE Journal of Quantum Electronics,* Vol. QE-14(3), pp. 177-184 (March 1978). ©1978 IEEE.

Parametric Study of a Constant *E/N* Pumped High-Power KrF* Laser

WALTER J. SARJEANT, MEMBER, IEEE, A. J. ALCOCK, SENIOR MEMBER, IEEE, AND KURT E. LEOPOLD

Abstract—The application of a novel constant voltage excitation technique has led to the production of volume glow discharges in a scalable multiatmosphere rare gas halide laser. Such discharges are obtained using a high-voltage discharge circuit which optimizes energy transfer from the power conditioning system into the load, up to the voltage limit of the system components. A detailed parametric study has been carried out for KrF* at pressures up to 6 atm and output energies in excess of 0.6 J were obtained from an active volume of 0.18 ℓ.

Manuscript received September 20, 1977.

The authors are with the National Research Council of Canada, Division of Physics, Ottawa, Ont., Canada.

INTRODUCTION

SINCE the application of fast electric-discharge pumping to rare gas halide excimer lasers was first reported [1] early in 1976, a considerable effort has been devoted to the further development of this relatively straightforward excitation technique [2]-[6]. Interest in the fast discharge approach has been stimulated not only by its low-cost and simplicity in comparison with electron beam excited or sustained devices, but also by the possibility that it may be particularly suited to high repetition rate operation.

A significant step in the developments which have taken place so far has been the application of UV preionization [7], [8] to permit the production of volume discharges at pressures in excess of 1 atm. This approach, in combination with highly overvolted constant *E/N* excitation from a pulse charged pulse forming network (PFN), has resulted in the first demonstration of a volume glow discharge at total gas pressures up to 6 atm [9], [10]. The applicability of this mode of operation to further scaling of the discharge volume and gas pressure appears promising and is of considerable relevance due to the current widespread interest in high-power lasers operating at UV and vacuum UV wavelengths.

The material presented in this paper comprises a full description of a laser using this new type of excitation scheme, as well as results from a detailed investigation of laser action in the F_2:Kr:He rare gas halide system. The dependence of laser output energy and pulse duration on various parameters, including total gas pressure, gas mixture and composition, charging voltage, and discharge electric field have been determined and provide further insight into the scaling characteristics of the device.

DESCRIPTION OF THE APPARATUS

A schematic representation of the complete laser system is shown in Fig. 1. The laser discharge region consists of an 80-cm long rectangular slot cut in an 11-cm thick panel of linen based phenolic. Two side panels 2.5 cm thick made from the same material are bolted to this panel, and all exposed surfaces treated with a highly fluorine resistant epoxy [11].

Two brass electrodes approximately 65 cm long are shaped to a uniform-field Rogowski profile with a 1-cm flat central region. This provides a 0.18-ℓ discharge volume ~60 cm long by 2.4 cm high and ~1.3 cm wide. The electrodes are each bolted to a collector plate that terminates the ten current

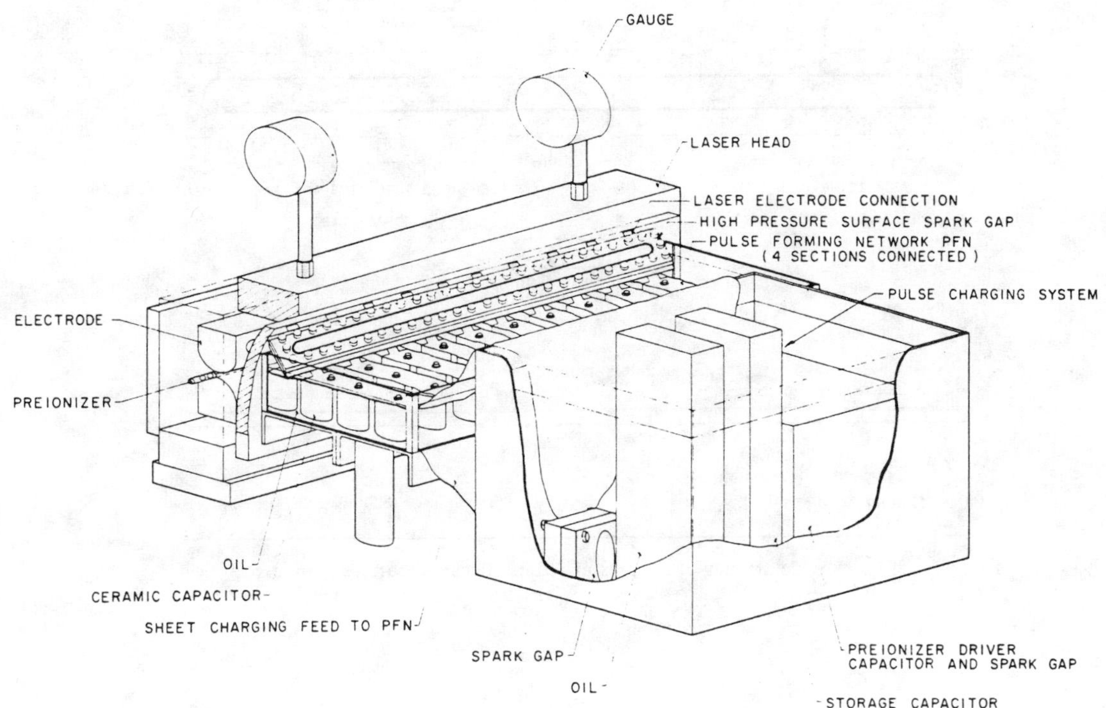

Fig. 1. Schematic representation of the complete laser system.

feeds, from the high-voltage driver, which pass through the side panel visible in Fig. 1. Mounted on the opposite side panel is the preionizer assembly which consists of a linear array of surface spark channels situated along the length of a glass tube placed in the center plane between the electrodes and 4 cm from them.

The electrical schematic of the system shown in Fig. 2, illustrates the method employed for rapid energy deposition into a volume discharge in the lasing gas. Plasma preconditioning is provided by UV photons generated by the auxiliary multiple spark discharge preionizer, preceding the main pump pulse by a delay so adjusted as to achieve glow discharge conditions.

As indicated in Figs. 1 and 2, the power conditioning system comprises a low impedance, type E, PFN coupled to the laser electrodes by means of a very rapidly closing multichannel surface spark gap. A scale drawing of the latter is presented in Fig. 3. The spark gap element is fabricated from type G-30 fiberglass epoxy board and reliable multichannel operation (~100 channels), with 80-kV hold-off in this circuit, has been obtained by etching the spark gap pattern symmetrically on both sides of the 2-oz copper cladding. The surface spark gap acts as a low-inductance switch, having a short resistive phase [12], [13] and applies the peak PFN voltage to the laser electrodes at a rate between 10 and 40 kV/ns, depending somewhat upon operating conditions in the spark gap and the charging dc voltage.

Two 0.1-μF, 100-kV storage capacitors are connected in parallel, and in conjunction with the spark gap shown in

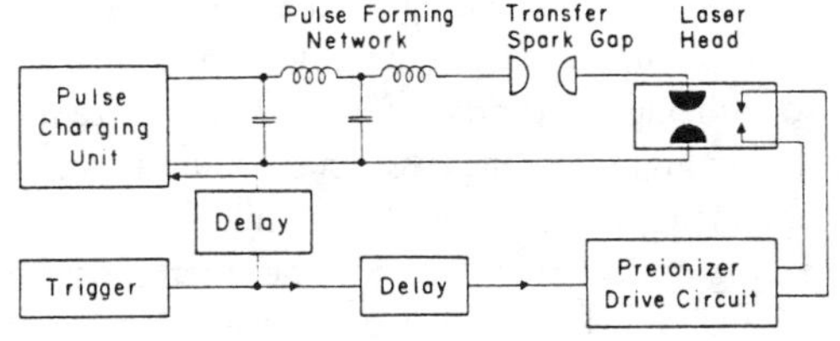

Fig. 2. Electrical schematic of the laser excitation circuit.

Fig. 1, form the pulse charging system which raises the PFN to full voltage in about 150 ns. Selection and preconditioning of the 20 ceramic capacitors (Sprague type 715, 2700 pF, 40 kV) in the PFN allowed satisfactory operation of the system up to a maximum charging voltage of 92 kV dc. Increasing this to 100 kV severely reduced capacitor lifetime to about 50 shots per unit, a generally unacceptably low figure. Energy for the preionizer was obtained from a circuit composed of a spark gap switch, connecting a low inductance 0.05-μF capacitor charged to 30 kV to the preionizer assembly via two short leads. Triggering of the field distortion spark gaps of the pulse charging unit and the preionizer was by means of high voltage (~100 kV) spiral transformer systems with krytron switches similar to those previously described [14]. The overall jitter between the preionizer and main voltage pulse was ~±25 ns, the same as between the input trigger and laser output pulse.

The gas handling system consists of a monel high-pressure mixing chamber (volume 1 ℓ) into which research grade NF_3 or F_2 could be mixed by partial pressure techniques with research grade Kr and raised to ~70 atm by adding high-purity

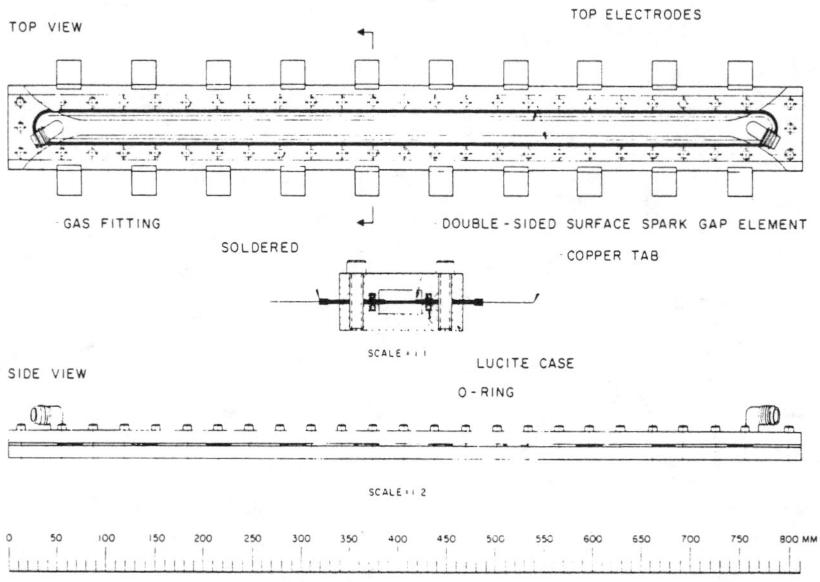

Fig. 3. Scale drawing of the pressurized multichannel surface spark gap.

helium. The mixtures were allowed to stand and mix for a short while before use. Additional experiments were conducted in which the actual mixing took place in the laser head itself. Since no significant differences appeared between the two techniques, the latter mixing approach was employed in the part of this study concerned with the effects of gas mixture composition upon output energy. Particular attention was paid to utilizing appropriate filters to minimize hydrocarbon backstreaming from the system's vacuum pumps, substantially enhancing the lifetime of each fill.

The 1-m long optical resonator for the laser consisted of an internal, 10-m radius of curvature concave UV-enhanced aluminum reflector and a two or four surface fused silica resonant reflector. The aluminum mirror and one of the resonant reflector elements were both exposed to the lasing gas, as they served as pressure windows for the discharge chamber.

Laser Performance

In marked contrast to previously reported excitation techniques using Blumlein or lumped LC circuits [1]-[8], the new type of driving circuit used in the present laser has permitted constant E/p pumping of uniform glow discharges in rare gas halide mixtures at total gas pressures of up to 6 atm [9], [10]. Visual and photographic observations clearly showed that such discharges could readily be obtained at 2.4-cm electrode spacings. Decreasing the spacing to ~1 cm with the same input energy resulted in filamentation of the glow discharge and reduced output energy, accompanied by occasional late arcs, caused most likely by electrode nonuniformities. For this reason, a gap spacing of 2.4 cm was selected and used during the parametric study of the electrical and optical performance obtained with Kr, F_2, He gas mixtures.

The control of the resonator over the laser action was demonstrated by misaligning both reflectors, with the result

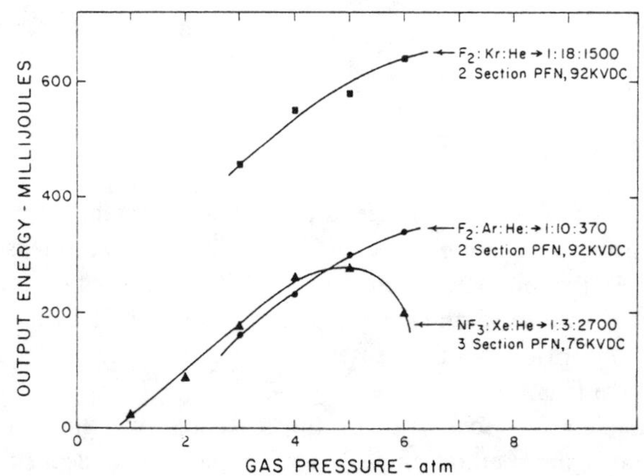

Fig. 4. Dependence of the laser output energy upon total gas pressure for several optimum rare gas halide mixtures.

that the optical output decreased into the detector noise region, i.e., less than 250 μJ. This and all other measurements of the laser output energy were made with a pyroelectric detector calibrated against a Scientech energy meter and also checked against an NBS calibrated detector unit at 10.6-μm wavelength. A complete determination of the optimum resonator parameters will require further more detailed study.

In Fig. 4 the dependence of the laser output energy on gas pressure is presented for several optimum rare gas halide mixtures for a constant dc voltage on the pulse charging capacitor. The number of sections in the PFN shown for each mixture is that yielding maximum output energy at 5-atm pressure. The behavior of the system with XeF and ArF previously described [9], [10] is compared to the particular gas species of interest here, namely KrF. A maximum energy per pulse of 0.61 J was measured with the pyroelectric energy detector, in a 6-atm mixture containing F_2:Kr:He in the ratio 1:18:1500.

Lower output energies were recorded with XeF and ArF; however, in all three cases the upper limit is presently determined by voltage limitations in the pulse forming network, which does not represent a fundamental obstacle to further scaling.

The dependence of the output energy and efficiency of the laser upon dc charging voltage is shown in Fig. 5. A mixture of F_2:Kr:He in the ratio of 1:18:1500 was synthesized in the laser head and the output energy recorded in two runs of both increasing and decreasing charging voltage. Point reproducibility for this data was better than ±5 percent. The energy stored in the PFN at each charging voltage was determined by calculation of $\frac{1}{2}CV^2$ where C was the total PFN capacitance at the peak voltage V on the PFN during the pulse charging cycle. The capacitance of these ceramic capacitors is strongly voltage dependent [15], giving rise to a PFN having a time varying line impedance. For driving this type of discharge, with an impedance which decreases with voltage, this type of PFN then matches the general load characteristic of decreasing impedance with time [16] providing the possibility of improved energy transfer and more rapid pulse termination [17] while maintaining a constant E/p during the discharge interval. As evident from Fig. 5, the conversion efficiency from electrical energy stored in the PFN into optical radiation, increased significantly with charging voltage, and consequently output energy. The increase in efficiency from 44 to 92 kV was from 0.12 up to 0.5 percent, strongly suggesting that higher operating voltages may result in a more than linear increase in output energy. Utilizing tapered, dispersive, liquid dielectric PFN's, energies in excess of 0.8 J have recently been achieved in the same device for a charging voltage of 100 kV [18]. The influence of higher charging voltages upon laser performance is currently under investigation.

With regard to Fig. 5, the energy stored in the PFN increased from 88 J at 44 kV up to 122 J at 92 kV charging voltage. For this 40 percent increase in stored electrical energy, an increase in output energy of more than 600 percent was obtained. It appears that this nonlinear increase in energy comes about primarily through the enhanced pumping efficiency achievable with the high E/p existing throughout the discharge interval [16], [19], [20]. The output energy at 6 atm was also measured as a function of the number of sections in the PFN for the same gas mix and charging voltage. Changing the PFN from one to two sections resulted in approximately a fivefold increase in energy and an efficiency of 0.5 percent. At this pressure, adding two additional sections to the PFN produced less than a 20 percent additional increase in energy. Because of this rapid decrease in efficiency, obtained using more than two sections in the PFN, the subsequent parametric studies were carried out with the 24 ±5-ns duration, two-section PFN.

It was observed that the output energy depended slightly (~20 percent) upon the time delay between the preionizer and the main discharge over the range from 0.2 to 10 μs. The delay was thus fixed at 2 μs for the duration of this study, although the sensitivity of any one parameter to the discharge delay was always checked as each set of data was taken. Changing the position of the preionizer over the range of ~1-4 cm and adjusting the capacitor charging voltage from 20 to 40 kV dc, yielded no noticeable effect on the output energy. These observations are at variance with a recently proposed model for UV preionization [21] and suggest that the threshold of ionization required for proper plasma conditioning might well correspond to substantially lower preionizer energies than currently employed. Recent measurements have been carried out on a similar system wherein several types and geometries of spark preionizers, having time durations as short as tens of nanoseconds, have been evaluated [18]. Virtually the same laser performance was obtained, further supporting the deduction that much smaller preionizer energies (<1 J) are equally effective in achieving the high-pressure operation described in the present work. With no preionization, the output energy was observed to decrease by ~5 times, accompanied by speckled output fluorescence patterns and severe arcing.

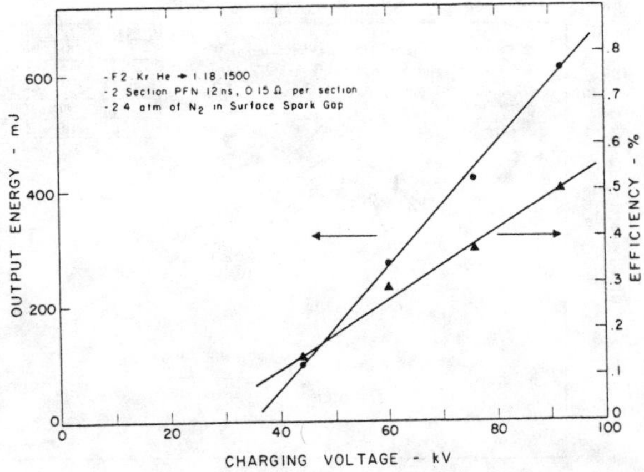

Fig. 5. Variation of output energy and efficiency of the laser with charging voltage. The 6-atm gas mixture was composed of F_2:Kr:He in the ratio of 1:18:1500.

The dependence of output energy upon gas pressure and composition was investigated to determine, in particular, the influence of F_2 concentration. Results are shown in Fig. 6, for a constant charging voltage of 92 kV dc and two sections in the PFN. The divergence of the curves at higher pressures indicates a relatively small range of gas compositions which yield high-output energies at the upper pressure limit of 6 atm. Based upon visual observation of the discharge, it was possible, in the case of the 1:5:460 mixture of F_2:Kr:He, to correlate the rapid decrease in output energy at higher pressures with the onset of arcing above 5-atm total pressure. The profile of this curve agreed well with the curve in Fig. 4 for XeF in which the same arcing behavior was observed. This arcing is attributed, partially at least, to the rapid degradation in multichanneling apparent in the surface spark gap for laser gas pressures in the region of 6 atm. Higher laser gas pressures increased the gas breakdown voltage to a level where, at the maximum PFN output voltage, the critical voltage for multichanneling could no longer be achieved [22]. Note that the surface spark gap pressure of 2.4-atm N_2 provided the maximum output energy from the laser at the highest operable pressure, 6 atm. It was not changed as the gas pressure in the laser was altered throughout this study.

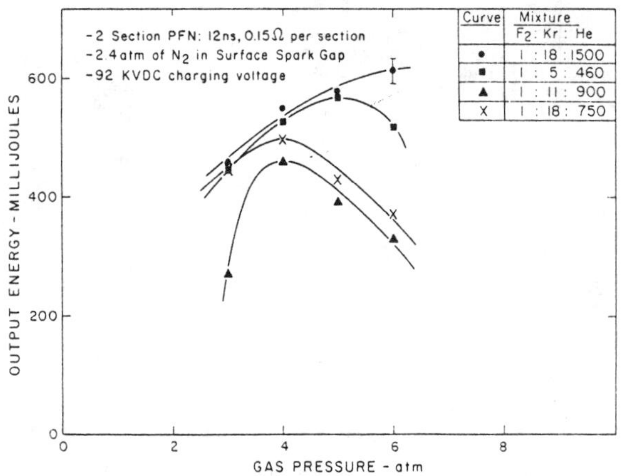

Fig. 6. Dependence of output energy upon gas pressure and composition for a fixed charging voltage of 92 kV dc.

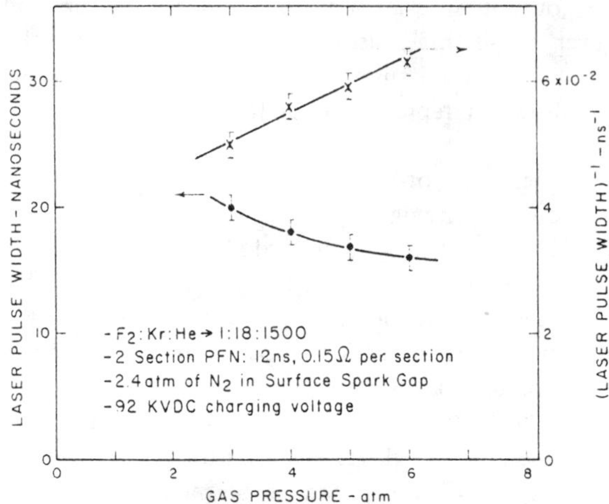

Fig. 7. Variation of laser pulsewidth with gas pressure for a fixed gas composition and charging voltage.

It was demonstrated experimentally that substantially reducing (~5X) the rate of application of voltage, limited the maximum pressure at which glow discharge operation could be obtained to less than 3 atm. Significant degradation of the discharge stability also followed, even at lower pressures, as well as increased energy fluctuations in pulse-to-pulse repeatability (±20 percent). Multichannel (~100 channels) operation of the switch reduced the inductive phase time constant substantially [13], [22] so that the full energy stored in the PFN could be deposited into the electrical discharge over the PFN period. The relatively high voltage hold-off and rapid breakdown time [Fig. 9(b)] are to be contrasted to the behavior of atmospheric surface discharges [15], [23].

The gas mixture, 1:18:1500 of F_2:Kr:He, for maximum energy per pulse was optimized in the following way: for a fixed molecular concentration of fluorine, the output energy was measured both as a function of krypton concentration and the total system pressure, as helium was added. This procedure was repeated as the fluorine donor partial pressure was further increased. In this way a maximum energy per pulse of 610 mJ was achieved. The energy output was still increasing with total gas pressure at the voltage limit of the present PFN and the optimum gas composition did not appear to change with pressure. In the case of the 1:11:900 and 1:18:750 mixtures, for pressures above 4 atm the output energy decreased with mounting pressure, although glow discharge operation appeared to be maintained.

A significant difficulty encountered in sustained pulsing of a nonflowing KrF laser is the degradation of the laser output energy caused by the chemical kinetics of the discharge [24]. In the present laser system, operating at the $\frac{1}{2}$ Joule level, the output energy was observed to decrease 1 percent per pulse, after a plateau level of ~30 pulses. This behavior appeared to be relatively insensitive to repetition rate over the range 0.1 pps to 1 ppm. Indeed, adding additional F_2 and/or Kr to the mixture after the output energy had decreased to ~10 percent of the initial value resulted in only a small enhancement in energy. Streak photographs of the discharge showed that a volume glow discharge existed before and after these additional gases were added. In addition, no significant changes

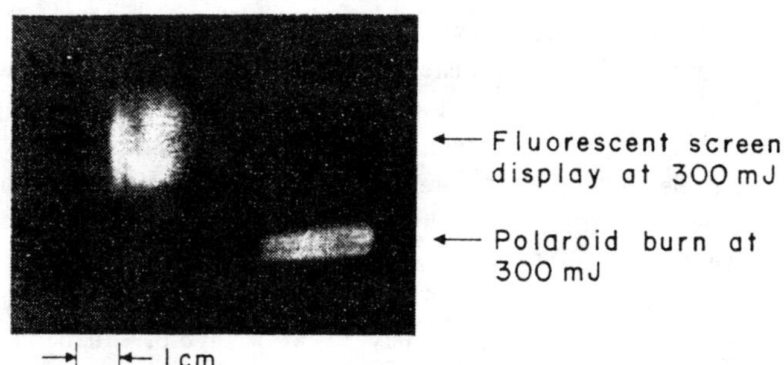

Fig. 8. Comparison of the attenuated output of the laser impinging upon a fluorescent screen to a burn on exposed Polaroid film, at 300-mJ output energy.

in the waveshape and amplitude of the voltage pulse on the laser electrodes were observed. This behavior is similar to the case of XeF (using NF_3 and F_2) but in marked contrast to ArF (using F_2) wherein energy was increased to more than 50 percent of the initial value by adding additional F_2 [18]. Detailed comparisons have not yet been carried out in all three cases using NF_3 or other halogen compounds as fluorine donors [8]. From this we conclude that this system is suitable for long-term sealed-off operation only by utilizing a gas recycling system [24].

Since high peak power is of specific interest for studying optical pumping and nonlinear phenomena with UV lasers, the variation of optical pulse duration with increasing pressure was studied. The laser pulse duration was monitored by means of a Hamamatsu model R 617 photodiode having an *S*-5 response, used in conjunction with a Tektronix 466 oscilloscope. Fig. 7 indicates that only a small pulse width decrease occurred for the pressure range of 3–6 atm. This is to be contrasted with the $1/p$ dependence observed in XeF and ArF [10] so that the KrF laser appears to be better suited to applications wherein a high total energy is the predominant requirement. The optical pulse shape was free of a tail or other observable structure and showed no dependence on cavity alignment and gas composition under lasing conditions.

A comparison is shown in Fig. 8 of the attenuated output of

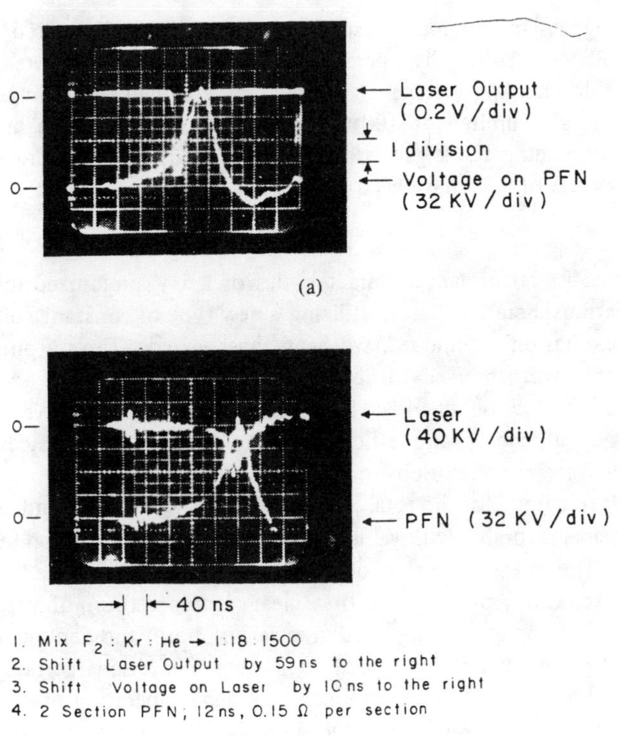

Fig. 9. (a) Optical output from the laser (upper) and voltage on the PFN (lower). Vertical scale for the laser output is uncalibrated. (b) Voltages on the laser electrodes (upper) and on the PFN (lower). Gas composition at 6 atm was F_2:Kr:He in the ratio 1:18:1500 and the charging voltage was 92 kV dc.

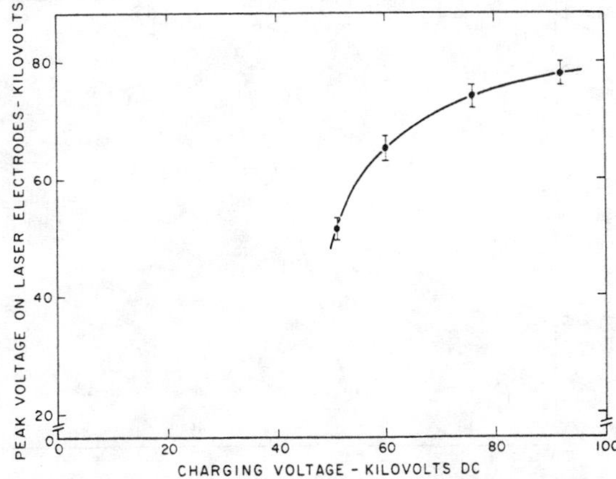

Fig. 10. Variation of the peak voltage on the laser electrodes with charging voltage. The gas mixture at 6 atm was composed of F_2:Kr:He in the ratio 1:18:1500.

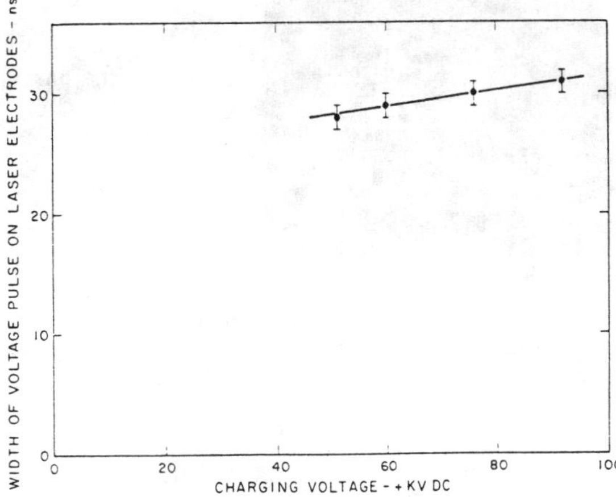

Fig. 11. Dependence of the width (FWHM) of the voltage pulse on the laser electrodes, upon charging voltage for a fixed gas pressure of 6 atm and a F_2:Kr:He ratio of 1:18:1500.

the laser impinging upon a fluorescent screen compared to a burn on exposed Polaroid film at the 300-mJ level. There is a substantial difference between the two areas in the photograph. The determination of maximum extractable laser energy depends upon which area is used in the calculation, giving values of 3.4 ± 0.4 or 6.1 ± 0.4 J/ℓ. These are obtained by taking the discharge widths at 6 atm as 1.3 and 0.7 cm, respectively. One then concludes that the minimum extractable energy density available from this system is 3 J/ℓ.

Electrical Characteristics

As a means of gaining further insight into the effect of charging voltage on laser output and efficiency, the electrical performance of this device was characterized by monitoring the voltages across the PFN and the laser electrodes. The voltage monitoring systems employed were variants of those described elsewhere [25] with an overall response time, including the 466 oscilloscope, of 3.5 ns. Fig. 9(a) displays the optical output of the laser and the voltage on the PFN. The pulse charging time is seen to be ~150 ns and the lasing action begins slightly past the crest of the PFN charging voltage. Comparing Fig. 9(b) with 9(a) it is evident that the optical output is beginning midway along the crest of the voltage applied to the laser electrodes. Note that the laser electrode voltage pulse is relatively flat topped, decaying rapidly through zero in the post lasing regime. The pulsewidth, FWHM, is 30 ± 5 ns, in reasonable agreement with 24 ns for the two-section PFN, whose impedance was ~0.15-Ω/section. The latter was solely a calculated value taking into consideration the lumped inductance and capacitance of each element in the PFN. The rate of rise of the voltage on the laser electrodes was observed by replacing the 466 oscilloscope with a 3.5-GHz Tektronix 519. In this case the measured risetime of the voltage pulse was ~2 ns. That of the measuring system, when tested with a pressurized liquid insulated spark gap discharging a transmission line charged to 60 kV dc, was 1.2 ns. Fig. 10 presents the variation of this peak voltage on the laser electrodes, with charging voltage. The slope of the curve decreases rapidly at the higher charging voltages.

It is important to note that, as Fig. 11 shows, in marked contrast to capacitor driven discharges, the width of the voltage pulse applied to the laser electrodes is essentially independent of charging voltage. This is as expected in an impedance matched system utilizing a PFN for energy storage [17]. In this way, by altering the characteristics of the PFN, the rectangular voltage pulse required for optimal constant E/p pumping and the impedance matching required for efficient operation of this class of fast discharge lasers can be achieved

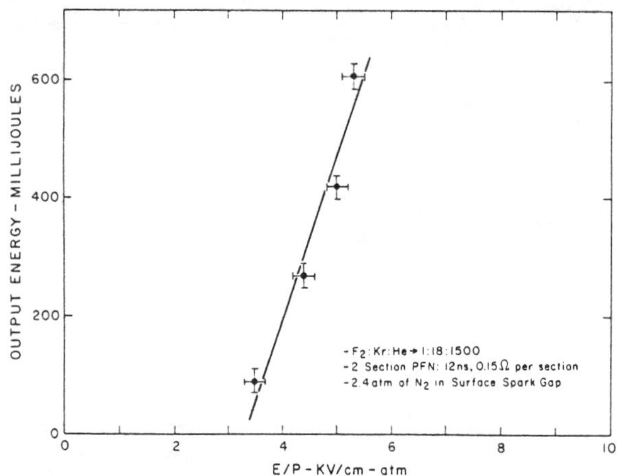

Fig. 12. Laser output energy versus E/p for a fixed gas pressure of 6 atm and a F_2:Kr:He ratio of 1:18:1500.

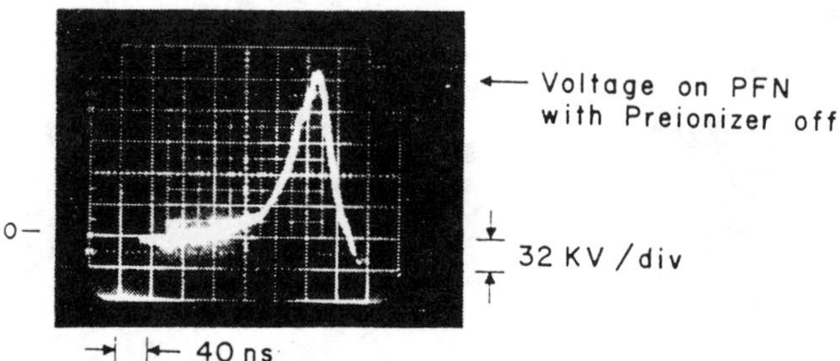

Fig. 13. Voltage on the PFN when the preionizer does not fire. The F_2:Kr:He ratio was 1:18:1500 and the charging voltage was 92 kV dc at a total gas pressure of 6 atm.

with independent control of pulse duration and applied electric field. Using this arrangement, the output energy was determined as a function of E/p by varying the dc charging voltage, at a constant gas pressure of 6 atm. As illustrated in Fig. 12, the output energy depends linearly upon E/p up to 5.2 kV/cm · atm and 0.61-J output energy. Since this relatively high field is sustained across the discharge during the transit time of the PFN, efficient pumping of other interesting laser systems, such as the N_2^+ + He charge transfer laser [26] has been possible. In KrF, unlike the case of the XeF laser [10], increasing the field at lower pressures in mixtures having the same specific number density of Kr and F_2, did not result in significant increases in output energy. Additionally, this effect was relatively independent of the number of sections in the PFN, with the increase in energy being 20 percent at 3 atm with four sections in the PFN. Laser action was not achievable for pressures less than ~2.5 atm, probably as a result of decreasing gain and consequent overcoupling of the cavity. It was noted that replacing the electrodes with those of higher field gradient geometry allowed laser action to be achieved down to subatmospheric pressures at the expense of energy, output uniformity and discharge area.

Improper firing of the preionizer resulted in a substantial loss of ceramic capacitors when operating at a charging voltage of 100 kV dc. Fig. 13 illustrates the very high (~170 kV) voltage applied to the ceramic capacitors in a case where the preionizer did not fire and the laser then arced. Proper triggering of the preionizer spark gap effectively eliminated this difficulty, aided by operation of the system at a more reasonable charging voltage of 92 kV dc. Provided the number of shots is limited at 100 kV dc, and the gas pressure in the sharpening spark gap is carefully adjusted, output energies in excess of 0.7 J have been achieved.

Discussion

The performance characteristics of a UV preionized multiatmosphere KrF laser, utilizing a new type of constant voltage excitation technique have been investigated. The output energy was observed to depend linearly upon E/p with a value of 0.61 J obtained at 5.2 ± 0.2 kV/cm · atm, however, the output energy and efficiency are presently limited by high-voltage considerations in the power conditioning system. The lower limit for the total extractable energy was 3 J/ℓ and compares favorably with values quoted for E-beam excitation [27].

The present results, obtained with highly overvolted PFN excitation, provide the first clear demonstration of volume excitation at pressures well in excess of 1 atm and demonstrate the potential scalability of such transverse discharge rare gas halide lasers to larger volumes and higher operating pressures. The possibility of operation at high repetition rates has not been investigated; however, aside from the problem of gas recycling, the present device has no inherent repetition rate limitations and should permit the development of high average power sources of coherent UV radiation.

Finally, although the present study has been concerned with the KrF gas laser it is to be noted that the excitation technique is of general applicability for the constant E/p pumping of high-pressure transverse discharge lasers other than the rare gas halides. A preliminary study of the N_2^+ + He system using <0.1 percent N_2 in helium at 6 atm yielded an output energy of 20 mJ, while, with a 1:1:8 mixture of CO_2:N_2:He, at a total pressure of 3 atm, output pulses of ~5 J having a duration of 20 ns were readily achieved.

Acknowledgment

The authors wish to thank I. V. Kovsh for participation in the measurements and acknowledge the valuable assistance of G. A. Berry in fabrication of the laser discharge chamber.

References

[1] R. Burnham, N. W. Harris, and N. Djeu, "Xenon fluoride laser excitation by transverse electric discharge," *Appl. Phys. Lett.*, vol. 28, pp. 86-87, Jan. 15, 1976.

[2] C. P. Wang, H. Mirels, D. G. Sutton, and S. N. Suchard, "Fast-discharge-initiated XeF laser," *Appl. Phys. Lett.*, vol. 28, pp. 326-328, Mar. 15, 1976; D. G. Sutton, S. N. Suchard, O. L. Gibb, and C. P. Wang, "Fast-discharge-initiated KrF laser," *Appl. Phys. Lett.*, vol. 28, pp. 522-523, May 1, 1976.

[3] R. Burnham, F. X. Powell, and N. Djeu, "Efficient electric discharge lasers in XeF and KrF," *Appl. Phys. Lett.*, vol. 29, pp. 30-32, July 1, 1976.

[4] C. P. Wang, "Performance of XeF/KrF lasers pumped by fast discharges," *Appl. Phys. Lett.*, vol. 29, pp. 103-105, July 15, 1976.

[5] V. N. Ishchenko, V. N. Lisitsyn, and A. M. Razhev, "Superradiative rare gas halide lasers excited by electric discharge," *Appl. Phys.*, vol. 12, pp. 55-58, 1977.

[6] B. Godard and M. Vannier, "Compact efficient discharge lasers in XeF, KrF and fluorine," *Opt. Commun.*, vol. 18, pp. 206-207, July 1976.

[7] R. Burnham and N. Djeu, "Ultraviolet-preionized discharge-pumped lasers in XeF, KrF and ArF," *Appl. Phys. Lett.*, vol. 29, pp. 707-709, Dec. 1, 1976.
[8] A. J. Andrews, A. J. Kearsley, C. E. Webb, and S. C. Haydon, "A KrF fast discharge laser in mixtures containing NF_3, N_2F_4 or SF_6," *Opt. Commun.*, vol. 20, pp. 265-268, Feb. 1977.
[9] W. J. Sarjeant, A. J. Alcock, and K. E. Leopold, "A scalable multiatmosphere high-power XeF laser," *Appl. Phys. Lett.*, vol. 30, pp. 635-637, June 15, 1977.
[10] —, "Constant *E/N* pumping of high-power rare-gas halide lasers," *IEEE J. Quantum Electron.*, vol. QE-13, pp. 104D-106D, Sept. 1977.
[11] Type E-7 epoxy: Techkits Inc., Demarest, NJ.
[12] J. C. Martin, "Multichannel gaps," AWRE Switching Notes, no. 10, Mar. 5, 1970.
[13] J. C. Martin, "Duration of the resistive phase and inductance of spark channels," AWRE Switching Notes, no. 9, Dec. 1965.
[14] K. E. Leopold and A. J. Alcock, "Simple, fully isolated, high voltage trigger generator," *Rev. Sci. Instr.*, vol. 47, pp. 254-255, Feb. 1976.
[15] L. P. Bradley, private communication.
[16] R. Sze, T. Loree, and R. Scott, "Performance characteristics of discharge excited excimer lasers," Laser Induced Chemistry, *2nd Wint. Conf.*, Park City, UT, Feb. 13-16, 1977; C. Brau, private communication.
[17] G. N. Glasoe and J. V. Lebacqz, *Pulse Generators*. New York: Dover, 1965.
[18] W. J. Sarjeant, A. J. Alcock, and K. E. Leopold, unpublished.
[19] C. A. Brau, A. E. Greene, and S. D. Rockwood, "Theoretical model for discharge excited rare gas halide lasers," presented at *2nd Wint. Coll. Laser Induced Chem.*, Park City, UT, Feb. 13-16, 1977; C. Brau, "Excimer lasers," presented at *3rd Int. Cong. Int. Trade Fair*, June 20-24, 1977, Munich, West Germany.
[20] W. H. Long, Jr., "Electron kinetics in the KrF laser," *Appl. Phys. Lett.*, vol. 31, pp. 391-394, Sept. 15, 1977.
[21] J. Hsia, "A model for uv preionization in electric-discharge-pumped XeF and KrF lasers," *Appl. Phys. Lett.*, vol. 30, pp. 101-103, Jan. 15, 1977.
[22] J. C. Martin, "Pressure dependency of the pulse breakdown of gases," AWRE Dielectric Strength Notes, no. 15, Sept. 26, 1967; —, "Pulsed surface tracking in air and various gases," AWRE SSWA/JCM/745/735, May 1974.
[23] A. V. Grigor'ev, P. N. Dushuk, S. N. Markov, V. L. Shutov, and M. D. Yurysheva, "Low-inductance megampere-current commutator based on sliding discharge," *Instrum. Exp. Tech.*, (USSR), vol. 19, pt. 2, pp. 1104-1105, July-Aug. 1976.
[24] C. P. Christensen, "High-repetition-rate XeF laser with gas recycling," *Appl. Phys. Lett.*, vol. 30, pp. 483-484, May 1, 1977.
[25] W. J. Sarjeant and A. J. Alcock, "High-voltage probe system with subnanosecond rise time," *Rev. Sci. Instr.*, vol. 47, pp. 64-68, Oct. 1976.
[26] J. B. Laudenslager, T. J. Pacala, and C. Wittig, "Electric-discharge-pumped nitrogen ion laser," *Appl. Phys. Lett.*, vol. 29, pp. 580-582, Nov. 1, 1976.
[27] J. M. Hoffman, A. K. Hays, and G. C. Tisone, "High-power uv noble-gas-halide lasers," *Appl. Phys. Lett.*, vol. 28, pp. 538-539, May 1, 1976.

Reprinted with permission from *Fusion Technology,* Vol. 11, pp. 497-531 (May 1987). ©1987 American Nuclear Society, La Grange Park, Illinois.

AURORA MULTIKILOJOULE KrF LASER SYSTEM PROTOTYPE FOR INERTIAL CONFINEMENT FUSION

LOUIS A. ROSOCHA, JOHN A. HANLON, JOHN McLEOD, MICHAEL KANG, BIRCHARD L. KORTEGAARD, MICHAEL D. BURROWS, and P. STUART BOWLING
University of California, Los Alamos National Laboratory
P.O. Box 1663, MS E548, Los Alamos, New Mexico 87545

Aurora is the Los Alamos National Laboratory short-pulse, high-power, KrF laser system. It serves as an end-to-end technology demonstration for large-scale ultraviolet laser systems of interest for short wavelength, inertial confinement fusion (ICF) investigations. The system is a prototype for using optical angular multiplexing and serial amplification by large electron-beam-driven KrF laser amplifiers to deliver stacked, 248-nm, 5-ns duration multikilojoule laser pulses to ICF targets using an ~1-km-long optical beam path.

The entire Aurora KrF laser system is described and the design features of the following major system components are summarized: front-end lasers, amplifier train, multiplexer, optical relay train, demultiplexer, target irradiation apparatus, and alignment and controls systems.

INTRODUCTION

Rare-gas-halide excimer lasers, such as KrF, have properties that make them highly promising candidates for inertial fusion drivers.[1,2] One particularly advantageous property is that KrF lasers produce a short wavelength that couples more efficiently to fusion targets than visible and infrared wavelength systems. Recent theoretical and experimental work on inertial confinement fusion (ICF) laser/target interactions has shown that the efficiency of coupling energy into fusion targets increases as the laser driver wavelength decreases.[3-7] Krypton fluoride is nearly optimum for a fusion driver because its wavelength is short enough to ensure efficient laser-target coupling, yet long enough to have a high transmission in practical optical materials. Because 248-nm light penetrates the target plasma to regions of high density, KrF laser drivers can provide high ablation pressures. Also, the hot electron production typical of longer wavelength lasers is drastically reduced. The KrF laser has a broad bandwidth, which provides further assurance that hot electron production will not occur. The output bandwidth of KrF lasers can be sufficiently increased to decrease the effects of the nonlinear processes that are thought to be the mechanism for the overheating.[9] Additionally, KrF lasers driven by electron beams (*e* beams) are shown to have a high intrinsic efficiency,[10-21] are scalable to high-energy output,[22-24] are relatively economical to build,[25] and have the potential for high repetition rate operation.

In spite of these many advantages, the KrF laser is constrained to output intensities of 10 to 20 MW/cm^2 by its relatively low saturation flux and relatively large nonsaturable absorption losses. To get high-energy outputs from KrF lasers, the aperture must be scaled to very large sizes to avoid both this saturation effect and high flux optical component damage. An additional constraint arises because KrF is a nonstorage laser medium; that is, the upper state lifetime is quite short, being only a few nanoseconds. Therefore, extraction of power from the laser medium is limited by the rate at which excitation energy is deposited in the medium. For practical excitation devices such as large area *e* guns operating at the multikilojoule level, electrical and laser efficiency limitations restrict the energy deposition to fairly long pump times (>100 ns). Because efficient coupling of the laser energy to a fusion target requires laser pulse durations with an energetic component of ~5 ns, some means of matching these target-pulse duration requirements to the pump-pulse duration must be devised. Two principal methods of accomplishing this match are optical multiplexing[17,26-33] and nonlinear optical techniques (e.g.,

Raman[34] and Brillouin[35–41] compression). The optical multiplexing technique creates a synthetic long pulse from a sequence of shorter pulses. This long pulse is more efficiently amplified by *e*-beam-excited KrF amplifiers. After amplification, the shorter pulses that comprise the long-pulse train are then appropriately delayed in time to arrive simultaneously (stacked into a single short pulse) at the target. Figure 1 shows the concept. At Los Alamos National Laboratory (LANL), we adopted the multiplexing approach because it utilizes conventional optical techniques and existing designs. So far, nonlinear pulse compression system concepts have not been proven to be more economical, efficient, or simple.

At LANL, we are investigating how KrF lasers may be applied to ICF (Refs. 42 and 43). The bulk of this investigation will be performed with the Aurora high-power KrF/ICF laser system prototype, which is now undergoing final construction and testing. The system employs optical angular multiplexing and serial amplification by *e*-beam-pumped KrF laser amplifiers to deliver 5- to 8-kJ laser pulses of 5-ns duration to ICF targets. Aurora is being built in two phases: The first phase includes the multiplexing and serial amplification features, while the second phase includes the additional end-to-end demonstrations of demultiplexing and delivery of laser pulses to fusion targets.

An overview of the Aurora system has been presented in an earlier publication[44]; the present paper has been expanded from Ref. 44 to provide a more complete description of the system. The performance of the main power amplifier [the large aperture module (LAM)] has been described in earlier more specific reports,[24,45] and a more complete treatment of the LAM performance is being planned for a future publication.[46] The LAM final amplifier has a 1- × 1-m laser aperture and is the largest and highest energy ultraviolet (UV) laser of its type so far reported, having produced more than 10 kJ of 248-nm laser light when operated as a nonoptimized unstable resonator device.

The Aurora prototype will serve as a test bed for specific technological aspects of larger laser fusion systems. In particular, Aurora will examine the following:

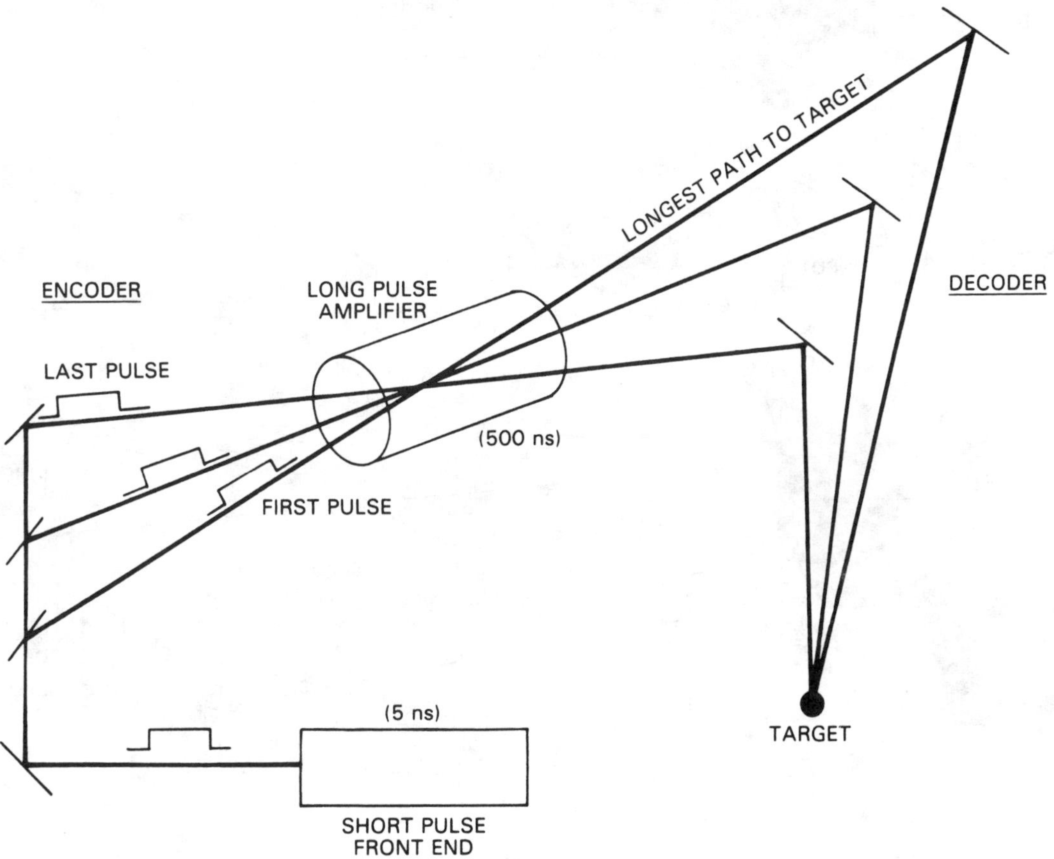

Fig. 1. A schematic diagram that illustrates the concept of optical angular multiplexing. From the front-end oscillator pulse, an encoder produces a head-to-tail train of pulses that are slightly separated in path angle. This pulse train is then amplified and the individual pulses are sent along appropriate flight paths such that all the pulses arrive at the target simultaneously. The use of multiplexing enables the short-pulse target requirement to be matched to long-pulse KrF lasers.

1. uniform e-beam pumping of large laser volumes
2. optical angular multiplexing and demultiplexing systems that are scalable to large system designs
3. control of amplified spontaneous emission (ASE) and parasitics for large amplifiers
4. staging of large KrF amplifiers
5. UV pulse propagation over long paths
6. alignment and real-time alignment control of multibeam multipath systems
7. novel approaches to optical hardware that can lead to cost reductions for even larger systems.

Figure 2 shows a conceptual layout of the Aurora system as it is presently configured. The first-phase portion of the system contains all of the main optical and laser elements from the front end to the final power amplifier output. In this first phase, the basic approach is to replicate the front-end output using aperture slicers, beam splitters, and mirrors to produce a 480-ns-long pulse train consisting of 96 beams, each of 5-ns duration. These encoded (multiplexed) pulses are spatially separated and individually adjusted at the entrance pupil of an optical relay system. The beam train is then relayed through two single-pass laser amplifiers [the preamplifier (PA) and intermediate amplifier (IA)], a double-pass laser amplifier (the LAM),

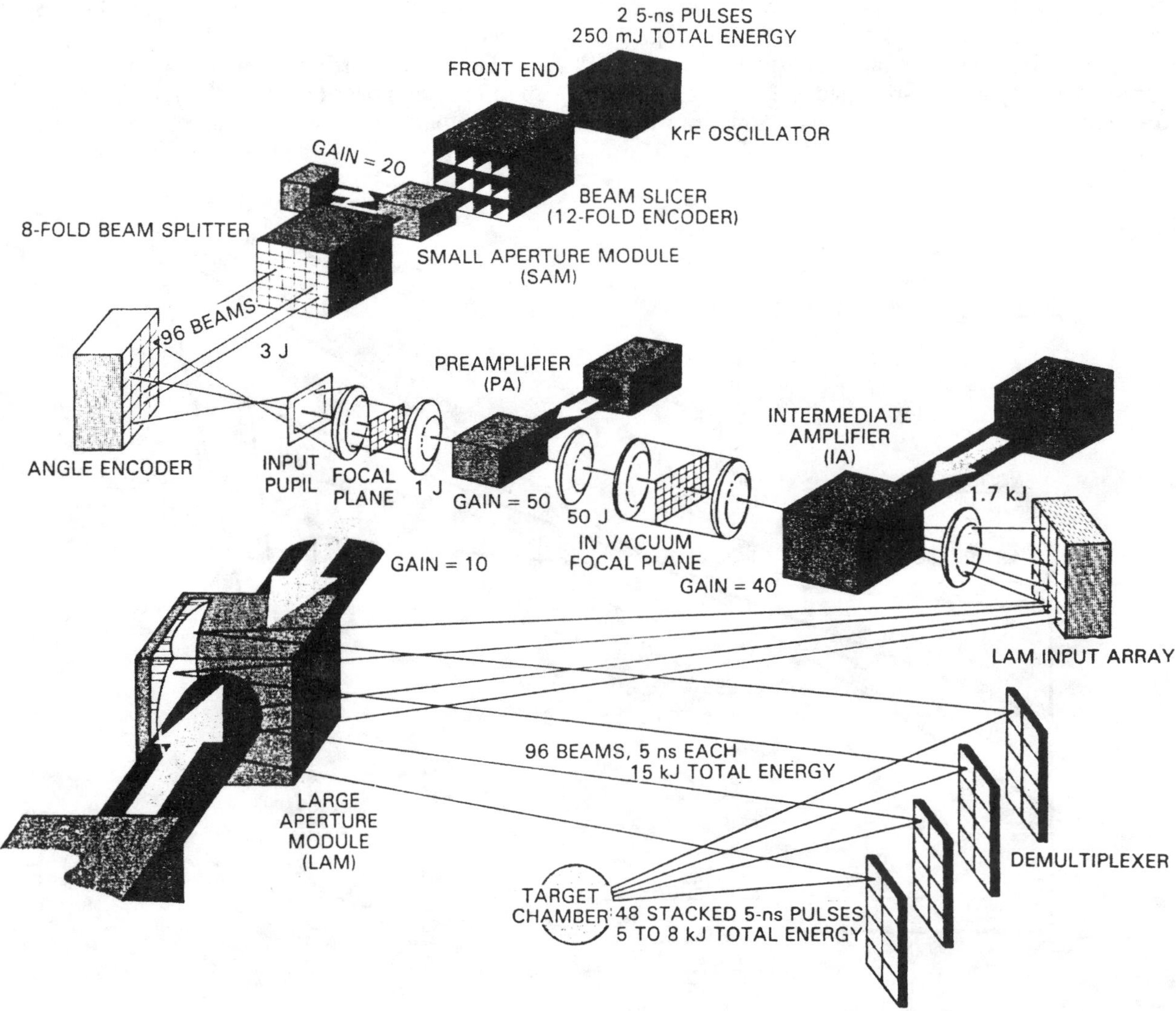

Fig. 2. A conceptual layout of the Aurora laser system. All of the main optical and laser elements from the front end, through the final amplifier output, and on to the target are shown. Stage gains, number of beams, and energy per beam are indicated at various points along the beam path. A final optimized design output of 10 to 20 kJ in a 480-ns pulse composed of a 96-element train of 5-ns pulses is expected at the output of the final LAM amplifier. Typical delivered energy at the target will be 5 to 8 kJ in 48 beams.

and delivered to a diagnostics station. Beam-train alignment to the diagnostics station is accomplished with two automated alignment control systems. In one system, the 96 beams at the entrance pupil are imaged on a single television (TV) camera, and a control system analyzes each beam location relative to its desired position and to fixed optical benchmarks. It then corrects the pointing of the 96 input pupil mirrors individually to correct for system drift and change. Pointing accuracies of ~5 μrad are continually maintained up until the actual instant of firing. The second alignment system keeps the LAM primary mirror aligned in real time. In principle, a final optimized design output of 15 to 20 kJ can be expected from the LAM.

To deliver short-pulse KrF laser energy to fusion targets, the system requires decoder (demultiplexer) optics to compress the multiplexed beam train and a target facility to house and perform diagnostics on fusion targets. The second phase of Aurora will be concerned with this end-to-end demonstration of multiplexing, amplification, demultiplexing, and delivery of energy to target. Figure 3 shows an artists's conception of the second-phase Aurora system as it will appear with a 48-beam demultiplexer and target building in place. As configured, this system is designed to stack 48 of the 96 multiplexed and amplified beams into a single multikilojoule 5-ns pulse at the fusion target.

In this paper, we present a description of the front end, the amplifiers, the multiplexer and relay optics, the alignment system, the demultiplexer optics, the target system, and the controls system.

FRONT END

The front-end system provides the initial pulse that is replicated and then amplified for delivery to the target. The Aurora front-end system will progress in stages that correspond to the two phases of the project. An interim front end will provide 5-ns pulses adequate for startup and initial integration of the amplifier chain. A front end to be installed later will provide high-contrast ratio and pulse shaping, as well as bandwidth flexibility.

First-Phase Front End for Multiplexing Demonstrations

The present Aurora front end is shown in Fig. 4. This system uses Pockels cells to switch out a 5-ns

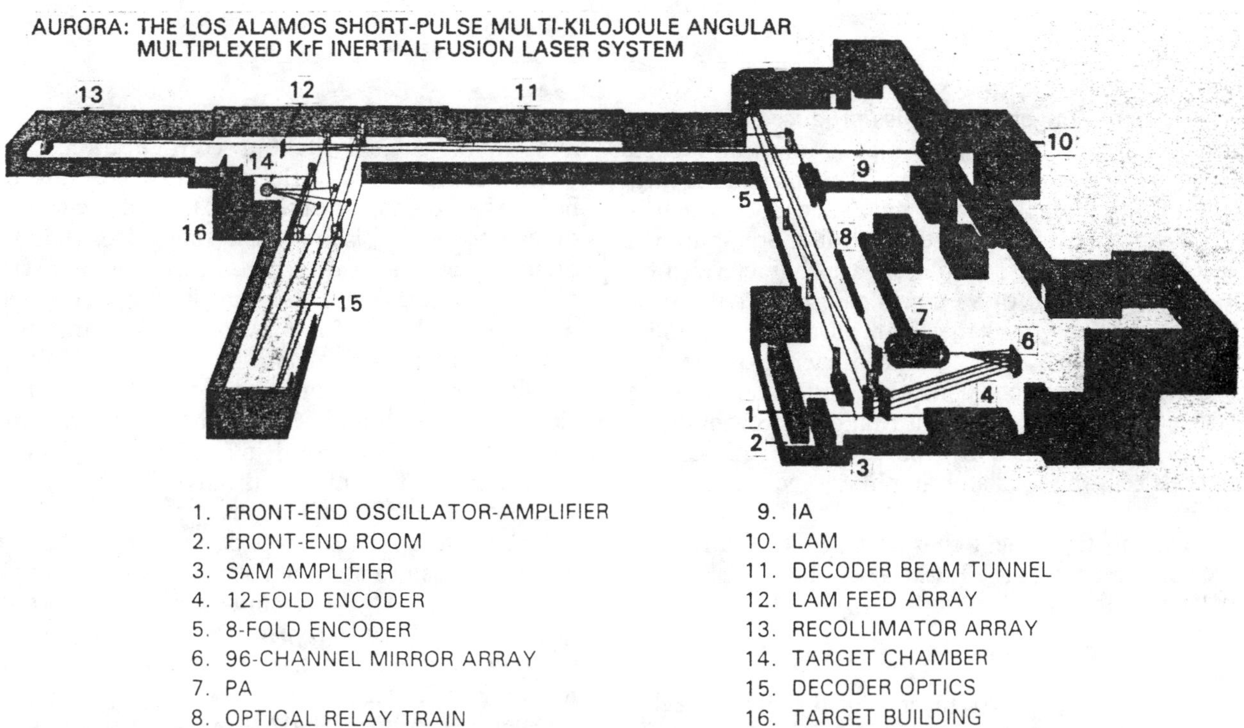

Fig. 3. An artist's conception of the Aurora system with a 48-beam decoder and target building in place. As configured, the system is intended to deliver multikilojoule 5-ns laser pulses to fusion targets. The decoder optics, mounts, and target chamber are under fabrication and final installation. The laser system shown on the right is presently in the final stages of system integration. The assembly of the decoder components has started in the building on the left.

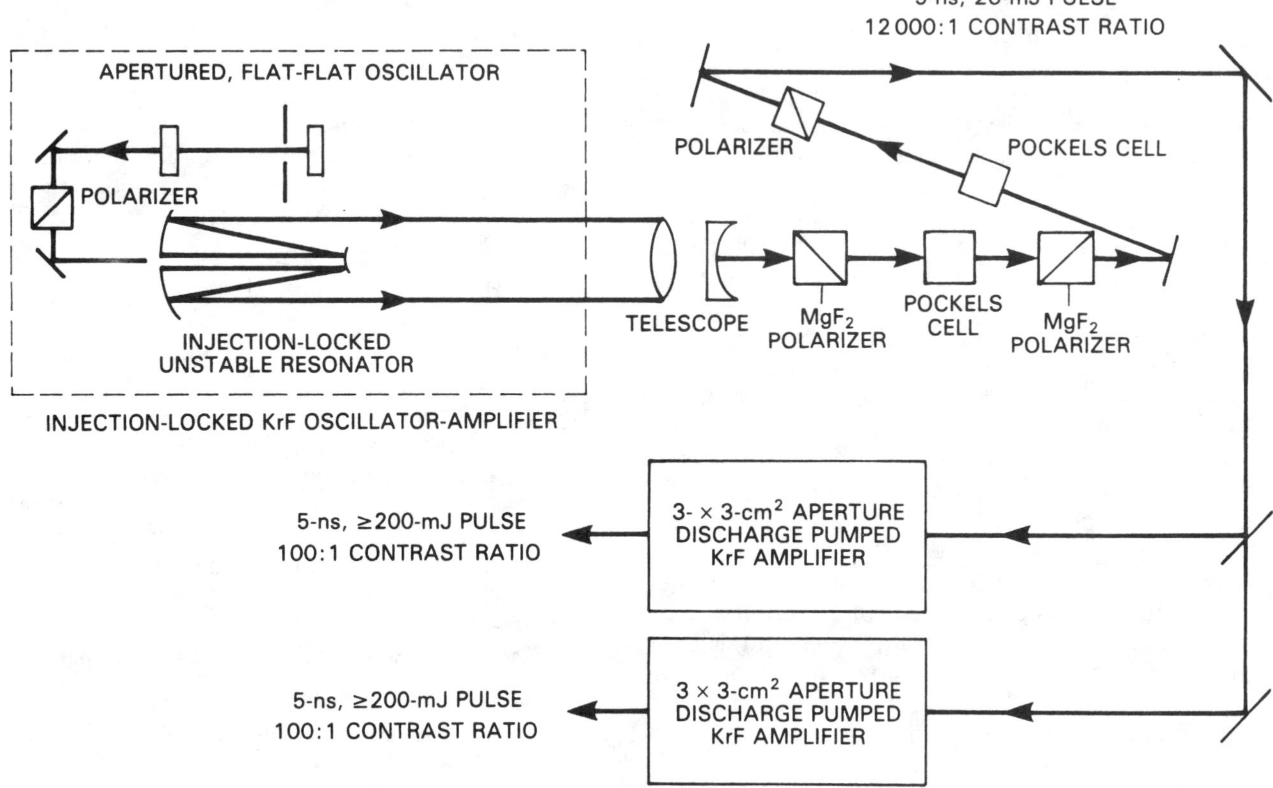

Fig. 4. Current Aurora front-end configuration and typical performance parameters obtained with Pockels cell switch-out approach.

pulse from a longer 25-ns pulse produced by a commercial electric discharge-pumped, injection-locked KrF oscillator-amplifier system. The 5-ns pulse is then split into two identical 5-ns pulses, each of which is single-pass amplified in a separate discharge-pumped KrF amplifier. These amplifiers are characterized by a discharge length of 93 cm, a gain of 7% per centimetre, a 25-ns discharge gain duration, and ASE levels of ≦20 mJ. The combined energy of the two amplified pulses is >400 mJ. The performance of the system[47] (total energy, contrast ratio, and beam divergence) is determined by the characteristics of the Pockels cell, the oscillator-amplifier, and the postamplifiers.

The most pertinent characteristics that influence the performance of the Pockels cell and its associated polarizers are

1. the transmission of the Pockels cell
2. the residual birefringence of the Pockels cell
3. the sensitivity of the Pockels cell to the beam divergence of the long-pulse (25-ns) input beam
4. the transmission of the polarizers
5. the damage resistance of the polarizers.

Calcite polarizers were initially used in both single- and double-stage switchout configurations. These worked satisfactorily at fluences of two to three times below their damage threshold. The damage threshold of calcite, which is obtained solely from naturally occurring crystals, is determined by its relatively strong absorption at 248 nm. Our calcite polarizers, which were hand-selected for maximum UV transmission, typically exhibit 30% absorption at 248 nm. Thus, the net single-stage switchout transmission due to the calcite polarizers alone is 50%. When coupled with the KDP Pockels cell transmission of 70% at 248 nm, the net switchout transmission is only 35%. Using calcite polarizers and a 900-mJ, 25-ns parent pulse, a single-stage switchout yielded 5-ns pulse energies of 10 mJ, which dropped to 5 mJ if a second switch was added. Custom-made MgF_2 Rochon polarizers were then obtained and used to replace the calcites in a double-stage switchout starting from the last, lowest energy handling polarizer and working up to the first, highest energy handling polarizer. We were able to replace all the calcites with MgF_2 Rochons without damage to the new polarizers, each of which is 93% transmitting at 248 nm. The residual 7% insertion loss consists primarily of reflection losses rather than absorption in the bulk material. With these new polarizers installed, a two-stage switchout routinely delivers 5-ns pulses at 20-mJ energies and a contrast ratio of 12 000:1.

The 30% absorption in the Pockels cell material (KDP) appears as heat and electro-optic stress, both of which contribute to the residual birefringence of the Pockels cell. This birefringence is most apparent when the parent 25-ns pulse passes through the switch when it is not electrically activated. In this instance, we observe that a 99.9% vertically polarized input beam yields a $\frac{1}{1000}$ replica of the input pulse. This parent replica is horizontally polarized after emerging from the switch crystal. When the switch is normally activated by a 5-ns high-voltage pulse, the resulting horizontally polarized 5-ns pulse emerges from the crystal accompanied by a low-intensity replica of the parent pulse. Because of its amplification in the small-signal gain regime of the postamplifier, the presence of this replica amounts to an unwanted noise signal, which lowers the contrast ratio of the system to 100:1.

This contrast ratio degradation upon amplification is the direct result of two basic features of KrF amplification that differ substantially from the long wavelength energy storage lasers previously used as ICF drivers. One of these is the KrF stimulated emission cross section of 2.6×10^{-16} cm^2, which is orders of magnitude larger than the respective CO_2 and Nd:glass cross sections of 1.5×10^{-18} and 2×10^{-20} cm^2. The other is the temporal behavior of the pumping mechanism. The long upper-laser-level lifetimes of energy storage media such as CO_2 and Nd:glass permit relatively slow energy deposition into the lasing medium, resulting in a gradual accumulation of the gain over hundreds of microseconds. The short 6.7-ns spontaneous emission KrF^* lifetime dictates very fast energy deposition, resulting in a rapid buildup of the gain. Furthermore, rapid KrF^* quenching by F_2, electrons, and krypton results in an effective KrF^* lifetime of 1.5 ns in a discharge-pumped laser. Thus, the sustained pump rate must be sufficiently high to overcome these losses, and the gain recovers from a delta function optical pulse with an exponential time constant of 1.5 ns. Regardless of the wavelength, a short pulse of 1- to 5-ns duration will always contain some energy on the temporal wings of the desired pulse envelope. If this pulse propagates through an energy storage amplifier, this "noise" will experience relatively low levels of amplification because of the small stimulated emission cross section. However, the main pulse, timed to arrive late in the pumping time envelope, will saturate the amplifier and strongly reduce the gain. In an excimer amplifier, the noise (parent-pulse replica) grows exponentially in the small-signal gain regime where the full gain is always present due to the high sustained pumping rate and the large stimulated emission cross section. The main pulse, however, grows linearly as it propagates in a strongly saturated regime. In essence, the high stage gain required to obtain useful 5-ns pulse energies also produces an extremely sensitive optical preamplifier capable of detecting minute amounts of stray 248-nm light outside the temporal extent of the main pulse. Thus, without temporal multiplexing the contrast ratio in a KrF system degrades exponentially upon amplification.

We have shown[47] that this problem can be circumvented by removing the parent 25-ns pulse after amplification rather than prior to amplification. In this setup, the 25-ns parent pulse was polarization "encoded" using the Pockels cell. Then this vertically polarized long pulse, with a 5-ns horizontally polarized pulse embedded within it, was amplified in a discharge-pumped KrF amplifier with a 25-ns gain duration. The 25-ns parent pulse was then removed by a second crossed polarizer placed after the amplifier. The resulting 5-ns output pulse energies were typically 70 mJ, and the leading edge spike on the output pulse (described below) was absent.[47] The utility of this approach is limited, however, by the large 25-ns pulse energies that the final polarizer must handle without damage. This is a real problem with the present MgF_2 polarizers that have an aperture of only 1.7-cm diameter through which one would have to transmit fluences of 1 to 2 J. Larger MgF_2 Rochon polarizers with a 3- × 3-cm clear aperture would be required, but the output contrast ratio of the 5-ns pulse prior to the 12-channel encoder would be $>10^4$:1. Such large-aperture MgF_2 polarizers could be custom-made at considerable cost, but the potential for damage would be small because of the much larger working aperture.

We have used injection locking in the master oscillator-amplifier portion of the front end to reduce the beam divergence. The discharge-pumped amplifier used in our present injection-locking configuration has a very high gain of >20% per centimetre and correspondingly high ASE output levels (140 mJ per pulse out of each end). Hence, the pulse energy from the highly apertured KrF master oscillator (a few microjoules) is not sufficient to dominate the ASE within the unstable resonator cavity of the injected amplifier, resulting in a low-locking efficiency. Furthermore, as the ASE increases with time, the locking efficiency is observed to decrease.[48] For this reason we typically switch out the 5-ns pulse near the front of the 25-ns parent pulse. Because of this high level of ASE, the beam divergence of our injection-locked laser is better than that obtained without injection locking, but the fraction of the total output beam energy contained within a 0.15-mrad divergence angle is modest. Some decrease in divergence, however small, is still useful because Pockels cells are quite sensitive to the divergence of the input beam. This beam divergence sensitivity, coupled with the typical injection-locked excimer-laser pulse energy versus the divergence curve, results in 5-ns pulse energies of 20 mJ from a 900-mJ, 25-ns parent pulse. The second Pockels cell in the system operates at a higher efficiency because the beam divergence has been reduced by the first switch and the higher divergence (effectively unswitched) portion of the input beam is rejected by the second crossed polarizer.

After emerging from the second switch and polarizer set, the single 5-ns pulse is split into two identical pulses by the beam splitter and then passes through two parallel postamplifiers. Upon emerging from the postamplifiers, the two 5-ns pulses contain a total energy of >400 mJ, which is more than sufficient for the multiplexing demonstration.

The shape of the 5-ns pulses emerging from the postamplifiers is determined by the effective excited-state lifetime of the KrF gain medium. Because of a short 6.7-ns spontaneous lifetime and the effect of collisional quenching, the effective lifetime of each KrF* molecule is ~2 ns, which is the fundamental lifetime for KrF amplifiers. The KrF gain medium is, in fact, an energy storage medium with an effective lifetime of 2 ns. Hence, the first portion of the 5-ns input pulse encounters an inverted medium and extracts energy while the KrF* population is also being simultaneously replenished. The net effect is that for the first 2.5 ns, energy is simultaneously extracted from two KrF* lifetimes. The remainder of the pulse then extracts energy from a highly saturated amplifier. This energy storage effect results in an amplified pulse with a strong spike on the leading edge. The spike contributes substantially to the observed 5-ns extracted energy because we effectively access a longer gain time of 7 to 7.5 ns with a shorter 5-ns pulse. The output pulse from the interim front end is shown in Fig. 5.

Proposed Second-Phase Front End for Target Shooting

The first-phase front-end configuration meets the requirements for the proof-of-principle demonstration of the angular multiplexing technique, but will not be adequate for the delivery of energy to fusion targets because the contrast ratio is too low (~100:1). To provide a high-quality target shooter front end, our current proposed design is to replace the injection-locked KrF laser and Pockels cell switch by the Nd:YAG-pumped dye laser system shown in block diagram in Fig. 6. The bulk of this system is commercially available; however, extensive modifications will be required to provide a pulse-shaping capability.

The initial 1064 nm per Nd:YAG pulse width in this system is 8 to 9 ns. Second harmonic generation converts this to a 6- to 7-ns, 532-nm beam to pump a dye laser, with the unconverted portion of the 1064-nm beam being saved for later use via optical delays. An additional second harmonic generation yields a 6- to 7-ns-long UV pulse. This frequency-doubled dye beam is then mixed with the residual 1064-nm beam to yield 248-nm pulses of 4- to 5-ns duration at measured pulse energies of 5 mJ. Although a large number of nonlinear mixing processes are required to reach 248 nm, the physics of these processes is very helpful for tailoring the output pulse shape at 248 nm. In essence, the temporal output pulse shape is determined by the product of the input pulse shape with itself at each instant in time. Hence, the doubling stages square up the pulse shape, and the contrast ratio increases after each frequency up-conversion stage.

To obtain a high contrast ratio 5-ns pulse from this system, the rising and falling edges of the initial 5-ns pulse must be fast. A fast switching time (≲160-ps) Pockels cell will be placed between the Nd:YAG oscillator and amplifier. The 7-kV, 5-ns pulse applied to the Pockels cell will be switched using laser-triggered spark gaps (≲150-ps rise time) or solid-state Auston switches[49] (≲50-ps rise time) triggered by the 100-ps light pulse from an actively mode-locked Nd:YAG laser. Accurate synchronization of the two Nd:YAG lasers will be ensured by slaving the fast clock of the active mode locker with the Q-switch of the main Nd:YAG laser. The resulting 5-ns, 1064-nm pulse will then have rise and fall times of 200 to 300 ps. These

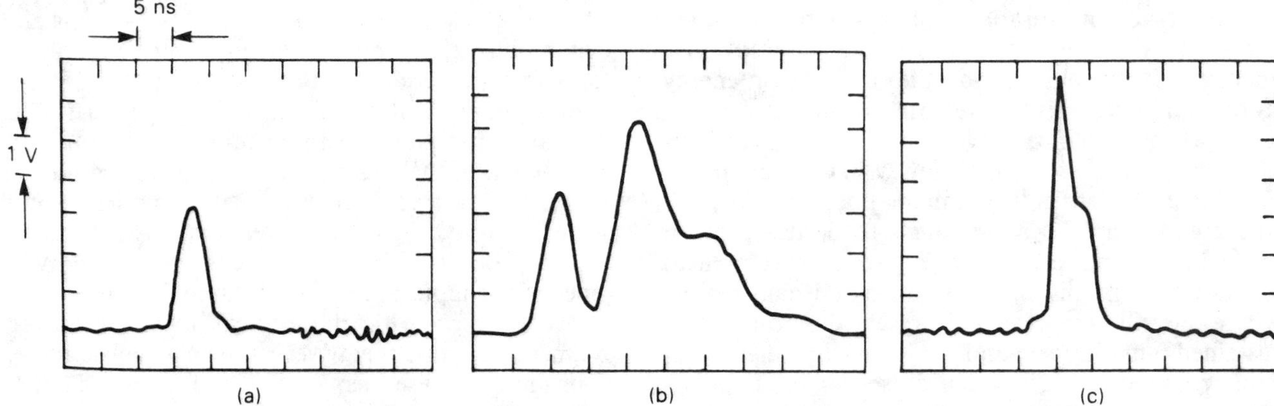

Fig. 5. (a) 5-ns pulse shape after switchout, and (b) parent 25-ns pulse with 5-ns switchout pulse removed. Gain saturation in the KrF postamplifier produces (c) the leading edge spike on the amplified 5-ns pulse.

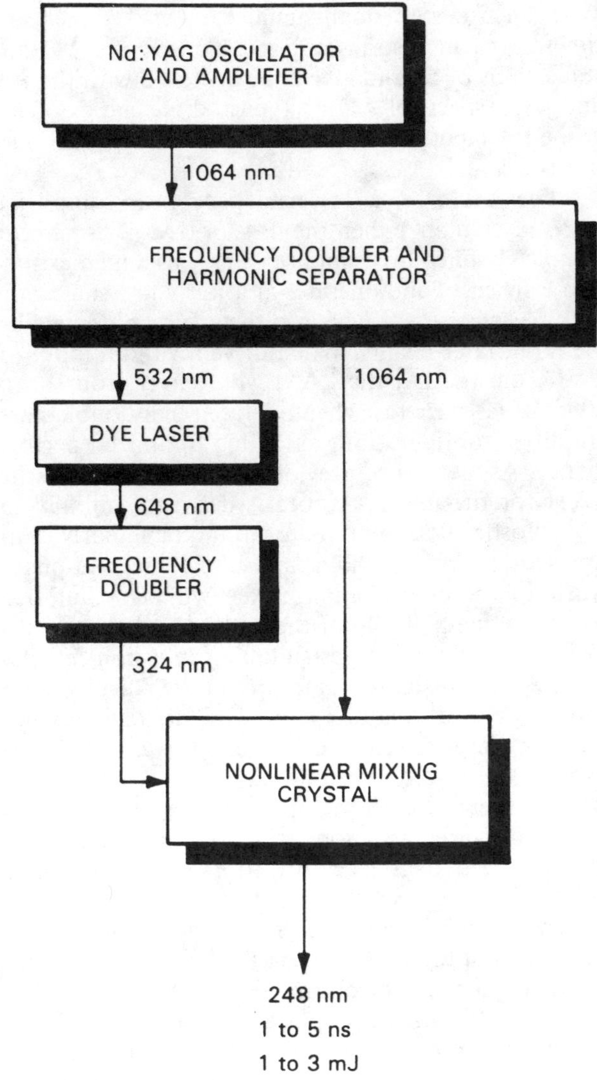

Fig. 6. Block diagram for the proposed Aurora second-phase front end.

fast rise and fall times will ensure that the nonlinear frequency up-conversion stages do not significantly shorten the initial 5-ns pulse width. The 300-ps leading and trailing edges will, however, be dramatically shortened by the doubling and mixing stages. A modest initial switchout contrast ratio of $10^4:1$ will be reduced to $10^3:1$ after Nd:YAG amplification. The 1064-nm doubling stage will increase this ratio to $10^6:1$, while dye laser frequency doubling is expected to provide a further increase to $10^{12}:1$. Thus, the contrast ratio of the 5-ns pulse at 248 nm will be very high because of the nonlinear frequency up-conversion process and the ability of the 532-nm pumped dye laser output to track the fast rise time of the 532-nm pump pulse temporally.

The plateau region between the 300-ps rising and falling edges of the initial 5-ns, 1064-nm pulse will not be perfectly flat, but will be somewhat peaked after conversion to 248 nm (result of squaring-up effect). Even if the pulse shape at 248 nm was perfectly square, amplification would produce the sharp leading edge spike that we currently observe. To avoid this leading edge spike after amplification in a KrF discharge amplifier, a tapered, variable impedance transmission line on the Pockels cell switchout will be used to provide a tailored pulse shape to compensate for amplifier pulse-shape distortion. Because this temporal taper will be imposed on the initial 1064-nm pulse, it can be slowly varying in time. The temporal squaring up provided by the doubling stages will then produce a much sharper taper. For example, a linear ramp with the functional form $y = t$ starting at the leading edge and increasing in amplitude to the trailing edge of the 5-ns pulse at 1064 nm assumes the form $y = t^2$ after doubling to 532 nm and $y = t^4$ upon doubling the dye laser. Hence, a sufficiently large taper can be introduced to compensate for KrF amplifier saturation. This same approach is used on the NOVA (Ref. 50) Nd:glass laser system. Further increases in the taper will produce a trailing edge spike for increased coupling of laser energy into the target.

The bandwidth of this system is determined primarily by the cavity components of the dye laser. Typically, the bandwidth at 248 nm is 1 cm^{-1}. Bandwidths of >100 cm^{-1} can be obtained by using lower order modes of the grating employed for dye-laser wavelength selection. Bandwidths of 100 cm^{-1} are feasible if this grating is replaced by a broadband mirror, with the tuning of the dye laser being accomplished by varying both the acidity and concentration of the laser dye mixture.

The postamplifier configuration for short pulses is shown in Fig. 7. The Lumonics[a] amplifiers are used here because we have demonstrated that their performance is well matched to the requirements of ICF short-pulse amplification. Thin film polarizers will be used to couple two counterpropagating "P" polarized 5-ns pulses into the amplifier. The quartz rotator will convert the amplified pulses to "S" polarized beams, which will then be outcoupled by the polarizers. Two such amplifier arrangements will provide four pulses that will be recombined to produce the required total 5-ns pulse energy. This will provide a flexible pulse shaping target shooter front-end system.

AMPLIFIERS

The main amplification chain for Aurora consists of four *e*-beam-driven KrF laser amplifiers ranging in aperture size from 10 × 12 cm to 100 × 100 cm. These devices are designated as the small aperture model

[a]Model TE-292K amplifiers, Lumonics Corporation, Ottawa, Canada.

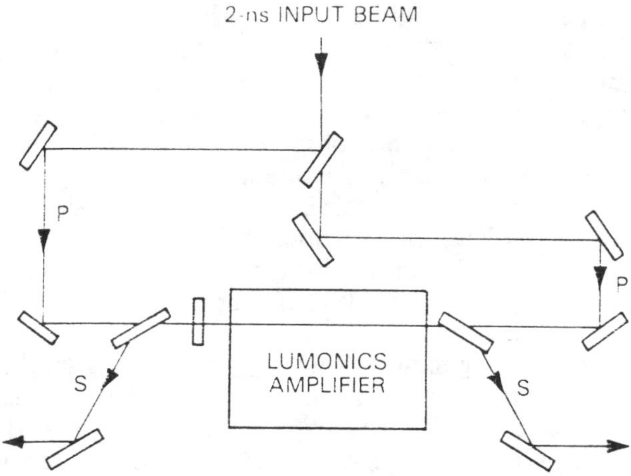

Fig. 7. Basic counterpropagating 2-ns pulse amplifier "building block" using a proven Lumonics amplifier. The thin film polarizers are at Brewster's angle and are used in combination with the λ/y Quartz rotator to allow efficient coupling of the pulses into and out of the amplifier. These polarizers also ensure that only half of the total amplifier ASE is out-coupled with the amplified 2-ns pulses.

(SAM), the PA, the IA, and the LAM. The characteristics of these four amplifiers are summarized in Table I.

The SAM is a double-pass amplifier that is placed between two sections of the encoder (multiplexer) and amplifies a portion (60 ns/12 × 5 ns) of the entire 96-beam pulse train. It has a stage gain of ~20 and is designed to deliver ~5 J of laser light to the eightfold encoder.

The PA and the IA are single-pass amplifiers with similar designs and gain characteristics. Both have large aspect ratios L/D (gain length divided by laser aperture width), operate at high stage gain, are driven by a relatively low fraction of a saturation flux, and are only partially filled by their input laser beams. With an expected small-signal gain of 3% per centimetre and an absorption-limited length of ~280 cm, stage gains of 50 and 40 can be achieved with the PA and IA, respectively. For a typical drive energy of 1 J at the PA input, the PA output is 50 J and the IA output is 2 kJ.

The LAM is a lower aspect ratio amplifier ($L/D = 2$) than either the PA or IA. It is almost completely filled by its input beams, has a high extraction efficiency, and operates at a fairly low stage gain of 10 because it is driven into the saturated regime by the input laser beams. When driven with an input of 2 kJ from the IA, the LAM will deliver from 10 to 20 kJ of laser energy when operated in a double-pass amplifier configuration, assuming optimized performance. As mentioned previously, the energy from the LAM for first-phase Aurora is delivered initially to a diagnostics station in the form of an angularly multiplexed, 96-beam, 480-ns pulse. For second-phase Aurora, a decoder (demultiplexer) will be installed to compress one-half (48) of the multiplexed beams into high-intensity 5-ns pulses suitable for fusion targets. The LAM is the largest amplifier in the Aurora chain and is intended to address many of the scaling issues regarding large aperture KrF lasers. It was first tested as a resonator to understand physics and engineering issues associated with the operation of so large a device. Configured as a nonoptimized unstable resonator, it produced in excess of 10 kJ of 248-nm laser radiation in the resonator cavity.[24]

The assembly drawing in Fig. 8 shows some of the main parts of the LAM. Of particular significance are the laser chamber, the output window, the guide magnets, the water dielectric pulse-forming lines (PFLs), and the electron-gun (e-gun) assembly. Figure 9 is a photograph of the LAM that was taken during the initial construction phase. The LAM is representative of all the amplifiers in the Aurora chain, except that the PA and IA use single-sided e-beam pumping and the SAM does not use a PFL. The pulsed power components for these amplifiers are discussed in a later section.

TABLE I

Summary of Amplifier Specifications

Unit	PFL Pulse Length (ns)	e-Gun Voltage (kV)	e-Gun J (in Gas) (A/cm^2)	e-Gun Area (cm^2)	Input Light Energy (J)	Output Light Energy (J)	Stage Gain	Clear Aperture (cm)
SAM	100	300	12	12 × 100	0.25	5	20	10 × 12
PA	650	675	10	40 × 300	1	50	50	20 × 20
IA	650	675	10	40 × 300	50	2000	40	40 × 40
LAM	650	675	12 (Each side)	100 × 200	2000	10 000 to 20 000	10	100 × 100

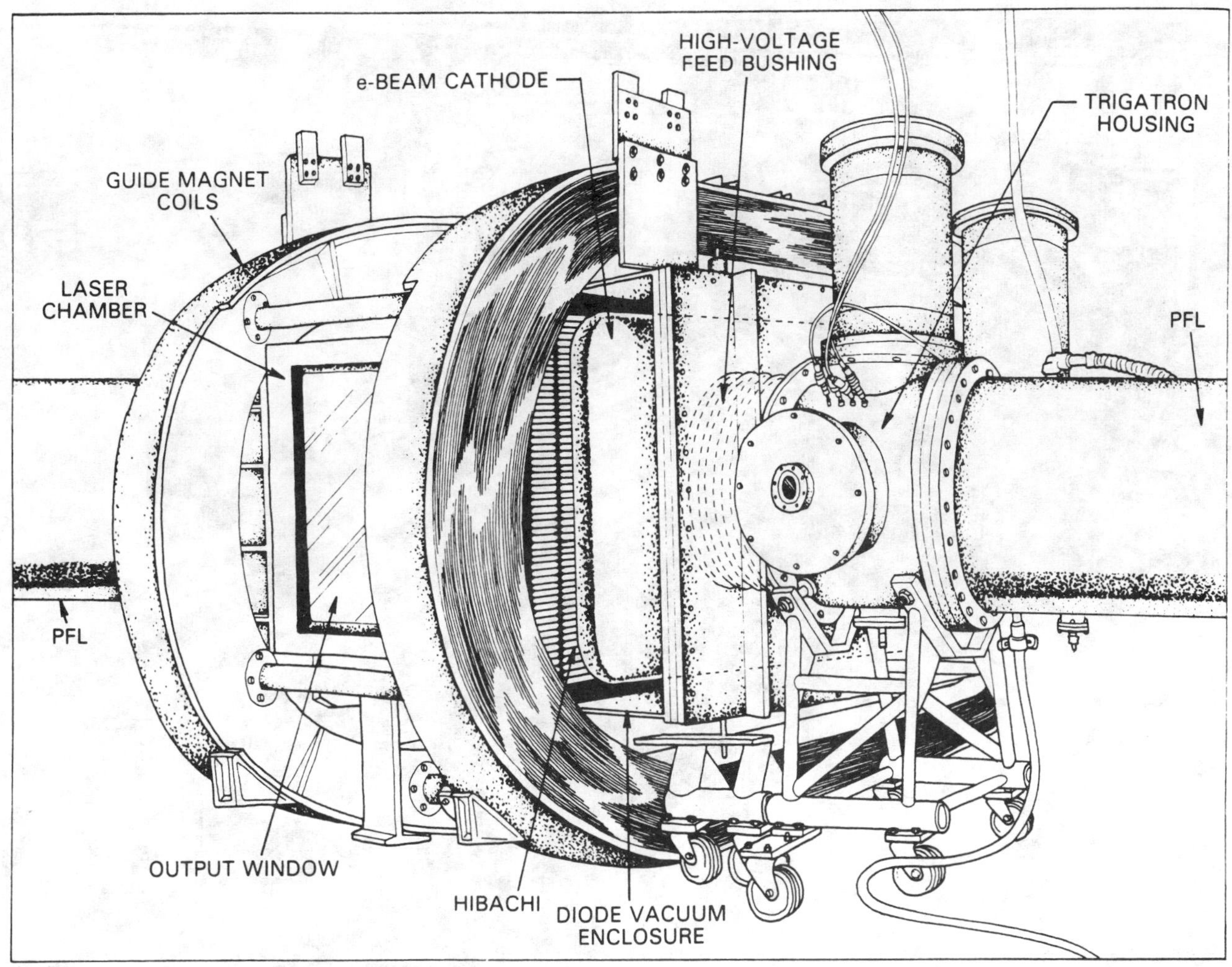

Fig. 8. Assembly drawing of the LAM. Shown are the laser chamber, the output window, the guide magnets, the water dielectric PFLs, and the *e*-gun assembly. This amplifier is representative of the amplifiers used in the Aurora chain. It is symmetrical in that it uses two sets of PFLs and two *e* guns in a double-sided pumping arrangement.

The stage gain, extraction efficiency, and ASE characteristics for amplifiers like the PA, IA, and LAM have been calculated previously.[22] The theory uses a one-dimensional steady-state radiative transport analysis, which incorporates bidirectional amplification, nonsaturable absorption, and ASE in a self-consistent manner. Assumed in the model are a uniform gain region of length L and a square aperture of dimension D on a side. The saturation flux I_{sat} and the ratio of small-signal gain to nonsaturable absorption g_0/α are other parameters necessary for the analysis. The saturation flux is taken to be 1.5 MW/cm^2. The main results of this model are that the stage gain of these KrF amplifiers increases as the driving flux is reduced. However, as the drive is lowered, more energy is lost as ASE output; therefore, less coherent energy will be extracted at low drive. The single-pass PA and IA both run at low drive, so they are fairly inefficient. A harder driven double-pass amplifier such as the LAM has relatively low stage gain, but a relatively high extraction efficiency. Consequently, there is a required compromise for higher efficiency because double-pass amplifiers will require greater optical complexity. We have chosen to employ single-pass amplifiers early in the amplification chain to minimize the optical complexity of the system and to relax the front-end output requirements. We have chosen to use a double-pass amplifier at the high-energy end of the amplification chain to maximize the energy extraction.

Figure 10 shows the performance of the PA, IA, and LAM as calculated using the model mentioned above. The stage gain and extraction efficiency are plotted as functions of the injection (drive) flux I_{in} for a family of g_0L (gain-length product) values at a given value of g_0/α. We have designed the PA, IA, and LAM to run at injection fluxes of $I_{in} \cong 0.4\%\ I_{sat}$, $4\%\ I_{sat}$, and $30\%\ I_{sat}$, respectively. These injection fluxes yield stage gains of ~50, 40, and 10 for the

Fig. 9. A photograph showing the Aurora LAM in the latter part of its initial assembly phase. The main laser cavity, which is pumped by two opposed broad-area cold-cathode *e* guns, is located between the coils that provide the guide magnetic field for the *e* guns. The *e* guns are housed in the vacuum enclosures adjacent to the laser chamber. Each *e* gun is powered by a parallel combination of two coaxial water dielectric PFLs, which are clearly visible in the foreground. Each pair of PFLs is charged by a separate Marx generator; the tank visible in the background contains one Marx. On a routine basis, the *e* guns deliver ≅160 kJ into the laser gas at electron energies of 550 to 600 kV and current densities of 12 A/cm^2. So far, the 1- × 1-m aperture LAM has produced in excess of 10 kJ of 248-nm laser light when configured as an unstable optical resonator.

parameters indicated on the PA, IA, and LAM graphs, respectively.

e-Beam Pumping

Because the laser gain medium is pumped by the *e* beam, the laser properties are closely linked to the *e*-beam properties. If the electron energy deposition in the laser gas is nonuniform, the gain, and hence the optical beam quality, will be nonuniform as well. There are four main sources of electron energy deposition nonuniformities:

1. variations in the spatial deposition profile resulting from the energy dependence of the electron stopping power in the laser gas
2. collisional diffusion of the *e* beam in the laser gas
3. *e*-beam pinching in the *e*-gun diode
4. temporal nonuniformities in the *e*-beam energy as a result of diode closure. Diode closure leads to a time-dependent impedance collapse, which in turn results in a diode voltage which decreases in time. This change in elecron energy with time results in a change in the spatial *e*-beam energy deposition.

The first nonuniformity can be avoided by double-sided *e*-beam pumping, which we employ in the LAM because of its very large aperture. Collisional diffusion

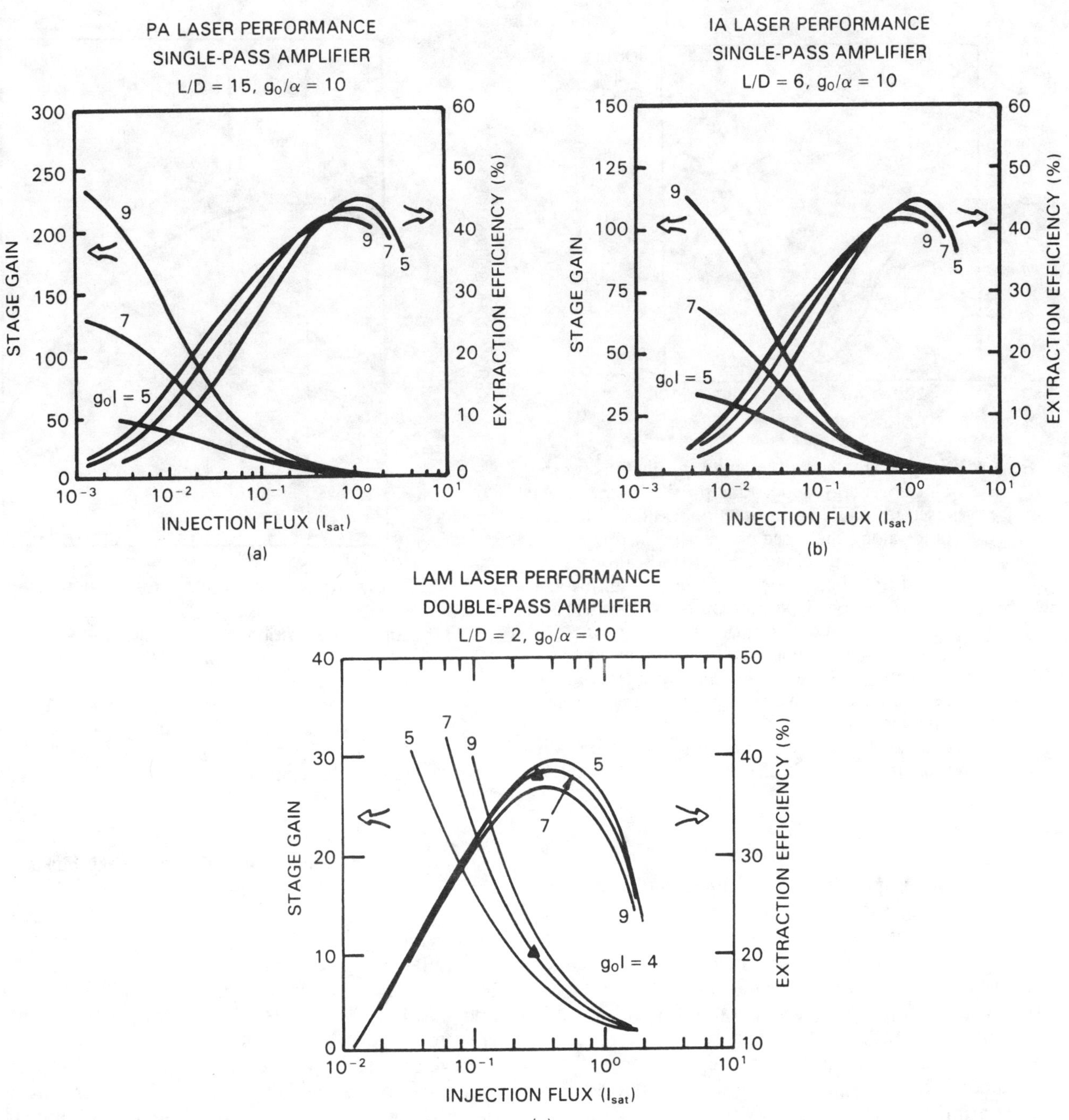

Fig. 10. Stage gains and extraction efficiencies for the (a) PA, (b) IA, and the (c) LAM plotted as a function of the injection flux (expressed in units of I_{sat}). This performance was calculated by means of a model that includes bidirectional amplification, nonsaturable absorption, and ASE in a self-consistent manner. The ratio of small-signal gain to nonsaturable absorption coefficient g_0/α is taken as ~10; the saturation flux is taken as ~1.5 MW/cm^2. A family of curves for different values of g_0L is shown in the figures. The nominal design points are a stage gain of 50, 40, and 10 and extraction efficiencies of ~10, 15, and 40% for the PA, IA, and LAM, respectively.

and pinching can be countered by the use of a guide magnetic field, which is used in all amplifiers except the SAM. Impedance collapse problems can be countered by proper impedance matching in the diode and pulsed power components.

We have designed the Aurora *e* guns to provide reasonably uniform *e*-beam pumping of all the laser amplifiers. Figures 11a and 11b display the results of sample calculations done to determine the energy deposition profile for the PA, IA, and LAM amplifiers.[51]

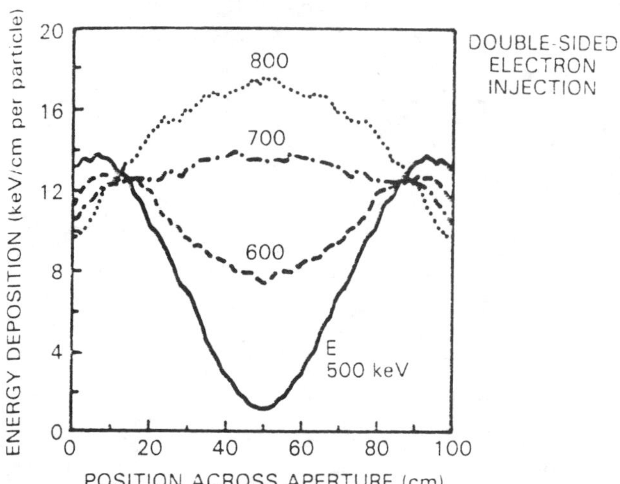

Fig. 11a. Sample Monte Carlo method calculations for the *e*-beam energy deposition profile in the LAM laser gas plotted as a function of horizontal distance along the *e*-beam centerline with electron energy as a parameter. Electron beams are injected from both the right and left, resulting in a uniform energy deposition profile across the laser aperture for an optimum electron energy of ~675 keV. Similar calculations done with an imposed magnetic guide field show improvements in the deposition at the vertical edges of the *e* beam. The gas mixture is 4% krypton, 95.5% argon, and 0.5% F_2 at a total pressure of 1.75 atm; the foils are 50-μm (2-mil) titanium for this calculation.

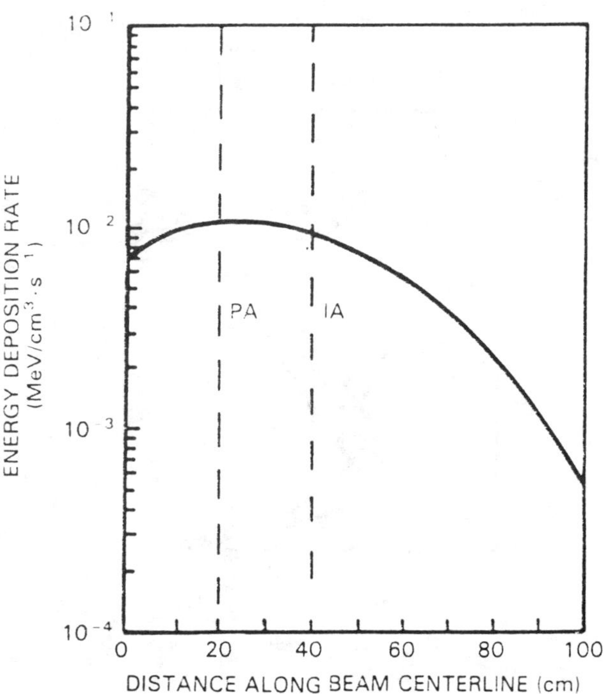

Fig. 11b. Energy deposition profile for the PA and the IA calculated by the Monte Carlo method. The *e* beams are injected from a single side. The relevant parameters for this calculation are a 1.5-atm target gas pressure of argon, 750-keV electron energy, 0-deg injection angle, and a foil of 50-μm (2-mil)-thick titanium.

For the 20-cm aperture PA, pumping uniformity at 1- to 1.5-amagat laser gas pressures is easily attained with a fairly broad range of voltages. The requirements for the IA are more stringent because single-sided pumping is used for the 40-cm aperture. The IA requires ~650-kV electron energies for 1.5-amagat pressure. For the 1-m LAM aperture, the required *e*-gun voltage is in the 600- to 700-kV range for a 1.5-amagat laser gas mix. Double-sided pumping yields a very uniform electron energy deposition profile.

The Aurora *e* guns have been described in detail in other articles.[52,53] A summary of the design details of the main pieces of *e*-gun hardware is presented below. The LAM design is representative of the designs used for most of the Aurora amplifiers, so we will use it as the basis for our discussions. A block diagram for the LAM is shown in Fig. 12.

Marx Generators and PFLs

Typically, the *e* guns that pump the laser amplifiers are powered by a combination of Marx generators and water dielectric PFLs. The LAM uses double-sided *e*-beam pumping and has two PFLs in parallel for each of its two *e* guns. The PA and the IA both use single-sided *e*-beam pumping, and each has a single PFL. The SAM also uses single-sided pumping, but is an exception in that it employs a Marx with a peaking circuit in place of a PFL. Each Marx generator is of similar design and construction,[54] except for the SAM, which is a commercial device.[b] The PA, IA, and LAM all employ 15-stage Marx generators that erect to an open-circuit voltage of ~1.8 MV and to a voltage of ~1.6 MV when charging the PFLs. These PFLs are coaxial cylinder transmission lines that use deionized water as a dielectric. The inner conductor has a 61-cm diameter, the outer conductor has a 91-cm diameter, and the length of the line is 10.8 m. The impedance of each line is ~2.7 Ω, the one-way electrical transit time of the line is 325 ns, and the energy storage per line is typically 150 kJ. Each PFL is connected to the *e*-gun cathode through an SF_6-insulated trigatron output switch and a high-voltage vacuum feed bushing. Depending on the particular amplifier, the output switches are triggered from 1.2 to 1.8 μs after the Marx erection. When the output switches fire, a voltage pulse of one-half the charge voltage and

[b]Modified "excitron" *e*-beam pumped laser, Maxwell Laboratories, Inc., San Diego, California.

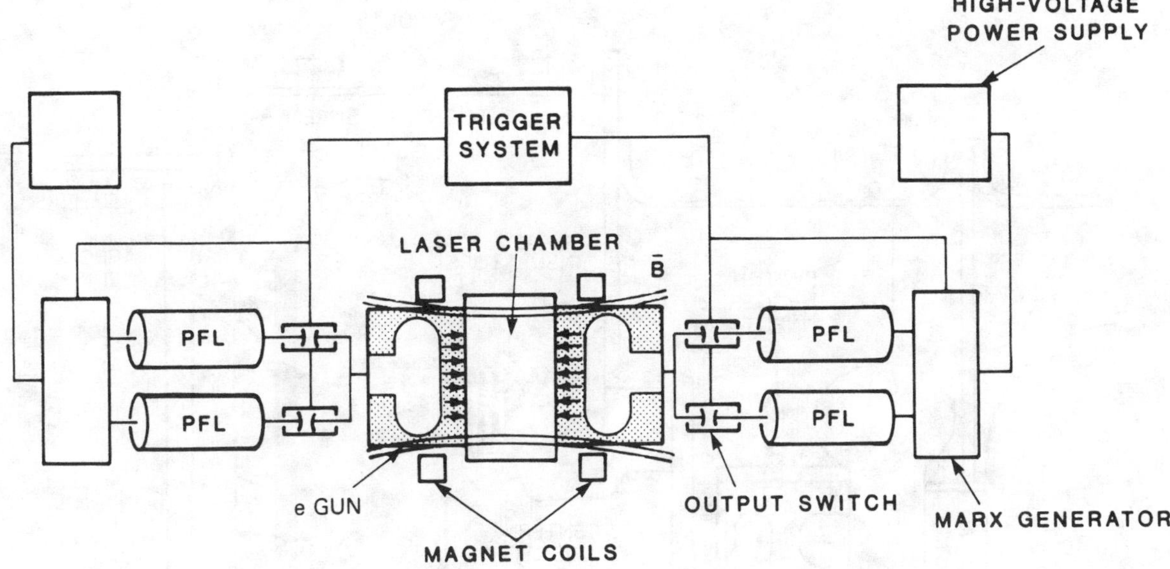

Fig. 12. A block diagram of the Aurora LAM showing the power conditioning, *e* guns, guide magnets, laser chamber, and high-voltage triggers. The LAM is representative of the large amplifiers in Aurora.

twice the electrical transit time of the PFL is delivered to the cathode.

e-Gun Assemblies

The *e* guns consist of the following main components: diode-feed bushing, cathode-corona shell, emitter, hibachi, and foil. These components are housed in a vacuum enclosure and maintained at a pressure of $\sim 5 \times 10^{-6}$ Torr. Any of the *e* guns (SAM, PA, IA, or LAM) is representative of the design and construction concepts used for Aurora, except that the SAM is considerably smaller than the other three and differs in some details not mentioned here. Figure 13 shows a cross section of the LAM *e* guns.

The diode-feed bushing electrically interfaces the output switch to the cathode. This bushing is a fairly common high-voltage design using 45-deg-angled acrylic insulator rings alternating with aluminum field-grading rings. The cathode-corona shell attaches to the end of this bushing, and the graphite felt emitter material is attached to a contoured boss on this shell. Graphite felt is used for the emitter because it exhibits a low ignition voltage and a reasonably uniform spatial distribution of electron emission. The emitter area for the SAM is 12×100 cm and the anode-cathode (A-K) gap spacing is 3.2 cm, which gives a calculated 6-Ω diode impedance at a nominal voltage of 350 kV. The current density at the cathode is 35 A/cm^2, with an observed hibachi transmission of 35%. The PA and IA *e* guns are almost identical. Both have ~8-cm A-K gaps and 40- × 280-cm emitter areas, although the PA beam is masked off to produce a 20-cm-wide beam compatible with its smaller laser aperture. The PA and IA diodes are designed to match the PFL impedance of 2.7 Ω and operate at a nominal cathode voltage of 675 kV and a nominal space-charge-limited current density of 22 A/cm^2 at the cathode. The LAM cathodes have 100- × 200-cm emitter areas and an A-K gap of ~7.5 cm. The nominal design cathode voltage and current density at the cathode are 675 kV and 25 A/cm^2, respectively, which matches the 1.35-Ω impedance of two PFLs in parallel.

The interface between the diode vacuum chamber and the laser-gas volume is provided by a titanium or Kapton[c] (polyimide film) foil of nominal 25-μm (1-mil) and 75-μm (3-mil) thicknesses, respectively. The foil is supported by an aluminum hibachi structure that typically has a geometrical transmission of 80%. The open-cell hibachi dimensions range from 13.5×1.6 cm for the SAM to 23.8×3.6 cm for the LAM. The laser chambers contain the krypton/F_2/argon laser gas mixtures at typical pressures in the range 600 to 1200 Torr: the open-cell sizes and hibachi thicknesses are designed to withstand the mechanical stresses resulting from these pressure differentials. A more detailed discussion of the hibachi design and an *e*-beam transport analysis is presented in Ref. 53. The transport of the *e* beam from the emitter surface to the pumped laser gas volume depends on many factors. Among these are the properties of the cathode emitter (emission uniformity in particular), scattering of the *e* beam by the foil and laser gas, energy loss in the foil, obstruction by the hibachi and other mechanical support structures, and the uniformity of the

[c]Registered trademark for polyimide film, E. I. DuPont de Nemours and Company, Inc., Wilmington, Delaware.

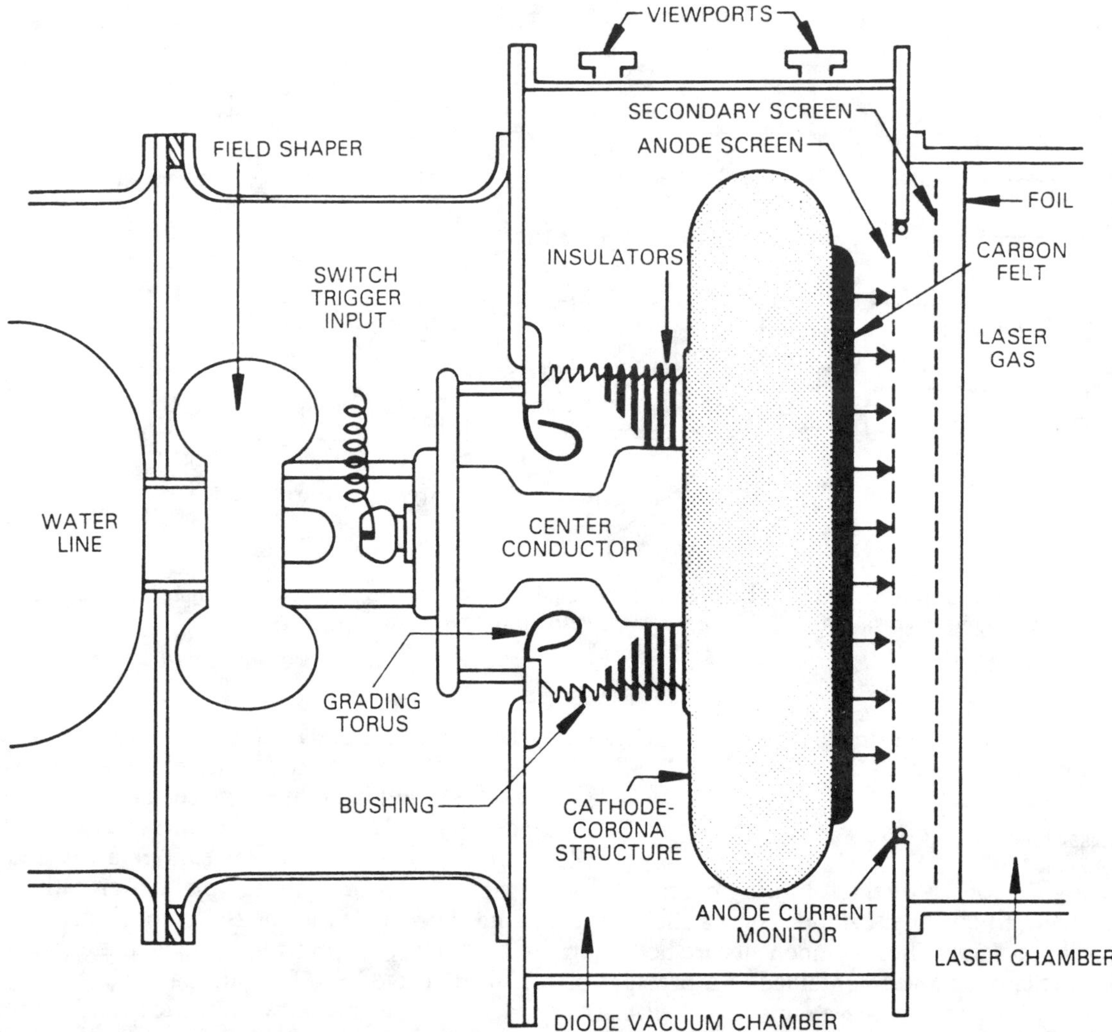

Fig. 13. Cross section for the Aurora LAM *e*-gun assembly. The LAM *e* gun is representative of the major Aurora devices. It employs two parallel-connected PFLs for each of its *e* guns in a double-sided excitation arrangement to achieve uniform pumping across its 1-m laser aperture. The laser axis is perpendicular to the plane of the figure. The *e*-beam emitter dimension is 200 cm along the laser axis and 100 cm transverse to the axis.

applied guide magnetic field. Typically, the transport efficiency is ~50%, although this depends to a large extent on the relative dominance of the previously mentioned factors.

Guide Magnets

Electromagnet coil pairs of a quasi-Helmholtz configuration are installed on all amplifiers but the SAM. The coil pairs are symmetrically placed about the center of the laser chambers and provide nearly uniform magnetic fields parallel to the *e*-beam paths. These fields stabilize the *e* beams against self-pinching and reduce collisional diffusion losses in the laser-gas volume.

The degree of beam pinching is related to the magnitude and direction of the self-magnetic field, which depend on the total beam current and the diode geometry. A device like the SAM has a small self-field that generates little beam pinching; therefore, it does not require a guide magnetic field to overcome the self-field. The PA, IA, and LAM have fairly large self-magnetic fields; thus the use of guide fields for these devices is mandatory. Loss of electrons from collisional diffusion is most important for diffusion perpendicular to the field direction. This diffusion is dependent on the mean-free-path of the electrons in the gas and the radius of the electron gyration about the field lines (Lamor radius). For large magnetic fields, diffusion perpendicular to the field direction is inversely proportional to the field strength.[55]

The main engineering considerations for the guide field are the magnitude of the applied field, the field tilt angle, and the spatial uniformity of the field.

If the guide field is sufficiently strong, it will add with the beam's own self-field in such a way as to produce a resultant field nearly parallel to the beam direction. The electrons within the beam will follow the resultant magnetic field lines in a helical orbit. If the deviation of the field lines from the normal to the cathode is small, the electrons will be transmitted with high efficiency through the hibachi and foil into the laser gas. If the deviation is larger, more beam current is intercepted by the hibachi ribs, which results in inefficient transmission. Once inside the laser-gas volume, the electrons will still be constrained to spiral along the field lines rather than scatter out. Practical experience has shown that the magnitude of the required guide magnetic field is generally a few times that of the self-field. Using a higher magnetic field strength is not advantageous because the closure velocity for the A-K gap increases with increasing applied field strength. This can lead to excessive cathode voltage fall-off and a consequent change in the pumping uniformity if the closure is too fast.

The main concerns in regard to tilt angle are how it affects transmission of the *e* beam through the hibachi and how it reduces the size of the beam cross section. We have designed the guide field tilt at the hibachi to be <5 deg for all the amplifiers. This keeps the transmission reduction resulting from the tilt <5%. Tilt at the cathode reduces the beam size, which may leave unpumped regions near the edge of the laser cavity. We have designed the guide magnets to allow a tilt at the cathode of ~10 deg. This results in a beam size reduction of ~8% for the PA, 4% for the IA, and 2% for the LAM.

The spatial variation in the magnitude of the guide field along the laser-cavity optical axis is a concern with two effects: A spatial variation in the guide field can lead to changes in the tilt angle of the resultant magnetic field, which gives a spatial variation in the hibachi transmission, and spatial variations in the guide field lead to spatial variations in the closure velocity. Both of these effects can result in nonuniform electron energy deposition in the laser gas. We have designed the Aurora guide magnets to have a field uniformity of ±10% over the length of the laser cavities. This leads to an ~8 to 10% increase in closure velocity from one end of the laser-gas volume to the other, which is not too severe for our applications.

The PA and IA coils have major and minor diameters of 5.5 and 1.65 m, respectively; the LAM coils have a major diameter of 4.2 m and a minor diameter of 2.6 m. Typical fields are 0.12 to 1.18 T for the PA and IA, and 0.2 to 0.3 T for the LAM. The measured total deviation in the field from the PA/IA coils has been found to be ~10% along the major axis and ≳5% along the minor axis. The usual magnet current waveform is a trapezoid with rise and fall times of a few seconds and a few second plateau. A summary of specifications of the PA, IA, and LAM magnet coils is shown in Table II; the PA and IA coils are identical.

TABLE II

Aurora Magnet Characteristics Summary

Device	B_{av} (T)	L^a (m)	W^b (m)	I (A)	V (V)
PA/IA	0.15 to 0.18	5.5	1.65	2100	680
LAM	0.20 to 0.40	4.2	2.6	4000	500

[a]Major diameter.
[b]Minor diameter.

OPTICAL SYSTEM

The Aurora optical system is representative of typical angularly multiplexed systems. It is designed to match the long amplifier electrical excitation pulse time, which is determined by electrical and laser kinetics considerations, to the much shorter pulse times required for efficient coupling of the laser pulse energy to inertial fusion targets. Angle and time multiplexing are necessary to accomplish this match. Distance is used to provide the time delays needed to time encode a 96-beam pulse train of 5-ns pulses. The 96 pulses are produced by a combination of aperture division (12-fold) and intensity division (i.e., beam spliting, which is 8-fold) encoding processes. These pulses are spatially separated, angle encoded, and sequentially passed through the KrF laser amplifier chain to produce an amplified 480-ns pulse train. This amplified pulse train is decoded after the final amplifier, using distance to take out the time delays; then all pulses in the train are delivered simultaneously to the fusion target. The major elements of the design are described in Ref. 56; a more detailed description of the optical system is given in Refs. 57 and 58. The major parts of the system are as follows:

1. an optical encoder that replicates the 5-ns front-end output pulse to produce a 480-ns-long pulse train consisting of 96 separate beams placed head-to-tail in time

2. an angle encoder that spatially separates the beams through the amplifiers and helps direct them so they can be decoded

3. a centered optical system that relays the beams through the amplifiers so they expand and fill the active gain volumes

4. an optical decoder to delay the earlier pulses in the pulse train relative to the later pulses so they all arrive at the target simultaneously

5. a set of final aiming mirrors and focusing lenses that direct the beams onto the target

6. isolated beam enclosures to provide a stable optical environment for the propagation of the UV beams
7. three optical alignment systems that control the alignment of the encoder, the final amplifier mirror, and the final aiming mirrors.

Figure 14 shows a plan view of the optical layout within the Aurora laser building. The temporal encoder design is made more complex because of the constraints imposed by fitting the system into an existing building.

Temporal Encoding

The front-end oscillator-amplifiers deliver two 5-ns pulses with two identical apertures to the encoder. The beam sizes are then shaped with prisms to the aspect ratio required for encoding. One beam is delayed by 30 ns with respect to the other, and both are expanded by parabolic-optics telescopes to an aperture size of ~15 × 23 cm. The expanded beams are divided spatially into six parts, each 7 × 7 cm in size, with each part given a 5-ns time delay. This produces a 12-element, 60-ns-long pulse train. This pulse train is then directed through one 10- × 12-cm aperture SAM amplifier in a double-pass mode with the use of 12 flat mirrors, which are part of a 24-element array. After amplification, the pulse train is returned to the second half of the 24-element mirror array, which creates a bundle of 12 parallel beams from the train. This bundle of 12 beams is handled as a unit by three stages of serial 50/50-intensity beam splitters, which produce an 8-fold replication to 96 beams. The time delays required to obtain the final 480-ns composite pulse are obtained by judicious location of the beam splitters. Figures 15 and 16 show photographs of some of the optical elements that comprise the 12- and 8-fold encoder sections.

The decision to place the 12-fold aperture division first in the encoding process was based on the following considerations:

1. Divergence and aiming problems inherent in the front end are reduced by immediate expansion.

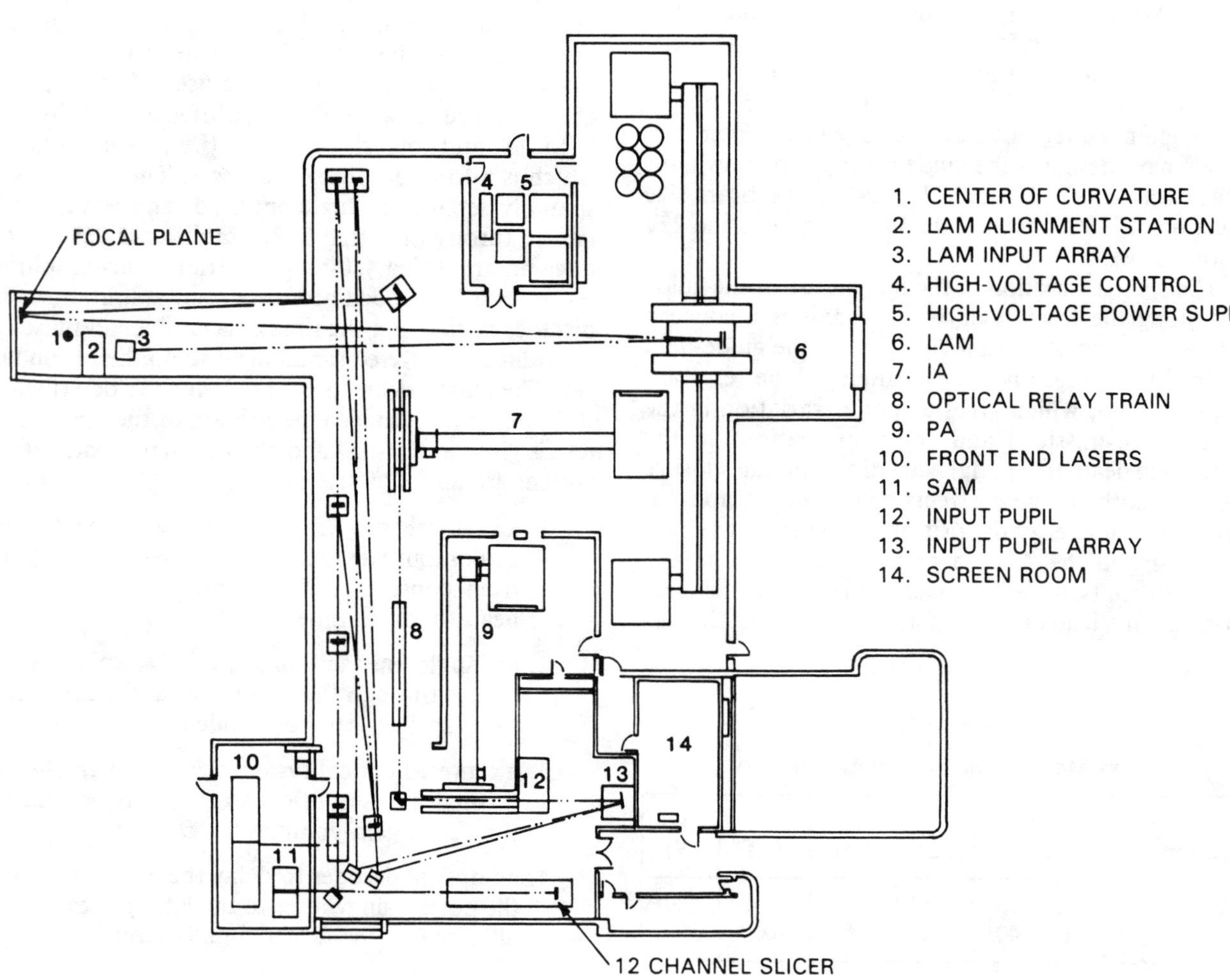

Fig. 14. Drawing of the first-phase Aurora laser system design now being built inside an existing building at LANL.

Fig. 15. The 12-channel slicer table. Two beams from the front end enter the table traveling toward mirrors in front of the array. One beam returns to the two mirrors in the center of the table, which redirect it again toward the array, creating a 30-ns delay. The two beams are magnified by two off-aperture telescopes; each beam passes six mirrors, which slice off portions of the magnified beam and return them to the mirror array. These 12 beams are amplified, returned again to the array, and then directed in a 12-beam parallel bundle, which forms the building block for the rest of the encoder.

2. A convenient station for the input-output array for the SAM amplifier results from this placement.
3. Aperture division with a low beam count avoids the use of a very large expansion telescope or the use of several parallel telescopes.
4. Intensity division as the second process provides more flexibility in fitting long time delays into the existing building.

The use of a multistage intensity division beam splitter placed stringent requirements on the splitting accuracy of each stage. For three stages, it was

Fig. 16. A photograph showing a portion of the 8-fold encoder. The 8-fold replication of the pulse train from the 12-fold encoder is accomplished with three stages of beam splitters resulting in 96 separate beams. Judicious placement of the beam splitters permits the proper time delays to obtain the 480-ns pulse train. Each of the beam-splitter elements is a coated 30- × 46- × 8-cm-thick fused-silica slab and has a 50:50 ±2% splitting ratio. The beam splitters are held in a motorized mount that is attached to the heavy stands.

Fig. 17. The 96-element input pupil feed array. This 8 × 12 mirror array angle encodes the Aurora beam train by directing each beamlet through the amplifier chain at slightly different angles relative to the central optical axis. Each mirror is 10 cm on an edge.

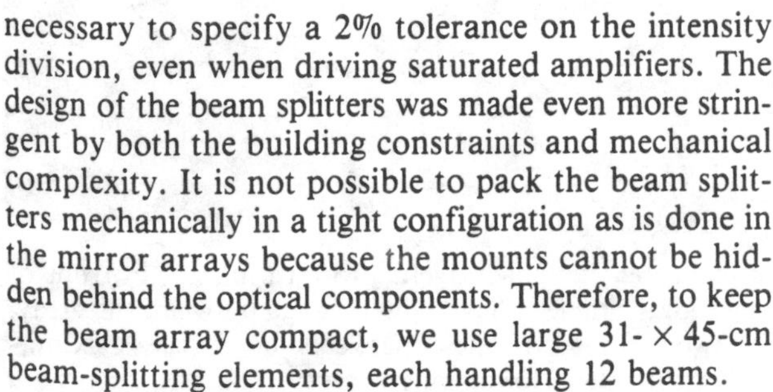

necessary to specify a 2% tolerance on the intensity division, even when driving saturated amplifiers. The design of the beam splitters was made even more stringent by both the building constraints and mechanical complexity. It is not possible to pack the beam splitters mechanically in a tight configuration as is done in the mirror arrays because the mounts cannot be hidden behind the optical components. Therefore, to keep the beam array compact, we use large 31- × 45-cm beam-splitting elements, each handling 12 beams.

Angular Multiplexing

In the temporal encoder, the beams are collimated and spatially distinct. They follow parallel paths to an 8 × 12 array of 96 separate flat mirrors called the input pupil array. Figure 17 is a photograph of this array. It is here the individual beams are angularly multiplexed; i.e., the beam paths are now slightly separated in angle. The angle of an extreme chief ray is 6.5 deg from the bundle centerline, while the channel-to-channel beam separation is ~1 deg. Each beam is of square cross section, 7 cm on an edge. The input pupil is a smaller square, 4 cm on an edge. Therefore, the beams are 1.5-cm oversize, which allows for a generous tolerance for alignment and diffraction losses. This also provides reasonable dynamic range for the target alignment control system, which must introduce offsetting pointing errors to compensate for real errors that occur in the form of physical changes elsewhere. The computer-based alignment control system, which controls the pointing of these beams, is described later in this paper. Each of the 96 mirrors that comprise the input pupil array is controlled by a pair of stepper motors, which are interfaced to the computer-controlled servo-alignment system. The chief ray of each beam in the array is independently aimed at the input pupil of the centered symmetric optical relay train.

Optical Relay Train

The primary function of the optical relay train (or the centered optical system) is to transport the 96 beams from the 8 × 12 input pupil array through the PA and IA to the 96-element LAM input mirror array. The relay train must interface to the encoder, provide a means to fill the amplifier gain media in an efficient manner, and separate the beams for the decoder. The PA and IA, which are placed toward the front of the amplification chain, are designed as single-pass amplifiers so that the beams use common optical elements throughout the relay train, thereby reducing the complexity and cost of the optical train. Relaying the input pupil through the amplifiers provides the best possible fill factor. The first section of the relay train is a centered symmetric lens train between the input pupil and the PA. This section consists of five lenses that image the input pupil to the output of the PA. From a purely optical design point of view, this is the most complex part of the laser system. Most of the system aberrations are balanced here because the parts are relatively small and inexpensive. The design employs two strong negative power lenses to cancel the positive power of the rest of the lenses so that the Petzval sum and, consequently, the field curvature at the focal plane behind the LAM input array are nearly zero. This allows all the LAM input array mirrors to have a common convex curvature and to be mounted on a plane surface. In this set of lenses, there is an intermediate focus that requires a modest vacuum.

The next section of the relay train images the input pupil from the output of the PA to the output of the IA. It consists of three lenses and a turning mirror. The beams from the PA output are relayed to the second set of relay lenses by the first turning mirror. The first lens in this set has an aspheric surface. These lenses form a pair that provides an intermediate hard focus that can be used for alignment and spatial filtering. The regions of hard focus require a moderate vacuum of $\sim 10^{-3}$ Torr to avoid air breakdown.

At the output of the IA, another lens focuses the beams to a surface behind the 96-element LAM input array. However, to fit the building, two turning mirrors are required between the IA and the LAM input array. Figure 18 shows a photograph of the optical relay train when it was set up for initial off-line testing.

LAM Input Array

The Aurora optical design employs a long flight path after the IA to spatially separate the 96 beams. At the end of this path, there is a 96-element array of small convex mirrors. This array consists of an 8 × 12

Fig. 18. A photograph showing the optical relay train during the setup and checkout phase. The hard focus and IA lens train is shown in the right background. At the right foreground is a turning mirror required to fit the test setup into this building. At left background and foreground are shown two large lightweight fused Pyrex turning mirrors.

matrix of small mirrors very similar to the input pupil mirror array. The mirrors in the LAM array are convex to avoid focusing, which would cause air breakdown. The radius of curvature of these mirrors was chosen to cause each beam to fill the full 1- × 1-m LAM aperture. For first-phase Aurora, the beams are brought to a focus at a diagnostics station ~40 m from the center of the LAM volume after making a double-pass trip through the LAM. For second-phase Aurora, the beams also make a double-pass trip through the LAM, but are then sent into the decoder optics for stacking into a single pulse and subsequent delivery to the target.

Materials and Coating Issues

The Aurora optical system requires materials for both transmissive and reflective elements. The transmissive elements consist of lenses and laser windows, both of which require antireflection coatings for 248-nm service. The laser windows are also required to operate in a fluorine environment. The reflective elements are high- and low-power relay mirrors, fold, and turning mirrors, as well as expansion telescopes. These elements require high-reflection coatings for both 248-nm and visible alignment service. Beam splitters have both reflective and transmissive elements.

Pyrex[d] is generally used for small mirrors with several other materials being used for other mirrors: Zerodur[e] for one turning mirror, Cervit[f] for the large LAM mirror, and novel lightweight Pyrex for two other turning mirrors. The novel lightweight Pyrex mirrors employ a sandwich design made from Pyrex flats fused to a honeycomb-shaped array of hexagonal close-packed Pyrex tubes. These mirror blanks are considerably lighter and less expensive than conventional mirrors made from quartz, Zerodur, or ULE.[g] They cost about the same as solid BK7[h] blanks, but have considerably better temperature characteristics. The material for transmissive optics is generally synthetic fused silica, with Corning 7940, homogeneity grade C, inclusion class II, being a common type used throughout the system.[i] The LAM output window is the largest piece of this type of material being a fused silica monolithic slab with a 1- × 1-m clear aperture and a thickness of ~7 cm. Smaller pieces of fused silica are also used for the beam splitters and fold mirrors in the encoder.

Optical component coatings for 248-nm service are a complicated issue because the technology involved in UV coatings is still being developed. Aurora uses various coatings produced by several different vendors: antireflection and high-reflection coatings for use within the fluorine-containing laser environment; 248-nm and visible alignment service high-reflection coatings for high- and low-power relay mirrors; and antireflection coatings for lenses. Antireflection coatings, which are not required to withstand fluorine, are made with conventional vacuum deposition coatings. Many of the mirrors in the fluorine-free beam train use an aluminum undercoat to give high reflectance for visible beam alignment.

High-reflection coatings from two different vendors are found to be acceptable for fluorine service; these have damage thresholds in the 0.6 to 4.0 J/cm^2 range, and tested samples appear serviceable after 200 h of exposure to the 0.5% fluorine-laser-gas mixture. The material in the highest part of the damage range is ThF_4/MgF_2, while that in the lower part of the range is HfO_2/ThF_4. Both have initial reflectivities of ~97%, with the smallest reflectivity after fluorine exposure being 93%.

Several sets of antireflection coatings for fluorine service were evaluated. The material with the best fluorine survivability characteristics is HfO_2/ThF_4 with a damage threshold in the 1.6 to 2.5 J/cm^2 range.

Other materials such as ThF_4/MgF_2 and ThF_4/Na_3AlF_6 have reasonable damage thresholds but poor fluorine survivability characteristics. In one test, low-power relay mirror designs used an aluminum film on a Pyrex substrate that was overcoated with a full 248-nm dielectric stack of HfO_2 and SiO_2. The aluminum film was intended to give high reflectance for visible beam alignment. Damage thresholds for these components are in the 1.3 to 1.5 J/cm^2 range. The reflectance is 99% at 248 nm and ~80% at 514 and 633 nm. In the same test, high-power relay mirror designs used a dielectric stack of Al_2O_3 and SiO_2 for UV service. The best samples obtained for these designs give a damage threshold of 4.0 J/cm^2, 99% reflectance at 248 nm, and 90% reflectance at 514 nm. A more detailed description of the Aurora optical materials and coatings experience is presented in Ref. 57.

Automated Alignment Systems

Multiplexer Alignment System

Aurora uses an electronic computer-controlled system that analyzes digitized TV images to position simultaneously the 96 elements of the multiplexed beam train to high accuracy. This control system is optimal and self-adaptive: Its algorithms constantly determine the optimal number of samples needed to resolve the

[d]Trade name of Corning Glass Works material, two-phase vitreous.

[e]Trade name of Schott Corporation, two-phase vitreous material; zero expansion coefficient near room temperature.

[f]Trade name of Owens-Illinois composite, semivitreous material.

[g]Trade name of Corning Glass Works material 7971; synthetic, non-UV transmissive, 7% TiO_2, 93% SiO_2.

[h]Borosilicate glass manufactured by Schott Corporation (or equivalent of other manufacturers).

[i]Corning Glass Works, Corning, New York.

actual alignment error for each of the beams. A schematic diagram of the multiplexer alignment system is shown in Fig. 19. The input pupil array does the angular portion of the multiplexing task; it must keep each beam aimed in its assigned direction with an accuracy of 30 μrad for first-phase Aurora and an accuracy of 2 μrad for second-phase Aurora. To control the 96 mirrors of the input array, the beams reflected from these mirrors are sampled and imaged on a TV camera as an 8×12 array. The image-plane position of each element of the image has a one-to-one correspondence with the angular position of the associated beam at the PA input pupil. Because each beam overfills the input pupil by a large margin, it is only necessary to control the angular positions of the beams and not their points in space. Positioning error information is obtained by a sophisticated analysis of the video signal produced by the far-field image of the beams at this entrance pupil. Once the positioning error is determined, the optical system is controlled by directing stepper motors to move the input array mirrors until the elements of the image are at the desired coordinates. Parallel processing of the alignment error information for all 96 beams and the use of inherent system noise in the sampling process lead to very short alignment times. Using binary decisions on a noisy sample space permits effective interpolating across beam boundary pixels to obtain precise and repeatable measurements of the beam position, without recourse to time-consuming and often unreliable software curve-fitting algorithms.

The alignment of the 96 beams is continuously maintained in real time, until the actual instant of firing. The types of disturbances expected are step displacements and velocity errors. The step errors result from mechanical settling or adjustments, and velocity errors may arise from thermal cycling of the building or from drifts in the alignment electronics itself. So far, the system has been able to align all 96 beams to a 2-μrad step correction accuracy in ~3 min. Velocity errors of 1 μrad/min or less have been controlled to 5-μrad total error. The velocity correction is predictive, permitting continuous interpolation and correction estimations during the times when the system is made open loop. In addition, the measurement analysis that permits the corrections provides error histories of all the beams, assisting diagnosis of significant disturbances.

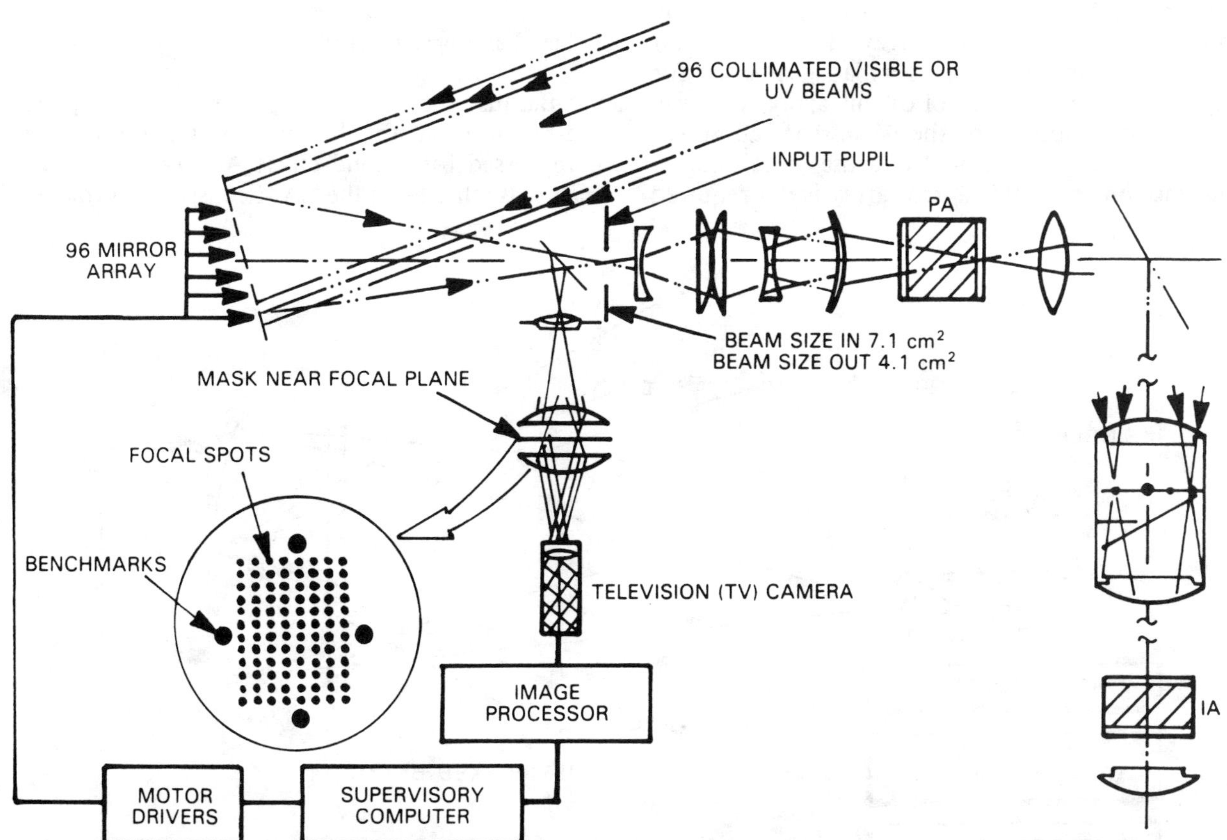

Fig. 19. The input pupil array, alignment station feedback loop. A dichroic beam splitter in front of the input pupil reflects colinear visible beams to a 96-spot focal plane on a mask with benchmarks. The spots are image-processed and positioned relative to the benchmarks by driving the input pupil array mirrors.

The far-field image is constantly available without interrupting the UV beams by using two dichroic beam splitters. One of these inserts a continuous wave visible laser beam before the temporal encoder; the second one diverts the visible beam at the input pupil. The visible laser is also used to perform an initial necessary manual alignment of the encoder. The encoder optics mounts are designed to hold the required coarse alignment accuracy for long periods of time. The stability of the relay optics that follows the encoder is also adequate for the immediate goal of filling the LAM. A more detailed description of the alignment system and the methods for image analysis have been presented elsewhere.[59,60]

Power Amplifier Alignment

A second part of the alignment system is concerned with keeping the input mirror array and the main mirror for the final power amplifier (LAM) aligned. The LAM mirror array is similar to the input pupil array, except that the LAM array mirrors are convex rather than flat. The main LAM mirror is a full 1- × 1-m clear aperture concave mirror having a 38-m radius of curvature for first-phase Aurora and a 110-m radius for the second phase. The beams coming from the IA are expanded to fill the LAM by means of the convex mirror array. The main LAM mirror compresses the beams to a manageable size for feeding the decoder. Control of this array is largely static; stepper motors for the 96 mirrors allow the beams to be aligned manually in the initial stages. Real-time control of this mirror array is not required because mount stability and overfill tolerances are adequate to hold the alignment for fairly long periods of time. Static alignment of the main LAM mirror, however, is not expected to be adequate because of the following: high-angular error sensitivity at this point in the system; mechanical perturbations caused by, for example, the gas pressure pulse generated when the LAM is fired; and the commonality of all 96 channels at the main mirror (any misalignment causes all the beams to be misdirected). Therefore, full-time feedback control of the LAM mirror is designed into the alignment system. This alignment mechanism, as shown in Fig. 20, depends on viewing the mirror from its center of curvature; a clear channel for this purpose has been included in the optical layout. A position-sensitive detector and a small laser are placed side by side at the center of curvature; the mirror returns an image of the laser beam onto the detector. Because the LAM mirror radius is large, only small motions at the mirror are required to produce motions at the detector that are easily within the step limits of the main mirror mount control motors. We are just beginning the design of this control system, and currently intend to use the same TV camera/video analysis system and much of the same software as was used in the 96-beam alignment system.

Optical Demultiplexer System

Because the ICF target requires a short pulse of ~5-ns duration, the 480-ns amplifier pulse must be compressed for second-phase Aurora. The synthetic long pulse that feeds the LAM consists of a train of 96

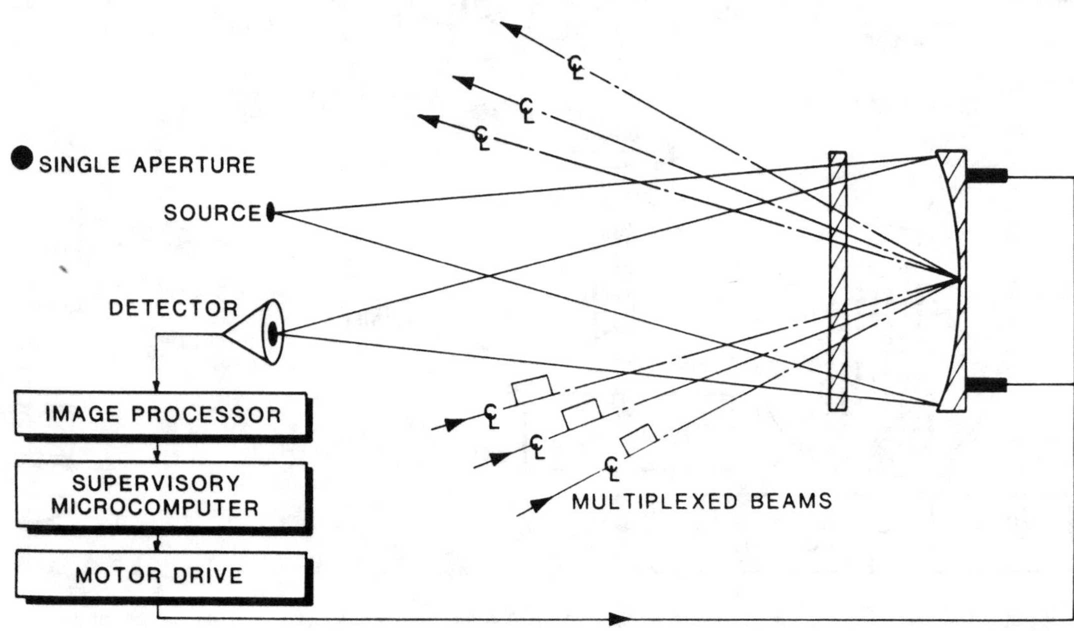

Fig. 20. The aiming of the LAM mirror is accomplished by using closed-loop feedback control.

separate 5-ns pulses. The 96 pulses have been encoded in the multiplexer to an assigned angle and an assigned time slot in the amplifiers. These assignations are then decoded in the demultiplexer to compress the long-pulse train into a single high-power pulse. This is accomplished by sending the beams along different flight paths to the target. For the Aurora prototype demonstration, only 48 of the 96 beams will be decoded and delivered to the target.

As a result of a deliberate effort to simplify the design of the encoder, the pattern of angle assignments naturally divides into four time blocks. Each quadrant of the pattern in space (or angle) is also one-quarter of the pulse train in time. The design of the decoder is also simplified by handling each of these quadrants as a block.

Figure 21 is a diagram that illustrates the demultiplexer (decoder) layout. The diagram is drastically foreshortened in the long dimension for ease of representation. The decoding process starts by recollimating the 96 slightly converging beams from the LAM and dividing them into four quadrants of 24 beams. Two of the quadrants encounter a 240-ns delay in the long separation tunnel after the LAM, which brings the two halves of the 480-ns pulse train into time coincidence. Two 120-ns time delays provided by the shorter beam tunnels at right angles to the main tunnel then bring all four quadrants into time coincidence. This scheme of decoding by quadrants is illustrated in Fig. 22.

A fine decoding process then provides appropriate 5-ns delays to allow all beams to arrive at the target simultaneously. Each beam must have an entirely separate mirror location within the shorter tunnels. Space is provided behind these mirrors for optical mounts and for the location of final optical diagnostics.

From the fine decoder, the beams are directed to the final aiming mirror array, which then aims the beams through the final focus lenses and onto the target. The precision alignment system required for final aiming is discussed in the next section. A more detailed description of the demultiplexer system is presented in Ref. 58.

The complicated path crossings produced by angular multiplexing and pulse stacking do not allow isolation of individual beam lines, either for evacuation or the control of air motion; hence, the optical quality of the long beam paths must be controlled. Propagation of the 248-nm light beams over long paths in air is affected by scattering (Rayleigh, aerosol, and Raman), absorption by atmospheric gases, thermal gradients and turbulence, beam alignment, control errors, and by optical component figure errors. Practical experience indicates that good beam quality cannot be obtained for modest path lengths (several tens of metres) unless an environmentally isolated beam

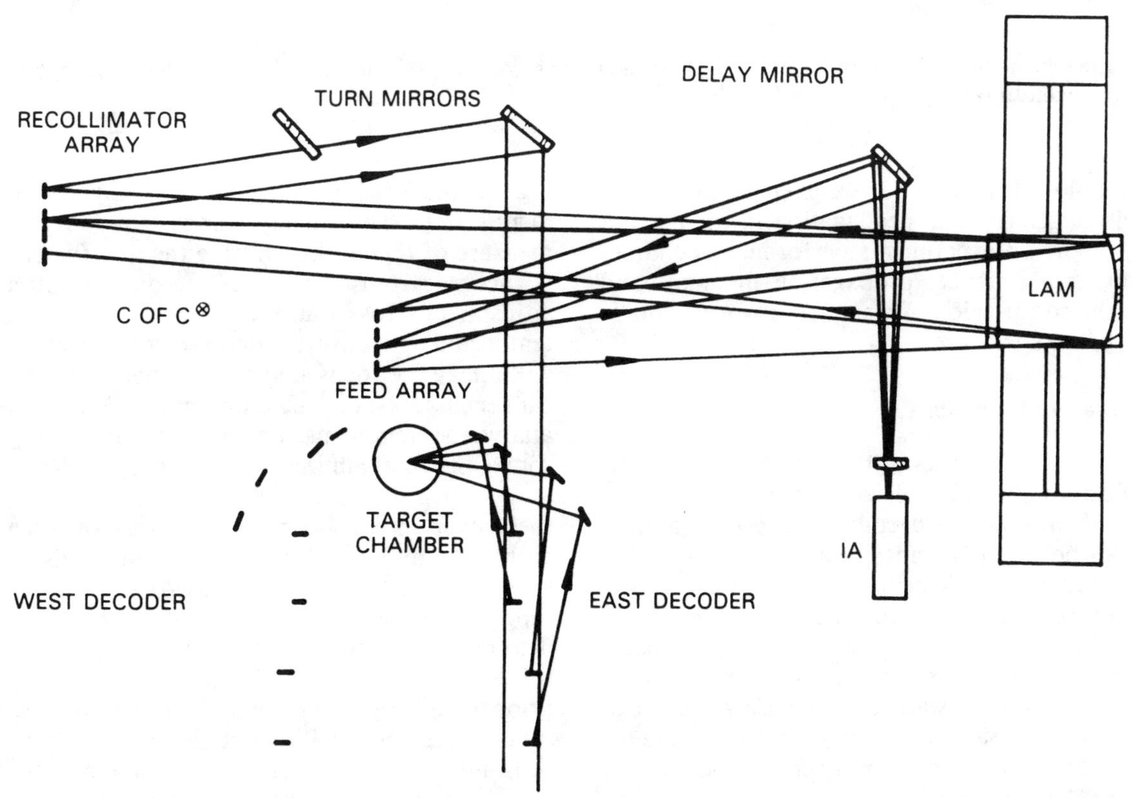

Fig. 21. The 48-beam decoder layout.

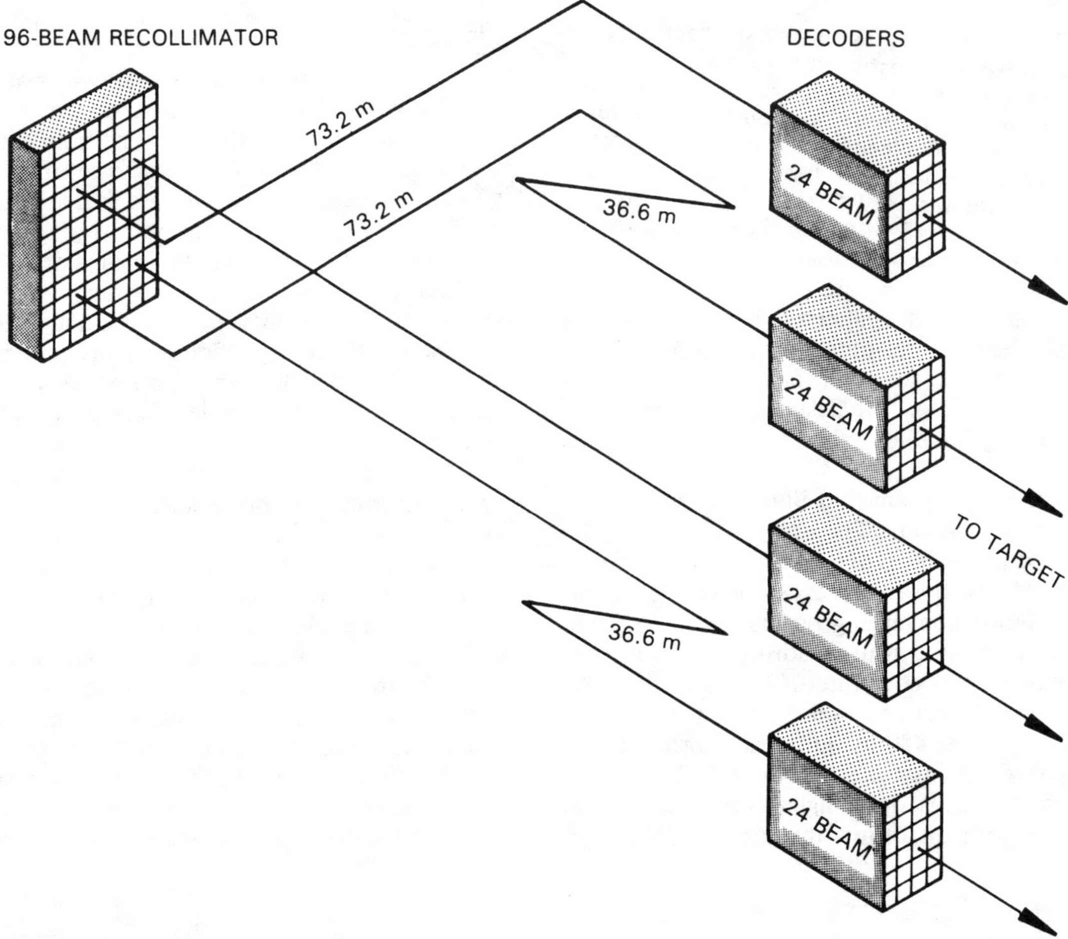

Fig. 22. The scheme of decoding by quadrants is illustrated (for second-phase Aurora, only two of the 24-beam blocks will be taken to target).

tube is employed. In Ref. 61, we examine how these mechanisms affect beam propagation in the Aurora system, report on experiments performed to characterize air as a practical propagation medium, and describe the construction of a suitable environmentally isolated beam enclosure.

Demultiplexer Alignment

To deliver laser pulses to the fusion target chamber, the beams must be directed from the main LAM mirror and through the decoder to the final aiming mirrors at the target chamber beam cone. Except for the last mirror in each beam path, each remaining decoder mirror needs to be aimed only well enough to direct the light to the next mirror. All optical elements in the decoder have been made oversize to permit several arc seconds of static alignment error at most locations. If necessary, the decoder optical elements can be manually aligned from a remote location by means of motorized mounts designed into the system.

The last mirror in each beam path is a final aiming mirror, which must be controlled by a third alignment system. This final aiming system does the largest measure of the work in hitting the tiny fusion target. Its accuracy must be one arc second or better, with adjustment steps of an even finer size. An optical system including an instrument inside the target chamber, will image the focused spot, together with fixed optical benchmarks, directly on a similar TV camera/video analysis system as used at the input pupil. Figure 23 shows the final aiming system concept. The software and control schedules for analyzing the properties of these overlapping beams will be very different than with the input pupil, but similar methods of high-speed data reduction will be used, and the effects of repositioning each of the beams will be observed to determine velocity errors schedules. The instrument in the target chamber will be withdrawn only seconds prior to delivery of energy to the target, but the velocity measurements will permit continuous error correction interpolation during that interval (predictive velocity correction must be used in real time anyway to minimize the average error bounds).

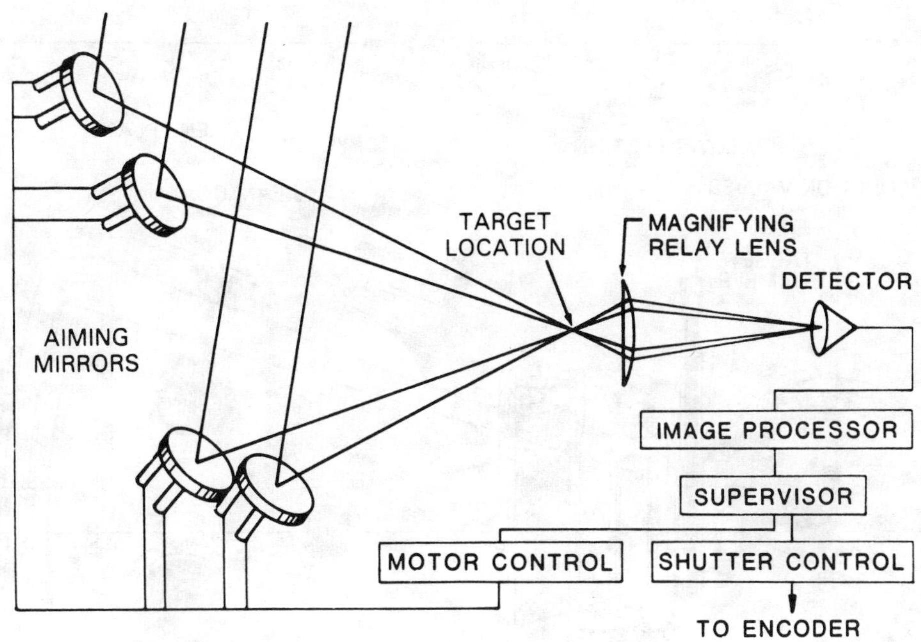

Fig. 23. The concept of the final aiming system is depicted.

Because the final aiming mirror system is large and of high mechanical Q, resonance stepper motor control of its pointing schedule may conceivably introduce pointing errors resulting from mechanical vibrations. Therefore, the target alignment system may have to work in conjunction with the input pupil system to minimize any such effects. In total, overall pointing errors of $<5\ \mu rad$ seem attainable with a direct extension of our present methods.

TARGET IRRADIATION SYSTEM

This section is based on earlier target irradiation work by Kristal.[62] The purpose in building a target irradiation subsystem is to demonstrate that the multiplexed KrF laser concept indeed produces a high-quality laser-fusion driver. Target irradiation is the only way to provide an end-to-end demonstration of the successful management of all the laser physics, optics, and associated technological issues involved in a laser-fusion prototype of this kind. A variety of targets will be illuminated, some of which put relatively stringent requirements on the quality of the illuminating beams. In addition, irradiation of targets will provide short wavelength laser/plasma interaction data that are of great interest to the laser-fusion community in general and are needed to design an ignition machine. Some of the properties of the KrF source will be exploited: short-wavelength, broad-bandwidth, and long-pulse (5- to 10-ns) operation characteristics. For example, while it is well-known that the optimal pulse shape for driving high-gain targets has an energetic component of ~5- to 10-ns width, so far no laser-fusion driver has operated in this regime. Aurora will do so. Also, a number of target physics issues relating to plasma motion and heat loss over the 5- to 10-ns pulse width are of interest, including questions of instability growth, electron preheat, deposition efficiency, and drive symmetrization.

As shown in Fig. 24, the target irradiation apparatus consists of three major parts: the target chamber, the beam cone, and the lens plate. The target chamber is designed to allow for attachment of two beam cones 180 deg apart. Each beam cone carries 48 separate beams, which would provide two-sided illumination if all 96 beams were used. As mentioned earlier, only half of the beams will be taken to target for the Aurora prototype demonstration, thus limiting the energy on target to about half of the maximum possible. The beams are directed to the beam cone by the final focusing lenses mounted to the lens plate and by the aiming mirrors located in the demultiplexer. The many ports in the target chamber provide access to the target for diagnostic instruments related to X-ray spectroscopy, laser light absorption, target-scattered light, ion blowoff, and other areas of target physics phenomena. A summary of the main elements of the target irradiation subsystem is presented below.

Target Chamber

The target chamber is a 1.57-m-diam, 7.6-cm-thick stainless steel sphere. It is attached to the beam cone by a valved cylindrical transition section and a bellows. The spherical shape of the target chamber has the advantages of exhibiting great stability against mechanical dimensional change under vacuum cycling and

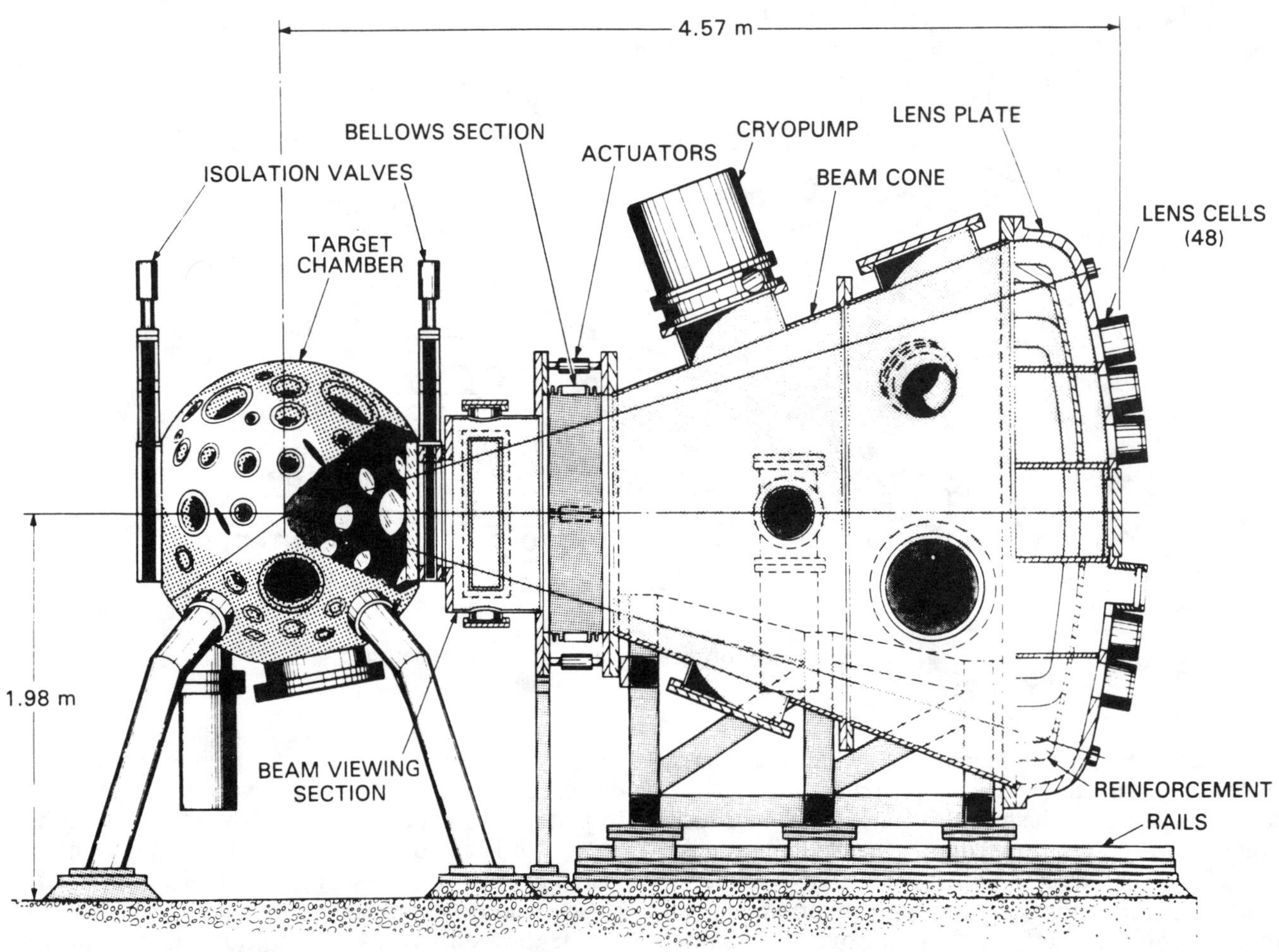

Fig. 24. South view/section assembly drawing of Aurora targeting hardware.

allowing for relatively easy diagnostic access to almost the entire 4-π solid angle around the target. Positive experience with this chamber shape at the University of Rochester Laboratory for Laser Energetics (Omega)[63] and at the Lawrence Livermore National Laboratory (Shiva),[64] plus instrument interchangeability considerations were reasons for us to adopt this shape. Information about the laser/target interaction is obtained from target diagnostic instruments, many of which are mounted on flanged ports machined into the wall of the target chamber. There are 75 ports in all, with 16 pairs of opposing ports.

Restrictions on mechanical stress and vibration are provided by the heavily reinforced concrete floor to which the target chamber support stand and beam cone are mounted, the heavy chamber leg supports, and the thick target chamber wall.

Beam Cone and Lens Plate

The beam cone expands from the target chamber joint with a cone angle of 30 deg to a diameter of 3 m and is terminated by the lens plate. The primary functions of this combined assembly are to provide a mounting structure for the focusing lenses, an evacuated beam path for the beams that are converging from the focusing lenses to the target chamber, and a means of varying the beam focal position in the target chamber. The previously mentioned Fig. 24 shows the combined beam tube and lens plate assembly, while Fig. 25 shows a more detailed view of the end of the lens plate.

The beam cone is constructed of two welded half-conical sections. This shape was mainly based on space considerations; that is, the cone provides more surrounding space than a cylinder. The beam cone holds the vacuum pumps required to evacuate the system to $\sim 10^{-6}$ Torr and also holds visual-, personnel-, and equipment-access ports. The beam cone is attached to a bellows at the small end. Mechanical expansion or contraction of this bellows provides adjustment of the beam focus at the reference target position.

The lens plate is constructed of a 447-cm radius dome section that is welded to a 305-cm-diam circular

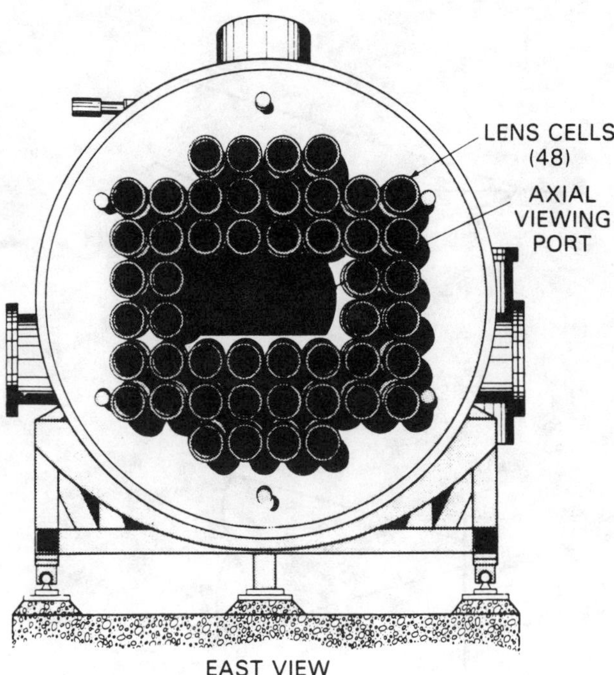

Fig. 25. A detailed view of the end of the lens plate is shown.

stainless steel flange. The 48 final focusing lenses are held in cells that are bolted to the dome over the beam penetrations. These penetrations are 18 cm in diameter and are spaced on 25-cm centers.

Beam Configuration and Delivery

The 48 collimated beams are directed radially toward the target by the final decoder aiming mirrors. The 48 focusing lenses are arranged on the lens plate dome to intercept and focus each beam on target a distance of 4.5 m away. The array of beams is basically rectangular, six rows by eight columns, as shown in Fig. 25. The four central columns are separated at their midplane to allow for target viewing. The most extreme rays at the diagonal edges of the bundle are at a 14.9-deg angle. In the horizontal and vertical planes, the edge rays are at a ~12-deg angle.

Each of the beams is expected to have a focal spot with 50% of the energy contained in a diameter of $<70\ \mu m$. This will provide a minimum attainable intensity of $\sim 5 \times 10^{+14}\ W/cm^2$ averaged over the central 50%. If all beamlets were precisely superimposed, then the total beam intensity would be $\sim 2 \times 10^{+16}\ W/cm^2$. However, we realistically expect to have the various beams distributed such that at best focus, 50% of the total energy is contained within a diameter of $<120\ \mu m$. This will provide an average intensity of $\sim 8 \times 10^{+15}\ W/cm^2$.

The beams will be pointable off axis by as much as 2.5 mm. This pointing is initially restricted so all the beams will point to the same place. Focusing of the beams to produce a desired spot size at the target plane is accomplished by precision translation of the entire beam cone and lens plate assembly. The focus range is continuous from ~6 cm in front to ~14 cm behind the reference target location. This will provide a maximum individual beam size of ~4 mm (at 90% energy) at the reference location. Focus adjustment resolution will be 100 μm throughout the focus range. A sketch of the possible illumination options appears in Fig. 26.

Target Diagnostics and Data Acquisition

Instruments for target plasma diagnostics and a data acquisition system are included as part of the target irradiation effort. Providing this equipment involves both near- and long-term efforts.

The near-term efforts mainly relate to four diagnostic measurements that are particularly valuable for yielding unequivocal data on the usefulness of the KrF laser beam in irradiating and heating laser-fusion targets. These measurements are based on previous LANL laser-fusion research experience (e.g., Helios[65] and Antares[66]) and are listed as follows:

1. time-resolved measurement of absolute soft X-ray emission
2. soft X-ray pinhole camera imaging of target emission
3. soft X-ray spectroscopy of target emission
4. laser-light absorption measurement.

The long-term efforts mainly relate to a number of additional measurements as well as improvements in existing hardware. The long-term measurements currently planned are as follows:

1. X-ray streak camera photography to determine both spatial and spectral target emission distributions
2. time-resolved measurements of hard X-ray (5- to 50-keV) target emission
3. time-, spatial-, and spectral-resolved target-scattered light (UV and visible)
4. angular distribution of soft X-ray emission
5. Faraday cup measurements of ion-blowoff fluence
6. coronal density profile measurements using UV and optical probes
7. X-ray microscopy of target emission.

Acquisition of shot data signals will be done by wideband oscilloscopes for the faster signals and CAMAC A/D converters for the slower ones. All data acquisition instrumentation will be located in a screen

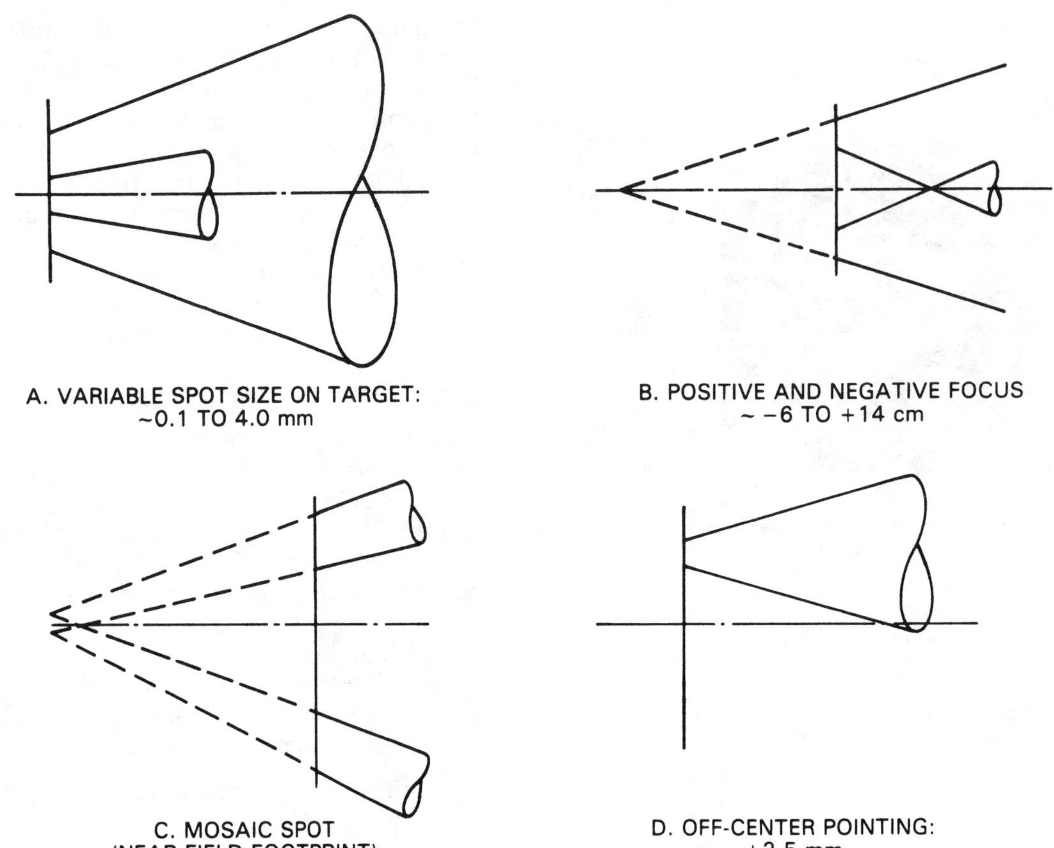

Fig. 26. Target illumination options using initial alignment and focusing capabilities.

room near the target chamber area. Much of the equipment will be taken from previous LANL laser-fusion projects and will include oscilloscopes with bandwidths up to ~3 GHz and a multitude of CAMAC digitizers with bandwidths up to ~100 MHz. Several newer items will also be added to enhance reliability, speed, and flexibility.

Initial acquisition of the digitized signals will be done on a PC/AT microcomputer using the general purpose interface bus (GPIB). Well-developed GPIB interface boards and drivers exist for this application. Some CAMAC drivers already exist and others are currently under development. The computer/digitizer interface will be accomplished using GPIB-CAMAC crate controllers. The acquired data will be stored locally on the PC/AT hard disk and then copied to a VAX 11/750 minicomputer. The VAX executes large analysis codes, archives data, generates data displays, and services remote terminals.

Additionally, photos of the fast oscilloscope traces will be digitized on a PC/AT-based video digitizer immediately after the target shot. Development of this system is near completion with a second PC/AT computer being used for this purpose. These digitized traces will also be sent to the VAX for archival and analysis.

LASER CONTROL AND DATA ACQUISITION SYSTEMS

Laser operations, optical alignment, optical and laser diagnostics, and target diagnostics will require several independent control and data acquisition systems to support the whole Aurora system. The most extensive control and data acquisition system supports the laser amplifiers. It is designed to prepare the amplifier chain for the firing sequence, to charge and fire the pulsed power components, and to collect, store, and analyze data from the system shots.

A complete description of this system is presented elsewhere.[67] The system design and hardware are from a previous LANL experience with the Antares/CO_2 laser-fusion system.[66] Brief descriptions of the control and data systems for other applications are included in the sections of this paper that correspond to those applications.

The control part of the laser amplifier control and data acquisition system consists of one host Digital Equipment Corporation (DEC) PDP 11/60 minicomputer, which is serially connected by RS232 fiber-optic links to three DEC LSI 11/2 microcomputers. These microcomputers serve as remote machine interfaces (MIs) to the laser system components. This portion of the system performs the functions of monitoring and controlling devices associated with the pulsed power components, *e* guns, and laser-amplifier gas and vacuum components. It also provides for proper timing between pulsed power components, firing of the entire laser system, and the acquiring and processing of binary, low-voltage analog, and timing data.

The fast transient data acquisition part of the system consists of two parts. The first part is one DEC PDP 11/34 minicomputer with four standard CAMAC crates, each holding up to eight LeCroy waveform digitizers of 10- to 200-MHz bandwidths. The second part is a turnkey Tektronix LSI 11/23 SPS system with CAMAC interfaces, a LeCroy 8212 32-channel digitizer, and Tektronix 7612, 7912, and 7D20 digitizers. Transient signals are connected directly to the digitizers from probes or transducers on the laser components by coaxial cables or fiber-optic links. These data are then saved on disk for postshot analysis. This minicomputer is also located in the electrically shielded room for noise suppression.

In maintenance mode, the control system allows an operator to actuate individual devices such as relays, valves, or similar devices; to turn power supplies on and off; and to examine monitors on many individual components of the laser system. In subsystem mode, it can be used to charge and fire individual Marx generators or amplifiers. In integrated mode, the control system charges and fires the entire Aurora laser system from the front end to the LAM.

Figure 27 is a block diagram for the laser-amplifier control and data acquisition system. It shows the main components and the functional interconnections between the minicomputers, which reside in the shielded control room, and the microcomputers, which reside within the MI enclosures.

One of the prime requirements of this control system is to provide synchronized timing for all electrical system elements related to the laser amplifiers. The pumping of the laser-gas volumes by the *e*-guns must be accurately synchronized with the flight time of the laser light pulses. Consequently, the charging and firing of the Marx generators and PFL output switches need to be controlled accurately. To synchronize the pumping of the amplifiers and the arrival of the pulse train requires that the pulsed power for the three main amplifiers (PA, IA, and LAM) be fired hundreds of nanoseconds before the front end. Accomplishing this requires an overall system jitter of ~25 ns.

To meet these timing requirements, the control system provides distinct programmable timing channels to the high-voltage devices that trigger the Marx generators and output switches. These channels are provided by LeCroy 4222 CAMAC-interface timing modules, which are located in one of the MIs. Each channel is delay programmable from 100 ns to 16.7 ms in 1-ns steps. Figure 28 is a timing diagram for the nontarget portion of the Aurora system.

Another major function of this system is to control and monitor various devices associated with the laser amplifiers; these may include relays, valves, power supplies, and others. The MI is a prime element in this control chain. It consists of an LSI 11/2 microcomputer, a 32-slot STD bus, and a CAMAC crate—all in a shielded enclosure located close to the particular laser subsystem that it controls.

The EMI environment created by the operation of the pulsed power system necessitates the use of fiber optics rather than metal conductors for communications between the MI and the devices to be controlled. The function of the STD-bus modules is to transmit and receive optical-level signals for the controlled devices. Aurora uses two categories of STD-bus modules. The first type of module handles control and monitor functions dealing with relatively low-speed binary and analog signals. The second type handles high-speed signals, which are interfaced by means of fiber optics to timing receivers. Examples of the low-speed functions are monitoring and/or controlling the charge of the Marx banks, the gas pressure in spark gaps or laser chambers, or the positions of switches or relays. Examples of the high-speed functions are the detection and recording of timing signals corresponding to current and voltage pulses within the Marx generators, *e* guns, and front-end lasers. Figure 29 shows these two types of STD-bus modules. Both reside in the STD bus with the connections to the microcomputer being made by a DRV-11 interface for the low-speed type and a CAMAC link for the high-speed type. The STD bus provides a modular approach in implementing these interfaces.

Data acquisition and data processing capability are provided by two independent systems. A DEC PDP 11/34-based system, designed and implemented internally at LANL, is used primarily for pulsed power diagnostics. An LSI 11/23 SPS turnkey system purchased from Tektronix is used for laser-beam and energy diagnostics.

The PDP 11/34 system acquires and processes transient waveform data (20 to 100 MHz) from the pulsed power system. The main signals of interest are voltage and current waveforms from Marx generators, PFLs, and *e* guns. These signals are sent via coaxial cables from the transducers (voltage dividers, current transformers) on the equipment to CAMAC-interfaced waveform digitizers. Commonly used digitizers are LeCroy 2256, 8837, and 8828 types with respective digitizing speeds of 20, 32, and 200 megasamples per second. The digitized data are transferred by a Kinetic Systems CAMAC crate controller to the PDP 11/34, which stores the data on hard disk for archival and analysis. A graphics terminal and printer are used for operator communication to the system.

The Tektronix LSI 11/23 SPS system acquires and processes temporal and energy-related laser performance data. These data consist of both slow and fast signals that are handled with appropriate bandwidth

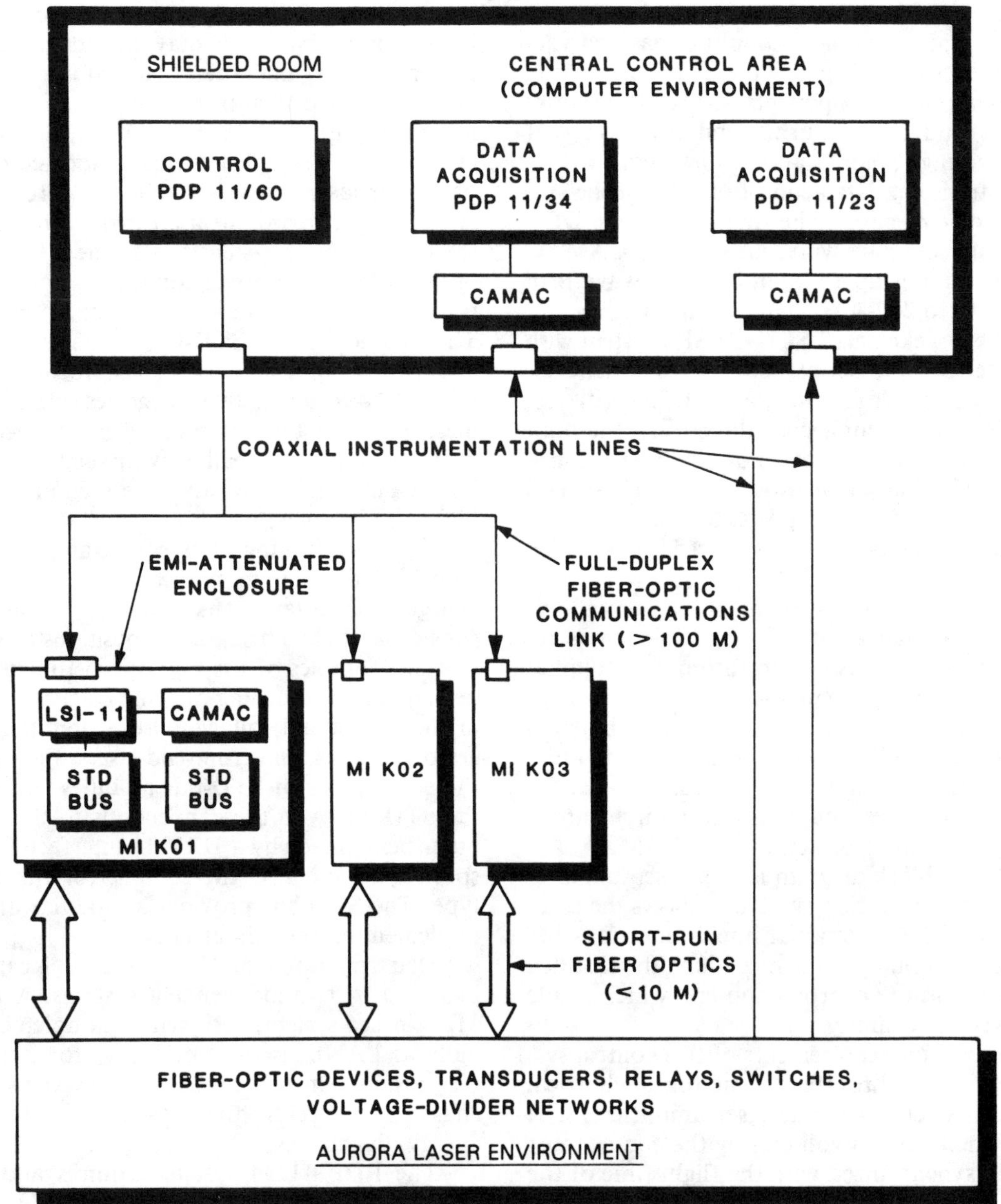

Fig. 27. Block diagram of the Aurora laser control system.

digitizers. The slow signals are from calorimeters, pyroelectric detectors, and capacitance manometers, which measure laser-beam energy and the energy deposited in the laser gas by the *e* beams. A 32-channel LeCroy 8212A CAMAC digitizer having a 5-kHz sampling rate is used. The fast signals are from photodiode detectors that measure the laser-beam intensity. These data have a bandwidth that necessitates a digitizer bandwidth in the gigahertz range in some cases. The fastest data are acquired by a Tektronix 7912AD/7A16 digitizer combination that has a bandwidth of 200 MHz and a sampling rate of 100 GHz. Signals of 10- to 80-MHz bandwidth are handled with a Tektronix 7612D digitizer, and those of a bandwidth <10 MHz are acquired with a Tektronix 7D20 digitizer.

Software is both standard and specialized. The reader is referred elsewhere for a more detailed description.[67]

Considerable diagnostic information of the overall system performance is available from the alignment control systems themselves. Position and velocity disturbances of the individual beams are continually being monitored, as well as corrected, and the history of

AURORA TIMING DIAGRAM

FE THYRATRON PULSE
FE OSCILLATOR PULSE
FE POCKEL PULSE
FE AMP 1 PULSE
FE AMP 2 PULSE
SAM TRIG PULSE
SAM PFL PULSE
SAM LASER PULSE
PA 50 kV TRIG
PA 100 kV TRIG
PA 200 kV TRIG
PA MARX PULSE
PA PFL PULSE
PA LASER PULSE
PA OS 50 kV TRIG
PA OS 100 kV TRIG
IA 50 kV TRIG
IA 100 kV TRIG
IA 200 kV TRIG
IA MARX PULSE
IA PFL PULSE
IA LASER PULSE
IA OS 50 kV TRIG
IA OS 100 kV TRIG
LAM 50 kV TRIG
LAM 100 kV TRIG
LAM 200 kV TRIG
LAM MARX PULSE
LAM PFL PULSE
LAM LASER PULSE
LAM OS 50 kV TRIG
LAM OS 100 kV TRIG
0 100 200 300 400 500
TIME (ns)
0 400 800 1200 1600 2000 2400 2800 3200 3600
TIME (ns)
FE WALL T_0 + 1752 ns

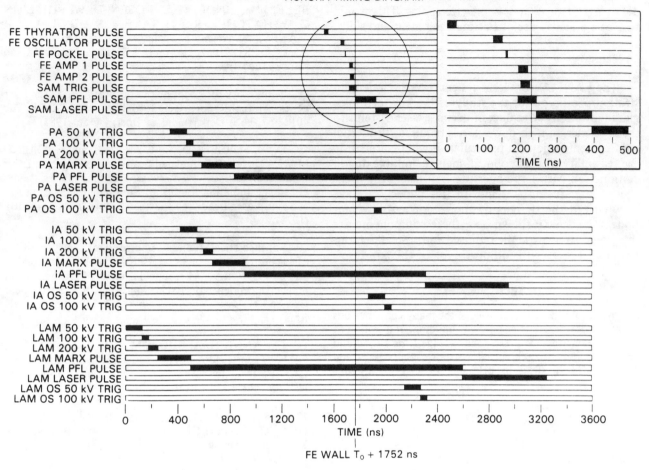

Fig. 28. Aurora laser electrical and control timing diagram.

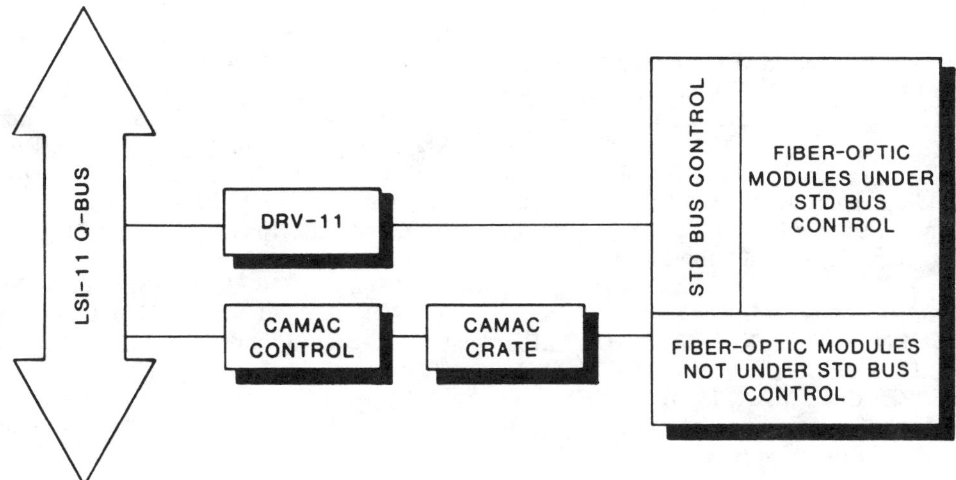

Fig. 29. Two basic categories of STD-bus modules.

such corrections is stored and available for display to the operator. In addition, it is conceivable that single events of any of the beams could be imaged onto a camera accessed by the alignment systems or seen on a separate dedicated analysis system. The events studied could give information about energy variations from event to event, for example, or information about hot spots in the optical system. The results of groups of single events could also be stored and their data correlated by these same electronics. This would be a cost-effective use of existing equipment and skills.

CONCLUSION

The LANL Aurora laser system serves as a demonstration prototype for the study of the key technologies involved in the scaling of excimer laser systems to the high-energy, high-power levels required for inertial confinement fusion. In particular, it will demonstrate the feasibility of using optical angular multiplexing in conjunction with large aperture KrF lasers for high-energy laser-fusion systems. In this paper, we have summarized the designs of the major system components and have shown how these components are integrated to provide the required end-to-end demonstration of a laser-fusion prototype of this kind.

ACKNOWLEDGMENTS

We would like to acknowledge the many contributions of all our coworkers in the design, building, and testing of the Aurora system. We also acknowledge Irma Lujan and Irene Bubernak for secretarial assistance, Sally Baca and Ruth Holt for illustration work, and Dianne Hyer for editing the manuscript.

REFERENCES

1. A. F. GIBSON, "Lasers for Compression and Fusion," *Contemp. Phys.*, **23**, 285 (1982).

2. J. F. HOLZRICHTER, D. EIMERL, E. V. GEORGE, J. B. TRENHOLME, W. W. SIMMONS, and J. T. HUNT, "High Power Pulsed Lasers," *J. Fusion Energy*, **2**, 5 (1982).

3. J. D. LINDL and J. W. K. MARK, "Recent Livermore Estimates on the Energy Gain of Cryogenics Single-Shell Ion Beam Target," *Laser Particle Beams*, **3**, 37 (1985).

4. R. J. JENSEN and P. D. GOLDSTONE, "KrF for Fusion: Target and Laser Issues," in "KrF Laser System for Inertial Confinement Fusion," LA-UR-86-620, p. 1, D. K. HYER, Ed., Los Alamos National Laboratory (1986).

5. W. C. MEAD, E. M. CAMPBELL, K. G. ESTABROOK, R. E. TURNER, W. L. KRUER, P. H. Y. LEE, B. PRUETT, V. C. RUPERT, K. G. TIRSELL, G. L. STRADLING, F. ZE, C. E. MAX, M. D. ROSEN, and B. F. LASINSKI, "Laser Irradiation of Disk Targets at 0.35 μm Wavelength," *Phys. Fluids*, **26**, 2316 (1983).

6. W. C. MEAD, E. M. CAMPBELL, W. L. KRUER, R. E. TURNER, C. W. HATCHER, D. S. BAILEY, P. H. Y. LEE, J. FOSTER, K. G. TIRSELL, B. PRUETT, N. C. HOLMES, J. T. TRAINOR, G. L. STRADLING, B. F. LASINSKI, C. E. MAX, and F. ZE, "Characteristics of Lateral and Axial Transport in Laser Irradiation of Layered-Disk Targets at 1.06 and 0.35 μm Wavelengths," *Phys. Fluids*, **27**, 1301 (1984).

7. F. ZE, L. J. SUTER, S. M. LANE, E. M. CAMPBELL, J. D. LINDL, M. D. ROSEN, D. W. PHILLION, C. W. HATCHER, R. P. DRAKE, J. S. HILDUM, K. R. MANES, "Wavelength Scaling of Laser-Driven Implosions," UCRL-91087, Lawrence Livermore National Laboratory (June 1984).

8. "University of Rochester Laboratory for Laser Energetics: Annual Report, Oct. 1983–Sept. 1984," DOE/DP/40124-67, U.S. Department of Energy (Jan. 1985).

9. D. W. FORSLUND, J. M. KINDEL, and E. L. LINDMAN, "Theory of Stimulated Scattering Processes in Laser-Irradiated Plasmas," *Phys. Fluids*, **18**, 1002 (1975); see also "Plasma Simulation Studies of Stimulated Scattering Processes in Laser-Irradiated Plasmas," *Phys. Fluids*, **18**, 1017 (1975).

10. For theoretical studies of improved efficiency by the use of krypton-rich mixtures see F. KANNARI, M. OBARA, and T. FUJIOKA, "Theoretical Studies of Output Performance Dependence on Excitation Rate for Electron-Beam Excited KrF Laser," *J. Appl. Phys.*, **53**, 135 (1982); see also Refs. 11, 12, and 13.

11. F. KANNARI, A. SUDA, M. OBARA, and T. FUJIOKA, "Theoretical Analysis of Electron-Beam-Excited KrF Laser Performance: New F_2 Concentration Optimization," *IEEE J. Quantum Electron.*, **QE-19**, 232 (1983).

12. F. KANNARI, A. SUDA, M. OBARA, and T. FUJIOKA, "Theoretical Evaluation of Electron-Beam-Excited KrF Lasers Using Argon-Free Mixtures of One Atmosphere," *Appl. Phys. Lett.*, **45**, 305 (1984).

13. M. TANIMOTO, A. YAOITA, I. OKUDA, Y. OWADANO, Y. MATSUMOTO, and T. KASAI, "Prospect of Efficient High-Power-Density Operation of KrF*-Excimer for Fusion Driver: Characteristics in Kr-Rich Gas Mixtures," *Laser Particle Beams*, **4**, 71 (1986).

14. For experimental studies on high-power, high-efficiency KrF lasers see G. C. TISONE, E. L. PATTERSON, and J. K. RICE, "Studies of an 80-kJ KrF Oscillator at Excitation Rates of 2–7 MW/cm^3," *Appl. Phys. Lett.*, **35**, 437 (1979); see also Refs. 15 through 21.

15. J. H. JACOB, J. C. HSIA, J. A. MANGANO, and M. ROKNI, "Pulse Shape and Laser Energy Extraction from E-Beam-Pumped KrF*," *J. Appl. Phys.*, **50**, 5130 (1979).

16. C. B. EDWARDS, F. O'NEILL, and M. J. SHAW, "60-ns E-Beam Excitation of Rare-Gas Halide Lasers," *Appl. Phys. Lett.*, **36**, 617 (1980).

17. J. C. SWINGLE, L. G. SCHLITT, W. R. RAPAPORT, J. GOLDHAR, and J. J. EWING, "Efficient Narrowband Electron Beam Pumped KrF Laser for Pulse-Compression Studies," *J. Appl. Phys.*, **52**, 91 (1981).

18. V. M. BUCHNEV, A. D. KLEMENTOV, and P. B. SERGEEV, "Electron-Beam-Excited KrF Laser with a Pump

Power Density of 1.6 GW liter^{-1} atm^{-1}," *Sov. J. Quantum Electron.*, **II**, 739 (1981).

19. A. SUDA, M. OBARA, and T. FUJIOKA, "Atmospheric Pressure Operation of an Electron Beam Excited KrF Laser Using Kr/F_2 Mixtures," *Appl. Phys. Lett.*, **45**, 1165 (1984).

20. E. T. SALESKY, W. D. KIMURA, "E-Beam Pumped KrF Laser Extraction Measurements for High Kr Concentration Gas Mixtures," *IEEE J. Quantum Electron.*, **QE-21**, 1761 (1985).

21. F. KANNARI, M. J. SHAW, and F. O'NEILL, "Parametric Studies of an Electron-Beam-Pumped Krypton-Rich KrF Laser," *Digest of Technical Papers CLEO '86*, paper TUN1, p. 128 (1986).

22. A. M. HUNTER and R. O. HUNTER, Jr., "Bidirectional Amplification with Nonsaturable Absorption and Spontaneous Emission," *IEEE J. Quantum Electron.*, **QE-17**, 1879 (1981).

23. J. A. SULLIVAN and C. W. von ROSENBERG, "High Energy Krypton Fluoride Amplifiers for Laser-Induced Fusion," *Laser Particle Beams*, **4**, 91 (1986).

24. G. W. YORK, Jr., S. J. CZUCHLEWSKI, L. A. ROSOCHA, and E. T. SALESKY, "Performance of the Large Aperture Module of the Aurora Krypton Fluoride Laser System," Digest of Technical Papers CLEO '85, p. 188 (1985).

25. D. B. HARRIS and J. H. PENDERGRASS, "Megajoule-Class Single-Pulse KrF Laser Test Facility as a Logical Step Toward Inertial Confinement Fusion," *Fusion Technol.*, **8**, 1868 (1985).

26. A. J. GLASS, "Optical Pulse Compression," in *Energy Storage, Compression, and Switching*, p. 399, W. H. BOSTICK, V. NARDI, and O. S. F. ZUCKER, Eds., Plenum Press, New York (1976).

27. M. A. DUGUAY, G. A. FISK, J. M. HOFFMAN, J. B. MORENO, R. E. PALMER, M. E. RILEY, and R. P. SANDOVAL, "Feasibility Study Relating to the Use of High Gain Lasers, Particularly HF, in Controlled Fusion Applications," SAND 76-0094, Sandia National Laboratories (Mar. 1976).

28. R. P. SANDOVAL, "Angular Multiplexing as a Technique for Short-Pulse Amplification in a High-Gain Xenon Amplifier," *J. Appl. Phys.*, **49**, 5745 (1978).

29. G. N. HAYS and J. M. HOFFMAN, "Pulse Compression Using Angular Multiplexing in a High-Gain 1.7 kJ Amplifier," *IEEE J. Quantum Electron.*, **QE-17**, 1836 (1981).

30. R. O. HUNTER, Jr., J. BERGER, S. CROW, R. FORKEY, D. FRIED, C. HUESTIS, E. KALASKY, D. LORENTS, and R. SCHEPS, "Key Technical Issues Associated with a Method of Pulse Compression," DOE/DP/40107-1, U.S. Department of Energy (June 1980).

31. M. W. TAYLOR and J. GOLDHAR, "Pulse Compression by Pulse-Stacking in a KrF Amplifier," *Appl. Optics*, **22**, 1288 (1983).

32. D. D. LOWENTHAL, J. J. EWING, R. E. CENTER, P. B. MUMOLA, W. M. GROSSMAN, N. T. OLSON, and J. P. SHANNON, "Conceptual Design of an Angular Multiplexed 50 kJ KrF Amplifier for ICF," *IEEE J. Quantum Electron.*, **QE-17**, 1861 (1981).

33. J. J. EWING, R. A. HASS, J. C. SWINGLE, E. V. GEORGE, and W. F. KRUPKE, "Optical Pulse Compression Systems for Laser Fusion," *IEEE J. Quantum Electron.*, **QE-15**, 368 (1978).

34. J. R. MURRAY, J. GOLDHAR, D. EIMERL, and A. SZOKE, "Raman Pulse Compression of Excimer Lasers for Application to Laser Fusion," *IEEE J. Quantum Electron.*, **QE-15**, 342 (1979).

35. M. J. DAMZEN and H. HUTCHINSON, "Laser Pulse Compression by Stimulated Brillouin Scattering in Tapered Waveguides," *IEEE J. Quantum Electron.*, **QE-19**, 7 (1983).

36. I. V. TOMOV, R. FEDOSEJEVS, and D. C. D. McKEN, "High-Efficiency Stimulated Brillouin Scattering of KrF Laser Radiation in SF_6," *Optics Lett.*, **9**, 405 (1984).

37. M. SLATKINE, I. J. BIGIO, N. A. KURNIT, and D. E. WATKINS, "Pulse Compression of Excimer Radiation by Backward-Stimulated Brillouin Scattering in Gaseous Media," *J. Opt. Soc. Am. B.*, **1**, 509 (1984).

38. V. A. EROSHENKO et al., "Numerical Investigation of the Possible Use of Stimulated Brillouin Scattering in Laser Fusion Facilities," *Sov. J. Quantum Electron.*, **10**, 1481 (1981).

39. V. A. GORBUNOV et al., "Time Compression of Pulses in the Course of Stimulated Brillouin Scattering in Gases," *Sov. J. Quantum Electron.*, **13**, 900 (1983).

40. S. B. KORMER et al., "Use of Stimulated Mandelstam-Brillouin Scattering for Peaking Pulses and Interstage Decoupling in Laser Fusion Experiments," *Sov. Phys. Tech. Phys.*, **25**, 757 (1980).

41. N. A. KURNIT et al., "Application of Nonlinear Optical Pulse Compression Techniques to Fusion Systems," in "KrF Laser System for Inertial Confinement Fusion," LA-UR-86-620, D. HYER, Ed., Los Alamos National Laboratory (1986).

42. R. J. JENSEN et al., "Los Alamos Krypton Fluoride Laser Program," *Laser Particle Beams*, **4**, 3 (1986).

43. R. J. JENSEN, L. A. ROSOCHA, and J. A. SULLIVAN, "High Power KrF Lasers for Fusion," *Proc. SPIE*, **622**, 70 (1986).

44. L. A. ROSOCHA, P. S. BOWLING, M. D. BURROWS, M. KANG, J. HANLON, J. McLEOD, and G. W. YORK, Jr., "An Overview of Aurora: A Multikilojoule KrF Laser System for Inertial Confinement Fusion," *Laser Particle Beams*, **4**, 55 (1986).

45. G. W. YORK, Jr. and F. D. FEIOCK, "Physics of Large Aperture KrF Lasers," *SOQUE Lasers '85 Conf.*, Las Vegas, Nevada, Paper HB-3, STS Press (Dec. 1985).

46. S. J. CZUCHLEWSKI, G. W. YORK, Jr., L. A. ROSOCHA, and B. J. KROHN, "A Large-Aperture 10-Kilojoule KrF Laser," (1986) (unpublished).

47. S. J. THOMAS and M. D. BURROWS, "Generation and Amplification of Single 5-ns, 248-nm Krypton Fluoride Pulses," *Digest of Technical Papers CLEO '85*, p. 172 (1985).

48. J. M. CHIQUIER, R. BUFFA, L. FINI, and F. PRADERE, "Diagnostic Measurements on the Locking Efficiency of an Injection Locked Unstable Resonator KrF Laser," *Opt. Commun.*, **56**, 267 (1985).

49. P. Le FUR and D. H. AUSTON, "A Kilovolt Picosecond Optoelectronic Switch and Pockels Cell," *Appl. Phys. Lett.*, **28**, 21 (1976).

50. For a description of NOVA, see "1981 Laser Program Annual Report," E. V. GEORGE, Scientific Ed., J. R. STRACK and G. R. GROW, Publication Eds., UCRL-50021-81, Lawrence Livermore National Laboratory (1982); see also W. W. SIMMONS and R. O. GODWIN, "NOVA Laser-Fusion Facility-Design, Engineering, and Assembly Overview," *Nucl. Technol./Fusion*, **4**, 8 (1983).

51. J. C. COMLY, Jr., unpublished calculations (1981); for further descriptions of Monte Carlo techniques see also J. C. COMLY, Jr., W. T. LELAND, C. J. ELLIOTT, A. M. HUNTER II, and M. J. KIRCHER, "Discharge and Kinetics Modeling in Electron-Beam Controlled CO_2 Laser Amplifiers," *IEEE J. Quantum Electron.*, **QE-17**, 1786 (1981); see also M. J. BERGER, "Monte Carlo Calculation of the Penetration and Diffusion of Fast Charged Particles," *Methods Comput. Phys.*, **1**, 135 (1963).

52. L. A. ROSOCHA, M. KANG, V. O. ROMERO, F. W. Van HAAFTEN, and J. P. BRUCKER, "Design and Performance of Large Area Monolithic Electron Guns for the Aurora KrF Laser System," *Digest of Technical Papers 5th IEEE Pulsed Power Conf.*, Albuquerque, New Mexico, p. 571, Institute of Electrical and Electronics Engineers (June 1985).

53. L. A. ROSOCHA and K. B. RIEPE, "Electron-Beam Sources for Pumping Large Aperture KrF Lasers," *Fusion Technol.*, **11**, 576 (1987).

54. K. B. RIEPE, L. L. BARRONE, K. J. BICKFORD, and G. H. LIVERMORE, "Antares Prototype 300-kJ 250-kA Marx Generator," LA-8491, Los Alamos National Laboratory (Jan. 1981).

55. J. JACOB, "Diffusion of Fast Electrons in the Presence of a Magnetic Field," *Appl. Phys. Lett.*, **31**, 252 (1977).

56. J. A. HANLON, J. McLEOD, J. SOLLID, W. HORN III, R. CARMICHAEL, B. L. KORTEGAARD, G. WOODFIN, and L. A. ROSOCHA, "The Aurora Project: Optical Design for a Kilojoule-Class KrF Laser," *Proc. SPIE*, **540**, 284 (1985).

57. J. HANLON and J. McLEOD, "The Aurora Laser Optical System," *Fusion Technol.*, **11**, 634 (1987).

58. J. McLEOD, "Output Optics for Aurora: Beam Separation, Pulse Stacking, and Target Focusing," *Fusion Technol.*, **11**, 654 (1987).

59. B. L. KORTEGAARD, "Superfine Laser Position Control Using Statistically Enhanced Resolution in Real Time," *Proc. SPIE*, **534**, 159 (1985).

60. B. L. KORTEGAARD, "PAC-MAN, A Precision Alignment Control System for Multiple Laser Beams Self-Adaptive Through the Use of Noise," *Fusion Technol.*, **11**, 671 (1987).

61. L. A. ROSOCHA, J. McLEOD, and J. A. HANLON, "Beam Propagation Considerations in the Aurora Laser System," *Fusion Technol.*, **11**, 624 (1987).

62. A more detailed description of earlier work on the target irradiation system can be found in L. A. ROSOCHA, M. D. BURROWS, P. S. BOWLING, L. BURCZYK, B. SHURTER, R. DINGLER, M. KANG, J. HANLON, B. KORTEGAARD, J. McLEOD, and R. KRISTAL, "Aurora: KrF Laser-Test System for Inertial Confinement Fusion Experiments," in "KrF Laser System for Inertial Confinement Fusion," LA-UR-86-620, p. 253, D. K. HYER, Ed., Los Alamos National Laboratory (1986).

63. J. BUNKENBERG, J. BOLES, D. C. BROWN, J. EASTMAN, J. HOOSE, R. HOPKINS, L. IWAN, S. D. JACOBS, J. H. KELLY, S. KUMPAN, S. LETZRING, D. LONOBILE, L. D. LUND, G. MOUROU, S. REFERMAT, W. SEKA, J. M. SOURES, and K. WALSH, "The Omega High-Power Phosphate-Glass System: Design and Performance," *IEEE J. Quantum Electron.*, **QE-17**, 1620 (1981).

64. For a description of Shiva, see C. F. BENDER and B. D. JARMAN, Eds., "Laser Program Annual Report-1977," UCRL-50021-77, Lawrence Livermore National Laboratory (1977); see also D. R. SPECK, E. S. BLISS, J. A. GLAZE, J. W. HERRIS, F. W. HOLLOWAY, J. T. HUNT, B. C. JOHNSON, D. J. KUIZENZA, R. G. OZARSKI, H. G. PATTON, P. R. RUPERT, G. J. SUSKI, C. D. SWIFT, and C. E. THOMPSON, "The Shiva Laser-Fusion Facility," *IEEE J. Quantum Electron.*, **QE-17**, 1599 (1981).

65. R. L. CARLSON, J. P. CARPENTER, D. E. CASPERSON, R. B. GIBSON, R. P. GODWIN, R. F. HAGLUND, Jr., J. A. HANLON, E. L. JOLLY, and T. F. STRATTON, "Helios: A 15-TW Carbon Dioxide Laser-Fusion Facility," *IEEE J. Quantum Electron.*, **QE-17**, 1662 (1981).

66. H. JANSEN, "Antares is Coming to Life," *Digest of Technical Papers 4th IEEE Pulsed Power Conf.*, Albuquerque, New Mexico, June 1983, p. 1.

67. P. S. BOWLING, L. BURCZYK, R. DINGLER, and R. B. SHURTER, "Aurora Inertial Confinement Fusion Laser Control and Data Acquisition System," *Fusion Technol.*, **11**, 612 (1987).

Reprinted with permission from *IEEE Journal of Quantum Electroncis,* Vol. 26(9), pp 1529-1534 (September 1990). ©1990 IEEE.

F_2 Pumped NO: Laser Oscillation at 218 nm and Prospects for New Laser Transitions in the 160–250 nm Region

SIMON M. HOOKER AND COLIN E. WEBB, MEMBER, IEEE

(Invited Paper)

Abstract—**We have recently proposed a scheme to produce powerful, coherent radiation at several wavelengths between 160 and 250 nm by optically pumping a high-lying electronic level of nitric oxide with radiation from a molecular fluorine laser. We present the details of this scheme, and the results of a kinetic model which describes the observed absorption of F_2 laser radiation by NO. The successful operation of the scheme to produce laser oscillation at 218 nm is described. The possibility of using this scheme to produce laser oscillation at other wavelengths is discussed, and further extensions to produce coherent radiation at wavelengths shorter than 158 nm are proposed.**

I. Introduction

THE major difficulty associated with producing laser oscillation at short wavelengths is the very high pumping power which is required to produce a population inversion. For this reason, there are relatively few laser sources which produce VUV radiation directly. Nearly all solids and liquids absorb strongly in the VUV, and so VUV lasers are restricted to gaseous media.

Nonlinear techniques have been used extensively to produce coherent VUV radiation. Four-wave mixing and frequency tripling of visible and ultraviolet laser radiation in metal vapors and rare gases enables tunable VUV radiation to be produced, but conversion efficiences and output pulse energies are low, usually no greater than 10^{12}–10^{14} photons/pulse. These sources are therefore restricted to applications in spectroscopy. The rare gas dimer lasers can produce VUV laser radiation, but until recently, they have always required electron beam excitation.

The most powerful discharge-excited VUV laser is the molecular fluorine laser which oscillates at 158 nm. Recently [1], a device has produced pulse energies in excess of 100 mJ, representing a peak power in excess of 1 MW. However, the F_2 laser is not tunable and its possible applications are therefore rather limited.

Manuscript received November 13, 1989; revised March 7, 1990.
The authors are with Clarendon Laboratory, University of Oxford, Oxford OX1 3PU, England.
IEEE Log Number 9037364.

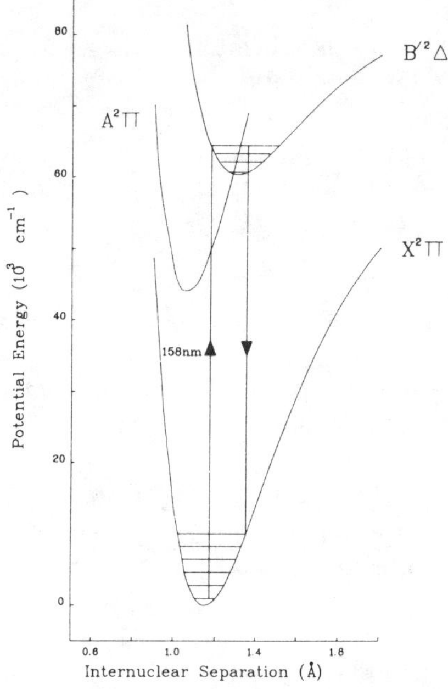

Fig. 1. Diagram showing the proposed optical pumping of NO by a molecular fluorine laser.

II. Optically Pumped NO: A New VUV Laser

A. The Proposed Scheme

We have proposed [2] a scheme (see Fig. 1) to optically pump a high-lying level of a molecule with F_2 laser radiation to produce population inversions with respect to excited vibrational levels of the ground state, which have only a very small thermal population. Laser oscillation should then be possible on several electronic transitions to the ground state, with wavelengths on the Stokes side of the F_2 laser wavelength. Since the excitation does not involve nonlinear processes, the scheme should convert F_2 laser radiation with a high efficiency (of order 10%), and pulse energies in the millijoule range are anticipated. If successful, this scheme would then provide powerful laser oscillation at many wavelengths in the range of 158–250 nm.

TABLE I
CALCULATED GAIN CROSS SECTIONS AND WAVELENGTHS FOR THE $B'^2\Delta(v' = 3) - X^2\Pi(v'' = v'')$ TRANSITIONS IN NO. THE CROSS SECTION OF A SINGLE ROTATIONAL TRANSITION IS OBTAINED BY MULTIPLYING THE LINE STRENGTH OF THE BRANCH.

v''	Cross Section (10^{15} cm^2)	Wavelength (nm)
0	3.7	157
1	2.0	162
2	0.16	167
3	2.5	173
4	1.1	178
5	0.23	184
6	2.4	190
7	1.8	196
8	0.03	203
9	1.3	210
10	3.8	217
11	4.2	225
12	2.8	233
13	1.3	242
14	0.44	251

The success of this scheme requires a molecule showing a strong absorption at the F_2 laser wavelength of 158 nm, leading to a bound state which does not predissociate. Only a few diatomic molecules, such as CO, NO, and N_2, remain bound after absorbing an F_2 laser photon of energy 7.8 eV.

B. Parameters of the Proposed Scheme

Excitation of a single rotational state of the $B'^2\Delta(v' = 3)$ level of nitric oxide by absorption of F_2 laser radiation has been reported by Taherian and Slanger [3]. This state has a radiative lifetime of 110.7 ns [4] and large Franck–Condon factors [5] for eight or more of its transitions to the ground state $X^2\Pi$. We have calculated the Doppler-broadened gain cross sections for the potential laser transitions, and these are presented in Table I. The cross-section for a single rotational transition is obtained by multiplying the tabulated cross-section value by the line strength of the branch (approximately 0.2 for the strongest branch). A single rotational transition therefore has a cross section of order $3 \cdot 10^{-16}$ cm^2, and hence laser oscillation should be possible if a population of order 10^{15} cm^{-3} can be produced in the upper level.

The F_2 laser oscillates on two close-lying transitions. The wavelength of the stronger of the two F_2 laser lines has been measured by McKee [6] as 157.6299 nm. In view of the number of significant figures given, the apparent error in this measurement is therefore ± 0.00005 nm, which corresponds to ± 0.02 cm^{-1}. However, in the same paper, the laser lines are stated to be about 1 cm^{-1} wide, and so it would seem likely that the true uncertainty in the F_2 laser wavelength must be about ± 0.3 cm^{-1}.

Miescher [7] has measured the wavelengths of the $B'^2\Delta(v' = 3) - X^2\Pi(v'' = 0)$ band of NO to an accuracy of ± 0.1 cm^{-1}. These data predict that the stronger F_2 laser line lies 0.02 cm^{-1} to longer wavelength from the $Q_{11}(7\frac{1}{2})$ transition of the B'-$X(3$–$0)$ band. Given the uncertainty in the F_2 laser wavelength, we conclude that the mismatch between the stronger F_2 laser line and the $Q_{11}(7\frac{1}{2})$ transition is in the range 0–0.4 cm^{-1}. The weaker F_2 laser line is not expected to be absorbed at all.

Taherian and Slanger also concluded that excitation of the $B'^2\Delta(v' = 3)$ state occurs via the $Q_{11}(7\frac{1}{2})$ transition. Their evidence was based on a coincidence they observed between an R and a P line in the emission spectrum of the B'-$B(3$–$1)$ band of NO after absorption of F_2 laser radiation. Using the spectroscopic constants of the $B'^2\Delta$ and $B^2\Pi$ states, they were able to identify the level excited by the F_2 laser radiation as the $J = 7\frac{1}{2}$ level of the $B'^2\Delta$ state. They then calculated that of the possible excitation transitions which produce the $J = 7\frac{1}{2}$ level, the wavelength of the $Q_{11}(7\frac{1}{2})$ transition was closest to the F_2 laser wavelength.

The Doppler width of the $Q_{11}(7\frac{1}{2})$ absorption transition in NO is 0.144 cm^{-1}. Because of the 0–0.4 cm^{-1} uncertainty in the frequency separation of the F_2 laser and the pumped transition of NO, the absorption cross section is uncertain by nine orders of magnitude over the probable range of line separation. With such a large uncertainty, it is not possible to predict with any accuracy the strength of the absorption of the F_2 laser radiation or the upper level population and the corresponding gain likely to be produced.

To evaluate the possibility of laser oscillation in this system, we have measured the absorption of F_2 laser radiation by NO, and we have interpreted the results with a kinetic model to determine the magnitude of the upper level population which can be produced.

III. THE ABSORPTION OF F_2 LASER RADIATION BY NO GAS

A. Experimental Technique

The apparatus used to determine the absorption is shown schematically in Fig. 2. The F_2 laser was a discharge-pumped device with automatic preionization of a design based on that of Kearsley *et al.* [8]. The external capacitor (70 nF) was rated for voltages of up to 45 kV, and the internal capacitor bank comprised 62 capacitors, each of 625 pF capacitance. The discharge dimensions were 58.5 cm (length) $\cdot$ 2 cm (the electrode spacing) $\cdot$ 0.7 cm (height). A laser gas mix of 6 mbar of fluorine in a buffer gas of 3.2 bar of helium was used. With the external capacitor charged to 45 kV, the F_2 laser produced output pulses of 30 mJ energy and 35 ns duration. For the absorption experiments, the external capacitor was charged to 35 kV, which reduced the F_2 laser pulse energy to approximately 10 mJ, thereby avoiding saturation of the detection equipment.

Light from the F_2 laser was transmitted via an evacuated glass pipe to the absorption cell. After propagating through the gas in the cell, the F_2 laser radiation was diffused by reflection from a roughened brass plate onto the cathode of a solar-blind photodiode. The distance from the scattering plate to the photodiode was small compared to the total path length, so that all light reaching the photodiode traveled through a length of gas close to the distance along the axis of the system (53 cm). The output

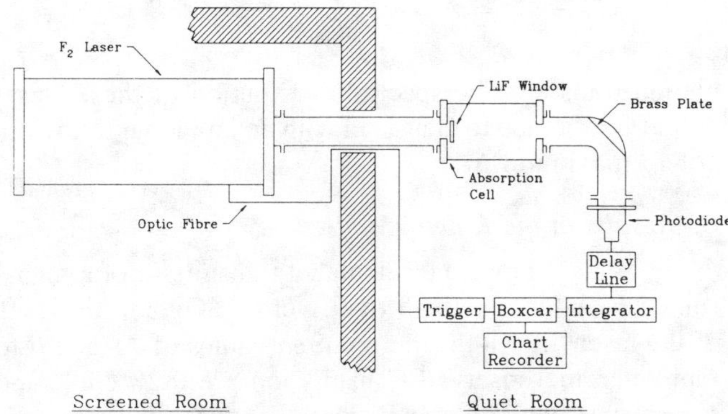

Fig. 2. Schematic representation of the experimental arrangement used to determine the absorption of radiation from a molecular fluorine laser by NO.

of the photodiode was integrated to give the total transmitted pulse energy and was averaged with a boxcar averager, the output of which was displayed on a chart recorder. The zero of the chart recorder trace was established by admitting air to the absorption cell. Air is totally opaque to F_2 laser radiation because of absorption on the strong Schumann–Runge band in molecular oxygen.

It is clearly important to ensure that the NO gas (BOC, stated purity 99.8%) is free from impurities if the true absorption is to be measured. With the exception of N_2, the major impurities of commercial NO are all triatomic (N_2O, NO_2, and CO_2) and have very low vapor pressures at temperatures close to that of liquid nitrogen. By cooling the gas to such temperatures, these impurities should be effectively removed. Fig. 3 shows the measured visible and ultraviolet transmission of a sample of gas before and after purification by a cryogenic gas purifier (Oxford Lasers GP2000). Unlike the unpurified gas, the purified gas does not absorb radiation with wavelengths longer than 227 nm, indicating a reduction in the concentration of impurities. The absorption below 227 nm observed in the purified gas corresponds to excitation to the first three vibrational levels of the $A^2\Sigma^+$ level of NO from the ground state. The gas used in the absorption experiments and the subsequent laser tests was always purified by this technique.

B. Experimental Results

The measured transmission as a function of NO pressure is shown in Fig. 4, together with the transmission predicted by the cross section measured by Taherian and Slanger ($3.7 \cdot 10^{-19}$ cm^2). The much greater absorption reported by Taherian and Slanger—almost an order of magnitude greater than that observed in the present experiment—we can only attribute to impurities in the gas sample they used. An impurity which is likely to be found in commercially suppled NO is nitrogen dioxide (NO_2). Nitrogen dioxide has an absorption cross section [9] of $1.6 \cdot 10^{-17}$ cm^2 at the F_2 laser wavelength. The presence of NO_2 in Taherian and Slanger's gas sample at a concentration of 2% would account for an apparent absorption cross section of the magnitude they report. In addition, as discussed in Section IV-C, the observed cross section for

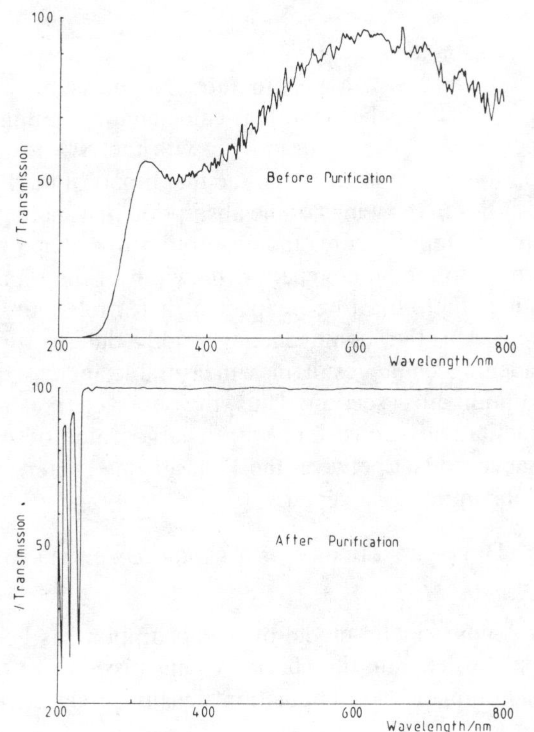

Fig. 3. Measured transmission of a sample of gas before and after cryogenic purification.

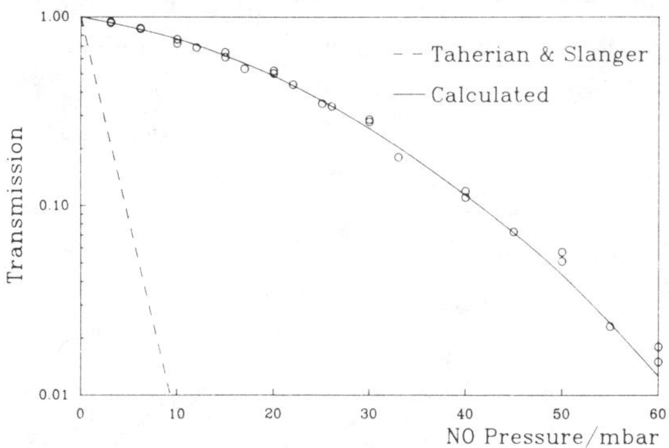

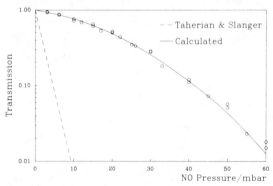

Fig. 4. Graph showing measured and calculated transmission as a function of NO pressure. The transmission calculated from the absorption cross section reported by [3] is also shown.

absorption of F_2 laser radiation by NO increases with pressure due to pressure broadening. Hence, the use of higher NO gas pressures than used in the present experiment would also result in the measurement of a larger absorption cross section than that determined here.

The presence of such low levels of impurities in Taherian and Slanger's gas sample would not have affected their determination of the radiative lifetime of the $B'^2\Delta(v = 3)J = 7\frac{1}{2}$ state of NO: (110.7 ± 1.1) ns, and is also unlikely to have produced a large error in their measurement of the quenching coefficient of this state: $(4.97 \pm 0.18) \cdot 10^{-10}$ cm^{-3} $\cdot$ molecules^{-1} $\cdot$ s^{-1} [4]. In this work, we have used their values for these quantities since they are consistent with other measurements [10], [11] and have the smallest quoted errors.

C. Conclusion

The plot of transmission versus the pressure shows a distinct curvature, implying an absorption cross section which increases with gas pressure. The measured absorption is much weaker than that calculated assuming exact coincidence of the F_2 laser line with the NO absorption transition, and it is clear that the major part of the F_2 laser output lies in the wings of the absorption line shape. Away from the Doppler core, the absorption line shape is very sensitive to the homogeneous linewidth of the transition, and it is therefore to be expected that a relatively small increase in the homogeneous width due to pressure broadening could result in a measurable increase in the absorption cross section. Thus, the observed transmission is qualitatively consistent with a large value of $\Delta\tilde{\nu}$, the frequency offset between the F_2 laser line center and the NO absorption line center.

IV. Detailed Theory of Absorption Experiments

A. Kinetic Model

A simple kinetic model of the absorption has been developed to explain the observed transmission and to predict the upper level population density produced by the absorption.

The spectral rate equations (i.e., treating intensities and populations on a frequency-resolved basis) of the simple two-level system were solved to predict the transmission. Assuming that the laser intensity is time-independent and that no depletion of the lower level population occurs, the transmission is given by a spectral form of Beer's Law:

$$T = \frac{1}{I_t}\int_0^{\infty} I(\nu, 0)e^{-k(\nu)l}\, d\nu \tag{1}$$

where

$$k(\nu) = \int_0^{\infty} \sigma_h(\nu - \nu')n_1(\nu')\, d\nu' \tag{2}$$

in which $I(\nu, z)$ is the spectral intensity of the laser at a distance z into the gas, $\sigma_h(\nu - \nu')$ is the homogeneous absorption cross section at a frequency ν for molecules with a homogeneous line center frequency ν', $n_1(\nu')$ is the lower level spectral population (i.e., the population per unit bandwidth which responds to frequencies around ν') described by a Gaussian distribution, I_t is the total incident laser intensity, and l is the total path length.

Since the lower level is long lived, the homogeneous linewidth $\Delta\tilde{\nu}_h$ of the pump transition is determined by the upper level lifetime τ_2, as well as the collisional quenching rate K_qN where K_q is the quenching rate coefficient of the upper level and N is the number density of molecules. However, there may also be processes, such as interruption of the phase of the molecular wavefunction, which give rise to an increase in the homogeneous width, but do not transfer population. We therefore describe $\Delta\tilde{\nu}_h$ in wavenumber units as

$$\Delta\tilde{\nu}_h = \frac{1}{2\pi c}\left\{\frac{1}{\tau_2} + \beta K_qN\right\} \tag{3}$$

where a value of β greater than unity indicates the presence of pressure broadening by processes other than population transfer. The spectral distribution of the F_2 laser output is assumed to Gaussian with an unknown full width at half maximum Δ_f.

B. Results of the Kinetic Model

Fig. 4 also shows the calculated transmission for an assumed F_2 laser linewidth of 0.1 cm^{-1}. Given this value of the laser linewidth, the required values of $\Delta\tilde{\nu}$ and β to reproduce the observed transmission are 0.28 cm^{-1} and 1.1, respectively. If the F_2 laser linewidth is increased, both $\Delta\tilde{\nu}$ and β must also be increased to obtain a good fit to the experimental data. With an assumed linewidth of 0.3 cm^{-1}, $\Delta\tilde{\nu}$ and β have to be increased to 0.465 cm^{-1} and 4.0. This latter value of the frequency offset is greater than the upper limit of 0.4 cm^{-1} as discussed above, and so we conclude that the linewidth of the molecular fluorine laser cannot be greater than 0.3 cm^{-1}. In order to obtain a good fit to the data, we find that the laser linewidth must be greater than 0.05 cm^{-1}.

We conclude, therefore, that the unknown parameters have values which lie within the following ranges.

F_2 laser linewidth:	$0.1 < \Delta_f < 0.3$ cm^{-1}
Offset between NO line center and F_2 laser:	$0.28 < \Delta\tilde{\nu} < 0.4$ cm^{-1}
Excess homogeneous broadening:	$1 < \beta < 4$.

The model can also predict the upper level population produced by the absorption at $z = 0$, i.e., at the point where the laser radiation enters the absorption cell. The upper level population increases as the NO pressure is increased. Assuming an F_2 laser linewidth of 0.1 cm^{-1}, the upper level population is calculated to reach a maximum during the pump pulse of $8.6 \cdot 10^{14}$ cm^{-3} at an NO pressure of 800 mbar.

C. Conclusions from the Absorption Experiment and Kinetic Model

The observed absorption of F_2 laser radiation by NO is about 10^4 times weaker than the calculated line center absorption. The experimental results are explained by the frequency offset $\Delta\tilde{\nu}$ being equal to at least two Doppler widths. Consequently, pressure broadening significantly increases the absorption cross section, giving rise to the observed curvature in the plot of transmission versus pressure.

The spectral width of the F_2 laser is predicted to be approximately 0.1 cm^{-1}, which is somewhat narrower than the 1 cm^{-1} reported by [6]. An F_2 laser linewidth of 1 cm^{-1} is *not* consistent with the transmission observed in our experiments, and we conclude that the previously reported value refers to an instrument-limited measurement. The Doppler width of a transition at 158 nm in molecular fluorine is of order 0.1 cm^{-1}, and hence an F_2 laser linewidth of order 0.1 cm^{-1} is consistent with the laser oscillation occurring on a single rotational transition.

Since the frequency offset $\Delta\tilde{\nu}$ is large, the absorption is weak, and high pressures are required to achieve the upper level population necessary for laser oscillation in NO. At a pressure of 800 mbar, the lifetime of the upper level against quenching is only 100 ps, a thousand times shorter than the radiative lifetime. The excitation is therefore inefficient, and nearly all molecules in the upper level are quenched before they radiate. The excitation of the upper level must be made more efficient if the proposed system is to work.

V. Inclusion of Magnetic Field Effects

A. Zeeman Shifting of the Transition Frequencies

The F_2 laser is not tunable, and so cannot be tuned into resonance with the absorption line. However, the $B'^2\Delta$ level of NO exhibits a large Zeeman splitting. We have calculated the Zeeman splitting of the upper level as a function of the applied magnetic field using the theory of Hill [12], and the result is presented in Fig. 5. To the first approximation, the ground state of NO $(X^2\Pi_{1/2})$ exhibits no Zeeman splitting. It should be possible to shift the B'–X transition frequencies close to resonance with the F_2 laser radiation by applying a magnetic field of order 1 T.

Preliminary experiments using a dc magnet indicated an increase in absorption cross section by a factor of 70 for an applied field of 1 T (see Fig. 6). It therefore seems promising to search for laser oscillation in a system employing an applied magnetic field.

B. A Test of the Proposed Scheme

The experimental arrangement to demonstrate laser oscillation in this system is shown schematically in Fig. 7. In these experiments, the external capacitor of the F_2 laser was charged to 45 kV, and the F_2 laser provided an output of about 30 mJ/pulse in a rectangular beam 20 mm wide and 7 mm high. The NO cell was connected to the F_2 laser output coupler via an O-ring seal. The body of the NO cell was constructed from brass. The top and bottom walls of the cell were formed from glass plates, sealed to the cell with epoxy, to avoid attenuation of the pulsed magnetic field by skin effects.

The magnetic field was provided by discharging a 100 μF capacitor through two coils fixed to the top and bottom of the cell. The coils, of 32 turns each, were connected in series and wound on formers of a "racetrack" cross section (16 · 26 mm) and 15 mm high. The separation of the coils was 14 mm. The current pulse through the coils had the form of a half sine wave with a duration of 200 μs and a peak value of up to 1.3 kA, depending on the charging voltage (0–1.3 kV) of the capacitor. The coils were calibrated with continuous currents of up to 10 A using a Hall probe, and were found to give 1.03 T/kA in the central region between the coils.

Two trigger pulses from a double pulse generator were used to switch the magnetic field and to trigger the F_2 laser. The relative timing of the trigger pulses was adjusted so that the F_2 laser emission occurred at the peak of the magnetic field. The jitter between the two pulses was negligible compared to the duration of the magnetic field.

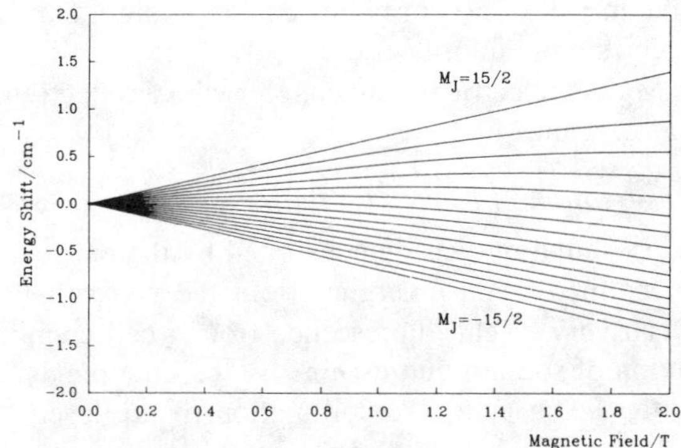

Fig. 5. Calculated Zeeman splitting of the $B'^2\Delta(v = 3)J = 7\frac{1}{2}$ level of NO as a function of applied magnetic field.

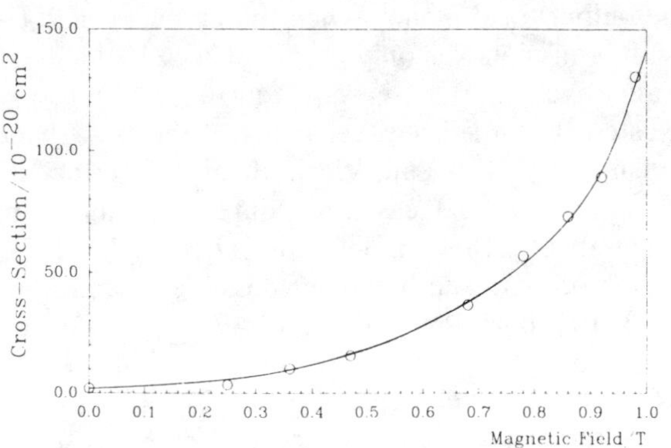

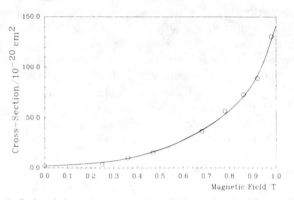

Fig. 6. Deduced absorption cross section of NO as a function of an applied dc magnetic field. The pole pieces of the magnet were of 25.4 mm diameter and were positioned so as to produce a magnetic field transverse to the propagation of the F_2 laser radiation. The NO pressure used in this experiment was 5 mbar.

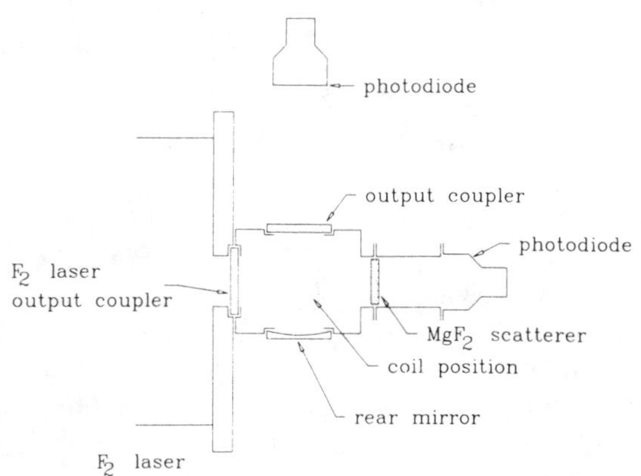

Fig. 7. Plan view of the apparatus for the experimental observation of laser oscillation in nitric oxide.

To demonstrate the proposed laser, it was decided to conduct an initial search for laser oscillation at wavelengths longer than 200 nm, thereby avoiding the need for a vacuum spectrometer. The resonator of the optically pumped laser was set up with its axis parallel to the 20 mm width of the F_2 laser beam. The cavity comprised one concave mirror of 50 cm radius coated in aluminum with a magnesium fluoride overcoat, and a 17-layer AlO_2–MgF_2 dielectric output coupler with a reflectivity of 82% at 218 nm.

C. *Observation of Laser Oscillation at 218 nm*

Laser oscillation was demonstrated by the existence of a well-defined beam emerging from the NO cell which produced very bright fluorescence from a cell containing a solution of sodium fluorescein. By tracking the dye cell along the beam path, the collimation of the laser beam was evident. The beam was approximately 7 mm high and 7 mm wide.

The NO laser radiation was passed to a spectrometer (Spex 1802) fitted with an optical multichannel analyzer in the output focal plane. When tuning between 200 and 300 nm, emission was only observed at (218.11 ± 0.02) nm (air wavelength), as is shown in Fig. 8.

A calculation of the wavelengths of the B'–X band of NO using the Hill–Van Vleck theory [13] for mixed Hund's case (a) and case (b) coupling predicts an air wavelength of 218.10 nm for the $Q_{12}(7\frac{1}{2})B'$–$X(3$–$10)$ transition of NO. The five other possible branches of the B'–$X(3$–$10)$ transition from the $J = 7\frac{1}{2}$ level of the upper level [(i.e., $P_{11}(8\frac{1}{2})$, $Q_{11}(7\frac{1}{2})$, $R_{11}(6\frac{1}{2})$, $P_{12}(8\frac{1}{2})$, $R_{12}(6\frac{1}{2})$] have wavelengths between 217.42 and 218.22 nm, and the dispersion of the spectrometer was sufficient to determine unambiguously that oscillation on these other branches did not occur. Laser oscillation occurs on a single branch of a single rotational transition. It is not known whether laser oscillation occurs on more than one transition between magnetic sublevels or, indeed, whether more than one magnetic sublevel in the upper level is populated.

D. *Laser Output Dependence on the Magnetic Field*

The dependence of the NO laser intensity on the applied magnetic field was investigated by passing the NO laser output through calibrated neutral density filters onto the cathode of a vacuum photodiode. Fig. 9 shows the peak intensity of the NO laser emission as a function of the applied magnetic field for various NO pressures. A distinct threshold at about 0.95 T is apparent, followed by an extremely rapid increase in intensity with applied magnetic field. At the maximum possible applied magnetic field of 1.3 T, the optimum NO pressure was found to be 20 mbar. The output energy of the NO laser was measured with a pyroelectric joulemeter (Gentec ED100) and was found to be 87 μJ under these conditions.

E. *Pulse Shape*

The temporal profiles of both the NO laser pulse and the F_2 laser radiation reaching the solar-blind photodiode at the far side of the cell (see Fig. 7) could be recorded. Fig. 10 shows the relative timing of these two pulses, where corrections have been made for the different distances of light propagation and different lengths of cable from the photodiodes to the oscilloscope (Tektronix 2440, 200 MHz single-shot bandwidth). The NO laser pulse duration was measured to be (9 ± 1) ns using an oscilloscope with a 350 ps rise time (Tektronix 519).

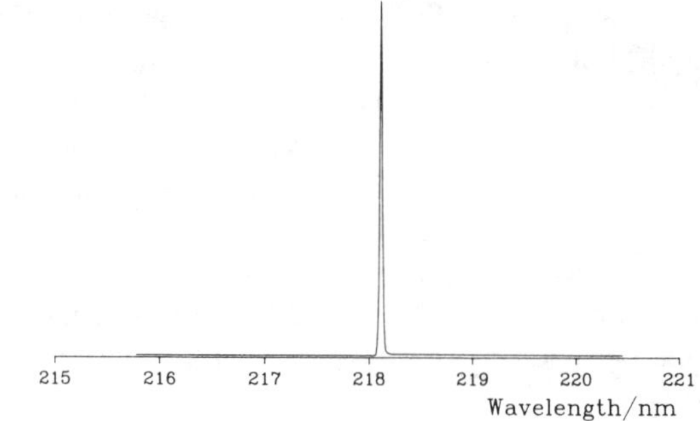

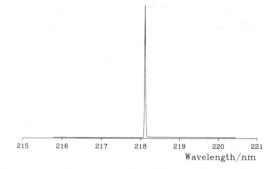

Fig. 8. Spectrum of the output of the NO cell with an applied magnetic field of 1.3 T.

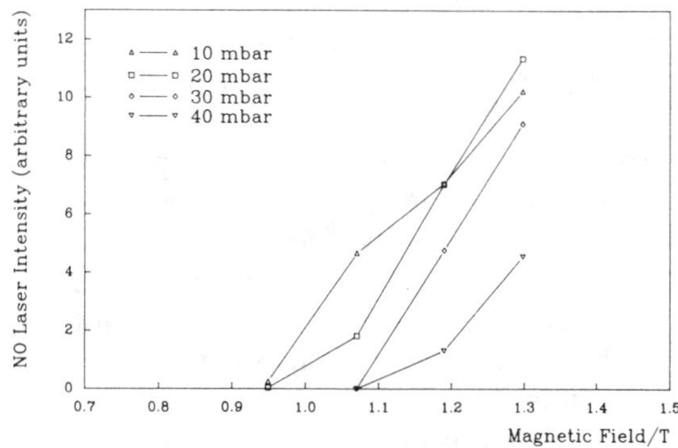

Fig. 9. Graph showing the peak NO laser intensity as a function of applied magnetic field for various gas pressures.

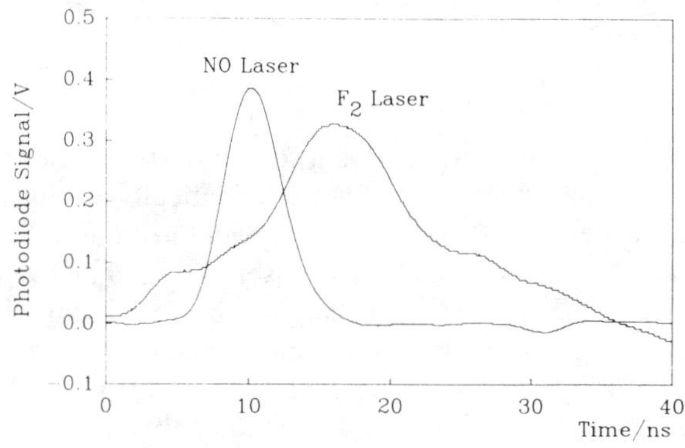

Fig. 10. The relative timing between the F_2 laser radiation reaching the solar-blind photodiode and the NO laser output for an NO pressure of 20 mbar and an applied magnetic field of 1.3 T.

It is clear that the NO laser pulse occurs during the first part of the F_2 laser pump pulse. It would therefore appear that the upper level population reaches the threshold value early in the pump pulse, and that laser oscillation then occurs. Since the lower laser level is long-lived compared to the rate at which it is filled, it is not surprising that the NO laser oscillation should be self-terminating.

VI. Conclusion

We have proposed a scheme to optically pump a high-lying electronic level of NO with F_2 laser radiation to produce powerful coherent radiation at several wavelengths in the VUV spectral region. Measurements of the absorption of F_2 laser radiation by NO show the absorption to be weak, and the results of a kinetic model indicate that this is due to a large separation of the F_2 laser line and the absorption line. The predicted upper level population density produced by the absorption is too small for the laser oscillation to occur.

Calculations of the Zeeman splitting of the upper level indicate that it should be possible to greatly increase the strength of the absorption by applying a magnetic field of order 1 T to the NO gas.

The scheme has been successfully demonstrated by observation of laser oscillation on the $B'-X(3-10)$ band of NO with a system employing a pulsed magnetic field. It is, to our knowledge, the first time that laser oscillation has been observed on a $B'-X$ transition in NO. Although the output energy that has been achieved so far is relatively small, this should be greatly increased by focusing the F_2 laser into the NO cell and by using a larger magnetic field.

The transition on which we have observed laser oscillation is not the strongest transition to the ground state, but is the transition for which the output coupler provides the greatest feedback. By employing a wavelength-selective cavity, it should be possible to produce laser oscillation on many transitions, with wavelengths in the range 158–250 nm. The system would then provide line-tunable, powerful, coherent radiation in the VUV.

The NO system could be extended in several ways. By introducing a buffer gas to the NO cell, it may be possible to induce J-changing collisions in the upper level. Provided that there is still sufficient gain, it would then be possible to tune the NO laser output to many different rotational transitions on each vibrational band. Ultimately, it might then be possible to continuously tune the NO laser output.

The successful demonstation of laser oscillation with this system indicates that a large population of the $B'^2\Delta$ state can be produced. It may be possible to transfer this population to an electronic state above the $B'^2\Delta$ state by absorption of intense radiation from a dye laser. It might then be possible to produce laser oscillation at wavelengths shorter than 158 nm. In any case, the inversion already produced would seem an ideal starting point for many new anti-Stokes Raman laser transitions in the VUV since, in the absence of a cavity, the upper level population is expected to last for a time of order 10 ns.

Acknowledgment

We would like to thank Prof. E. Miescher for sending us the results of his absorption measurements on the $B'-X(3-0)$ band of NO. We also acknowledge many helpful discussions with Prof. J. B. Atkinson.

References

[1] K. Yamada, K. Miyazaki, T. Hasama, and T. Sato, "High-power discharge-pumped F_2 molecular laser," *Appl. Phys. Lett*, vol. 54, pp. 597–599, 1989.

[2] S. M. Hooker and C. E. Webb, "Proposed vacuum ultraviolet laser in nitric oxide," in *Tech. Dig. Conf. Quantum Electron. Laser Sci.*, Apr. 1989.

[3] M. R. Taherian and T. G. Slanger, "Photoexcitation of NO at 1576 Å," *J. Chem. Phys.*, vol. 81, pp. 3796–3799, 1984.

[4] ——, "Radiative and kinetic properties of NO ($B'^2\Delta$)," *J. Chem. Phys.*, vol. 83, pp. 5349–5351, 1985.

[5] R. W. Nicholls, "Franck-Condon factors to high vibrational quantum numbers IV: NO band systems," *J. Res. Nat. Bur. Stand.*, vol. 68A, pp. 535–540, 1964.

[6] T. J. McKee, "Spectral-narrowing techniques for excimer laser oscillators," *Can. J. Phys.*, vol. 63, pp. 214–219, 1985.

[7] E. Miescher, unpublished data.

[8] A. J. Kearsley, A. J. Andrews, and C. E., Webb, "A novel preionization technique for discharge excited rate gas halide lasers," *Opt. Commun.*, vol. 31, pp. 181–184, 1979.

[9] T. Nakayama, M. Y. Kitamura, and K. Watanabe, "Ionization potential and absorption coefficients of nitrogen dioxide," *J. Chem. Phys.*, vol. 30, p. 1180, 1959.

[10] J. Brzozowski, P. Erman, and M. Lyyra, "Predissociation rates and perturbations of the *A, B, B', C, D* and *F* states in NO studied using time resolved spectroscopy," *Phys. Scr.*, vol. 14, pp. 290–297, 1976.

[11] D. J. Hart and J. W. Hepburn, "Vacuum ultaviolet laser spectroscopy: Radiative lifetimes of interacting $^2\Delta$ states of NO," *J. Chem. Phys.*, vol. 86, pp. 1733–1742, 1987.

[12] E. L. Hill, "On the Zeeman effect in doublet band spectra," *Phys. Rev.*, vol. 34, pp. 1507–1516, 1929.

[13] I. Kovacs, *Rotational Structure in the Spectra of Diatomic Molecules*. Adam Hilger, 1969.

Simon M. Hooker was born in Bromley, Kent, England in 1965. He received the B.A. degree in physics from Exeter College, Oxford, England, in 1986.

Since October 1986 he has worked with the Gas Laser Research Group at the Clarendon Laboratory, University of Oxford, on developing optically pumped VUV lasers. This research forms the basis of his doctoral dissertation. He has coauthored several publications and conference papers on this subject. Since October 1987 he has been a Stipendiary Lecturer at Jesus College, Oxford.

Mr. Hooker is a student member of the Institute of Physics.

Colin E. Webb (M'87) was born in Erith, Kent, England in 1937. He received the B.Sc. degree from Nottingham University, Nottingham, England, in 1960 and the D.Phil. degree from the Clarendon Laboratory, University of Oxford, Oxford, England, in 1964.

From 1964 to 1968 he was a member of the Technical Staff at Bell Laboratories, Murray Hill, NJ, where he worked on the early development of the argon ion laser and studies of its excitation mechanism. He returned to Clarendon in 1968 to head the Gas Laser Research Group. In the 1970's the group carried out studies of thermal energy charge transfer as a laser excitation mechanism, and worked on the development of multianode hollow cathode metal ion lasers. More recently, the group has been responsible for the development and study of the physical mechanisms of discharge-excited excimer lasers and high-power metal vapour lasers. Since 1971 he has been a University Lecturer at the University of Oxford, and from 1973 to 1989 he held the position of Official Tutorial Fellow at Jesus College, Oxford, where he is currently a Senior Research Fellow. In 1977 he was a founder member of Oxford Lasers Ltd., and has been Chairman of the company since that time. He is a Visiting Professor at the University of Salford.

Dr. Webb is a Fellow of the Institute of Physics and was awarded its Duddell Medal and Prize in 1985. He is a Fellow of the Optical Society of America, and is currently the European Representative of the IEEE LEOS Advisory Committee. He is the author of over 50 papers in the field of gas laser excitation mechanisms.

Section Four

Short Wavelength Generation by Nonlinear Processes

Concurrent with the development of rare gas excimer lasers was the development of nonlinear optical techniques for generation of harmonics of long wavelength lasers. While the nonlinear solid materials available for harmonic generation had little transmission in the vacuum ultraviolet, low pressure gas vapors were fine for this purpose.

The group led by Steve Harris at Stanford University quickly recognized the potential of third harmonic up-conversion in vapors and developed wavelengths as short as 882 Å. Workers at IBM promoted the idea of four wave mixing, thus producing a degree of tunability in these sources. Generation of higher harmonics was carried farther (5th and 7th) by Reintjes at the Naval Research Laboratory using harmonic generation in the rare gases. This process was driven by a neodymium laser operating in the infrared and doubled twice to reach the UV prior to the higher harmonic process.

Another idea for generating short wavelength lasers worked on the principle of filling an upper metastable state and then optically transferring the population to a higher state from which lasing occurs, termed anti-Stokes Raman lasing. The scheme was pursued unsuccessfully for very short VUV wavelengths for several years at Stanford but was shown to work fine at longer UV and VUV wavelengths by White.

Reprinted with permission from *Applied Physics Letters,* Vol. 19(10), pp. 385-387 (November 15, 1971).

Proposed Third-Harmonic Generation in Phase-Matched Metal Vapors*

S. E. Harris and R. B. Miles
Microwave Laboratory, Stanford University, Stanford, California 94305
(Received 30 August 1971)

This letter considers the use of alkali metal vapors, phase matched with inert buffer gases for generation of third-harmonic radiation. For example, calculations show that 1.8 MW will be required for 50% conversion of 1.06-μ radiation to 0.35-μ radiation using a 1 : 412 part mixture of rubidium and xenon. Generation to frequencies above the ionization potential of the metal vapors is considered.

This letter proposes a technique for the effecient production of ultraviolet radiation by third-harmonic generation in phase-matched metal vapors. As a result of their large oscillator strengths and resonant frequencies located in the visible region of the spectrum, we calculate nonlinear susceptibilities about 10^5 times greater than those of the inert gases which have been previously studied.[1] Of key importance, the high localized oscillator strengths of vapors such as Rb, Cs, Na, etc., cause their refractive indices at frequencies below their fundamental resonance lines to be greater than their refractive indices at the third harmonic of these frequencies.[2] It is then possible to add an inert buffer gas to attain phase matching ($n_1 = n_3$). Calculations show the ratio of the necessary partial pressure of metal vapor to buffer gas to typically be about 1 : 400. Other potentially interesting features of the metal-vapor inert-gas system are wide acceptance bandwidth and thus the ability to utilize subpicosecond pulses; and the ability to generate to frequencies above the metal-vapor ionization potential and thus to regions of the uv where most solids or liquids are opaque. The possibility of using anomalous dispersion to achieve phase matching was noted by a number of early workers,[3] and has been demonstrated in liquids by Bey *et al.*[4]

The principal results of this letter are summarized in Table I and will be discussed in the paragraphs below. We consider three possible tripling experiments, i.e., 10640 → 3547 Å in Rb and 6943 → 2314 Å and 6000 → 2000 Å in Na. In each case, the number of metal atoms/cc is chosen to yield a maximum transmission loss at the fundamental or third harmonic of

TABLE I. Calculated parameters for third-harmonic generation in metal vapors.

$\lambda_F \rightarrow \lambda_{3rd}$	10 640→ 3547 Å	6943→ 2314 Å	6000→ 2000 Å
Metal vapor	Rb	Na	Na
Buffer Gas	Xe	Xe	Xe
Metal atoms/cc[a]	2.25×10^{17}	7.73×10^{16}	2.12×10^{16}
Partial pressure of metal vapor (mm Hg)	16.0	6.40	1.61
Cell temperature	415 °C	527 °C	461 °C
$\chi_{\text{metal vapor}}$ (esu)	7.42×10^{-32}	5.86×10^{-33}	-6.36×10^{-33}
L_c (cm)	9.62×10^{-2}	2.60×10^{-1}	1.10×10^{-1}
$\frac{\text{Number atoms buffer gas}}{\text{Number atoms metal vapor}}$	$\frac{412}{1}$	$\frac{100}{1}$	$\frac{476}{1}$
P_F/A (50% conversion, $L=50$ cm) (W/cm^2)	7.27×10^{8}	1.75×10^{10}	5.07×10^{10}
P_F (50% conversion) (W)	1.93×10^{6}	3.04×10^{7}	7.61×10^{7}
α_F (cm^{-1})	4.17×10^{-3}	2.13×10^{-4}	5.74×10^{-3}
α_{3rd} (cm^{-1})	5.74×10^{-3}	5.74×10^{-3}	3.73×10^{-4}
P_{sat}/A (W/cm^2)	1.68×10^{8}	3.24×10^{9}	3.82×10^{7}
J_{sat}/A (J/cm^2)	5.04	51.8	0.611
Δt_{min} (sec)	3.80×10^{-13}	1.43×10^{-13}	7.63×10^{-12}

[a]Number of metal-vapor atoms adjusted for maximum loss of 25% for 50 cm at fundamental or third-harmonic wavelengths.

25% in a 50-cm-long cell in the presence of the higher pressure buffer gas which is necessary for phase matching.

Calculations of the third-harmonic nonlinearity were carried out using the formula of Armstrong *et al.*,[3] i.e.,

$$\chi(3\omega,\omega,\omega,\omega)=(e^4/\hbar^3)\sum_{ijk} A_{ijk}Z_{gi}Z_{ij}Z_{jk}Z_{kg} \text{ (esu)}, \quad (1)$$

where the A_{ijk} are frequency-dependent coefficients with resonant denominators at $(\omega_{gp}-\omega)$, $(\omega_{gp}-2\omega)$, and $(\omega_{gp}-3\omega)$, where ω is the fundamental laser frequency and ω_{gp} corresponds to any atomic transition frequency to ground. To evaluate (1) all terms (a total of 128) involving all levels between the 5*s* and 7*d* states for Rb and between the 3*s* and 6*d* states for Na were retained. Magnitudes of matrix elements were obtained from calculated oscillator strengths,[5,6] while the signs of matrix elements were determined from the tables of Bates and Damgaard.[7] The fine splitting of a multiplet was accounted for via degeneracy factors and a weighted average frequency. The calculated magnitudes of $\chi(3\omega,\omega,\omega,\omega)$ are given on line 7 of Table I.

The refractive indices of the metal vapors were calculated from the standard Sellmeier formulas and are in agreement with the early experimental data of Wood.[2] (It is of interest to note that the refractive index of Na is less than 1 over the wavelength region $\lambda=5890$ Å to $\lambda=3320$ Å.) The coherence length ($L_c=\lambda_F/6\Delta n$) for third-harmonic generation for a non-phase-matched metal vapor is given on line 8 of Table I, and corresponds to the metal-vapor pressure given on line 5.

To obtain phase matching and thus to increase the conversion efficiency by $(L/L_c)^2$ we add a normally dispersive buffer gas at a partial pressure to cause the refractive indices at the fundamental and third-harmonic frequencies to be equal. Refractive indices for Xe were obtained from the formula of Kock.[8] Line 9 of Table I gives the ratio of the number of atoms of Xe to the number of atoms of metal vapor which is necessary to obtain phase matching.

Assuming no depletion of the fundamental, the ratio of generated third-harmonic power to incident fundamental power is given in mks units by

$$\frac{P_3}{P_1}=\frac{9\pi^2\eta^4c^2L^2\chi_T^2}{4\lambda_1^2}\left(\frac{P_1}{A}\right)^2\cong\frac{9\pi^2\eta^4c^2\chi_T^2}{\lambda_1^4}P_1^2 \text{ (mks)}, \quad (2)$$

where $\chi_{mks}=(10^{-17})\chi_{esu}$, $\eta=377\ \Omega$, λ_1 is the wavelength of the fundamental, L is the cell length, and A is the area of all beams. To obtain χ_T in Eq. (2), the per atom χ of line 7 is multiplied by the total number of atoms (all assumed to be in the ground state) and is divided by the total degeneracy of the ground state (two for the alkali metals). To obtain the second equality in Eq. (2) we assume a Gaussian beam with a confocal parameter equal to the cell length L. For such a confocally focused beam the conversion efficiency to the third harmonic is independent of the cell length. Lines 10 and 11 of Table I give the necessary fundamental power density and fundamental power (assuming confocal focusing) which are necessary to obtain 50% conversion efficiency to the third harmonic. These values are based on a cell length of 50 cm and the number of metal-vapor atoms given in line 4.

Absorption loss at both the fundamental and third-harmonic frequencies was computed using the standard formulas for pressure broadened Lorentzian lines, with all transitions to ground which contribute significant loss at either frequency accounted for. Continuum losses were obtained from the experimental data of Ditchburn.[9] For tripling 1.06 μ in Rb the dominant loss occurred at the third harmonic and was due to the $5s$-$7d$ transition. For tripling 6943 Å or 6000 Å in Na, the dominant losses are at the third harmonic and fundamental, respectively. It is of particular interest that once past the ionization potential the continuum absorption is very small. For example, at 2000 Å, the absorption cross section for Na is about 1.7×10^{-20} cm^2. Discrete losses were calculated based on the pressure of xenon necessary to achieve phase matching and make use of the inert gas-alkali pressure broadening data given by Ch'en and Takeo.[10]

Lines 13 and 14 of Table I give the saturation power density and saturation energy density for the given operating conditions. If the length of the incident pulse substantially exceeds the decay time of the absorbing level then the saturation power density $P_{sat}/A = \hbar\omega/2\sigma T_1$ (where σ is the cross section and T_1 is the decay time of the absorbing level) is the power density which will reduce the population difference by 50%. For an incident pulse length less than T_1, $J_{sat}/A = (P_{sat}/A)\, T_1$ is the energy density for 50% population reduction. Since the inert gases have little quenching effect on the alkali metals,[11] T_1 for Rb and Na are about 16 and 30 nsec, respectively. From lines 13 and 10 of Table I we see that saturation power density is of the same order or less than the power density necessary for 50% conversion to the uv. For high conversion efficiencies, it will thus be necessary to work with pulses of length $\ll T_1$. For subnanosecond or picosecond pulses the saturation joule requirement will not pose a problem. Optical breakdown in metal vapors has been studied by Rizzo and Klewe[12] who find a breakdown threshold of 10^9 W/cm^2 at 10^{17} atoms of Cs for a 65-nsec-long ruby pulse. Wang[13] has shown that for short pulse lengths breakdown is dependent on energy density (as opposed to power density); thus further suggesting the use of short pulses.

Finally we calculate the minimum allowable width of a picosecond pulse to ensure that the third-harmonic pulse does not separate from the fundamental pulse over the cell length. This minimum width depends on the relative dispersion (group velocity difference) at the fundamental and third harmonic and for 50% walk off of a rectangular pulse is

$$\Delta t_{min} = \frac{n_1 n_3 L}{c^2}\left(\frac{\partial\omega_2}{\partial k_2} - \frac{\partial\omega_1}{\partial k_1}\right) \quad . \tag{3}$$

Dispersions were evaluated numerically, again accounting for all contributing transitions; and for the given operating conditions they are given in line 15 of Table I.

Experiments aimed at demonstrating the ideas of this letter are now being constructed in our laboratory. Other metal-vapor inert-gas systems for generation further into the uv, for example Cd-He for 3547 → 1182 Å generation, will also be studied.

The authors gratefully acknowledge helpful discussions with J.F. Young, G. Bjorklund, A.H. Kung, and A.E. Siegman. R. B. Miles gratefully acknowledges the Fannie and John K. Hertz Foundation for its generous support.

---

*Work sponsored by the Air Force Cambridge Laboratories under Contract No. F19(628)-70-C-0057, and by the U.S. Army Research Office—Durham under Contract No. DAHC04-68-C-0048.

[1]J. F. Ward and G.H.C. New, Phys. Rev. 185, 57 (1969).
[2]R.W. Wood, Phil. Mag. Suppl. 8, 293 (1904).
[3]J.A. Armstrong, N. Bloembergen, J. Ducuing, and P.S. Pershan, Phys. Rev. 127, 1918 (1962).
[4]Pole P. Bey, John F. Giuliani, and Herbert Rabin, Phys. Rev. Letters 19, 819 (1967).
[5]E.M. Anderson and V.A. Zilitis, Opt. Spectrosc. 16, 211 (1964).
[6]W. L. Wiese, M.W. Smith, and B.M. Miles, Natl. Bur. Std. Report NSRDA-NBS 22, Vol. II, 1969 (unpublished).
[7]D. R. Bates and Agnete Damgaard, Phil. Trans. Roy. Soc. 242, 101 (1949).
[8]John Koch, Kungl. Fysiografiska Sällskapets I Lund Fördhandlingar 19, 173 (1949).
[9]R.W. Ditchburn, P.J. Jutsun, and G.B. Marr, Proc. Roy. Soc. (London) A219, 89 (1953).
[10]Shang-Yi Ch'en and Makoto Takeo, Rev. Mod. Phys. 29, 20 (1957).
[11]E.R. Fisher and G.K. Smith, Appl. Opt. 10, 1803 (1971).
[12]J.E. Rizzo and R.C. Klewe, Brit. J. Appl. Phys. 17, 1137 (1966).
[13]Charles C. Wang and L.I. Davis, Jr., Phys. Rev. Letters 26, 822 (1971).

Third-Harmonic Generation in Phase-Matched Rb Vapor*

J. F. Young, G. C. Bjorklund, A. H. Kung, R. B. Miles, and S. E. Harris
Microwave Laboratory, Stanford University, Stanford, California 94305
(Received 18 October 1971)

We report the generation of 0.3547-μm radiation by tripling 1.064-μm radiation in a phase-matched mixture of rubidium and xenon. We find $\chi(3\omega) = 1.4\times 10^{-32}$ esu, which is about 10^6 times greater than that of He. Phase matching occurs for Xe and Rb atoms in the ratio 412:1.

This Letter reports the generation of 0.3547-μm radiation by tripling 1.064-μm radiation in a phase-matched mixture of rubidium vapor and xenon.[1] We experimentally confirm a third-harmonic nonlinear susceptibility in Rb vapor which is about 10^6 times greater than that of He.[2] This large susceptibility is due to the large oscillator strengths and resonant enhancements resulting from Rb transitions in the near infrared, visible, and uv. The closest of these transitions is 3200 cm^{-1} from 1.064 μm and 315 cm^{-1} from 0.3547 μm, and thus significant loss is not introduced at either of these frequencies.

As a result of the large oscillator strengths of the 0.7800- and 0.7948-μm transitions ($f_{ij} = 0.9$ and 0.3, respectively), the refractive index of Rb vapor at 1.064 μm is greater than its refractive index at 0.3547 μm. The addition of Xe, in the ratio of 412 atoms of Xe to each atom of Rb, causes the refractive index at 1.064 μm to equal the refractive index at 0.3547 μm (achieves phase matching) and increases the generated third-harmonic power by $(L/L_c)^2$, where L is the cell length and L_c is the coherence length of the Rb vapor in the absence of Xe. In the experiments reported here we have observed a phase-matching third-harmonic power enhancement of a factor of 33, and believe that much greater enhancements will be possible with engineering improvements.

The possibility of using anomalous dispersion to achieve phase matching was suggested by a number of early nonlinear-optics workers,[3] and has been demonstrated in liquids by Bey, Giuliani, and Rabin.[4]

The experimental apparatus consisted of an acousto-optically Q-switched Nd-doped yttrium aluminum garnet laser and amplifier which furnished up to 100 kW of TEM_{00}-mode radiation at 1.064 μm. The Rb cells were 19 cm long and were constructed of Pyrex. The Rb metal was placed in a side arm which was maintained at a somewhat lower temperature than the main cell. By controlling the side-arm temperature from about 100 to 320°C, the vapor pressure of Rb could be continuously varied between 2×10^{-4} and 2 Torr. Different pressures of Xe were placed in the cells before sealing. The 0.3547-μm light was detected using an RCA 1P28 photomultiplier with an S5 photocathode, which followed filters and a monochromator used to discriminate against the 1.064-μm radiation.

The first experiment was performed without Xe present and was aimed at determining the nonlinearity of the Rb vapor. The incident laser beam was focused to a beam diameter of 0.52 mm positioned at the output window of the Rb cell. The confocal parameter for this focus was 40 cm, thus yielding a slightly converging beam over the length of the Rb cell. The points in Fig. 1 show generated third-harmonic power as a function of the temperature of the Rb side arm. The solid

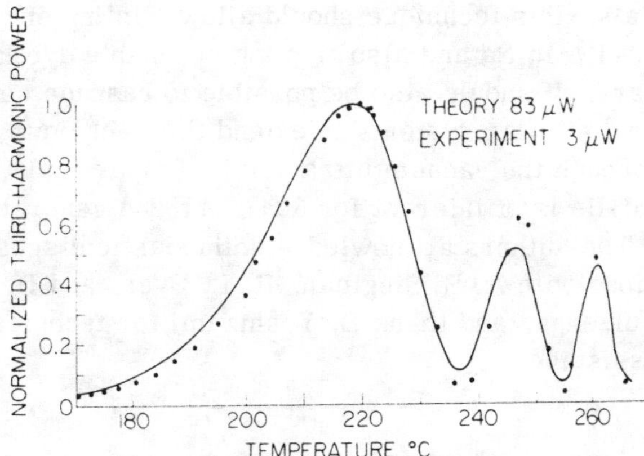

FIG. 1. Normalized third-harmonic power versus temperature for pure Rb vapor. The 50-kW 1.064-μm beam was focused on the output cell window with a confocal parameter of 40 cm.

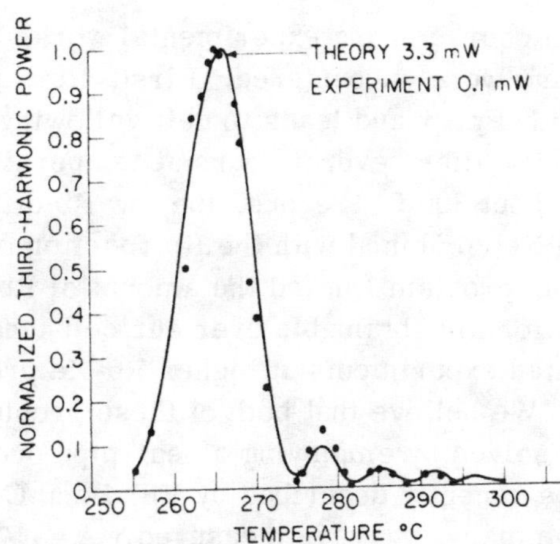

FIG. 2. Normalized third-harmonic power versus temperature for Rb with 81 Torr Xe at 20°C. Experimental points were uniformly translated toward cooler temperatures by 5°C. Incident power, focusing, and confocal parameter are as in Fig. 1.

curve is obtained from

$$\frac{P_3}{P_1^3}=\frac{3\pi^2N^2\chi^2}{\lambda^4c^2\epsilon_0^4g^2}\left|\int_{-\zeta}^{0}\frac{\exp(\frac{1}{2}jb\Delta k\xi')}{(1+j\xi')^2}\,d\xi'\right|^2 \text{ (mks)}, \quad (1)$$

which is obtained by appropriately integrating an expression given by Ward,[2] where P_3 and P_1 are the third-harmonic and fundamental powers, respectively, N is the number of Rb atoms/cm^3, $g=2$ is the degeneracy of the 5s level, χ is the third-harmonic susceptibility ($\chi_{mks}=\frac{1}{81}\times10^{-17}\chi_{esu}$), λ_1 is the fundamental wavelength, and b is the confocal parameter of the fundamental beam—assumed to be focused on the output window of the gas cell. ζ, a normalized z coordinate, is related to the position of the focus at $z=f$ by $\zeta=2z/b$. The $\vec{k}$ mismatch $\Delta k=6\pi(n_1-n_3)/\lambda_1$ is obtained from the Sellmeier equations for Rb.

For a nearly collimated beam, $b\gg L$, the right-hand side of Eq. (1) is proportional to $\sin^2(\frac{1}{2}\pi L/L_c)$, where $L_c=\pi/\Delta k$; this predicts maximum output power for a Rb vapor pressure such that L_c equals the cell length L. Based on the Sellmeier equation for Rb, $L_c=19$ cm (our cell length) for $N=1.14\times10^5$ atoms/cm^3, which occurs at a temperature of $T=210$°C. As a result of the converging input beam, Eq. (1) predicts that the height of the first lobe should exceed that of the latter lobes and should occur about 9°C hotter than would be the case for a perfectly plane wave. Both experimental and theoretical results were normalized to a peak amplitude of unity. The excellent agreement of periodicities indicates that the Sellmeier equation for Rb is accurately known, and that the Rb temperature was correctly measured.

With an input power $P_1=50$ kW and a confocal parameter $b=40$ cm (thus a peak power density of about 47 MW/cm^2) we obtained a third-harmonic power $P_3=3$ μW at $T=219$°C. At this temperature there are 1.59×10^{15} Rb atoms/cm^3 in the cell. From Eq. (1) we obtain χ_{Rb}(meas) $=1.4\times10^{-32}$ esu. Considering experimental uncertainties, this agrees reasonably well with the previously calculated value χ_{Rb}(calc) $=7.42\times10^{-32}$ esu.[1]

The second experiment was aimed at demonstrating that the Rb vapor could be phase matched by introducing a normally dispersive gas such as Xe, thus allowing the interaction to extend over many coherence lengths. In this experiment, 81 Torr of xenon at 20°C was introduced into the cell before sealing. From the Sellmeier equations of Xe and Rb we calculate that phase matching should occur at a Rb vapor pressure corresponding to a cell temperature of $T=262$°C.

Experimental results are shown in Fig. 2. Note that for the same input power and focus, the peak power obtained in the phase-matched case exceeds that of the pure-Rb case (Fig. 1) by a factor of 33. To achieve the best experimental-theoretical fit, it was necessary to translate the experimental points uniformly by 5°C. Fitting the peak experimentally observed power by the peak of the theoretical curve of Eq. (1), with the use of Sellmeier equations for both Rb and Xe, yields $\chi_{Rb}=1.3\times10^{-32}$ esu, in close agreement with the pure Rb case.

In the course of the experimental work, two problems were encountered. First, Rb vapor reacts with Pyrex and leads to cell yellowing and uv opacity after several hours at temperatures above about 300°C. Second, the low Rb diffusion rate in Xe combined with the Rb reaction or clean-up problem limited the amount of Rb which was uniformly obtainable over our cell length and prevented experiments at higher Rb-Xe pressures. We believe that both of these problems can be solved by employing a heat-pipe oven of the type recently described by Vidal and Cooper.[5]

In summary, we have measured $\chi_{Rb} = 1.4 \times 10^{-32}$ esu for tripling 1.064 to 0.3547 μm, and have demonstrated that metal vapors may be phase matched via the addition of inert gases. Based on these measurements and on previous calculations,[1] we believe that if the Rb vapor pressure could be increased to 16 Torr (415°C) and the cell length extended to 50 cm, 50% conversion efficiency to 0.35 μm should be obtainable with an input power of about 10 MW. Peak powers exceeding this are now readily available with picosecond lasers, and calculations have shown that subpicosecond pulses are acceptable in a system of this type.[1]

Since metal vapors are often nearly transparent for wavelengths above their ionization potentials,[6] this technique should allow tripling of 6943 Å in Na and also tripling of tunable dye lasers. It should also be possible to cascade several similar systems to extend this technique through the vacuum ultraviolet. For example, Cd-He is of interest for 3547 → 1182 Å generation.

The authors acknowledge enthusiastic discussions with A. E. Siegman, R. L. Byer, and D. J. Kuizenga, and thank B. Yoshizumi for technical assistance.

---

*Work sponsored jointly by the National Aeronautics and Space Administration under NASA Grant No. NGL-05-020-103 and by the U. S. Air Force Cambridge Research Laboratories under Contract No. F19(628)-70-C-0057.

[1]S. E. Harris and R. B. Miles, "Proposed Third Harmonic Generation in Phase-Matched Metal Vapors" (to be published).

[2]J. F. Ward and G. H. C. New, Phys. Rev. 185, 57 (1969).

[3]J. A. Armstrong, N. Bloembergen, J. Ducuing, and P. S. Pershan, Phys. Rev. 127, 1918 (1962).

[4]P. P. Bey, J. F. Giuliani, and H. Rabin, Phys. Rev. Lett. 19, 819 (1967).

[5]C. R. Vidal and J. Cooper, J. Appl. Phys. 40, 3370 (1969).

[6]R. W. Ditchburn, P. J. Jutsun, and G. B. Marr, Proc. Roy. Soc., Ser. A 219, 89 (1953).

Reprinted with permission from *Physical Review Letters,* Vol. 29(15), pp. 985-988 (October 9, 1972). ©1972 American Physical Society.

Generation of Vacuum Ultraviolet Radiation in Phase-Matched Cd Vapor*

A. H. Kung, J. F. Young, G. C. Bjorklund, and S. E. Harris
Microwave Laboratory, Stanford University, Stanford, California 94305
(Received 17 July 1972)

We report the generation of 1773-, 1520-, and 1182-Å radiation by frequency tripling and summing in a phase-matched mixture of Cd and Ar. For the third-harmonic process, 5320→1773 Å phase matching occurs for Cd and Ar atoms in the ratio 1 : 25, and $\chi^{(3)} \cong 2 \times 10^{-34}$ esu/atom. The energy conversion efficiency to 1773 Å was about 10^{-4}, yielding a peak picosecond power of 7 kW.

Because of the increased difficulty of obtaining laser oscillations in the vacuum-ultraviolet (vuv) and soft x-ray regions of the electromagnetic spectrum,[1,2] it is of interest to consider other techniques which are capable of generating coherent radiation in these spectral regions. One possible approach is to use cascaded frequency triplers to convert the very high peak power now available at 1.06 μm to much shorter wavelengths. In this Letter we report the generation of 1.06-μm harmonic vuv radiation at 1773, 1520, and 1182 Å.

To obtain radiation at the above frequencies we employed the technique of phase-matched harmonic generation and frequency summing in a mixture of a metallic vapor and an inert gas. This technique was first suggested by Harris and Miles[3] and experimentally demonstrated by Young *et al.*[4] In these first experiments a mixture of Rb vapor and Xe was used for the third-harmonic process 1.06 μm → 3547 Å. To extend this technique to the vuv we employed a mixture of Cd and Ar. The choice of Cd was indicated for two reasons: First, its nonlinear susceptibility in the vuv should be enhanced by its strong atomic transitions which extend from the fundamental resonance line at 2288 Å to the beginning of the continuum at 1378 Å. Second, as is the case for the alkali metals, Cd has a relatively small absorption cross section in the spectral region just above its ionization potential ($\sigma = 7\times10^{-20}$ cm^2 at $\lambda = 1182$ Å).[5] To obtain efficient harmonic or sum-frequency generation it is necessary that the driving dipole polarization wave travel at the same velocity as the electromagnetic wave which it is desired to generate. This phase-matched condition is obtained by correctly choosing the ratio of Cd to Ar atoms.

We describe three nonlinear processes. These are (1) tripling of 5320 Å to yield 1773 Å, (2) summing of 1.064 μm with 3547 Å to yield 1520 Å, and (3) tripling of 3547 Å to yield 1182 Å. The exper-

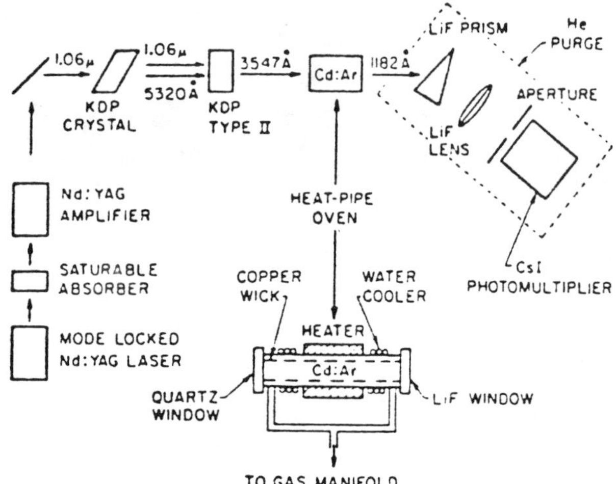

FIG. 1. Schematic of experimental apparatus for generation of 1182 Å.

imental apparatus is shown schematically in Fig. 1. As the 1.064-μm source we used a mode-locked Nd:YAlG (Nd-doped yttrium aluminum garnet) laser followed by a Kodak 9740 saturable dye absorber cell and a Nd:YAlG amplifier. The resulting 1.064-μm output consisted of about ten pulses, spaced by 5 nsec, and each about 50 psec long. The total energy of these pulses was about 10 mJ, yielding a peak power of about 20 MW. A potassium dihydrogen phosphate crystal doubled this radiation to 5320 Å with an energy conversion efficiency of up to 80%. For the experiments requiring 3547 Å, this efficiency was reduced to 50% and a second, type-II phase-matched potassium dihydrogen phosphate crystal was used to sum the remaining 1.064-μm radiation with the 5320-Å radiation to yield 3547 Å at an overall 1.064-μm to 3547-Å energy conversion of about 10%.

The Cd cell was modeled after the open-ended heat-pipe oven described by Vidal and Cooper[8] and consisted of a copper wick inside a stainless steel tube, with water cooling to protect the quartz (input) and LiF (output) end windows. The cell was wound with a 20-cm-long heating coil and had an inner diameter of 2.5 cm. Based on thermocouple measurements on the outer surface of the oven, we estimate that temperature was constant to within ± 1°C (the estimated necessary temperature tolerance) over about a 2-cm length. Ar or He was introduced near the ends of the cell and appeared to mix homogeneously with the Cd vapor in several seconds.

The generated vuv radiation was incident on a homemade, He-purged, LiF-prism monochromator, and was detected using a solar-blind EMR 542-G photomultiplier with a CsI photocathode.

A first set of experiments was aimed at determining whether the Cd vapor was negatively dispersive and thus whether it would be possible to obtain phase matching by adding a normally dispersive buffer gas. Generated third-harmonic power at 1773 Å is shown as a function of cell temperature in Fig. 2. An important feature is the fact that the height of the first lobe exceeds that of the latter lobes. This only occurs in a negatively dispersive medium, and results since in such a medium, off-axis converging and diverging light rays are in effect phase matched.[7,8] In this experiment the 5320-Å radiation is focused to a beam with a confocal parameter of $b = 100$ cm. As the cell temperature and thus the density of the Cd vapor is further increased, the cell becomes an increasing number of coherence lengths long, resulting in the oscillating output power. From the fringe spacing versus temperature, an effective cell length ($L = 2$ cm), and the vapor-pressure curve of Cd, the coherence length may be estimated. Table I gives the coherence length at 10^{17} atoms/cm^3 ($p = 8$ Torr, $T = 475°$C) for the first two of the nonlinear processes considered in this Letter. The signal at 1182 Å was at just about the noise level produced by scattered 3547-Å light, and a measurement of its coherence

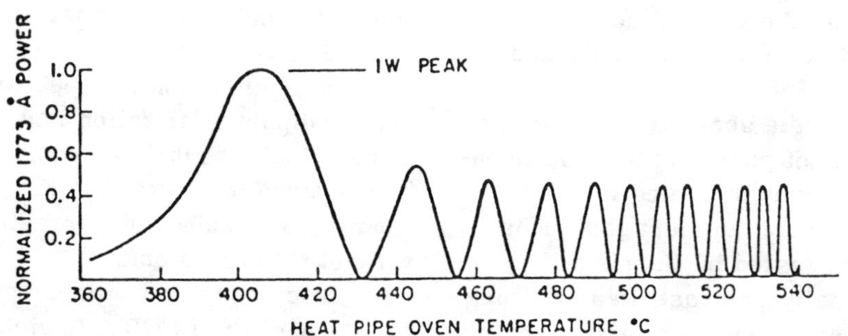

FIG. 2. Normalized 1773-Å output power versus oven temperature without phase matching. 5320-Å input power, 20 MW. Confocal parameter of input beam, 100 cm.

TABLE I. Summary of experimental data.

Input wavelengths (Å)	Generated wavelength (Å)	L_c at 10^{17} atom/cm^3 (cm)	Phase-matching ratio $N_{Cd}:N_{Ar}$	Energy conversion efficiency	$\chi^{(3)}$ (esu/atom)
5320	1773	−0.57	1:25	10^{-4}	2×10^{-34}
1.064×10^4, 3547	1520	−0.23	1:15	10^{-6}	2×10^{-33}
3547	1182	···	1:2.5	10^{-7}	···

length could not be made. To prevent condensation of the Cd vapor on the cell end windows, 455 Torr of He was also present in the cell; however, its dispersion is sufficiently small that the correction introduced to the measured coherence lengths is negligible.

In the next set of experiments, phase matching was obtained by establishing an appropriate Cd:Ar ratio. Experimental results for phase-matched 1773-Å generation are shown in Fig. 3. With 700 Torr of Ar present, the phase-matched peak occurred at a cell temperature of 536°C, corresponding to a Cd:Ar ratio of 1:25. For the same input power and focusing, the phase-matched peak power is 30 times greater than that obtained for the Cd:He combination. The failure of the higher temperature side lobes to decrease as rapidly as expected is probably due to temperature, and thus vapor density, gradients within the cell.

In another experiment at 1773 Å, we reduced the confocal parameter of the incident 0.53-μm beam to 5 cm, and at 700 Torr of argon obtained an energy conversion efficiency of about 10^{-4}, corresponding to a peak picosecond power of about 7 kW. Based on the effective cell length, power density, and vapor pressure of Cd, we obtain $\chi^{(3)}=1\times10^{-34}$ esu/atom. Based on a normalized measurement to the third-harmonic power generated in the last coherence length of a LiF

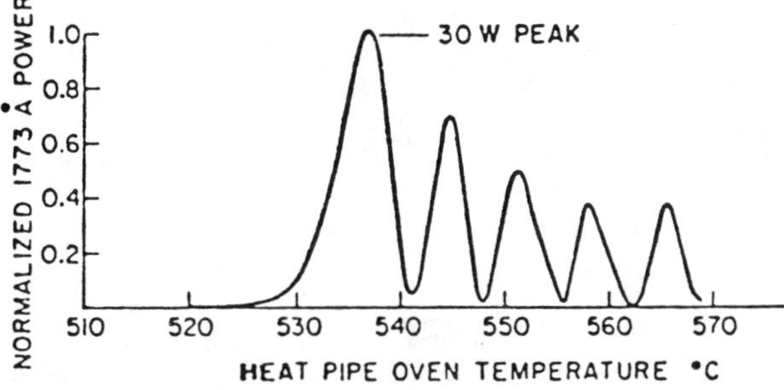

FIG. 3. Normalized 1773-Å output power versus oven temperature with 700 Torr (at 536°C) of Ar present. Input power and focus are the same as in Fig. 2. Note the enhancement of peak output power by a factor of 30.

crystal, we obtain $\chi^{(3)}=2\times10^{-34}$ esu/atom.

For the generation of 1520-Å radiation, both the 3547-Å and the 1.064-μm beams were focused to a confocal parameter of 20 cm. For 100 Torr of argon, phase matching occurred at 460°C at an Ar:Cd ratio of 15:1, and the enhancement due to argon, as compared to the phase-unmatched case, was a factor of 8.5. For this process the observed energy conversion efficiency was about 10^{-6}, which yields a lower bound of $\chi^{(3)}\cong2\times10^{-33}$ esu/atom. For 1182-Å generation, phase matching to 200 Torr of Ar occurred at 579°C at an Ar:Cd ratio of 2.5:1, and the observed energy conversion was about 10^{-7}. Experimental results are summarized in Table I.

In considering the results of these experiments it is clear that conversion efficiencies should be improved if this process is to yield practical devices. Based on the measured $\chi^{(3)}\cong2\times10^{-34}$ esu/atom for 1773 Å, a 50-cm-long cell with a Cd vapor pressure of 20 Torr would yield 50% peak power conversion efficiency for an incident confocally focused beam with a peak power of about 57 MW. This assumes that the harmonic process does not saturate, which at high incident pulse energies may not be the case. The dominant saturation process is caused by small absorption of the fundamental or third-harmonic frequency by the metal vapor. As atoms are excited to higher states, the metal-vapor refractive index is reduced, the phase-matching condition broken, and the beam thermally defocused. These problems are under study in a Na:Xe system and results will be reported subsequently.[8] Other practical problems such as maintaining a zone of sufficiently constant temperature and homogeneity over the required length must also be solved.

We note that radiation generated by this technique preserves the characteristics of the lower-frequency laser radiation. It is thus diffraction limited, polarized, of picosecond time scale, and of relatively narrow bandwidth. We believe that high efficiencies will be obtained, and experiments to extend the technique further into the vuv are underway.

The authors gratefully acknowledge discussions with R. B. Miles and A. E. Siegman, and thank D. Carson, B. Yoshizumi, and J. McMenamin for help with construction of the experimental apparatus and aid in calibrating the vuv photomultiplier.

---

*Work sponsored jointly by the U. S. Office of Naval Research under Contract No. N00014-67-A-0112-0036 and by the U. S. Air Force Cambridge Research Laboratories under Contract No. F19(628)-70-C-0057.

[1]R. T. Hodgson and R. W. Dreyfus, Phys. Rev. Lett. 28, 536 (1972); W. Waynant, Phys. Rev. Lett. 28, 533 (1972).

[2]M. A. Duguay and P. M. Rentzepis, Appl. Phys. Lett. 10, 350 (1967).

[3]S. E. Harris and R. B. Miles, Appl. Phys. Lett. 19, 385 (1971).

[4]J. F. Young, G. C. Bjorklund, A. H. Kung, R. B. Miles, and S. E. Harris, Phys. Rev. Lett. 27, 1551 (1971).

[5]R. B. Cairns, H. Harrison, and R. I. Schoen, J. Chem. Phys. 51, 5440 (1969).

[6]C. R. Vidal and J. Cooper, J. Appl. Phys. 40, 3370 (1969).

[7]J. F. Ward and G. H. C. New, Phys. Rev. 185, 57 (1969).

[8]R. B. Miles and S. E. Harris, "Optical Third Harmonic Generation in Alkali Metal Vapors" (to be published).

Reprinted with permission from *Applied Physics Letters*, Vol. 22(6), pp. 301-302 (March 15, 1973).

Generation of 1182-Å radiation in phase-matched mixtures of inert gases*

A.H. Kung, J.F. Young, and S.E. Harris

Microwave Laboratory, Stanford University, Stanford, California 94305

Coherent radiation at 1182 Å is obtained by third-harmonic generation in a phase-matched mixture of Xe and Ar. For generation from 3547 to 1182 Å, Xe is negatively dispersive, and phase matching is obtained at a ratio of Xe : Ar = 1 : 430. A conversion efficiency of 2.8% is obtained at an input power of 13 MW. As predicted by theory the conversion efficiency increases linearly to the limit of our available input power.

Third-harmonic generation in phase-matched mixtures of metal vapors and inert gases has recently been described both theoretically and experimentally.[1-3] In the first experiments, 1.064-μ radiation was tripled to yield 3547-Å radiation in a mixture of rubidium and xenon. Recently, the technique was extended to the vacuum ultraviolet where 1773-, 1520-, and 1182-Å radiation was generated in a mixture of Cd and Ar. Though the metal-vapor—inert-gas system is attractive theoretically,[4] a number of practical problems concerned with the homogeneous mixing of the metal vapor and inert gas have thus far limited the conversion efficiency to about 10^{-4}.

In the present letter, we report the generation of 1182-Å radiation in a phase-matched mixture of Xe and Ar. No metal vapor is employed. The large nonlinearity of Xe and the homogeneous mixing of the inert gases allows a conversion efficiency of 2.8% at an input power of 13 MW. This efficiency increases linearly to the limit of our available input power at 3547 Å.

To obtain efficient third-harmonic generation it is essential that one of the inert gases be negatively dispersive (have a refractive index at the third-harmonic frequency less than its refractive index at the fundamental frequency). This allows the use of a positively dispersive gas to phase match, or of equal importance, the use of very tight focusing to the center of a gas cell.[4,5] In the case of the metal vapors, the negative dispersion is obtained by allowing the lower or fundamental frequency to be less than and relatively close to the resonance frequency of the metal vapor. In the case of Xe, the negative dispersion is obtained by allowing the third-harmonic frequency to be greater than and relatively close to a transition of high oscillator strength. (In these experiments, the 1192-Å $5p$-$5d$ transition of Xe is probably the dominant transition involved.) The lowest energy level of any inert gas is the 1469.5-Å line of xenon; thus inert-gas—inert-gas generation is possible over the spectral region of 1469 to at least 500 Å, where the continuum of helium begins.

We note that third-harmonic generation in inert gases has been demonstrated much earlier by Ward and New.[5] In these important early experiments, the third harmonic of ruby at 2314 Å was generated in each of the inert gases. However, in this spectral region, the inert gases are not negatively dispersive and their nonlinearity is much lower ($\chi^{(3)} = 9.8 \times 10^{-37}$ esu for xenon). The conversion efficiency reported by Ward is about eleven orders of magnitude lower than that reported here.

Our experimental setup is similar to that reported in Ref. 3 and is shown in Fig. 1. A single pulse from a mode-locked 1.064-μ Nd:YAG laser is amplified by a Nd:YAG amplifier to yield an estimated peak power of 3×10^8 W and a pulse length of 25 psec at 1.064 μ. The pulse is frequency doubled in an ADP crystal to 5320 Å, and mixed with remaining 1.064-μ radiation to yield 3547 Å. A maximum peak power of 1.3×10^7 W is obtained at 3547 Å. Two Xe:Ar gas cells were employed in these experiments. Each had a quartz input window and a lithium fluoride output window. The generated 1182-Å radiation was directed into a helium-purged lithium fluoride prism spectrometer. Detection was accomplished with a solar blind model EMR 542G photomultiplier with a cesium iodide photocathode. A sensitive lithium tantalate pyroelectric detector[6] was used for absolute intensity measurements at 1182 Å.

In the first set of experiments, the laser was focused to a spot with 70-μ diameter (confocal parameter, 2.1 cm), and a 0.95-cm-long cell was placed at the center of the focus. The xenon pressure was fixed at 1 Torr. Generated third-harmonic power at 1182 Å was monitored as the argon pressure was gradually increased. Experimental results are shown in Fig. 2. Peak third-harmonic power was obtained at an Ar:Xe ratio of 430:1. The Xe pressure was then increased to 5.7 Torr, and the experiment was repeated. Peak third-harmonic power was again obtained at a ratio of 430:1, and was 2500 times greater than that obtained with pure Xe. The conversion efficiency for these experimental conditions

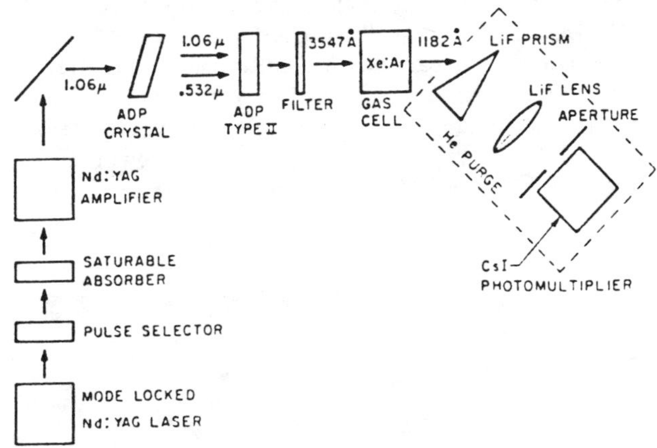

FIG. 1. Schematic of experimental apparatus for 1182-Å generation.

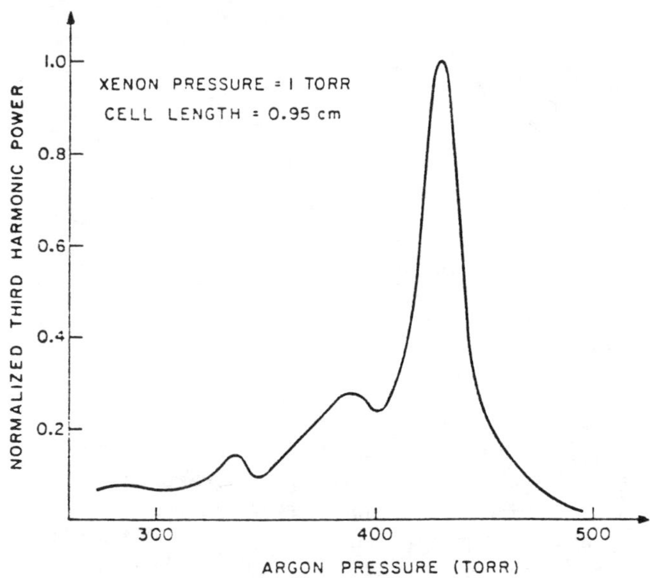

FIG. 2. Normalized 1182-Å output power vs argon pressure. Confocal parameter of input beam is 2.1 cm.

was 0.13%. A further increase in Xe pressure did not yield significantly higher output powers. The ratio of third-harmonic power outputs with argon present to that with argon absent, yields a coherence length for pure xenon of − 0.033 cm at 10^{17} atoms/cm^3. The measured conversion efficiency, cell length, and coherence length yield a nonlinear susceptibility $\chi^{(3)} \simeq 2.5 \times 10^{-34}$ esu.

To obtain higher conversion efficiency, the 3547-Å radiation was focused to a confocal parameter of 0.25 cm in the center of a 9.5-cm cell. At an input power of 13 MW the power density on the cell windows was still reasonable, while the density at the focus was about 6.3×10^{12} W/cm^2. For these tight focusing conditions, the ratio of Ar to Xe which was necessary to achieve phase matching was reduced to about 50:1. This reduction in ratio is a result of the tighter focusing employed.[4] At an input power of 13 MW and an optimized Xe pressure of 3 Torr, an energy conversion efficiency of 2.8% from 3547 to 1182 Å is obtained. For these tight focusing conditions, even pure Xe at a pressure of 3 Torr yields a conversion efficiency of 0.9%.

In general, to obtain maximum conversion efficiency, it is desirable to work at the highest power density allowed by either breakdown or multiphoton ionization. For the 25-psec pulses employed in our experiment, we found that the third-harmonic power output varied as the cube of the incident power up to an incident power density of 7×10^{12} W/cm^2. This may be compared with a four-photon ionization density of 1.7×10^{12} W/cm^2 estimated by Morton,[7] and 1×10^{13} W/cm^2 estimated by Bebb and Gold.[8]

A different type of saturation of the third-harmonic output power results due to absorption at the third-harmonic frequency causing a change in the refractive index and a breaking of the phase-matching condition. If the pressure of the Xe is reduced as the square root of the incident energy density, theory[4] predicts that conversion efficiency should increase linearly with input power. This was found to be the case to the limit of our available power. On the basis of the measured susceptibility and with the assumption that theory continues to hold, 20% conversion efficiency should be obtained at an input power of about 9.3×10^7 W. For this input power the laser should be focused to a confocal parameter of 1.8 cm ($P/A = 5.8 \times 10^{12}$ W/cm^2), and 1.1 Torr of Xe and 28 Torr of Ar should be used.

The general technique of phase-matched harmonic generation in mixtures of inert gases should be applicable to the spectral region from 1469 to at least 500 Å. Tripling of the second harmonic of a mode-locked ruby laser to yield radiation at 1157 Å should be obtained at a ratio slightly less than that reported here, and with a nonlinearity which is approximately the same. By tripling the radiation obtained from dye lasers and frequency-doubled dye lasers,[9,10] high-power tunable radiation over much of the vacuum ultraviolet should also be obtainable.

The authors gratefully acknowledge many helpful discussions with G.C. Bjorklund, thank C.B. Roundy and R.L. Byer for the use of their pyroelectric detector, and thank B. Yoshizumi for help with the experimental apparatus.

---

*Work sponsored jointly by the Office of Naval Research, the Air Force Cambridge Research Laboratories, and by the U.S. Army Research Office.

[1]S.E. Harris and R.B. Miles, Appl. Phys. Lett. 19, 385 (1971).
[2]J.F. Young, G.C. Bjorklund, A.H. Kung, R.B. Miles, and S.E. Harris, Phys. Rev. Lett. 27, 1551 (1971).
[3]A.H. Kung, J.F. Young, G.C. Bjorklund, and S.E. Harris, Phys. Rev. Lett. 29, 985 (1972).
[4]R.B. Miles and S.E. Harris, IEEE J. Quantum Electron. (to be published).
[5]J.F. Ward and G.H.C. New, Phys. Rev. 185, 57 (1969).
[6]C.B. Roundy and R.L. Byer, J. Appl. Phys. 44, 929 (1973).
[7]V.M. Morton, Proc. Phys. Soc. Lond. 92, 301 (1967).
[8]H.B. Bebb and A. Gold, Phys. Rev. 143, 1 (1966).
[9]D.J. Bradley, J.V. Nicholas, and J.R.D. Shaw, Appl. Phys. Lett. 19, 172 (1971).
[10]R.W. Wallace, Opt. Commun. 4, 316 (1971).

Reprinted with permission from *IEEE Journal of Quantum Electronics,* Vol. QE-9(4), pp. 470-484 (April 1973). ©1973 IEEE.

Optical Third-Harmonic Generation in Alkali Metal Vapors

RICHARD B. MILES AND STEPHEN E. HARRIS

Abstract—**This paper considers third-harmonic generation in phase-matched mixtures of alkali metal vapors and inert gases. Calculations show that the combination of near-resonant nonlinear susceptibilities, the ability to phase match, and the relatively high UV transparency of these vapors should allow high conversion efficiency for picosecond laser pulses with a peak power of $10^8 - 10^9$ W. Calculations of the nonlinear susceptibility and of the ratio of xenon atoms to metal vapor atoms which is necessary to achieve phase matching are given for each of the alkalies as a function of incident laser wavelength. Processes that limit the allowable peak power density and energy density are discussed and guides for determining the metal vapor pressure, cell length, and beam area are given.**

I. Introduction

THIS PAPER presents a theoretical analysis of phase-matched optical third-harmonic generation in alkali metal vapors. Calculations predict the efficient conversion of high-power picosecond laser pulses into the ultraviolet. Three complementary phenomena combine to produce the potentially high conversion efficiency: 1) resonant nonlinear susceptibility, 2) phase matching, and 3) ultraviolet transparency.

The resonant enhancement of the third-harmonic nonlinear susceptibility arises from resonant denominators at the first, second, and third harmonics of the incident frequency. Susceptibilities of the alkalies in the visible and near-infrared spectral region are typically five orders of magnitude greater than those of the inert gases in the same region. The conversion efficiency is proportional to the square of this susceptibility.

Phase matching is possible because alkali metal vapors are anomalously dispersive if the driving frequency is chosen below and its third harmonic chosen above the primary resonance line. A normally dispersive buffer gas such as xenon may be added to vary the indices of refraction until both the first and third harmonics travel at the same velocity through the gas mixture. Third-harmonic generation then becomes cumulative over the entire length of the gas cell and a substantial increase of the power conversion is possible.

The small absorption cross sections of the alkali vapors above their ionization potentials assure that the third harmonic is not reabsorbed by the vapor itself. This ultraviolet transparency allows generation to spectral regions that are not accessible to nonlinear optical crystals.

Assuming that high efficiencies can be experimentally realized, third-harmonic generation in gas mixtures will have a number of significant advantages over third-harmonic generation or sequential second-harmonic generation in nonlinear crystals. Nonlinear crystal

Manuscript received October 25, 1972. This work was supported jointly by the U. S. Air Force Cambridge Research Laboratories, the Office of Naval Research, NASA, and the U. S. Army Research Office, and by a grant to R. B. Miles from the Fannie and John K. Hertz Foundation.

R. B. Miles is with the Department of Aerospace and Mechanical Sciences, Engineering Quadrangle, Princeton, N. J. 08540.

S. E. Harris is with the Hansen Microwave Laboratory, Stanford University, Stanford, Calif. 94305.

transparency is now limited to below the cutoff of ammonium dihydrogen phosphate at about 2000 Å, while gases have no such limitation. The isotopic nature of gas mixtures eliminates Poynting vector walkoff characteristic of birefringent phase matching in crystals. Breakdown power and energy densities are higher in gases and breakdown does not destroy the medium. Gas cells may ultimately be made with very large apertures to handle large incident optical energies.

Conversely, metal vapor tripling cells are not nearly as simple and will be more expensive than nonlinear crystals. Even theoretically, the required incident power is much higher for efficient tripling in vapors than for efficient doubling in crystals. At this time the highest experimental conversion efficiency obtained in metal vapors is about 10^{-4}, and considerable experimental effort will be necessary to attempt to verify the calculations and predictions of this paper.

In the following sections, the third-harmonic nonlinear susceptibility is calculated and plotted as a function of wavelength for each of the alkalies. Tables of matrix elements, oscillator strengths, and transition energies are given. The power conversion equation is developed and the ratio of xenon atoms to alkali atoms, which is necessary to obtain phase matching, is given for each of the alkalies. Experimental results confirm the calculation of the susceptibility to within 15 percent and correlate almost perfectly with the theoretical phase-matching behavior.

Processes that limit the maximum metal vapor density, and thus the maximum conversion efficiency, are discussed. These include: single and multiphoton absorption and ionization, Kerr effect, breakdown, thermal defocusing, and breaking of the phase-matching condition as a result of atomic saturation. Typically this latter process will be the most severe and will probably limit the energy density to about 1 J/cm² for tripling 1.064-μ radiation. Formulas for determining the metal vapor pressure, cell length, and beam area are given.

Before proceeding, we note that third-harmonic generation in the inert gases has been extensively studied by Ward and New [1]. The concept of phase matching by gas mixing was suggested by Armstrong *et al.* [2]. The metal vapor inert gas system was proposed by Harris and Miles [3], and demonstrated by Young *et al.* [4].

II. Calculation of the Susceptibility

Third-harmonic light is generated from a radiating power-density-dependent third-harmonic component of the induced polarization. For high power densities, this third-harmonic nonlinearity becomes large and radiation may be substantial. The creation of the third-harmonic component can be visualized as a step-by-step process beginning with a strong electric field that interacts with ground state electrons and produces an induced dipole moment at the driving frequency. This induced dipole moment interacts with the field to create a 2ω variation of excited and mixed state populations. These populations again interact with the field to produce a third-harmonic component of the dipole moment. These interactions occur simultaneously and no transitions are involved.

If the incident electric field is written as

$$\mathcal{E}(t, r) = \tfrac{1}{2}[\mathcal{E}(r)e^{-i\omega t} + \mathcal{E}^*(r)e^{i\omega t}], \tag{1}$$

we can define the polarization at the third-harmonic frequency as

$$\mathcal{P}^{(3)}(t, r) = \tfrac{1}{2}[\mathcal{P}^{(3)}(r)e^{-i3\omega t} + \mathcal{P}^{(3)*}(r)e^{i3\omega t}] \tag{2}$$

where

$$\mathcal{P}^{(3)}(r) = \frac{N\chi^{(3)}(3\omega)[\mathcal{E}(r)]^3}{4} \tag{3}$$

and N is the density of atoms/cubic centimeter. Armstrong *et al.* [2] have shown $\chi^{(3)}(3\omega)$ to be given by

$$\chi^{(3)}(3\omega) = \frac{1}{\hbar^3}\sum_g \sum_{a,b,c} \mu_{ga}\mu_{ab}\mu_{bc}\mu_{cg}\rho_{gg}A_{abc}, \tag{4}$$

where μ_{ij} are the dipole matrix elements, ρ_{gg} is the probability of occupancy of the ground level, and A_{abc} are frequency factors:

$$\begin{aligned} A_{abc} = {} & \frac{1}{(\Omega_{ag} - 3\omega)(\Omega_{bg} - 2\omega)(\Omega_{cg} - \omega)} \\ & + \frac{1}{(\Omega_{ag} + \omega)(\Omega_{bg} + 2\omega)(\Omega_{cg} + 3\omega)} \\ & + \frac{1}{(\Omega_{ag} + \omega)(\Omega_{bg} + 2\omega)(\Omega_{cg} - \omega)} \\ & + \frac{1}{(\Omega_{ag} + \omega)(\Omega_{bg} - 2\omega)(\Omega_{cg} - \omega)} \end{aligned} \tag{5}$$

where Ω_{ij} are the atomic transition frequencies. We assume the incident laser field to be linearly polarized in the z direction and thus take $\mu_{ij} = e\langle i\,|z|\,j\rangle$.

The Hamiltonian from which the eigenstates $|i\rangle$ are derived includes a term describing the $L - S$ coupling that is characteristic of the alkalies and other multielectron atoms. This coupling accounts for the splitting of the energy levels with quantum numbers L greater than zero and is responsible, for instance, for the two closely separated sodium D lines. If the driving frequency is much farther from the resonances than the splitting, the $L - S$ coupling may be neglected by replacing the split resonance lines with an average resonance. Angular and spin eigenstates then become identical to those of the hydrogen atom. The radial quantum number n, however, must be derived from the particular alkali's radial wavefunctions. Equation (6) results from ignoring the $L - S$ coupling and is used for the ensuing calculations:

$$\begin{aligned} \chi^{(3)}(3\omega) = \frac{e^4}{\hbar^3}\sum_{a,b,c} \{ & \langle g\,s\,0\,\tfrac{1}{2}\,|z|\,a\,p\,0\,\tfrac{1}{2}\rangle\langle a\,p\,0\,\tfrac{1}{2}\,|z|\,b\,s\,0\,\tfrac{1}{2}\rangle \\ & \cdot\langle b\,s\,0\,\tfrac{1}{2}\,|z|\,c\,p\,0\,\tfrac{1}{2}\rangle\langle c\,p\,0\,\tfrac{1}{2}\,|z|\,g\,s\,0\,\tfrac{1}{2}\rangle A_{ap,bs,cp} \\ & + \langle g\,s\,0\,\tfrac{1}{2}\,|z|\,a\,p\,0\,\tfrac{1}{2}\rangle\langle a\,p\,0\,\tfrac{1}{2}\,|z|\,b\,d\,0\,\tfrac{1}{2}\rangle \\ & \cdot\langle b\,d\,0\,\tfrac{1}{2}\,|z|\,c\,p\,0\,\tfrac{1}{2}\rangle\langle c\,p\,0\,\tfrac{1}{2}\,|z|\,g\,s\,0\,\tfrac{1}{2}\rangle A_{ap,bd,cp}\}. \end{aligned} \tag{6}$$

TABLE I

MATRIX ELEMENTS OF THE ALKALIES

Lithium

Transition	f	ΔE(Ry)	$\langle z \rangle$ (Bohr Radii)	Transition	f	ΔE(Ry)	$\langle z \rangle$ (Bohr Radii)
2s-2p	0.744	0.1359	-2.34	2p-3d	0.635	0.1494	2.26
2s-3p	0.00428	0.2620	0.123	2p-4d	0.122	0.1980	0.860
2s-4p	0.00398	0.3325	0.109	2p-5d	0.0462	0.2206	0.501
2s-5p	0.00239	0.3557	0.082	2p-6d	0.0229	0.2328	0.345
3s-2p	- 0.327	- 0.1122	1.71	3p-3d	0.0742	0.0033	5.23
3s-3p	1.21	0.0339	- 5.97	3p-4d	0.521	0.0519	3.47
3s-4p	0.0000364	0.0845	- 0.021	3p-5d	0.130	0.0745	1.45
3s-5p	0.00125	0.1077	0.108	3p-6d	0.0543	0.0867	0.867
4s-2p	- 0.0378	- 0.1833	0.454	4p-3d	- 0.302	- 0.0473	0.876
4s-3p	- 0.667	- 0.0373	4.23	4p-4d	0.136	0.0014	-10.76
4s-4p	1.64	0.0133	-11.11	4p-5d	0.490	0.0240	4.95
4s-5p	0.000990	0.0365	- 0.165	4p-6d	0.132	0.0362	2.09
5s-2p	- 0.0127	- 0.2133	0.244	5p-3d	- 0.00530	- 0.0705	0.314
5s-3p	- 0.0775	- 0.0672	1.07	5p-4d	- 0.0735	- 0.0218	2.01
5s-4p	- 1.01	- 0.0167	7.78	5p-5d	0.191	0.00076	-17.37
5s-5p	2.05	0.0065	-17.74	5p-6d	0.487	0.0130	6.70

Potassium

Transition	f	ΔE(Ry)	$\langle z \rangle$ (Bohr Radii)	Transition	f	ΔE(Ry)	$\langle z \rangle$ (Bohr Radii)
4s-4p	1.04	0.11875	-2.96	4p-3d	0.839	0.07760	3.60
4s-5p	0.0154	0.22534	-0.261	4p-4d	0.00121	0.13105	0.105
4s-6p	0.00277	0.26446	-0.102	4p-5d	0.00163	0.15647	-0.112
4s-7p	0.000968	0.28332	-0.0585	4p-6d	0.00226	0.17025	-0.126
5s-4p	-0.525	-0.07297	2.68	5p-3d	-0.234	-0.02899	-3.11
5s-5p	1.50	0.03362	-6.68	5p-4d	1.19	0.02446	7.64
5s-6p	0.0316	0.07274	-0.659	5p-5d	0.00779	0.04988	0.433
5s-7p	0.00602	0.09160	-0.256	5p-6d	0.0000153	0.06366	-0.0170
6s-4p	-0.0500	-0.13154	0.617	6p-3d	-0.0110	-0.06811	-0.440
6s-5p	-0.957	-0.02495	6.19	6p-4d	-0.502	-0.01466	-6.41
6s-6p	1.94	0.01417	-11.7	6p-5d	1.51	0.01076	12.98
6s-7p	0.0499	0.03303	- 1.23	6p-6d	0.0159	0.02454	0.882
7s-4p	-0.0164	-0.15728	0.323	7p-3d	-0.00317	-0.08697	0.209
7s-5p	-0.0810	-0.05069	1.26	7p-4d	-0.0324	-0.03352	-1.08
7s-6p	-1.37	-0.01157	10.88	7p-5d	-0.762	-0.00810	-10.62
7s-7p	2.37	0.00729	-18.03	7p-6d	1.82	0.00568	19.61

Sodium

Transition	f	ΔE(Ry)	$\langle z \rangle$ (Bohr Radii)	Transition	f	ΔE(Ry)	$\langle z \rangle$ (Bohr Radii)
3s-3p	0.972	0.1547	-2.51	3p-3d	0.855	0.1113	-3.04
3s-4p	0.0153	0.2760	-0.235	3p-4d	0.0996	0.1603	-0.864
3s-5p	0.00251	0.3195	-0.0886	3p-5d	0.0311	0.1830	-0.452
3s-6p	0.000821	0.3401	-0.0491	3p-6d	0.0140	0.1953	-0.293
4s-3p	-0.502	-0.0800	2.51	4p-3d	-0.195	-0.0100	4.83
4s-4p	1.44	0.0413	-5.90	4p-4d	0.948	0.0390	-5.40
4s-5p	0.0385	0.0848	-0.677	4p-5d	0.142	0.0617	-1.66
4s-6p	0.00779	0.1054	-0.272	4p-6d	0.0493	0.0740	-0.894
5s-3p	-0.0412	-0.1480	0.528	5p-3d	-0.000275	-0.0535	-0.079
5s-4p	-0.937	-0.0267	5.92	5p-4d	-0.382	-0.0045	10.09
5s-5p	1.88	0.0168	-10.58	5p-5d	1.05	0.0182	- 8.32
5s-6p	0.0620	0.0374	- 1.29	5p-6d	0.173	0.0305	- 2.61
6s-3p	-0.0131	-0.1769	0.272	6p-3d	-0.0000517	-0.0741	- 0.0289
6s-4p	-0.0696	-0.0556	1.12	6p-4d	-0.00141	-0.0251	- 0.260
6s-5p	-1.36	-0.0121	10.59	6p-5d	-0.558	-0.0024	16.80
6s-6p	2.31	0.0084	-16.56	6p-6d	1.17	0.0099	-11.88

Rubidium

Transition	f	ΔE(Ry)	$\langle z \rangle$ (Bohr Radii)	Transition	f	ΔE(Ry)	$\langle z \rangle$ (Bohr Radii)
5s-5p	1.09	0.1161	-3.06	5p-4d	0.594	0.0604	3.44
5s-6p	0.0243	0.2167	-0.335	5p-5d	0.0273	0.1182	-0.526
5s-7p	0.00535	0.2540	-0.145	5p-6d	0.0233	0.1455	-0.438
5s-8p	0.00209	0.2721	-0.0876	5p-7d	0.0144	0.1600	-0.329
6s-5p	-0.562	-0.0674	2.89	6p-4d	-0.141	-0.0402	-2.05
6s-6p	1.54	0.0331	-6.82	6p-5d	0.935	0.0177	7.97
6s-7p	0.0412	0.0704	-0.765	6p-6d	0.0182	0.0449	-0.698
6s-8p	0.00883	0.0886	-0.316	6p-7d	0.0172	0.0594	-0.589
7s-5p	-0.0523	-0.1238	0.650	7p-4d	-0.0115	-0.0775	-0.422
7s-6p	-1.00	-0.0232	6.56	7p-5d	-0.331	-0.0196	-4.50
7s-7p	1.98	0.0141	-11.85	7p-6d	1.23	0.0076	13.95
7s-8p	0.0613	0.0322	- 1.38	7p-7d	0.0122	0.0221	- 0.814
8s-5p	-0.0172	-0.1487	0.340	8p-4d	-0.00353	-0.0957	0.210
8s-6p	-0.0808	-0.0481	1.30	8p-5d	-0.0352	-0.0378	- 1.06
8s-7p	-1.42	-0.0108	11.48	8p-6d	-0.521	-0.0106	- 7.69
8s-8p	2.40	0.0074	-18.06	8p-7d	1.50	0.0040	21.29

The eigenstates in the equation above are $|n\ l\ m_l m_s\rangle$, where $m_l = l, l-1, \cdots, -l$, and $m_s = \pm\frac{1}{2}$. Selection rules for the dipole z-matrix elements state that $\Delta l = \pm 1, \Delta m_l = 0$, $\Delta m_s = 0$ [5]. These differ from the total dipole matrix-element selection rules that include x and y components and also allow $\Delta m_l = \pm 1$.

The ground state of the alkalies, for which $l = 0$, is indicated by $n = g$, $l = s$, and it is assumed that this is the only populated level. We see from the selection rules that the energy levels associated with $n = a$ and $n = c$ in (6) must be p levels ($l = 1$). Those associated with $n = b$ may be either s levels ($l = 0$) or d levels ($l = 2$). Thus (6) has two terms: those for which the b levels are s states, and those for which the b levels are d states. The $A_{ap,bd,cp}$ factor is the frequency factor of (5) with resonances Ω between $|ap\rangle$ and ground, $|bd\rangle$ and ground, and $|cp\rangle$ and ground.

Values for the dipole matrix elements in terms of l and m values and the radial $\mathcal{R}$ factor are given in Slater [6]. For the z component

$$\langle n\ l\ m_l\ |z|\ n'\ l+1\ m_l\rangle = \sqrt{(l+1)^2 - m_l^2}\ \mathcal{R}_{nl;n'l+1}, \quad (7)$$

where

TABLE I
CONTINUED

Cesium

Transition	f	ΔE(Ry)	$\langle z \rangle$ (Bohr Radii)	Transition	f	ΔE(Ry)	$\langle z \rangle$ (Bohr Radii)
6s-6p	1.13	0.1053	-3.28	6p-5d	0.197	0.0275	2.93
6s-7p	0.0270	0.1995	-0.368	6p-6d	0.281	0.1009	-1.83
6s-8p	0.00631	0.2349	-0.164	6p-7d	0.0902	0.1323	-0.904
6s-9p	0.00255	0.2523	-0.101	6p-8d	0.0407	0.1484	-0.574
7s-6p	-0.576	-0.0637	3.01	7p-5d	-0.0240	-0.0668	-0.657
7s-7p	1.58	0.0306	-7.19	7p-6d	0.354	0.0066	8.00
7s-8p	0.0401	0.0659	-7.80	7p-7d	0.283	0.0381	-2.99
7s-9p	0.00862	0.0833	-0.322	7p-8d	0.0933	0.0541	-1.44
8s-6p	-0.0565	-0.1164	0.670	8p-5d	-0.00284	-0.1022	-0.183
8s-7p	-1.02	-0.0222	6.78	8p-6d	-0.0955	-0.0287	-2.00
8s-8p	2.01	0.0132	-12.34	8p-7d	0.470	0.0027	14.45
8s-9p	0.0580	0.0305	- 1.38	8p-8d	0.285	0.0187	- 4.27
9s-6p	-0.0189	-0.1401	0.367	9p-5d	-0.000854	-0.1195	- 0.0926
9s-7p	-0.0858	-0.0458	1.37	9p-6d	-0.0156	-0.0461	- 0.638
9s-8p	-1.44	-0.0105	11.73	9p-7d	-0.0173	-0.0147	- 3.76
9s-9p	2.43	0.0069	-18.78	9p-8d	0.578	0.00138	22.42

$$\mathcal{R}_{nl;n'l+1} = \frac{1}{\sqrt{(2l+1)(2l+3)}} \int_0^\infty r^3 R_{nl} R_{n'l+1}\, dr \tag{8}$$

and R_{nl} is the radial wave function.

The matrix elements to be used in (6) for calculation of the third-harmonic nonlinear susceptibility include only states with $m_l = 0$. Thus we find

$$\langle n\, l\, 0\, |z|\, n'l+1\, 0\rangle = (l+1)\mathcal{R}_{nl;n'l+1}. \tag{9}$$

Values for this matrix element may be found from the Bates and Damgaard [7] approach, which assumes a Coulombic radial potential field and tabulates the values of the radial function in terms of the effective quantum number of each level. They define σ, which is $e\mathcal{R}$ in our notation. The sign of $\mathcal{R}$ is important and is included in their derivation; however, Bebb [8] mentions a sign error of $(-1)^{(n-n')+1}$ in his work.

An alternative, and perhaps superior, approach to the evaluation of matrix elements is to find their absolute value from tabulated oscillator strengths and the sign from Bates and Damgaard. Solving for the matrix element $\langle n\, l\, 0 \cdot |z|\, n'l+1\, 0\rangle$ in terms of the oscillator strength yields

$$|\langle n\, l\, 0\, |z|\, n'l+1\, 0\rangle|^2 = f_{nl;n'l+1} \frac{\hbar}{2m_e \Omega_{n'l+1;nl}} \frac{3(l+1)}{2l+3}, \tag{10}$$

where $f_{nl;n'l+1}$ is the oscillator strength, $\hbar\Omega_{n'l+1;nl}$ is the energy difference associated with the $|n\, l\, 0\rangle$ to $|n'l+1\, 0\rangle$ transition, and m_e is the electron mass. If the resonant frequency Ω is written as an energy difference in rydbergs and the matrix element is found in Bohr radii, then

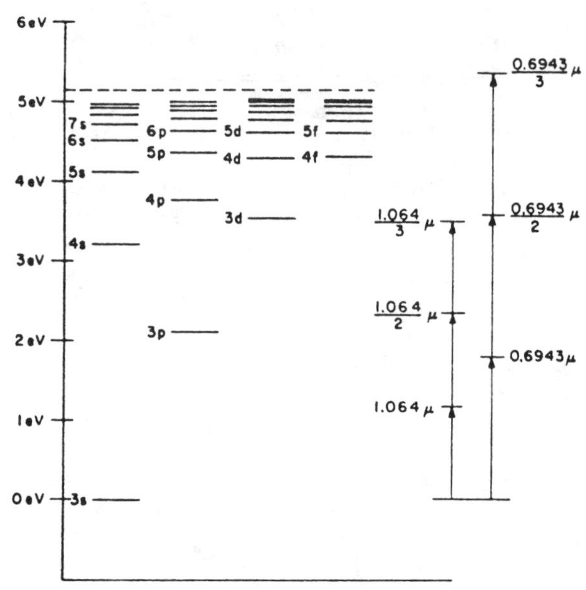

Fig. 1. Energy levels of sodium.

$$|\langle n\, l\, 0\, |z|\, n'l+1\, 0\rangle| = \sqrt{\frac{f_{nl:n'l+1}}{E_{n'l+1} - E_{nl}} \frac{3(l+1)}{2l+3}}. \tag{11}$$

The average frequency factors to be used in (6) are calculated from the $L - S$ split levels weighted by the relative line strengths:

$$\tfrac{2}{3}E_{np(j=3/2)} + \tfrac{1}{3}E_{np(j=1/2)} = E_{np}$$

$$\tfrac{2}{5}E_{nd(j=3/2)} + \tfrac{3}{5}E_{nd(j=5/2)} = E_{nd}. \tag{12}$$

The average energy levels are used in Table I to give allowed transition energies between the lowest four s, p, and d states for each of the alkalies. These 12 levels create 128 terms in the summation and constitute our approximation of the nonlinear susceptibility.

Fig. 1 shows the average energy levels of sodium. It is apparent that the approximation is not good for driving frequencies whose first, second, or third harmonic is above the levels used and below the ionization potential. Continuum absorption is small for the alkalies and is neglected in this derivation. Table I gives the $\langle n\, l\, 0\, |z|\, n'l+1\, 0]$ matrix elements with the oscillator strengths and energy differences from which they are calculated. For consistency, these oscillator strengths have all been taken from calculations by Anderson [9], [10]. The signs of the matrix elements are from Bates and Damgaard with the correction factor mentioned by Bebb.

Figs. 2–6 give $|\chi^{(3)}(3\omega)|$ in electrostatic units versus wavelength for each of the alkalies. The regions where our approximation does not include resonant levels are marked as invalid. Substantial cancellations from the signs of both frequency factors and matrix elements account for the numerous zeros. It is important to note that the 2ω resonances (occurring with the excited s or d levels) do not correspond to allowed single photon absorption, and, if approached by 2ω, could be used to enhance the third-harmonic susceptibility without substantially increasing the loss at the fundamental frequency.

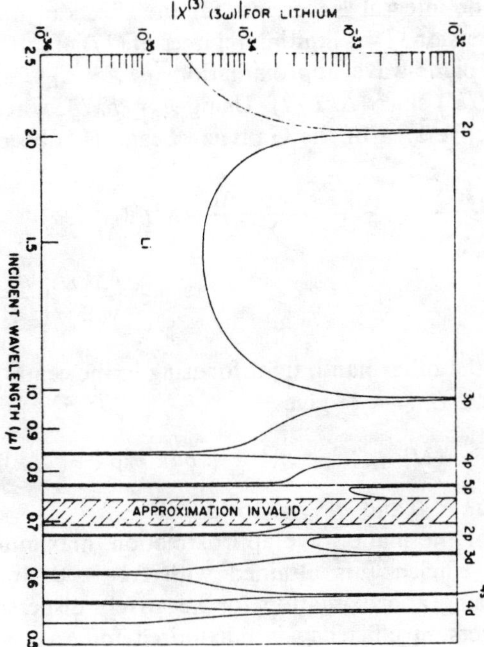

Fig. 2. Nonlinear susceptibility of lithium versus incident wavelength.

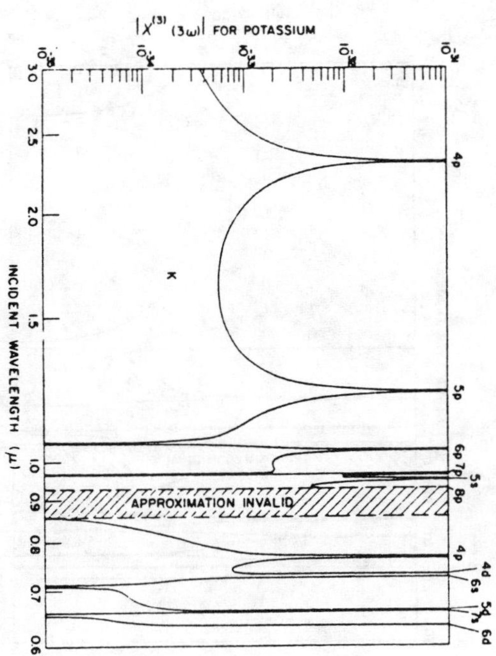

Fig. 4. Nonlinear susceptibility of potassium versus incident wavelength.

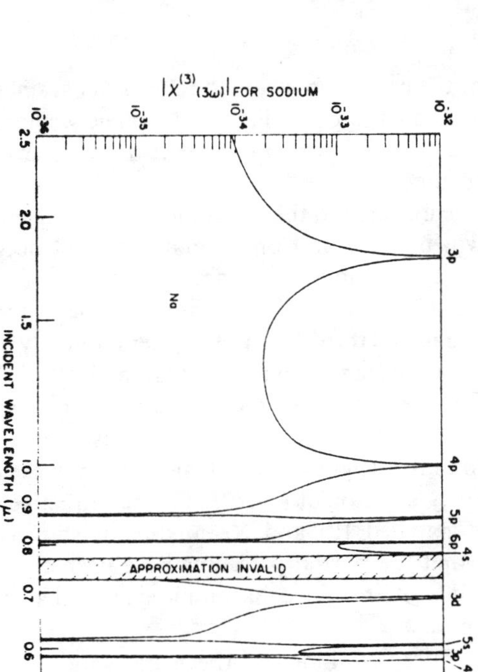

Fig. 3. Nonlinear susceptibility of sodium versus incident wavelength.

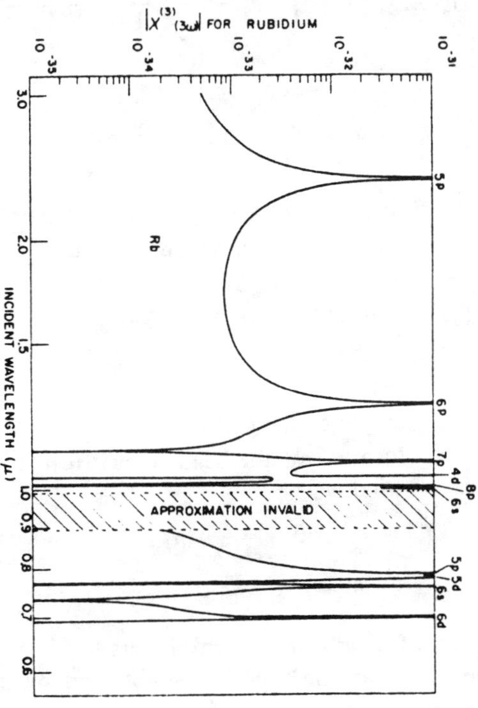

Fig. 5. Nonlinear susceptibility of rubidium versus incident wavelength.

III. Third-Harmonic Power Conversion

We assume the incident electric field to be a TEM_{00} Gaussian mode focused at $z = f$ with a confocal beam parameter b. Then

$$\mathcal{E}(r) = \mathcal{E}_0 e^{ik_1 z}(1 + i\xi)^{-1} \exp\left[-k_1(x^2 + y^2)/b(1 + i\xi)\right]. \quad (13)$$

In this expression $k_1 = 2\pi n_1/\lambda$, where n_1 is the index of refraction at the incident wavelength λ; $b = 2\pi w_0^2/\lambda$, where w_0 is the beam radius; and $\xi = 2(z - f)/b$. From Ward and New [1], the generated third-harmonic electric field is given by

$$\begin{aligned}\mathcal{E}^{(3)}(r) = {} & [i \tfrac{1}{16}\, \eta\, c\, k_0^2\, b\, N\, \chi^{(3)}(3\omega)\mathcal{E}_0^2/k_3] \\ & \cdot \exp\,[3ik_1 z](1 - i\xi)^{-1} \\ & \cdot I(\Delta k, \xi, \zeta) \exp\left(-\frac{3k_1(x^2 + y^2)}{b(1 + i\xi)}\right) \quad (14)\end{aligned}$$

where

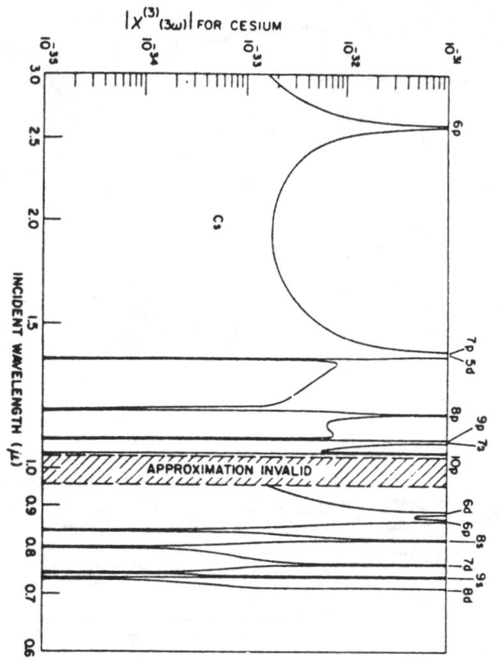

Fig. 6. Nonlinear susceptibility of cesium versus incident wavelength.

$$I(\Delta k, \xi, \zeta) = \int_{-\zeta}^{\xi} d\xi' \frac{\exp\left[\frac{1}{2}\, i\, b\, \Delta\, k\, (\xi - \xi')\right]}{(1 + i\xi')^2} \qquad (15)$$

and

k_0	$= 6\pi/\lambda$,
k_3	$= n_3 k_0$,
n_3	index of refraction at the third harmonic,
N	number of atoms/cubic centimeter,
η	$= \sqrt{\mu_0/\epsilon_0} \cong 377$,
$\chi^{(3)}(3\omega)$	$= (1/81 \times 10^{-17})\chi^{(3)}(3\omega)_{ESU}$,
ξ	$= 2(L - f)/b$,
ζ	$= 2f/b$,
L	length of the gas cell,
f	location of the beam focus from the entrance window,
Δk	$= k_3 - 3k_1 = \frac{6\pi}{\lambda}(n_3 - n_1)$ = wave-vector mismatch.

All units of length are in centimeters.

The third-harmonic power is obtained by integrating over r, and in terms of the incident power $P^{(1)}$, is

$$P^{(3)} = \frac{3\eta^4\pi^2 c^2}{\lambda^4} N^2[\chi^{(3)}(3\omega)]^2\, |I(\Delta k, \xi, \zeta)|^2\, [P^{(1)}]^3. \qquad (16)$$

The conversion efficiency is defined as the ratio of third- to first-harmonic power. With the power in watts, the alkali atom density N in atoms/cubic centimeter, the nonlinear coefficient $\chi^{(3)}(3\omega)$ in ESU, and the incident wavelength λ in centimeters, the conversion efficiency becomes

$$\frac{P^{(3)}}{P^{(1)}} = \frac{8.215 \times 10^{-2}}{\lambda^4} N^2[\chi^{(3)}(3\omega)]^2\, |I|^2\, [P^{(1)}]^2. \qquad (17)$$

The integral I accounts for the effects of focusing and dispersion. Two limiting regimes of (17) are of interest. In the plane-wave approximation ($b >> L$), I^2 reduces to $(4L^2/b^2)\,\mathrm{sinc}^2(\Delta kL/2)$. Using $A = b\lambda/4$, where A is the effective area of the Gaussian beam, (17) becomes

$$\frac{P^{(3)}}{P^{(1)}_{(\text{plane wave})}} = \frac{5.134 \times 10^{-3}}{\lambda^2} N^2 L^2[\chi^{(3)}(3\omega)]^2 \cdot \mathrm{sinc}^2\left(\frac{\Delta kL}{2}\right)\left[\frac{P^{(1)}}{A}\right]^2. \qquad (18)$$

On the other hand, tight focusing in the center of the cell ($b << L$, $\xi = \zeta$) gives

$$|I|^2_{(\text{tight focusing})} = [\pi b\Delta k \exp(+\tfrac{1}{2}b\Delta k)]^2, \qquad (19)$$

for $\Delta k < 0$ and $|I|^2 = 0$ for $\Delta k \geq 0$.

For the plane-wave approximation, maximum conversion efficiency is attained with $\Delta k = 0$. In the tight focusing approximation for negatively dispersive media, conversion efficiency is maximized for $b\Delta k = -4$. For confocal focusing ($b = L$, $\xi = \zeta$) at the center of a negatively dispersive media, $|I|^2$ maximizes at 2.46 when $\Delta kL = -3.5$.

A. Phase Matching

For the condition where the confocal parameter is much longer than the gas cell, i.e., the plane-wave approximation, Δk must be made equal to zero. If two gases are mixed together, one with a negative and the other with positive dispersion, then at some ratio of partial pressures, Δk will be zero and phase matching will occur. It thus suffices to mix some nonreactive gas, such as xenon, with the alkali vapor to phase match. In the absence of this buffer gas, the third-harmonic generation only occurs over the short distance that the first and third harmonics overlap. This is called the coherence length and is $L_c = |\pi/\Delta k|$. Phase matching will increase this interaction length to the length of the cell and thus increase the output power by a factor of $(\pi L/2L_c)^2$. The refractive index of a phase-matched Rb and Xe mixture is shown in Fig. 7. Note that the partial pressures have been chosen so that the index at the third harmonic equals that at the fundamental.

The refractive index of the metal vapors is calculated from the standard Sellmeier equation

$$n - 1 = \frac{Nr_e}{2\pi} \sum_i \frac{f_i}{[(1/\lambda_i^2) - (1/\lambda^2)]}, \qquad (20)$$

where

r_e	$= 2.818 \times 10^{-13}$ cm,
f_i	oscillator strength of the ith transition,
λ_i	wavelength of the ith transition in centimeters.

Values of the f_i and λ_i for Li, Na, K, Rb, and Cs are given in Table V. The refractive index of Xe is taken from Koch [11], who derived the following equation from experimental data at STP:

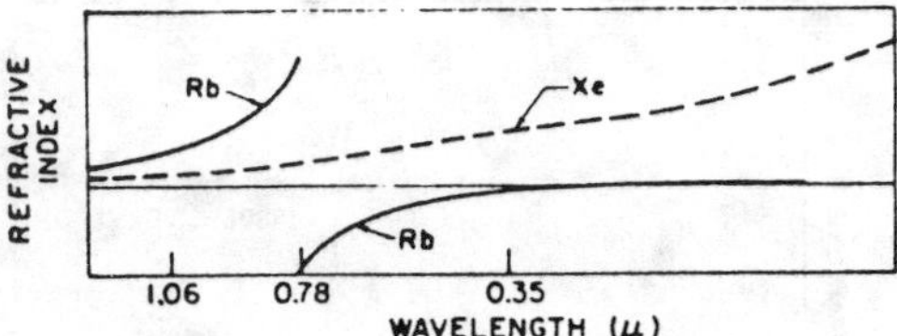

Fig. 7. Refractive indices of rubidium and xenon versus wavelength.

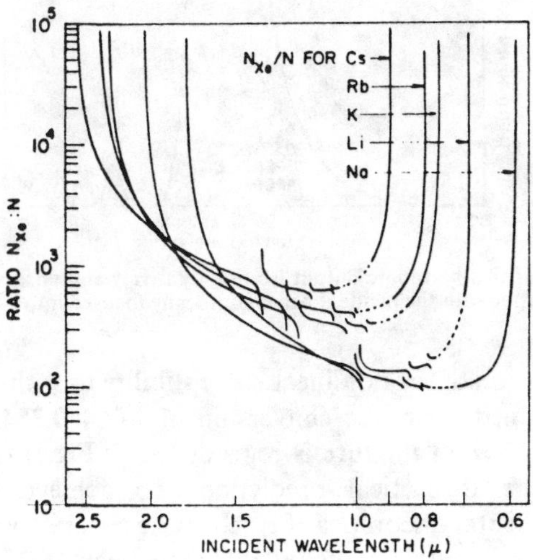

Fig. 8. Required ratio of Xe to alkali atoms versus incident wavelength for phase-matched third-harmonic generation.

$$n_{Xe} - 1 \cong \left\{ \frac{393235}{46.3012 - 10^{-8}/\lambda^2} + \frac{393235}{59.5779 - 10^{-8}/\lambda^2} + \frac{7366100}{139.8310 - 10^{-8}/\lambda^2} \right\} \times 10^{-8} \quad (21)$$

where λ is in centimeters. Fig. 8 plots the ratio of the number of Xe to alkali atoms versus the incident wavelength for phase-matched third-harmonic generation in each of the alkalies.

When picosecond pulses are used for third-harmonic generation, it is necessary that the broad frequency spectrum that comprises the pulse be simultaneously phase matched; or equivalently that the fundamental and third harmonic maintain at least 50-percent temporal overlap. The minimum allowable pulse length Δt_{min}, which satisfies this condition, is determined by the difference in group velocities Δv_g of the fundamental and third harmonic, and is given by

$$\Delta t_{min} = \frac{n_1 n_3 L}{c^2} \left[\frac{\partial \omega_3}{\partial k_3} - \frac{\partial \omega_1}{\partial k_1} \right] = \frac{n_1 n_3 \Delta v_g}{c^2} L = BL. \quad (22)$$

The term $(n_1 n_3 \Delta v_g)/c^2$ is labeled B and is proportional to the density of atoms; the normalized constant B/N is given in Table II for 1.064- and 0.6943-μ tripling experiments. From these data we see that 50 cm of Rb vapor at 10^{17} atoms/cm^3 will phase match a 0.17-ps or longer pulse of 1.064-μ radiation. This is to be compared with a minimum pulse time of 6.1 ps for a 1-cm crystal of $LiNbO_3$ and 0.07 ps for a 1-cm crystal of KDP for doubling 1.064-μ radiation [12].

TABLE II

PARAMETERS FOR THIRD-HARMONIC GENERATION

Element	$\chi^{(3)}(3\omega)$ [ESU]	L_cN	Ratio $N_{Xe}:N$	B/N
		1.064 μ To 0.3547 μ		
Li	$1.[illegible]5 \times 10^{-3[illegible]}$	$5.79 \times 10^{1[illegible]}$	19[illegible]	$1.[illegible] \times 10^{-3[illegible]}$
Na	-3.95×10^{-34}	5.86×10^{16}	15[illegible]	$2.7[illegible] \times 10^{-32}$
K	2.61×10^{-34}	2.73×10^{16}	376	1.81×10^{-32}
Rb	6.15×10^{-33}	2.15×10^{16}	411	3.30×10^{-32}
Cs	$-1.17 \times 10^{-3[illegible]}$	1.35×10^{16}	699	$5.5[illegible] \times 10^{-32}$
		0.6943 μ To 0.2314 μ		
Li	3.00×10^{-34}	5.03×10^{16}	400	1.23×10^{-30}
Na	3.16×10^{-34}	2.01×10^{16}	100	3.69×10^{-32}
K	$4.17 \times 10^{-3[illegible]}$	9.60×10^{15}	---	---
Rb	$8.[illegible]5 \times 10^{-34}$	9.34×10^{15}	---	---
Cs	$3.75 \times 10^{-3[illegible]}$ [a]	$1.65 \times 10^{1[illegible]}$	---	---

[a] Includes extra energy levels that are near the 0.6943-μ resonance.

Table II presents other relevant data for the 1.064- and 0.6943-μ conversion experiments. Li and Na are the only alkalies that phase match 0.6943 μ; thus the ratio of xenon to alkali atoms and B/N are given only for those two vapors. The coherence length is inversely proportional to the density of alkali atoms and is tabulated as L_cN, which may be derived from (20).

The density of atoms of each alkali is calculated from the vapor pressure. A good approximation of the vapor pressure for pressures near 1 mmHg is

$$p(\text{mm}) \cong \exp[-(a/T) + d], \quad (23)$$

where the constants a and d are given in Table III for each of the alkalies and T is the temperature in degrees Kelvin. The density of atoms is, then,

$$N = 9.66084 \times 10^{18} \frac{p(\text{mm})}{T} \text{ atoms/cm}^3. \quad (24)$$

As the temperature and thus the density of alkali atoms increase, the allowed temperature tolerance necessary to maintain phase matching decreases. A maximum allowed variation on Δk of $\delta(\Delta k) = \pi/L$ yields a maximum allowed temperature variation of

$$\delta(T) = \frac{L_c}{L} T \left[\frac{a}{T} - 1 \right]^{-1}, \quad (25)$$

where a is the constant in Table III. A temperature of 814 K gives 10^{17} atoms of Na. From Tables II and III, L_c is 5.86×10^{-1} cm and $a = 1.2423 \times 10^4$. These numbers yield $\delta(T) = 33.4/L$ K, where L is in centimeters. Typically the vapor pressure will be low because of other limiting processes and the temperature tolerance will be no problem.

B. Tight Focusing

In the tight focus regime ($b \ll L$), setting $\Delta kb = -4$ maximizes the conversion efficiency. As opposed to the

TABLE III
VAPOR PRESSURE CONSTANTS

	Li	Na	K	Rb	Cs
a	19[illegible]1.4	12[illegible].3	10210.4	9140.07	[illegible]827.[illegible]
d	19.130	17.3914	16.539	16.0628	16.0007

TABLE IV
THIRD-HARMONIC GENERATION BY TIGHT FOCUSING

Element	$N_{\text{tight focusing}}$ (atoms/cm³)	K
	1.064 μ To 0.3547 μ	
Li	$7.37 \times 10^{16}/b$	1.11×10^{-28}
Na	$7.46 \times 10^{16}/b$	1.13×10^{-27}
K	$3.47 \times 10^{16}/b$	1.08×10^{-28}
Rb	$2.75 \times 10^{16}/b$	3.75×10^{-26}
Cs	$1.72 \times 10^{16}/b$	5.31×10^{-26}
	0.6943 μ To 0.2314 μ	
Li	$6.40 \times 10^{15}/b$	1.14×10^{-29}
Na	$2.56 \times 10^{16}/b$	2.02×10^{-28}

plane-wave condition where the sinc² function is identical for positive or negative Δk, the integral is only nonzero for negative Δk in the tight focus approximation and thus a negatively dispersive medium is necessary. Since the wave-vector mismatch Δk is proportional to N, the number of atoms/cubic centimeter required for maximum conversion by tight focusing is

$$N_{\text{tight focusing}} = 4(L_c N)/b\pi. \tag{26}$$

Substituting this value of N into (17), we obtain

$$\frac{P^{(3)}}{P_{\text{tight focusing}}^{(1)}} = K(P/A)^2. \tag{27}$$

Values of $N_{\text{tight focusing}}$ and K are given in Table IV for tripling 1.064- and 0.6943-μ radiation.

Though this type of phase matching is of interest because of its simplicity, it is likely that multiphoton absorption [8], [22] will limit the allowable incident power density to about 10^{11} W/cm² and thus (in Cs, for instance) will limit the maximum conversion efficiency to about 5.31×10^{-4}.

Fig. 9 shows calculated third-harmonic power versus temperature for a beam confocally focused ($b = L$) into a 10-cm cell filled with Rb vapor and a similar experiment using an imaginary vapor with the same characteristics as Rb except positively dispersive. The difference is easily noted and provides a method of distinguishing positively from negatively dispersive media. The large first peak occurs only if Δk is negative and equal to $-3.5/L$.

C. Experimental Results

Experimental results have been presented elsewhere [4]. A recent correction of the theory yielded experimental verification of the nonlinear susceptibility to within 15 percent. Third-harmonic conversion of 1.064–0.3547 μ in a Rb and xenon mixture is reproduced in Fig. 10 together with the theoretical prediction. To achieve the best experimental–theoretical fit, it was necessary to translate the experimental points by 5°C. The peak at 267°C corresponds to the temperature at which the rubidium vapor density was in the proper ratio to the xenon density to cause phase matching.

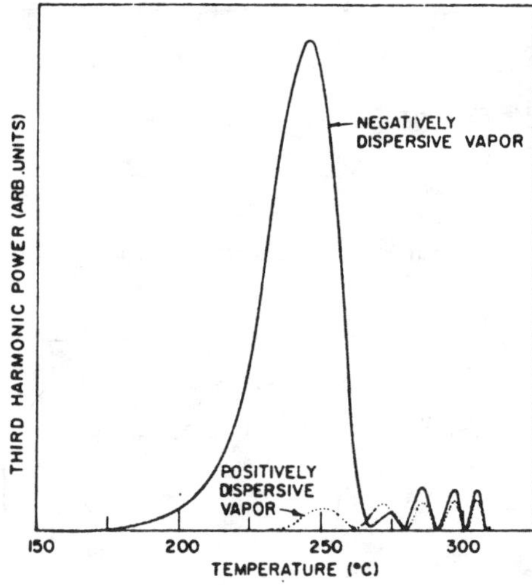

Fig. 9. Third-harmonic output from a negatively and positively dispersive vapor with the incident beam confocally focused into a 10-cm cell.

IV. LIMITING PROCESSES

Third-harmonic generation is limited at high powers and high-power densities by competing processes. Absorption will, of course, deplete the pump or the third-harmonic radiation. Off line center, however, absorption is generally not as severe a problem as are saturation (with the associated breaking of phase matching and self focusing), multiphoton absorption, and gas breakdown. Other processes will cause additional refractive index variations and the dominant limiting process depends on the particular experimental configuration.

A. Absorption

The single-photon absorption cross section is

$$\sigma^{(1)}(\omega) = \frac{\pi e^2 \eta \omega}{\hbar} |\langle f \, |z| \, g \rangle|^2 \, \rho(\omega). \tag{28}$$

Third-harmonic generation will most likely be done in relatively high-pressure gas cells and far off single-photon absorption resonances. Since the Lorentzian line shape decreases much slower off resonance than does the Gaussian and also characterizes pressure broadening,

$$\rho(\omega) = \frac{1}{\pi} \left\{ \frac{2\, \Omega_{fg}\, \omega \Delta\omega}{[\Omega_{fg}^2 - \omega^2]^2 + (\omega \Delta\omega)^2} \right\}, \tag{29}$$

where $\Delta\omega$ is the Lorentzian broadened full width at the half-power points.

The single-photon cross section may also be expressed

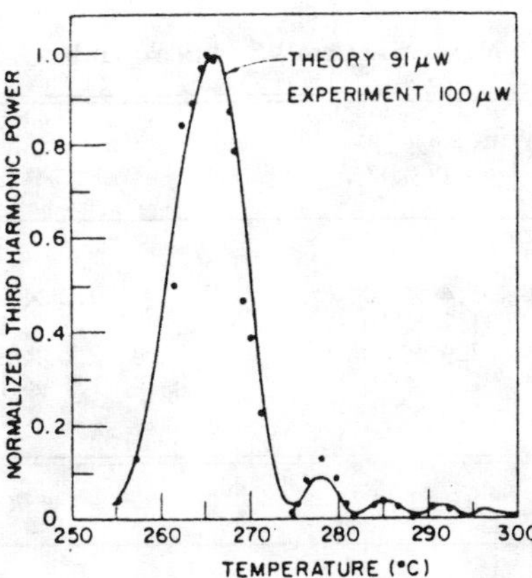

Fig. 10. Third-harmonic power output from rubidium vapor phase matched with xenon: theory and experiment.

in terms of the oscillator strength of the $g \to f$ transition. If we let $\omega = 2\pi c\nu$, where ν is in centimeter^{-1}, c is in centimeters/second, and use (29) for the line shape, the cross section far off line center becomes

$$\sigma^{(1)}(\omega) \cong 2r_e f_{of} \frac{\nu^2 \Delta\nu}{[\nu_{fo}^2 - \nu^2]^2}. \tag{30}$$

Measurements of the pressure-broadened linewidth of alkali gases in argon are tabulated by Ch'en and Takeo [13] and show that the line width is proportional to the relative density of the gas. Relative density is the pressure of the same number of atoms at 0°C; thus the pressure-broadened linewidth is proportional to the number of buffer gas atoms present.

More generally, the linewidth must include contributions from natural, or lifetime, broadening and from self-broadening effects. If the number of buffer gas atoms is R times the number of alkali atoms, where R is determined by the phase-matching criterion, the Lorentzian linewidth is

$$\Delta\nu = \Delta\nu_{\text{natural}} + \delta\nu_s N/N_0 + \delta\nu RN/N_0. \tag{31}$$

$\delta\nu$ is the pressure broadened, $\delta\nu_s$ is the self-broadened linewidth at standard temperature and pressure, and $N_0 = 2.69 \times 10^{19}$ atoms/cm^3. Values for $\Delta\nu_{\text{natural}}$, $\delta\nu_S$, and $\delta\nu$ are given in Table V for the absorption lines of the alkalies. The numbers for $\delta\nu$ enclosed in parentheses are estimates; the other numbers of $\delta\nu$ are taken from Ch'en and Takeo's tables for argon broadening and are only approximately correct for broadening with xenon. Oscillator strengths are taken from the sources referenced and do not necessarily correspond to those from which the matrix elements given in Table I were derived. There, for the sake of consistency, Anderson's calculations were used exclusively. The resonant wavelengths are from Landolt and Bornstein [14].

The natural width is calculated from the natural lifetime, or quenching time [18],

$$\tau_c = 1.51\left(\frac{g_f}{g_o}\right)\frac{\lambda_{fo}^2}{f_{of}}, \tag{32}$$

TABLE V
ABSORPTION LINE PARAMETERS

Element	Resonance (μ)	f	$\delta\nu_s$ (cm^{-1})	$\delta\nu^a$ (cm^{-1})	τ_c (s)	$\Delta\nu_N$ (cm^{-1})
Li [10]	0.6708	0.744	56.8	(0.72)	2.7×10^{-8}	1.9×10^{-4}
	0.3234	0.00428	0.10	(2.5)	1.1×10^{-6}	4.8×10^{-6}
	0.2742	0.00398	0.081	(2.5)	8.6×10^{-5}	6.2×10^{-6}
Na [15]	0.5892	0.982	42.7	0.72	1.6×10^{-8}	3.3×10^{-4}
	0.3303	0.0142	0.35	(2.5)	3.5×10^{-7}	1.5×10^{-5}
	0.2853	0.0022	0.046	(2.5)	1.7×10^{-6}	3.1×10^{-6}
K [15]	0.7676	1.04	59.0	1.01	2.5×10^{-8}	2.1×10^{-4}
	0.4045	0.0154	0.46	2.5	4.8×10^{-7}	1.1×10^{-5}
	0.3447	0.00277	0.071	(2.5)	2.0×10^{-6}	2.7×10^{-6}
Rb [16]	0.7948	0.395	69.6	0.627	2.4×10^{-8}	2.2×10^{-4}
	0.7800	0.805	69.6	0.855	2.3×10^{-8}	2.3×10^{-4}
	0.4216	0.00532	0.50	2.21	5.0×10^{-7}	1.1×10^{-5}
	0.4202	0.01068	0.50	2.56	5.0×10^{-7}	1.1×10^{-5}
	0.3592	0.000979	0.078	(2.56)	2.0×10^{-6}	2.7×10^{-6}
	0.3587	0.00196	0.078	(2.56)	2.0×10^{-6}	2.7×10^{-6}
Cs [17]	0.8944	0.394	78.1	(0.627)	3.1×10^{-8}	1.7×10^{-4}
	0.8521	0.814	76.9	(0.855)	2.7×10^{-8}	2.0×10^{-4}
	0.4593	0.00284	0.29	1.63	1.1×10^{-6}	4.8×10^{-6}
	0.4555	0.0174	0.88	2.22	3.5×10^{-7}	1.5×10^{-5}
	0.3890	0.000317	0.027	2.69	7.3×10^{-6}	7.3×10^{-7}
	0.3876	0.00349	0.15	2.69	1.3×10^{-6}	4.0×10^{-6}

[a] Values of $\delta\nu$ in parentheses are estimates; others are from Ch'en and Takeo [13].

by

$$\Delta\nu_N = \frac{1}{2\pi c\tau_c}. \tag{33}$$

g_g and g_f are degeneracies of the lower- and upper-energy levels and λ_{fg} is the transition wavelength in centimeters. Values for τ_c are included in Table V and are important for the saturation process discussed in the following section. The self-broadened linewidth $\delta\nu_s$ is calculated from the relation [19]

$$\delta\nu_s = \frac{3 \times 6^{1/2}}{4\pi} \frac{r_e \lambda_{fo} f_{of}}{g_f} N_0. \tag{34}$$

For convenience we will ignore the self-broadened and natural linewidths in (31) when calculating the pressure-broadened cross section. The error will not be large since typical values of R are greater than 100 and the xenon pressure-broadened linewidths are only approximate.

Table VI gives values of $\sigma^{(1)}(\omega)/N$ for tripling 1.064 and 0.6943 μ in the alkali vapors phase matched with xenon. Single-photon cross sections at the third harmonic, $\sigma^{(1)}(3\omega)/N$, and two-photon cross sections, $\sigma^{(2)}(\omega)/N$, are included as well. The single-photon cross section at the third harmonic corresponds to the absorption of the generated third harmonic. For tripling 0.6943 μ, $\sigma^{(1)}(3\omega)$ is derived from the continuum cross section and is assumed independent of N. The absorption coefficient is, of course, $\alpha = N\sigma L$, and forms an upper limit on the length and density of the gas cell.

Single-photon absorption to the continuum is of con-

TABLE VI

SINGLE- AND TWO-PHOTON ABSORPTION CROSS SECTIONS (σ IN cm^2, N IN ATOMS/cm^3, P/A IN W/cm^2)

Element	Ratio $N_{Xe}:N$	Phase Matched With Xe $\sigma^{(1)}(\omega)/N$	$\sigma^{(1)}(3\omega)/N$	$\sigma^{(2)}(\omega)/N$
		1.064–0.3547 μ		
Li	154	8.5×10^{-39}	5.4×10^{-39}	$9.2 \times 10^{-52} P/A$
Na	152	5.0×10^{-39}	1.3×10^{-38}	$1.8 \times 10^{-51} P/A$
K	326	9.6×10^{-38}	3.9×10^{-38}	$2.6 \times 10^{-49} P/A$
Rb	414	1.3×10^{-37}	1.8×10^{-37}	$1.1 \times 10^{-42} P/A$
Cs	658	5.7×10^{-37}	1.0×10^{-37}	$2.2 \times 10^{-46} P.A$

Element	Ratio $N_{Xe}:N$	$\sigma^{(1)}(\omega)/N$	$\sigma^{(1)}(3\omega)^{a}$	$\sigma^{(2)}(\omega)/N$
		0.6943–0.2314 μ		
Li	400	4.3×10^{-36}	2.5×10^{-18}	$2.2 \times 10^{-47} P/A$
Na	100	4.7×10^{-38}	8.0×10^{-20}	$8.3 \times 10^{-48} P/A$

[a] Continuum absorption cross section from Ditchburn [20] assumed independent of N.

cern if the third-harmonic frequency is above the ionization potential of the alkali atom, as is the case for tripling 0.6943 μ. A summary of measurements is presented by Ditchburn *et al.* [20]. It shows that the cross sections of the alkalies are typically less than 10^{-18} cm^2. Sodium, for example, has a cross section of 1.2×10^{-19} cm^2 at its ionization threshold. The cross section then drops to 2×10^{-20} at 0.1900 μ and rises slowly toward higher frequencies. This behavior is typical of alkalies and indicates that the generated third-harmonic signal will not be significantly absorbed if it is above the ionization energy. The Kuhn–Thomas sum rule predicts this low absorption since the sum of the discrete level oscillator strengths is very nearly 1 for all the alkalies.

At pressures of a few torr, the alkali metal vapors contain from 1 to 10 percent diatomic molecules. The absorption bands are diffuse and the value of the absorption cross sections in the IR and UV do not appear to have been determined.

Preliminary experimental measurements in our laboratory indicate, at least at pressures of a few torr for tripling of 1.064 μ in Na vapor, that molecular absorption should not be a problem. If the fundamental or third-harmonic frequency should fall in the middle of a molecular band, it is likely that the molecular absorption will bleach very rapidly and will not affect the refractive index as much as atomic absorption. The absence of knowledge of molecular absorption is a weak point of this paper and requires experimental study.

A derivation of the two-photon cross section to discrete levels is given by Bebb [21]. With the matrix elements in Bohr radii, the power density in watts/centimeters², and the resonant and incident energies in rydbergs (1 Ry = 109 737.31 cm^{-1}),

$$\sigma^{(2)}(\omega) = 4.597 \times 10^{-34} \cdot \left| \sum_{a_1} \frac{\langle f\,|z|\,a_1\rangle\langle a_1\,|z|\,g\rangle}{E_{a_1,g} - E} \right|^2 \omega\rho(2\omega)\,\frac{P}{A}\ \text{cm}^2. \quad (35)$$

The lineshape is again Lorentzian.

Values of the two-photon absorption cross section for tripling 1.064 and 0.6943 μ are given in Table VI. The linewidth used for these calculations is $\delta^{(2)}\nu = 2.7\ \text{cm}^{-1}$ and represents an approximation of the widths of the upper d and s levels. For typical conditions away from resonances, two-photon absorption can be ignored.

Morton [22] has derived multiple-photon ionization transition probabilities for the alkalies for incident wavelengths of 1.059, 0.6943, 0.5295, and 0.3472 μ. The multiple-photon absorption cross section is found from these transition probabilities by the relation

$$\sigma^{(q)} = \frac{q\hbar\omega W}{P/A} \quad (36)$$

where q is the number of photons absorbed and W is the transition probability in second^{-1}. Values for $\sigma^{(q)}$ are given in Table VII. It is likely that multiphoton ionization will be the dominant process that limits the allowable power density, and at typical pressures and cell lengths this ionization will limit this density to about 10^{10} or 10^{11} W/cm^2. Once high efficiency is reached, multiple-photon ionization caused by the generated third-harmonic radiation may further restrict the allowable incident power density.

B. Saturation

The energy density that is applied in a time less than the quenching time and that reduces the ground state population by e^{-1} is termed the saturation energy density:

$$J_{sat}/A = \frac{\hbar\Omega_{fg}}{2\sigma^{(1)}(\omega)}. \quad (37)$$

If the energy is applied in a time longer than the quenching time τ_c, then the pulse length is no longer of importance and the saturation power density becomes

$$P_{sat}/A = \frac{\hbar\Omega_{fg}}{2\sigma^{(1)}(\omega)\tau_c}. \quad (38)$$

The saturation energy density can be written in terms of

TABLE VII
MULTIPLE-PHOTON IONIZATION CROSS SECTIONS[a]

	1.059 μ	0.6943 μ	0.5295 μ	0.3472 μ
Li	$6.8 \times 10^{-66}\ (P/A)^4$	$7.8 \times 10^{-50}\ (P/A)^3$	$6.4 \times 10^{-42}\ (P/A)^2$	$1.9 \times 10^{-30}\ (P/A)$
Na	$2.2 \times 10^{-65}\ (P/A)^4$	$3.4 \times 10^{-40}\ (P/A)^2$	$6.3 \times 10^{-41}\ (P/A)^2$	$3.2 \times 10^{-30}\ (P/A)$
K	$1.7 \times 10^{-52}\ (P/A)^3$	$3.3 \times 10^{-41}\ (P/A)^2$	$1.4 \times 10^{-30}\ (P/A)$	$5.8 \times 10^{-29}\ (P/A)$
Rb	$7.5 \times 10^{-51}\ (P/A)^3$	$2.7 \times 10^{-39}\ (P/A)^2$	$1.8 \times 10^{-30}\ (P/A)$	$1.9 \times 10^{-30}\ (P/A)$
Cs	$3.7 \times 10^{-49}\ (P/A)^3$	$3.9 \times 10^{-39}\ (P/A)^2$	$3.8 \times 10^{-30}\ (P/A)$	$3.8 \times 10^{-28}\ (P/A)$

[a] From Morton [22].

the cross-section off line center given in (29):

$$J_{sat}/A = \frac{hc[\nu_{fg}^2 - \nu^2]^2}{4\, r_e f_{gf}\, \nu \Delta\nu}. \tag{39}$$

The linewidth depends on the total density of atoms; if it is below about 10^{16} atoms/cm³, then the natural linewidth is to be used (see Table V); for higher pressures, the expression of (31) gives the linewidth. Pressure broadening is generally anticipated, so

$$J_{sat}/A = 4.74 \times 10^8 \frac{[\nu_{fg}^2 - \nu^2]^2}{f_{gf}\, \nu \delta\nu R N}\ \text{J/cm}^2. \tag{40}$$

The saturation energy density is maximized when the total density of atoms is so low that the natural linewidth dominates. The first two columns of Table VIII give this maximum saturation energy density and J_{sat}/A as given by (40) for tripling of 1.064- and 0.6493-μ radiation.

Though J_{sat}/A is comfortably large, a more severe limitation is imposed on the allowable incident energy density by the tolerance on the phase-matching condition and by thermal defocusing. For $J/A \ll J_{sat}/A$, the fractional variation in atomic population δN is

$$\frac{\delta N}{N} = \frac{J/A}{J_{sat}/A}. \tag{41}$$

We may accept a half-power tolerance on the phase-matching condition $\delta(\Delta k)$ of

$$\delta(\Delta k)_{alk} L = \pi. \tag{42}$$

The coherence length L_c of the alkali vapor is defined as

$$\Delta k_{alk} L_c = \pi. \tag{43}$$

Assuming that only the alkali vapor experiences saturation and noting that both $\delta(\Delta k_{alk})$ and Δk_{alk} are proportional to the atomic population, then

$$\frac{\delta(\Delta k_{alk})}{\Delta k_{alk}} = \frac{\delta N}{N} = \frac{L_c}{L}. \tag{44}$$

Equation (44) is somewhat in error since it neglects the contribution of excited atoms to the refractive index. This error depends on the particular alkali and incident wavelength and is generally less than a factor of 2. Combining the above equations, we obtain the maximum allowable incident energy density that will not break the phase-matching condition as

TABLE VIII
SATURATION DENSITY IN PHASE-MATCHED GAS MIXTURES (J/A IN J/cm², N IN ATOMS/cm³, L IN cm)

Element	Maximum J_{sat}/A	$(J_{sat}/A) \times N$	$(J_{phase\ matching}/A) \times N^2$
	1.064–0.3547 μ		
Li	2.37×10^6	1.09×10^{19}	$6.39 \times 10^{35}/L$
Na	2.29×10^5	1.88×10^{18}	$1.09 \times 10^{36}/L$
K	5.64×10^4	9.77×10^{17}	$2.67 \times 10^{34}/L$
Rb	4.14×10^4	7.14×10^{17}	$1.54 \times 10^{34}/L$
Cs	1.77×10^4	1.62×10^{18}	$2.22 \times 10^{33}/L$
	0.6943–0.2314 μ		
Li	1.84×10^3	3.28×10^{16}	$1.67 \times 10^{32}/L$
Na	2.47×10^4	2.99×10^{18}	$5.76 \times 10^{34}/L$
K	8.05×10^3	—	—
Rb	1.03×10^4	—	—
Cs	3.11×10^4	—	—

[a] Assumes natural linewidth in (39).

$$J_{phase\ matching}/A = \frac{L_c}{L}(J_{sat}/A). \tag{45}$$

Values for this quantity are given in the third column of Table VIII. Since both L_c and J_{sat} vary as $(1/N)$, $J_{phase\ matching}/A$ varies as $1/N^2$. In general, this quantity will impose the most severe limitation on the allowable incident energy density.

Saturation of the alkali metal vapor may also lead to thermal focusing or defocusing of the incident beam. For a Gaussain beam profile the variation of refractive index across the beam is

$$n(x) \cong n_0 - \delta n + \delta n \frac{2x^2}{w_0^2}, \tag{46}$$

where w_0 is the beam radius and $\delta n = n_0(J/A)/(J_{sat}/A)$. We assume a beam with its waist at the center of the cell and a complex beam parameter q_0 [23]. The ray transfer matrix is

$$\begin{bmatrix} A & B \\ C & D \end{bmatrix} = \begin{bmatrix} 1 & L \\ \frac{4\delta n L}{w_0^2} & 1 \end{bmatrix}, \tag{47}$$

which yields a q_0 at the cell exit of

$$q_1 = \frac{q_0 + (L/2)}{(2\delta n L/w_0^2)q_0 + 1}. \tag{48}$$

The beam waist at the cell exit is then

$$w_1^2(L/2) = \left(\frac{\lambda}{\pi}\right)^2 \left[\frac{L^2/4 + (\pi^2 w_0^4/\lambda^2)}{w_0^2 - \delta n L^2}\right]. \tag{49}$$

Normalization to the beam waist in absence of thermal defocusing ($\delta n = 0$) gives the ratio

$$\frac{w_1^2(L/2)_{\text{focusing}}}{w_1^2(L/2)_{\text{no focusing}}} = \frac{1}{(w_0^2 - \delta n L^2)/(1/w_0^2)}. \tag{50}$$

If we assume that a rough criterion for significant thermal defocusing is that this ratio = 2, then

$$\delta n_{\text{allowable}} = \frac{w_0^2}{2L^2}, \tag{51}$$

and

$$\frac{\delta N}{N} = \frac{\delta n}{n} = \frac{w_0^2}{2L^2 n} = \frac{3L_c}{L^2}\frac{w_0^2}{\lambda}. \tag{52}$$

For confocal focusing, $w_0^2 = (L\lambda/2\pi)$ and

$$\frac{\delta N}{N} = \frac{3}{2\pi}\left(\frac{L_c}{L}\right), \tag{53}$$

which differs from the tolerance imposed by the breaking of phase matching (44) by a factor of $3/2\pi$.

C. Breakdown

Gas breakdown at high optical intensities appears to be a two-step process. Initially a small number of free electrons are created in the focal volume through multiple-photon ionization. These electrons then gain energy through inverse bremsstrahlung absorption of radiation and collide with atoms to create more free electrons in an avalanche process that finally leads to an opaque plasma.

Kishi *et al.* [24] have found that free electrons are created at much lower power intensities than observed breakdown thresholds, indicating that only the avalanche process need be analyzed. The theoretical threshold power density for inverse bremsstrahlung behaves as [24], [25]

$$\left(\frac{P}{A}\right)_{\text{breakdown}} \approx \frac{\omega^2}{N}\left(\frac{1}{t_p} + \frac{1}{\tau_b}\right) \tag{54}$$

where t_p is the laser pulse length. The steady-state response time τ_b is determined by whatever competing loss process is dominant: at high pressures, electrons lose energy from elastic collisions and at low pressures the electrons diffuse very rapidly away from the focal volume. Observations of breakdown in air by Wang and Davis [26] yield τ_b on the order of $\frac{1}{2}$ ns. Krasyuk *et al.* [27], however, find that their results with picosecond pulses in inert gases scale approximately by $1/t_p$ to measurements done with 30-ns lasers.

Rizzo and Klewe [28] have measured the breakdown thresholds of Rb and Cs. Although the vapor densities were low, they observed a behavior characteristic of the avalanche processes. Their results show that a 65-ns ruby laser pulse breaks down 10^{16} atoms/cm^3 at a focal density of about 10^{10} W/cm^2, and that breakdown threshold varies as $1/N$. It seems likely that with picosecond pulses, $t_p \ll \tau_b$ and that breakdown is determined by energy density (as opposed to power density). Furthermore, the maximum energy density that is allowed by the stringent condition on the breaking of phase matching will almost certainly be less than that which will cause gas breakdown.

TABLE IX
QUADRATIC KERR SUSCEPTIBILITY

Element	$\chi^{(3)}(\omega)$ (ESU)	Kerr Effect[a] (W/cm^2)
	1.064–0.3547 μ	
Li	6.7×10^{-34}	2.0×10^{12}
Na	8.2×10^{-34}	1.6×10^{12}
K	1.7×10^{-32}	8.0×10^{10}
Rb	6.9×10^{-32}	2.0×10^{10}
Cs	-2.1×10^{-31}	6.3×10^{9}
	0.6943–0.2314 μ	
Li	3.2×10^{-32}	2.8×10^{10}
Na	6.3×10^{-32}	1.4×10^{10}
K	-2.8×10^{-32}	3.2×10^{10}
Rb	-3.0×10^{-32}	3.0×10^{10}
Cs	1.5×10^{-32}	6.0×10^{10}

[a] Assumes 10^{16} atoms/cm^3 and a 1-m cell.

D. Quadratic Kerr Effect

The contribution of the third-order nonlinear susceptibility to the polarization at the driving frequency causes a change in refractive index that may also break phase matching and cause focusing or defocusing of the incident laser beam. The third-order polarization at ω is derived similarly to the third-harmonic polarization of (3) and leads to a variation of the refractive index as a function of incident power density given by

$$\delta n = \frac{\eta N \chi^{(3)}(\omega)(P/A)}{4\epsilon_0}. \tag{55}$$

Given N in atoms/cubic centimeter, χ in ESU, and P/A in watts/square centimeters, the variation of index is

$$\delta n = 1.316 \times 10^{-8} N\chi^{(3)}(\omega)(P/A). \tag{56}$$

Again we require $\delta(\Delta k)L \leq \pi$, and thus

$$\delta n \leq \frac{\lambda}{6L}. \tag{57}$$

Values of $\chi^{(3)}(\omega)$ for 1.064- and 0.6943-μ upconversion are given in the first column of Table IX. The second column gives the power density that will cause difficulty according to the criterion of (57). An atom density of 10^{16} atoms/cm^3 and a cell length of 1 m are assumed. Positive values of $\chi^{(3)}(\omega)$ indicate self-focusing (as opposed to defocusing) and will probably not cause a reduction in third-harmonic efficiency.

V. Optimization

If limiting processes are neglected, the third-harmonic conversion efficiency [(17) and (18)] varies as the square of

TABLE X

LIMITING ATOM DENSITIES FOR TRIPLING—PHASE MATCHING BY MIXING WITH XE IS ASSUMED
(N IN ATOMS/cm^3, L IN cm, J/A IN J/cm^2, P/A IN W/cm^2)

Element	N Single-Photon Absorption (ω)	N Single-Photon Absorption (3ω)	N Two-Photon Absorption	N Kerr Effect	N Phase Matching
			1.064–0.3547 μ		
Li	$5.8 \times 10^{18}/L^{1/2}$	$7.3 \times 10^{18}/L^{1/2}$	$1.78 \times 10^{25}(A/LP)^{1/2}$	$1.88 \times 10^{30}(A/LP)$	$7.95 \times 10^{17}(A/LJ)^{1/2}$
Na	$7.6 \times 10^{18}/L^{1/2}$	$4.7 \times 10^{18}/L^{1/2}$	$1.26 \times 10^{26}(A/LP)^{1/2}$	$1.39 \times 10^{30}(A/LP)$	$1.05 \times 10^{18}(A/LP)^{1/2}$
K	$1.7 \times 10^{18}/L^{1/2}$	$2.7 \times 10^{18}/L^{1/2}$	$1.05 \times 10^{24}(A/LP)^{1/2}$	$7.89 \times 10^{28}(A/LP)$	$1.63 \times 10^{17}(A/LJ)^{1/2}$
Rb	$1.5 \times 10^{18}/L^{1/2}$	$1.3 \times 10^{18}/L^{1/2}$	$1.63 \times 10^{23}(A/LP)^{1/2}$	$1.88 \times 10^{28}(A/LP)$	$1.24 \times 10^{17}(A/LJ)^{1/2}$
Cs	$7.1 \times 10^{17}/L^{1/2}$	$1.7 \times 10^{18}/L^{1/2}$	$3.68 \times 10^{22}(A/LP)^{1/2}$	$6.01 \times 10^{27}(A/LP)$	$4.65 \times 10^{16}(A/LJ)^{1/2}$
			0.6943–0.2314 μ		
Li	$2.6 \times 10^{17}/L^{1/2}$	$1.2 \times 10^{17}/L^{a}$	$1.19 \times 10^{23}(A/LP)^{1/2}$	$2.71 \times 10^{28}(A/LP)$	$1.30 \times 10^{16}(A/LJ)^{1/2}$
Na	$2.5 \times 10^{18}/L^{1/2}$	$3.8 \times 10^{18}/L^{a}$	$1.87 \times 10^{23}(A/LP)^{1/2}$	$1.33 \times 10^{28}(A/LP)$	$2.4 \times 10^{17}(A/LJ)^{1/2}$

[a] Continuum loss: cross section assumed independent of N.

susceptibility, power density, cell length, and density of atoms. The maximum incident power density is determined by multiphoton ionization and is in the range of 10^{10}–10^{12} W/cm^2 for tripling in the alkali metals. For confocal focusing in a cell of length L ($A = L\lambda/4$), the length of the cell is an invariant with regard to conversion efficiency. For a laser with a given peak input power the cell should be chosen sufficiently long that with confocal focusing, the multiphoton ionization power density is not exceeded. For high-power lasers this may not be possible unless multipass techniques are employed. The limit on the maximum atom density is now determined by the most severe of the following: single-photon absorption at the fundamental, single-photon absorption at the third harmonic, two-photon absorption, Kerr effect, or, as will most often be the case, by the requirement that the incident energy density not destroy the phase-matching condition. Table X gives the value of the maximum atom density as determined by each of the above processes for tripling of 1.064- and 0.6943-μ radiation. The limit for each process is calculated assuming xenon phase matching at the required ratio. Laser pulses of length shorter than the atomic decay or quenching time are assumed.

As an example, assume an incident 1.064-μ pulse with a peak power of 10^8 W and a pulse length of 10^{-11} s. Assume that Na is to be used for tripling and that $P/A = 10^{11}$ W/cm^2 is the maximum power density allowed by multiple-photon (five) ionization (Table VII). For a 50-cm path length, the confocal area at 1.064 μ is 1.36×10^{-3} cm^2 and thus confocal focusing is just possible. From Table X, the maximum atom densities as determined for each of the limiting processes are as follows: single-photon absorption at (ω), $N_{max} = 1.07 \times 10^{18}$ atoms/cm^3; single-photon absorption at (3ω), $N_{max} = 6.65 \times 10^{17}$ atoms/cm^3; two-photon absorption, $N_{max} = 6.5 \times 10^{18}$ atoms/cm^3; Kerr effect, $N_{max} = 4.3 \times 10^{17}$ atoms/cm^3; and phase matching, $N_{max} = 1.71 \times 10^{17}$ atoms/cm^3. The most stringent tolerance is imposed by the joule tolerance on the phase-matching condition; and thus we take $N = 1.71 \times 10^{17}$ atoms/cm^3. At this pressure the cell is about 145 coherence lengths long and requires that temperature be constant to within about ±0.6°C. For these conditions, (17) yields a conversion efficiency of 7.1 percent.

Table XI gives the maximum conversion efficiency, based on the joule limitation on the phase-matching condition, for each of the alkalies for 1.064- and 0.6943-μ third-harmonic generation. The first column assumes confocal focusing; thus cell length and area do not appear and the conversion efficiency depends only on the square of the incident power divided by the number of joules incident in an atomic decay time. The second column gives the maximum conversion efficiency in terms of incident power density, energy density, and cell length. The atom densities used to obtain these conversion efficiencies are given in the fourth column of Table X. The first column of Table XI applies under power-limited conditions. The second column applies once the limiting allowable power density is reached. For example, if we assume that five-photon ionization in sodium will allow a maximum incident power density of 1×10^{11} W/cm^2, then a 10-ps pulse (1 J/cm^2) in a 1-m-long cell will yield a conversion efficiency of 19 percent. Fig. 11 plots necessary power versus pulse length for 50-percent conversion.

VI. CONCLUSION

This paper has presented a theoretical study of third-harmonic generation in alkali metal vapors. Principal results of the analyses include the calculation of the third-order susceptibility as a function of wavelength for each of the alkalies, a derivation of the xenon buffer gas to alkali vapor mixing ratios required for phase matching, and a detailed study of the various limitations on efficient third-harmonic generation. It has been shown that the principal limitation process will be the breaking of phase matching caused by the change of the index of refraction due to absorption. Generally, lasers with 10-ps pulses will require $10^8 - 10^9$ W peak power to achieve 50-percent conversion to the third harmonic.

A number of possibilities exist which may allow the energy density that may be passed through metal vapor

TABLE XI

MAXIMUM CONVERSION EFFICIENCIES AS LIMITED BY PHASE MATCHING

Element	Maximum Conversion Efficiency (Confocal Focusing-Power Limited)	Maximum Conversion Efficiency (Power Density Limited)
	1.064–0.3547 μ	
Li	$4.1 \times 10^{-22}(P^2/J)$	$1.09 \times 10^{-26}(P/A)^2L/(J/A)$
Na	$7.1 \times 10^{-21}(P^2/J)$	$1.89 \times 10^{-25}(P/A)^2L/(J/A)$
K	$7.6 \times 10^{-23}(P^2/J)$	$2.02 \times 10^{-27}(P/A)^2L/(J/A)$
Rb	$2.4 \times 10^{-20}(P^2/J)$	$6.38 \times 10^{-25}(P/A)^2L/(J/A)$
Cs	$1.3 \times 10^{-20}(P^2/J)$	$3.46 \times 10^{-25}(P/A)^2L/(J/A)$
	0.6943-0.2314 μ	
Li	$2.2 \times 10^{-24}(P^2/J)$	$3.82 \times 10^{-29}(P/A)^2L/(J/A)$
Na	$9.1 \times 10^{-22}(P^2/J)$	$1.58 \times 10^{-26}(P/A)^2L/(J/A)$

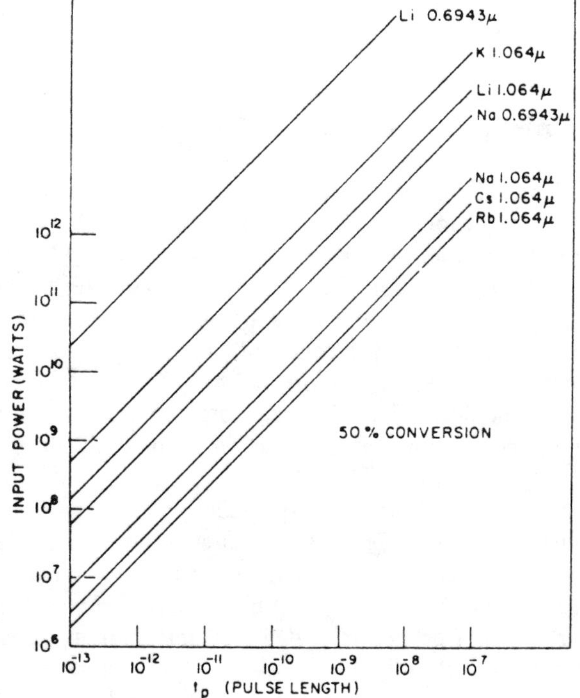

Fig. 11. Power necessary for 50-percent conversion versus pulse length for the alkalies.

tripling cells to be substantially increased. These include the following.

1) The reduction of the phase-matching ratio by replacing the inert gas with a media with higher refractive index per atom; for example Cd or Hg.

2) The use of a molecular quenching agent such as N_2 or H_2 to reduce the atomic decay time (for example, at ten atmospheres of nitrogen, the decay time of sodium is reduced by about a factor of 100 [30]; this should at least allow the use of a train of picosecond pulses instead of only a single pulse).

3) The use of multipass techniques combined with tight-focusing-type phase matching. This would allow operation at very low pressures with the associated natural linewidth, and as shown in Table VIII, yield very large saturation densities.

4) Finally, Bjorklund has suggested the use of discrete periodic phase matching. In this technique, cells of positively and negatively dispersive media are alternately spaced and their pressures independently adjusted. Here again, the metal vapor cell could be operated at very low pressure with very high energy saturation density.

The procedures developed in this paper can also apply to sequential third-harmonic steps further into the ultraviolet by the selection of other materials similar to those discussed, but having appropriate resonances in the ultraviolet rather than the visible spectral region. In recent months third-harmonic generation from 5320 to 1773 Å and from 3547 to 1182 Å has been obtained in cadmium and argon mixtures [29]. It is probable that this system has a significantly higher energy saturation density than does the alkali metal vapor system. It is possible to envision cascaded harmonic generators, possibly all within one heat pipe oven, leading to the generation of very short wavelengths. A four-stage system, for example, would yield 132 Å from a 1.064-m source. Although a system of this type would be complex, its output radiation will maintain many of the desirable features of the original radiation. It would thus be nearly diffraction limited, narrow band, polarized, and of picosecond duration.

ACKNOWLEDGMENT

The authors would like to express gratitude for many helpful discussions with A. E. Siegman, G. C. Bjorklund, A. H. Kung, and particularly J. F. Young. Experimental work done by the latter three was used to verify the theory, and the fine job of computer programming by L. B. Wigton was essential for the numerical results.

REFERENCES

[1] J. F. Ward and G. H. C. New, "Optical third harmonic generation in gases by a focused laser beam," *Phys. Rev.*, vol. 185, p. 57, 1969.

[2] J. A. Armstrong, N. Bloembergen, J. Ducuing, and P. S. Pershan, "Interactions between light waves in a nonlinear dielectric," *Phys. Rev.*, vol. 127, p. 1918, 1962.

[3] S. E. Harris and R. B. Miles, "Proposed third harmonic generation in phase-matched metal vapors," *Appl. Phys. Lett.*, vol. 19, p. 385, 1971.

[4] J. F. Young *et al.*, "Third harmonic generation in phase-matched Rb vapor," *Phys. Rev. Lett.*, vol. 27, p. 1551, 1971.

[5] L. I. Schiff, *Quantum Mechanics*, 3rd ed. New York: McGraw-Hill, 1968, p. 417.

[6] J. C. Slater, *Quantum Theory of Atomic Structure*. New York: McGraw-Hill, 1960, vol. I, ch. 6, vol. II, ch. 25.

[7] D. R. Bates and A. Damgaard, "The calculation of the absolute strengths of spectral lines," *Phil. Trans. Roy. Soc. London*, vol. A242, p. 101, 1949.

[8] H. B. Bebb, "Quantitative theory of the two-photon ionization of the alkali atoms," *Phys. Rev.*, vol. 149, p. 25, 1966.

[9] E. M. Anderson and V. A. Zilitis, "Oscillator strengths for sodium and potassium atoms calculated by a semiempirical method," *Opt. Spectrosc. (USSR)*, vol. 16, p. 99, 1964.

[10] —— "Semiempirical calculation of oscillator strengths for lithium, rubidium, and cesium atoms," *Opt. Spectrosc. (USSR)*, vol. 16, p. 211, 1964.

[11] J. Koch, "On the refraction and dispersion of the noble gases krypton and xenon," *Kungl. Fysiografiska Sallskapets I Lund Forhandlingar*, vol. 19, p. 173, 1949.

[12] W. H. Glenn, "Second-harmonic generation by picosecond optical pulses," *IEEE J. Quantum Electron.*, vol. QE-5, pp. 284–290, June 1969.

[13] S. Ch'en and M. Takeo, "Broadening and shift of spectral lines due to the presence of foreign gases," *Rev. Mod. Phys.*, vol. 29, p. 20, 1957.

[14] Landolt and Bornstein, *Zahlenwerte und Funktionen aus Physik*, vol. I, pt. 1, 6th ed. Berlin, Germany: Springer, 1950.

[15] W. L. Wiese, M. W. Smith, and B. M. Miles, N.B.S. Rep. NSRDA-NBS 22, vol. II, 1969.

[16] G. I. Goldberg, *Izv. Gl. Astron. Obser. Pulkove*, vol. 156, p. 126, 1956; results also given by Anderson [10].

[17] P. M. Stone, "Cesium oscillator strengths," *Phys. Rev.*, vol. 127, p. 1151, 1962.

[18] A. C. G. Mitchell and M. W. Zemansky, *Resonance Radiation and Excited Atoms*. New York: Cambridge, 1961.

[19] W. W. Houston, "Resonance broadening of spectral lines," *Phys. Rev.*, vol. 54, p. 884, 1938.

[20] R. W. Ditchburn, P. J. Jutsun, and G. B. Marr, "The continuous absorption of light in alkali-metal vapours," *Proc. Roy. Soc.*, vol. 219, p. 89, 1953.

[21] H. B. Bebb and A. Gold, "Multiphoton ionization of hydrogen and rare-gas atoms," *Phys. Rev.*, vol. 143, p. 1, 1966.

[22] V. M. Morton, "Multi-photon absorption in monatomic gases," *Proc. Phys. Soc.*, vol. 92, p. 301, 1967.

[23] H. Kogelnik and T. Li, "Laser beams and resonators," *Appl. Opt.*, vol. 5, p. 1550, 1966.

[24] K. Kishi, K. Sawada, T. Okuda, and Y. Matsuoka, "Two photon ionization of cesium and sodium vapors," *J. Phys. Soc. Japan*, vol. 29, p. 1053, 1970.

[25] Ya. B. Zel'dovitch and Yu. P. Raizer, "Cascade ionization of a gas by a light pulse," *Sov. Phys.—JETP*, vol. 20, p. 772, 1965.

[26] C. C. Wang and L. I. Davis, Jr., "New observations of dielectric breakdown in air induced by a focused Nd^{3+}-glass laser with various pulse widths," *Phys. Rev. Lett.*, vol. 26, p. 822, 1971.

[27] I. K. Krasyuk, P. P. Pashinin, and A. M. Prokhorov, "Investigation of breakdown in argon and helium produced by a picosecond ruby laser light pulse," *Sov. Phys.—JETP*, vol. 31, p. 860, 1970.

[28] J. E. Rizzo and R. C. Klewe, "Optical breakdown in metal vapours," *Brit. J. Appl. Phys.*, vol. 17, p. 1137, 1966.

[29] A. H. Kung, J. F. Young, G. C. Bjorklund, and S. E. Harris, "Generation of vacuum ultraviolet radiation in phase matched Cd vapor," to be published.

[30] P. K. Kibble, C. Copley, and L. Krause, "Inelastic collisions between excited alkali atoms and molecules. II. The quenching of sodium resonance radiation by N_2, H_2, HD, and D_2," *Phys. Rev.*, vol. 159, p. 11, 1967.

Tunable Coherent Vacuum-Ultraviolet Generation in Atomic Vapors*

R. T. Hodgson, P. P. Sorokin, and J. J. Wynne
IBM Thomas J. Watson Research Center, Yorktown Heights, New York 10598
(Received 26 December 1973)

Two tunable dye lasers have been used to generate coherent radiation at a tunable sum frequency in the vacuum-ultraviolet spectral region. Spectral ranges of ~3500 cm^{-1} around 1895 Å and ~1200 cm^{-1} around 1798 Å have been covered. These ranges may easily be extended. Large (~$\times 10^4$) enhancements of $2\nu_1+\nu_2$ sum mixing are seen when $2\nu_1$ is tuned to a double-quantum allowed transition from the ground state in Sr vapor.

The original work by Harris and co-workers[1] on extending nonlinear optical-mixing methods into the vacuum-ultraviolet (vuv) spectral range has raised great interest in such techniques. We have employed tunable dye lasers to take advantage of the resonant enhancements of the nonlinearities in atomic vapors in order to generate easily detectable, tunable, coherent, vuv radiation via third-order sum mixing. With the use of several combinations of dyes, spectrally narrow vuv beams were generated and continuously tuned from 1778 to 1817 Å (a range of ~1200 cm^{-1}) and from 1833 to 1957 Å (a range of ~3500 cm^{-1}). Tunable coherent radiation in this range will be useful for a variety of absorption and resonance fluorescence studies in simple atoms and molecules.

The resonant enhancements occur when the input lasers are tuned to double-quantum transitions. With a single dye laser, we have observed that the intensity of third harmonic generation (THG) in Sr vapor increases by many orders of magnitude when the fundamental frequency is tuned to the half-frequency of a two-photon allowed transition. Since only two photons are needed for this resonance, one is free to mix in the light from a second dye laser with no constraint on its frequency, thereby generating tunable output at the frequency $2\nu_1+\nu_2$, where ν_1 is the frequency of the fixed laser at the half-frequency of the double-quantum transition, and ν_2 is the frequency of the tunable laser.

A block diagram of the experiment is shown in Fig. 1. The Molectron UV-1000 nitrogen laser produces ~1-MW, 7.5-nsec long pulses at ~15 pulses/sec. The collinear, orthogonally polarized dye laser beams leaving the Glan prism have powers between 15 and 100 kW each. The dye lasers incorporated optics[2] that narrowed the spectral bandwidths to ~0.1 and ~1 cm^{-1}, respectively. The beams were focused, via a 33-cm focal-length lens, into the center of a simple Sr vapor cell made of nickel and heated to the 800–900°C range. Helium gas at pressures from 100 to 700 Torr and two $\frac{1}{4}$-in. apertures placed 25 cm apart (the approximate length of the hot zone) prevented the Sr vapor from diffusing to, and coating, the Pyrex input and LiF output windows. The output light could be observed either directly or through a McPherson model 225 vuv spectrometer using an EMR 541GX-08-18 solar-blind photomultiplier. This detector has no response to direct beams from the dye lasers with $\lambda > 4500$ Å.

The importance of resonant enhancement was dramatically illustrated when a single, linearly polarized beam from a sodium-fluorescein dye laser was tuned from 5337 to 5710 Å. The vuv frequency-tripled light displayed enormous resonant enhancements—the signal increasing ~10^4 times from its weak, off-resonance value—at four wavelengths: 5380, 5409, 5605, and 5681 Å. These wavelengths correspond to exact half-frequencies of the following doubly excited, even-parity states of Sr: $(5p^2)\ ^1S_0$, $^1D_2$, $^3P_2$, and $^3P_0$, respectively. An energy-level diagram of Sr showing one such $5p^2$ state is given in Fig. 2. Strong THG was also observed when a rhodamine 6-G laser was tuned to 5757 Å, the half-frequency of the singly excited $5s5d\ ^1D_2$ state. Smaller resonant enhancements were noted when a 7-diethylamino-4-methylcoumarin laser was tuned to the half-frequencies of the $5s8s\ ^1S_0$, $5s7d\ ^1D_2$, $5s9s$

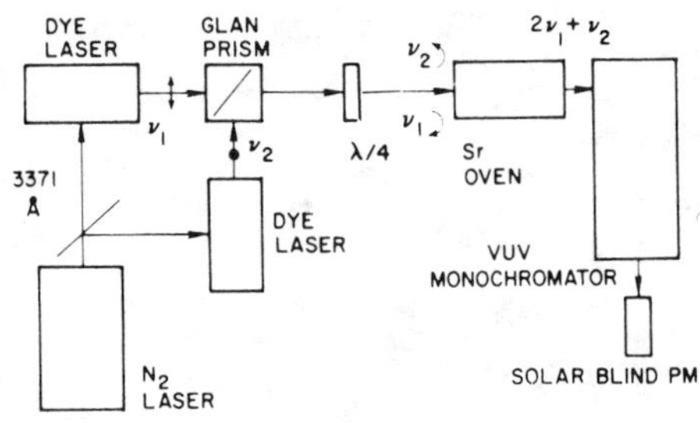

FIG. 1. Block diagram of the experiment.

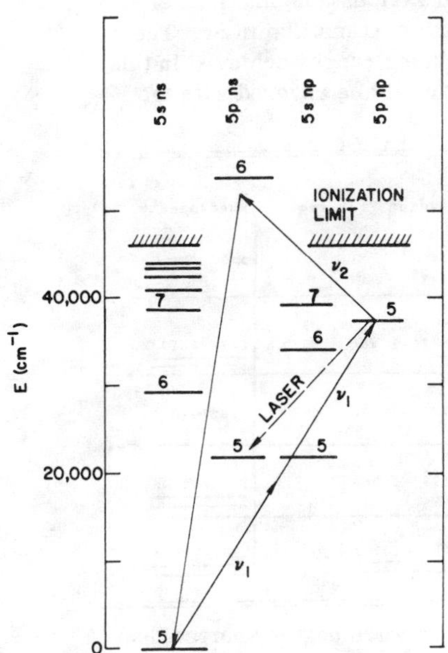

FIG. 2. Partial energy-level diagram of Sr atoms, showing resonantly enhanced tunable $2\nu_1+\nu_2$ generation using a $5p^2$ intermediate state.

$^1S_0$, and $5s8d\,^1D_2$ states. The shortest vuv wavelength obtained in this way was 1550 Å.

Using light at 5757 Å for THG, the vuv signal increased about 5 times when a few hundred Torr of xenon gas was added to the Sr vapor maintained at ~10 Torr. The addition of more Xe resulted in a sharp decrease of the vuv signal. We attribute this behavior to the dependence of the coherence length on the Xe pressure.[1]

By means of a simple technique to eliminate THG, a single-frequency tunable vuv light source was made using two dye lasers in the configuration of Fig. 1. Circularly polarized light cannot be frequency tripled in isotropic media since angular momentum would not be conserved.[3] A linearly polarized dye laser (ν_1) was tuned to 5757 Å and the THG signal was nulled using a $\lambda/4$ plate to convert the light to circular polarization. A second input tunable dye laser (ν_2) was then added collinearly by means of the Glan prism. The $\lambda/4$ plate converted some part of this light to circular polarization in the opposite sense, allowing strong vuv generation at $2\nu_1+\nu_2$. Tuning ν_2 sweeps the output at $2\nu_1+\nu_2$ over a tuning range as wide as that of ν_2. This tuning was verified for various combinations of dyes with the use of the vuv monochromator and also, in the case of direct photomultiplier detection, by sweeping the generated output wavelength over various known absorption lines such as one in CH_3I at 1927 Å.[4]

In Table I we present results for the tuning ranges we have covered. Table I also shows the tuning ranges to be expected through the use of other combinations of four commonly used dyes.[5] In each case, one laser is fixed at a double-quantum resonance while the other is tuned over its complete tuning range.

The nature of the resonant enhancement of the nonlinearity may be easily understood by considering the nonlinear susceptibility, $\chi^{(3)}$, which describes the sum mixing of the type $\nu_3=2\nu_1+\nu_2$. The nonlinear susceptibility may be expressed as[6]

$$\chi_{ijkl}{}^{(3)}\propto\sum_{\substack{g,m\\n,o}}N_g\frac{\langle g|\mu_i(3)|o\rangle\langle o|\mu_j(2)|n\rangle\langle n|\mu_k(1)|m\rangle\langle m|\mu_l(1)|g\rangle}{(\nu_{og}-\nu_3)(\nu_{ng}-2\nu_1)(\nu_{mg}-\nu_1)} \qquad (1)$$

plus the sum of similar terms with the frequencies permuted. The summation in Eq. (1) is taken over all states of the nonlinear medium. N_g is the density of occupied states in the quantum state g, and $\langle n|\mu_k(\alpha)|m\rangle$ is the dipole matrix element of the kth component of $\mu(\alpha)$ between states m and n, where $\mu(\alpha)$ is the dipole operator component parallel to the input electric field at ν_α. In the frequency denominators, ν_{ng} is the energy difference (in units of frequency) between states n and g. Equation (1) shows the resonant enhancement which may be obtained by setting $2\nu_1$ equal to ν_{ng}. The use of a two-photon resonance has important advantages.[7] If ν_1, ν_2, or ν_3 is set equal to a resonance frequency, $\chi^{(3)}$ will be resonantly enhanced but the input light will be strongly absorbed. Similarly, if ν_3 equals a resonance frequency, the output light at the sum frequency is absorbed. In addition, it is hard to phase match[1,8] if ν_1, ν_2, or ν_3 is close to an allowed single-photon resonance. If, however, $2\nu_1$ equals the frequency of a double-quantum allowed transition, the light can only be absorbed by the relatively weak two-photon absorption. But Eq. (1) shows that the resonant enhancement of $\chi^{(3)}$ can be just as strong as for single-photon resonances. To realize the full potential of the resonant enhancement, the laser linewidth must be as narrow as the material linewidth, which may be

TABLE I. Tuning ranges in the vuv obtainable with various combinations of dyes with λ_1 tuned to the half-frequency of a two-quantum transition in Sr. The underlined entries show dye combinations used and tuning ranges achieved in this work. The other entries show the tuning ranges that would be covered with the remaining combinations of these four dyes.

Dye Resonant State λ_1	7-Diethylamino-4-methylcoumarin $5s7d\ ^1D_2$ 4779A	Mixture Coumarin 6 and Coumarin 102 $5s5d\ ^1D_2$ 5032A	Sodium Fluorescein $5p\ ^1D_2$ 5409A	Rhodamine 6G $5s5d\ ^1D_2$ 5757A
7-Diethylamino-4-methylcoumarin[a] 4648-4525A	1578-1609A	1632-1666A	1710-1746A	<u>1778-1817A</u>
Mixture Coumarin 6 and Coumarin 102[b] 5000-5350A	1617-1651A	1674-1712A	1756-1797A	1827-1872A
Sodium Fluorescein 5337-5710A	1657-1685A	1710-1747A	1795-1836A	<u>1870-1914A</u>
Rhodamine 6G 5680-6111A	1682-1718A	1744-1783A	<u>1833-1875A</u>	<u>1907-1957A</u>

[a] One may tune 7-diethylamino-4-methylcoumarin to wavelengths shorter than 4400 Å, but for sum mixing, phase matching becomes impractical below 4648 Å since λ_2 approaches the main Sr resonance line at 4607 Å.

[b] Ref. 5.

~0.1 cm^{-1} for atomic vapors.

In order for a resonantly enhanced term of the type expressed in Eq. (1) to make a large contribution to $\chi^{(3)}$, the matrix elements must correspond to allowed transitions. On this basis one expects a very strong effect from tuning $2\nu_1$ into resonance with the singlet $5p^2$ states, since the one-electron $5s$-$5p$ transition has an oscillator strength of order unity, and the two-photon resonance from the ground state to a $5p^2$ state can be viewed as two successive virtual transitions of this type, e.g., $5s^2\,{}^1S_0 \rightarrow 5s5p\,{}^1P_1{}^0 \rightarrow 5p^2\,{}^1S_0$. However, the large enhancement observed for the triplet states ${}^3P_2$ and ${}^3P_0$ of the $5p^2$ configuration is unexpected because the $\Delta S = 0$ selection rule is violated.

Another manifestation of the large $5s$-$5p$ two-photon cross section was the appearance of superradiant laser beams at 6566, 6550, and 4811 Å, corresponding to the transitions $5p^2\,{}^1S_0$-$5s5p\,{}^1P_1{}^0$, $5p^2\,{}^1D_2$-$5s5p\,{}^1P_1{}^0$, and $5p^2\,{}^3P_2$-$5s5p\,{}^3P_2{}^0$, respectively, when these upper levels were pumped via two-photon absorption. However, the two-photon absorption did not prevent large resonant enhancement of the THG or sum mixing.

In the course of tuning ν_2, we observed further strong vuv signal enhancement in the form of resonances. These additional enhancements appear to correspond to the sweeping of $2\nu_1 + \nu_2$ over various excited states lying above the first ionization limit. The location of such states is currently a subject of research.[9] With a $5p^2$ state acting as the intermediate double-quantum resonance, additional enhancement would *a priori* be expected to occur for such autoionizing states in Sr as $6s5p\,{}^1P_1{}^0$ (see Fig. 2), $5d5p\,{}^1P_1{}^0$, etc., which are optically connected to both the ground state and the $5p^2$ state. Using $5p^2$ and other known double-quantum resonances, it should be possible to elucidate the quantum numbers of the autoionizing levels.

We have further observed that the strongest vuv generation occurs when rather special conditions of resonance are met. For instance, the vuv signal generated at 1791 Å, with ν_1 tuned to 5757 Å and ν_2 tuned to 4742 Å so that $\nu_1 + \nu_2$ equals the frequency of the $5s7s\,{}^1S_0$ state, is stronger than all other observed vuv signals. vuv power measurements were performed under these conditions. With the laser power at ν_1 measured at 16 kW and the laser power at ν_2 measured at 1.6 W at the entrance to the Sr oven, the vuv power measured was 5.2×10^{-5} W. The Sr vapor pressure was 25 Torr, and 460 Torr of Xe was added for phase matching. The laser at ν_2 was attenuated by a factor of 1.1×10^4 to avoid saturating the detector. The power conversion efficiency from 4742 to 1791 Å was thus 3.3×10^{-5}. The vuv power output was measured to be linear in the power at ν_2 and quadratic in the power at ν_1 for powers low enough not to saturate the detector. Assuming that this linearity applies for much higher powers, the unattenuated input power at ν_2 of 18 kW produces a vuv signal of 4×10^9 photons/pulse.

In summary, we have used the resonant enhancement of the nonlinear optical response in Sr vapor to produce tunable vuv radiation. Extension of the tuning range should be possible through the use of other vapor systems such as mercury and cadmium, and other dye lasers and frequency-doubled dye lasers. This method should produce diffraction-limited coherent light, tunable with a <0.1 cm^{-1} bandwidth from ~2300 Å, the present limit of frequency-doubled dye lasers, to ~800 Å.

Technical assistance by L. Manganero and C. G. Wood is gratefully acknowledged. We thank Dr. J. A. Armstrong and Dr. E. Courtens for stimulating discussions.

---

*Work partially supported by the U. S. Army Research Office, Durham, N. C.

[1]S. E. Harris and R. B. Miles, Appl. Phys. Lett. 19, 385 (1971); J. F. Young, G. C. Bjorklund, A. H. Kung, R. B. Miles, and S. E. Harris, Phys. Rev. Lett. 27, 1551 (1971); R. B. Miles and S. E. Harris, IEEE J. Quantum Electron. 9, 470 (1973).

[2]T. W. Hänsch, Appl. Opt. 11, 895 (1972).

[3]P. P. Bey and H. Rabin, Phys. Rev. 162, 794 (1967).

[4]G. Herzberg and G. Scheibe, Z. Phys. Chem., Abt. B 7, 390 (1930).

[5]F. B. Dunning, F. K. Tittel, and R. F. Stebbings, Opt. Commun. 7, 181 (1973).

[6]J. A. Armstrong, N. Bloembergen, J. Ducuing, and P. S. Pershan, Phys. Rev. 127, 1918 (1962).

[7]J. A. Armstrong, R. W. Dreyfus, R. T. Hodgson, A. L. Lurio, and J. J. Wynne, IBM Technical Disclosure Bulletin No. 15 (unpublished), p. 2209.

[8]P. D. Maker, R. W. Terhune, M. Nisenhoff, and C. M. Savage, Phys. Rev. Lett. 8, 21 (1962).

[9]See, for example, G. H. Newsom, S. O'Connor, and R. C. N. Learner, J. Phys. B: Proc Phys. Soc., London 6, 2162 (1973).

Generation of tunable picosecond VUV radiation*

A. H. Kung

Microwave Laboratory, Stanford University, Stanford, California 94305

A coherent tunable vacuum ultraviolet picosecond source has been constructed by third-order nonlinear mixing of a broadly tunable picosecond visible source and the fourth harmonic of a mode-locked Nd:YAG laser in xenon. Tunable radiation in the VUV covering portions of the region from 1180 to 1470 Å and continuously from 1631 to 1946 Å is obtained.

We report the generation of tunable picosecond vacuum ultraviolet (VUV) radiation in xenon using third-order nonlinear processes. The tuning range covers portions of the region from 1180 to 1470 Å and is continuously tunable from 1631 to 1946 Å. A high-power broadly tunable picosecond source in the visible is used as the pump radiation. Intense picosecond radiation at harmonics of the 1.064-μ line of the mode-locked Nd:YAG laser has been previously generated in mixtures of a metal vapor and an inert gas or a mixture of two inert gases.[1,2] The shortest wavelength generated to date is the 12th harmonic of the Nd:YAG laser at 886 Å.[2] In addition, using two N_2-laser-pumped dye lasers, Hodgson *et al.* have obtained tunable VUV radiation from 1570 to 1960 Å in strontium vapor in a pulse several nanoseconds long.[3]

A schematic of the experiment is shown in Fig. 1. The tunable visible source consists of a 2660-Å pumped ammonium dihydrogen phosphate (ADP) parametric generator,[4] a spatial filter, and an ADP parametric amplifier. The ADP crystals are 5 cm long with a 5 ×5-mm aperture. Each is oriented with its optic axis at 90° to the pump propagation direction and is placed in an oven whose temperature can be controlled to better than 0.1 °C in the range of the phase-matching temperature from 50 to 105 °C. The unfocused 2660-Å pump beam, obtained by frequency quadrupling a passively mode-locked Nd:YAG laser, is incident on the ADP generator with a power density of about 10^9 W/cm^2. The calculated single-pass on-axis parametric gain is 5×10^{13}. This high single-pass gain, together with the near-plane-wave focusing, results in a broad-band amplified fluorescence with a beam divergence of ~10^{-2} rad corresponding to signal and idler frequencies that satisfy the phase-matching condition $\Delta k = 0$ both at and slightly off 90°. Spatial and frequency filtering is thus necessary. It is achieved by separating the crystals by 100 cm with an aperture placed midway between the crystals. The aperture size is such that its radius is equal to twice the waist of the pump beam. The portions of the signal and idler waves which are collinear with the pump are then selected and amplified in the second ADP crystal. By varying both ADP oven temperatures from 50 to 105 °C a tuning range from 4200 to 7200 Å can be obtained.[4] Increased ultraviolet absorption in the ADP prevents operation at temperatures higher than 105 °C. The bandwidth of the tunable output varies from about 5 to as much as 20 Å close to degeneracy. At oven temperatures of 60 °C, corresponding to a signal wavelength of 4760 Å and an idler wavelength of 6000 Å, the total parametric energy conversion efficiency is more than 10% (> 100-μJ tunable output for 1-mJ uv input) which is equivalent to a peak power of over 10^6 W for both the signal and the idler assuming pulsewidths of 30 psec. The beam divergence is 0.77 mrad which is about 3 times the diffraction of a TEM_{00} beam of similar cross section. The pump, signal, and idler outputs are focused tightly into the center of a gas cell via a 7.5-cm-focal-length SiO_2 lens. The cell is about 10 cm long with a quartz window at the input and a LiF window at the output. It contains xenon as the nonlinear medium. The pressure of xenon could be varied from 0 to ~1 atm. The generated output is detected using a McPherson model 225 vacuum monochromator and a EMR model 541G solar blind photomultiplier.

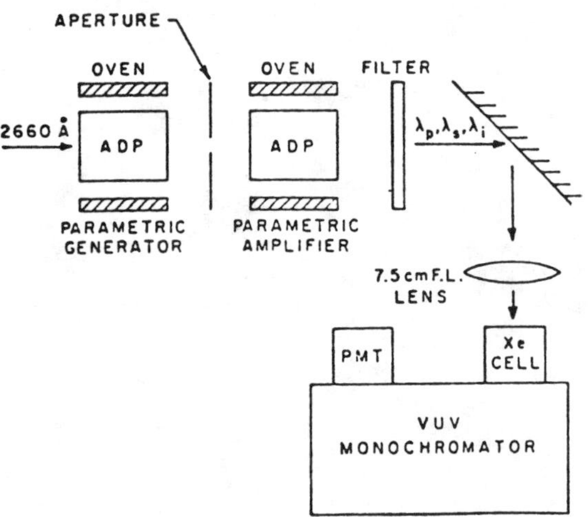

FIG. 1. Schematic diagram of the experiment.

By a combination of third-order sum generation, difference generation, and third harmonic generation of the pump, signal, and idler, tunable radiation spanning the region from 1180 to 1946 Å has been obtained. A summary of the results is shown in Fig. 2. The slashed area represents the predicted tuning range and the cross-hatched area represents the observed output range. We find that for this experiment it is necessary to focus tightly in the cell to obtain high input power densities to make up for the relatively low third-order nonlinearity in xenon.[5] Ward and New[6] and Bjorklund[7] have shown that under the conditions of tight focusing, the output for sum generation will be reduced by several orders of magnitude from the plane-wave case if the process is positively dispersive. This is caused by a cancellation from the intrinsic π phase shift at the waist of a Gaussian beam. Although precise data on the index of refraction of xenon are not available, xenon is prob-

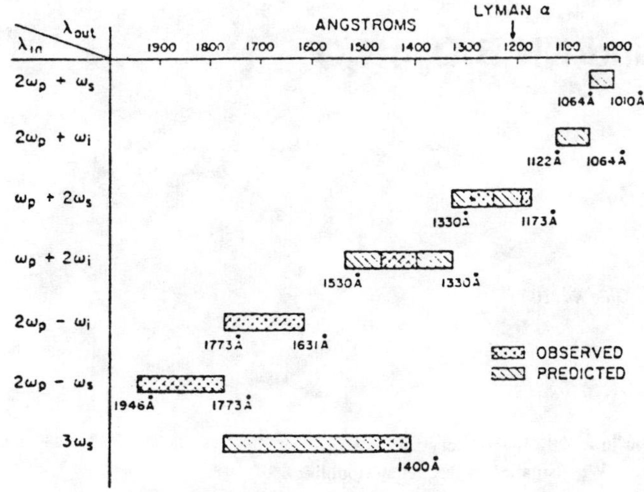

FIG. 2. Summary of the tunable VUV output. ω_p, pump frequency at 2660 Å; ω_s, signal frequency tunable from 5320 to 4200 Å; ω_i, idler frequency tunable from 7200 to 5320 Å

ably positively dispersive unless the radiation is within several thousand wave numbers of one of its strongest resonance lines because of the strong contribution to the refractive index by the continuum.[8] Thus, a strong coherence length VUV signal is observed from 1400 to 1470 Å, corresponding to the region above the $(5p^5 6s)\ ^3P_1$ level of xenon, from 1265 to 1296 Å $[(5p^5 6s)\ ^1P_1]$ and from 1180 to 1192 Å $[(5p^5 5d)\ ^3P_1]$. In other regions the signal is below our sensitivity of detection. Bjorklund has also shown that the cancellation is not present in the case of difference generation.[7] This accounts for the observed continuously tunable signal from 1631 to 1946 Å. The measured output peak power is typically 1 W, corresponding to ~10^7 photons in a 20-psec pulse. Using appropriate phase-matching techniques, this output could in some cases be increased by several orders of magnitude.[9]

In conclusion, we have demonstrated the use of parametric processes to generate coherent tunable picosecond VUV radiation in inert gases. Tunable picosecond VUV radiation will be useful for picosecond spectroscopy, for studying various high-pressure excimer systems, for high-density plasma diagnostics, for laser fusion studies, and for generation of soft x-ray pulses.

The author wishes to thank Dr. S. E. Harris and Dr. J. F. Young for helpful discussions, and Ben Yoshizumi for help in constructing the oven controllers.

*Work supported in part by the Advanced Research Projects Agency under Contract N00014-67-A-0112-0036 and by the Office of Naval Research under Contract N00014-67-A-0112-0036.

[1]S. E. Harris and R. B. Miles, Appl. Phys. Lett. 19, 385 (1971).

[2]For summary, see S. E. Harris, J. F. Young, A. H. Kung, D. M. Bloom, and G. C. Bjorklund, in *Proceedings of the First Tunable Laser Spectroscopy Conference, Vail, Colorado*, 1973 (Plenum, New York, to be published).

[3]R. T. Hodgson, P. P. Sorokin, and J. J. Wynne, *Digest of Technical Papers, Eighth International Quantum Electronics Conference* (IEEE, New York, 1974), p. 49.

[4]J. M. Yarborough and G. A. Massey, Appl. Phys. Lett. 18, 438 (1971).

[5]S. E. Harris, Phys. Rev. Lett. 31, 341 (1973).

[6]J. F. Ward and G. H. C. New, Phys. Rev. 185, 57 (1969).

[7]G. C. Bjorklund, Ph. D. dissertation, M. L. Report No. 2339 (Stanford University, Stanford, California, 1974) (unpublished).

[8]J. A. R. Samson, *Advances in Atomic and Molecular Physics* (Academic, New York, 1966), Vol. 2, p. 177.

[9]A. H. Kung, J. F. Young, and S. E. Harris, Appl. Phys. Lett. 22, 301 (1973).

Reprinted with permission from *Applied Physics Letters,* Vol. 26(12), pp. 714-716 (June 15, 1975).

Frequency doubling in $KB_5O_8 \cdot 4H_2O$ and $NH_4B_5O_8 \cdot 4H_2O$ to 217.3 nm

C. F. Dewey, Jr.*

Massachusetts Institute of Technology, Cambridge, Massachusetts 02139

W. R. Cook, Jr.

Cleveland Crystals Incorporated, 19306 Redwood Avenue, Cleveland, Ohio 44110

R. T. Hodgson and J. J. Wynne

IBM Thomas J. Watson Research Center, Yorktown Heights, New York 10598

We have produced tunable phase-matched second-harmonic radiation in a $KB_5O_8 \cdot 4H_2O$ crystal between 217.3 and 234.5 nm. Phase matching was achieved by crystal rotation. We also studied frequency doubling in $NH_4B_5O_8 \cdot 4H_2O$.

Potassium pentaborate ($KB_5O_8 \cdot 4H_2O$) is a biaxial uncolored crystal with optical properties which make it possible to produce phase-matched second-harmonic generation (SHG) at wavelengths as short as 216.8 nm. This wavelength is shorter than that generated by phase-matched SHG in any other material. In this paper we shall present some of the details of an experimental study of SHG in both $KB_5O_8 \cdot 4H_2O$ and a homologue, ammonium pentaborate ($NH_4B_5O_8 \cdot 4H_2O$).

Until 1973, the shortest wavelength obtained by phase-matched SHG was from the crystal ADP. As a frequency doubling crystal, ADP has been used since 1962.[1] The combination of transmission to wavelengths as short as 200 nm,[2] sufficient birefringence to phase match SHG to 244.2 nm,[3] and high-power-density damage threshold have served to make ADP the most widely used frequency-doubling material for short-wavelength generation. In 1973, low-power SHG was observed at a short-wavelength limit of 225 nm by Dunning, Tittel, and Stebbings[3] in lithium formate monohydrate. This crystal is limited at short wavelengths by linear uv absorption, so that below 237.5 nm the conversion efficiency falls rapidly.

Potassium pentaborate shows excellent transmission to wavelengths as short as 200 nm. An uv transmission spectrum revealed no significant change in transmission across the entire region from 200 to 400 nm.[4] Figure 1 shows the measured indices of refraction of $KB_5O_8 \cdot 4H_2O$. From the crystalline symmetry of this material (orthorhombic, C_{2v}),[5] the nonvanishing components of the second-order nonlinear electric susceptibility tensor yielding second-harmonic (SH) polarizations are

$$P_x(2\omega) = 2d_{15}E_x(\omega)E_z(\omega), \tag{1a}$$

$$P_y(2\omega) = 2d_{24}E_y(\omega)E_z(\omega), \tag{1b}$$

$$P_z(2\omega) = d_{31}E_x^2(\omega) + d_{32}E_y^2(\omega) + d_{33}E_z^2(\omega). \tag{1c}$$

Kleinman's symmetry condition[6] predicts $d_{15} = d_{31}$ and $d_{24} = d_{32}$. From Fig. 1 and Eq. (1c) it is clear that the optimum geometry for phase-matching SHG at the shortest wavelengths is one which polarizes the SH along the c axis, with the fundamental polarized along the a axis.[7] In order to tune toward longer wavelength, two options are open. One may propagate the fundamental in the bc plane keeping it polarized along a. This geometry is shown in Fig. 2(a). With ϕ as the angle between the direction of propagation and the b axis, the index of refraction for the SH (which is polarized *in* the bc plane) is given by

$$[n(2\omega)]^{-2} = [n_b(2\omega)]^{-2}\sin^2\phi + [n_c(2\omega)]^{-2}\cos^2\phi,$$

while the index of refraction for the fundamental is just n_a. Then the phase-matching angle ϕ_m is given by

$$\sin^2\phi_m = \{[n_a(\omega)]^{-2} - [n_c(2\omega)]^{-2}\}\{[n_b(2\omega)]^{-2} - [n_c(2\omega)]^{-2}\}^{-1}. \tag{2}$$

This geometry has the advantage that $n(2\omega)$ varies relatively slowly with ϕ. In the present experiments, it was also useful in generating information on both n_b and n_c at short wavelengths (the triangular points in Fig. 1). Note that this geometry has the following limitations. First, as one tunes toward longer wavelengths (larger ϕ_m), the effective component of the nonlinear polarization decreases as $\cos\phi_m$ (only that component

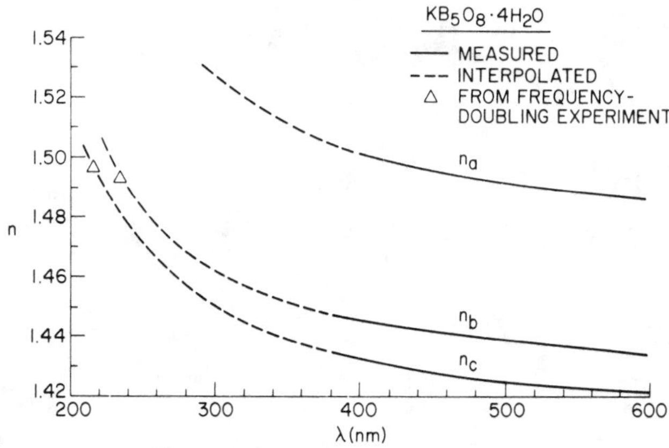

FIG. 1. Measured indices of refraction of $KB_5O_8 \cdot 4H_2O$ in the visible. The values were found by the angle of minimum deviation method. The curves are interpolated into the uv by using a one-term Sellmeir formula. The values represented by the triangles are calculated from the measured wavelengths of $\phi_m = 0°$ and $\phi_m = 90°$ phase matching in the geometry of Fig. 2(a).

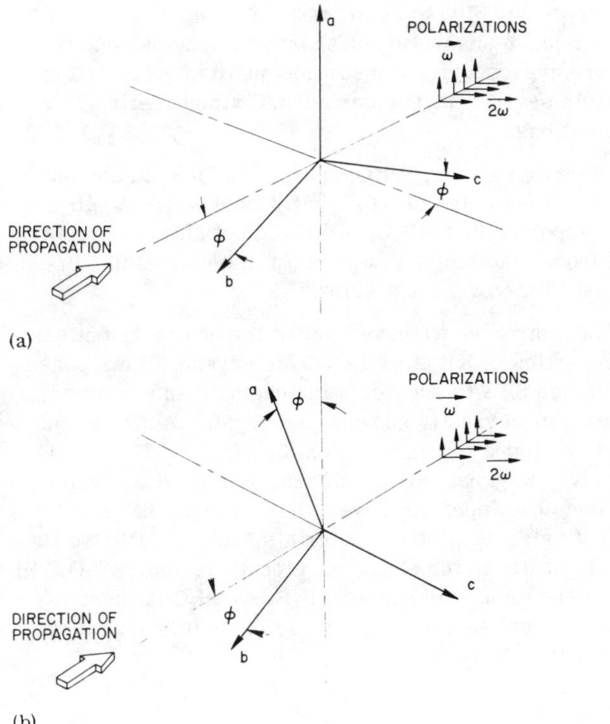

FIG. 2. Geometry for SHG. Phase matching is achieved by varying ϕ as the fundamental wavelength is tuned. The configuration of (a) was employed for tuning SHG from $KB_5O_8 \cdot 4H_2O$. The configuration of (b) was used in investigating $NH_4B_5O_8 \cdot 4H_2O$ and provides a larger tuning range than the configuration of (a), as described in the text.

normal to the direction of propagation can radiate). Second, the long-wavelength limit ($\phi_m = 90°$) corresponds to $n_a(\omega) = n_b(2\omega)$. As is evident from Fig. 1, this limit can be extended to much longer wavelengths if the fundamental index of refraction is reduced below n_a, and a geometry which accomplishes this is shown in Fig. 2(b). Now, the laser propagates and is polarized in the *ab* plane with the SH polarized along *c*. The index of refraction at the fundamental is given by

$$[n(\omega)]^{-2} = [n_b(\omega)]^{-2} \sin^2\phi + [n_a(\omega)]^{-2} \cos^2\phi,$$

while the index of the SH is just n_c. The phase-matching angle is then given by

$$\sin^2\phi_m = \{[n_c(2\omega)]^{-2} - [n_a(\omega)]^{-2}\}\{[n_b(\omega)]^{-2} - [n_a(\omega)]^{-2}\}^{-1}. \qquad (3)$$

Here $n(\omega)$ varies relatively rapidly, resulting in a more critical setting of ϕ for phase matching. The long-wavelength limit corresponds to $n_b(2\omega)$. By a simple extrapolation of the index data of Fig. 1, we estimate that this limit corresponds to a SH wavelength longer than 550 nm. *Thus, in this one crystal it should be possible to achieve phase-matched* SHG *from* 216.8 nm *to greater than* 550 nm, by rotating the crystal about a single axis.

For the experiments, we used a 10-mm cube of $KB_5O_8 \cdot 4H_2O$, cut so that the a axis was perpendicular to the entrance face normal and the *b* axis made an angle of 63° with the entrance face normal. The sides were polished using techniques common to rocksalt crystals. Under normal atmospheric conditions the surface quality deteriorates on a time scale of several weeks. The fundamental beam came from a dye laser pumped by a Molectron UV-1000 nitrogen laser. The dye laser employed a beam expander and diffraction grating as one cavity reflector[8] and produced a linearly polarized beam with ~30 kW of power in a 7-ns pulse at a repetition rate of 15 Hz. The spectral linewidth was ~0.3 cm^{-1}. Either a 10 or 15-cm-focal-length lens was used to focus the fundamental radiation into the crystal. Using the geometry of Fig. 2(a), phase-matched SHG was observed from 217.3 to 234.5 nm.[9] The short-wavelength limit corresponds to an external angle of incidence of 70° to normal. For a larger angle of incidence, our sample did not offer a clear aperture. The SH radiation intensity was too low (i.e., a conversion efficiency of less than 1%) to yield an absolute power measurement with an accurately calibrated detector. But the unattenuated uv could easily be deteced by eye by observing the fluorescence which it produced upon striking a microscope slide coated with a thin film of sodium salicylate. A solar-blind photomultiplier tube, EMR type 541GX-08-18, easily detected the SH even when the fundamental beam power was reduced by a factor of 100. The uv intensity was quadratic in the fundamental power, as expected.

An important property of nonlinear crystals is the damage threshold for high power density. We observed no optical damage to the $KB_5O_8 \cdot 4H_2O$ crystal when the focused fundamental intensity at 450 nm was ~1 GW/cm^2 and the dye laser operated at 15 Hz.

At the longest wavelength of the tuning range, the uv power dropped due to the decrease of the effective nonlinear polarization, since the *c* axis was being inclined toward the direction of propagation (larger ϕ_m). At the shortest wavelength of the tuning range there was no great change in uv power until the aperture became too small for clear transmission. We estimate that one could produce phase-matched SH at 216.8 nm when propagating along the *b* axis. This estimate is based on

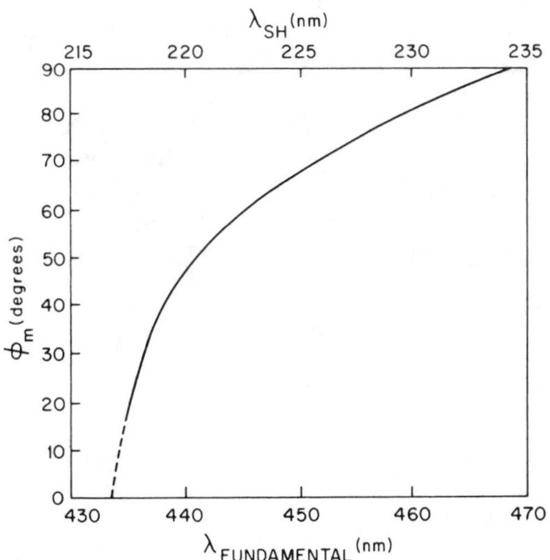

FIG. 3. Measured phase-matching angle vs wavelength (solid line) for $KB_5O_8 \cdot 4H_2O$. The dotted line is the extrapolation to the short-wavelength limit ($\phi_m = 0°$).

an extrapolation of the tuning curve of wavelength vs phase-matching angle. The tuning curve is shown in Fig. 3. Temperature tuning to shorter wavelengths does not appear promising; the phase-matched wavelength shifts to the blue about 0.025 nm per °C of cooling.[10]

No attempt was made to find an accurate value for d_{31}. Since no other known material is phase matchable at the wavelengths we measured, we had no standard to which we could compare our crystal. From the approximate calibration of the solar-blind photomultiplier, we could estimate the uv power generated. With an input power of 30 kW at 450 nm, and focusing with a 10-cm-focal-length lens, we measured a conversion efficiency of 2×10^{-3} to within a factor of 3. The dye laser beam was multimode, with an approximate cross-sectional area at the focus of 10^{-4} cm^2. Larger conversion efficiencies would be expected at higher input powers[11] or if the fundamental beam contained fewer modes.

While no further measurements were made on $KB_5O_8 \cdot 4H_2O$, it is clear from the earlier discussion that by inclining the a axis toward the direction of propagation, phase-matched SHG to much longer wavelengths may be obtained. For SHG at wavelengths longer than 260 nm, a direct comparison can be made with ADP to find the values of the nonlinear optical coefficients d_{ij}. The signal will result from some combination of d_{31} and d_{32}. While we have not used d_{32} for SHG, a prediction based on Miller's rule[12] results in $d_{32}/d_{31} = 0.78$ (using the measured values for n_a and n_b at 400 nm).

We have also made some measurements on $NH_4B_5O_8 \cdot 4H_2O$. We produced phase-matched SHG between 240.4 and 222.2 nm in this crystal by rotating about the c axis [geometry of Fig. 2(b)]. The crystal was cut with all faces normal to the crystallographic directions and measured ~7 mm on a side. In tuning toward shorter wavelengths we found that our sample showed strong absorption. Transmission measurements were obtained by using $KB_5O_8 \cdot 4H_2O$ to generate SH and then measuring the signal with and without $NH_4B_5O_8 \cdot 4H_2O$ in front of the detector. The transmission of the sample varied from 10% at 222.5 nm to 30% at 230.3 nm. At 222.2 nm, our $KB_5O_8 \cdot 4H_2O$ sample generated more than ten times as much radiation as the $NH_4B_5O_8 \cdot 4H_2O$ sample. The short-wavelength limit, 222.2 nm, corresponded to propagating directly along the b axis. Wavelengths longer than 240.4 nm were not detectable by our solar-blind photomultiplier. In comparison to $KB_5O_8 \cdot 4H_2O$, $NH_4B_5O_8 \cdot 4H_2O$ cannot be phase matched for SHG to as short a wavelength, it shows much more absorption at short wavelengths, and it is more hygroscopic, the surface quality deteriorating within several days under normal atmospheric conditions.

Finally we note that Graja[13] made SHG studies on powered samples of $KB_5O_8 \cdot 4H_2O$ and $NH_4B_5O_8 \cdot 4H_2O$. He reported that $KB_5O_8 \cdot 4H_2O$ did not show a direction of index matching and was not phase matchable, in contrast to the present results.

In summary, we have studied the nonlinear optical properties of $KB_5O_8 \cdot 4H_2O$. This crystal allows phase matched SHG to shorter wavelengths than any other material currently known. The crystal is biaxial and may be tuned to phase match SHG from 216.8 nm all the way to greater than 550 nm. For longer wavelengths it does not appear to have as high a nonlinear coefficient as several other materials such as ADP, so its main utility in the short-wavelength region. $KB_5O_8 \cdot 4H_2O$ appears to be superior to $NH_4B_5O_8 \cdot 4H_2O$ in most essential properties relevant for use in nonlinear optical devices.

*Partially supported by the Advanced Research Projects Agency under Contract DAHC04-71-C-0049 and N00014-67-A-0204-0092.

[1]R.C. Miller and A. Savage, Phys. Rev. **128**, 2175 (1962).
[2]M.W. Dowley and E.B. Hodges, IEEE J. Quantum Electron **QE-4**, 552 (1968).
[3]F.B. Dunning, F.K. Tittel, and R.F. Stebbings, Opt. Commun. **7**, 181 (1973).
[4]Dr. Robert Rippon (private communication).
[5]W.R. Cook, Jr., and H. Jaffe, Acta Crystallogr. **10**, 705 (1957).
[6]D.F. Kleinman, Phys. Rev. **126**, 1977 (1962).
[7]To avoid any possible ambiguities in notation, the c axis is the polar axis of the crystal also referred to as the z direction. The a and b axes are synonymous with the x and y directions, respectively. In reduced notation d_{31} is equivalent to d_{zxx} or d_{caa}, etc.
[8]T.W. Hänsch, Appl. Opt. **11**, 895 (1972).
[9]Preliminary results were presented by C.F. Dewey, Jr., W.R. Cook, Jr., R.T. Hodgson, and J.J. Wynne at VIII IQEC, San Francisco, 1974 (unpublished).
[10]R. Deslattes and H. Dewey (private communication).
[11]In preliminary experiments conducted at the National Bureau of Standards by R. Deslattes and H. Dewey, SHG conversion efficiencies in excess of 1% were measured on the same $KB_5O_8 \cdot 4H_2O$ crystal used in our experiments. A dye laser input power of about 100 kW (multimode) was used to obtain this result.
[12]R.C. Miller, Appl. Phys. Lett. **15**, 17 (1964).
[13]A. Graja, Phys. Status Solidi **27**, K93 (1968).

Reprinted with the permission of the IEEE from *IEEE Journal of Quantum Electronics,* Vol. QE-14(8), pp. 581-596 (August 1978).

Generation of Coherent Radiation in the XUV by Fifth- and Seventh-Order Frequency Conversion in Rare Gases

JOHN REINTJES, CHIAO-YAO SHE, MEMBER, IEEE, AND ROBERT C. ECKARDT

(Invited Paper)

Abstract—Results of experimental studies of the generation of coherent radiation in the XUV by high order optical nonlinearities in the rare gases are described. Fifth- and seventh-harmonic conversion and six wave mixing of harmonic pulses from an Nd:YAG laser were used to produce radiation at several discrete wavelengths between 38 and 76 nm. Experimental measurements of fifth-harmonic conversion of pump pulses at 266.1 nm in helium are compared with theoretical predictions. Discrepancies between theory and experiment are observed at high laser powers, and the role of competing processes is discussed.

I. Introduction

THE nonlinear optical processes of harmonic generation and frequency conversion have been used to produce coherent radiation in wavelength ranges extending from the infrared to the vacuum ultraviolet (VUV) [1]-[5]. In particular, frequency mixing of radiation from dye lasers has been used to generate narrow-band tunable radiation throughout much of the range between 100 and 200 nm [6]-[8]. Most of the work to date has involved the use of second- and third-order frequency mixing since these are the lowest order nonzero optical nonlinearities in crystals and vapors, respectively. In recent years there has been considerable interest in the use of higher-order optical nonlinearities for frequency conversion [9]-[11]. Harmonic radiation generated through such higher-order interactions is generally expected to be weaker than that generated through lower-order processes. However, at the intensity levels which are available today from focused mode-locked laser pulses, significant conversion efficiency is predicted for fifth- and higher-order harmonic generation.

The higher-order nonlinear processes offer several advantages over lower-order ones, especially with regard to the extension of coherent radiation into the extreme ultraviolet (XUV) and soft X-ray ranges. Although initial work involving the generation of coherent radiation in the XUV at wavelengths of 88.6 [12] and 57 nm [13] was done using third-harmonic conversion, continued use of the lower-order interactions is not without difficulty. In order to generate radiation at still shorter wavelengths in the XUV by third-harmonic conversion, one must use pump radiation at still shorter wavelengths in the VUV. Unfortunately, it is just in this region of the spectrum that high quality coherent primary lasers become scarce.

On the other hand, the use of higher-order interactions allows a larger step along the frequency scale to be taken in a single conversion process. This means, for example, that a given wavelength can be reached from a longer-wavelength pump. Thus radiation at XUV wavelengths which could be generated only from VUV pump sources by third-harmonic conversion can be produced from pumps in the visible or near UV if the higher-order processes are utilized. As a result, a much wider choice of pump sources, including tunable dye lasers, becomes available for the generation of XUV radiation. Alternatively the higher-order processes make it possible to reach a shorter wavelength from a given pumping wavelength. Thus, as high quality pumping sources are developed at shorter wavelengths in the VUV, these processes will extend the range of available coherent radiation to still shorter wavelengths in the XUV.

Fifth-harmonic conversion of Nd:glass laser radiation at 1.06 μm has been studied both experimentally and theoretically. Experimental observations of both direct and cascade genera-

Manuscript received March 3, 1978.

J. Reintjes and R. C. Eckardt are with the Laser Physics Branch, Optical Sciences Division, Naval Research Laboratory, Washington, DC 20375.

C. Y. She was on sabbatical at the Optical Sciences Division, Naval Research Laboratory, Washington, DC 20375. He is now with the Department of Physics, Colorado State University, Fort Collins, CO 80523.

tion of the fifth-harmonic wavelength at 212.5 nm in solids have been reported [14]. Later, fifth-harmonic conversion in vapors was analyzed theoretically [11]. More recently, conversion of Nd:glass laser light by fifth- [15] and ninth-harmonic [16] generation in metal vapors has been reported. The use of fifth- and higher-order processes for the generation of radiation in the XUV and soft X-ray ranges has been suggested [9] but only preliminary experimental results were reported.

In this paper we describe the results of a series of experiments which we have performed to investigate the use of these higher-order nonlinearities for generating coherent radiation in the XUV [17]-[19]. In Section II, we present a theoretical treatment of fifth-harmonic conversion of focused beams in transparent vapors. In Section III, we describe the laser system which we used to generate the XUV radiation and in Section IV, we review our progress in short-wavelength generation in the rare gases.

In Section V, we compare our experimental results with the theoretical predictions of Section II. Although reasonable agreement between theory and experiment is found at low laser powers and gas pressures, significant deviation from theory is observed at higher values of optical power and gas pressure. In Section VI, we discuss possible mechanisms which can account for the observed behavior and present additional measurements which indicate the relative importance of the various competing processes in our experiments. Finally, in Section VII, we summarize our progress and indicate possible paths of future work.

II. Theory

Several theoretical treatments of harmonic generation in vapors by focused beams have been given in the literature. Ward and New [2] derived general expressions for the power radiated into the qth harmonic by focused beams which took into account wave-vector mismatch between the fundamental and harmonic wavelengths. Their results for third-harmonic generation, especially with regard to the effects of negative dispersion and phase matching, were expanded upon by others [3], [20]. Similar analyses have been given for fifth-harmonic generation, which included the effects of cascade as well as direct conversion processes [11].

In this section, we will summarize briefly the theory of direct qth-harmonic generation in focused beams. We will restrict our attention to conversion in a single component medium. Thus, phase matching by mixtures of vapors, which has been treated for third- [3] and fifth- [11] harmonic conversion, will not be considered. Since all of our experiments were done in single component vapors, these theoretical results can be compared directly with our measurements. At various stages of the development of the theory, comparison will be made between theoretical behavior of third-harmonic conversion, which has been analyzed at length in the literature, and conversion to the higher harmonics. Although our general results are applicable to harmonic generation of arbitrary order, specific examples will be presented for fifth-harmonic conversion since the bulk of our experimental work was done with this process. Cascade processes, which are in general important for generation of harmonics of order higher than two will also not be included in the present theoretical discussion [21]. It will be shown, however, that in helium, for which sufficient information exists for a quantitative comparison of theory and experiment, the cascade fifth-harmonic conversion of radiation at 266 nm (which was used in our measurements) is smaller than the direct conversion by at least two orders of magnitude and is therefore negligible for our purposes. Finally competing mechanisms, such as multiphoton ionization, Stark shifts, or Kerr effects will also not be included in this theoretical treatment. Such effects have been considered theoretically for third- and higher-order harmonic generation [9], [22]-[24]. The importance of these processes can be estimated from the extent to which the theoretical predictions outlined in this section disagree with our measurements, and the effects of these processes will be discussed later in Section VI.

A. *Harmonic Generation in a Focused Beam*

Harmonic generation occurs as the result of a nonlinear polarization that is induced by successive interactions between the electrons in a medium and an intense optical field. A polarization linear in the field at the fundamental frequency ω is created by the action of the pump light on the ground state electrons. This polarization can interact again with the driving field to produce a polarization which depends on the square of the field and oscillates at 2ω. Similar subsequent interactions can result in a polarizarion at $q\omega$ depending on the qth power of the incident field. The dominant interaction between the light and the medium is through electric dipole coupling, so that in centrosymmetric media, such as atomic vapor systems, only the polarizations at the odd harmonic frequencies can radiate energy. When the pumping wavelength is chosen such that the fundamental and harmonic frequencies are not coincident with allowed atomic transitions, the multiple interactions described above occur simultaneously and the atom is left in its original ground state with no real transitions having taken place.

For qth-harmonic generation, the nonlinear polarization is given by

$$P_q(r, z) = N\chi^{(q)}(-q\omega, \omega)\,\frac{E_1^q(r, z)}{2^{q-1}}, \qquad q = 3, 5 \cdots \tag{1}$$

where $P_q(r, z)$ is the complex amplitude of the time dependent polarization given by

$$P_q(r, z, t) = \tfrac{1}{2}\,[P_q(r, z)\exp -i(q\omega t - k_q z) + P_q^*(r, z)\exp i(q\omega t - k_q z)]. \tag{2}$$

$E_1(r, z)$ is the complex amplitude of the incident field

$$E_1(r, z, t) = \tfrac{1}{2}\,[E_1(r, z)\exp -i(\omega_1 t - k_i z) + E_1^*(r, z)\exp i(\omega_1 t - k_1 z)]. \tag{3}$$

N is the atomic number density and $\chi^{(q)}(-q\omega, \omega) \equiv \chi^{(q)}(-q\omega, \omega, \omega, \cdots, \omega)$ is the qth-order susceptibility per atom. The expression for $\chi^{(q)}$ depends on the properties of the atomic medium and can be calculated from quantum mechanical perturbation theory. For example, in an atomic medium, the fifth-harmonic susceptibility has the form in ESU

$$\chi^{(5)}(-5\omega,\omega) = \frac{(ea_0)^6}{(\hbar c)^5} \sum \mu_{ga}\mu_{ab}\mu_{bc}\mu_{cd}\mu_{de}\mu_{eg}$$

$$\times \left\{ \frac{1}{(\omega_{ag}-\omega)(\omega_{bg}-2\omega)(\omega_{cg}-3\omega)(\omega_{dg}-4\omega)(\omega_{eg}-5\omega)} \right.$$

$$+ \frac{1}{(\omega_{ag}-\omega)(\omega_{bg}-2\omega)(\omega_{cg}-3\omega)(\omega_{dg}-4\omega)(\omega_{eg}+\omega)}$$

$$+ \frac{1}{(\omega_{ag}-\omega)(\omega_{bg}-2\omega)(\omega_{cg}-3\omega)(\omega_{dg}+2\omega)(\omega_{eg}+\omega)}$$

$$+ \frac{1}{(\omega_{ag}-\omega)(\omega_{bg}-2\omega)(\omega_{cg}+3\omega)(\omega_{dg}+2\omega)(\omega_{eg}+\omega)}$$

$$+ \frac{1}{(\omega_{ag}-\omega)(\omega_{bg}+4\omega)(\omega_{cg}+3\omega)(\omega_{dg}+2\omega)(\omega_{eg}+\omega)}$$

$$\left. + \frac{1}{(\omega_{ag}+5\omega)(\omega_{bg}+4\omega)(\omega_{cg}+3\omega)(\omega_{dg}+2\omega)(\omega_{eg}+\omega)} \right\} \quad (4)$$

where a_0 is the Bohr radius, μ_{ij} is the electric dipole moment between states i and j, in atomic units, ω is the angular frequency of the pump radiation in cm^{-1}, and g refers to the ground state while $a, b \cdots$ refer to all intermediate states.

It has been pointed out in the literature [6] that near resonances with atomic levels can be used to enhance the nonlinear susceptibility. Two photon resonances are particularly important in third-harmonic generation because they provide strong enhancement for the harmonic process without causing significant absorption at either the fundamental or harmonic frequencies. From (4) it can be seen that additional resonances involving three or four photons can be used to enhance fifth-harmonic generation without introducing loss at either the pump or generated frequencies.

In general one expects that the higher-order harmonics, which involve higher orders of perturbation theory, will be weaker than the lower-order ones. However, for sufficiently intense incident optical fields, the higher-order polarization can be comparable to or larger than the lower-order ones. This can be seen by considering the ratio

$$\frac{P_{q+2}}{P_q} = \frac{\chi^{(q+2)}}{\chi^{(q)}} \left[\frac{E}{2}\right]^2 \quad (5)$$

where the quantity $[E/2]^2$ is related to the intensity of the incident field I by $I = [cn/2\pi]\,(E/2)^2$. In helium, for example, typical values of the susceptibilities for experiments which will be described later give $\chi^{(5)}/\chi^{(3)} = 10^{-10}$ and the fifth-harmonic polarization becomes comparable to the third for an incident intensity of $I = 5 \times 10^{12}$ W/cm^2, a level which can easily be achieved in the focus of an intense ultrashort laser pulse. Of course, the mere fact that P_5 exceeds P_3 does not mean automatically that conversion to the fifth harmonic will exceed conversion to the third. At the intensities needed to achieve this result, conversion in a given medium may be limited by any one of a number of competing mechanisms, preventing significant generation of the higher harmonic. However, as will be shown later, experimental conditions can exist in which conversion to the fifth harmonic exceeds conversion to the third.

If we assume that the pump field is not depleted and that the harmonics of different order are generated independently, the qth harmonic field radiated by the nonlinear polarization is given by Maxwell's equation

$$\nabla \times \nabla \times E_q(r,z,t) + \frac{1}{c^2}\frac{\partial^2}{\partial t^2} E_q(r,z,t) = -\frac{4\pi}{c^2}\frac{\partial^2}{\partial t^2} P_q(r,z,t) \quad (6)$$

where $P_q(r, z, t)$ is given by (1) and (2). In the slowly varying envelope approximation, (6) simplifies to

$$\nabla_\perp^2 E_q(r,z) + 2ik_q \frac{\partial Eq(r,z)}{\partial z} = -\frac{4\pi\omega_q^2}{c^2} P_q(r,z)\, e^{-i\Delta kz} \quad (7)$$

where the wave vector mismatch Δk is given by

$$\Delta k = k_q - qk_1, \text{ where } k_q = n_q\omega_q/c,\ \omega_q = q\omega,$$

and n_q is the refractive index at ω_q. The choice of sign for Δk is consistent with that of Miles and Harris [3], but opposite to that of Ward and New [2]. With this choice of sign, negative values of Δk are associated with negative (anomalous) dispersion. Solutions to (7) have been given in the literature [2], [20], [22] for a pump beam with a Gaussian profile of the form

$$E_1(r,z) = E_0(1+i\xi)^{-1} \exp\,[-k_1 r^2/b(1+i\xi)] \quad (8)$$

where $\xi = 2(z - f)/b$, f is the focal length of the lens used for focusing, $b = 2\pi\omega_0^2/\lambda$ is the confocal parameter of the focused beam, and ω_0 is the $1/e$ field radius of the beam waist. Under the approximation that $\Delta k << k_q, qk_1$ the harmonic field has a Gaussian profile with the same confocal parameter as the fundamental field [20]. For an interaction region extending from $-z'$ to $+z$, the solution of (7) using (8) and (1) is

$$E_q(r,z) = -i\,\frac{\pi\omega_q^2}{2^{q-3}k_q c^2}\,\frac{N\chi^{(q)}E_0^q}{(1+i\xi)}\, b \exp\left(\frac{-qk_1 r^2}{b(1+i\xi)}\right) e^{iqk_1 z} \cdot \int_{-\xi'}^{\xi} (1+i\xi'')^{1-q} \exp\left[\frac{-ib\Delta k}{2}(\xi''-\xi)\right] d\xi''. \quad (9)$$

The generated power may be obtained by integrating the intensity of the qth harmonic over the transverse coordinates:

$$P_q(\xi) = \int dr^2\, \frac{cn_q}{8\pi}\, |E_q(r)|^2. \quad (10)$$

By carrying out the integration of (10) we obtain

$$P_q(\xi) = \frac{2^{q-1}\pi^{q+1}}{qn_1 n_q c^{q-1}} \times \left| \frac{N}{n_1 - n_q}\chi^{(q)}(\omega_1,\omega_q) \right|^2 \times |(b\Delta k)F(b\Delta k)|^2 \times \left(\frac{4P_1}{b\lambda_1}\right)^{q-1} P_1 \quad (11)$$

where $P_1 = cn_1|E_0|^2 b/16k_1$ is the pump power, $4P_1/b\lambda_1$ is the pump intensity at the focus, $\Delta k = k_q - qk_1 = 2\pi q(n_q - n_1)/\lambda_1$, and $F(\Delta kb)$ is a phase-optimization integral given by

$$F = \int_{-\xi'}^{\xi} (1 + \xi'')^{1-q} \exp -i\left[\left(\frac{\Delta kb}{2}\right)(\xi'' - \xi)\right] d\xi''. \quad (12)$$

The first factor in (11) is a constant which is independent of vapor density and the properties of the nonlinear medium, except for a minor dependence on n_1 and n_q. The second factor depends on the nonlinear medium through $\chi^{(q)}$ but is independent of density for a single component vapor since the quantity $(n_1 - n_q)/N$ is the dispersion per atom. The third factor $|(\Delta kb)F(\Delta kb)|^2$ is a dimensionless function of vapor density N, confocal parameter b, and dispersion in the vapor. It describes the effect of focusing and phase matching on the harmonic conversion and contains all of the pressure dependence for conversion in a single component vapor. For a tightly focused beam in which $\xi, \xi' >> b$ conversion can occur only for negative values of Δk, corresponding to anomalous dispersion in the refractive indices. This effect arises because of the need to balance the phase slippage of the harmonic field in the focused beam relative to its driving polarization with a refractive-index dispersion of the proper sign. This phase slippage arises because of the complex amplitude in the description of the propagation of the focused Gaussian beam [see (8)]. If, on the other hand, integration of (12) is carried out between the limits $\xi' = \infty$, $\xi = 0$, some conversion can occur for both positive and negative values of Δk. This situation would arise experimentally, for example, if the beam were focused onto a window as was done for measurements reported in [2]. As will be pointed out later, these integration limits also approximately describe the conditions present in our experiments.

Variation of the third factor $|b\Delta kF(b\Delta k)|^2$ is shown in Fig. 1 as a function of $b\Delta k$ for $q = 3, 5$, and 7, for integration between the limits $\xi' = \infty$, $\xi = 0$. The curves peak at values of $b\Delta k \approx -6.2$, -10.4, and -14.6 for $q = 3, 5, 7$, respectively. This means that one may maximize conversion by choosing a proper combination of b and N. In practice, however, unless a very large value of b is used (several millimeters to centimeters), the density at which maximization occurs is usually very high (several hundred torr). Under these conditions, conversion may be limited by other processes such as breakdown, absorption, or the Kerr effect. Although a finite level of conversion exists for positive values of Δk, the maximum conversion which can be obtained is considerably smaller than the peak conversion for negative Δk.

B. Cascade Processes

In addition to the direct-conversion processes described above, higher harmonics can be generated by cascade processes involving multiple lower-order interactions. For example, fifth-harmonic radiation can be produced by a stepwise process in which the third harmonic is generated in a third-order interaction and is subsequently combined with two fundamental photons to generate the fifth harmonic in another third-order process. In general, this cascade process has the

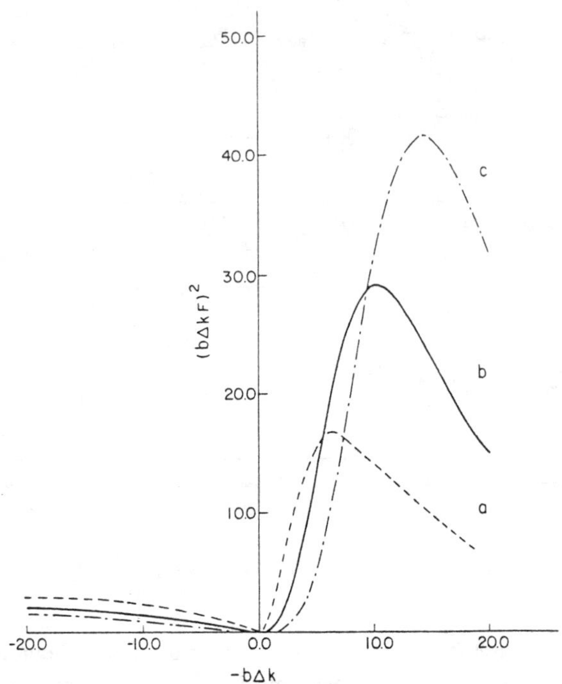

Fig. 1. Variation of the quantity $|b\Delta kF|^2$ as a function of the product $b\Delta k$ for third harmonic (a), fifth harmonic (b), and seventh harmonic (c). The phase optimization integral F was evaluated between the limits $\xi' = \infty$ and $\xi = 0$ for all three cases.

same resonant enhancements as the direct fifth-order process and in solids it is of the same order of magnitude as the direct process [21]. It has been shown that the two processes can in principle be simultaneously phase matched in vapors and can be of comparable magnitude under appropriate conditions [11].

The net fifth-harmonic signal is determined by interference between the harmonic fields generated by the direct and cascade process. The effect of the cascade process was treated in [11] where it was shown that the net harmonic field is given by an expression similar to (11) (with $q = 5$) with the function F replaced by $F' = F_1 + \eta F_2$, where F_1 and F_2 are the phase matching integrals for one- and two-step processes, respectively, and η is the ratio of their strengths,

$$\eta = i\frac{6\pi^2}{n_3\lambda_1} bN \frac{\chi^{(3)}\chi^{(3)'}}{\chi^{(5)}}. \quad (14)$$

Here $\chi^{(5)}$ is the susceptibility for the direct fifth-order process, $\chi^{(3)}$ the susceptibility for the third harnomic, and $\chi^{(3)'}$ for the mixing of one third harmonic and two fundamental photons. The quantity $|b\Delta kF'|$ is plotted in Fig. 2 as a function of pressure in helium for the direct process alone and for the direct and cascade processes combined. In evaluating F and F' for Fig. 2, we used parameters that were typically encountered in our experiments. The nonlinear susceptibilities for helium considering only the contributions of the discrete levels were calculated to be $\chi^{(5)} = 3.39 \times 10^{-48}$ ESU, $\chi^{(3)} = 3.86 \times 10^{-38}$ ESU, and $\chi^{(3)'} = 3.4 \times 10^{-37}$ ESU. The dispersion Δk was determined from calculations of the refractive indices at the fundamental ($\lambda_1 = 266.1$ nm) and the fifth-harmonic ($\lambda_5 = 53.2$ nm) wavelengths which included the contributions of the continuum and gave a value for

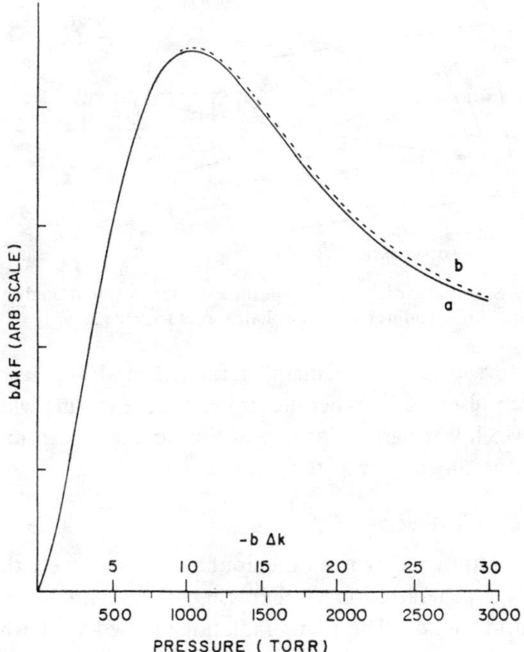

Fig. 2. Variation of the quantity $|b\Delta kF|$ as a function of the quantity $b\Delta k$ for fifth-harmonic conversion by the direct process only (a), and the direct and cascade processes combined (b). The pressure scale is appropriate for a value of b of 0.5 mm and dispersion corresponding to frequency conversion of 266 nm pulses in helium.

$(n_1 - n_5)/N$ of 4.92×10^{-24} cm^3/atm. The confocal parameter b was taken to be 0.5 mm, corresponding to use of a 5 cm focal length lens in our experiments.

The relative contributions of the two effects is a function of vapor pressure. At pressures less than 100 torr, which were typically encountered in our experiments, the two-step process makes a negligible contribution. A rough estimate from (14) shows that the two-step process becomes comparable to the single-step process at a value of N near 10^{22}/cm^{-3}, approaching the density of condensed matter. Although this calculation shows that the direct generation of fifth-harmonic radiation dominates the cascade generation in our experiments, the relative importance of the two effects depends on the confocal parameter of the focused beam b, and on the absolute magnitude of the third- and fifth-order susceptibilities. Thus, under different experimental conditions, the contributions from the direct and cascade processes could be comparable, as was found in [11].

C. Numerical Examples

To gain some feeling for the orders of magnitude involved in fifth-harmonic generation, we can calculate the expected fifth-harmonic conversion of pump pulses at λ_1 = 266.1 nm in helium using (11). Since most of the necessary matrix elements are known for helium, the second factor in (11) can be calculated from first principles. Values for the nonlinear susceptibility $\chi^{(5)}(-5\omega, \omega)$ and the dispersion per atom are the same as used in Fig. 2. Using these values together with parameters appropriate to experiments which will be described later (P_1 = 300 MW, b = 2 mm, corresponding to a lens of 10 cm focal length in our experiments, and the optimum value for $|(\Delta kb) F(\Delta kb)|^2 = 28.98$, corresponding to a pressure of 250 torr of He), we estimate the conversion efficiency P_5/P_1 to be 135 percent. A calculated conversion level this high indicates that the theory is invalid in that it ignores pump deletion. However, it also indicates that significant conversion to the fifth harmonic can be expected in the absence of other competing effects.

D. Summary of Theoretical Predictions

The theory given above shows that the harmonic power depends on a combination of laser intensity, gas pressure, dispersion, and resonant structure of the medium. In order to make comparisons with the experimental results that follow, we may summarize the conclusions for fifth-harmonic generation ($q = 5$) in a single component atomic gas as follows:

1) the harmonic power P_5 should vary as the fifth power of the pump power P_1.

2) For optimum conversion in a focused beam it is necessary to have negative dispersion.

3) Harmonic generation of any order is favored by using as tight a focus as possible and adjusting the value of $b\Delta k$ accordingly to optimize the phase integral. This conclusion follows from (11) and is valid only for harmonic conversion in a single component vapor. If phase matching is done by using mixtures of gases, as in [3], this conclusion is valid only for harmonics of order greater than three.

4) Under certain conditions more fifth harmonic than third harmonic can be generated.

5) For a fixed confocal parameter b the shape of the P_5 versus N curve should be independent of the pump power P_1.

6) The harmonic power can be increased by resonant enhancements involving two, three, or four photons.

Additional predictions can be made for fifth-harmonic conversion in helium.

7) At the available laser power, the conversion efficiency should be high enough to deplete the pump.

8) The conversion efficiency and optimum gas density N for a given confocal parameter b can be calculated and compared with experiment.

It should be emphasized again that these theoretical predictions are the result of a theory that accounted only for harmonic generation and did not consider possible limiting effects. Evidence for the importance of such effects can be obtained by observing the extent to which our experimental results fail to agree with these predictions.

III. Experimental Apparatus

A. Laser System

The laser system used in the present experiments is shown schematically in Fig. 3. The Nd:YAG laser oscillator was passively mode locked and produced a train of pulses 30 ps long with a peak energy per pulse of about 0.1 mJ. A single pulse was selected from the train and was amplified in three YAG amplifiers to a level of about 60 mJ, corresponding to a peak power of 2 GW. At this output power level, temporal measurements done with an ultrafast streak camera showed a smoothly varying intensity profile with a duration of 30 to 35 ps. Simultaneous spectral measurements showed a smooth spectral distribution with a width that was about 10

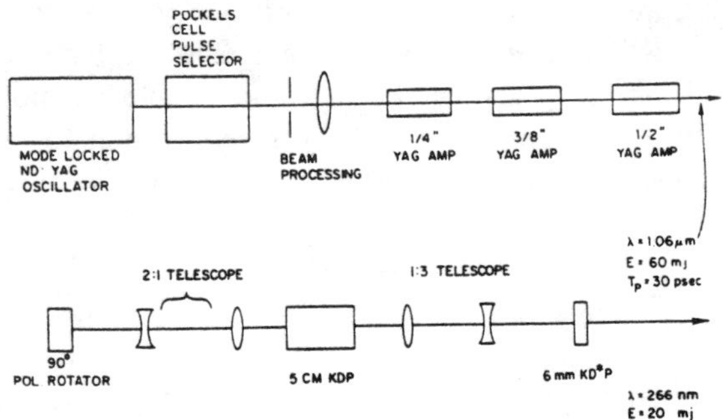

Fig. 3. Schematic diagram of laser system used to generate higher harmonics in rare gases.

percent greater than the time-bandwidth limit due to self-phase modulation in the amplifier chain. Operation of the system at higher output levels resulted in increased self-phase modulation which seriously reduced the efficiency of the second-harmonic generation that followed. In order to minimize effects due to self-focusing in the amplifiers, beam processing optics, consisting of a 2 m lens and an aperture with a diameter equal to the $1/e$ intensity diameter of the beam, were used after the first amplifier. The last two amplifiers were placed so that the rod edges coincided with the first minimum of the Airy pattern in the far field of the 2 m lens.

The output from the last amplifier was converted to the fourth harmonic in two successive stages of second-harmonic generation. The first frequency doubling stage consisted of a 2 in long KDP crystal oriented for angle tuned type I phase matching. The major factor limiting conversion efficiency in this stage is the angular acceptance of the phase-matching peak. In order to insure that the divergence of the infrared beam was fully contained within the phase-matching peak, the beam had to be expanded by a factor 2 before entering the KDP crystal. Internal energy conversion efficiency of about 75 percent was obtained in this stage for an input intensity of about 500 MW/cm^2. For the second stage of frequency doubling, a KD*P crystal, again oriented for angle tuned type I phase matching at room temperature, was used. In this stage the main factor limiting conversion efficiency was the spectral width of the fundamental pulse. A crystal length of 6 mm was used to insure the entire bandwidth of the incident second-harmonic pulses was effectively phase matched and, at an input intensity of about 5 GW/cm^2, 75 percent conversion between the second and fourth harmonics was obtained [25]. Since the pump is severely depleted in the two doubling stages, the pulse duration was reduced by only about 10 percent (from about 33 to 30 ps). Because of losses due to Fresnel reflection at the uncoated optical surfaces, the linear transmission of the optical system in Fig. 3 is 0.54, resulting in output pulse energies at 266.1 nm of about 20 mJ. Although the net energy throughput of this cascade harmonic system was only about 33 percent, energy throughputs of up to 50 percent should be possible in such a system if properly antireflection coated optical components are used.

For experiments involving only higher-order harmonic generation from 266 nm, two fused quartz dispersing prisms were

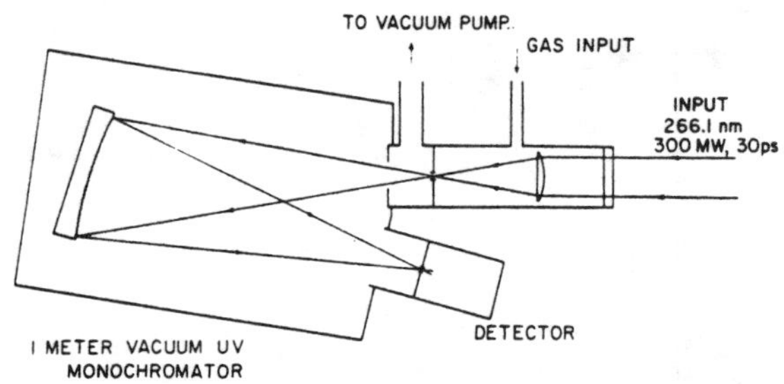

Fig. 4. Schematic diagram of experimental arrangement used to generate and detect higher harmonics in rare gases.

used to separate the remaining fundamental and second-harmonic pulses. For experiments in six-wave mixing which used the two lower harmonics in addition to the fourth harmonic, the dispersing prisms were removed.

B. *XUV Generation*

The output pulses from the doubling crystals were then used for XUV generation in the experimental system which is illustrated in Fig. 4. The pump radiation entered a cell which was attached to the front of a 1 m normal incidence vacuum monochromator. It was focused with a CaF_2 lens to a spot at the center of a 250 μm diameter aperture which replaced the entrance slit of the monochromator. The gas used for nonlinear mixing was flowed into the cell and was differentially pumped behind the aperture. A two stage differential pumping arrangement was used which allowed pressures up to several hundred torr to be used in the sample cell while the pressure in the main spectrometer was maintained below 5×10^{-4} torr.

Lenses with focal lengths of 5, 10, and 20 cm were used in the experiments. The distribution of the pump light at the focus of each of these lenses was measured using a silicon diode array. For each of the lenses, the focal spot intensity followed a Gaussian distribution to about the 10 percent points with spot sizes ($1/e$ field radius) of 5, 10, and 20 μm, respectively. The peak intensity of the pump light at the focus of the 5 cm lens was about 10^{15} W/cm^2.

Detection of the generated XUV radiation was done at the exit plane of the monochromator both photographically and photoelectrically. Photographic detection was done with Kodak 101-01 film. Because of the intensity of the scattered pump radiation at 266 nm, a 1000 Å thick aluminum window was used in front of the film. As a result, photographic measurements were limited to wavelengths shorter than about 75 nm. Photoelectric detection was done with a visible-photomultiplier-scintillator combination and a solar-blind windowless photomultiplier. The visible multiplier required use of two aluminum filters (transmission about 10 percent each at 50 nm) because the scintillator was sensitive to the scattered pump radiation, again limiting detection to wavelengths below about 75 nm. The windowless solar-blind multiplier had BeCu photocathode and dynodes and was insensitive to the pump radiation. This detector could be used out to its long-wave cutoff of about 120 nm and so could be used to compare the fifth-harmonic conversion with conversion in lower-order processes. Although the gain of

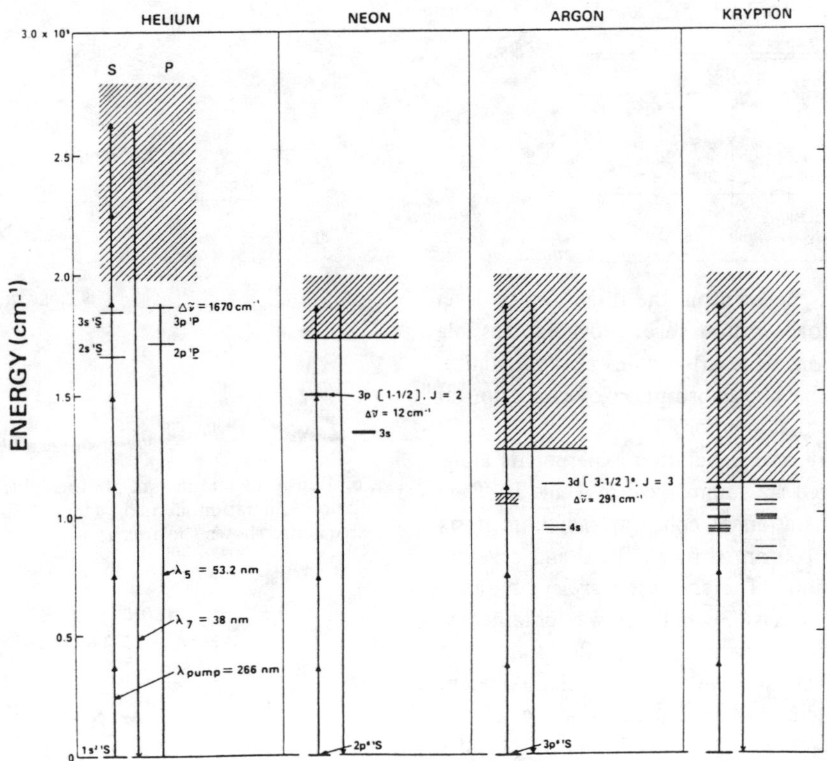

Fig. 5. Energy level diagrams for fifth- and seventh-harmonic conversion of pump radiation at 266 nm in four of the rare gases.

the windowless multiplier was less than that of the visible tube, no aluminum filters or scintillator had to be used and the sensitivity of the two detection systems at 53.2 nm was about equal.

IV. Short Wave Generation

We have investigated experimentally several aspects of coherent XUV generation using higher-order optical frequency conversion. All of our measurements were done in the noble gases because these are the only neutral atomic vapors which are transparent at wavelengths below 100 nm (helium, for example is transparent to 50.4 nm and neon to 75 nm). We felt that the ease of handling these gases along with the lack of photoionization absorption in some of them in the wavelength range of interest would more than offset the relatively low nonlinear susceptibilities which they have when compared, for example, with metal vapors.

In this section we will describe the results of our experiments in short wave generation. First we will present results of fifth- and seventh-harmonic conversion of pump pulses at 266.1 nm in helium and neon. Then we will describe observations of six-wave mixing which involve the lower-order harmonics of the YAG laser as well as the fourth harmonic. Finally, we will compare the strength of the fifth-harmonic conversion of the 266.1 nm pump pulses in several of the rare gases.

Energy level diagrams are shown in Fig. 5 for fifth-harmonic conversion of radiation at 266.1 nm in He, Ne, Ar, and Kr along with the seventh-harmonic process in helium. Different experimental conditions are encountered in each of the rare gases. For the fifth-harmonic process in helium, there are detunings of about 1700 cm^{-1} between the $3P$ level and the fifth-harmonic frequency and 16 000 cm^{-1} between the $2S$ state and the frequency of four pump photons. Although these detunings are quite large, the $3P$ level does provide modest enhancement of the fifth-order susceptibility. In addition, helium is transparent at the fifth-harmonic wavelength and it has negative dispersion for this process. Therefore, it is expected that the fifth-harmonic conversion can be maximized through phase optimization in a tight focus.

In neon there is a near four-photon resonance with the even parity $3p[1\frac{1}{2}]\ J = 2$ level for which the detuning from line center is about 12 cm^{-1}. Estimates of the laser linewidth indicate that there actually is some overlap of the laser with the four-photon resonance level. In the absence of large Stark shifts this resonance is expected to enhance the conversion efficiency significantly. However, the fifth-harmonic frequency is in the photoionization continuum of neon and therefore efficient conversion is expected only for pumping geometries in which the waist of the focused beam is shorter than the absorption length. For example, at a pressure of 40 torr the absorption length at 53.2 nm is about 1 mm. As a result, conversion may be limited by absorption in our experiments with the 10 and 20 cm focal length lenses. In argon, there is a moderate three-photon resonance with the $3d[3\frac{1}{2}]^0 J = 3$ level ($\Delta\tilde{\nu} = 291$ cm^{-1}), but the fifth-harmonic wavelength is further into the continuum than in neon, with a larger

TABLE I

Order	Process	λ	Gas
7	7 x 266.1 nm	38 nm	He
5	5 x 266.1	53.2	He, Ne, Ar, Kr
	4 x 266.1 + 532	59.1	He, Ne
	4 x 266.1 + 1064	62.6	He, Ne
	4 x 266.1 - 1064	70.9	He, Ne
	4 x 266.1 - 532	76.0	He, Ne
3	3 x 266.1	88.6	He, Ne
	2 x 266.1 + 532	106.4	He, Ne
	2 x 266.1 + 1064	118.2	Ne

absorption cross section. In krypton, the three photon level lies just below the photoabsorption edge, providing possible resonant enhancement from odd parity states near the ionization continuum, while the photoabsorption cross section at 53.2 nm is comparable to that in argon.

The results of the short wave generation experiments along with the processes involved are summarized in Table I. They have resulted in the generation of coherent radiation at six new wavelengths below 100 nm through fifth- and seventh-order frequency conversion. The shortest wavelength radiation which we observed was at 38 nm. It was obtained as the seventh harmonic of the pump pulses at 266.1 nm. At this writing this is the shortest wavelength at which coherent radiation has been reported. The fifth-order processes of harmonic generation and six-wave mixing were used to produce radiation at 5 wavelengths from 53.2 to 76 nm. In addition to the higher-order processes, third-order interactions were used to generate radiation at three more wavelengths out to 118 nm.

A. Fifth Harmonic

Fifth-harmonic conversion was observed in all of these gases. Initial experiments were performed to detect the generated light at 53.2 nm and to verify its origin as due to fifth-harmonic conversion. Measurements of the signal at 53.2 nm were made both photographically and photoelectrically as described in the previous section. A densitometer tracing of a photographic spectrum taken in neon at a pressure of 40 torr is shown in Fig. 6. The generated signal (top tracing) shows a single spectral line with a width which is instrument limited by the size of the beam at the entrance aperture. The wavelength of this line was measured by maximizing the photomultiplier signal as the spectrometer setting was varied, giving a value of $\lambda = 53.2 \pm 0.1$ nm. This wavelength is in good agreement with the expected value of 53.225 nm which was determined by calibrating the laser second harmonic wavelength against a neon discharge spectrum. For comparison, a helium discharge spectrum is also shown in Fig. 6 (lower trace) with three of the helium emission lines evident.

The variation of the strength of the generated signal with the incident pump power in neon at a pressure of 40 torr was measured with the scintillator and visible photomultiplier (Fig. 7). A least-square fit to the data shows a power law dependence with an exponent of 4.7, in reasonable agreement with the expected fifth power dependence. This combination of correct power dependence combined with a single narrow isolated spectral line at the correct frequency serves to confirm that the observed signal arose from the fifth-harmonic process.

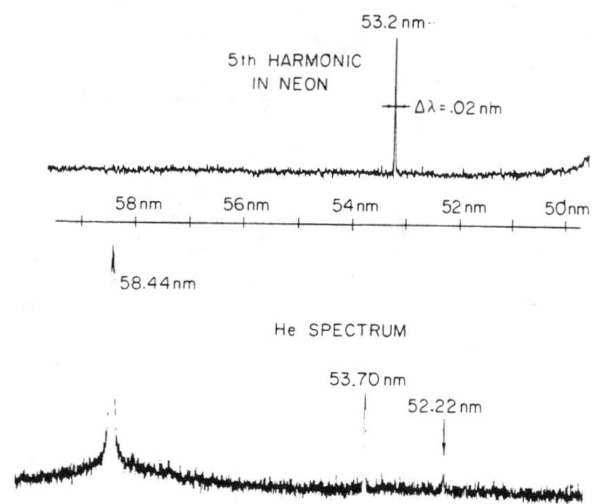

Fig. 6. Densitometer trace of photographic spectrum of fifth-harmonic radiation generation in neon (top). Spectrum from a helium discharge is also shown (bottom).

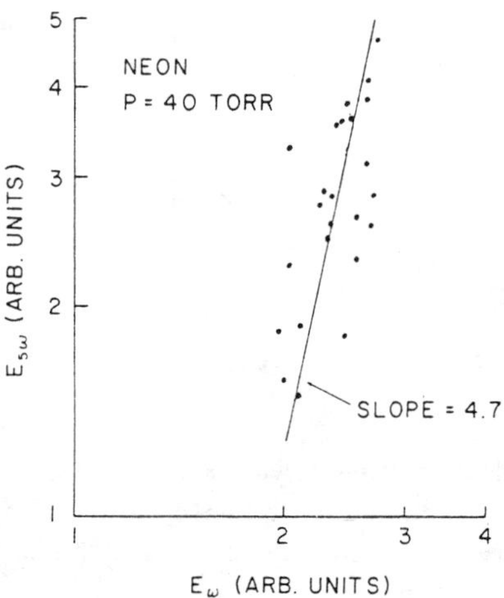

Fig. 7. Variation of fifth-harmonic signal with pump strength in neon at a pressure of 40 torr. Line is least square fit to data and shows a power low dependence with an exponent of 4.7.

B. Seventh Harmonic

Similar measurements were made to generate and detect radiation at the seventh harmonic of the 266.1 nm pump at 38 nm. This process is indicated for helium in Fig. 5. Although the generated radiation lies in the photoionization continuum, the absorption cross section is only 4.5 Mb, slightly more than one-half of the cross section for 53.2 nm radiation in neon. Absorption cross sections for the other rare gases at 38 nm are much larger than that in helium and indeed helium is the only material in which we have seen seventh-harmonic signals.

Observation of the seventh-harmonic signals were again made both photographically and photoelectrically. A densitometer trace of a photographic spectrum of the harmonic radiation in the vicinity of 38 nm is shown in Fig. 8. For these measurements, a 5 cm CaF_2 focal length lens was used. Single isolated spectral lines whose widths were again instrument limited were observed at the wavelengths expected for both the seventh- and fifth-harmonic signals. Variation of the seventh-harmonic signal with pump strength was also observed (Fig. 9). The results show reasonable agreement with the ex-

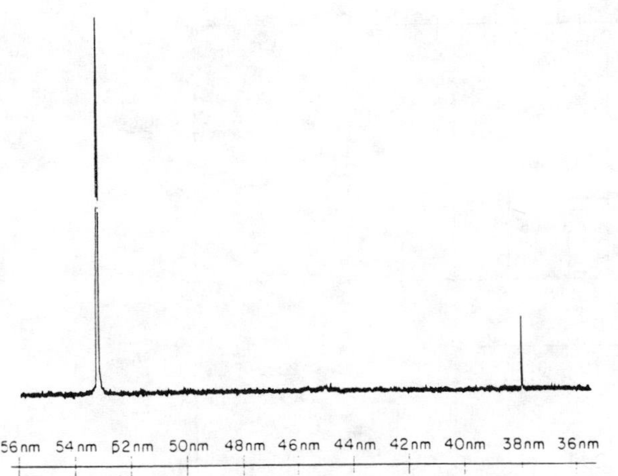

Fig. 8. Densitometer trace of photographic spectrum showing fifth- and seventh-harmonic lines generated in helium.

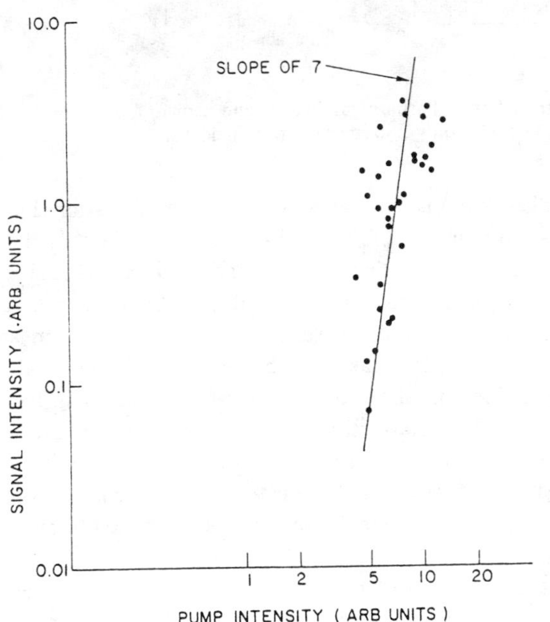

Fig. 9. Variation of seventh-harmonic signal in helium with pump strength. Data show agreement with expected seventh power law dependence.

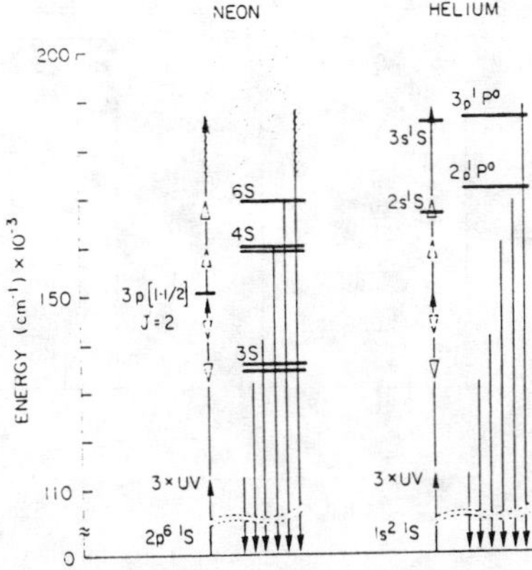

Fig. 10. Energy level diagram showing six-wave mixing processes in helium and neon. New radiation is generated by the processes 4 × 266.1 nm (solid arrows) ± 532.2 nm (open arrows) and 4 × 266.1 nm ± 1064.4 nm (dashed arrows). Fifth- and third-harmonic generation of 266.1 nm radiation is also shown.

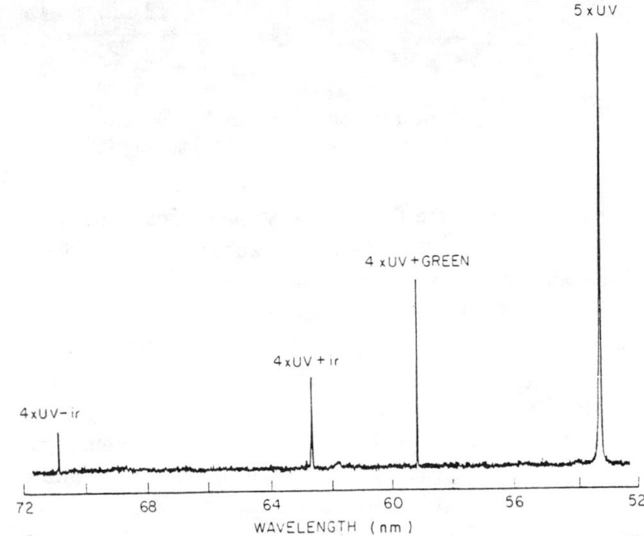

Fig. 11. Densitometer tracing of photographic spectrum showing three of the fifth-order mixing lines. Fifth-harmonic line is also present.

pected seventh power-law dependence. The center wavelength of the signal was found to be 38.05 ±0.1 nm by varying the spectrometer setting, in good agreement with the expected value of 38.02 nm.

C. Six-Wave Mixing

In addition to harmonic conversion of the 266 nm radiation, six-wave mixing involving the other harmonics of the YAG laser can be used to generate coherent radiation at additional wavelengths in the XUV. Energy level diagrams of He and Ne are shown in Fig. 10 for one type of six-wave mixing process. In these interactions, one photon at the YAG fundamental or second harmonic is either added to or subtracted from four photons at the YAG fourth harmonic. Of the many possible fifth-order processes, this class of interaction is expected to be the strongest in our experiments because the YAG laser fundamental and second harmonic are severely depleted in the second harmonic conversion stages. Third-harmonic generation is also shown for each gas.

Helium is transparent at all of the wavelengths generated in these processes (see Table I), but all except the fifth harmonic of 266.1 nm lie below the $2p$ resonance level. As a result, the mixing processes will be positively dispersive in helium and no significant resonant enhancement is expected. Neon is transparent to the third harmonic and all of the fifth-order lines except the fifth harmonic. Various amounts of detuning from odd parity levels, indicating possible resonant enhancement, are encountered for the different wavelength combinations as well as both positive and negative dispersion. In addition, the near four photon resonance with the $3P[1\frac{1}{2}]\ J = 2$ level is involved in all of the fifth-order processes. In the next section, data will be given which indicate that in neon, the four photon resonance is not effective in enhancing the fifth-harmonic conversion over that observed in other rare gases, indicating the possible presence of strong Stark shifts.

A densitometer tracing of a photograph of a spectrum taken in neon at a pressure of 30 torr using a 5 cm focal length lens is shown in Fig. 11. Three of the fifth-order mixing lines are

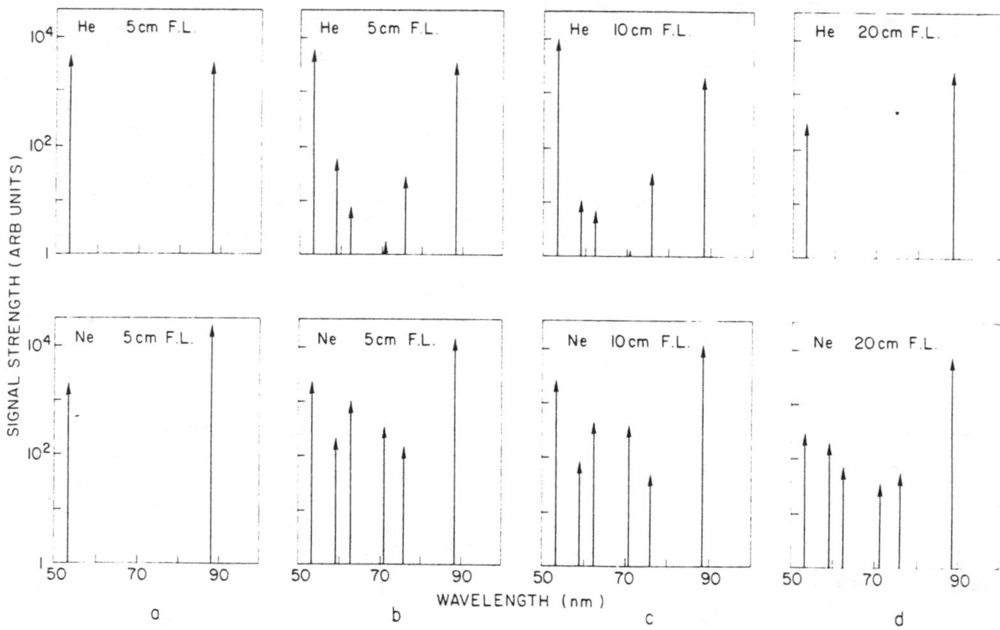

Fig. 12. Comparison of strength of fifth-order mixing lines and fifth and third harmonic in helium and neon at a pressure of 30 torr for various focusing lenses. Data in (a) were taken with only 266 nm radiation incident.

evident, along with the fifth harmonic line. The longer wavelength radiation could not be photographed because of the increasing absorption of the aluminum filter.

The variation of the intensities of the fifth-order lines in both helium and neon was measured at a pressure of 30 torr as the strength of the focusing lens was changed. These results are shown in Fig. 12 for the 5, 10, and 20 cm lenses, along with data taken with only the UV pump present [Fig. 12(a)]. The signals were detected with the solar blind photomultiplier and, for purposes of comparison, were corrected relative to the fifth-harmonic signal for the spectral dependence of the detection system.

Data taken with only the UV pump incident into the cell show only harmonics of the UV signal, indicating that the mixing lines did indeed require the presence of the other laser harmonics. A detailed theoretical understanding of the relative intensities of the various lines requires exact knowledge of the energy and beam waist dimensions of each of the laser harmonics, the degree of spatial and temporal overlap of the various harmonics at the focus of the lens, and the gas density variation near the beam focus. Comparison of the observed signal strengths can, however, give qualitative indications of some of the major features of the various interactions. For example, the fifth-order mixing lines are stronger in neon than in helium for each of the lenses used. This effect is especially evident in data taken with the 20 cm focal length lens. This observed difference is likely to be due to a larger nonlinear susceptibility in neon than in helium arising from a larger nonresonant polarizability combined with possible resonant enhancements. In helium, on the other hand, generation of the fifth-order combination lines is likely to be discriminated against by the positive dispersion which exists for these processes. The importance of dispersion is also reflected in the dominance of the fifth-harmonic signal in helium, for which the dispersion is favorable, over the combination lines. A similar dominance of the fifth-harmonic signal over the fifth-order combination lines is not seen in neon. This characteristic may be due to unfavorable dispersion in neon or to loss at the fifth-harmonic wavelength due to continuum absorption. Finally, data taken with the 5 and 10 cm focal length lenses in helium show that conversion to the fifth harmonic is greater than conversion to the third. To our knowledge, this is the first time conversion to a higher harmonic has been observed to exceed conversion to a lower one in the same system and confirms one of the theoretical predictions given in Section II.

In addition to the lines shown in Fig. 12, radiation was seen at spectrometer settings of 106.4 and 118.2 nm, corresponding to the third-order processes 2×266.1 nm + 532 nm and 2×266.1 nm + 1064.4 nm, respectively.

D. Comparison of Fifth-Harmonic Conversion in Rare Gases

The relative strength of fifth-harmonic generation in several of the rare gases was also investigated. Results are shown in Fig. 13 for measurements taken in He, Ne, Ar, and Kr using the 10 cm focal length lens and the full laser power (peak intensity near 2×10^{14} W/cm^2). As was pointed out earlier, helium is transparent at 53.2 nm while neon, argon, and krypton can be photoionized by the fifth-harmonic radiation with cross sections of 7, 36, and 32 Mb, respectively. At low pressures (0.5–1 torr) the fifth-harmonic conversion in the three absorbing gases is greater for the heavier gases. This trend is the same as that for the nonresonant third-order susceptibility at longer wavelengths [2] and very likely reflects the relative size of the fifth-order susceptibility for these materials.

The relatively low conversion in neon as compared to the other gases indicates that the four photon resonance is not

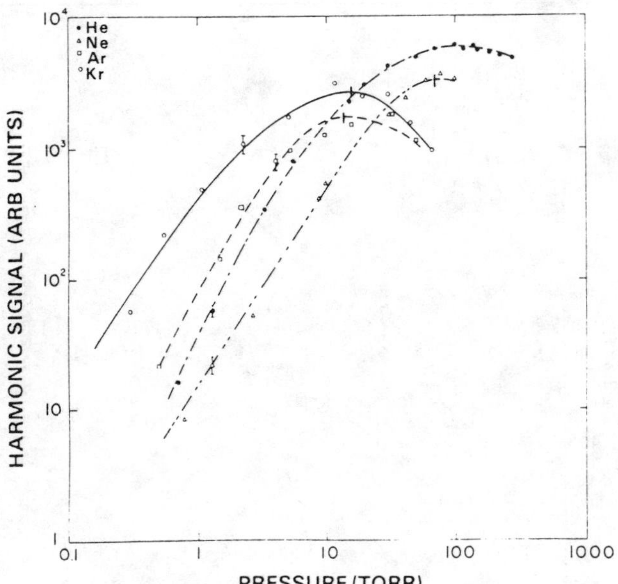

Fig. 13. Comparison of fifth-harmonic signal in four of the rare gases as a function of pressure. Data were taken using a 10 cm focal length lens ($b = 2$ nm) and vertical line near the peak of each curve indicates the pressure at which the absorption length in each gas was equal to $\frac{1}{4}$ of the confocal parameter.

effective in enhancing the susceptibility for fifth-harmonic conversion. Stark shifts of the order of 1000 cm^{-1} have been calculated [24] for other atomic systems under conditions of near two-photon-resonant excitation at pump intensities of the order of 10^{15} W/cm^2. Stark shifts of similar magnitude may also be present here preventing significant resonant enhancement from taking place.

As the pressure is increased, the conversion reaches a maximum for each gas and then decreases. The vertical line near the peak of each curve indicates the pressure at which the photoionization absorption length equals the distance required for the focused intensity to drop by 20 percent (~0.5 mm). The good correlation between this pressure and the pressure at which each curve peaks indicates that the limitation observed in these gases is due to photoabsorption of the harmonic radiation. At the highest pressures used here, the order of increasing conversion has changed from that observed at low pressures, with more conversion being seen in the gases with the lower absorption cross section. Conversion in helium lies between that in neon and argon at low pressures. At high pressures, the greatest conversion is observed in helium, which is the only gas which is transparent at 53.2 nm. Saturation of the conversion is also observed in helium near 100 torr. Since helium is transparent it is not expected that this behavior is due to the same cause as in the absorbing gases. The origins of this saturation will be discussed in more detail in the following sections.

These results show that significantly more conversion can be obtained in argon and krypton than in helium and neon at low pressures where absorption is negligible. This indicates that considerable improvement in efficiency should be possible for the generation of radiation at wavelengths which lie below the absorption edges of krypton and argon (88.5 and 78.6 nm, respectively).

V. Comparison with Theory

The variation of fifth-harmonic conversion in helium as a function of gas pressure can be compared directly with the theoretical predictions given in Section II. As was pointed out earlier, for a single component vapor, the theoretical variation of the harmonic power is given by the quantity $|(b\Delta k)F(b\Delta k)|^2$ [see (11)]. This function is replotted in Figs. 14 and 15 for fifth-harmonic generation with the phase optimization integral F evaluated between the limits $(\xi', \xi = \infty)$ (curve b) and $(\xi' = \infty, \xi = 0)$ (curve a). For a constant value of b, corresponding to the use of a single focusing lens, the quantity $b\Delta k$ is proportional to gas pressure. As was pointed out earlier, the calculated harmonic power rises at low pressures and peaks when the dispersion is optimum to offset the phase shift in the focus. At low pressures, the calculated harmonic power for the full focus varies as N^8 because of the near cancellation of the harmonic signal in the front and back half of the focus. The calculated conversion for one-half of the focus has a much weaker dependence at low pressures, varying as N^2. The greatest harmonic conversion is obtained at the peak of the full focus curve but at low pressures more conversion is obtained for interaction with one-half of the focus.

Experimental measurements of fifth-harmonic conversion as a function of pressure for focusing with the 5 and 10 cm lenses are compared with the theory in Figs. 14 and 15, respectively. Measurements for two different laser powers are shown for each lens. The horizontal scale for these measurements was fixed by the measured value of b and the calculated value of the dispersion Δk. The value of $b\Delta k$ which corresponds to a pressure of 10 torr is indicated for each set of measurements. The vertical scale is fixed by estimating the absolute conversion from the observed photomultiplier signals and measured values of filter transmission and comparing this measured value with the theoretical one. The expected theoretical fifth power dependence on pump strength has been divided out of the experimental data so that measurements with the same lens but different laser power can be compared with the same theoretical curve.

The measurements with the 5 and 10 cm lenses show similar qualitative trends. At low pressures the measured harmonic signals follow a square law dependence on gas pressure but deviate from this behavior at higher pressures. This density dependence at low pressures is in agreement with the behavior predicted by theory for interaction with one-half of the focused beam. This can be understood by considering the vapor density distribution near the aperture. Flow of a relatively high pressure gas through a constricting aperture into a vacuum will result in the development of a shock front accompanied by a sharp drop in density at, or down stream from, the aperture [26]. Consequently, the aperture behaves as if it were a window at the focus of the beam. While this analogy is not exact, the very different behavior between the half and full focus curves indicates that the window-like effect is strong enough to enable us to restrict attention to calculations using one half of the focus. The deviation of the harmonic signals from

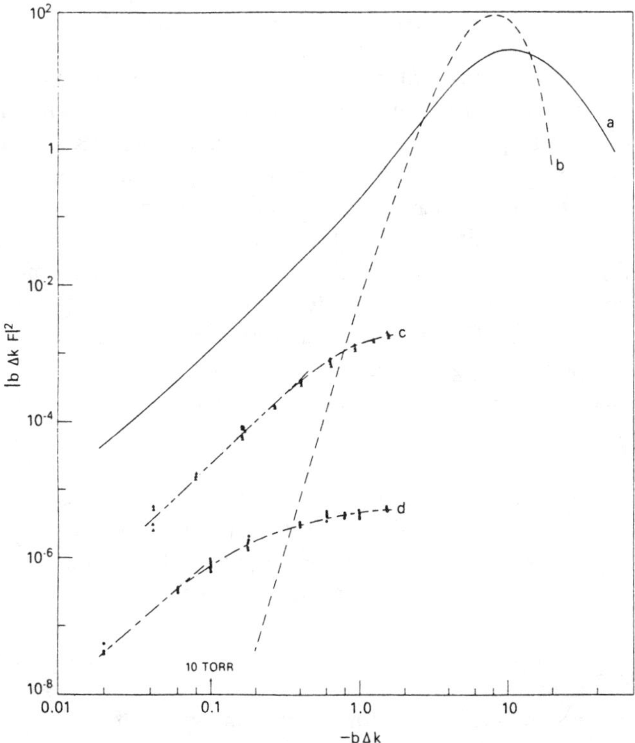

Fig. 14. Comparison of measured fifth-harmonic conversion in helium with theory for data taken with a 5 cm focusing lens (b = 0.5 mm). Curves (a) and (b) were calculated for phase optimization integral F evaluated between limits ($-\infty$, 0) and ($-\infty$, ∞), respectively. Data curve (c) was obtained with reduced laser power ($I_{peak} \approx 2.5 \times 10^{14}$ W/cm^2) while data curve d was obtained with full laser power ($I_{peak} \approx 10^{15}$ W/cm^2). The fifth power law dependence has been divided out of the two sets of data so that they can be compared with a single theoretical curve. Horizontal scale is proportional to gas pressure and vertical arrow indicates position corresponding to 10 torr.

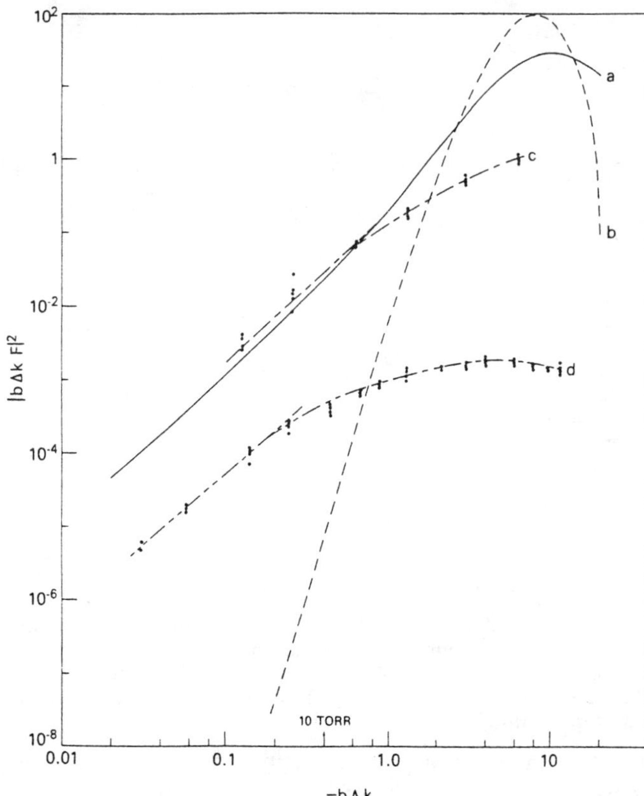

Fig. 15. Comparison of measured fifth-harmonic conversion in helium with theory for data taken with 10 cm focusing lens, (b = 2 mm). Curves (a) and (b) were calculated for phase optimization integral F evaluated between limits ($-\infty$, 0) and ($-\infty$, ∞), respectively. Data curve (c) was obtained with reduced laser power ($I_{peak} \approx 0.5 \times 10^{14}$ W/cm^2) and data curve (d) was obtained with full laser power ($I_{peak} \approx 2.5 \times 10^{14}$ W/cm^2). The fifth power law dependence has been divided out of each set of experimental data so that they can be compared with the same theoretical curve. Arrow indicates value of $b\Delta k$ corresponding to 10 torr.

the N^2 behavior occurs at lower pressures than the theory predicts for all of the combinations of lens focal length and laser power which we used. Such behavior indicates that additional effects may become important at these pressures in limiting the observed conversion.

The absolute conversion level is lower than that predicted by theory for all of the measurements taken with the 5 cm lens. The greatest conversion efficiency which we observed, 10^{-5}, was obtained with the 5 cm focal length lens at full laser power. Although the largest measured conversion efficiency is several orders of magnitude below the theoretical values, the power in the harmonic pulse was of the order of 10^3 W, comparable to powers obtained from some visible dye lasers. Less absolute conversion was observed with the 5 cm lens at the lower laser power but agreement with theory was better.

The same general trends were observed when the 10 cm focal length lens was used. Again the measured values of harmonic conversion were well below the corresponding theoretical values for the higher laser power and better agreement between theory and experiment was obtained with reduced laser power. For measurements done with the 10 cm lens at reduced laser power, agreement between experiment and theory is within a factor 2 at low pressures. These trends again indicate that additional effects become important at higher pressures and laser powers and serve to limit attainable conversion. Some of the processes which can be responsible for such effects will be discussed in the next section.

VI. Competing Processes

The results presented in the last section indicate that one or more additional effects which can limit fifth-harmonic conversion becomes important at high gas pressure and high incident laser power. Several processes, such as multiphoton ionization, dielectric breakdown, saturation of excited state population through multiphoton absorption, Stark shifts, and intensity dependent changes of the refractive index (quadratic Kerr effect) have been suggested in the literature as being responsible for the saturation of third-order frequency conversion [3], [9], [22]-[24], [27]-[30]. Experimental evidence has been given for some of these processes, although some experimental results appear to be open to more than one interpretation [23]. In this section we will discuss the extent to which these mechanisms affect our experiments and will present further measurements which indicate the relative importance of the various processes in limiting the fifth-harmonic conversion.

The effects of the competing processes on harmonic generation can be grouped into two broad categories: changes in the magnitude of the nonlinear susceptibility and changes in the

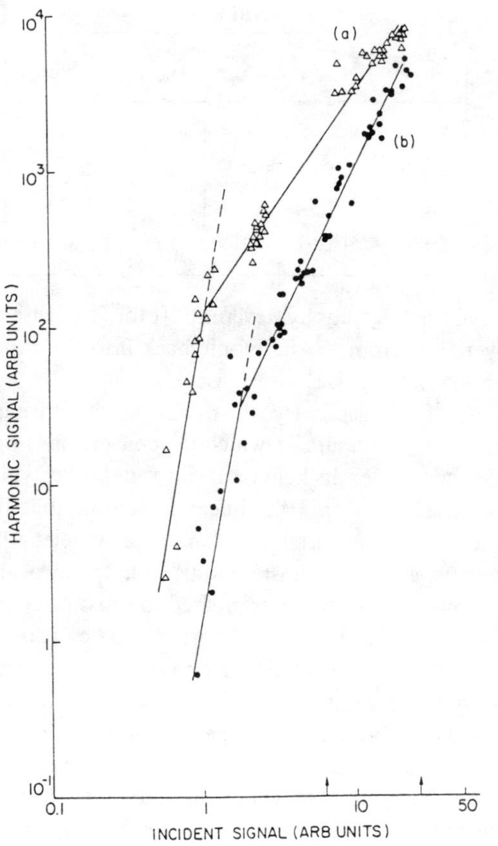

Fig. 16. Dependence of fifth-harmonic signal on pump strength for helium pressure of 100 torr (a), and 30 torr (b).

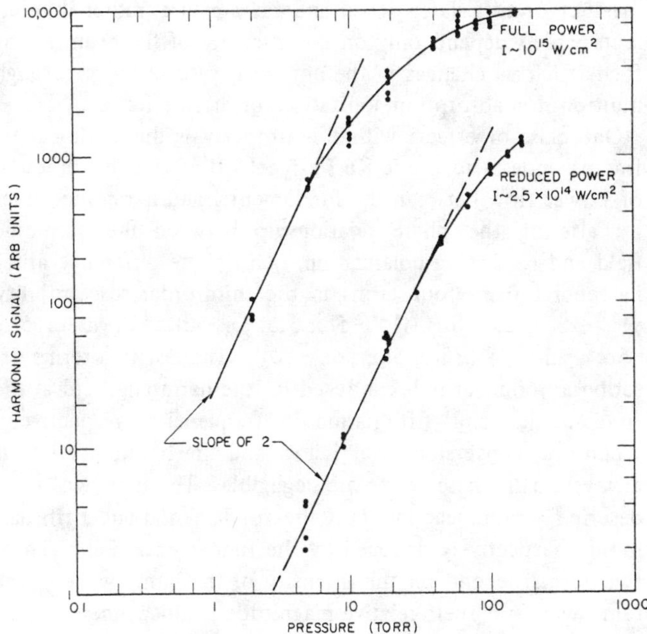

Fig. 17. Dependence of fifth-harmonic signal on helium pressure for full laser power (a), and reduced laser power (b).

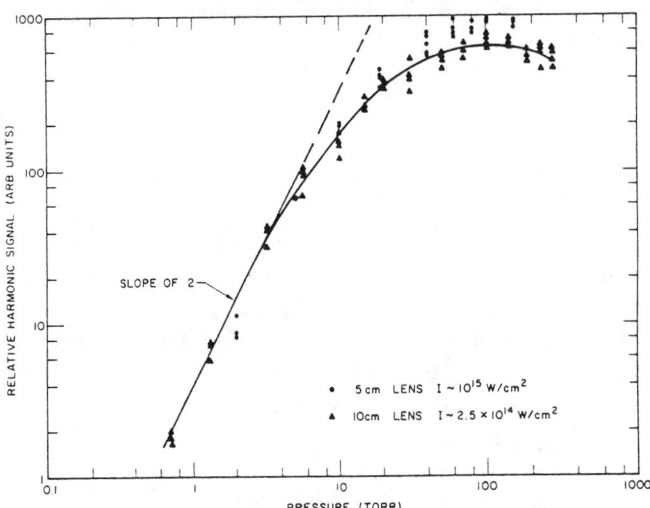

Fig. 18. Comparison of fifth-harmonic signal as function of helium pressure for two different focal length lenses at full laser power.

refractive indices. Changes in the nonlinear susceptibility affect harmonic conversion by changing the strength of the nonlinear interaction, while the nonlinear refractive index affects conversion by changing the direction of power flow from the fundamental to the harmonic wave. Some of the processes listed above can contribute to both of these effects. For example, saturation of excited state population by multiphoton absorption can affect the nonlinear susceptibility by changing the electron population distribution [this changes N in (1)]. The Stark effect can change the susceptibility by changing resonant denominators [see (4)] during the time the driving pulse is on. These terms also contribute to the total nonlinear refractive index, again through population changes or level shifts and comprise part of the nonlinear index coefficient which is calculated from perturbation theory. In the experimental results which follow, we will attempt to identify the relative importance of these effects in limiting fifth-harmonic conversion in helium.

Measurements of the harmonic signal as a function of pump strength are shown in Fig. 16 for helium pressures of 30 and 100 torr. At low pump levels the harmonic signals follow a fifth power law dependence on pump strength for each pressure, as is expected from theory. However, the harmonic signals deviate from this ideal behavior at higher pump levels, following a much weaker dependence on pump strength.

The same general behavior is evident in the pressure dependent data discussed earlier. The measurements using the 5 cm lens showing harmonic signal strength variation with helium pressure at two different pump levels is shown again in Fig. 17. The point at which the harmonic signals deviate from the theoretical dependence on pressure occurs at a higher gas pressure for the lower pump power.

The behavior of the harmonic conversion on pump strength and gas pressure shown in Figs. 16 and 17 is qualitatively consistent with all of the effects mentioned above. In an effort to distinguish among them further we compared the harmonic conversion obtained with two different lenses (5 and 10 cm focal length) at a constant pump power (Fig. 18). Very little difference is seen between the curves obtained with different focal lengths lenses. This means that although the saturation of the harmonic conversion depends on the incident laser power and the gas pressure, it does not depend on how tightly the beam is focused at the maximum laser power. This behavior is characteristic of effects which depend only on the product of total laser power and gas pressure, rather than effects which depend only on the intensity of the beam at the focus such as changes in the nonlinear susceptibility through multiphoton absorption, ionization, or Stark effects.

One class of effects with this property is the nonlinear refractive index (quadratic Kerr effect). It affects the direction of power flow between the fundamental and harmonic waves by altering the phase relationship between the harmonic field and its driving polarization. This phase difference arises in general from four terms in the third-order susceptibility $\chi^{(3)}(-\omega, \omega, \omega, -\omega)$, $\chi^{(3)}(-5\omega, 5\omega, \omega, -\omega)$, $\chi^{(3)}(-\omega, \omega, 5\omega, -5\omega)$, and $\chi^{(3)}(-5\omega, 5\omega, 5\omega, -5\omega)$. The last two terms describe a nonlinear index induced by the harmonic field at the fundamental and fifth-harmonic frequencies, respectively. When the conversion level is low and the harmonic field is always small, these terms are negligible. The first two terms describe a nonlinear index at the fundamental and fifth harmonic, respectively, induced by the fundamental field. These two terms depend on the intensity of the pump wave in the same way and their relative magnitude is independent of the strength of the harmonic field.

The importance of this effect may be estimated by evaluating the total on-axis accumulated nonlinear phase shift between the nonlinear polarization and the harmonic field in one-half of the focus:

$$\Delta\phi_{NL} = \Delta\phi^{NL}_{E_{5\omega}} - \Delta\phi^{NL}_{P_{5\omega}}$$

$$= N\left[k_{5\omega} n_2(5\omega, \omega) - 5k_\omega n_2(\omega, \omega)\right] \int_{-\infty}^{0} \langle E^2_\omega(z)\rangle dz \tag{15}$$

where k is the optical wave vector, n_2 is the nonlinear coefficient of refractive index per atom and is related to the susceptibility by $n_2(q\omega, \omega) = (\pi/n_0)\chi^{(3)}(-q\omega, q\omega, \omega, -\omega)$, and $E_\omega(z)$ is the peak on axis optical field at the fundamental frequency. For a beam with a Gaussian profile

$$\langle E^2(z)\rangle = \langle E_0^2\rangle/(1 + (2z/b)^2),$$

(15) becomes

$$\Delta\phi_{NL} = \frac{4\pi^2 k_{5\omega}(n_2(5\omega, \omega) - n_2(\omega, \omega))}{c n_0 \lambda_\omega} PN \tag{16}$$

where P is the peak power in the fundamental beam. Equation (16) shows that the accumulated nonlinear phase shift depends only on the product of laser power and gas pressure since an increase in the peak disturbance of the refractive index due, for example, to tighter focusing, is exactly offset by a decrease in the depth of focus.

The value of the quantities $n_2(\omega, \omega)$ and $n_2(5\omega, \omega)$ are shown in Table II for helium along with the contribution each makes to the nonlinear phase change at two gas pressures for a pump power of 300 MW. The contribution of the nonlinear index at the fundamental wavelength is small even at 100 torr. The nonlinear coefficient at the harmonic frequency, however, is more than two orders of magnitude greater than that at the fundamental due to the near-resonance with the $3P$ level. As a result the nonlinear phase change of the harmonic field is large enough even at 20 torr to cause a reversal of power flow from the harmonic back into the fundamental at the peak of the pulse.

TABLE II

$\frac{n_2}{N}$	Frequency	$\Delta\phi_{NL}$	Pressure
2×10^{-37}	$(-\omega,\omega,-\omega,\omega)$	$0.04\ \pi$	100 Torr
2×10^{-37}	$(-\omega,\omega,-\omega,\omega)$	$0.008\ \pi$	20 Torr
2.6×10^{-35}	$(-5\omega,\omega,-\omega,5\omega)$	$-5\ \pi$	100 Torr
2.6×10^{-35}	$(-5\omega,\omega,-\omega,5\omega)$	$-1\ \pi$	20 Torr

In a tight-focus geometry, the nonlinear refractive index will also change the pressure at which the conversion is optimized. The nonlinear index in helium at 5ω is negative, while that at ω is positive, enhancing the linear dispersion already present between the fundamental and harmonic wavelengths. Thus the pressure at which the harmonic conversion peaks should shift to lower values when compared to those calculated using the theory in Section II. Therefore, on the basis of these preliminary estimates, the optical Kerr effect can account at least qualitatively for some of the discrepancies we have observed between the theoretical and experimental variation of the harmonic signal with gas pressure. Further studies are needed to determine the extent to which the quadratic Kerr effect or other mechanisms can account for our remaining observations.

VII. Discussion

We have presented experimental results in this paper which demonstrate that useful amounts of radiation in the XUV can be generated by frequency conversion using higher-order optical nonlinearities. Because of the high intensities needed for these higher-order processes they probably will not replace second- and third-order conversion processes in the visible and near UV. However, for generation of coherent light in the XUV, they offer very real advantages over the lower-order processes, especially with regard to the choice of pumping wavelengths, without significant sacrifice in conversion efficiency in this wavelength range.

Our measurements of fifth-order frequency mixing indicate the feasibility of using dye lasers, already available in the visible and near UV, to generate tunable coherent radiation in the XUV range between about 40 and 100 nm. Although our experiments were done with fixed frequency pump sources, they indicate that these processes should provide tunable radiation in the XUV just as the third-order frequency mixing processes do at longer wavelengths in the vacuum UV [6]-[8].

Theoretical conversion efficiencies to the XUV are well into the range of pump depletion for existing laser powers indicating the possibility of conversion well in excess of 50 percent. Experimentally observed conversion efficiencies, however, fall several orders of magnitude below these values indicating that, under the conditions of the present experiments, additional mechanisms are acting to limit attainable conversion. On the basis of additional experimental measurements we have suggested that the quadratic Kerr effect can account qualitatively for some of the differences between theory and experiment.

Similar conclusions have been reached with third-order frequency mixing processes [22], [30]. With the third-order interactions, the Kerr effect is an absolute limiting process, since both the nonlinear index and the third-order susceptibility governing frequency conversion carry the same resonant denominators and dependence on laser power. With the fifth-harmonic process, however, it is possible to discriminate against the limitations due to the quadratic Kerr effect by taking advantage of the differences in the two processes with respect to beam focusing, pump intensity, or resonant structure of the susceptibility. For example, use of tighter focusing would increase the fifth-harmonic signal [see (11)] while leaving the nonlinear phase change unaltered. In this manner, conversion efficiency could be maintained while at the same time the effect of the nonlinear index could be reduced by lowering the incident laser power. Unfortunately, the absolute harmonic signal will drop with decreases in laser power. A second possibility is to use resonant enhancements to favor the fifth-harmonic process. A third-order resonance will enhance the fifth-order susceptibility without changing either of the terms which contribute to the nonlinear phase changes arising from the third-order nonlinear index. All other resonances contained in the fifth-order susceptibility are also contained in one or the other of the nonlinear index terms. Thus, by judicious choice of pump wavelength and mixing medium, the fifth-harmonic conversion efficiencies reported here could be expected to be increased. Of course, such a change could also result in other differences, such as an increased importance of third-harmonic generation and the cascade fifth-harmonic process, as well as possible increased importance of higher-order limiting processes such as the fifth-order Kerr effect. As a final example of a possible method for improving the fifth-harmonic conversion, we can consider increasing the detuning of the harmonic frequency from the nearest level (e.g., the $3P$ level in helium). Since the major contribution to the nonlinear index comes from the term resonant with this level, increased detuning would reduce the effect of the nonlinear index by decreasing the magnitude of n_2. A similar reduction in the magnitude of the fifth-harmonic susceptibility would also occur. However, this reduction could be offset by changing the pump power or the focusing. Because of the difference in the dependence on beam focusing and pump power of the two effects, it is then possible to maintain the fifth-harmonic conversion while reducing the effects of the nonlinear index. Thus it is possible, in principle at least, to increase both the fifth-harmonic conversion efficiency and output power over the levels reported here when the dominant limiting mechanism is the quadratic Kerr effect. Future experimental and theoretical results are needed to determine the extent to which the fifth-harmonic conversion process can actually be improved by these techniques.

The present results can be extended to the generation of radiation at still shorter wavelengths either by using even higher-order processes or shorter wavelength pump sources. Recently, ninth-harmonic conversion to 118 nm in sodium vapor with an efficiency of 10^{-16} was reported [16]. Such low conversion efficiencies indicate that amplification in the XUV may be desirable to raise the harmonic power to useful levels. Our attempts to observe the ninth-harmonic of the 266 nm pulses at 29.6 nm were unsuccessful since we could not detect a signal at that wavelength above our noise level, again indicating very low conversion for this process. Alternatively, shorter wavelength pump sources should be capable of generating shorter wavelength radiation through fifth- and seventh-order processes similar to those reported here. As in all frequency mixing processes, however, these interactions are extremely sensitive to the bandwidth of the pump radiation. We have seen evidence in our experiments that an increase in pump bandwidth, due for example to an increase in the self phase modulation occurring in the YAG amplifiers, results in a decrease in conversion efficiency, even for a constant peak intensity. Thus, it is desirable to emphasize the spectral quality of pump sources at shorter wavelengths if they are to be used for pumping frequency conversion processes into the XUV.

Acknowledgment

The authors wish to thank R. C. Elton and R. A. Andrews for support and encouragement of this work, and N. E. Karangelen for assistance with many of the early experiments. They also wish to thank R. H. Lehmberg, S. E. Harris, J. F. Young, G. C. Bjorklund, and E. A. Stappaerts for many helpful discussions. One of the authors (C. Y. She) also wishes to thank R. C. Elton for giving him assistance and hospitality during his sabbatical leave at the Naval Research Laboratory where this work was performed.

References

[1] The field of frequency conversion is so widespread and has so many contributors that it is impossible to reference every paper. The references given below list either first reports of various effects or are papers that have direct bearing on the work being reported here. It is not meant to be a complete list of references to this topic.

[2] J. F. Ward and G. H. C. New, "Optical third harmonic generation in gases by a focused laser beam," *Phys. Rev.*, vol. 185, pp. 57–72, 1969.

[3] R. B. Miles and S. E. Harris, "Optical third-harmonic generation in alkali metal vapors," *IEEE J. Quantum Electron.*, vol. QE-9, pp. 470–484, Apr. 1973.

[4] A. H. Kung, J. F. Young, G. C. Bjorklund, and S. E. Harris, "Generation of vacuum ultraviolet radiation in phase matched Cd vapor," *Phys. Rev. Lett.*, vol. 29, pp. 985–988, 1972.

[5] A. H. Kung, J. F. Young, and S. E. Harris, "Generation of 1182 Å radiation in phase matched mixtures of inert gases," *Appl. Phys. Lett.*, vol. 22, pp. 301–302, 1973.

[6] R. T. Hodgson, P. P. Sorokin, and J. J. Wynne, "Tunable coherent vacuum ultraviolet generation in atomic vapors," *Phys. Rev. Lett.*, vol. 32, pp. 343–346, 1974.

[7] A. H. Kung, "Generation of tunable picosecond VUV radiation," *Appl. Phys. Lett.*, vol. 25, pp. 653–654, 1974.

[8] K. K. Innes, B. P. Stoicheff, and S. C. Wallace, "Four wave sum mixing (130–180 nm) in molecular vapors," *Appl. Phys. Lett.*, vol. 29, pp. 715–717, 1976.

[9] S. E. Harris, "Generation of vacuum ultraviolet and soft X-ray radiation using high order nonlinear optical polarizabilities," *Phys. Rev. Lett.*, vol. 31, pp. 341–344, 1973.

[10] S. A. Akhmanov, *et al.*, "Direct and cascade processes in higher optical harmonic generation," in *Abstracts 7th All-Union Conf. Coherent and Nonlinear Optics*, Tashkent, USSR, May 1974. Moscow, USSR: Moscow State Univ. Press, pp. 15–17.

[11] I. V. Tomov and M. C. Richardson, "Fifth-harmonic generation in isotropic media," *IEEE J. Quantum Electron.*, vol. QE-12, pp. 521–531, Sept. 1976.

[12] S. E. Harris, J. F. Young, A. H. Kung, D. M. Bloom, and G. C. Bjorklund, "Generation of ultraviolet and vacuum ultraviolet

radiation," in *Laser Spectroscopy*, R. G. Brewer and A. Mooradian, Ed. New York: Plenum, 1973, pp. 59-75.

[13] M. H. R. Hutchinson, C. C. Ling, and D. J. Bradley, "Generation of coherent radiation at 570 Å by frequency tripling," *Opt. Commun.*, vol. 18, pp. 203-204, 1976.

[14] S. A. Akhmanov, V. A. Martynov, S. M. Salficl, and V. G. Tunkin, "Observation of nonresonant six-photon processes in a calcite crystal," *Pis'ma Zh. Eksp. Teor. Fiz.*, vol. 22, pp. 143-147, 1975; also in *JETP Lett.*, vol. 22, pp. 65-67, 1975.

[15] D. I. Metchkov, V. M. Mitev, L. I. Pavlov, and K. V. Stamenov, "Fifth harmonic generation in sodium vapor," *Opt. Commun.*, vol. 21, pp. 391-394, 1977.

[16] M. G. Grozeva, D. I. Metchkov, V. M. Mitev, L. I. Pavlov, and K. V. Stamenov, "Direct ninth harmonic conversion of picosecond laser pulses," *Opt. Commun.*, vol. 23, pp. 77-79, 1977.

[17] J. Reintjes, R. C. Eckardt, C. Y. She, N. E. Karangelen, R. C. Elton, and R. A. Andrews, "Generation of coherent radiation at 53.2 nm by fifth harmonic conversion," *Phys. Rev. Lett.*, vol. 37, pp. 1540-1543, 1976.

[18] J. Reintjes, C. Y. She, R. C. Eckardt, N. E. Karangelen, R. A. Andrews, and R. C. Elton, "Seventh harmonic conversion of mode locked laser pulses to 38 nm," *Appl. Phys. Lett.*, vol. 30, pp. 480-482, 1977.

[19] C. Y. She and J. Reintjes, "Generation of step tunable coherent radiation in the XUV by fifth-order frequency mixing," *Appl. Phys. Lett.*, vol. 31, pp. 95-97, 1977.

[20] G. C. Bjorklund, "Effects of focusing on third-order nonlinear processes in isotropic media," *IEEE J. Quantum Electron.*, vol. QE-11, pp. 287-296, June 1975.

[21] E. Yablonovitch, C. Flytzanis, and N. Bloembergen, "Anisotropic interference of three-wave and double two-wave frequency mixing in GaAs," *Phys. Rev. Lett.*, vol. 29, pp. 865-868, 1972.

[22] H. Puell, K. Spanner, W. Falkenstein, W. Kaiser, and C. R. Vidal, "Third-harmonic generation of mode locked Nd-glass laser pulses in phase matched Rb-Xe mixtures," *Phys. Rev. A*, vol. 14, pp. 2240-2257, 1976.

[23] A. T. Georges, P. Lambropoulos, and J. H. Marburger, "Theory of third-harmonic generation in metal vapors under two-photon resonance conditions," *Phys. Rev. A*, vol. 15, pp. 300-307, 1977.

[24] E. A. Stappaerts, "Harmonic generation at high field strengths. Frequency shifts and saturation phenomena," *Phys. Rev. A*, vol. 11, pp. 1664-1667, 1975.

[25] J. Reintjes and R. C. Eckardt, "Efficient harmonic conversion from 532 to 266 nm in ADP and KD*P," *Appl. Phys. Lett.*, vol. 130, pp. 91-93, 1977.

[26] J. P. Valleau and J. M. Deckers, "A study of molecular interactions in molecular beams isolated from the exhaust of supersonic nozzles," *Can. J. Chem.*, vol. 42, pp. 225-245, 1964.

[27] C. C. Wang and L. I. Davis, Jr., "Saturation of resonant two-photon transitions in thallium vapor," *Phys. Rev. Lett.*, vol. 35, pp. 650-653, 1975.

[28] J. F. Ward and A. V. Smith, "Saturation of two-photon-resonant optical processes in cesium vapor," *Phys. Rev. Lett.*, vol. 35, pp. 653-656, 1975.

[29] A. T. Georges, P. Lambropoulous, and J. H. Marburger, "Two-photon resonant third-harmonic generation in cesium vapor," *Opt. Commun.*, vol. 18, pp. 509-512, 1976.

[30] L. J. Zych and J. F. Young, Limitation of 3547 to 1182 Å conversion efficiency in Xe," *IEEE J. Quantum Electron.*, vol. QE-14, pp. 147-149, Mar. 1978.

Reprinted with permission from *Optics Letters*, Vol. 5(7), pp. 282-284 (July 1980).

Generation of high-spectral-brightness tunable XUV radiation at 83 nm

H. Egger, R. T. Hawkins,* J. Bokor,† H. Pummer, M. Rothschild, and C. K. Rhodes

Department of Physics, University of Illinois at Chicago Circle, Chicago, Illinois 60680

Received March 24, 1980

High-spectral-brightness coherent XUV radiation has been produced by third-harmonic generation of a transform-limited-bandwidth KrF* laser in gaseous xenon. The observed XUV output, which was continuously tunable from 82.8 to 83.3 nm, had a peak power of 40 mW, a bandwidth <0.01 cm^{-1}, and absolute frequency control to within 0.04 cm^{-1}. The utility of this XUV source for high-resolution spectroscopic applications is demonstrated by absorption studies in molecular hydrogen.

The rapid development of rare-gas–halogen excimer lasers is permitting the detailed study of many nonlinear processes in the ultraviolet region. These include high-resolution multiquantum spectroscopy of high-lying atomic and molecular states,[1–3] state-selective collisional processes,[1,2] isotopically selective mechanisms involving excited molecular electronic levels,[3] and third-harmonic generation.[4] In this Letter, we report new results on third-harmonic conversion of excimer-laser radiation. The excimer-laser systems provide highly attractive fundamental sources for frequency conversion to the XUV because of their demonstrated ability to deliver tunable, very-high-spectral-brightness radiation in the ultraviolet region. This ability was clearly demonstrated by the early work of Hutchinson *et al.*,[5] who produced tunable, coherent radiation at ~57 nm by frequency tripling a xenon excimer laser.

The shortest-wavelength coherent radiation produced to date is at 38 nm, the 28th harmonic of the Nd:YAG laser.[6] That result was obtained in a cascade process by first generating the fourth harmonic (266.1 nm) of the Nd:YAG laser in two stages of frequency doubling and then directly generating the seventh harmonic of the 266.1-nm radiation in gaseous helium. The earlier work[6] stressed the need for new, powerful, narrow-bandwidth pump sources in the ultraviolet region for frequency conversion to the XUV.

Recently, a tunable, narrow-bandwidth KrF* laser was developed that exhibits performance parameters closely approaching the fundamental limits governing spectral linewidth, beam divergence, and absolute wavelength control.[7] This instrument combines the property of continuous tunability over the full KrF* gain profile with the following experimentally established characteristics: pulse energy ~60 mJ, pulse duration ~10 nsec, spectral linewidth 150 ± 30 MHz, absolute frequency control to within 300 MHz, and beam divergence ~50 μrad.

In this Letter, we report the generation of high-spectral-brightness, coherent, and continuously tunable XUV radiation in the vicinity of 83 nm by two-photon resonant frequency tripling in gaseous xenon. The experimental apparatus is shown schematically in Fig. 1. The ultraviolet laser radiation is focused by a 10-cm focal-length lens into a 350-μm-diameter pinhole, through which xenon flows from the tripling cell to the differentially pumped chamber. The generated third-harmonic radiation is dispersed by a 1-m scanning vacuum-ultraviolet monochromator (MacPherson model 225) and is detected with a windowless electron multiplier (EMI model 9603/2B), which has a quantum efficiency of 17% at 83 nm and less than 0.01% at 250 nm. This configuration is similar to that used in previous studies.[5,6] The optimum xenon pressure was found to be ~10 Torr, independent of input wavelength or intensity.

No attempt was made to compensate for the phase mismatch, Δk, in these initial experiments. Since 83 nm, the third-harmonic wavelength, is above the photoionization threshold for xenon, the index of refraction at this wavelength is complex. (The absorption cross section at 83 nm in xenon is[8] $\sigma_{abs} \cong 6.5 \times 10^{-17}$ cm^2.) For lossless nonlinear media, the variation in third-harmonic output as a function of gas density may be related to the variation in phase mismatch.[6,9] For absorbing media, the third-harmonic output peaks and then begins to drop as a function of pressure when the absorption length becomes comparable with the confocal parameter of the fundamental beam.[6] Because appreciable harmonic conversion is observed in our case,

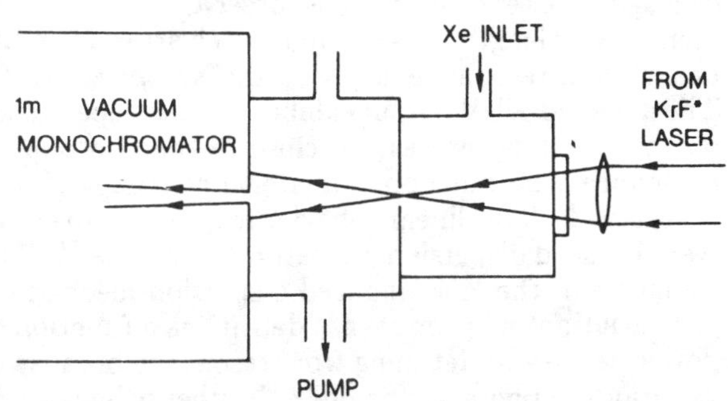

Fig. 1. The experimental apparatus for tripling KrF* radiation in xenon (see text).

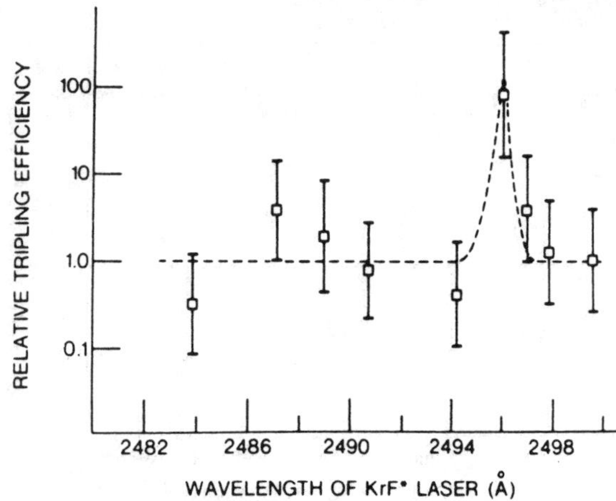

Fig. 2. Relative tripling efficiency as a function of the fundamental wavelength. Peak absolute efficiency is estimated to be $\sim 10^{-8}$.

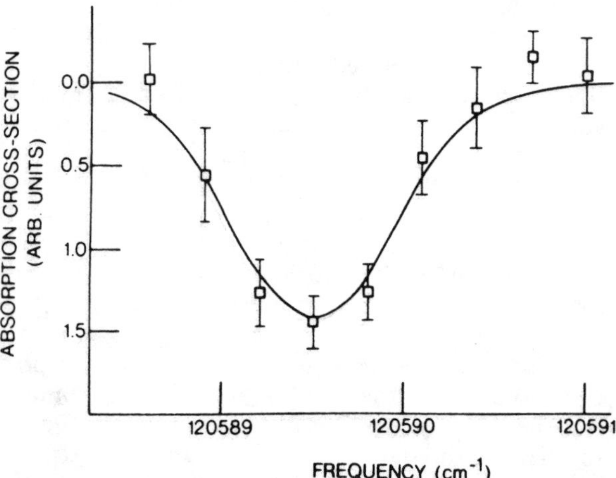

Fig. 3. Absorption cross section of H_2 at the $D \leftarrow X(4,0)$ $Q(3)$ line as observed in transmission of the tripled light. The solid line is a Gaussian profile with Doppler width (31 GHz).

we may at least infer that the sign of Δk is negative.[6,9]

Tunable XUV radiation was obtained from 82.8 to 83.3 nm. Figure 2 illustrates the conversion efficiency versus fundamental wavelength. More than an order-of-magnitude enhancement is observed at a fundamental wavelength of 249.63 nm, which arises from the two-photon resonance involving the Xe $6p(½)_0$ state. The detected XUV output exhibits a cubic dependence on the input power, except close to the two-photon resonance, where an approximately linear dependence is observed. This linear behavior may be due to either Kerr-induced dispersion[10] or saturation effects.[11] The signature of the Kerr-induced dispersion mechanism is a variation in optimum gas density as a function of power density or detuning from resonance because of variations in phase mismatch.[10] Neither behavior was observed. As noted above, since the conversion efficiency is limited by loss at the third harmonic before optimal phase matching is achieved, it is believed that the variation in the power dependence near the two-photon resonance condition is primarily due to saturation. To support this view we note that the laser intensity in the focal region is estimated to be $\sim 10^{13}$ W/cm^2. Using the estimated two-photon absorption parameter $\alpha \cong 10^{-27}$ cm^4/W applicable for the $^1S_0 \rightarrow 6p(½)_0$ transition[12] with the narrow-linewidth 248-nm radiation, we confirm that saturation behavior is expected.

In order to demonstrate explicitly the spectroscopic utility and narrow linewidth of the tunable XUV radiation, several transitions in molecular hydrogen have been studied. This was done by introducing $\sim$100 mTorr of H_2 into the differential pumping chamber, as shown in Fig. 1. At the wavelength λ = 82.926 nm, strong absorption was observed that was due to the $Q(3)$ line of the $D^1\Pi_u \leftarrow X^1\Sigma_g{}^+$ (4,0) band. In Fig. 3, the absorption profile for this line is shown. The linewidth of the absorption is 31 ± 3 GHz, in agreement with the Doppler width of the transition at room temperature. Since the gas-flow characteristics in the differentially pumped chamber are not well known, we are only able to give a lower limit to the absorption cross section $\sigma \gtrsim 7 \times 10^{-16}$ cm^2. Many other absorption lines in H_2, HD, and D_2 are within the available XUV tuning range. Some of these lines are expected to be Doppler broadened, like the one shown in Fig. 3, whereas others are appreciably broadened and distorted by predissociation.[13] Detailed studies of these predissociation linewidths and line profiles will furnish considerable detailed information regarding diabatic interactions among the Rydberg states in hydrogen. Such an investigation is currently under way in this laboratory.

In conclusion, a coherent, tunable 83-nm light source has been developed using third-harmonic generation of tunable KrF* radiation in xenon and has been demonstrated to be a useful spectroscopic tool. We note that this source, in comparison with the outputs obtained from the brightest synchrotron radiation sources[14] at the same wavelength, provides a spectral brightness approximately 2 orders of magnitude greater.

The authors wish to thank K. Skala and S. Vendetta for their expert technical assistance.

This research was supported by the National Science Foundation under grant PHY78-27610, the U.S. Department of Energy under contracts DE-AC02-80ET33065.A000 and DE-A02-79-ER-10350, the U.S. Air Force Office of Scientific Research under grant AFOSR-79-0130, and the U.S. Office of Naval Research.

* Present address, Amoco Research Center, P.O. Box 400, Naperville, Illinois 60540.

† Present address, Bell Laboratories, Holmdel, New Jersey 07733.

References

1. J. Bokor, J. Zavelovich, and C. K. Rhodes, "Multiphoton ultraviolet spectroscopy of some $6p$ levels in krypton," Phys. Rev. A (to be published).

2. D. J. Kligler, J. Bokor, and C. K. Rhodes, "Collisional and radiative properties of the H_2 $E, F\ {}^1\Sigma_g{}^+$ state," Phys. Rev. A **21,** 607 (1980).
3. J. Bokor, J. Zavelovich, and C. K. Rhodes, "Isotope effect in multiphoton ultraviolet photolysis of carbon monoxide," J. Chem. Phys. **72,** 965 (1980).
4. J. Reintjes, Opt. Lett. **4,** 242, (1979).
5. M. H. R. Hutchinson, C. C. Ling, and D. J. Bradley, Opt. Commun. **18,** 203 (1976).
6. J. Reintjes, C. Y. She, and R. C. Eckardt, IEEE J. Quantum Electron. **QE-14,** 581 (1978).
7. R. T. Hawkins, H. Egger, J. Bokor, and C. K. Rhodes, Appl. Phys. Lett. **36,** 391 (1980).
8. R. D. Hudson and L. J. Kieffer, At. Data **2,** 205 (1971).
9. G. C. Bjorklund, IEEE J. Quantum Electron. **QE-11,** 287 (1975).
10. L. J. Zych and J. F. Young, IEEE J. Quantum Electron. **QE-14,** 147 (1978).
11. C. C. Wang and I. I. David, Phys. Rev. Lett. **35,** 650 (1975); J. F. Ward and A. V. Smith, Phys. Rev. Lett. **35,** 653 (1975).
12. W. K. Bischel, J. Bokor, D. J. Kligler, and C. K. Rhodes, IEEE J. Quantum Electron. **QE-15,** 380 (1979).
13. P. M. Guyon, J. Breton, and M. Glass-Maujean, Chem. Phys. Lett. **68,** 314 (1979).
14. H. Winick and A. Bienenstock, in *Annual Review of Nuclear and Particle Science,* J. D. Jackson *et al.,* eds. (Annual Reviews, Palo Alto, Calif., 1978), Vol. 28, p. 52; C. Kunz, in *Synchrotron Radiation,* C. Kunz, ed. (Springer-Verlag, Berlin, 1979), p. 1.

Reprinted with the permission of the Optical Society of America from *Applied Optics,* Vol. 19(23), pp. 3889-3896 (December 1, 1980).

Frequency mixing in the extreme ultraviolet

J. Reintjes

The generation of coherent XUV radiation through harmonic generation and frequency mixing is described. Results that have been obtained using third- to ninth-order nonlinear interactions are summarized. The use of rare gas halide lasers for generating tunable XUV radiation is discussed.

I. Introduction

Optical frequency mixing has provided a source of narrowband coherent radiation in various regions of the spectrum, often ones in which there are no primary lasers available. For example, it has been an important source of coherent radiation in the VUV and is currently the only source of coherent radiation in the XUV. The range of wavelengths that is currently accessible by laser radiation is indicated in Fig. 1. Primary laser radiation is available from the IR through the visible and UV down to wavelengths of ~116 nm [Fig. 1(b)]. Frequency conversion of primary laser radiation also provides coherent light in most of this region and has enabled us to extend the range of wavelengths at which coherent radiation is available to the XUV reaching almost to the soft x-ray range [Fig. 1(c)].

II. Nonlinear Polarizations

Frequency conversion occurs as a result of nonlinear terms in the dielectric response function of a medium to incident radiation. For incident fields that are much weaker than the intra-atomic fields that bind the electrons in the atoms, the dielectric response in the electric dipole approximation can be written as

$$P = \chi^{(1)}E_i + \chi^{(2)}E_iE_j + \chi^{(3)}E_iE_jE_k + \ldots, \tag{1}$$

where the E_i are the electric fields of the incident optical waves, and the coefficients are the susceptibilities of the medium of various orders. In the gases and vapors that are used for VUV generation only the odd-order terms make a contribution to the electric dipole response of the medium. If only one frequency is present in the incident radiation, oscillating polarizations will be developed through the terms in Eq. (1) at odd harmonics of the incident laser frequency. If the incident field contains more than one frequency, polarizations can be created at sum and difference frequency combinations of the incident frequencies. If one or more of the incident frequencies is tunable, the generated radiation will also be tunable. In this way tunable radiation in the VUV can be produced from tunable radiation generated in lasers at longer wavelengths.

III. Generated Fields

The polarizations given by Eq. (1) radiate energy at new frequencies resulting in generated fields that are described by the Maxwell equation

$$\nabla^2 E_g - \frac{1}{c^2}\frac{\partial^2}{\partial t^2}E_g = \frac{4\pi\partial^2}{c^2\partial t^2}P_g^{NL}. \tag{2}$$

If the incident fields are assumed to have the form

$$E_{(r,z,t)} = \tfrac{1}{2}\sum_i \{A_i(r,z)\exp[-i(\omega t - kz)] + \text{c.c.}\}, \tag{3}$$

the amplitude of the generated wave at ω_g is given by

$$\nabla_\perp^2 A_g + 2ik_g\frac{\partial A_g}{\partial z} = -\frac{4\pi}{c^2}\omega_g^2 P_g^{NL}\exp(-i\Delta kz), \tag{4}$$

where $\Delta k = k_g - \Sigma k_i$ is the wave vector mismatch between the generated field and the polarization that drives it.

Expressions for the power in the generated wave and for its dependence on the wave vector mismatch depend on the geometry of the experimental arrangement. Most commonly conversion to the VUV is done in beams that are tightly focused in the nonlinear medium to take advantage of the high intensities in the focus. If we assume that the incident beam has a Gaussian variation of the form

$$A_i = A_o(1 + i\xi)^{-1}\exp[-kr^2/b(1 + i\xi)], \tag{5}$$

where $\xi = 2z/b$, b is the confocal parameter of the focused beam, and that conversion is done in a single-

The author is with U.S. Naval Research Laboratory, Optical Sciences Division, Washington D.C. 20375.

Received 6 June 1980.

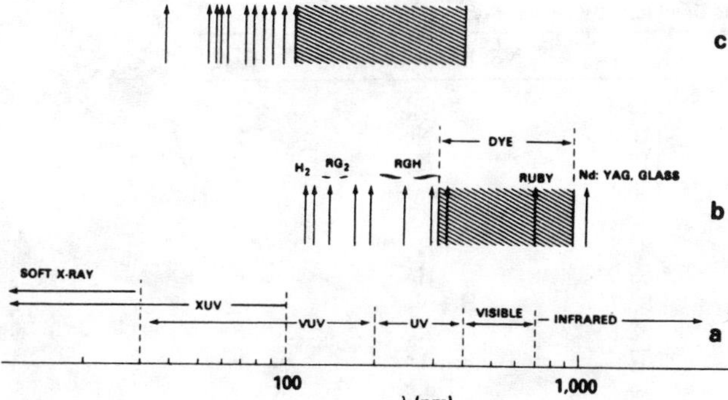

Fig. 1. (a) Designation of spectral regions. (b) Spectral range covered by primary laser radiation. RGH—rare gas halide lasers; RG_2—rare gas excimer lasers. (c) Spectral range covered by frequency conversion. Dashed region is covered by continuously tunable radiation generated by conversion of dye laser radiation.

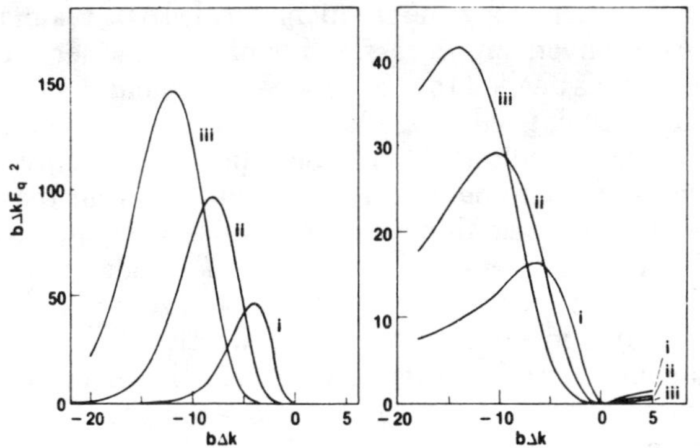

Fig. 2. Variation of quantity $|G|^2 = |b\Delta kF|^2$ with $b\Delta k$ for the third (i), fifth (ii), and seventh (iii) harmonics. Beam is focused (left) to center of infinite medium, (right) at edge of semi-infinite medium extending to one side of beam waist.

component medium, the power in the qth harmonic is given by

$$P_q = \frac{2^{q-1}\pi^{q+1}}{qn_1n_qc^{q-1}}\left|\frac{N}{n_1-n_q}\chi^{(q)}\right|^2\left(\frac{4P_1}{b\lambda_1}\right)^{q-1}P_1\,|b\Delta kF_q|^2, \quad (6)$$

where P_1 is the power in the fundamental field, and

$$b\Delta kF_q = G = b\Delta k\int_{-\xi'}^{\xi}\frac{\exp(-ib\Delta k\xi''/2)}{(1+i\xi'')^{q-1}}d\xi'', \quad (7)$$

with the nonlinear medium extending from $-z'$ to $+z$.

An example of the variation of $|G|^2$ for a beam focused to the center of an infinite medium is shown in Fig. 2(a) for harmonics three, five, and seven. Conversion is possible only in media with negative dispersion. Optimum conversion occurs for a phase mismatch given by

$$b\Delta k = -(2q-2). \quad (8)$$

In many experiments involving VUV generation the beam is focused at the center of an aperture that forms the window in a differential pumping arrangement. In such a situation the nonlinear medium can behave as if it were semi-infinite, occupying the space to one side of the beam waist. The variation of the quantity $|G|^2$ for such a semi-infinite medium for the third, fifth, and seventh harmonics is shown in Fig. 2(b). Optimum conversion still occurs for negative dispersion at values of $b\Delta k = -6.2, -10.2$, and -14.0 for harmonics three, five, and seven, respectively. A small, but nonzero, conversion is now possible for media with positive dispersion as well.

The negative dispersion required for phase optimization can be obtained by arranging the incident and harmonic wavelengths so that the incident wavelength falls in a region of positive dispersion, while the harmonic wavelength lies above a dispersive resonance so that the refractive index of the harmonic is less than that at the fundamental. This requirement generally restricts the choice of media in which radiation of a given wavelength may be tripled. The optimum value of $b\Delta k$ may be obtained either by mixing an appropriate ratio of media in which the dispersion has opposite signs or by adjusting the pressure of a single negatively dispersive medium.

IV. Experimental Results

Frequency conversion has been used to generate coherent radiation at wavelengths near and below 100 nm using a wide range of pump sources, nonlinear media, and nonlinear interactions. Fixed frequency pulsed lasers have been used to generate radiation at discrete wavelengths in the XUV at wavelengths down to 38 nm. Tunable radiation over a limited range can be obtained from lasers such as excimer or exciplex lasers that are themselves tunable over restricted wavelength ranges. Examples of this type of generation are conversion of radiation from rare gas excimer lasers or rare gas halide (RGH) lasers. Tunable radiation over wider spectral ranges has been obtained by the frequency conversion of radiation from dye lasers and parametric generators, either by themselves or in conjunction with the fixed frequency radiation from pulsed lasers. A summary of the reported experimental results is given in Table I.

Third-harmonic generation and third-order frequency mixing have been used to generate radiation at wavelengths down to 57 nm.[1–9] Most of the results have been obtained in rare gases, although some results have been reported in metal vapors. Radiation from pulsed YAG and glass lasers, RGH lasers, and rare gas excimer lasers have been used as pump sources. Occasionally resonant enhancement is possible for these processes as in the case of third-harmonic conversion of Xe laser emission in Ar and conversion of KrF laser radiation in Xe. In general, however, resonant enhancement has not played as great a role to date in the generation of radiation in the XUV as it has in the generation of radiation at longer wavelengths.

Higher-order frequency conversion has been used to generate radiation at still shorter wavelengths extending down to 38 nm. In these experiments[2] the fundamental, second, and fourth harmonics of a mode-locked

Table I. **Nonlinear Processes Used for XUV Generation**

Order	Process	Laser	λ(nm)	Nonlinear medium	Ref.
3	3 × 354.7 nm	Nd:YAG	118.2	Cd	1
	2 × 266.1 + 1064	Nd:YAG	118.2	Ne	2
	3 × 351	XeF	117	Kr	3
	2 × 266.1 + 532	Nd:YAG	106.4	He, Ne	2
	3 × 308	XeCl	102.7	Ar	4
	2 × 243 + 486	Dye	97.2	H	5
	3 × 268.8	Nd:glass	89.6	Hg	6
	3 × 266.1	Nd:YAG	88.7	He, Ne, Ar	7,2
	3 × 249	KrF	83	Xe	8
	3 × 171	Xe_2	57	Ar	9
5	4 × 266.1 − 532	Nd:YAG	76	He,Ne	2
	4 × 266.1 − 1064	Nd:YAG	70.9	He,Ne	2
	4 × 266.1 + 1064	Nd:YAG	62.6	He,Ne	2
	4 × 266.1 + 532	Nd:YAG	59.1	He,Ne	2
	5 × 266.1	Nd:YAG	53.2	He,Ne,Ar,Kr	2
7	7 × 266.1	Nd:YAG	38	He	
9	9 × 1060	Nd:glass	118	Na	10

Nd:YAG laser were used as a pump source, and conversion was done through fifth- and seventh-harmonic conversion and six-wave mixing. The wavelengths obtained in this way are given in the lower portion of Table I. Fifth-harmonic conversion of the fourth harmonic of the Nd:YAG laser at 266.1 nm gave radiation at 53.2 nm. It was observed in four of the rare gases: He, Ne, Ar, and Kr. At low gas pressure the highest conversion was observed in Kr, but at the highest gas pressures that were used the highest conversion was observed in He. Maximum conversion efficiency was $\sim 10^{-5}$, giving peak pulse powers of the order of 1 kW in the XUV. Seventh-harmonic conversion of the YAG fourth-harmonic pulses was used to produce radiation at 38 nm, just at the edge of the soft x-ray range. Conversion was observed only in He, and the peak signal level was about an order of magnitude less than the maximum fifth-harmonic signals, giving peak pulse powers of the order of 100 W at 38 nm.

Six-wave mixing using the fundamental, second, and fourth harmonics of the YAG laser in combinations of the form $4\omega_{UV} \pm \omega_{IR,g}$ where ω_{UV} is the fourth-harmonic frequency, and $\omega_{IR,g}$ is either the fundamental or second-harmonic frequency, was used to generate radiation at additional wavelengths in the XUV. These interactions were observed in both He and Ne. The signal levels were stronger in Ne than in He presumably because of the resonances that are possible. Peak signal levels were 1–2 orders of magnitude smaller than those observed for the fifth harmonic in He. These results are nonetheless very encouraging for the generation of tunable radiation in this wavelength range, because the fundamental and second harmonics were severely depleted in the generation of the YAG fourth harmonic. As a result the intensity of these waves in the region of overlap with the fourth harmonic wave was considerably less than the fourth-harmonic intensity.

Finally ninth-harmonic[10] conversion of Nd:glass laser radiation at 10.6 μm has been reported, giving coherent light at 118.2 nm.

In generating radiation at short wavelengths the higher-order interactions offer certain potential advantages over the lower-order interactions. They allow a larger step along the frequency scale to be taken in a single conversion process, reducing the number of cascade steps needed to reach a given wavelength or eliminating their need altogether. In the case of generation of radiation below 700 nm, they allow pump sources in the near UV to be used rather than ones that require vacuum propagation or special optical components. These advantages will, of course, be academic if the higher-order processes are too weak to generate significant amounts of radiation. It is worthwhile therefore to compare the relative strengths of the higher-order processes with the lower-order ones in the same medium.

The relative conversion to harmonics of different order is determined by a combination of phase matching parameters, pump intensities, and the behavior of the nonlinear susceptibilities. Conversion to higher-order harmonics can be favored over conversion to lower-order ones through proper choice of the phase matching parameters. This effect is indicated in Fig. 2, which shows that the optimum value of $b\Delta k$ depends on the order of the harmonic. In addition the power series expansion of Eq. (1) indicates that at sufficiently high pump intensities the nonlinear polarization generated in the higher-order interactions can be larger than that generated in the lower-order ones. If the magnitudes of the susceptibilities decrease uniformly with increasing order, as, for example, in media with no resonant enhancements in any order, this condition will not usually be met unless the assumptions leading to the perturbation expansion of Eq. (1) are violated. However, in media in which certain higher-order susceptibilities contain resonant enhancements that are not present in the lower-order ones, larger nonlinear polarizations can be generated in the higher-order interactions than in the lower-order ones without violating the assumptions of perturbation theory. In principle then the higher-order interactions can be as effective as the lower-order ones in generating new radiation under certain circumstances. In practice, however, other nonlinear effects can and usually do become important at high pump

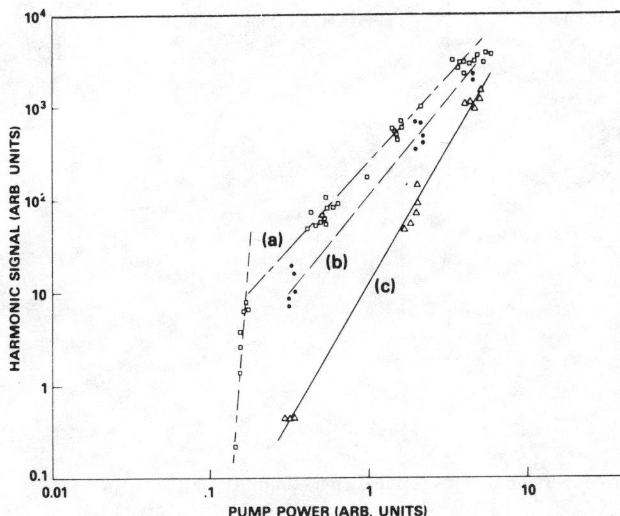

Fig. 3. Comparison of fifth- and third-harmonic conversion of 266-nm radiation in He: (a) fifth harmonic, He pressure—25 Torr; (b) fifth harmonic, He pressure—18 Torr; (c) third harmonic, He pressure—18 Torr.

Table II. Harmonic of RGH Lasers in XUV

	λ (nm)	λ/3 (nm)	λ/5 (nm)	λ/7 (nm)
XeF	351	117	70	50.1
XeCl	308	102.7	61.6	44
KrF	249	83	49.8	35.6
ArF	193	64.3	38.6	27.6

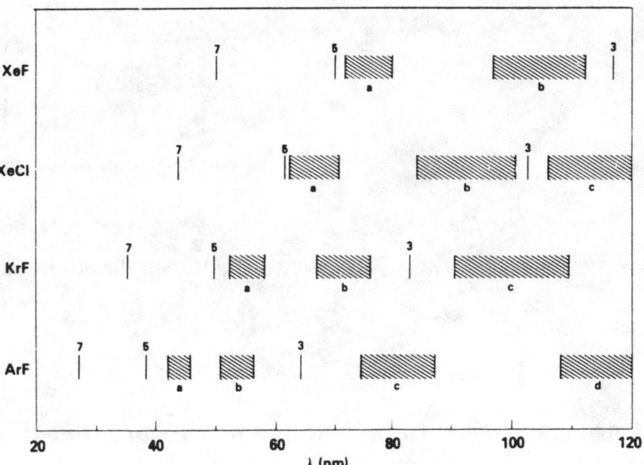

Fig. 4. Wavelength range covered with RGH lasers using harmonic generation and frequency mixing with dye laser radiation extending from 330 to 900 nm. Each RGH laser is specified at left. Harmonic order is indicated over appropriate spectral positions. Process a—$4\,\omega_{RGH} + \omega_{Dye}$; b—$4\,\omega_{RGH} - \omega_{Dye}$; c—$2\,\omega_{RGH} + \omega_{Dye}$; d—$2\,\omega_{RGH} - \omega_{Dye}$.

intensities and effectively limit the conversion efficiency that can be obtained in a given frequency conversion process. In such situations it may be impossible to obtain significant power in the higher-order harmonics before the conversion efficiency is limited.

To investigate this problem, conversion of radiation at 266.1 nm through third- and fifth-harmonic generation in He has been compared,[11] and results are shown in Fig. 3. The third-harmonic signal shows a cubic variation with pump power over the entire range of pump powers that were used. The fifth-harmonic signal was larger than the third harmonic by factors that range from ~20 at a pump power of 12 MW to a factor of 2 at a pump power of 300 MW. The saturation that is evident in the fifth harmonic is due to competing processes and has been discussed in detail in Ref. 2. Conversion to the fifth harmonic was favored over conversion to the third by a near five-photon resonance between the ground state and the $1s3s\ ^1P_0$ level that enhanced the fifth-order susceptibility but not the third. Eventually however the conversion to the higher-order harmonics must decrease with increasing harmonic order, or the perturbation expansion of Eq. (1) will be invalid. In our experiments conversion to the seventh harmonic was less than that to the fifth presumably because of a decrease in the nonlinear susceptibility. These results indicate that conversion to a higher-order harmonic can be as effective as conversion to a lower-order one in particular media. They furthermore indicate that different harmonics can be favored in different media depending on the relation of the wavelengths and energy levels.

V. RGH Lasers

Our most recent experiments have involved the frequency conversion of radiation from RGH lasers. As a class these lasers are an efficient source of medium to high power in the near UV and as such are a convenient source of pump radiation for generating coherent VUV and XUV radiation. They are tunable over a narrow region in the near UV and can be used to generate radiation through harmonic conversion that is tunable over a restricted range in the VUV and XUV. In addition, they are effective in pumping dye lasers and can be used in conjunction with dye laser radiation to generate radiation that is tunable over a wider range in the XUV. The wavelengths of four of the more common RGH lasers along with the XUV wavelengths that can be generated through third-, fifth-, and seventh-harmonic conversion are given in Table II. The wavelength range that can be covered using these processes as well as four- and six-wave mixing with dye laser radiation extending from 330 to 900 nm is shown in Fig. 4.

To investigate the usefulness of the RGH laser radiation in driving the frequency mixing processes we have studied third-harmonic conversion of radiation from a XeCl laser in rare gases.[4] Energy level diagrams for this process in Ne, Ar, and Kr are shown in Fig. 5. The pump radiation lies below the resonance lines in all three gases. In Ar the harmonic lies above the resonance lines providing the negative dispersion that is necessary for optimizing the phase mismatch in a tight focus or in a mixture with a medium that has positive dispersion. In Kr the harmonic lies just above the $4d[1/2]^0$ level. Although this is the correct position for negative dispersion, calculations show that the reso-

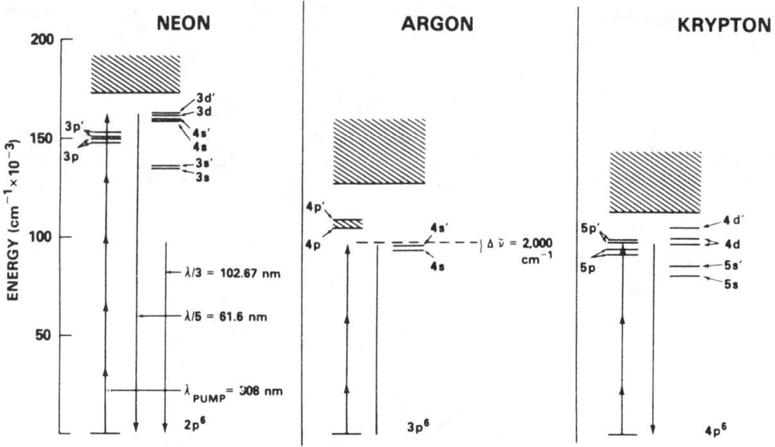

Fig. 5. Energy level diagram of Ne, Ar, and Kr, showing third-harmonic conversion with negative dispersion in Ar. Fifth harmonic is also shown in Ne.

nance is too weak to provide the needed negative dispersion. In Ne the harmonic lies below the resonance lines, and the dispersion is positive.

Third-harmonic conversion was observed in Ar (Ref. 4) but not in Kr in accordance with expectations based on consideration of the sign of the dispersion. Kr and Ne along with He would be appropriate for use in phase matching by gas mixtures. The third harmonic showed a cubic power-law dependence on the pump power up to pump power levels of the order of 500 kW and pump intensities of the order of 10^{11} W/cm^2, the limit of pump powers that were available. The conversion efficiency observed at these power levels was rather low, of the order of 10^{-8}, providing peak pulse powers of the order of 1–10 mW in the VUV. They are, however, of the same order of magnitude as that which could be expected from conversion of other laser sources, such as the harmonics of a Nd:YAG laser in this wavelength range at similar power levels.[12] The lack of saturation in the power-law dependence indicates that no competing mechanisms are present at these pump powers that can limit conversion efficiency, and improvements in both conversion efficiency and third-harmonic power levels can be expected at higher pumping levels. For comparison, in experiments involving conversion of 354.7-nm radiation from the third harmonic of a Nd:YAG laser,[12] saturation of conversion efficiency was not observed until the pump intensity reached a level of 5×10^{12} W/cm^2.

Typical variation of the harmonic power as a function of Ar pressure is shown in Fig. 6 for beams focused with 5- and 10-cm focal length lenses. The solid lines were calculated following the theory outlined earlier. An elliptical Gaussian profile with an aspect ratio of 3:1 was assumed for the cross section of the input beam in accordance with our measurements. Such a profile is typical of electric-discharge-excited RGH lasers that are preionized from the side as was the one used in these experiments. The effect of this property of the laser emission on the conversion efficiency is illustrated in

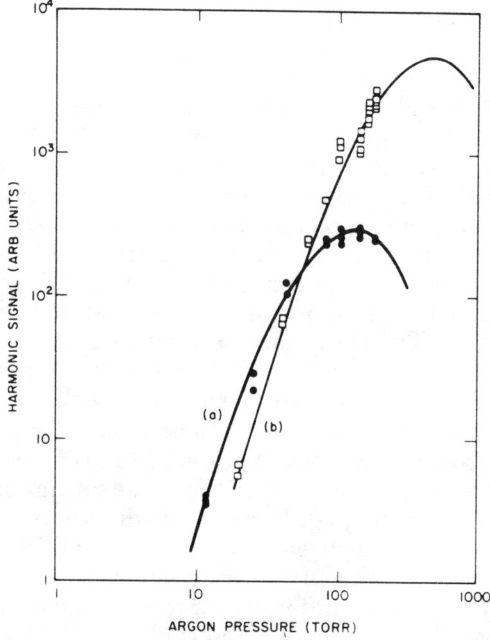

Fig. 6. Variation of power in third harmonic of XeCl laser radiation using 10-cm focal length (a) and 5-cm focal length (b) lenses. Solid curves were calculated using theory of Eq. (7) and an elliptical beam profile with aspect ratio of 3:1. Theoretical curves were normalized at peak of 10-cm lens data.

Fig. 7. In curve (a) the conversion is calculated for an elliptical beam of the kind used in our experiments. In curve (b) a circular profile with a dimension corresponding to the smaller dimension of the elliptical cross section used in curve (a) was assumed. The same total laser power was used for both calculations. The conversion of the circular beam is seen to be higher than that of the elliptical beam by almost a factor of 20 due to the improved phase optimization and increased intensity in the focus. If we consider the improvements

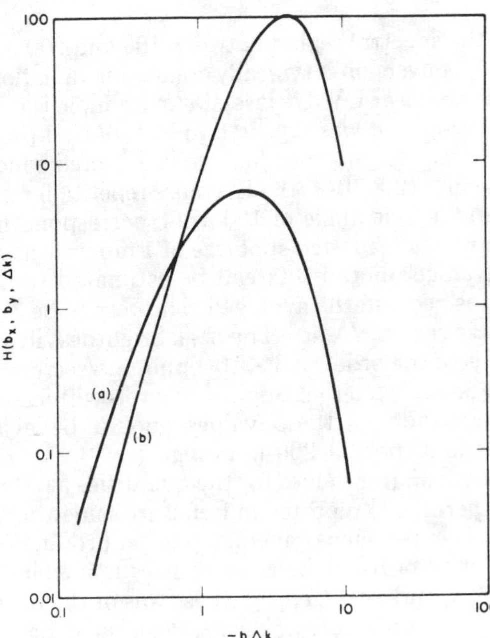

Fig. 7. Theoretical comparison of conversion possible at a fixed power level for an elliptical Gaussian beam with 3:1 aspect ratio (a) and a circular Gaussian beam (b).

to be had in beam profile and increases in pump power to values of the order of 10 MW, a level that has been reported in some RGH lasers, conversion levels of the order of 10^{-4} are possible, leading to peak pulse powers of the order of 1 kW in the VUV.

To test some of these considerations we have constructed an electric discharge laser with a wide aperture discharge formed by preionizing through the negative electrode. The discharge region varies in dimension from 1.5 × 2.5 to 2 × 2.5 cm depending on the gas mixture that was used. The laser was operated as an injection-locked oscillator in an unstable resonator configuration in conjunction with a master oscillator that was operated in a stable cavity. When a 0.5-mm aperture was used in the master oscillator its output was effectively diffraction limited, and its low divergence was maintained when amplified in the injection-locked oscillator. The output from this laser was in the form of an approximately square beam that could be focused to an effectively circular spot that was within ~10% of its diffraction limit.

The pressure dependence of the third-harmonic generation from the injection-locked oscillator now showed the characteristic dependence of a beam with circular symmetry rather than elliptical symmetry, indicating the feasibility of the technique for improving beam quality. It also provides better mode matching for frequency mixing with radiation from a dye laser.

Operation of the laser as an injection-locked device also provides the opportunity to take advantage of the tunability of the XeCl laser to generate tunable VUV radiation.[13] A spectrum of the single-pass axial fluorescence of the XeCl laser is shown in Fig. 8(a) with the

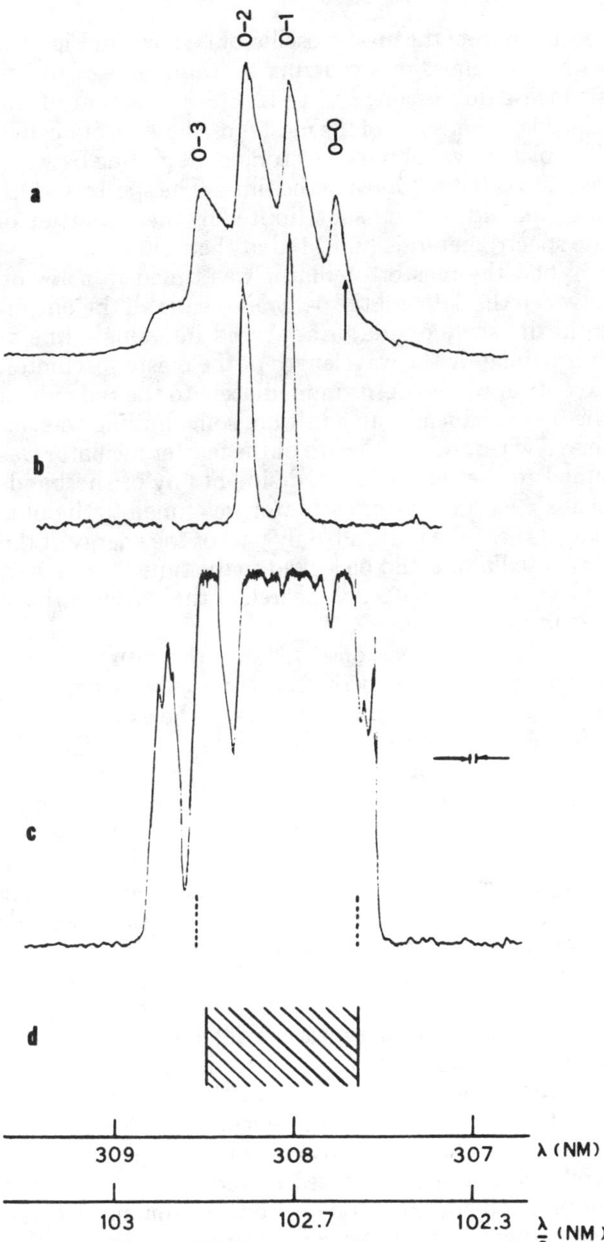

Fig. 8. (a) Densitometer tracing of single-pass axial fluorescence spectrum of XeCl laser discharge. Band designations are indicated. Arrow indicates position of three times the wavelength of the Lyman-β transition of H. (b) Normal untuned XeCl laser spectrum. (c) Range of tuned laser emission obtained by turning grating between laser shots. Approximate width of single-frequency tuned laser emission is indicated at right. Dashed lines indicate range over which laser emission could be tuned using 0.5-mm aperture. (d) Wavelength range over which third-harmonic conversion to VUV was observed. (a), (b), and (c) use upper wavelength scale; (d) uses lower wavelength scale.

band designations indicated. A wavelength of 307.71 nm, corresponding to three times the wavelength of the Lyman-β transition of H, lies to the blue side of the 0–0 bandhead as indicated by the arrow. An untuned laser spectrum from the master oscillator is shown in Fig. 8(b) with laser emission occurring on the bands with the strongest fluorescence. In Fig. 8(c) the extent of the tuned laser emission of the master oscillator is indicated. This picture was obtained by tuning the grating between laser shots but not moving the film. The spectral width of an individual laser shot, limited by the resolution of the spectrometer, is indicated at the right.

When the master oscillator was tuned in a region between the 0–0 and the 0–3 bandheads all the output from the slave oscillator appeared in a single line at approximately the wavelength of the master oscillator, except for wavelengths immediately to the red side of the 0–0 bandhead. In addition, some pulling was observed when the wavelength of the master oscillator was tuned to the immediate red side of any of the bandheads. As the master oscillator was tuned to the blue side of the 0–0 bandhead, only part of the energy of the slave oscillator could be locked to the tuned frequency, and some of the output appeared at the wavelengths of the untuned output.

VUV radiation was observed over the entire range of wavelengths to which the master oscillator could be tuned using the 0.5-mm aperture. The extent of this range is indicated by the shaded region in Fig. 8(d). The wavelength of the VUV signal followed the position of the tuned pump radiation even for pump wavelengths at which the injection locking was incomplete. When the aperture of the master oscillator was opened, the slave oscillator could be locked completely over a wider wavelength range, but the VUV signal disappeared, reflecting the degradation in beam quality.

The VUV tuning range covered in Fig. 8(d) includes the Lyman-β transition of atomic hydrogen. One application of such radiation is the detection of neutral H atoms by resonance fluorescence from the Hα transition (656 nm) following excitation at the Lyman-β wavelength. This technique for neutral particle detection is similar to that using Lyman-α fluorescence[14,15] but offers potential advantages in terms of background suppression and ease of detection. Resonance Raman scattering can also be used to discriminate against fluorescence radiated from excited H atoms.

VI. Comparison with Other Sources

Finally, it is of interest to compare the power levels that can be obtained in the frequency converted laser sources with the power levels that are available from other VUV and XUV sources such as synchrotron radiation and arc lamps. The properties of the radiation sources that are of primary importance depend to a large extent on particular experimental needs, and a comparison of a given set of properties may not be appropriate for all applications. Nevertheless, a comparison of such properties as total photon flux, average brightness, and peak pulse brightness can provide some indications of the relative usefulness and capabilities of the various sources. The numbers that are given in this section are meant only to reflect typical quantities that are currently available and not to indicate ultimate performance levels.

In the spectral region between 100 and 200 nm, frequency conversion is typically done using radiation from visible and near UV dye lasers. An example is the VUV conversion that was reported in Ref. 16 that produced $\sim 10^{11}$ photons/pulse at 143.6 nm in a quoted bandwidth of 0.1 cm^{-1} (2×10^{-3} Å). If a pulse repetition rate of 10 pps and a cone angle of 100 μrad, corresponding to a beam with a Gaussian spot size of 1 mm, are assumed, the average photon flux can be estimated to be 10^{12} photons/sec and the average brightness to be 3×10^{24} photons/sec/cm^2/Å/sr. The peak brightness in a single pulse is of the order of 3×10^{31} photons/sec/cm^2/Å/sr. It can be expected that brightness levels within an order of magnitude of these values should be available throughout the 100–200-nm range.

Corresponding values for the quantities at 53 nm for the experiments reported in Ref. 2 are somewhat lower. In those experiments average photon production was of the order of 10^8 photons/sec in an estimated linewidth of 0.04 Å, and average brightness was of the order of 6×10^{18} photons/sec/cm^2/Å/sr. Peak pulse brightness is of the order of 6×10^{30} photons/sec/cm^2/Å/sr comparable with peak brightness at 143 nm. The large increase in peak brightness is due to the shorter duration (20 psec) of the 53-nm pulses.

Typical values for photons in the 100-nm range available at a target from a synchrotron are of the order of 10^{10}–10^{12} photons/sec in a 1-Å bandwidth and a cone with divergence of 1×10 mrad. If a beam aperture of the order of 0.1 mm is assumed, the average brightness is of the order of 10^{19}–10^{21} photons/sec/cm^2/Å/sr, and peak brightness is of the order of 10^{21}–10^{23} photons/sec/cm^2/Å/sr.

Total photon flux from arc lamps is of the same order of magnitude, but brightness is considerably lower due chiefly to the large divergence of the arc lamp.

Comparison of these values indicates that the frequency converted laser sources in the XUV exhibit properties that are characteristic of laser sources in other spectral ranges, namely, high spectral brightness and high peak intensities. The advantage they enjoy in these areas over other sources is due chiefly to their narrow linewidth and excellent collimation. It can be anticipated then that they should prove useful in areas that take advantage of these properties such as high resolution spectroscopy or nonlinear spectroscopy. Currently the tuning range available from these sources at wavelengths below 100 nm is quite restricted, but increased tuning capability at least to 40 nm should be possible.

References

1. A. H. Kung, J. F. Young, G. C. Bjorklund, and S. E. Harris, Phys. Rev. Lett. **29**, 985 (1972).
2. J. Reintjes, C. Y. She, and R. C. Eckardt, IEEE J. Quantum Electron. **QE-14**, 581 (1978).
3. D. Cotter, Opt. Commun. **31**, 397 (1979).
4. J. Reintjes, Opt. Lett. **4**, 242 (1979).
5. B. I. Troshin, V. P. Chebotayev, and A. A. Chernenko, Pis'ma Zh. Eksp. Fiz. **27**, 293 (1978) [JETP Lett. **27**, 273 (1978)].
6. V. V. Slabko, A. K. Popov, and V. F. Lukinykh, Appl. Phys. **15**, 239 (1977).

7. S. E. Harris, J. F. Young, A. H. Kung, D. M. Bloom, and G. C. Bjorklund, in *Laser Spectroscopy,* R. G. Brewer and A. M. Mooradian, Eds. (Plenum, New York, 1973).
8. H. Egger, R. T. Hawkins, J. Bokor, H. Pummer, M. Rothschild, and C. K. Rhodes, at Eleventh International Quantum Electronics Conference, Boston (June 1980), paper Q.4.
9. M. H. R. Hutchinson, C. C. Ling, and D. J. Bradley, Opt. Commun. **18,** 203 (1976).
10. M. G. Grozeva, D. I. Metchkov, V. M. Mitev, L. I. Pavlov, and K. V. Stamenov, Opt. Commun. **23,** 77 (1977).
11. J. Reintjes and C. Y. She, Opt. Commun. **27,** 469 (1978).
12. L. J. Zych and J. F. Young, IEEE J. Quantum Electron. **QE-14,** 147 (1978).
13. J. Reintjes, Opt. Lett. **5,** 342 (1980).
14. T. J. McKee, B. P. Stoicheff, and S. C. Wallace, Opt. Lett. **3,** 207 (1978).
15. R. Mahon, T. J. McIlrath, and D. W. Koopman, Appl. Phys. Lett. **33,** 305 (1978).
16. S. C. Wallace and G. Zdasivk, Appl. Phys. Lett. **28,** 449 (1976).

Reprinted with permission from *Optics Letters,* Vol. 6(4), pp. 182-184 (April 1981).

Generation of high-brightness coherent radiation in the vacuum ultraviolet by four-wave parametric oscillation in mercury vapor

J. Bokor, R. R. Freeman, R. L. Panock, and J. C. White

Bell Laboratories, Holmdel, New Jersey 07733

Coherent radiation at several wavelengths in the vacuum ultraviolet (VUV) has been generated by four-wave parametric oscillation in mercury vapor. When a powerful ultraviolet pump laser of frequency ω_p is tuned to a two-photon resonance, VUV signal photons at frequency ω_s, as well as idler photons at frequency ω_i, are generated such that $\omega_s + \omega_i = 2\omega_p$. A frequency-doubled dye laser tuned to two-photon resonance with the $6s6d\ ^1D_2$ level near 280.3 nm produced output at 184.9 and 143.5 nm. A tunable krypton fluoride excimer laser tuned to two-photon resonance with the $6s10s\ ^1S_0$ level near 248.7 nm produced output at 140.1, 130.7, 130.1, 125.9, and 125.0 nm. Approximately 1-μJ, 200-W pulses were observed at 143.5 and 125.9 nm.

Third-harmonic generation and four-wave sum-frequency mixing in atomic vapors have been used extensively for the production of coherent radiation in the vacuum-ultraviolet (VUV) region of the spectrum.[1] These nonlinear processes involve the combination of three input frequencies to produce output at the sum frequency. When fundamental radiation derived from visible- and near-ultraviolet-wavelength laser sources has been used, such mechanisms have provided the means for the generation of tunable coherent radiation in the region below 200 nm. However, with the availability of powerful laser sources in the 200–300-nm range, another type of four-wave interaction may be considered for the generation of coherent VUV radiation, namely, four-wave parametric oscillation (FWPO). In FWPO, pairs of optical waves at frequencies ω_s and ω_i are generated on irradiation of an appropriate nonlinear medium by an intense pump wave at frequency ω_p such that $\omega_s + \omega_i = 2\omega_p$.

In atomic vapors, resonance enhancements of the nonlinear susceptibility are generally exploited. Thus $2\omega_p$ is tuned to a two-photon resonance while ω_i and ω_s are generated such that $2\omega_p - \omega_i$ is near a hyper-Raman resonance. This type of resonantly enhanced FWPO leading to up-conversion of visible radiation to the near ultraviolet has been observed by several groups.[2–6] Because of the resonance enhancements of the nonlinear susceptibility, the conversion efficiency of pump photons to signal photons can be quite high; up to 5% conversion of 579-nm pump radiation to 330-nm output radiation was observed by Hartig[5] in sodium vapor.

We have performed two experiments in which FWPO has been used for the first time to our knowledge to generate coherent radiation in the VUV. In the first case, outputs at 184.9 and 143.5 nm were produced in mercury vapor by using 280-nm pump radiation. The tunable pump radiation was produced by frequency doubling the output of a Nd:YAG-pumped dye laser in a KDP crystal. Pulses of up to 20 mJ at 280 nm, with a 4–5-nsec duration and 0.3-cm^{-1} bandwidth, were available at a repetition rate of 10 pulses per second. The pump radiation was focused by a 250-mm focal-length lens into a 450-mm-length cell containing mercury at a density of 10^{16}—10^{17} cm^{-3} and helium buffer gas at a pressure of up to 300 Torr. Peak intensities in the focal region were not measured but are estimated to be between 10^{10}–10^{11} W/cm^2. When the pump radiation was tuned to two-photon resonance with the $6s^2\ ^1S_0$–$6s6d\ ^1D_2$ transition in mercury at 280.3 nm, strong coherent emission at 143.5 and 184.9 nm was observed, corresponding to additional resonance with the $6s7p\ ^3P_1$ and $6s6p\ ^1P_1$ levels, respectively [see Fig. 1(a)]. The VUV wavelengths were measured with a 0.3-m focal-length scanning monochromator to an accuracy of 0.2 nm. The relative magnitude of the output at each wavelength was also measured by using the monochromator.

Other characteristics of the output were determined

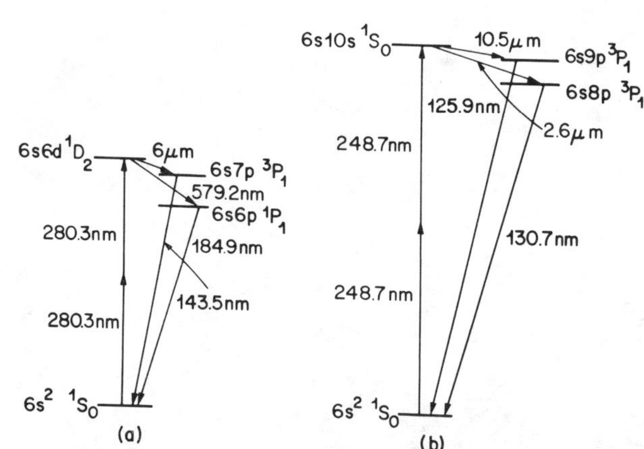

Fig. 1. Partial energy-level diagram of mercury showing resonances involved in generation of coherent VUV radiation by four-wave parametric oscillation. (a) Generation of 184.9- and 143.5-nm radiation by pumping with a frequency-doubled dye laser at 280.3 nm. (b) Generation of 125.9- and 130.7-nm radiation by pumping with a tunable krypton fluoride excimer laser at 248.7 nm. In this configuration, output was also observed at 140.1, 130.1, and 125.0 nm (see text).

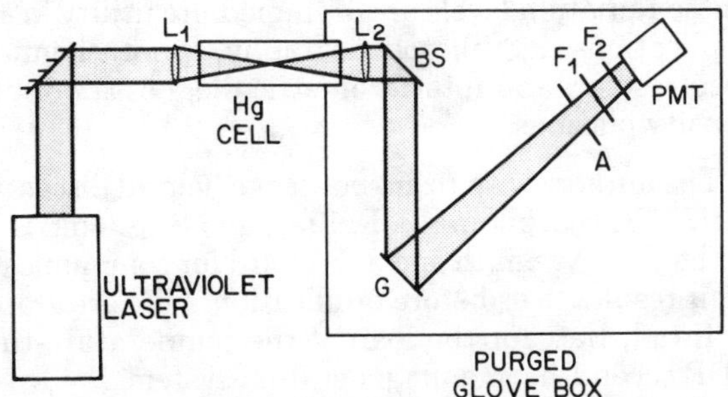

Fig. 2. Schematic diagram of experimental setup used to generate and characterize the VUV outputs. The ultraviolet laser represents either the frequency-doubled dye laser or the tunable krypton fluoride excimer laser. L1, 250-mm focal-length quartz lens; L2, 400-mm focal-length calcium fluoride lens or lithium fluoride lens; BS, ~10% reflecting beam splitter; G, 1200-groove/mm grating; A, variable aperture; F_1, F_2, calibrated VUV filters; PMT, solar-blind photomultiplier tube.

by using a nitrogen-purged glove-box arrangement, as shown in Fig. 2. The VUV outputs were found to be highly directional and were generated in the forward direction only. Strong directional emission at 579 nm, the idler wavelength associated with the 184.9-nm signal, was observed in both the forward and backward directions. No attempt was made to detect 6-μm radiation, which is the idler wavelength associated with the 143.5-nm signal. Measurements of the absolute VUV output pulse energies were obtained by using the optical system shown in Fig. 2. Emission from the cell was recollimated by a 400-mm focal-length calcium fluoride lens L2, then split by a flat, uncoated calcium fluoride beam splitter BS and directed onto a 1200-groove/mm grating G, blazed for 120 nm in the first order. The dispersed radiation was attenuated by using calibrated VUV filters and detected by a solar-blind photomultiplier tube. The beam splitter BS was used to attenuate both the signal and the pump radiation, preventing optical damage to the grating by the strong pump. Our purging system was imperfect, and residual absorption in the VUV optical paths was always present. This absorption was accounted for by translating the phototube over a measured distance while noting the change in signal and then extrapolating to obtain the total absorption over the full path length using Beer's law. With this adjustment, and including the absorption loss at L2 and the reflectivity of BS and using manufacturer's data for the grating efficiency,[7] phototube quantum efficiency, and gain,[8] we inferred an output energy of 1 μJ at 143.5 nm with an estimated uncertainty of a factor of 3. Output at 184.9 nm was a factor of 3 smaller than that at 143.5 nm, with a relative uncertainty of 50%.

The VUV output was found to be relatively insensitive to the helium buffer-gas pressure over the range of 5–100 Torr. Above 100 Torr, the output began to decrease, and it was undetectable above 250 Torr. As is shown in Fig. 3, the output at 143.5 nm increased approximately as the square of the mercury density until a value of 0.1 Torr was reached, at which point the output leveled off to a constant value. Tuning of the pump radiation was found to be critical; with a detuning of more than $\pm 0.5\ cm^{-1}$, the signal was completely extinguished.

We have also used a tunable krypton fluoride excimer laser to observe FWPO in mercury vapor. In this case, output at several discrete wavelengths from 125.0 to 140.1 nm was generated by using 249-nm pump radiation. The tunable excimer-laser system is based on the design of Hawkins *et al.*[9] A tunable dye laser operating near 498 nm is frequency doubled by a temperature-tuned ammonium dihydrogen phosphate (ADP) crystal. The second-harmonic radiation is then amplified in a single pass through a krypton fluoride discharge device (Lambda Physics model EMG 200). In this way, tunability over the krypton fluoride gain band from 247 to 250 nm may be obtained. In our case, approximately 100 mJ of radiation per pulse were produced at the peak of the krypton fluoride gain band (248 nm) with 100 μJ per pulse of input second-harmonic radiation. The output bandwidth was approximately $0.4\ cm^{-1}$, the pulse duration was 5–7 nsec, and the pulse repetition rate was 10 pulses per second.

When this laser system was used as the pump source for FWPO in mercury by tuning it to the $6s^2\ ^1S_0$–$6s10s\ ^1S_0$ two-photon resonance at 248.7 nm, strong coherent emission at 125.0, 125.9, 130.1, 130.7, and 140.1 nm was observed, corresponding to resonance with the $6s9p\ ^1P_1$, $6s9p\ ^3P_1$, $6s8p\ ^1P_1$, $6s8p\ ^3P_1$, and $6s7p\ ^1P_1$ levels, respectively [see Fig. 1(b)]. By using the optical system shown in Fig. 2, but substituting lithium fluoride optics for the calcium fluoride optics, an output energy of 1 μJ per pulse was measured at 125.9 nm. The measurement uncertainty is again a factor of 3. Output at each of the other wavelengths was about an order of magnitude smaller. As in the first experiment, no attempt was made to detect the infrared and far-infrared idler wavelengths. The dependence of the 125.9-nm output on helium buffer and mercury densities, as well as on pump detuning, was found to be similar to that found for the 143.5-nm output described above.

It is somewhat surprising that triplet intermediate states lead to the dominant output signals. However, spin-orbit mixing is well known to be strong in mercury.

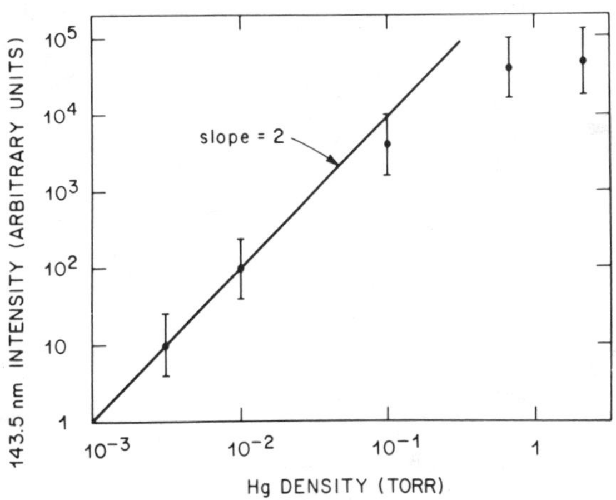

Fig. 3. Dependence of 143.5-nm output signal on Hg density.

Recent measurements[10] have shown that the Einstein A coefficient for the intercombination line $6s6d\ ^1D_2$–$6s6p\ ^3P_1$ is actually 4.1 times larger than that for the $6s6d\ ^1D_2$–$6s6p\ ^1P_1$ transition. This provides a qualitative explanation for the dominance of intercombination pathways in our experiments.

In the course of these experiments, we have also observed second-harmonic generation (SHG) of VUV radiation in mercury. Although collinear SHG is strictly forbidden for plane-wave propagation in isotropic media,[1,11] Freeman *et al.*[12] have recently demonstrated that SHG may be observed by using a focused single beam in an isotropic vapor. With our pump laser tuned near the $6s6d\ ^1D_2$ level in Hg, tunable radiation at the second harmonic near 140 nm was observed. This signal was strongly peaked at the resonance but was observable at pump-frequency detunings as large as 100 cm^{-1}, with the output wavelength appropriately tracking with pump-laser tuning. At its peak, this signal was about a factor of 10 smaller than the 143.5-nm FWPO signal. When the pump laser was tuned near the $6s10s\ ^1S_0$ level in Hg, no SHG could be observed. This restriction of the observation of resonantly enhanced SHG to states of angular momentum greater than 1 is in agreement with the observations of Freeman *et al.*[13]

In summary, we have observed the generation of coherent radiation at several wavelengths in the vacuum-ultraviolet region by four-wave parametric oscillation in mercury vapor. Approximately 1-μJ, 200-W pulses were obtained at 143.5 nm using 10-mJ, 2-MW input pulses at 280.3 nm for an overall conversion efficiency of 10^{-4}. Approximately 1-μJ, 200-W pulses were obtained at 125.9 nm using 100-mJ, 20-MW pulses at 248.7 nm for an overall conversion efficiency of 10^{-5}. These radiation levels are of immediate utility in such applications as photolithography, photochemistry, spectroscopy and interferometric diagnostics of high-density plasmas.

The authors wish to acknowledge helpful discussions with J. E. Bjorkholm, P. F. Liao, and S. E. Harris and to thank A. V. Smith and J. F. Ward for communicating their results to us before publication. We are grateful to Inrad, Inc., for the loan of the temperature-tuned ADP second-harmonic-generation system.

References

1. A comprehensive review is given in D. C. Hanna, M. A. Yuratich, and D. Cotter, *Nonlinear Optics of Free Atoms and Molecules* (Springer-Verlag, New York, 1979).
2. D. M. Bloom, J. T. Yardley, J. F. Young, and S. E. Harris, Appl. Phys. Lett. **24,** 427 (1974).
3. J. R. Taylor, Opt. Commun. **18,** 504 (1976).
4. Q. H. F. Vrehen and H. M. J. Hikspoors, Opt. Commun. **21,** 127 (1977); D. Cotter, D. C. Hanna, W. H. W. Tuttlebee, and M. A. Yuratich, Opt. Commun. **22,** 190 (1977).
5. W. Hartig, Appl. Phys. **15,** 427 (1978).
6. A. V. Smith, Ph.D. thesis (University of Michigan, Ann Arbor, Mich., 1977); A. V. Smith and J. F. Ward, to be published.
7. Bausch & Lomb, Inc., Rochester, N.Y.
8. EMR Photoelectric, Princeton, N.J.
9. R. T. Hawkins, H. Egger, J. Bokor, and C. K. Rhodes, Appl. Phys. Lett. **36,** 391 (1980).
10. F. H. M. Faisal, R. Wallenstein, and R. Teets, J. Phys. B **13,** 2027 (1980).
11. P. S. Pershan, Phys. Rev. **130,** 919 (1963); T. Hänsch and P. Toschek, Z. Phys. **236,** 373 (1970).
12. R. R. Freeman, J. E. Bjorkholm, R. Panock, and W. E. Cooke, submitted to Phys. Rev. A.

Reprinted with permission from *Physical Review A*, Vol. 26(5), pp. 3029-3030 (November 1982). ©1982 American Physical Society.

Four-wave parametric mixing in optically inverted barium ions

R. R. Freeman
Bell Laboratories, Murray Hill, New Jersey 07974

J. Bokor
Bell Laboratories, Holmdel, New Jersey 07733

W. E. Cooke
Department of Physics, University of Southern California, Los Angeles, California 90007

(Received 2 June 1982)

Optically inverted barium ions in the $6p_{(1/2)}$ excited state served as the nonlinear medium for doubly resonant four-wave parametric generation of coherent radiation at 167 nm. The excited barium ions were produced via selective autoionization. Stimulated-emission photons at 650 nm corresponding to the $6p_{(1/2)}$-$5d_{(3/2)}$ transition were mixed with input 451-nm laser photons tuned to the $6p_{(1/2)}$-$6f_{(5/2)}$ two-photon resonance to produce the 167-nm output photons.

If an atom is excited to an autoionizing state, it will in general decay to a multitude of final ionic states with corresponding distribution of ejected electron energies. Under some conditions, preferential decay to specific excited ionic states occurs. Recently, Bokor *et al.*[1] produced laser action in barium ions by exploiting this principle. Neutral barium was excited to an autoionizing state of the configuration $6p_{(3/2)}np$ with $n \geqslant 12$ by stepwise two-photon laser excitation. This class of autoionizing states was found to selectively decay to yield excited Ba^+ in the $6p_{(1/2)}$ state. We refer to this behavior as selective autoionization. Amplified spontaneous emission (ASE) was observed at 493 and 650 nm corresponding to the $6p_{(1/2)}$-$6s_{(1/2)}$ and $6p_{(1/2)}$-$5d_{(3/2)}$ transitions, respectively. In this Communication, we report the utilization of the excited $Ba^+ 6p_{(1/2)}$ ions produced in this way as a nonlinear medium for four-wave parametric generation of coherent radiation in the vacuum ultraviolet region of the spectrum.

A schematic energy-level diagram showing the relevant barium states and the optical excitation scheme is shown in Fig. 1. The autoionizing states of interest belong to the nominal configuation $6pnp$ and were excited via the $6snp$ resonant intermediate state. In the experiments reported here, the $n = 12$ configurations were used. The apparatus consisted of a barium vapor cell mounted with its output at the entrance slit of a 1-m focal length, normal incidence, vacuum ultraviolet monochromator. An evacuated chamber containing optics for the measurement of backward propagating vacuum ultraviolet emissions was fitted to the input of the cell. The input laser beams were obtained from pulsed dye lasers pumped by the second harmonic of a Nd:YAG laser and standard nonlinear optical techniques. Ultraviolet radiator tunable near 247 nm was produced with an energy up to 1 mJ per pulse at 10 pps and a 2-cm^{-1} bandwidth. This beam was used for excitation of the $6s^2$-$6s12p$ transition in neutral Ba. Visible radiation tunable near 450 nm was produced with an energy of up to 10 mJ per pulse at 10 pps and a 0.5-cm^{-1} bandwidth. This beam was used for the second step in the excitation scheme, $6s_{(1/2)}12p$-$6p_{(3/2)}12p$.

The transition $6s_{(1/2)}12p$-$6p_{(3/2)}12p$ involves primarily a one-electron, nearly unity oscillator strength transition of the ion $6s_{(1/2)}$-$6p_{(3/2)}$, with the $12p$ Ryd-

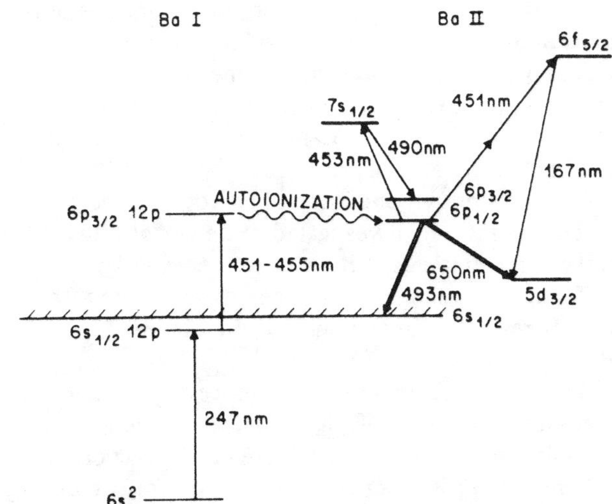

FIG. 1. A schematic energy-level diagram showing the relevant neutral and first ionic states of barium. The autoionization $6p_{(3/2)}12p \rightarrow 6p_{(1/2)} + e^-$ provides an inversion in the ion; the resulting ASE is observed at 650 and 493 nm (double arrows). This process remained saturated as the laser driving the $6s_{(1/2)}12p \rightarrow 6p_{(3/2)}12p$ was tuned from 451–455 nm. As explained in the text, this allowed the production of ASE and four-wave mixing output in the ion using only the original lasers used in the pumping of the autoionization level in the neutral.

berg electron acting as an observer.[2] Using focused excitation, this transition was easily depletion broadened[3] to a width of up to 10 nm. Under these conditions, selectivity in the autoionization process was preserved, and ASE at 650 nm was produced over this entire tuning range. This fact allowed off-resonant production of the $6p_{(1/2)}$ ions and subsequent excitation of these ions to higher-lying states using the same input laser. Two such processes were investigated. When the input laser was tuned to exact resonance with the $6p_{(1/2)}$-$7s_{(1/2)}$ transition at 452.6 nm, strong ASE on the $7s_{(1/2)}$-$6p_{(3/2)}$ transition at 490 nm was observed, indicating efficient transfer of population from the $6p_{(1/2)}$ to $7s_{(1/2)}$ level. The $6p_{(1/2)}$ level was sufficiently depleted that the 650- and 493-nm ASE outputs were fully quenched. Well-collimated output at 490 nm was observed from both ends of the cell, with a wavelength which was identical (to within our measurement accuracy of ± 0.02 nm) to that given for the $7s_{(1/2)}$-$6p_{(3/2)}$ transition in Moore.[4] Further, the wavelength of the output was independent of the density of barium, and the wavelength of the excitation laser.

In the second case, the visible laser was tuned near 451 nm, corresponding to the $6p_{(1/2)}$-$6f_{(5/2)}$ two-photon transition in Ba^+. In this case, the 650-nm ASE was not quenched; in fact, no significant decrease in 650-nm output was observed for any tunings of the visible laser in this vicinity. Nevertheless, strong collimated emission at 167 nm was detected in the forward direction. The peak output was estimated to be 10^{12} photons per pulse. Because no emission was detected in the backward direction, this output cannot be due to ASE and is instead attributed to a doubly resonant four-wave parametric interaction involving the excited Ba^+ as the nonlinear medium. Here, two of the input 451-nm photons mix with the internally generated 650-nm ASE photons to produce the 167-nm output photons. This process closely resembles recently investigated examples of four-wave parameteric oscillation[5] with the important difference that the large nonlinearity arises from the doubly resonant susceptibility of the *excited* $Ba^+ 6p_{(1/2)}$ *ions.*

The parametric nature of this process is further illustrated by the data of Fig. 2. Here, the output emission at 167 nm was monitored as a function of the input laser wavelength near 451 nm for two different temperatures of the barium vapor cell. Optimum output is achieved for a laser tuning of approximately 7 cm^{-1} to the red side of the true two-photon resonance as given in Moore.[4] The tuning curve is seen to be density dependent, broadening the red shifting with increased barium density. This type of excitation spectrum is characteristic of phase-matching behavior in four-wave mixing processes.[6]

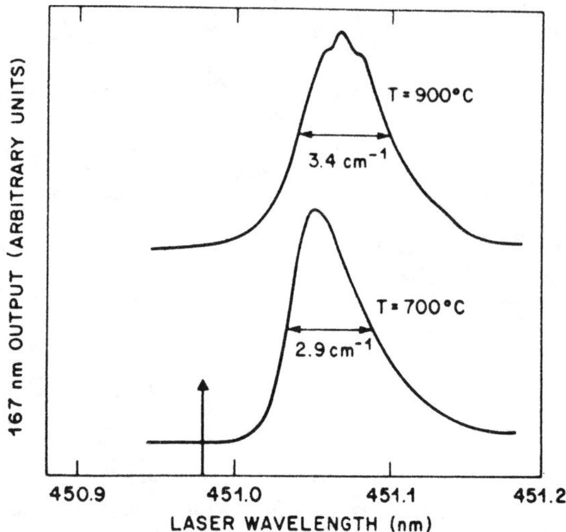

FIG. 2. Plot of the intensity of emission at 167 nm as a function of the input wavelength near 451 nm for two different temperatures of the barium cell. The arrow marks the laser wavelength for exact two-photon resonance as given by Moore. The tuning curve is seen to be density dependent, broadening and red shifting with increased barium density.

In conclusion, excited $Ba^+ 6p_{(1/2)}$ ions produced by decay of the neutral $Ba^+ 6p_{(3/2)} 12p$ autoionizing state have been exploited as a nonlinear medium for the efficient generation of coherent vacuum ultraviolet radiation. Up to 10^{12} photons per pulse at 10 pps were generated at 167 nm. These results indicate the potential of the selective autoionization mechanism acting in combination with additional nonlinear processes for the generation of high-brightness coherent radiation in the deep ultraviolet region of the spectrum.

The authors wish to acknowledge the technical assistance of R. H. Storz. Work done at the University of Southern California was supported in part by the National Science Foundation under Grant No. PHY-7916444. One of us (W.E.C.) acknowledges the support of an Alfred P. Sloan Foundation Fellowship.

[1]J. Bokor, R. R. Freeman, and W. E. Cooke, Phys. Rev. Lett. 48, 1242 (1982).

[2]W. E. Cooke, T. F. Gallagher, S. A. Edelstein, and R. M. Hills, Phys. Rev. Lett. 40, 178 (1978).

[3]W. E. Cooke, A. S. Bhatti, and C. L. Cromer, Opt. Lett. 7, 69 (1982).

[4]C. E. Moor, Report No. NSRDA-NBS35 (unpublished).

[5]J. Bokor, R. R. Freeman, R. L. Panock, and J. C. White, Opt. Lett. 6, 182 (1981) and references contained therein.

[6]P. P. Sorokin, J. J. Wynne, and J. R. Lankard, Appl. Phys. Lett. 22, 342 (1973); a more general discussion of phase matching in four-wave mixing processes can be found in D. C. Hanna, M. A. Yuratich, and D. Cotter, *Nonlinear Optics of Free Atoms and Molecules* (Springer, New York, 1979).

Section Five

X-Ray Lasers

The possibility of extending laser wavelengths into the x-ray region, by various means such as those of Gudzenko and Shelepin or of Rentzepis and Duguay, caught immediate attention following the progress of lasers in the ultraviolet. Predictions of swift x-ray laser progress initiated programs in the early 1970s. The slow progress that resulted during these programs, accompanied by difficult to interpret results and claims of lasing, led to a decline in activity in the early 1980s.

Although solid x-ray laser results have been produced by the Lawrence Livermore group, which used an extremely high power laser intended for fusion experiments, and by others using laser pumping facilities, x-ray laser research moves slowly due in large part to the difficulty of working with large machines. Current activity is directed toward searching for new transitions with high power lasers while trying new techniques that may enable more modest "laboratory size" pumping systems to be used to excite x-ray lasers.

The wavelengths currently producible approach the 20-44 Å region, where transmission through the water associated with biomolecules is possible. It is hoped that transmission in this "water window" will allow holography to display the three-dimensional structure of biomolecules.

Reprinted with permission from *Soviet Physics-Doklady,* Vol. 10(2), pp. 147-149 (August 1965). ©1965 American Institute of Physics.

RADIATION ENHANCEMENT IN A RECOMBINING PLASMA

L. I. Gudzenko and L. A. Shelepin

(Presented by Academician M. A. Leontovich, September 18, 1964)
P.N.Lebedev Institute of Physics, Academy of Sciences of the USSR,
Translated from Doklady Akademii Nauk SSSR, Vol. 160, No. 6, pp. 1296-1299, February, 1965
Original article submitted September 3, 1964

The analysis of radiation enhancement in a highly ionized plasma with inversely populated energy levels requires taking account of the entire set of relaxation times. The detailed solution of this problem is far from complete; even in a qualitative consideration of the processes accompanying the decay of such a plasma, it is convenient to distinguish the following three stages: 1) a strongly-ionized plasma with "instantaneously" cooled free electrons when the lower levels are still almost unpopulated; 2) a substantially-ionized plasma in which "stationary drainage" has been established, with superpopulated upper levels; 3) a weakly-ionized plasma.

In a strongly-ionized plasma of average density ($N_e \sim 10^{11}$ - 10^{17} cm^{-3}) the electron relaxation times over discrete levels considerably exceed the time for establishing a distribution in a continuous spectrum and, consequently, such mixed cooling of the free electrons is found to be possible that the initially small population of a number of discrete levels is not increased significantly. Thus, a medium is formed which enhances electromagnetic radiation [1];its properties are determined by specific conditions of cooling and by the kinetics of recombination. Papers [2-4] are devoted to the relaxation of a plasma whose high degree of ionization exceeds by far the equilibrium value (at a temperature T_e of the free electrons); recombination is initiated with the capture of an electron into one of the upper excited levels as a result of triple collisions, then the electron transfers to a lower level as a result of collisions of the second kind or spontaneously, and it may even transfer to higher discrete levels or return to the continuous spectrum as a result of a collision of the first kind. Inelastic collisions sharply reduce the role of states which are metastable for radiative transition and, also, we may anticipate, the well-known similarity of processes occurring in the decay of highly-ionized homogeneous plasma of different compositions.

Let us consider an optically thin hydrogen plasma. If, after "prompt" cooling of the free electrons, their kinetic temperature is maintained unchanged, the equations for the occupation of the energy levels assume the form

$$\frac{dN_n}{dt} = -N_e N_n\Big[\sum_{m>n} V(n, m) + \sum_{m<n} R(n, m)\Big] - N_e N_n B_\varepsilon(n) + N_n \sum_{m<n} A(n, m) + N_e\Big[\sum_{m>n} R(m, n) N_m + \sum_{m<n} V(m, n) N_m\Big] + N_e^3 B_\varepsilon'(n) + N_e^2 A_\varepsilon(n) + \sum_{m>n} A(m, n) N_m,$$

$$N = N_e + \sum_n N_n. \tag{1}$$

Here N is the total number of electrons in 1 cm^3 of plasma, N_e is the free electron density, N_n is the number of electrons per 1 cm^3 in a discrete level with principal quantum number n. The quantities $A(n, m)\,dt$ and $A_\varepsilon(n)\,dt$ are equal respectively to the probabilities of radiative transition $n \to m$ and spontaneous recombination at the level n after a time dt; similarly, V(n, m) and R(n, m) are proportional to the probabilities of nonradiative transitions within the atom; $B_\varepsilon(n)$ and $B_\varepsilon'(n)$ and the probabilities of nonradiative ionization and recombination.

For densities of $N \sim 10^{13}$ - 10^{16} cm^{-3} and temperature $kT_e \sim 0.1$ - 0.5 eV the general relaxation scheme appears qualitatively to be this: After capture of an electron in an upper level, collision relaxation predominated, the probability of which falls with decreasing n, while the role of radiative tran-

TABLE 1

	$N_e = 10^{12}$				$N_e = 10^{13}$			
	$kT_e = 0.1$	0.2	0.3	0.4	0.1	0.2	0.3	0.4
N_2	$4.6\cdot10^4$	$4.7\cdot10^3$	$1,8\cdot10^3$	$1.0\cdot10^3$	$2.2\cdot10^7$	$1.2\cdot10^6$	$3.6\cdot10^5$	$1.7\cdot10^5$
N_3	$1,8\cdot10^5$	$1,9\cdot10^4$	$7,0\cdot10^3$	$3.9\cdot10^3$	$9.6\cdot10^7$	$8.1\cdot10^6$	$2.2\cdot10^6$	$9.7\cdot10^5$
N_4	$1.0\cdot10^6$	$7.9\cdot10^4$	$2,5\cdot10^4$	$1.3\cdot10^4$	$8.8\cdot10^8$	$2.6\cdot10^7$	$6.6\cdot10^6$	$2.8\cdot10^6$
N_5	$2.3\cdot10^6$	$1,8\cdot10^5$	$5,7\cdot10^4$	$2.8\cdot10^4$	$3.8\cdot10^8$	$2.4\cdot10^7$	$7.3\cdot10^6$	$3.4\cdot10^6$
N_6	$2.3\cdot10^6$	$2.3\cdot10^5$	$8,0\cdot10^4$	$4.1\cdot10^4$	$2,6\cdot10^8$	$2.5\cdot10^7$	$8.3\cdot10^6$	$4.3\cdot10^6$

	$N_e = 10^{14}$				$N_e = 10^{15}$			
	$kT_e = 0.1$	0.2	0.3	0.4	0.1	0.2	0.3	0.4
N_2	$9.6\cdot10^9$	$3.6\cdot10^8$	$1.2\cdot10^8$	$4.9\cdot10^7$	$2.0\cdot10^{12}$	$2.7\cdot10^{11}$	$3.2\cdot10^{10}$	$2.3\cdot10^{10}$
N_3	$3.2\cdot10^{10}$	$6.1\cdot10^9$	$1.2\cdot10^9$	$3.6\cdot10^8$	$1.7\cdot10^{12}$	$3.5\cdot10^{12}$	$3.9\cdot10^{11}$	$6.3\cdot10^{10}$
N_1	$4.1\cdot10^{11}$	$3.9\cdot10^9$	$8.7\cdot10^8$	$3.5\cdot10^8$	$6.5\cdot10^{13}$	$4.4\cdot10^{11}$	$9.8\cdot10^{10}$	$3.7\cdot10^{10}$
N_5	$4.7\cdot10^{10}$	$2.6\cdot10^9$	$7.7\cdot10^8$	$3.6\cdot10^8$	$5.2\cdot10^{12}$	$2.6\cdot10^{11}$	$7,8\cdot10^{10}$	$3.6\cdot10^{10}$
N_6	$2.7\cdot10^{10}$	$2.5\cdot10^9$	$8.6\cdot10^8$	$4.4\cdot10^8$	$2.7\cdot10^{12}$	$2.5\cdot10^{11}$	$8.6\cdot10^{10}$	$4.4\cdot10^{10}$

sitions increases; at lower levels ($n < n^*$) radiative transitions play the primary role. The rate of relaxation can be estimated from the rate of passage through the level n^*; for $n > n^*$ the electrons rapidly assume a quasiequilibrium distribution

$$\tilde{N}_n = n^2 N_e^2 \left(\frac{2\pi\hbar}{mkT_e}\right)^{3/2} \exp\left(\frac{E_n}{kT_e}\right). \tag{2}$$

The first stage of relaxation is characterized by the time τ_1 for establishing stationary drainage at excited discrete levels; the order of magnitude of τ_1 is estimated to be the lesser of the time of triple recombination at the second level and the sum of the relaxation times between adjacent levels. For values of N_e and T_e of interest to us, $\tau_1 \sim 10^{-8}$ - 10^{-7} sec.

The second stage is initiated after a time τ_1 after sudden cooling of the free electrons and is concluded at $\sum_{n=2}^{n_{max}} N_n(t) \simeq N_e(t)$; in calculating the population $\bar{N}_n$ at stage (2) of the "stationary drain" it is necessary to put $d\bar{N}_n/dt = 0$, $n = 2, 3, \ldots, n_{max}$ in Eq. (1) (see also [3, 4]). The calculation of $\bar{N}_n$ was carried out on the M-20 electronic computer of the P. N. Lebedev Physics Institute; the modified Born cross sections for collision processes [5] were used for the coefficients of system (1), the value of n_{max} was determined from the Debye radius and $\bar{N}_n$ was taken equal to $\tilde{N}_n$ for $n > 10$. Transition cross sections from states with $n > 10$ to lower discrete levels are estimated by asymptotic continuation of the triple recombination formula. Table 1[1] shows the occupation number $\bar{N}_n$ for the levels $n = 2$ to 6, where $\bar{N}_n$ differs significantly from $\tilde{N}_n$.

The coefficient of negative absorption of radiation with wavelength $\lambda_{n,m}$ (corresponding to the transition $n \to m$) per 1 cm photon path is equal to

$$\varkappa_{m,n} \simeq \frac{\lambda_{n,m}^2}{4\Gamma_{m,n}} A(n, m)(N_n - N_m). \tag{3}$$

Let us estimate, for example, $\varkappa_{5,2}$ for the first and second stages of relaxation. The line width is determined here by collisions with ions [5]: $\Gamma_{m,n} = 12.5(m^2 - n^2) N_e^{2/3}$. For the first stage, assuming $N_s \simeq \tilde{N}_s$, $N_2 = 0$ for $kT_e = 0.1$ eV, we find $\varkappa_{5,2}^{(1)} = 2 \cdot 10^{-28} N_e^{4/3}$; consequently, for $N_e = 10^{15}$ cm^{-3} we have $\varkappa_{5,2}^{(1)} \simeq 4 \cdot 10^{-2}$ cm^{-1}. For the second stage, according to Table 1, for $kT_e = 0.1$ eV, $N_e = 10^{15}$ cm^{-3}, we find $\varkappa_{5,2}^{(2)} = 2 \cdot 10^{-3}$ cm^{-1}. Thus, during the entire interval of the stationary drainage ($\tau_2 \sim 10^{-5}$ sec) an inverted population is maintained, sufficient for creating a laser. Even during the time $\tau_1 \sim 10^{-8}$ sec, corresponding to stage (1), the enhancement in a hydrogen plasma enables lasing to be produced at a length of several centimeters. In an optically thin plasma the values of N_n are independent of N_1 but in actual systems for $N_e > 10^{14}$ cm^{-3} it is necessary to take account of radiation reabsorption, which leads to an increase of $\bar{N}_2$ and $\bar{N}_3$, of their dependence on N_1 and to reduction of τ_2, $\varkappa_{n,2}^{(2)}$, $\varkappa_{n,3}^{(2)}$. It should be noted that hydrogen is not the best medium for a plasma laser, since as a consequence

[1]The collision cross sections for the first levels, even in the case of hydrogen, are determined as yet only with an accuracy of a factor of $\sim$ 1-3. Consequently, it is of interest to compare the values of N_n calculated by us with the values calculated in previously appearing papers [4], where quasiclassical cross sections were used. The corresponding values of $\bar{N}_n$ were found to agree to order of magnitude.

of the linear Stark effect it has large values of $\Gamma_{m,n}$; moreover, the absence of metastability in a hydrogen plasma decreases the times τ_1 and τ_2.

No account is taken in Eq. (1) of imprisonment of radiation, effect of undecomposed molecules and neutral atoms, and also of electron attachment. In stage (1) and, to a certain extent in stage (2), taking account of all these phenomena should have only a refining character, which is meaningless without a specific definition of the method of cooling. At stage (3) these effects may become decisive. The situation is further complicated in that in a weakly-ionized plasma the significance of nonradiative transitions is reduced, which emphasizes the role of metastable states. In contrast to stages (1) and (2), the state with inverted population in a weakly-ionized plasma can easily be maintained stationary, and it is achieved in a gas laser. We shall consider one property of a gas-discharge plasma.

The heating and cooling of free electrons in a gas discharge are time-coincident: The heater is the electric field and the cooler is the large specific heat of the heavy particles (ions, atoms, and molecules) as well as the walls. For low degrees of ionization the frequency ν_e of electron-electron collisions falls, and the distribution N(E) of the free electrons is different from Maxwellian; this is well-known for large energies $E > 2kT_e$. It is important to note the deviation N(E) from a Maxwellian distribution at low energies. With decrease of energy, for $E \ll kT$ collisions of an electron with cold heavy particles become all the more important; the efficiencies of heating impacts with faster electrons and cooling impacts with ions are comparable at $E \sim E_0$:

$$\frac{\nu_i(E_0)\,\delta}{\nu_e(E_0,\,E > E_0)} \simeq \frac{\sqrt{\pi}}{2}\,\delta\left(\frac{kT_e}{E_0}\right)^{3/2}\left[-\mathrm{Ei}\left(-\frac{E_0}{kT_e}\right)\right]^{-1} \simeq 1, \quad (4)$$

where ν_i is the frequency of collision with ions δ is the relative fraction of the energy transferred by the collisions. Having substituted in Eq. (4) the usual parameters of a gas laser plasma $kT_e = 8$ eV, $kT_i = 0.04$ eV we find, for example, that for hydrogen $E_0 \sim 0.6$ eV. That is, for $E_0 < 0.6$ eV collisions with heavy particles lead to a definite increase in the density of cold electrons above the value corresponding to a Maxwellian distribution for temperature T_e and, consequently, to an intensification of recombination at the upper discrete levels. The decrease of cold electrons as a consequence of recombination is compensated by their influx as a result of inelastic collisions. As a consequence of some upper level metastability, their population exceeds the quasiequilibrium values, which may be one of the reasons for population inversion of a gas-discharge plasma. The effect should be enhanced as a result of pulse modulation of the field, and this is verified qualitatively by experiment. We note finally the significance of "diffusion cooling" [6], which determined the dependence of the enhancement on the distance to the walls and which governs the dependence of the operation of the entire gas laser on the diameter of the tube; the role of the walls is reduced by the introduction of the magnetic field.

It must be emphasized again that in analyzing the enhancement in a nonequilibrium recombining plasmas with different degrees of ionization, the kinetics of the entire multilevel system should be taken into account; taking account of the electron distribution only over two or three levels (see, for example, [7]), which has been done hitherto, is here unjustified.

The authors express their thanks to A. T. Matachun, for assistance with the numerical calculations, and to A. M. Prokhorov, I. I. Sobel'man and N. N. Sobolev for discussions.

LITERATURE CITED

1. L. P. Gudzenko and L. A. Shelepin, ZhÉTF, 46, 1445 (1963) [Soviet Physics – JETP, see Vol. 12].
2. N. D'Angelo, Phys. Rev., 121, 505 (1961); S. Byron, R. C. Stabler, and P. I. Bortz, Phys. Rev. Lett., 8, 376 (1962); E. Hinnov and J. G. Hirschberg, Phys. Rev., 125, 795 (1962).
3. D. R. Bates, A. E. Kingston, and R. W. P. McWhirter, Proc. Roy. Soc., A267, 297 (1962).
4. R. W. P. McWhirter and A. G. Hearn, Proc. Phys. Soc., 82, 641 (1963); D. R. Bates and A. E. Kingston, Planetary and Space Sci., 11, 1 (1963).
5. I. I. Sobel'man, Introduction to the Theory of Atomic Spectra [in Russian], (Moscow, 1963).
6. M. A. Biondi, Phys. Rev., 93, 1136 (1954).
7. W. R. Bennett, UFN, 81, 119 (1963) [Soviet Physics – Uspekhi, see Vol. 12].

Reprinted with permission from *Applied Physics Letters,* Vol. 10(12), pp. 350-352 (June 15, 1967).

SOME APPROACHES TO VACUUM UV AND X-RAY LASERS

M. A. Duguay and P. M. Rentzepis
Bell Telephone Laboratories, Inc.
Murray Hill, New Jersey
(Received 3 April 1967)

The ejection of electrons from inner shells of atoms through photoionization is suggested as a straightforward means of creating population inversions at vacuum uv and x-ray wavelengths. This can be accomplished by photon sources covering broad bands. Sodium vapor and solid copper are examined as possible candidates for laser action at 372 Å and 1.54 Å, respectively. A first-rise traveling wave pump must be used; pumping powers required for superradiant operation run into several gigawatts, with rise times ranging from 10^{-9} sec in the near-vacuum uv to 10^{-15} sec in the x-ray region.

In this Letter we wish to point out that the ejection of inner shell atomic electrons through photoionization appears to be a straightforward mechanism for creating population inversions for transitions at vacuum ultraviolet and x-ray wavelengths. When an electron has been ejected from, say, the K shell of a copper atom, the residual copper ion is left in an excited state which can decay by virtue of an L-shell electron dropping down into the K shell. Since there are initially no copper ions, the process of photoionization has created a population inversion in a single step, which is reminiscent of Bennett's single-step excitation process in ion gas lasers.[1]

Ejection of electrons from preferentially inner shells of atoms is made possible by the very nature of the photoionization process: The probability of ejecting a tightly bound electron, at a given wavelength, is larger than that for ejecting a more loosely bound electron by a factor which is larger than that for ejecting a more loosely bound electron by a factor which is severalfold in the x-ray region, but may be much larger in the vacuum uv. A striking example in the vacuum uv is provided by sodium vapor. The photoionization cross section of sodium vapor[2] has been sketched in Fig. 1. In a broad energy range extending above the threshold for ejection of a $2p$ electron (38 eV), the cross section for ejecting a $2p$ electron is seen to be more than one hundred times that for ejecting the outer $3s$ electron! It is clear that broad-band photon sources can be used very effectively to selectively produce sodium ions in the excited states of the $2p^5\,3s$ configuration, which lie at about 33 eV above the ion ground state.

As is also apparent from Fig. 1, a pump source covering a band above 1.1 keV could produce population inversions for the 1.04-keV L shell to K shell transition. Photoionization cross sections exhibit the same general behavior in all elements, and the same principles would apply there. From the behavior of *electron* impact ionization cross sections,[3] electrons do not appear to be nearly as well suited as photons for selectively removing electrons from inner shells.

To give an idea of the numbers involved, we estimate here the pump requirements of a sodium vapor laser operating on the 33-eV transition described above, and of a solid copper laser operating on the 8-keV L shell to K shell transition.

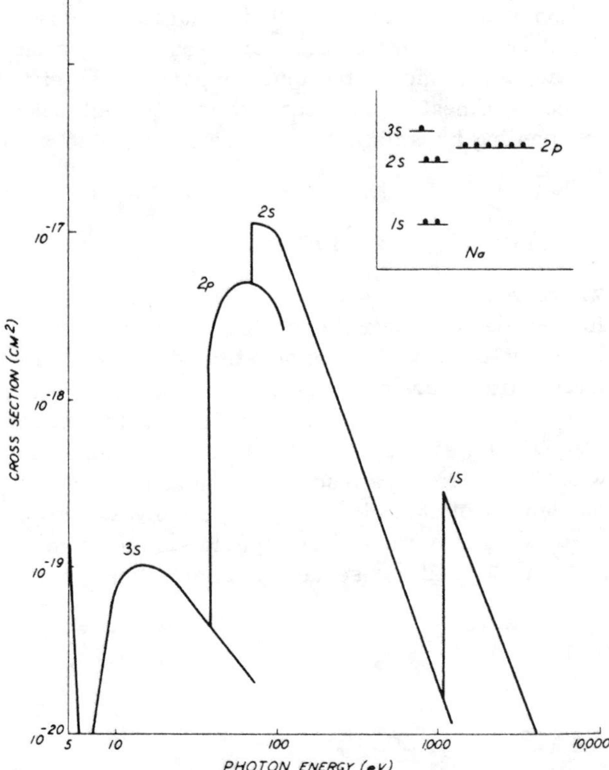

Fig. 1. Photoionization cross section of sodium as obtained from ref. 2. The labels on the curve indicate which electronic shell is contributing to the total cross section. The insert indicates the gross shell structure of Na.

The photoemission of a $2p$ electron from the sodium atom predominantly populates the four states of the $2p^5\,3s$ configuration of Na II. The shortest-lived state among these is the $3s_2\;^1P_1$ state which decays to the $2p\;^1S_0$ ion ground state by emitting a 33.3-eV photon ($\lambda = 372$ Å). The lifetime of this state is unknown, but for the purpose of this discussion it is sufficient to retain the estimate of 0.4 nsec, that one obtains by assuming that the transition has the same oscillator strength (0.16 absorption) as the corresponding transition (736-Å line) in isoelectronic Ne.[4] The other three states are much longer lived, and their presence will be ignored here.

Since the ground state is stable, laser action on this transition is said to be "self-terminating" because a population inversion can only be maintained for times of the order of the upper state lifetime. With the short lifetimes we are encountering here, it becomes necessary to pump the laser in the traveling wave fashion which has been pioneered by Shipman[5] for the 3371-Å nitrogen laser. Shipman applied to his laser medium a fast rising current pulse which traveled down the length of the laser at the speed of light, thereby amplifying in its wake a short pulse of uv light. Besides allowing in principle arbitrarily large lengths for the active medium, the traveling wave pump also provides for an economy of pumping power, since at any given time one is only pumping a short length of the active medium.

Let the sodium vapor laser have dimensions 1 cm × 1 cm × 500 cm, and the pressure be 0.02 torr (temperature, 310°C). Let the traveling wave pumping vacuum uv radiation cover a band centered at a quantum energy of 50 eV, and be incident perpendicularly to the length of the laser. At a pressure of 0.02 torr only 0.3% of this pumping radiation is absorbed in the 1-cm-wide laser medium. While higher pressures would lead to higher efficiencies and lower pumping power requirements, they cannot be used here because of one weakness of this laser: Namely, the ejected $2p$ electrons can ionize other neutral sodium atoms by ejecting the $3s$ electron, thereby reducing the population inversion sought for. At 0.02 torr, the probability of these electrons causing ionization during the short laser pulse is about 1%.[6]

The gain G per centimeter is given by:[7]

$$G = \frac{\lambda^2}{8\pi}\left(\frac{4\ln 2}{\pi}\right)^{1/2}\frac{A}{\Delta\nu}\left(N_2 - \frac{g_2}{g_1}N_1\right)$$

where λ is the wavelength (372 Å), A is the Einstein coefficient (2.5 GHz), $\Delta\nu$ is the Doppler width (30 GHz), N_2 and N_1 are the number of atoms per cm^3 in the upper and lower state, respectively, and g_2/g_1 is the ratio of their statistical weights (3 here).

Let us assume that the traveling wave pump has a linear rise with time. Let Pt be the rate at which sodium atoms in any given cm^3 are pumped to the upper laser state, where t is the time and P is in units of atoms/sec/sec/cm^3. Integrating the rate equations, we find that the weighted population excess ($N_2 - g_2N_1/g_1$) reaches a broad maximum of $0.056\;P\tau_2^2$ at a time $0.6\;\tau_2$ after the beginning of the pumping pulse, where τ_2 is the upper state lifetime (0.4 nsec). The effect of the photoejected $2p$ electrons is to reduce this maximum by about 20% and shift it to $0.55\;\tau_2$. The direct production of ground state ions by the pump ($3s$ electron photoionization), reduces this maximum further by about 10%.

Evaluating the gain equation we find that pumping power rising at the rate of 4 GW/nsec/cm^2 would result in a gain of 40 dB/m, thereby assuring superradiant laser action. Note that the losses due to absorption at 372 Å ($3s$ electron photoionization) are only 0.3% per meter. The laser pulse would be about 0.1 nsec long. The saturated power output would be about 3 kW/cm^3, for a maximum possible total of 1.5 MW for a 5-m-long laser.

Following ejection of an electron from the K shell of copper, laser action on the 8.0 keV (1.537 Å) transition from the $^2S_{1/2}$ K-shell hole state to the $^2P_{3/2}$ L_{III}-subshell hole state would be favored by the 1 to 2 ratio of statistical weights. One is fighting much shorter lifetimes here: 0.45 femtosecond (10^{-15} sec) for the upper state, 1.35 fsec for the lower state.[8] Again the transition is self-terminating, and laser action requires a traveling wave pump. Imagine the active medium to be a strip 1 μ × 1 μ × 5 mm on a very smooth surface of copper. With pumping x rays of 12 keV average energy, about 10% of the pumping radiation is absorbed in 1 μ. At this energy the cross section for ejecting an electron is about 8 times larger in the K shell than in the L shell.

We find in this case that traveling-wave pumping power rising linearly at the rate of 25 GW per femtosecond per square micron would result in a gain of 400 dB per mm, thereby comfortably exceeding the 200 dB/mm absorption losses at 1.537 Å, for a net gain of 200 dB/mm.

The estimates given above make it clear that pumping a 33-eV laser and especially an 8-keV x-ray laser is a formidable problem. The sheer power and rise-time requirements are not far, however, from being within the grasp of laser technology. Pulses as short as 4×10^{-12} sec have been observed recently[9] with the Nd glass laser, and pulses as short as 10^{-13} sec seem possible[10] with this laser. The problem of converting this optical power to x-ray wavelengths is a formidable one. The Compton scattering of light by relativistic electrons[11] and the production of laser sparks[12] would appear to offer interesting possibilities, provided conversion efficiencies are high enough.

Clearly other atomic and molecular systems can be pumped by the ejection of inner-shell electrons. In general, one must, however, pay close attention to the very fast Auger processes, whereby the atom decays with the emission of electrons rather than photons. The case of sodium and other atoms with a single electron orbiting outside a closed shell core is favorable in this respect, since there is no other electron available for the Auger process to take place.

Finally, it is worth pointing out that ejection of inner shell electrons with subsequent Auger processes taking place, can lead to population inversions in highly ionized species, of the type suitable for CW laser action. The ejection of a K-shell electron in aluminum vapor, for example, in a large fraction of the cases would result through Auger processes in a triply ionized ion (Al IV) with an electron in the $3p$ shell, none in the $3s$ shell, and with one vacancy in the $2p$ shell. Laser action would take place in the same fashion as in the neon ion lasers,[13] between states in the $3p$ and $3s$ configurations.

---

[1] W. R. Bennett, Jr., J. W. Knutson, Jr., G. N. Mercer, and J. L. Betch, *Appl. Phys. Letters* **4,** 180 (1964).

[2] Anne H. Boyd, *Planet. Space Sci.* **12,** 729 (1964); A. H. Compton and S. K. Allison, *X-Rays in Theory and Experiment* (Van Nostrand, Princeton, New Jersey, 1935), p. 799.

[3] L. J. Keiffer and G. H. Dunn, *Rev. Mod. Phys.* **38,** 1 (1966).

[4] F. A. Korolev, V. I. Odintsov, and E. V. Furova, *Opt. and Spectr.* (USSR, English translation), **16,** 304 (1964).

[5] J. D. Shipman, Jr., *Appl. Phys. Letters* **10,** 3 (1967).

[6] Estimate based on an electroionization cross section equal to $\approx 5 \times 10^{-16}$ cm^2, see ref. 3.

[7] A. C. G. Mitchell and M. W. Zemansky, *Resonance Radiation and Excited Atoms* (Cambridge University Press, New York, 1934), p. 95.

[8] L. G. Parratt, *Rev. Mod. Phys.* **31,** 616 (1959).

[9] J. A. Armstrong, *Appl. Phys. Letters* **10,** 16 (1967).

[10] A. J. DeMaria, D. A. Stetser, and H. Heynau, *Appl. Phys. Letters* **8,** 174 (1966).

[11] F. R. Arutyunian and V. A. Tumanian, *Phys. Letters* **4,** 176 (1963).

[12] S. L. Mandelshtam, P. P. Pashinin, A. M. Prokhorov, Yu. P. Raizer, and N. K. Sukhodrev, *Zh. Eksperim. i Teor. Fiz.* **49,** 127 (1965) [translation, *Soviet Phys. JETP* **22,** 91 (1966)].

[13] P. K. Cheo and H. G. Cooper, *J. Appl. Phys.* **36,** 1862 (1965).

Reprinted with permission from *Applied Physics Letters,* Vol. 10(8), pp. 216-218 (April 15, 1967). ©1967 American Institute of Physics.

PROPOSED RESONATOR FOR AN X-RAY LASER

W. L. Bond, M. A. Duguay, and P. M. Rentzepis
Bell Telephone Laboratories, Inc.
Murray Hill, New Jersey
(Received 2 March 1967)

A simple scheme for an x-ray laser resonator is proposed. It involves a three-dimensional "puckered-ring" type arrangement of crystals set at the Bragg angle. The polarization eigenmodes and losses are discussed for such a system.

An objection frequently raised against the feasibility of x-ray lasers is the unavailability of low-loss resonators at x-ray wavelengths. We wish to propose here a simple scheme for such a resonator.

It has long been known[1] that the reflectivity of perfect crystals set at the Bragg angle should approach unity. Recent measurements[2] on the 220 planes of highly perfect crystals of germanium have revealed peak reflectivities better than 95% for highly monochromatic and parallel copper $K\alpha$ x rays polarized normal to the plane of incidence.

The high efficiency of the Bragg reflection immediately suggests a ring-like structure for a resonator, much as has been used at optical frequencies.[3] The Bragg angle is, however, so sharply defined—within a few seconds of arc—that it would be an extremely improbable occurrence to find for a given x-ray wavelength a set of planes, among the available crystals, with a Bragg angle precisely matching the angle required by the geometry of the ring, viz. a submultiple of 360°, 720°, etc. for regular polygonal rings. This is so if the ring is restricted to a *plane*. If, however, one "puckers" the ring, i.e., deforms it so that it takes the shape of a three-dimensional polygon, it becomes possible to "tune" the Bragg angle, so to speak.

To see how this could be done in a practical device consider the square puckered-ring resonator shown in Fig. 1. In a case where the Bragg angle for a given x-ray wavelength and set of planes in a crystal happened to be precisely 45°, one would simply put four crystals at the corners of the square, set such that their surfaces were perfectly vertical and at 45° to the sides of the square, along which the x rays travel (to simplify the discussion we assume that the crystal surfaces are perfectly parallel to the Bragg planes). In the more probable case, however, where the Bragg angles were some-

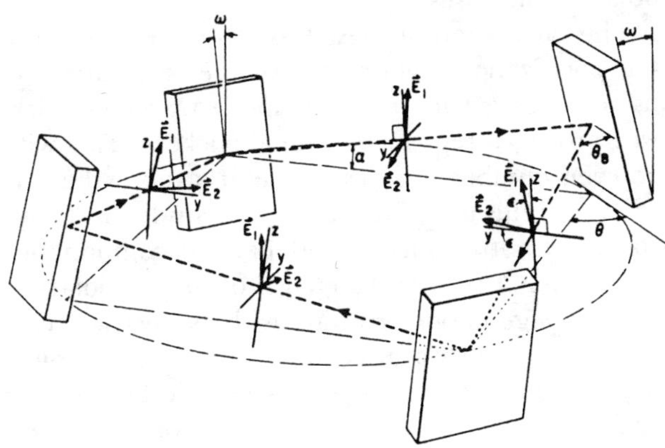

Fig. 1. Puckered square ring geometry for the resonator of an x-ray laser. The x rays follow a path shown as a heavy dotted line, the projection of which on the reference plane is a square (light dashed line). The vectors E_1 and E_2 represent the low-loss and high-loss polarization eigenmodes, respectively.

what larger than 45°, one would move the crystals to the positions shown in Fig. 1. Each leg of the circuit, over which the x rays travel, has been "puckered" by an angle α, and each crystal has been tilted about a tangent to the circumscribed circle by angle ω until its normal lies in the plane defined by the puckered legs. Consecutive crystals are tilted alternately towards and away from the center of the circle, and are alternately lying above and on the horizontal reference plane. The same remarks apply to regular hexagonal, octogonal, etc., puckered rings and also to star-like puckered rings.

The Bragg angle θ_B at each crystal is now larger than the Bragg angle θ which would be required of a planar ring by an amount controlled by the puckering angle α. By elementary trigonometry one can show that

$$\cos \theta_B = \cos \alpha \cos \theta .$$

For the square puckered ring, θ is 45°, and varying α from 0 to 15° causes θ_B to vary from 45° to 46.9°.

Adopting a three-dimensional circuit has one drawback: It introduces polarization losses. These are brought about by the poor reflectivity of the polarization component of the incident wave which is parallel to the plane of incidence. When the ratio of the reflected to the incident amplitude is nearly unity for the normal component, it is nearly $\cos 2\theta_B$ for the polarization component parallel to the plane of incidence. In a planar ring an x-ray wave with its electric vector parallel to the vertical direction will be reflected optimally at each crystal and maintain the same polarization all around the circuit. For a puckered ring the directions of optimum polarizations will change on every leg, leading to polarization losses.

The calculation of these losses is done by finding the polarization eigenmodes of the resonator. Let us consider a running wave mode traveling clockwise around a regular polygonal puckered ring with an even number of sides $2n$. Let us assume that the ratio of reflected to incident amplitudes is 1 and $\cos 2\theta_B$ for the normal and parallel components, respectively. In the language of plane polarizations an eigenmode is a wave with its electric vector polarized in such a direction that after a complete trip around the ring it has its electric field vector again parallel to its original direction, albeit attentuated. We shall use as polarization reference axis a system of axes y and z normal to the ray in each leg and oriented such that the y axis is horizontal and points toward the center of the ring (see Fig. 1).

The n-fold symmetry reduces the problem to diagonalizing the product of two matrices, each representing the attenuation and change of polarization suffered by the wave at each of two consecutive crystals. Under the assumption of small puckering angles α, the eigenvalues are found to be

$$\lambda_1 = 1 - 4\alpha^2$$
$$\lambda_2 = \cos^2 2\theta_B(1 + 4\alpha^2) . \qquad (1)$$

The eigenvalue λ_1 belongs to a low-loss eigenmode which has its electric field vector $\mathbf{E}_1$ tilted alternately clockwise and counterclockwise from the z axis by a small angle ϵ equal to $\alpha \tan^2 \theta_B$. The eigenvalue λ_2 belongs to a high-loss eigenmode which has its electric field vector $\mathbf{E}_2$ tilted alternately above and below the y axis by the same angle ϵ. Note that $\mathbf{E}_1$ and $\mathbf{E}_2$ (see Fig. 1) are not orthogonal, this being a result of the asymmetrical character of the matrix describing the reflection from two consecutive crystals.

The intensity loss after two crystals is therefore $8\alpha^2$ for the low-loss mode, or $4\alpha^2$ per crystal. It is convenient to express this loss as a function of $\theta_B - \theta$, the number of radians by which the available Bragg angle exceeds the angle required for a planar geometry. One has

$$\text{Intensity loss} = 8(\theta_B - \theta) \tan \theta \qquad (2)$$

where $(\theta_B - \theta)$ is expressed radians. Small puckering angles α have been assumed.

To give some specific examples we have listed in Table I the parameters of three geometries which could be used for an x-ray laser operating of the copper $K\alpha_1$ line ($\lambda = 1.53737$ kxu) if highly perfect crystals of only germanium and silicon were available; the small refractive index correction was neglected in computing the Bragg angles. Clearly the germanium square is ideal in this instance. In general, polygons with small Bragg angles are favored over star-like polygons if one is to have small losses: first, because of the $\tan \theta$ factor in Eq. (2) and, second, because the Bragg reflectivity is itself better at small angles.[4]

Power could be coupled out of the resonator by various means, such as Borrmann effect x-ray beam splitters, for example,[5] or by making one of the crystals thin enough so as to be partially transmitting. To insure low diffraction losses, one of the crystals could be bent into a spherical shape. Practical dimensions for an active medium and a resonator, however, are likely to result in such a high

Table I. **Parameters of three practical geometries for the resonator of an x-ray laser to operate on the copper $K\alpha_1$ line ($\lambda = 1.53737$ kxu). The lattice parameters used for Ge and Si were 5.64605 and 5.41968 kxu, respectively. The loss is the intensity loss per crystal due to polarization (*see text*).**

Geometry	Crystal	Plane	θ_B (deg)	θ (deg)	α (deg)	Loss
Square	Ge	333	45.0265	45.	1.7432	0.37%
Octagon	Ge	220	22.6486	22.5	2.6602	0.86%
Octagon	Si	220	23.6508	22.5	7.4851	6.6%

Fresnel number, due to the short x-ray wavelength, that plane mirrors would be more than adequate.[6]

In practice, aligning the puckered ring arrangement would not be easy, although not impossible. Although not tunable, *flat* square rings would however be immensely easier to build from cubic crystals such as silicon or germanium. Taking advantage of the four-fold symmetry, one would simply drill a square hole along the *a* axis of a single block of germanium or silicon such that the sides would be parallel to the four 220 planes.

Informative discussions with George W. Brady are gratefully acknowledged.

[1]C. G. Darwin, *Phil. Mag.* **27,** 315 (1914) (I); **27,** 675 (1914) (II).

[2]B. Okkerse, *Philips Res. Repts.* **18,** 413 (1963) and G. W. Brady (private communication).

[3]W. M. Macek and D. T. M. Davis, Jr., *Appl. Phys. Letters* **2,** 67 (1963).

[4]R. W. James, *The Optical Principles of the Diffraction of X-rays,* (Cornell University Press, Ithaca, N. Y., 1965), Chap. 2.

[5]U. Bonse and M. Hart, *Z. Physik* **188,** 154 (1965) and **190,** 455 (1966).

[6]H. Kogelnik and T. Li, *Appl. Opt.* **5,** 1550 (1966).

Reprinted with permission from *Journal of Applied Physics,* Vol. 41, pp. 3549-3550 (1970).

Some Characteristics of the Resonators for X-Ray Frequencies

A. V. Kolpakov, R. N. Kuz'min, and V. M. Ryaboy

Department of Physics, Moscow State University, Leninskie Gory, Moscow, U.S.S.R.

(Received 15 September 1969; in final form 11 February 1970)

The high efficiency of Bragg's reflection from perfect monocrystals[1,2] permits the creation of resonators in the x-ray frequency range.

The question concerning the geometry of the x-ray resonators has already been examined.[2-5] The tunable resonator proposed by Cotterill[5] has been proved to be most successful.

The question concerning power coupling into and out of these resonators has not been examined in detail. The system for coupling power in and out must satisfy the following conditions:

(i) It should not disturb the reflection geometry, which ensures the beam a closed trajectory.

(ii) There should not be any additional loss of energy.

(iii) The outgoing beam should have the minimum angular divergence.

A power coupling scheme using the Borrmann Effect and satisfying the above conditions is shown in the Fig. 1 (a) and (b). Although Borrmann crystal can be used in the monolithic resonator of Deslattes,[4] the preservation of the high Q-factor additional correction is required since Bragg and the Laue angles differ somewhat from each other. The use of Borrmann crystal in the Cotterill's resonator is more promising, as in this case the resonator has the ability of being tuned at any wavelength. Similarly there exists an interesting possibility of using some active substance, for example, some Mössbauer nuclei of the isotopes ^{57}Fe, ^{119}Sn, ^{121}Sb, ^{125}Te, etc. in the Borrmann crystal. These elements can be introduced in the crystal either as the basic component[6] or in the form of impurity without destroying the perfectness of the crystal.[7]

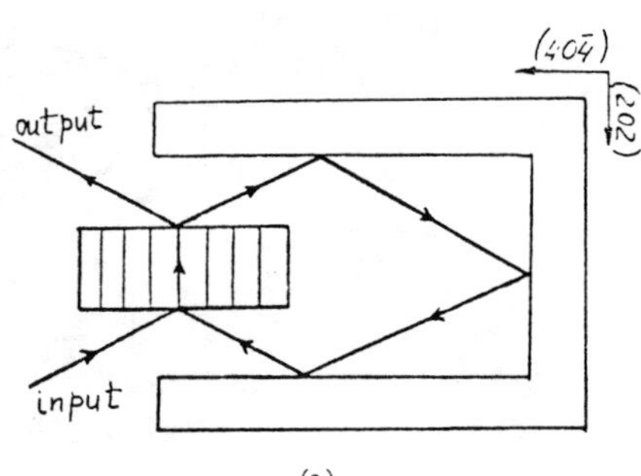

(a)

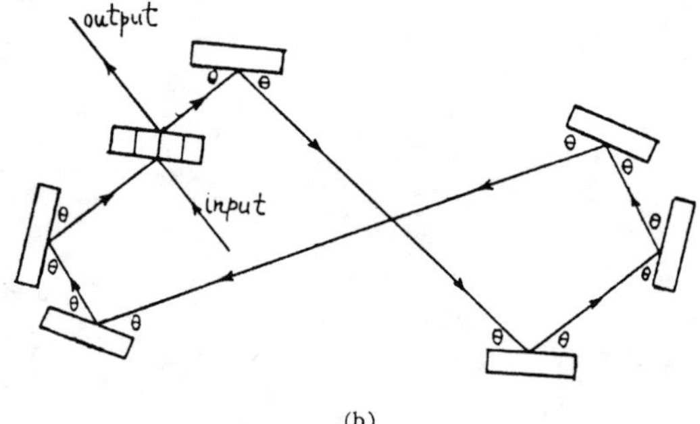

(b)

Fig. 1. Use of Borrmann effect for coupling power into and out of x-ray resonators: (a) Deslattes monocrystal resonator; (b) Cotterill's tunable resonator.

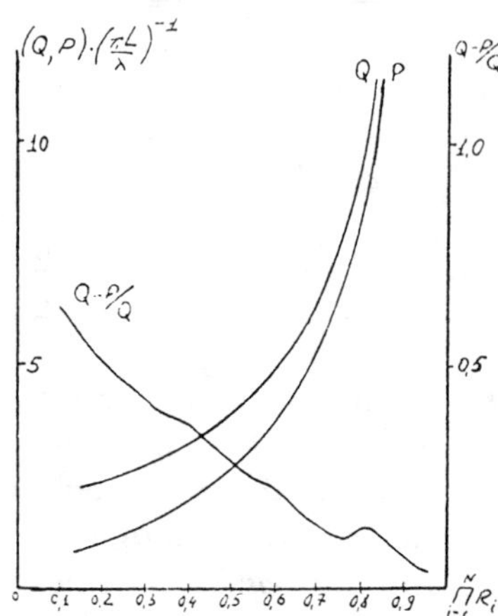

Fig. 2. Dependence of the quality factor Q, the resolving power P of the interferrometer, and the ratio $(Q-P)/Q$ with the product of the reflection coefficients $\prod_{i=1}^{N} R_i$.

We will consider here some basic characteristics of these resonators and will numerically estimate them.

The energy loss in the resonator in time $\Delta t = L/c$ (where Δt is the time of the revolution of the beam along the trajectory of length L) is determined from the expression

$$\Delta W = -W\left(1-\prod_{i=1}^{N} R_i\right), \tag{1}$$

where N is the number of resonator's reflecting surfaces and R_i is the reflection coefficient from the ith crystal. Then the quality factor Q of the resonator which is defined as the ratio of the stored energy in the resonator to the energy loss in time ω^{-1} can be written in the form

$$Q = \omega \frac{W}{|\Delta W/\Delta t|} = \frac{2\pi L}{\lambda}\left(1-\prod_{i=1}^{N} R_i\right)^{-1}. \tag{2}$$

If for the output power Borrmann crystal is used, then one of the coefficients R_i in Eqs. (1) and (2) is the anamalous transmission coefficient, which for simplicity we assume to be close to $\frac{1}{2}$. The Bragg reflection coefficients are also assumed to be of the order of unity.

Considering the resonator as a circular interferrometer, the resolving power analogus to optics[8] can be expressed in the form

$$P = (\pi L/\lambda)\left\{\left(\prod_{i=1}^{N} R_i\right)^{1/4} \Big/ \left[1-\left(\prod_{i=1}^{N} R_i\right)^{1/2}\right]\right\}. \tag{3}$$

The dependence of the quality factor Q and the resolving power P with the product of the reflection coefficient

$$\prod_{i=1}^{N} R_i$$

is shown in Fig. 2. In the same figure the curve $(Q-P)/Q$ has also been shown, which shows that, in the region

$$\prod_{i=1}^{N} R_i < 0.2,$$

the quality factor very well coincides with the resolving power of the interferrometer.

The quality factor according to Eq. (2) on the assumption that $\lambda \simeq 10^{-8}$ cm and $L \simeq 5$ cm is of the order $Q \simeq 6\times10^{9}$. As $Q = \lambda/\Delta\lambda$, the linewidth for the resonator $\Delta\lambda \simeq 1.7\times10^{-18}$ cm.

Time for the existence of mode in the resonator $\tau = Q/\omega \simeq$

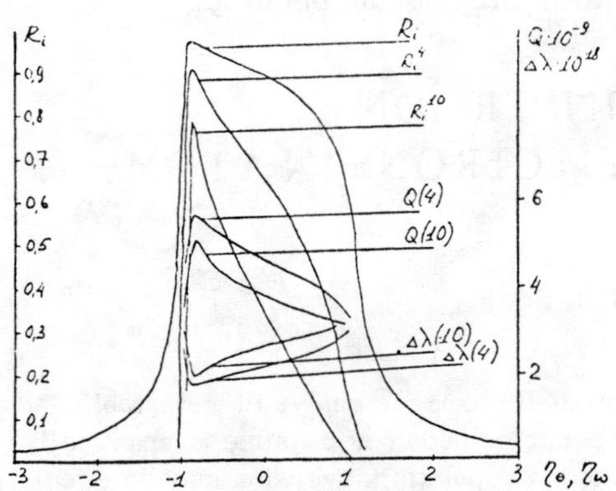

FIG. 3. Frequency (angular) dependence of the reflection coefficients R_i, R_i^4, and R_i^{10}, quality factor Q, and the resonator's linewidth in the case of 4th and 10th reflecting surfaces.

3×10^{-10} sec. During this time the beam travels the path $c\tau\simeq10$ cm, which means that it completes two revolutions along the trajectory and experiences $2N$ reflections.

The distance $\delta\lambda$ between two neighboring resonances can be determined from the expression

$$\delta\lambda=\lambda^2/L, \tag{4}$$

from which we find $\delta\lambda\simeq2\times10^{-17}$ cm.

The linewidth for the characteristic x ray is $\Delta\lambda_x\simeq10^{-12}$ cm and for the γ transition in Mössbauer isotope ^{57}Co, $\Delta\lambda\gamma\simeq10^{-20}$ cm. Thus we have $\Delta\lambda_x/\Delta\lambda\simeq5\times10^5$ and $\Delta\lambda_\gamma/\Delta\lambda\simeq5\times10^{-3}$. From this it is clear that the lines for the resonator are much narrower than for the characteristic radiation, but essentially they are wider than the γ lines. From this, as well as from Eq. (4), it follows that excitation of the resonator by the characteristic radiation is more convenient, since in this case the condition for the resonance $n\lambda=L$ is automatically satisfied, when for γ radiation additional correction is required.

X-ray resonators, unlike optical resonators, are always dispersive systems[9] as long as the Bragg reflection coefficient from the thick crystal has a sharp angular and frequency maximum:

$$R_i=\left|\frac{1+i(B/A)}{[\eta_\omega+\eta_\theta+(1/\gamma)-i(\beta/A)]\pm\{[\eta_\omega+\eta_\theta+(1/\gamma)-i(\beta/A)]^2-[1+i(B/A)]^2\}^{1/2}}\right|^2$$

where

$$\eta_\theta=(\theta-\theta_1)/\gamma\Delta\theta_0,\qquad \eta_\omega=(\omega-\omega_1)/\gamma\Delta\omega_0,$$

$2\Delta\omega_0$ is the frequency width of the reflection curve, θ_1 is the corrected Bragg's angle, and ω_1 is the center of gravity of the spectral distribution R_i. All other terms have the usual meaning.[1]

Reflection curves R_i, as well as R_i^4 and R_i^{10}, giving the reflection coefficient at $N=4$ and $N=10$ respectively, are shown in Fig. 3. These curves illustrate the dispersion character of the resonator.

Comparing the frequency width of the reflection curve with the estimated width for the resonator $\Delta\lambda$ and the distance $\delta\lambda$ between them, we see that a number of resonator lines may be excited, the quality factor for which, however, depends on their positions relative to reflection curve maximum (Fig. 3).

Finally, we give some parameters for the resonator [Fig. 1(b)] using the Ge (220) plane and Cu$K\alpha_1$ radiation ($\lambda=1.54050$ Å). For this the Bragg's angle $\theta=22°38'$ and the necessary number of reflector pairs is five ($N=10$). The reflection coefficients[2] $R_i=0.95$ and the absorbtion coefficient in anomalous transmission $\mu^1=14.4$ cm^{-1}.[10] Assuming $L=5$ cm, $d=0.05$ cm we find $Q\simeq2.5\times10^9$ (d is the thickness of Borrmann crystal).

The authors wish to thank Mr. V. K. Agarwal for the help in the preparation of the manuscript.

1 R. W. James, *The Optical Principles of the Diffraction of X-Rays* (Bell, London, 1950).
2 B. Okkerse, Philips Res. Rep. **18**, 413 (1963).
3 W. L. Bond, M. A. Duguay, P. M. Rentzepic, Appl. Phys. Lett. **10**, 216 (1967).
4 R. D. Deslattes, Appl. Phys. Lett. **12**, 133 (1968).
5 R. M. T. Cotterill, Appl. Phys. Lett. **12**, 403 (1968).
6 V. K. Voitovetskii, I. L. Korsunskii, A. I. Novikov, and Yu. F. Pazhin, ZhETF. Pis. Red **7**, 330 (1968) [JETP Lett. **7**, 258 (1968)].
7 S. Maruyama, J. Phys. Soc. Japan **20**, 1339 (1965).
8 F. A. Jenkins, H. F. White, *Fundamentals of Optics* (McGraw-Hill Book Co., New York, 1957), 3rd ed.
9 *Lasers and Applications* (Ohio State University, Columbus, 1963), p. 96.
10 V. I. Kisin (private communication).

Reprinted with permission from *Soviet Journal of Quantum Electronics*, Vol. 1(3), pp. 242-247 (November-December 1971). ©1971 American Institute of Physics.

ESTABLISHMENT OF POPULATION INVERSION BY PHOTOIONIZATION OF INNER ELECTRONS IN ATOMS

V. B. Rozanov

Translated from Kvantovaya Élektronika, Vol. 1, No. 3, pp. 54-60, 1971

It is shown that the photoionization of the inner-shell electrons can yield metastable ions. Therefore, the accumulation of excited particles becomes possible at practically realizable optical pumping powers. This method of population inversion may be effective because a large part of the emission spectrum of an optically transparent plasma in a radiation source is in the form of "hard" photons, which are emitted when electrons are captured and atoms or ions go over to their ground state.

There are various methods of achieving population inversion by optical pumping [1-3]. If a photon of sufficiently high energy impinges on an atom, it may photoionize electrons in the outer or the inner shells. In the latter case, the ion formed in this way remains in the excited state. Duguay and Rentzepis [4] considered the photoionization of the 2p electrons of sodium in their attempt to construct a laser operating in the ultraviolet range. In spite of the very favorable ratio of the ionization cross sections of the 3s and 2p electrons (the latter is approximately one hundred times larger than the former [5]), laser emission was not observed in sodium. This was because the excited state N_2 of the sodium ion (configuration $2p^5 3s$) had a large statistical weight and was related to the ground state N_1 ($2p^6$) by an optically allowed transition. Under these conditions, the populations of the states ($N_2/g_2 - N_1/g_1$) rapidly become equal (here, g_1 and g_2 are the corresponding statistical weights of the levels). Duguay and Rentzepis [4] estimated that the pumping power would have to rise rapidly ($4 \cdot 10^{18}$ W/cm^2 · sec) before such a laser could operate under the action of the leading edge of a light pulse.

In a recent paper, the present author [6] drew attention to the fact that, in some cases, the photoionization of the inner-shell electrons could give rise to ions in metastable states. Therefore, the accumulation of a sufficiently large number of excited particles would become possible at practically realizable optical pumping powers. This problem is considered in greater detail in the present paper. The efficiency of this method of establishing population inversion is influenced strongly by the selection of the composition of the plasma in the radiation source since, under certain conditions, the fraction of the "hard" photons which can photoionize deep electrons may reach 50% of the total radiation energy. This happens because photons are emitted as a result of the capture of electrons, which leaves the atoms or ions concerned in their ground states. Figure 1 shows a calculated emission spectrum of neon plasmas of various optical thicknesses. Similar spectra may be obtained also for other inert gases, for hydrogen, halogens, alkali metals (for these metals, the emission peak lies in the second ionization region), and for several other elements.

Let us now consider the electron configurations of the atoms and the ions given in Table 1 below.

The well-known classification of the spectra of many-electron atoms and an analysis of the origin of a given ion resulting from photoionization [7] show that an excited ion may have an allowed transition to the ground state in the case of alkali and alkaline-earth elements [$np^6(n+1)s^\lambda$, $\lambda = 1, 2$], oxygen-group elements, halogens, and inert gases

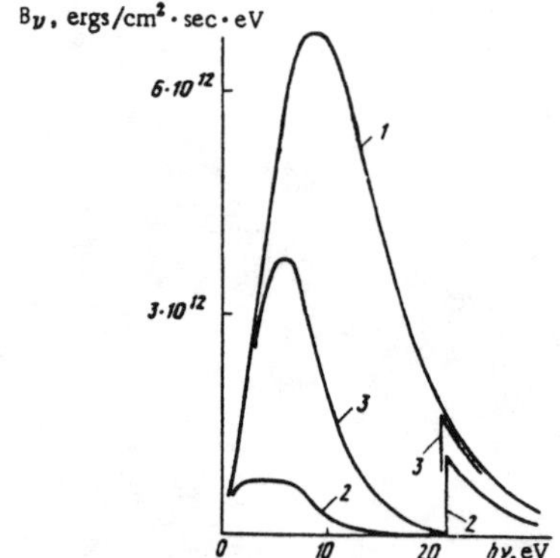

Fig. 1. Emission spectrum at 36,000°K (B_ν is the spectral brightness): 1) blackbody; 2, 3) neon plasma layer 1 cm thick, with particle (atom and ion) densities of $4.8 \cdot 10^{18}$ and $1.6 \cdot 10^{19}$ cm^{-3}, respectively.

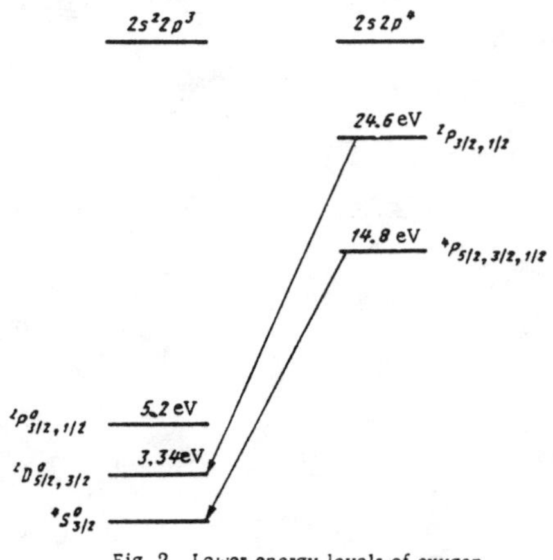

Fig. 2. Lower energy levels of oxygen.

TABLE 1

Atom	$np^6(n+1)s^\lambda$, $\lambda = 1, 2$	$ns^2(n+1)p^k$, $k = 1, 2, \ldots, 6$	$nd^m(n+1)s^\lambda$, $m = 1, 2, \ldots, 10$
Excited ion	$np^5(n+1)s^\lambda$	$ns(n+1)p^k$	$nd^{m-1}(n+1)s^\lambda$
Ion in ground state	$np^6(n+1)s^{\lambda-1}$	$ns^2(n+1)p^{k-1}$	$nd^m(n+1)s^{\lambda-1}$

[$ns^2(n+1)p^k$, k = 4, 5, 6]. Figure 2 shows, by way of example, the energy level scheme of the oxygen ion.

The energy levels of elements belonging to the boron, carbon, and nitrogen groups are given in Table 2 (the downward sequence of terms corresponds to increasing excitation energy).

For all these elements, the decay of the lowest of the excited states is forbidden by the multiplet rule and this means that the probability of a transition from such an excited state is reduced (relative to the allowed transitions) by a factor of 10^4-10^5 in the case of light atoms, and by a factor of 10^2-10^3 for heavy atoms [7]. The threshold of formation of an excited ion with a lower multiplicity is much higher and, therefore, a suitable selection of the pumping spectrum can ensure that only ions with a higher value of the total spin are generated. Data on the energies of various states of ions can be found in [8].

In the case of elements with d electrons [$nd^m(n+1)s^\lambda$], the ground-state and the excited configurations of ions have the same parity. Therefore, a transition between them is of the electric quadrupole type and its probability is 10^5-10^6 times lower than that in the case of optically allowed transitions [7]. In some cases, there is an additional forbiddenness because of multiplicity. Table 3 gives the energy level scheme of the Cd and Zn ions and of the Zn atom [8]. In the case of ions of these elements, a term $^2P_{3/2,\,1/2}$ of the $nd^{10}(n+1)p$ configuration is located between the ground state and the state resulting from the photoionization of a d electron. This term can serve conveniently as the lower level of a laser transition because lifetimes should be very short (it decays by an allowed transition to the ground state). The energy level scheme of the Zn atom illustrates the possibility of the resonance transfer of the energy from the ion to the atom of this element.

The terms $4s5p\,^3P$ and $4s6s\,^3S$ of the Zn atom have ionization energies close to the ionization energy of the term $3d^94s^2\,^2D$ of the Zn ion. Consequently, in the case of this element, we have the possibility of resonance transfer of the excitation energy from the ion to the atom and of subsequent laser transitions in which the atomic levels are involved.

The $nd^9(n+1)s^2 \rightarrow nd^{10}(n+1)p$ transition in the Zn and Cd ions involves two electrons but its probability can be considerable because the $nd^9(n+1)s^2\,^2D_{5/2,\,3/2}$ state includes, because of the electrostatic interaction, an admixture of the $nd^{10}(n+1)d\,^2D_{5/2,\,3/2}$ state. This can be proved by analyzing, within the framework of the perturbation theory, the splitting of sublevels with different values of the total angular momentum.

It is reported in [11] that coherent emission can be obtained when a discharge takes place in a mixture of Zn or Cd vapor with He. The emitted coherent radiation is due to transitions in the Zn and Cd ions, including the $s^2\,^2D \rightarrow p^2P^0$ transition. The measured lifetime of the $s^2\,^2D_{5/2}$ level of the Cd ions is $0.77 \cdot 10^{-6}$ sec, whereas the lifetimes of the levels $s^2\,^2D_{5/2}$ and $s^2\,^2D_{3/2}$ of the Zn ion are $1.6 \cdot 10^{-6}$ and $2.2 \cdot 10^{-6}$ sec, respectively. The excitation in a discharge results from the collisions between metastable He atoms and Zn or Cd atoms, and the resultant formation of excited ions of these metals.

The Zn and Cd ions are only two examples of the many elements with d electrons which have one or more levels between the ground state and the state excited by the photoionization of the inner electrons. If the lower state of the laser transition becomes empty (as in the case of Zn or Cd) or if this state has a large statistical weight [as, for example, in the $nd(n+1)s^2$ elements], a laser can operate directly on the basis of a transition in an ion. The other possibility is to use transitions in impurity ions to which energy is transferred by resonance collisions. This process is used widely in gas lasers. Recombination of an ion gives rise to an atom which can participate once again in the photoionization process. Therefore, in principle, continuous operation becomes possible. The electron density is determined by the pumping power and the rate of recombination in triple collisions; this density governs the rate of ionization of atoms and the rate of excitation (as well as deactivation) of atoms and ions by electron impact. These processes populate primarily the lower levels and they can destroy inversion. The formation of excess electrons can be avoided if the impurity in question has a small photoionization cross section. In this case, a satisfactory variant is provided by the transfer of the excitation energy from the ion to the atom of the same element (as in the case of Zn).

Let us consider a laser utilizing the transition $2 \rightarrow 1$ in an ion, which results in the accumulation of particles in the lower state (as in [4]):

$$\left.\begin{aligned} dn_2/dt &= \nu_p n_0 - \nu_2 n_2, \\ dn_1/dt &= \nu_2 n_2, \\ n_1 + n_2 + n_0 &= N, \end{aligned}\right\} \quad (1)$$

where n_0 is the density of atoms; N is the total number of particles in 1 cm^3; ν_2 is the probability of the $2 \rightarrow 1$ transition; $\nu_p = I\sigma$ is the probability of photoionization resulting in the formation of an ex-

TABLE 2

Atom	$ns^2(n+1)p$		$ns^2(n+1)p^2$		$ns^2(n+1)p^3$	
Ion	ns^2	$ns(n+1)p$	$ns^2(n+1)p$	$ns(n+1)p^2$	$ns^2(n+1)p^2$	$ns(n+1)p^3$
		$^1P^0_1$		$^2P_{3/2,\,1/2}$		$^3S^0_1$
		$^3P^0_{2,1,0}$		$^4P_{5/2,\,3/2,\,1/2}$		$^5S^0_2$
					$^1S_0$	
					$^1D_2$	
Ground state	$^1S_0$		$^2P^0_{3/2,\,1/2}$		$^3P_{0,1,2}$	

TABLE 3

Configuration	Term	Total ang momen-tum	Excitation energy of ions, cm^{-1}	
			Zn ($n = 3$)	Cd ($n = 4$)
$nd^{10}(n+1)s$	^2S	1/2	0.0	0.0
$nd^{10}(n+1)p$	$^2P^0$	1/2	48 480.6	44 136.08
		3/2	49 354.4	46 618.55
$nd^9(n+1)s^2$	^2D	5/2	62 721.9	69 258.91
		3/2	65 441.1	74 893.66
$nd^{10}(n+2)s$	^2S	1/2	88 436.8	82 990.66
$nd^{10}(n+1)d$	^2D	3/2	96 909.0	89 689.25
		5/2	96 959.7	89 843.78

TABLE 4

Configura-tion	Term	Excitation energy of ions, cm^{-1}	Configura-tion	Term	Excitation energy of ions, cm^{-1}
$3d^{10}4s^2$	$^1S_0$	0.0	$3d^{10}4s5p$	$^3P^0_{0,1,2}$	61 247 — 61 330
$3d^{10}4s4p$	$^3P_{0,1,2}$	32 311 - 32 890	$3d^{10}4s4d$	$^1D_2$	62 458
$3d^{10}4s4p$	$^1P^0_1$	46 745	$3d^{10}4s4d$	$^3D_{1,2,3}$	62 768 — 62 776
$3d^{10}4s5s$	$^3S_0$	53 672	$3d^{10}4s5p$	$^1P^0_1$	62 910
$3d^{10}4s5s$	$^1S_0$	55 789	$3d^{10}4s6s$	$^3S_1$	65 432

cited ion (this probability is proportional to the photon flux I and the photoionization cross section σ). We shall assume that only excited ions are formed. This is justified because the photoionization cross sections are proportional to $(h\nu)^{-3}$ and the spectrum is of the form shown in Fig. 1. The photoionization cross sections of deep (inner) electrons can be determined experimentally or by more rigorous calculations. The semiempirical method of Burgess and Seaton would hardly provide the required refinement because its validity in the case of the photoionization of the inner electrons has not yet been fully established. The photon flux which occurs in the expression for ν_p can be estimated from Planck's equation

$$I = \frac{2\pi k^3}{h^3 c^2} \int_{\varepsilon_1}^{\infty} \frac{\varepsilon^2 d\varepsilon}{\exp(\varepsilon/T) - 1};$$

for $\varepsilon/T = 7$, we have

$$I = 1.4 \cdot 10^{19} \varepsilon_2^3 \ \text{cm}^{-2} \cdot \text{sec}^{-1}. \tag{2}$$

Here, ε_2 is the photon energy, expressed in electron volts, above which a discontinuity is found in the emission spectrum of the source. The gas in the pumping source should be selected so that its ionization potential ε_2 is equal to the photionization threshold of the inner electrons in the illuminated medium $\varepsilon_1 + \varepsilon^*$ (ε_1 is the ionization potential of the atoms in this medium and ε^* is the excitation energy of the ions): for many atoms $\varepsilon_1 + \varepsilon^* = 10$-$20$ eV and, consequently, $I \approx 10^{22}$-10^{23} $cm^{-2} \cdot sec^{-1}$. In high-current discharges characterized by photon fluxes of this order of magnitude, the leading edge of a pulse can be of the order of 10^{-5} sec. Therefore, we shall consider a linearly rising pumping intensity $\nu_p = \alpha t$, where $\alpha \approx 10^9$-10^{10} sec^{-2} (it is assumed that $\sigma = 10^{-18}$ cm^2). The solution of Eq. (1),

$$\left.\begin{aligned} &n_1 = \int_0^{\tau} n_2\, d\tau, \quad \tau = \nu_2 t, \quad \beta = \alpha \nu_2^{-2}, \\ &\Phi(x) = \sqrt{\frac{2}{\pi}} \int_0^x e^{-t^2/2} dt, \\ &n_2 = N \left\{ e^{-\tau} - e^{-\beta\frac{\tau^2}{2}} + \sqrt{\frac{\pi}{2\beta}}\, e^{\frac{1}{2\beta} - \tau} \right. \\ &\left. \times \left[\Phi\left(\sqrt{\beta}\,\tau - \sqrt{\frac{1}{\beta}}\right) + \Phi\left(\sqrt{\frac{1}{\beta}}\right) \right] \right\}, \end{aligned}\right\} \tag{3}$$

shows that the establishment of inversion is governed by the dimensionless parameter β, which should be of the order of or larger than unity. To achieve this, the probability of decay should be sufficiently low ($\nu_2 \lesssim \sqrt{\alpha} \approx 10^4$-$10^5$ sec^{-1}), which can be realized for the metastable ions we have considered. It is reported in [4] that $\nu_2 \sim 10^{10}$ sec^{-1} and, therefore, the pumping should ensure that $\alpha \approx 10^{20}$ sec^{-2}.

We shall now consider continuous stimulated emission on the assumption that the lower state of the 3 → 2 laser transition becomes empty:

$$\left.\begin{aligned} &\frac{dn_3}{dt} = \nu_p n_0 - \nu_3 n_3, \quad \frac{dn_1}{dt} = \nu_2 n_2 - b n_1^3, \\ &\frac{dn_2}{dt} = \nu_3 n_3 - \nu_2 n_2, \quad \frac{dn_0}{dt} = -\nu_p n_0 + b n_1^3, \\ &n_3 + n_2 + n_1 + n_0 = N. \end{aligned}\right\} \tag{4}$$

Here, the subscripts 3, 2, and 1 represent the states of an ion; ν_3^{-1} and ν_2^{-1} are the lifetimes of states 3 and 2; n_0 is the density of atoms; $n_e = n_1 + n_2 + n_3$ is the density of electrons; b is the triple-recombination constant, given by $b = 8.75 \cdot 10^{-27}/T^{9/2}$ cm^6/sec [9].

The slowest process is the triple recombination (therefore, $n_1 \gg n_2$ and $n_1 \gg n_3$), whose rate depends on the spectrum of those electrons which are created with an energy of several electron volts. Under certain conditions, the translational equilibrium between electrons, ions, and atoms is established quite rapidly. Then, the average energy of electrons is determined by the number of electrons relative to the total number of particles. These conditions are achieved if the degree of ionization is of the order of 0.01-0.1 for $N = 10^{16}$-10^{18}

cm^{-3}. The rate of establishment of this equilibrium is determined by the Coulomb cross sections (the relevant time constants are of the order of 10^{-5}-10^{-6} sec). The radiation energy transferred to the electrons is distributed between a large number of particles.

Substituting numerical values, we find that for $n_e \approx n_1 = (\nu_p N/b)^{1/3}$ and for $N = 10^{16}$ cm^{-3}, $\nu_p = 10^4$ sec^{-1}, $T^{9/2} = 1$, we obtain $n_1/N = 0.2$, whereas for $N = 10^{18}$ cm^{-3}, we obtain $n_1/N = 0.01$; consequently, we find that $n_0/N \approx 1$. If the $2 \rightarrow 1$ transitions is allowed, the inversion population may be considerable and we then find that $n_3 = \nu_p N/\nu_3$ and $n_3/n_2 = \nu_2/\nu_3$. It must be pointed out that energy is transferred to the illuminated gas in each photoionization event and, therefore, the duration of continuous stimulated emission is determined by the heating and the heat losses.

The calculated values of the electron density can be used to estimate the deactivation time of level 3. The quasiclassical cross section for the excitation of a quadrupole transition in an ion by a charge (excitation energy ~10 eV) is of the order of 10^{-19} cm^2 [7]. The deactivation cross section is of the same order of magnitude. Consequently, the lifetime of level 3 is of the order of 10^{-4} sec. A similar estimate of the time constant of the resonant transfer of the energy from an ion to an atom gives values of the order of 10^{-7}-10^{-6} sec (for a concentration of impurity atoms of 10^{16} cm^{-3}). Thus, in the case being considered, the deactivation times are such that we can achieve stimulated emission by means of transitions in ions and in impurity atoms (bearing in mind the time constant for the resonant transfer of the excitation energy to such atoms).

A comparison of the system (4) and of the pumping spectrum (Fig. 1) shows that the energy parameters and the efficiency of the lasers being considered may be quite high. The electrical energy consumed in high-current discharge is practically all converted to radiation. It follows from Fig. 1 that the proportion of the "hard" photons may be 50%. This proportion corresponds to an extremely wide pumping band whose width is approximately 2T (T is the temperature of the plasma source). The efficiency may be a few percent because the emission of a stimulated photon may be 10 times easier than the emission of a pumping photon. The stimulated radiation power is governed by the number of excitation events, $\nu_p n_0$, which may be three to four orders of magnitude higher than the power emitted by gas-discharge lasers [10].

In practice, the outlined method for establishing population inversion is fraught with difficulties, particularly those encountered in the generation of an atomic vapor of the illuminated gas of sufficient density, the separation of the source plasma from the active medium, etc. The presence of molecules in the atomic active medium may complicate considerably the activation and the quenching processes.

We have not considered the laser transition linewidth or the laser gain. These parameters can be found only if we specify more accurately the conditions in a laser. All that we can do at this stage is to point out that, under the conditions considered, the absorption of the radiation by free electrons is slight.

The author is deeply grateful to I. A. Poluéktov, F. A. Nikolaev, and G. V. Mikhailov for valuable discussions of the problems considered in the present paper.

LITERATURE CITED

1. T. H. Maiman, Phys. Rev., 123, 1145 (1961).
2. S. G. Rautian and I. I. Sobel'man, Zh. Eksp. Teor. Fiz., 41, 2018 (1961) [Sov. Phys. – JETP, 14, 1433 (1962)].
3. N. G. Basov, A. Z. Grasyuk, and V. A. Katulin, Dokl. Akad. Nauk SSSR, 161, 1306 (1965) [Sov. Phys. – Dokl., 10, 343 (1965)].
4. M. A. Duguay and P. M. Rentzepis, Appl. Phys. Letters, 10, 350 (1967).
5. A. H. Boyd, Planet. Space Sci., 12, 729 (1964).
6. V. B. Rozanov, ZhETF Pis. Red., 12, 486 (1970) [JETP Lett., 12, 340 (1970)].
7. I. I. Sobel'man, Introduction to the Theory of Atomic Spectra [in Russian], Fizmatgiz, Moscow (1963).
8. C. E. Moore, Atomic Energy Levels, National Bureau of Standards, Washington (1949).
9. Ya. B. Zel'dovich and Yu. P. Raizer, Elements of Gas Dynamics and the Classical Theory of Shock Waves, Academic Press, New York (1968).
10. V. F. Kitaeva, A. I. Odintsov, and N. N. Sobolev, Usp. Fiz. Nauk, 99, 361 (1969) [Sov. Phys. – Usp., 12, 699 (1970)].
11. Y. Sugawara, Y. Tokiwa, and T. Iijima, Digest of technical papers presented at Sixth Intern. Conf. on Quantum Electronics, Kyoto (1970), p. 320.

Reprinted with permission from *Soviet Journal of Quantum Electronics,* Vol. 2(1), pp. 13-17 (July-August) 1972). ©1972 American Institute of Physics.

PLASMA PRODUCED BY LASER IRRADIATION OF SOLID TARGETS AS A SOURCE OF HIGHLY STRIPPED IONS*

F. E. Irons, N. J. Peacock, and R. S. Pease

UKAEA Research Group, Culham Laboratory, Abingdon, Berks., England
Published in Kvantovaya Élektronika, No. 7, pp. 20-25, 1972

The plasma produced from a solid target which is irradiated by an intense, pulsed laser beam is considered as a source of highly stripped ions. The populations of the various ions and their spatial distributions are deduced from emission spectroscopy. The most highly ionized atoms are located at the front of the plasma expanding away from the target and are followed later in time by lower stages of ionization. A separation of the ion stages in space and time can thus be effected. With the appropriate shaped Q-spoiled laser pulse, 10^{14} to 10^{16} ions can be produced with a mean charge state approaching +20. Potentially the laser-produced plasma is an attractive source of ions for heavy-ion accelerators.

1. INTRODUCTION

As has been pointed out by Peacock and Pease [1] the generation of highly ionized atoms in laser-produced plasmas may have some application in experiments using these ions as projectiles in heavy-ion accelerators to create, for example, new transuranic elements. This is a topical problem.

Recently Flerov at Dubna and Ghiorso at UCRL have reported the successful creation of element 105 (hahnium$^{260}_{105}$). In the latter instance (Ghiorso et al. [2]) a Cf^{249} target was bombarded with N^{15} ions. It can be expected that higher-mass-number transuranic elements can be created as suitable ion sources become available. Table 1 shows possible reaction rates taken from [3].

Ideally one would like a source of arbitrary ion species with a charge/mass ratio ε of near 0.5, from which the ions can be accelerated up to 5 to 10 MeV per nucleon with a current of between 10^6 and 10^{13} particles/sec. Such a source is not available at present.

This paper discusses only conceptually the laser-produced plasma as an ion source, and reviews previous work on the ion stages which can be achieved with intense laser irradiation. It does not report work on the extraction of ions from the plasma, nor have we as yet any results to report with laser powers greater than 0.5 GW, which is much less than the optimum laser power necessary

*This paper was presented at the International Conference on Laser-Produced Plasmas, Moscow, November, 1970.

TABLE 1

Reaction	Spallation product	Peak cross section (mb)	Ion energy MeV	MeV per nucleon
$Cf^{252}_{98} + Ni^{60}_{28}$	126^{311}	0.002	344	5.7
	126^{310}	1	346	5.8
	126^{309}	22	350	5.8
	126^{308}	65	366	6.1
$Hf^{180}_{72} + Xe^{132}_{54}$	126^{310}	64	754	5.7
$Th^{232}_{90} + Kr^{80}_{36}$	126^{310}	19	441	5.5

to produce $\varepsilon \approx 0.5$ in, for example, elements of the first long period.

Following the work of Boland, Irons, and McWhirter [4] on the temperature density and ion species in a laser-produced carbon plasma, measurements of each carbon ion species have been made. A spectroscopic analysis of the emission line intensities as a function of wavelength, time, and location in an expanding carbon plasma allows the population density of the ions, their velocities, and their flight paths to be evaluated. The ion density, evaluated from those lines which are predominantly Stark broadened, are compared with previous measurements from absolute line intensities, while the ion velocity is deduced from other lines, whose source function is due to Doppler broadening.

When irradiating a massive target of carbon (i.e., massive relative to the size of the focal spot) it is apparent that the ion stages occupy a discrete position in space at any given time. It is possible therefore to separate the most highly ionized fraction of the plasma through an aperture placed in front of the target with an appropriate, fast-acting shutter to screen off the remainder of the plasma. Peacock and Pease [1] have pointed out that a maximum charge state of about +20 can be expected after expansion of the laser-produced plasma blob. It is shown in the present paper that their model of spherical expansion with all the ions in a single charge state Z is inappropriate when a massive target is irradiated. Their recombination rates at densities greater than 10^{20} cm^{-3} are also somewhat in error. These discrepancies do not, however, materially affect the general conclusions of Peacock and Pease [1].

2. SPATIAL DISTRIBUTION OF IONS

The spatial variation of the ion species during the expansion of the plasma from a laser-irradiated carbon target has been deduced from the shape and intensity of emission lines in the visible spectrum. The experimental setup is the same as that described by Boland, Irons, and McWhirter [4]. Close to the target the visible lines are Stark broadened and overlaid by continuum. But at distances from the target greater than 1 mm, the profiles of the lines are readily derivable and the linewidths are determined by Stark broadening and by mass motion.

A comparison of CV ion linewidths as a function of distance from the target is shown in Fig. 1. The target is orthogonal to the incident laser beam and these observations are made transverse to the laser beam axis. Stark broadening makes no contribution to the 2271 Å, 2s − 2p transition and the linewidth due to ion streaming is constant with distance from the target. The velocity transverse to the laser axis is approximately $1.5 \cdot 10^7$ cm/sec at 1 mm from the target.

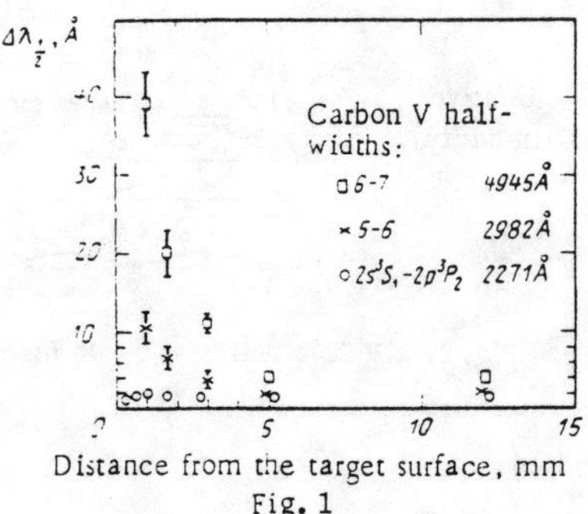

Fig. 1

The 5 − 6 and 6 − 7 transitions, on the other hand, are degenerate in azimuthal quantum number and exhibit the first-order Stark effect. These degenerate level transitions, which have only been observed in high-density plasmas such as laser-produced plasmas and in plasma focus (Irons and Peacock [5]), are broad close to target, but since the density decreases rapidly away from the surface, the linewidth falls to the Doppler value at distances greater than 10 mm from the target surface.

The major contribution to the Stark broadening is from the ion microfield. The quasistatic approximation has been used to deduce the ion density as a function of distance from the target. On comparison with the ion density evaluated from the absolute line intensities [4] it is found that the Stark effect underestimates the ion density by about a factor of 2. The fall-off in density from the target surface is adiabatic, with an approximately constant value for $T_e/(n_i)^{2/3}$, where T_e is the electron temperature, n_i the ion density, and V, the ion volume, varies as n_i^{-1}. At 1 mm from the target surface the electron density is $n_e = 1.8 \cdot 10^{18}$ cm^{-3} and $T_e = 34$ eV.

The intensity of those CV lines which exhibit no Stark broadening at times later than 5 nsec after the peak of the laser irradiation shows a double hump when scanned in planes transverse to the laser beam axis and parallel to the target surface. The CV intensity at 45 nsec after the start of the laser pulse, whose peak intensity occurs at 20 nsec, is shown in Fig. 2. The double hump can be attributed to ions lying on a conical surface which is

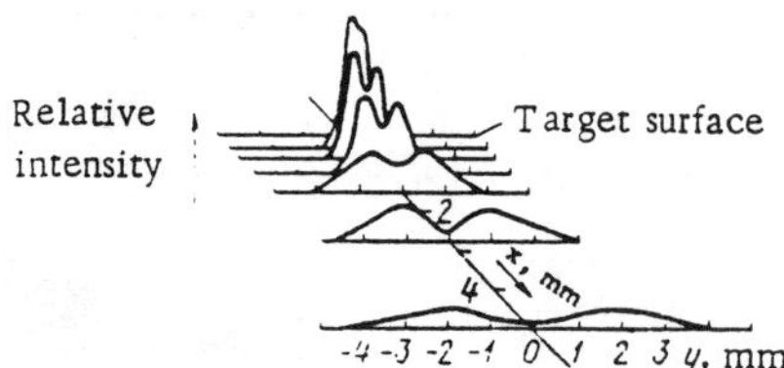

Fig. 2. CV 2271 Å line at t = 45 nsec.

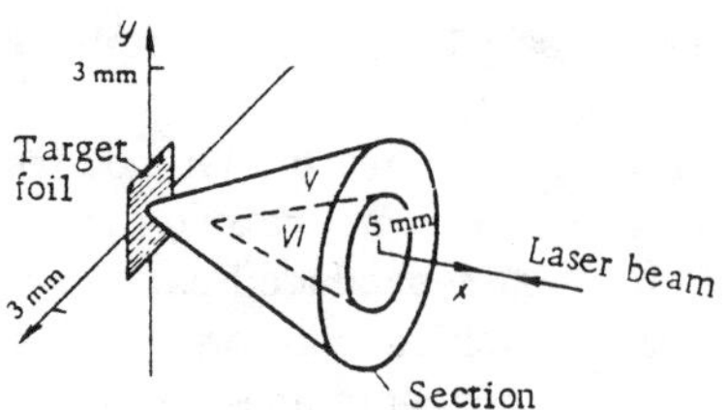

Fig. 4. Space distribution of CV and CVI lines at t = 45 nsec.

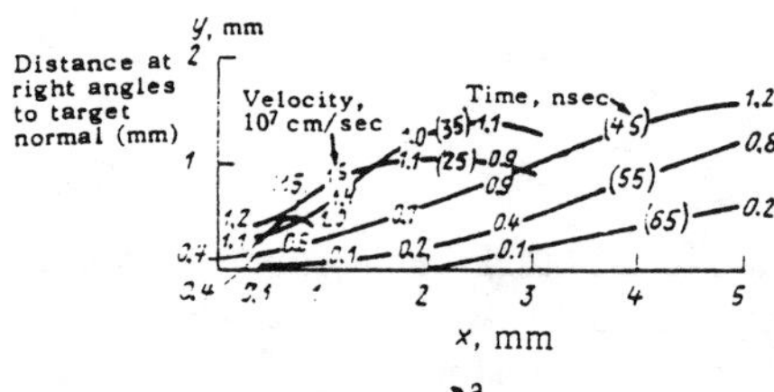

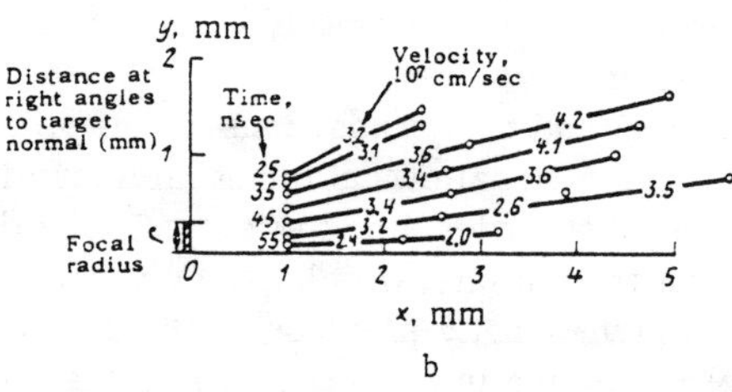

Fig. 3

expanding away from the target (x axis) and from the axis of symmetry (y axis). The Doppler-derived velocity of the CV ions transverse to the axis of symmetry is plotted at the location of maximum line intensity for different times during the plasma expansion, in Fig. 3a. The numbers (t) represent different times in nsec after peak laser intensity, while the number v represents the velocity orthogonal to the axis of symmetry. The locus of these curves in time gives the actual flight paths of the ions. This is shown in Fig. 3b, where v now represents the velocity along the flight path. The results are consistent with the ions lying within an expanding conical annulus.

The spatial distributions of different ion species CV and CVI are shown to scale in Fig. 4 at 45 nsec after the peak laser intensity. The velocities of these ions away from the target have been derived from the appropriate mass-motion wavelength shift. Velocities of $2.5 \cdot 10^7$ cm/sec and $2.2 \cdot 10^7$ cm/sec are typical for CVI and CV ions, respectively. It is clear that the time for the cone of ions to flow past its own length is 30 to 40 nsec. Since the continuum and line intensities show that the loss of ions (by recombination) is small while the plasma is expanding from 1 mm to 5 mm from the surface, it can be said that the flux of ions across any plane normal to the surface is constant for this duration. If then only the 40-nsec pulse of highly ionized species were allowed to expand through an aperture of, say, 2 mm diameter placed 3 mm from the target, the remainder of the lower ionized species could be shuttered off by a pulsed electric field or even a mechanical shutter placed between the target and the aperture. It would then be possible to produce a beam of ions all approximately in the same charge state.

3. RELATIVE AND TOTAL POPULATION OF IONS

Previous work on a carbon plasma by Boland, Irons, and McWhirter [4] has shown that $1.4 \cdot 10^{15}$ ions with an ionization potential $\psi_i = 400$ eV are produced using a modest laser power of 5 J in 17 nsec. These numbers were deduced from the intensity of the free–bound continuum and from the absolute intensity of visible lines, whose level populations are tied to the continuum by the Boltzmann factor. Each of these measured quantities is proportional to $n_e n(C^{Z+})$, and so $n(C^{Z+})$ can be deduced.

Even if a small fraction (10^{-4}) of the total ion population were extracted, this still would give an ion current sufficient for accelerator purposes.

4. IONIZATION AND RECOMBINATION IN EXPANDING PLASMA

The presence of ions more highly stripped than CVI in laser-produced plasmas is evident from the emission spectrum in the far vacuum ultraviolet. Ions of FeXVII and NiXVIII have been produced with a peak laser power level of 0.5 GW in a 20-nsec pulse and are observed to extend more than 2 mm from the target surface [1]. Further than this, the ion stages are effectively frozen since the recombination time exceeds the expansion time. It is clear that the important phase for ion loss by recombination is expansion within 1 mm of target surface.

There is no difficulty in explaining the initial appearance of FeXVIII since ionization equilibrium is reached within the laser-heating pulse, i.e., within a few nanoseconds. The temperature of the dense plasma at equilibrium is here taken to be 100 eV, a value consistent with that derived from the free–bound continuum from a metal oxide in laser-produced plasma (Burgess, Fawcett, and Peacock [6]).

For optimum plasma heating, however, a pulse rise time of 0.1 to 1 nsec is indicated (Haught et al. [7]). Electron temperatures approaching 1 keV have been measured with recent multigigawatt subnanosecond-rise-time laser pulses (Floux et al. [8]). It is probable that with a subnanosecond rise time the ionization equilibrium will not be reached and in this case the maximum degree of ionization will be determined by a balance between photon absorption and plasma expansion.

The decay of the degree of ionization due to recombination in an expanding Fe plasma has been calculated to occur mainly at densities $>10^{20}$ cm^{-3} (Peacock and Pease [1]). Three-body and radiative recombination appropriate to hydrogen ions and symmetrical expansion of a plasma sphere were assumed, with all the ions initially in the single-ionization stage. The calculations predict a more rapid decay in ionization than is actually observed and this discrepancy could be due to an error in the assumed recombination rates at very high densities or in the model chosen for the plasma expansion.

The recombination coefficient α at high densities is not well known. The scaling of α with Z, the effective ion charge (where $13.6Z^2 = \psi_i$; ψ_i is ionization potential) varies markedly with density. Gurevich and Pitaevskii [9] quote a Z-dependence given by

$$\alpha = 1.7\cdot 10^{-[illegible]} Z^3 T_e^{-9/2} \text{ cm}^6/\text{sec},$$

where T_e is in °K. At high temperatures and at very high densities ($\geq 10^{21}$ cm^{-3}), where local thermodynamic equilibrium may hold for some of the Fe ions (e.g., FeXVI), α scales as Z^{-2} (Bates et al. [10]). The three-body coefficient assumed by Peacock and Pease [1] also scales as $1/Z^n$ ($n \simeq 3$) and the total recombination rate is within an order of magnitude of that given by Bates et al. [10]. The collisional radiative rates tabulated by Bates et al. [10] would perhaps have been more appropriate to the problem but would in fact have increased the calculated ionization decay rather than the reverse. The position is complicated by the fact that the recombination rate for each Fe ion species ought to be treated on its own merits.

A more likely explanation for the observed decay in ionization is to be attributed to the model assumed for heating and expansion of the laser-produced plasma. It is clear from the work reported here that a spherical expansion model is not valid. The front of the expanding plasma, in which are embedded the most highly stripped ions, will be continuously irradiated during the laser pulse. Sustainment of the electron temperature during the initial stages of the expansion (< 1 mm) from an "overdense" condition [11] will allow the degree of stripping at 1 mm from the target to remain high. It is probable then that the limit to the maximum ionization stage which can be extracted from the laser-produced plasma can exceed somewhat the value of +20 suggested by the simple model of Peacock and Pease [1].

5. CONCLUSIONS

The populations of various ion species and their spatial distributions in a laser-produced plasma have been deduced from emission spectroscopy. It is shown that the most highly ionized atoms in a plasma produced by irradiation of a solid target are located at the front of the plasma expanding away from the target. The volume which each ion species occupies is unique in space and time and appears to correspond to the surface of an expanding cone whose axis is the input laser beam. A separation of the ion species in space and time can thus in principle be effected.

The number of ions, between 10^{14} and 10^{16}, is sufficiently high to make the plasma potentially useful as a source for heavy-ion acceleration. We can expect a maximum charge state which is somewhat higher than the value of +20 previously calculated. The extraction of the ions and their utilization in an accelerator is the main problem and is due to the unavoidable pulsed nature of the source.

LITERATURE CITED

1. N. J. Peacock and R. S. Pease, J. Phys. D., 2, 1705 (1969).
2. A. Ghiorso, M. Nurmia, K. Eskola, J. Harris, and P. Eskola, Phys. Rev. Letters, 24, 1498 (1970).
3. A. Ghiorso, IEEE Trans. Nucl. Sci., NS-14, No. 3, 5 (1967); Lawrence Radiation Laboratory Report, UCRL 16828 (1966).

4. B. C. Boland, F. E. Irons, and R. W. P. McWhirter, J. Phys. B, 1, 1180 (1968).
5. F. E. Irons and N. J. Peacock, unpublised article (1970).
6. D. D. Burgess, B. C. Fawcett, and N. J. Peacock, Proc. Phys. Soc. London, 92, 805 (1967).
7. A. F. Haught, D. H. Polk, and W. J. Fader, United Aircraft Research Labs. Report F920365-6 (1967).
8. F. Floux, D. Cognard, L. G. Denoeud, G. Piar, D. Parisot, J. L. Bobin, F. Delobeau, C. Fauquignon, Phys. Rev., A, 1, 821 (1970).
9. A. V. Gurevich and L. P. Pitaevskii, Zh. Eksp. Teor. Fiz., 46, 1281 (1964) [Sov. Phys. – JETP, 19, 870 (1964)]; T. S. Green, ESRIN Internal Report 72 (1970).
10. D. R. Bates, A. E. Kingston, and R. W. P. McWhirter, Proc. Roy. Soc. London, A267, 297 (1962).
11. J. Schluter and W. Winkelmann, Proc. Fourth European Conference on Controlled Fusion and Plasma Physics, Rome, 1970, CNEN, Rome (1970), p. 113.

Reprinted with permission from *Physics Letters*, Vol. 36A(3), pp. 167-168 (August 30, 1971). ©1971 Elsevier Science Publishers B.V., The Netherlands.

EXPERIMENTAL EVIDENCE FOR THE POSSIBLE EXISTENCE OF A STIMULATED EMISSION IN THE EXTREME UV RANGE

P. JAEGLE, A. CARILLON, P. DHEZ, G. JAMELOT, A. SUREAU and M. CUKIER
Laboratoire de Chimie Physique de l'Université Paris VI, Orsay, France

Received 5 July 1971

Comparison between absorption and emission spectra due to several discrete transitions in ions produced by an aluminium laser-plasma, suggests that a laser effect at a wavelength of 117.41 Å may exist in the hot zone of the plasma.

We have recently described an experiment for the study of laser-plasma absorption in the extreme uv region [1,2]. Absorption measurements are given here for a spectral region where the aluminium emission line intensities are highly anomalous [3].

These anomalies are shown in columns 5 and 6 (table 1) and on the densitograms a and b in fig. 1. This suggests that there exists a population inversion between the $2p^6\ {}^1S_0$ and $2p^5\ 4d\ {}^3P^o_1$ levels, which may be attributed though this is not the only possibility, to an intrachannel interaction [4] between nd states and the continuum. This favorises the strongly metastable states ${}^3P^o_1$ produced by the recombination of the Al^{4+} ions with free electrons [5]. The transition wavelengths are given in column 1 and the levels in column 2. For theoretical reasons, identification of the lines corresponding to ${}^1P^o_1$ and ${}^3D^o_1$ is reversed with respect to earlier interpretations [6]. The relative intensities calculated from *jj* coupling are given in column 3. The intensities observed in the spark spectra and in the laser-plasma cold zone appear in column 4. The intensities measured 1.25 mm and 0.4 mm from the target surface (hot zone) for a laser power of 80 MW are given in column 5 and 6 respectively, the a and b spectra in fig. 1 being photographic recordings at the same distances.

Table 1

λ(Å)	Transition	Intensity			
1	2	3	4	5	6
116.46	$2p^6\ {}^1S_0 - 2p^5\ 4d\ {}^1P^o_1$	5	7	5	-1
116.92	$2p^6\ {}^1S_0 - 2p^5\ 4d\ {}^3D^o_1$	9	5	5	-1
117.41	$2p^6\ {}^1S_0 - 2p^5\ 4d\ {}^1P^o_1$	1	0	2	3

It is noticed that the transition from the initial state ${}^3P^o_1$, although forbidden in *LS* coupling and only weakly allowed in *jj* coupling, give rise to a line whose intensity increases, whereas transitions from ${}^3D^o_1$ and ${}^1P^o_1$ disappear and show up as a weak absorption.

A population inversion in favour of ${}^3P^o_1$ should be revealed as a negative absorption, i.e., a stimulated emission at a wavelength of 117.41 Å. Our absorption measurements are given by the curve d, for which some of the details have yet to be confirmed. For the three lines situated at 116.4 Å, 116.9 Å and 118.5 Å large absorption peaks of 60 to 80% show up quite clearly, but, corresponding to the 117.4 Å emission line, an absorption minimum (10%) appears followed by a narrow peak (40%) on the high energy side. It should be noted that the profiles resemble resonance profiles calculated for discrete states interacting with the continuum. Confirmation of this by other experiments would tend to suggest that ${}^3P^o_1$ is populated by interactions of this type.

The fact that no negative absorption is observed can be attributed to the too low power (25 MW) at which, for experimental reasons, the measurements were carried out. Indeed, in the emission spectrum (curve c) corresponding to these experimental conditions, the ${}^1P^o_1$ and ${}^3D_1$ lines are not inverted. Reabsorption must also be taken into account, for the peripheral zones of the plasma.

The negative absorption should be observable using higher plasma powers. But, henceforth, we consider that the results set out here constitute a serious argument in favor of a stimulated emission line at 117.41 Å. This phenomenon has never been observed at such a short wavelength and it can only be revealed at the

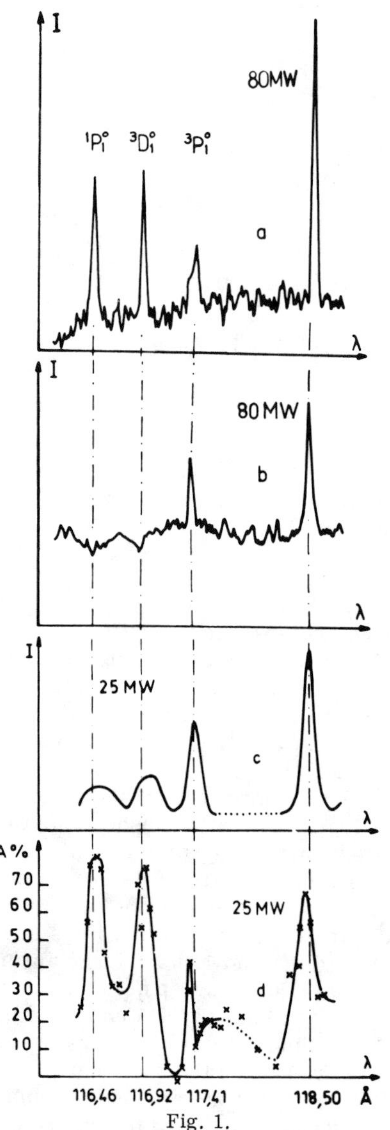

Fig. 1.

high temperatures and electron densities present in a laser-plasma.

The authors are very grateful to Professor Y. Cauchois for her interest and support in this work.

References

[1] A. Carillon, P. Jaegle and P. Dhez, Phys. Rev. Letters 25 (1970) 140(C).
[2] A. Carillon, P. Jaegle and P. Dhez, Colloque CNRS no. 196, Paris 1970, J. de Phys., to be published.
[3] P. Dhez, P. Jaegle S. Leach and M. Velghe, J. Applied Physics 40 (1969) 2545.
[4] U. Fano and J. W Cooper Rev. of Mod. Phys. 40 (1968) 441.
[5] A. Carillon, P. Jaegle, G. Jamelot, P. Dhez and M. Cukier, Colloques d'Evian de la Sté. Francaise de Physique (May 1971) J. de Phys., to be published.
[6] J. Söderquist, Nova Acta Reg. Soc. Sci. Upsaliensis 9 (1934) Ser. IV.

Reprinted with permission from *Applied Physics Letters*, Vol. 24(12), pp 598-599 (June 15, 1974).

Possibility of a distributed-feedback x-ray laser*

Robert A. Fisher

Department of Applied Science, Davis-Livermore, and Lawrence Livermore Laboratory, University of California, Livermore, California 94550

It is suggested that distributed feedback might greatly improve the chances of achieving x-ray laser action in a crystalline material. We have considered the case where the cavity mirror structure is provided by internal Bragg scattering which is distributed throughout the lasing medium. In addition to providing efficient feedback, higher effective gains can be achieved by eliminating the influence of periodic absorbers which occur in selectively x-ray-pumped polyatomic crystals. This is accomplished by establishing a standing wave with its nulls on the periodically spaced absorbers.

Various x-ray laser resonator cavities have been proposed.[1] It has been suggested that an external cavity can be formed by a multiple set of Bragg crystals or by glancing angle scattering. Both of these schemes can suffer from the problems of multiple-element alignment, and both possess a cavity transit time which is far greater than the x-ray fluorescence emission time. Typical cavity transit times in these configurations are of the order of 50 or more picoseconds. This paper is specifically intended to implement the x-ray laser scheme[2] in which the sample is to be pumped by a fast-rising (10^{-14} sec) pulse of x rays. Optical pulse compression schemes[3] may be crucial in the preparation of the fast-rising x-ray pump.

We suggest a distributed-feedback design which incorporates the reflectors (cavity) and the active material as one piece. For visible emitting dye laser systems, distributed feedback has been provided by impression of a permanent periodic index variation[4] and by periodic spatial pumping.[5] X-ray distributed feedback can be achieved by choosing a crystal with the appropriate periodic lattice spacing for backward Bragg scattering at the characteristic emission frequency of one of its constituents. A schematic of this approach is shown in Fig. 1. The x-ray laser emission would come out much like a "Laue spot" and would be the stimulated counterpart of the emission phenomenon known as "Kossel lines".[6] This device has a far shorter cavity transit time (approximately 100 lattice spacings correspond to the 10^{-14}-sec x-ray fluorescence lifetime), and eliminates problems associated with the alignment of multiple elements. Since a number of experimental efforts are now underway,[7] this note suggests an additional criterion for selecting potential samples. With this distributed feedback, the required pumping power could be reduced and thus x-ray laser action could possibly be achieved at an earlier date. An early attempt at such an x-ray scheme should employ a long-wavelength emitter, since the fluorescence lifetime in the electric dipole approximation is approximately proportional to the square of the wavelength. A longer "storage time" corresponds to more easily achieved pumping requirements. For our example we will discuss the case of oxygen in which the K_α wavelength is 23.61 Å.[8] Since numerous crystals have water of hydration, it is possible to choose a crystal with the appropriate spacing. A cubic millimeter would probably be sufficient and the crystal would be destroyed in a single shot.

TABLE I. Selected candidates for oxygen K_α emission.

	d(Å)		d(Å)
First-order diffraction $d=\lambda/2=11.8$ Å			
$Ca_3Fe_2Si_3O_{12}$	12.00	$K_2HgCl_4\cdot H_2O$	11.63
$Ca_3Cr_2Si_3O_{12}$	11.95	$Ce_2(WO_4)_3$	11.62
$5CaO\cdot 3Al_2O_3$	11.95	CaB_2O_4	11.60
$AgRhO_3$	11.92	Ho_2O_3	11.58
$MgSO_4\cdot 7H_2O$	11.91	$Cs_2S_2O_6$	11.54
$W(CO)_6$	11.90	$Mg_3Al_2Si_3O_2$	11.51
$MgCrO_4\cdot 7H_2O$	11.89	$Fe_3Al_2Si_3O_{12}$	11.50
$BaNi(CN)_4\cdot 4H_2O$	11.89	$NH_4H_2PO_2$	11.47
$3CdSO_4\cdot 8H_2O$	11.87	$CaMoO_4$	11.44
$Ca_3Al_2Si_3O_{12}$	11.87	$UO_2(NO_3)_2\cdot 6H_2O$	11.42
$LiAlSiO_4\cdot 3SiO_2$	11.87	$(Fe'', Mn'')_3Al_2(SiO_4)$	11.40
$Cr(CO)_6$	11.72	$CaCrO_4\cdot 2H_2O$	11.39
$C_6H_5HC:COOH$	11.65	$CaWO_4$	11.38
Second-order diffraction $d=\lambda=23.61$ Å			
$H_3PW_{12}O_{40}\cdot 29H_2O$	23.38	$GdPMo_{12}O_{40}\cdot 30H_2O$	23.1
$NdPMo_{12}O_{40}\cdot 30H_2O$	23.1	$FeHSiW_{12}O_{40}\cdot 30H_2O$	23.1
$SmPMo_{12}O_{40}\cdot 30H_2O$	23.1	$Mg_2SiMo_{12}O_{40}\cdot 31H_2O$	23.14
$H_3PMo_{12}O_{40}\cdot 30H_2O$	23.1		

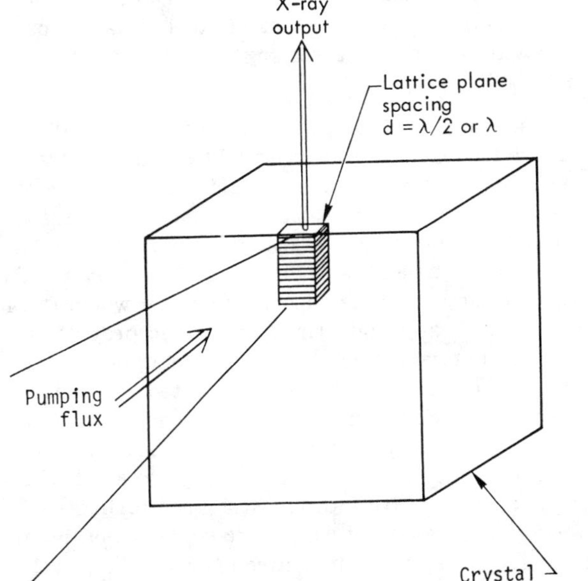

FIG. 1. A possible setup for observing distributed-feedback x-ray laser action.

Although Table I lists some possible crystals for oxygen, many other emitters can be considered. Another excellent candidate is β-Cristobalite[9] (SiO_2), which is cubic with a lattice spacing of $d = 7.138 \pm 0.001$ Å. Silicon has two K-emission lines; one is at $\lambda = 7.12791$ Å, and one is at $\lambda = 7.12542$ Å.

We have no new insight into pumping the x-ray emitter. A bright subpicosecond x-ray source may serve as the pump, and the inner-shell electrons must be preferentially removed. The pumping and gain conditions have been discussed by Lax and Guenther,[10] Duguay and co-worker,[2] and Wood *et al.*[11]

In the scheme presented here the electron density distribution must remain periodic while the inversion is established. If all atoms become highly ionized, for instance, then the electron distribution (which must do the Bragg scattering) would no longer be concentrated at the atomic sites. We can estimate the time at which a pumped crystal loses its periodicity by the following argument: We assume that the ion satisfies the one-dimensional equation $\frac{1}{2}mv^2 = \frac{1}{2}KT(t)$, where T is the ion temperature and t is the time. We let $T(t) = T_f[1 - \exp(-t/\tau)]$, where T_f is the final free-electron temperature and τ is the electron-ion coupling time. For times short compared to τ, the ionic velocity satisfies the equation $v = c(KT_f/E_R)^{1/2}(t/\tau)^{1/2}$, where E_R is the rest mass energy of the ion. For $KT_f \approx 5$ eV and $\tau = 24$ psec, this equation is integrated to find for oxygen that the displacement becomes 20 Å in ≈ 2 psec. This shows that the duration of the periodicity can exceed the fluorescence lifetime, although the Bragg scattering function will be spectrally broadened, and its peak value will be correspondingly decreased. This broadened Bragg line may mean that a precise crystal lattice spacing coincidence would not be necessary. Since the material may have expanded a bit prior to emission of x rays, one might choose x-ray crystals with a slightly reduced lattice spacing. As the material expands through the proper spacing, "Q-switched" emission could ensue. Table I also includes some of these candidates with reduced spacings. It is also possible that a plasma oscillation with the requisite spacing could provide the feedback.

As an example of the potential advantage of a distributed-feedback system, we find that the presence of some highly absorbing atoms might not be detrimental to laser action. Consider the one-dimensional linear diatomic chain case for alternating atoms A and B. If the electronic densities at the two sites are equal, the structure factor for the unpumped crystal would forbid first-order Bragg scattering. This could provide output coupling. Let us assume that the pumping event has inverted the A sites, but has not affected the B sites. If it were not for Bragg reflection, a *traveling* wave would experience alternating regions of amplification and attenuation, which could even correspond to a net loss for the wave. Yet, in first-order Bragg scattering, a *standing* wave could sit with its nodes on all of the amplifying A sites, while its antinodes would be on all of the absorbing B sites. Thus only the amplifying sites would influence this standing wave. Clearly, there is also a standing wave which sits oppositely and experiences only the lossy sites. It is the former *standing* wave which will grow, and *traveling* wave gain may not be necessary. For a particular crystal, the laser threshold condition could probably be calculated by an extension of the coupled-wave theory of Kogelnik and Shank.[12] One should avoid operating with x-ray K vectors that touch corners of the Brillouin zone, because some will be scattered in directions other than those of interest. If there is a large number of excited atoms relatively uniformly distributed throughout each unit cell, then the standing waves will see a reduced fraction of the excited atoms. The corresponding reduction in gain is a manifestation of the Borrmann effect.[13]

In conclusion, this paper has brought attention to the possibility of a distributed-feedback x-ray laser. Although it will not be an easy task, it is not too early to include distributed-feedback considerations when choosing samples in presently ongoing experiments.

Conversations with L. L. Wood are gratefully acknowedged. D.W. Gregg is thanked for suggestions concerning the manuscript.

*Work performed under the auspices of the U.S. Atomic Energy Commission.

[1]B. Okkerse, Phillips Res. Rep. **18**, 413 (1963); W. L. Bond, M.A. Duguay, and P.M. Rentzepis, Appl. Phys. Lett. **10**, 216 (1967); R.D. Deslattes, Appl. Phys. Lett. **12**, 133 (1968); R.M.T. Cotterill, Appl. Phys. Lett. **12**, 403 (1968); A.V. Kolpakov, R.W. Kuz'min, and V.M. Ryaboy, J. Appl. Phys. **41**, 3549 (1970).

[2]M.A. Duguay and P.M. Rentzepis, Appl. Phys. Lett. **10**, 350 (1967); M.A. Duguay, Laser Focus **9** (No. 11), 41 (1973).

[3]M.A. Duguay and J.W. Hansen, Appl. Phys. Lett. **14**, 14 (1969); R.A. Fisher, P.L. Kelley, and T.K. Gustafson, Appl. Phys. Lett. **14**, 140 (1969).

[4]H. Kogelnik and C.V. Shank, Appl. Phys. Lett. **18**, 152 (1971); I.P. Kaminow, H.P. Weber, and E.A. Chandross, Appl. Phys. Lett. **18**, 497 (1971).

[5]C.V. Shank, J.E. Bjorkholm, and H. Kogelnik, Appl. Phys. Lett. **18**, 395 (1971).

[6]W. Kossel, V. Loeck, and H. Voges, Z. Phys. **94**, 139 (1935); W. Kossel and H. Voges, Ann. Phys. **23**, 677 (1935); H. Voges, *ibid.* **27**, 694 (1936); G. Borrmann, *ibid.* **27**, 669 (1936).

[7]A list of some present experimental efforts has been prepared by M.A. Duguay and R.A. Andrews, Laser Focus **9** (No. 11), 42 (1973).

[8]J.A. Bearden, Rev. Mod. Phys. **31**, 78 (1967).

[9]*Handbook of Chemistry and Physics*, edited by R.C. Weast (The Chemical Rubber Company, Cleveland, Ohio, 1970), 51st ed. p. B-210.

[10]B. Lax and A.H. Guenther, Appl. Phys. Lett. **21**, 361 (1972).

[11]L. Wood, G. Chapline, S. Slutz, and G. Zimmerman, Lawrence Livermore Laboratory Report No. UCRL-75184, 1973 (unpublished).

[12]H. Kogelnik and C.V. Shank, J. Appl. Phys. **43**, 2327 (1972).

[13]G. Borrmann, Z. Phys. **127**, 297 (1950); M. von Laue, Acta Cryst. **2**, 106 (1949).

Reprinted with the permission of the Optical Society of America from *Applied Optics,* Vol. 14(1), pp. 97-101 (January 1975).

Extension of 3*p*→3*s* Ion Lasers into the Vacuum Ultraviolet Region

R. C. Elton

The feasibility of extending existing near-ultraviolet ion lasers into the vacuum ultraviolet spectral region is analyzed with a simplified three-state model. Single-pass amplification in a laser-produced plasma of reasonable length, pump power, and rise-time requirements is predicted, especially for high electron temperatures. The results are intended to serve as a basis and incentive for detailed numerical modeling and for experiments.

I. Introduction

Lasing in multiply ionized atoms has been demonstrated in the visible and near-ultraviolet spectral regions with gas discharges in resonant cavities.[1] It would be of great interest and importance to translate these results to shorter wavelengths isoelectronically.[2] At vacuum ultraviolet (vuv) wavelengths shorter than 2000 Å, conventional cavities become inefficient, and impractical below 1600 Å. However, for amplification of, for example, a frequency upconverted coherent vacuum-uv beam,[3] a resonant cavity is not required, provided significant gain can be achieved in a single photon pass through an inverted medium of reasonable length. Higher inverted state densities are required for single-pass amplification and for short wavelengths, with an upper density limit set by rapid depletion due to charged particle collisions. Population inversions are often self-terminating in time as equilibrium population distributions are approached, and the required rise time of the pumping source usually decreases with decreasing wavelength according to increasing transition probabilities for spontaneous decay. Also, the higher excitation energy in the heavier elements required for short wavelengths (isoelectric extrapolation) requires increased particle energies and densities for collisional pumping.

With these general guidelines we have attempted to analyze the scalability to shorter wavelengths. The highest degrees of ionization in heavy elements are obtained in high density plasmas, in short bursts, and in small volumes with a limited amount of available energy. A conceivably practical device, compatible with present technology, would be a linear plasma of about 1 cm in length, with the necessary ions and particle densities produced from a solid target by a line-focused laser beam. Longer plasmas may eventually be generated to produce increased overall gain, or perhaps decreased density for improved efficiency, as more powerful lasers are developed. Longer lengths may also become a possibility with axial heating of gaseous media by long wavelength lasers, a concept similar to that proposed for fusion plasma heating.[4] However, absorption and heating is a function of the plasma temperature and density, and uniform heating with narrow channeling[5] must first be proved. For short wavelengths and high Z materials, solid targets are generally more readily available than gases. It therefore seems reasonable to model the present analysis around a transverse irradiated and vaporized solid target plasma medium.

After expansion the initial plasma would be pumped axially with a separate short-pulse laser; this would preferentially heat the electrons, which in turn would produce the inversion by electron-ion collisions. A high electron temperature T_e is often very beneficial in producing a high inversion when, as here, the electron density is limited; also a low ion temperature reduces the (Doppler) line width and increases the possible gain (see Eq. (1) below). Thus, an electron-ion temperature differential is desirable, and this may be achieved by allowing the ions to expand and cool (faster than recombination takes place) and by heating the electrons in times shorter than the electron-ion energy equipartition time.

Considering resonance-lin absorption and stimulated emission, the gain in a homogeneous medium of length L is given by $I/I_0 = \exp(\alpha L)$, where α is the gain coefficient[6]:

The author is with the U.S. Naval Research Laboratory, Washington, D.C. 20375.

Received 17 June 1974.

$$\alpha = [\lambda^2(\pi \ln 2)^{1/2}/4\pi^2\Delta\nu]A[N_u - (g_u/g_l)N_l]. \quad (1)$$

Here, λ is the laser wavelength, A the transition probability, $\Delta\nu$ the Doppler line width in frequency units, and g_u, g_l, N_u, N_l the statistical weights and population densities for the upper and lower laser levels, respectively. Photoionization losses are omitted here, since only (K and) L shell electrons are present, and the photon energy of the short wavelength laser lines is insufficient to remove L electrons; likewise competition from Auger decay does not exist. Loss of laser photons through scattering has also been neglected here. A selection of a particular αL product (unity for threshold, $\gtrsim 5$ desirable) determines the minimum length of the medium, since the other parameters (e.g., density) are fixed or limited in the medium. Thus, we intend to show that a practical length of the order of 1 cm is reasonable for a particular transition.

Laser transitions between two states, both with $n = 3$ principal quantum number, were chosen for detailed analysis. Electron pumping is assumed to proceed directly from a $n = 2$ ground state of a particular ion through a nondipole transition (slowly decaying) by electron collisions to a $n = 3$ state, followed by lasing through a dipole transition to a lower $n = 3$ state, after which the electron decays more rapidly to the $n = 2$ ground state. (It is not necessary to invoke a seemingly less probable combined ionization-excitation single-step collisional process in the analysis.) Laser transitions from a $n = 4$ upper state (pumped from $n = 2$) to a $n = 3$ lower state would produce shorter wavelength lines. However, the proximity of other $n = 4$ dipole-decaying states limits the maximum electron (and ion) density to too low a value to give reasonable laser lengths. Also, $n = 3$ to $n = 2$ transitions in helium like ions, pumped from the $1s^2$ ground state, were considered; however, the large $1s \rightarrow 3s$ energy gap severely limits the collisional excitation rates (see Eq. (5)) and therefore the available inversion density and the minimum laser length obtainable. (Note that this 3→2 laser scheme may prove practical when pumped from above by rapid downward cascading following electron capture.)

Pumping into a $n = 3$ upper laser state that is not dipole-coupled to $n = 2$ levels is one necessary condition for maintaining a large population density, since spontaneous depopulation of this state is limited to the $\Delta n = 0$ laser transition with a relatively low rate. Conversely, the lower laser state population is kept low by a high $n = 3 \rightarrow 2$ dipole depopulation rate. The collisional transition for populating the upper laser state can be monopole; e.g., $2p \rightarrow 3p$ ($2p \rightarrow 3s$ is not followed by 3→3 dipole decay). Quadrupole $2s \rightarrow 3d$ excitation is also conceivable. However, in the two instances where this might be particularly important, namely, the lithiumlike and berylliumlike (singlet) ground state ions, an inverted population will not be obtained, since the pumped $3d$ upper laser state has a shorter lifetime than the lower laser state due to a low-lying $2p$ state.

Lasing following monopole $2p \rightarrow 3p$ excitation has been observed in ions belonging to the beryllium (triplet system) through the fluorine isoelectronic sequences.[1] For a particular element (such as oxygen for which data are available), the trend is towards shorter wavelengths (and correspondingly lower gains) for the more highly ionized species (Be-like). Also, pumping by collisional excitation becomes more difficult for the larger 2→3 energy gap in the highly stripped ions. It is also desirable to have a large energy separation between the upper lasing state and any nearby states that are dipole-coupled to the ground state, in order to reduce collisional-radiative depopulation; here, the boron- and carbonlike ions are slightly favored.

II. Analysis

While observations of lasing in multiply ionized atoms have been reported,[1] no similar attempt towards analysis of the mechanisms and limitations has been found in the literature. The present three-state analysis for carbon-like ions is intended to serve as a guide and stimulus for a more sophisticated and complete time-dependent numerical analysis (presently underway). Pumping is assumed to take place in a $2p^2\ ^3P \rightarrow 2p3p\ ^3D$ monopole ($\Delta l = 0$) transition, followed by lasing in a $2p3p\ ^3D \rightarrow 2p3s\ ^3P$ dipole transition, with the final state rapidly decaying by a dipole transition to the $2p^2\ ^3P$ ground state. Lasing from a $2p3p\ ^3S$ upper term is also possible. Two-electron radiative-Auger decay to a $2s2p^3$ configuration is expected to have a negligible effect.[7] Along the isoelectronic sequence, data are generally available up to neon.[7-11] Beyond that, wavelengths are scaled[12] as z^{-1}, where z is the charge seen by the active electron ($z - 1$ = ion charge). The oscillator strength for the laser transition is extrapolated according to a $Z^{-1.1}$ empirical best fit (Z is the nuclear charge of the ion), and the associated laser transition probability is deduced[9] from $A \propto f/\lambda^2$. The equilibrium kinetic temperature of the plasma in which the ions are produced is taken as $kT \approx 0.25\chi_{z-2}$, where χ_{z-2} is the ionization potential of the next lower ion state. For estimating the excitation rate, and consequently the inversion density, it is assumed that the monopole excitation rate is approximately equal to a corresponding dipole rate. This assumption is supported by experimental and theoretical results[13] on plasma ions and is further discussed below for the high electron temperature situation. For this, the $2p^2\ ^3P \rightarrow 2p3d\ ^3D$ allowed transition was used and the oscillator strength was extrapolated empirically to unity with higher Z. This oscillator strength, as well as the n = 2–3 energy difference ΔE_{23}, are required in the approximation used for calculating the excitation rate in Eq. (5) for $\Delta n \neq 0$ transitions. The energy difference ΔE_{23} was estimated through extrapolation by keeping the ratio $\Delta E/\chi$ constant along the isoelectronic sequence.

In evaluating the collisional mixing rate between the upper laser state and a nearby state that has a short lifetime for dipole decay to the ground state,

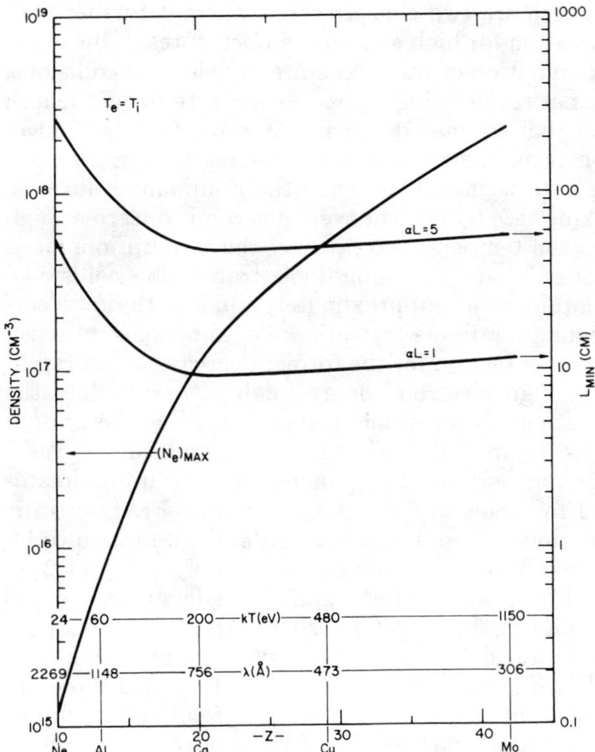

Fig. 1. Minimum length $L_{\min}$ for amplification in carbonlike ions with gain $\exp(\alpha L)$ vs atomic number Z, wavelength λ, and temperature, where the electron (kT_e) and ion (kT_i) temperatures are assumed equal. Maximum electron density $(N_e)_{\max}$ is also shown.

the lower laser state was chosen, since—for the carbon sequence at least—it was close and thereby had a typical overlap. (In carbonlike ions there are six clustered $n = 3$ states that should be properly considered in a more sophisticated collisional analysis.) The electron collisional mixing rate C_e at an electron temperature T_e and density N_e is best estimated for $\Delta n = 0, l = 1 \rightarrow l = 0$ transitions from twice the line width given by the portion of Eq. (526) of Ref. 14, which pertains to $l \rightarrow l - 1$ transitions:

$$C_e = 6\pi N_e(2m/\pi kT_e)^{1/2}(\hbar/mz)^2 n^2(n^2 - l^2)[l/(2l + 1)] \times \ln\{5 - (4.5/z) + \xi^{-1}[(1 + kT_e n^2)/\chi_H z(z - 1)]^{-1}\}, \quad (2)$$

where $n = 3$, $l = 1$, and where $\xi = (z - 1)\, e^2\, \omega/mv_e{}^3$ from Eq. (515) of the same reference. Here, χ_H is the ionization potential of hydrogen and ω is the laser angular frequency. The ratio C_e/N_e has been tabulated[15] for $T_e = T_i$.

The ion collisional mixing rate C_i has also been evaluated by Eqs. (517) and (518) of Ref. 14 (with the former multiplied by the square of the ion charge $(z - 1)^2$ for ions heavier than protons):

$$C_i = [4\pi^2/(2l + 1)]\ \frac{3}{5}(\hbar n/mz)^2[N_e/(z - 1)](z - 1)^2 \times (M/kT_i)\left[\, l(n^2 - l^2)v \times \exp\left(-\frac{5}{6}\, Mv^2/kT_i\right)\right], \quad (3)$$

where

$$v = [6\pi(z - 1)e^2\omega kT_i/M^2]^{1/5}\,. \quad (4)$$

Here, M is the ion mass, T_i the ion temperature, and $N_e/(z - 1)$ is used for the ion density. The parameter C_i/N_e has also been tabulated[15] and is found to range from about five to two orders of magnitude less than C_e/N_e for the neon to molybdenum ions, respectively.

The maximum electron density is determined by setting the collisional mixing rate equal to the spontaneous emission probability A_{33} for the laser transition. Then, $(N_e)_{\max} = A_{33}/(C_e N_e)$, for $C_i \ll C_e$. This density upper limit has been tabulated[15] and is plotted in Figs. 1 and 2. The maximum electron densities shown are quite consistent with those available in an expanding and cooling laser-produced plasma.

If the upper and lower laser terms are assumed to be populated by electron collisions from the $n = 2$ ground state (density $= N_g$) only (see Introduction), final coronal equilibrium values, given in a first approximation by $N_g(C_{23}/A_{32})$, are reached in a characteristic e-folding time of $\sim A_{32}{}^{-1}$. This time is much shorter for the lower laser level than for the upper, and the lower level reaches a much lower equilibrium concentration more rapidly. The collisional excitation rate C_{23} is calculated with the effective Gaunt factor approximation in the convenient form[16]:

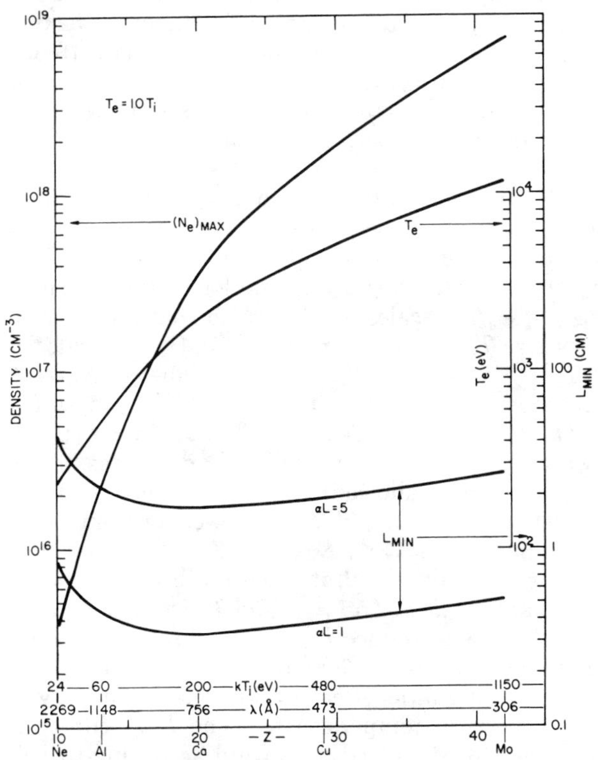

Fig. 2. Minimum length $L_{\min}$ for amplification in carbonlike ions with gain $\exp(\alpha L)$ vs atomic number Z, wavelength λ, and ion kinetic temperature kT_i. The electronic kinetic temperature kT_e is assumed equal to $10\,kT_i$ and is plotted. Maximum electron density $(N_e)_{\max}$ is also shown.

$$C_{23} = [1.6 \times 10^{-5} f_{23} \bar{g} \exp(-\Delta E_{23}/kT_e)/\Delta E_{23}(kT_e)^{1/2}] \times N_e \text{ sec}^{-1}, \quad (5)$$

for ΔE_{23} and kT_e in eV and where $\bar{g}$ is the average Gaunt factor ($\approx$0.2). By setting $N_g \approx N_e/(z - 1)$, the upper laser state density may be calculated and is found[15] to be $\approx 10^{-3}N_g$.

A question remains as to how long an inversion is maintained; i.e., what equilibrium population distribution is reached and in what time interval? At first glance it appears possible that inversion can be sustained for an indefinite period. Clearly, a detailed time-dependent numerical rate equation analysis is needed, including as many effects from other levels (such as cascading) as possible. This refinement is now underway.

III. Results

It is now possible to estimate the minimum length necessary to achieve a particular gain product αL. For Doppler line broadening (Stark broadening is estimated from $0.5C_{e,i}$ and found to be negligible), this length is given for large inversion by[6]

$$L \geq (8\pi\alpha L/A_{33}N_u\lambda_{33}^3)(2\pi kT_i/M)^{1/2}. \quad (6)$$

This is plotted as $L_{\min}$ vs element, temperature, and wavelength in Fig. 1 for $\alpha L = 1$ and 5, and for $T_e = T_i$. The analysis is carried up to molybdenum ($Z = 42$), which is the heaviest element for which high stages of ionization have been reported.[17] It is seen that the parameters involved scale with Z such that $L_{\min}$ is approximately constant for elements heavier than $Z \approx 17$ and never becomes less than 10 cm, which is somewhat long for laser-produced plasmas. However, for neon, the length is consistent with 1-m cavity discharge experiments, since $\alpha l \approx 1.5\%$ is sufficient.

Since it is hoped that the ions may cool in expansion and that subsequently the electrons may be heated preferentially, it is of great interest to observe the effect here. Neglecting the logarithmic term in Eq. (2), C_e/N_e scales as $T_e^{-1/2}$ so that $(N_e)_{\max}$ increases as $T_e^{1/2}$. Also, from Eq. (5), C_{23}/N scales as $(\bar{g}/T_e^{1/2})\exp(-\Delta E_{23}/kT_e)$, as does N_u/N_e^2. Therefore, $N_u \propto \sqrt{T_e} \exp(-\Delta E_{23}/kT_e)$, and $L \propto (T_i/T_e)^{1/2} \exp(\Delta E_{23}/kT_e)$. The advantage in allowing the ions to cool (while N_e decreases to the maximum value allowed) is indicated here, although the dependence upon T_i is much weaker than on T_e, particularly for $kT_e < \Delta E_{23}$. In Fig. 2, the ion temperature is maintained at the equilibrium value assumed above (i.e., $0.25\,\chi_{z-1}$) and T_e is taken as $10T_i$. The effect is to reduce $L_{\min}$ below unity for threshold gain and as low as 1.7 cm for $\alpha L = 5$. This indicates the dramatic effect of increased pumping at higher electron temperatures. The $L_{\min}$ curves in Fig. 2 are to be shifted downward according to $\sqrt{T_i}$ for significant cooling with frozen-in ions. Just which ions will be most useful (i.e., the carbonlike sequence analyzed here or another sequence) will probably be determined by experiments (presently underway[18]).

There are two concerns that warrant further consideration for high electron temperatures. One is the depopulation of the laser states by electron collisions, the net result being a possible increase in gain length over that estimated above. An estimate[16] for ionization from the $n = 3$ states indicates that in all cases the rate is much less than the dominant collisional mixing rate C_e used above. A second concern at high electron temperatures involves the assumption, made above, that the nondipole-transition collisional pumping rate is approximately equal to that of a corresponding dipole transition; i.e., for atoms, at least, the cross section for the former decreases more rapidly at high electron energy (high T_e) than does the cross section for dipole transitions. For the present $T_e = T_i$ analysis, $kT_e/\Delta E_{23} < 1$, and for the $T_e/T_i = 10$ analysis, $kT/\Delta E_{23}$ increases from approximately 3 for neon to 5 for molybdenum. From existing experimental and theoretical data[13,19] for multiply-ionized atoms, there is no evidence that the $n = 2 \rightarrow 3$ nondipole rates will be significantly less than the corresponding dipole rates for $kT_e/\Delta E_{23}$ up to 5. Furthermore, data exist[20] for $n = 3 \rightarrow 3$ transitions with $kT_e/\Delta E_{33}$ varying from 4 to 15, which also shows no significant deterioration in the relative nondipole rates (although the absolute value of the cross section is reduced below that for dipole transitions in this case). Data on relative nondipole excitation rates at high electron temperatures are important, not only to the present analysis, but to other short wavelength ion laser approaches[21] that depend directly on a *weak* monopole excitation rate for the lower laser level at anomalously high electron energies in plasmas.

The required internal pump power density can be found from $N_g C_{23} \Delta E_{23}$, assuming $N_g = N_e/(z - 1)$. With a volume determined by the product of the cross-sectional area a and the length L, and assuming a fractional absorption of L/L_{abs} along with a total energy conversion efficiency of η, the axial pumping laser irradiance P/a that is required is given by

$$P/a = N_e C_{23} \Delta E_{23} L_{\text{abs}}/\eta(z - 1). \quad (7)$$

Here, L_{abs} is the classical inverse-bremsstrahlung absorption length, given by[4]

$$L_{\text{abs}} = 5 \times 10^{27} T_e^{3/2}/N_e^2\lambda^2(z - 1) \text{ cm} \quad (8)$$

for densities much less than the critical value ($\approx 10^{21}$ cm^{-3} for $\lambda = 1.06$ μm radiation) at the plasma frequency. Here, T_e is in eV, λ is in cm, and N_e is in cm^{-3}. Then,

$$P/a = (2 \times 10^{11})[T_e f \exp(-\Delta E_{23}/kT_e)/(z - 1)^2\eta] \text{ W/cm}^2, \quad (9)$$

with Eq. (5). Within the present approximations, P/a is therefore independent of density and medium length.

Numerical results indicate, for an estimated total conversion efficiency of 1%, a required irradiance up to approximately 10^{14} W/cm^2 for the ions indicated in the figures, and for $T_e = 10T_i$. This may be obtained with a 0.1-J, 10-psec laser focused to a 100-μm diam. The 1% efficiency estimate is arrived at by assuming 10% for laser heating and 10% for excitation of the particular upper configuration, in competition both with other excitation modes and with ionization (ionization from the $n = 2$ orbit proceeds at a rate[16] comparable to that for excitation to $n = 3$ levels for the enhanced electron temperature case).

IV. Discussion

The experimental scheme proposed above involves the transverse generation and subsequent expansion of a cylindrical plasma and the additional heating and pumping by an axial laser beam. A Maxwellian electron distribution has implicitly been assumed in the analysis. The electron equilibration time scales as $N_e^{-1}T_e^{3/2}$ and reaches the nanosecond range for the high electron temperature cases, which is comparable both to the upper laser state lifetimes and the collisional excitation times. Electron-ion equipartition times are, however, still much longer, so that high T_e/T_i ratios may be maintained. A more sophisticated analysis will either have to account for this relatively slow electron equilibration or depend upon electron heating at higher densities with an associated risk of excessive cooling during the ensuing expansion phase. The latter approach would not require additional pump irradiance, according to the present analysis; however, a complicated dynamic numerical plasma model would be required for analysis. Experiments will undoubtedly be done wtih various heating times.

V. Summary

The present three-state analysis indicates that it is promising to extrapolate successful near-ultraviolet ion laser transitions into the vacuum-uv region for amplification, by using expanding laser-produced cylindrical plasma as an initial medium that is subsequently pulse-heated axially with available lasers to increase the electron temperature for efficient pumping. The particular ion species that are generated and maintained in a frozen-in state will be identified in experiments. The added effects of other levels, as well as the true time dependence of the gain, will hopefully evolve from a numerical model presently under development. Such modeling of increasing sophistication will require more refined extrapolation methods and more basic data, particularly as it proceeds to higher Z elements.

The author is grateful to H. R. Griem for helpful suggestions towards evaluating the collisional rates involved here. Valuable discussions with his colleague R. A. Andrews are also recalled with appreciation.

References

1. R. S. Pressley, Ed. *Handbook of Lasers,* (Chemical Rubber Co., 1972) p. 242; C. K. Rhodes, IEEE J. Quantum Electron. **QE-10,** 153 (1974); Y. Hashino, Y. Katsuyama, and K. Fukuda, Japan J. Appl. Phys. **11,** 907 (1972); **12,** 470 (1973), for recent low-Z ion lasing in a z-pinch discharge.
2. M. Duguay, Laser Focus **9,** 45 (1973); R. A. Andrews, NRL Memo. Rept. 2677 (1973).
3. S. E. Harris, A. H. Kung, and J. F. Young, J. Opt. Soc. Am. **64,** 556 (1974).
4. J. M. Dawson, A. Hertzberg, R. E. Kidder, G. C. Vlases, H. G. Ahlstrom, and L. C. Steinhauer, *IAEA Symposium on Plasma Physics and Controlled Fusion Research, Madison* (IAEA, Vienna, 1971), p. 673.
5. L. C. Steinhauer and H. G. Ahlstrom, Phys. Fluids **14,** 1109 (1971).
6. R. C. Elton, R. W. Waynant, R. A. Andrews, and M. H. Reilly, "X-Ray and Vacuum-UV Lasers: Current Status and Prognosis," NRL Rept. 7412, (May 2, 1972).
7. R. L. Kelly with L. J. Palumbo, "Atomic and Ionic Emission Lines Below 2000 Å, NRL Rept. 7599 (1973).
8. C. E. Moore, "Atomic Energy Levels" NSRDS-NBS 35 (Dec. 1971); NSRDS-NBS 3 (1965–1971); NBS Circular 488.
9. W. L. Wiese, M. W. Smith, and B. M. Glennon, "Atomic Transition Probabilities, Vol. 1 Hydrogen through Neon" NSRDS-NBS-4 (May 1966); W. L. Wiese, M. W. Smith and B. M. Miles, "Vol. II, Sodium through Calcium" NSRDS-NBS 22 (October 1969).
10. W. L. Wiese, Appl. Opt. **7,** 2361 (1958).
11. M. W. Smith and W. L. Wiese, Astrophys. J. **23,** 103 (1971).
12. B. Edlen, in *Handbuch der Physik* (Springer Verlag, Berlin, 1964), Vol. 27, p. 80.
13. H.-J. Kunze, Space Sci. Rev. **13,** 565 (1972).
14. H. R. Griem, *Broadening of Spectral Lines by Charged Particles in Plasmas* (Academic Press, New York, 1974).
15. R. C. Elton, NRL Memo. Rept. 2799 (May 1974); Proceedings IV Int. Conf. on Vacuum-Ultraviolet Radiation Physics, Hamburg, 1974.
16. R. C. Elton, in *Methods of Experimental Physics-Plasma Physics,* H. R. Griem and R. H. Lovberg, Eds. (Academic Press, New York, 1970), Vol. 9A.
17. J. J. Turechek and H.-J. Kunze (to be published).
18. T. N. Lee, J. Davis, J. F. Reintjes, R. H. Dixon, R. C. Eckardt, K. Whitney, J. L. DeRosa, R. A. Andrews, and R. C. Elton, Bull. Am. Phys. Soc. **19,** 558 (1974); Proc. VIII IEEE International Quantum Electronics Conf. (1974).
19. H.-J. Kunze and W. D. Johnson, III, Phys. Rev. A **3,** 1384 (1971); W. D. Johnson III and H.-J. Kunze, Phys. Rev. A **4,** 962 (1971).
20. R. U. Datla, H.-J. Kunze, and D. Petrini, Phys. Rev. A **6,** 38 (1972).
21. T. C. Bristow, M. J. Lubin, J. M. Forsyth, E. B. Goldman, and J. M. Sources, Opt. Commun. **5,** 315 (1972).

Reprinted with permission from *Physical Review Letters,* Vol. 35(7), pp. 435-438 (August 18, 1975).

Population Inversions and the Measurement of Gain in Laser-Produced Plasmas

W. T. Silfvast, J. M. Green, and O. R. Wood, II
Bell Telephone Laboratories, Holmdel, New Jersey 07733

We consider plasma conditions leading to a population inversion with respect to the ground state of an ion and problems arising in the measurement of gain in laser-produced plasmas. These considerations indicate that recent reports of superradiant emission in a laser-produced aluminum plasma at 117.41 Å might be subject to reinterpretation.

In this paper, population inversions with respect to the ground state of ions in a high-density plasma are considered and some general problems that can arise in the interpretation of gain measurements in laser-produced plasmas are described. These results suggest that explanations other than the presence of gain might be considered in interpreting measurements made by Jaegle *et al.*[1] in a laser-produced aluminum plasma. Specifically, calculations of plasma conditions for which a population inversion with respect to an ion ground state might occur indicate that such an inversion would almost always favor transitions from the first excited state. From higher excited states of similar energy, gain on the transition with the highest radiative rate (not the 117.41-Å transition suggested in Ref. 1) would dominate. Also, experimental evidence is presented indicating that for the measurement of gain in a laser-produced plasma the two-plasma technique (one plasma playing the role of a source and the other acting as a sample) such as that used in Ref. 1 can be unreliable. Qualitative explanations for the origin of these measurement difficulties are given. Finally, a simple two-component-plasma model is presented that can explain the intensity anomalies observed in an aluminum plasma[2] without speculating on the existence of gain.

Although population inversions with respect to ion ground states in a plasma are generally considered to be unlikely situations, the existence of such inversions was found to be possible theoretically by calculating individual populations of the ground state and first few excited states for hydrogenic ions at various electron temperatures and densities.[3] These calculations, based on a rate-equation approach,[4] indicate that population inversions with respect to the ground state would almost always be largest for the first excited state. These results also apply qualitatively to nonhydrogenic ions. Favorable conditions for attaining such an inversion in a laser-produced plasma are created by generating a plasma of sufficiently high electron density and temperature such that initially some higher ionization stage, $E^{(x+1)+}$, would have a greater population than the next lower stage, E^{x+} (where E denotes the element and x specifies its charge). During the subsequent recombination phase of the plasma evolution, a population inversion of duration $\sim 10^{-10}$ – 10^{-11} might then occur in the E^{x+} ionization stage under conditions of unusually rapid cooling.

If these conditions for a population inversion were achieved in a laser-produced aluminum plasma, then the highest gain in the Al^{3+} ion would almost always occur on the $2p^53s\,^3P_1 \rightarrow 2p^6\,^1S_0$ transition at 161.69 Å. The minimum electron density required to achieve such a population inversion increases as the electron temperature increases. For example, at an electron temperature of 5 eV the threshold electron density for population inversion in the Al^{3+} ion is $\sim 10^{20}$ cm^{-3}. Population inversions of higher excited states, such as those in the closely spaced $4d$ multiplet considered by Jaegle *et al.*, are also possible. In this case gain would be greatest on those transitions with the largest radiative rates, since the populations of these levels are estimated to collisionally equilibrate in times less than 10^{-10} sec for electron densities greater than 10^{17} cm^{-3}. Experimentally measured collisional mixing rates in other metal ions[5] (when scaled by the ratio of the appropriate Bohr radii) support this estimate. Thus, because of rapid collisional mixing, gain would be greater at 116.46 and 116.92 Å (the transitions to the ground state from the $4d$ multiplet with the highest radiative rates) than at 117.41 Å, and it is unlikely that any particular collisional process which preferentially populates the $^3P_1$ level over the $^1P_1$ and $^3D_1$ levels of the $4d$ multiplet, as suggested by Carillon *et al.*,[6] could have a rate large enough to alter this conclusion. Therefore, since gain is not expected to dominate at 117.41 Å, alternative explanations of the enhancement measured by Jaegle *et al.* might be considered.

In this laboratory, in the course of measurements of excited-state densities in laser-produced metal-vapor plasmas formed in a vacuum and in the presence of a background gas, both the two-plasma technique and a laser-probe technique were used to study the upper and lower levels of the 4416-Å transition in the Cd^+ ion. A cadmium plasma was formed by focusing the 10.6-μm output from a high-pressure, pulsed, CO_2 laser with a cylindrical lens onto a cadmium target inside a vacuum chamber. The 10.6-μm output was focused in such a way that two collinear regions of the cadmium target (each 3 mm long and 0.4 mm wide, separated by 2 mm) were irradiated with intensities of 10^8–10^9 W/cm². The resulting collinear plasmas (formed above the target surface) emitted strong radiation during the recombination phase of the plasma in both the neutral and the ionized spectra of cadmium. An optical-detection scheme permitted a small, approximately cylindrical region (parallel to the common axis of the plasmas) to be sampled at any particular height above the target by a high-resolution monochromator. For the two-plasma technique this region was imaged onto a pinhole with $f/25$ optics and subsequently focused onto the slit of the monochromator. For the laser-probe technique, the laser beam passed unfocused through the plasma and continued over a relatively long path (to minimize background light from the plasma) before being focused into the monochromator.

In the two-plasma measurement, the intensity from the two identical plasmas viewed together (I_T) and separately (I_S) gave a measure of the apparent enhancement $[\Delta I = (I_T - 2I_S)/I_S]$ of radiation from the plasma furthest from the detection system in the presence of the plasma nearest the detection system. Enhancements were observed over a wide range of background-gas pressures and in vacuum. As an example of a particularly large enhancement, Fig. 1(a) shows the recorded time dependence of I_S and I_T for the plasma emission at 4416 Å observed 1 mm above the target surface with a background gas of helium at 30 Torr. The resulting enhancement, ΔI, is shown as a dashed curve in Fig. 1(b). Hence, at certain spatial and temporal positions the two-plasma technique indicates (through an apparent enhancement of the 4416 Å emission) the presence of as much as 200% "gain" at 4416 Å in the laser-produced cadmium plasma. A time-integrated measurement of intensity would have shown a smaller enhancement of ~25% which is comparable in magnitude to the 17% gain deduced from photographic measurements by Jaegle *et al.* at 117.41 Å in a laser-produced aluminum plasma.

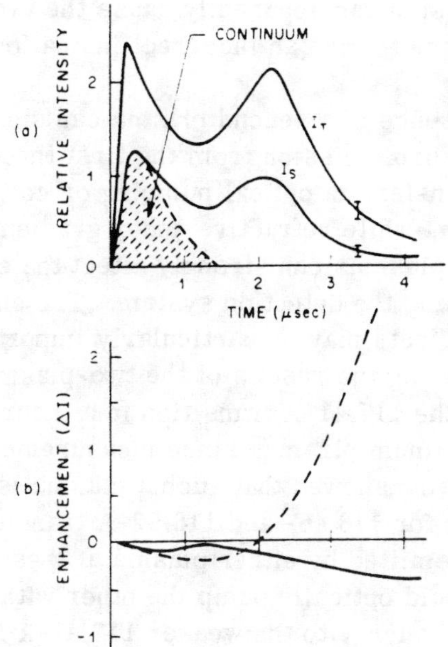

FIG. 1. Experimental comparison of two-plasma and laser-probe techniques at 4416 Å in a laser-produced cadmium plasma. (a) Intensity (average of five pulses) from a single plasma (I_S) and from two plasmas produced together (I_T) as measured by the two-plasma technique. (b) Enhancement measured by two-plasma technique (dashed curve) and absorption from laser-probe measurement (solid curve).

A 4416-Å He-Cd laser was subsequently used to probe the laser-produced cadmium plasma in the identical spatial and temporal regions where the presence of gain was indicated by the two-plasma technique. These results, shown as a solid curve in Fig. 1(b), indicate a loss of 40% where the two plasma technique indicated a 200% gain. When using the laser-probe method it was observed that the plasma produced focusing and deflection of the probe beam. Therefore great care was taken to ensure that all of the laser radiation was properly collected by the detection system. The possibility that the two-plasma technique was monitoring emission or absorption at a frequency shifted from that of the probe laser was also considered. However, a high-resolution measurement of the frequency distribution of the plasma emission at 4416 Å indicated that the frequency of the probe laser was near the center of the broadened line. When these effects were taken into account it was concluded that the laser-probe technique gave a reliable measurement of plasma absorption. Therefore, effects other than stimulated emission can apparently cause the two-plasma technique to give an incorrect indication of gain.

The presence of a second plasma can significantly perturb emission from the first through energy transfer via optical pumping or collisional interaction, while refractive-index gradients within the plasmas can strongly affect the emission reaching the detection system. The energy-transfer effects may be particularly important in interpreting the results of the two-plasma technique for the 117.41-Å transition in a laser-produced aluminum plasma, since measurements by Carillon *et al.* showed that such a plasma is optically thick for 116.46- and 116.92-Å transitions.[6] Radiation emitted by either plasma at these wavelengths would optically pump the other with a net transfer of energy to the weaker 117.41-Å line through strong collisional coupling within the $4d$ multiplet. Also, if the plasmas overlap while still strongly radiating, the interaction could produce changes in plasma conditions resulting in increased emission at 117.41 Å. The presence of index gradients due to large spatial variations in electron density or strong plasma absorption could produce strong focusing and deflection effects in the laser-produced plasmas. For example, the plasma nearest the detection system might act as a lens concentrating radiation from the other plasma onto the detection system. Since focusing and deflection of 4416-Å radiation by a cadmium plasma was observed during the laser-probe measurement it is possible that refractive-index gradients are at least partially responsible for the apparent enhancement measured at 4416 Å.

Prior to their report of measured gain at 117.41 Å, the possibility of stimulated emission at this wavelength had already been suggested by Jaegle *et al.* to explain the occurrence of some "intensity anomalies" appearing in a spectrogram of a laser-produced aluminum plasma.[2] Near the target the transitions from the $4d$ multiplet to the Al^{3+}-ion ground state having large radiative rates (i.e., the 116.46- and 116.92-Å lines) appeared as broad absorption features on a continuum background, whereas the 117.41-Å line with the smaller radiative rate appeared as a narrow emission line above the background. Such anomalies were recently attributed by Valero[7] to the presence of an absorbing region in the plasma.

A two-component model (not necessarily intended to describe specific details of a laser-produced plasma) when fitted with specific ab-

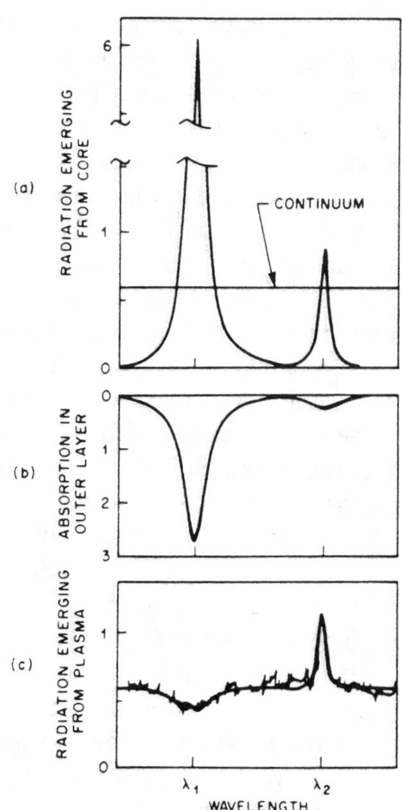

FIG. 2. Plasma emission resulting from a two-component plasma model compared to the 116.92- and 117.41-Å emission from a laser-produced Al plasma of Jaegle *et al.* ["experimental" curve of Fig. 2(c)].

sorption and emission values can reproduce the "intensity anomalies" reported by Jaegle *et al.* without speculating on the existence of gain. As a simplification, the model considers emission in the region of two wavelengths (λ_1 and λ_2) corresponding to transitions having a 10-to-1 ratio of radiative rates from two excited levels to the ground state of an ion. One component of the model is the plasma core and the other component is an outer layer which absorbs emission from the core but whose own emission is negligible. The emission emerging from the core is shown in Fig. 2(a). The continuum emission might occur during the heating phase when the plasma is hot and dense while the narrow-line emission might occur at a later time [as suggested by experiments in this laboratory, see Fig. 1(a)] during recombination when the plasma has cooled. The intensities for the line emission have been calculated under the assumption of equal upper-level populations (e.g., by collisional coupling) and core absorptions of 1.0 at λ_1 and 0.1 at λ_2. This assumption results in the stronger transition at λ_1 being broadened and partially self-absorbed as shown in Fig. 2(a). The absorption of the outer layer is given in Fig. 2(b). The radiation emerging from such a plasma (core radiation passing through outer absorbing layer) is shown in Fig. 2(c). The anomalous features of a portion of the spectrogram obtained by Jaegle *et al.* for laser-produced aluminum plasma are also reproduced in Fig. 2(c) and are seen to be in good agreement with the predictions of the model. A slightly more complex plasma model, incorporating different absorptions for the continuum and line radiation to simulate a time-dependent outer-layer absorption [as suggested by the results of the laser-probe measurement shown in Fig. 1(b)], leads to an even better fit to the results of Jaegle *et al.*

[1]P. Jaegle, G. Jamelot, A. Carillon, A. Sureau, and P. Dhez, Phys. Rev. Lett. 33, 1070 (1974).

[2]P. Jaegle, A. Carillon, P. Dhez, G. Jamelot, A. Sureau, and M. Cukier, Phys. Lett. 36A, 167 (1971).

[3]J. M. Green and W. T. Silfvast, to be published.

[4]See, for example, D. R. Bates and A. E. Kingston, Planet. Space Sci. 11, 1 (1963); R. W. P. McWhirter and A. G. Hearn, Proc. Phys. Soc., London 82, 641 (1963).

[5]J. M. Green, G. J. Collins, and C. E. Webb, J. Phys. B: At. Mol. Phys. 6, 1545 (1973); T. Sakurai, J. Appl. Phys. 45, 2666 (1974).

[6]A. Carillon, P. Jaegle, G. Jamelot, and A. Sureau, in *Proceedings of the International Conference on Inner Shell Ionization Phenomena and Future Applications, Atlanta, Georgia, 1972,* edited by R. W. Fink, J. T. Manson, I. M. Palms, and R. V. Rao, CONF 720404 (U. S. Atomic Energy Commission, Oak Ridge, Tenn., 1973), Vol. 4, p. 2373.

[7]F. P. J. Valero, Appl. Phys. Lett. 25, 64 (1974).

Reprinted with permission from *Soviet Journal of Quantum Electronics,* Vol. 6(4), pp. 456-457 (April 1976). ©1976 American Institute of Physics.

X-ray laser with a distributed feedback: output power and coherence

G. A. Lyakhov

M.V. Lomonosov State University, Moscow
Kvantovaya Elektron. (Moscow) 3, 838–839 (April 1976)

A theoretical analysis is made of the energy and statistical characteristics of a distributed-feedback laser. Estimates are made of the output energy and times needed to establish a practically complete coherence of the output radiation in the x-ray wavelength range.

PACS numbers: 42.60.—v

1. The possibility of constructing an x-ray laser is currently the subject of intensive theoretical[1] and experimental[2] investigations. The main problem in these investigations is the population inversion. However, it is clear that x-ray lasers will fulfil the expectations only if they are considerably superior to luminescence sources in respect of the output power, monochromaticity, and degree of spatial coherence of the output radiation.

Improvements in these characteristics can be achieved using a distributed-feedback (DFB) scheme ensured by the Bragg reflections of radiation from periodic inhomogeneities in the crystal lattice.[3,4]

We shall give the results of an analysis of the energy and statistical characteristics of a DFB laser and we shall obtain estimates for the x-ray wavelength range.

2. In a superluminescence laser the spatial coherence of the radiation is due to the finite transverse cross section of the pump beam. A solution of the equation for the spatial correlation function describes narrowing of a superluminescence beam with increasing distance and a simultaneous increase in the correlation radius. The value of the "coherent" gain, i.e., of the gain for which the correlation radius becomes approximately equal to the beam radius, is given by the relationships $gl_{coh} \approx l_{diffr}/l$ for $l_{diffr} < l_{gr}$ and $gl_{coh} \approx l^2_{diffr}/ll_{gr}$ for $l_{diffr} > l_{gr}$. Here, g is the gain, l is the length of the active medium, l_{diffr} and l_{gr} are the diffraction and group lengths. Estimates based on the available results give a requirement which is impossible to satisfy: $gl_{coh} \approx 3\times 10^2$.

3. The output energy of a DFB laser in the linear regime is (it is assumed that the laser is pumped with rectangular pulses of duration τ_p).

$$W = W_{sl} \exp(x)/x, \quad x = 2c(g - g_{th})(\tau_p - l/c)$$

where g_{th} is the threshold gain given by the transcendental equation $\sinh(g_{th}l) = g_{th}/\beta$ and β is the gain modulation coefficient. If $\beta/g = 10^{-4}$ (Ref. 4) and for a 1.5-fold excess over the threshold, the energy gain over superluminescence is of the order of 10^3.

4. The factor which limits the output power is the lattice damage (characteristic time t_d) resulting from strong heating caused by the pumping. If we assume that, beginning from an instant t_0 the modulation coefficient decreases exponentially: $\beta = \beta_0 \exp[(t_0 - t)/t_d]$, the quenching time of the laser action t in which the output power falls to the superluminescence level can be found from

$$\exp(\bar{t}/2t_d) - 1 = (\bar{t} + t_0)g/2t_d g_{th}.$$

Since the lattice damage is governed by the pump energy, a suitable optimization may ensure that it begins when the stimulated emission is already achieved and, consequently, such emission is extended in time: $\bar{t} > t_d$ for $t_0 \lesssim 3t_d g_{th}/g$.

5. Equations describing nonlinear steady-state operation were solved numerically in the two-level approximation. The dependences of the threshold gain on the rate of pumping were obtained for different values of the modulation coefficient. It was found that in the case of active media of considerable length the DFB laser efficiency should be independent of the degree of modulation.

6. In the case of a moderate excess over the threshold the situation is described by an equation of the diffusion type for changes in the temporal correlation function. This function has the Gaussian form

$$\Gamma(t, \tau, l) \sim \exp(-\tau^2/\tau^2_{corr}),$$

where the correlation time is proportional to the square root of a linear function of the pump pulse duration:

$$\tau_{corr} = [6(\tau_p - l/2c)/cg_{th}]^{1/2}.$$

The radiation emitted by a DFB laser should be practically coherent (the emission line width is governed by the pulse duration) in a time of the order of 10^{-14} sec.

7. In the approximation which is paraxial with respect to the spatial "correlation" coordinate the spatial correlation function satisfies the diffusion equation with a biharmonic spatial operator. Estimates of the time needed to establish the diffraction-limit divergence

$$\Delta\theta = \left[\frac{8g_{th}}{2ck^2(t - l/2c)}\right]^{1/4} = \Delta\theta_{diffr} = (kl)^{-1/2}$$

show that it occurs when the pump pulse duration τ_p is ≈ 10 times as long as the transit time of the waves through the system.

The results obtained indicate that, in spite of the obvious difficulties (the main of which is the difficulty of obtaining population inversion which is common to all laser systems), a laser with the Bragg DFB may provide a suitable alternative to a mirror resonator in the x-ray range of wavelengths.

The author is deeply grateful to S. A. Akhmanov for his great help.

[1]M. A. Duguay and P. M. Rentzepis, App. Phys. Lett. 10, 350 (1967).
[2]J. G. Kepros, E. M. Eyring, and F. W. Cagle Jr, Proc. Natl. Acad. Sci. USA 69, 1744 (1972).
[3]R. A. Fisher, Appl. Phys. Lett. 24, 598 (1974).
[4]A. Yariv, Appl. Phys. Lett. 25, 105 (1974).

Translated by A. Tybulewicz

DIRECT OBSERVATION OF POPULATION INVERSION BETWEEN Al^{+11} LEVELS IN A LASER-PRODUCED PLASMA

V.A. BHAGAVATULA and B. YAAKOBI

Laboratory for Laser Energetics, University of Rochester, Rochester, New York 14627, USA

Received 23 December 1977

Measured X-ray intensities of the resonance line series of Al^{+11} in a laser-produced plasma shows population inversion between the $n = 4, 5$ levels and the $n = 3$ level at a plasma density $N_e \sim 10^{20}$ cm^{-3}. The cooling of the expanding plasma leading to inversion is enhanced by a special target configuration. The gain coefficient in the $4 \rightarrow 3$ transition at 129.7 Å is estimated to be ~ 10 cm^{-1}, using both measured line intensities and numerical simulation.

Population inversion in an expanding laser-produced carbon plasma has been reported in two previous experiments [1,2]. Here we report on the observation of population inversion of the levels $n = 3$ and 4 (also of $n = 3$ and 5) of Al^{+11} by measuring the X-ray lines from these levels to the ground state. Even though the basic mechanism producing the inversion (i.e., recombination in an expanding plasma) is the same, there are several important differences between this and previous experiments:

(1) Here the observed line ($1s^2$–$1s4p$) starting on the upper level is actually stronger than the line ($1s^2$–$1s3p$) starting on the lower level of the inverted pair, beyond a certain distance from the target. This means that the deduced population inversion is not subject to doubts due to the imprecise knowledge of film calibration. Similar evidence was reported recently by Dixon and Elton [3] in a different inversion scheme: resonant charge exchange.

(2) Our spectra represent a single experiment per exposure.

(3) By employing a laser of power one to two orders of magnitude higher, we were able to achieve inversion in a higher-Z target (Al as compared with C). Consequently, we observe an inversion at a higher density, $N_e \sim 10^{20}$ cm^{-3}, as compared with $\sim 10^{17}$ cm^{-3} in ref. [1] and $\sim 10^{19}$ cm^{-3} in ref. [2]. Higher densities lead, of course, to a higher gain.

(4) We employ a full-fledged hydrodynamic numerical code rather than a similarity model as in refs. [2] and [4], and we come to different conclusions: cylindrical expansion is not really advantageous over planar expansion. The expanding plasma in both cases goes through a similar succession of parameter values (temperature, density, population), only in plane expansion this is extended over longer time and distance spans.

(5) The most important feature of the present experiment is the employment of a stepped target designed to cool the plasma at a certain distance from the initial surface. The idea here is that unlike expansion, cooling due to an additional plate is not accompanied by a drop in density and with it in gain.

Fig. 1 shows the experimental configuration: a glass:Nd laser of energy typically 10 J in 200 ps is

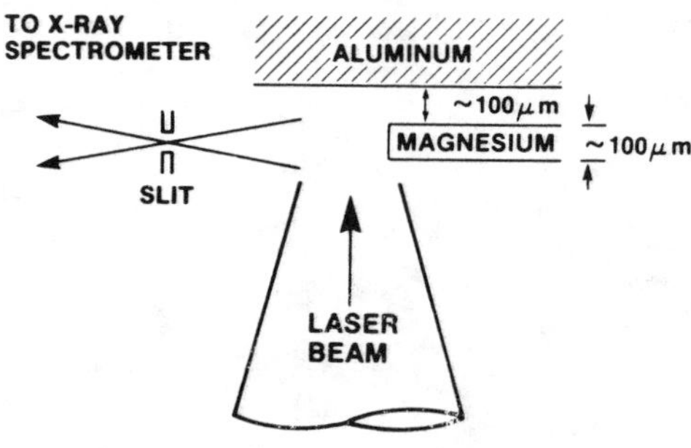

Fig. 1. The experimental configuration.

focused onto a stepped target: an aluminum slab and a magnesium plate in front of it for cooling the expanding Al plasma. Magnesium was chosen because Al and Mg lines can be registered on the same film. A small portion of the laser beam hits the magnesium plate giving rise to weak emission of the two resonance lines of Mg^{+10} and Mg^{+11} ions. The high density Mg plasma close to the Mg plate surface where the temperature drops to the metal bulk temperature is a heat sink, drawing heat from the low density high temperature Al expanding plasma. An X-ray crystal spectrograph equipped with a slit measured Al and Mg lines as a function of the distance perpendicular to the target. Spectra registered on Kodak No-Screen and Kodak RAR2490 films gave very similar results except that the latter film has a better signal to background ratio. Elaborate calibration of No-Screen film has been carried out in our laboratory [5] whereas for RAR2490 film we relied on the curves given by Benjamin et al. [6]. The reflectivity of the analyzing crystal (Tl.A.P.) was measured by Henke and Tester [7].

Fig. 2 shows the aluminum spectra before calibration at two distances from the aluminum surface. The line $1s^2-1s4p$ was found to be consistently stronger than the $1s^2-1s3p$ line for all distances $\gtrsim 300\ \mu m$, showing unequivocally an inversion between the n = 4 and 3 levels. For larger distances ($\gtrsim 500\ \mu m$) even the line $1s^2-1s5p$ becomes more intense than the two preceding ones. For smaller distances but larger than 150 μm we derive population inversion of the $n = 3, 4$ levels even though the line intensities themselves decrease along the series. Flat (non-stepped) targets of Al or Mg do not show such intensity inversion (even though some population inversion was deduced). This behavior is consistent with recombination in a cooling plasma which will show population inversion if $N_e \lesssim 10^{14}\ Z^7$ (so that excitation colli-

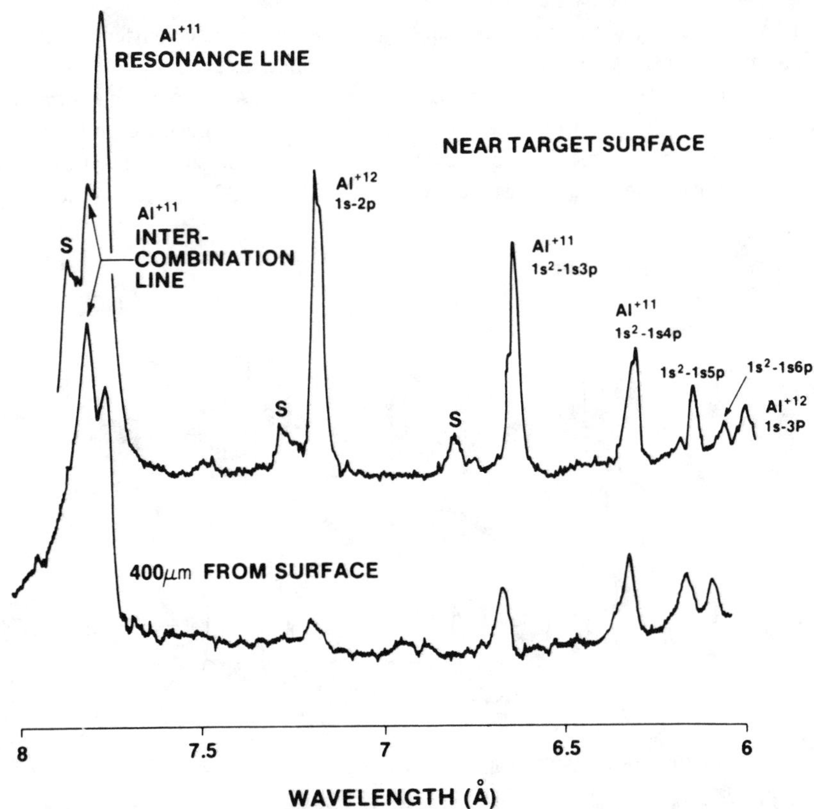

Fig. 2. Single-shot aluminum spectra from a stepped target (spatial resolution 50 μm). The lower spectrum shows inversion of the (1s3p, 1s4p) pair. S denotes dielectronic satellites. These are plots of film density with different scales (see also fig. 3).

sions are unimportant [8]), the temperature is sufficiently low and the density ratio $Q = n(\mathrm{Al}^{+12})/n(\mathrm{Al}^{+11})$ is sufficiently high. This implies the relative "freezing" of the Al^{+12} ion density which provides the pumping source for the inversion.

We compare the experimental results with the one-dimensional two-temperature hydrodynamic code SUPER [9] which includes an atomic physics group of subroutines similar to what is described in ref. [4]: rate equations for the evolution of Al ions charge states and excited level populations, and the escape factor approximation for line radiation transport. Using code calculations (and the experimental results), the opacity of the $1s^2-1s3p$ and $1s^2-1s4p$ lines can be estimated and it turns out to be much smaller than 1 at the large distances where inversion is observed (along the narrow dimension of the plasma). Opacity effects can then by no means account for the observed intensity inversion.

Fig. 3 shows that the plasma expands in a narrow axial channel (this was also found by Feldman et al. [10]): line widths obtained by the non-focusing spectrograph are determined by the source width. Fig. 3 indicates a plasma width $\lesssim 200\ \mu$m over a large distance ($> 500\ \mu$m) from the target. A numerical simulation assuming a planar expansion is therefore justified. Also, the lines intensity decay with distance is

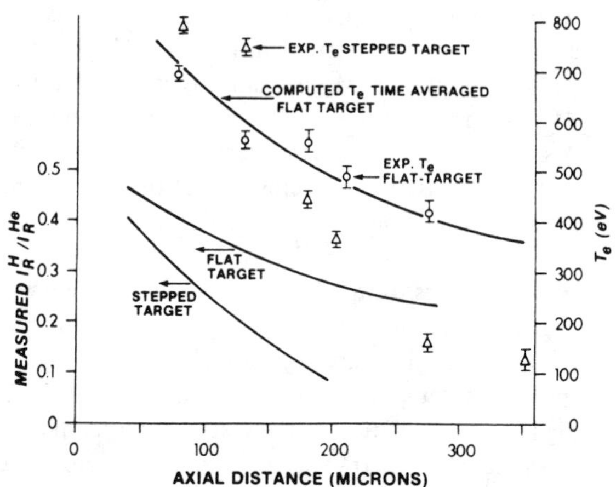

Fig. 4. Computed and measured electron temperature as a function of distance from the aluminum surface. Triangles denote experimentally determined temperature values for the stepped target of fig. 1, circles-for a flat aluminum target. Lower curves: measured intensity ratios of the resonance lines of hydrogen-like to helium-like aluminum ions.

found to be consistent with planar, but not hemispherical expansion.

Fig. 4 compares measured and computed profiles of T_e. The measured intensity ratio of the Al^{+12} to Al^{+11} resonance lines drops faster with distance when the Mg plate is added. This is evidence of addi-

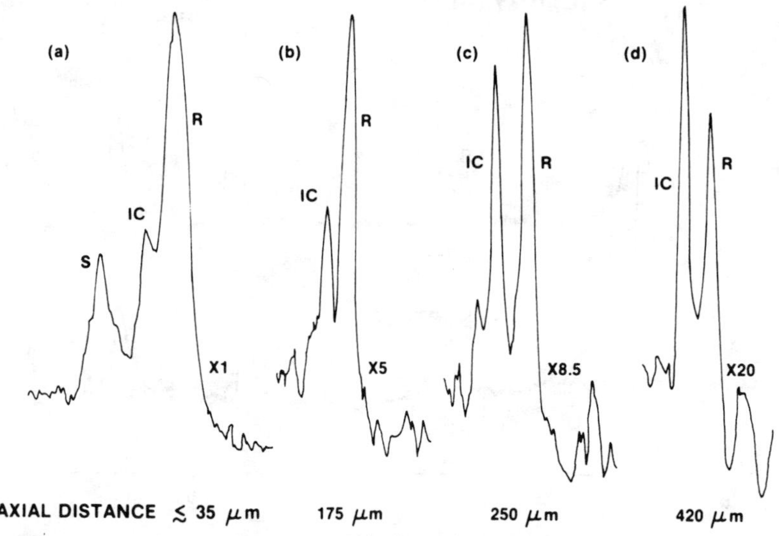

Fig. 3. Film density traces of Al^{+11} lines used to determine the plasma density profile. R: $1s^2-1s^2p^1P$, IC: $1s^2-1s2p^3P$. S denotes dielectronic satellites. Note that the curves have slightly different horizontal scales and different height scale factors. Spatial resolution was 38 μm.

tional cooling due to the plate. For the recombination regime pertinent to our case simple coronal or LTE models are not relevant in determining the electron temperatures. The experimental electron temperatures are derived using the more appropriate steady state excited level model of ref. [8] by comparing the observed intensity ratio of the inverted lines to the tabulated values. As fig. 4 shows, the values thus derived are consistent with the code predictions. The intensity of each resonance line is affected by opacity but the ratio is relatively independent of absorption. However, the addition of the Mg plate causes T_e to fall faster with distance. To model this cooling in the code we assumed a lateral temperature gradient scale of 200 μ, conducting heat into a sink of $N_e = 10^{21}\ \mathrm{cm}^{-3}$ at a location corresponding to the Mg plate. This is an approximate model designed only to show qualitatively the effect of additional cooling.

Fig. 5 shows the ratio of reduced populations (i.e., after division by the statistical weights) for the $n = 3$, 4 shells derived from the measured intensities of the lines $1s^2$–1s3p and $1s^2$–1s4p. The electron density is derived from the intensity ratio of the resonance line and the intercombination line (R and IC in fig. 3), using cross-sections given by Vinogradov et al. [11]. We see that inversion exists in a region where N_e is of order $10^{20}\ \mathrm{cm}^{-3}$. Neglecting opacity of the resonance line yields a conservative estimate of N_e (and the gain) and is probably responsible in part for the

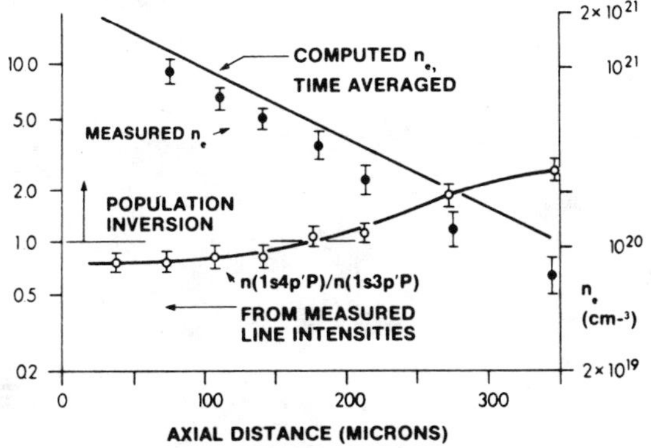

Fig. 5. Upper curve: comparison between computed and measured electron density profile. Measured values (full circles) are derived from I_R/I_{IC} values (fig. 3). Lower curve: the line through the open circles denotes reduced population ratio of the inverted level pair as deduced from the measured line intensities.

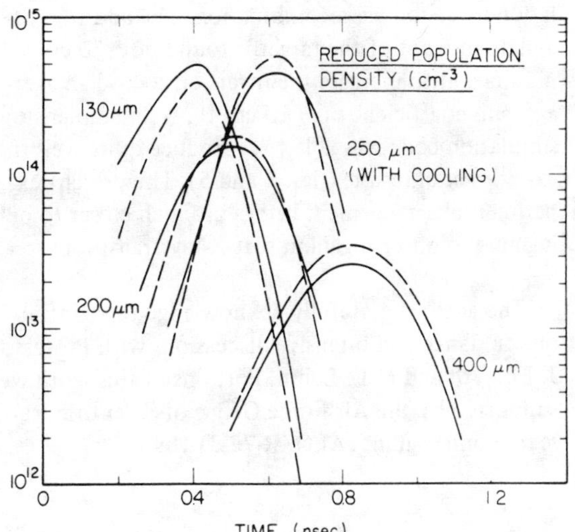

Fig. 6. Numerical code calculation of reduced population densities. Distances are from initial aluminum surface. The pair of curves at 250 μm corresponds to a calculation with provision to simulate the cooling effect of the magnesium plate. The other three pairs correspond to a simple flat aluminum target.

experimental N_e points being lower than the calculated curve.

Finally, we show in fig. 6 a sample calculation of population density evolution, with and without additional cooling. There is no inversion at 130 μm because the streaming plasma arrives there, first, with too high a temperature, then with too low a Q. On the other hand, plasma conditions are right to obtain small inversion at 200 μm and 400 μm. Notice that enhanced cooling (the curves at 250 μm) increases the peak reduced inversion density by a factor of 4 to 5 (compare with curves at 200 μm) and also increases the population ratio of the inverted level pairs. This agrees with the fact that with a stepped target large population ratios and even intensity inversions of the inverted level pair are observed. Fig. 6 also shows that spatial resolution at these distances is partially equivalent to temporal resolution. Using either the calibrated line intensities or the curves "with cooling" in fig. 6, we estimate the gain coefficient for the $4\,^3F$–$3\,^3D$ manifold [12] at 129.7 Å to be $\sim 10\ \mathrm{cm}^{-1}$ which for the measured plasma width $\sim 200\ \mu$m yields a gain of exp (0.2).

In conclusion, we find that plasma expansion far from a flat target is one-dimensional and shows population inversion via recombination. The addition of a plate in front of the target is found both to cool the plasma and to increase the inversion to give an average gain coefficient of $\sim 10\ cm^{-1}$. A one-dimensional simulation code was able to reproduce quite well the experimental results (figs. 4 and 5). The present experimental arrangement brings us much closer to being able to observe gain in soft X-ray transitions.

The authors gratefully acknowledge the continuous guidance and intensive discussions with Professors J. Forsyth and M.L. Lubin. Portions of this work were supported by the Air Force Office of Scientific Research under grant (AFOSR-77-3) 189.

References

[1] F.E. Irons and N.J. Peacock, J. Phys. B 7 (1974) 1109.
[2] R.J. Dewhurst et al., Phys. Rev. Letters 37 (1976) 1265.
[3] R.H. Dixon and R.C. Elton, Phys. Rev. Letters 38 (1977) 1072.
[4] G.J. Pert, J. Phys. B 9 (1976) 3301.
[5] A. Hauer and G. Harvey, Soft X-ray calibration of no-screen film, Tech. Note No. 2, X-Ray Group, LLE, University of Rochester (1975).
[6] R.F. Benjamin et al., Appl. Optics 16 (1977) 393.
[7] B.L. Henke and M.A. Tester, Adv. in X-Ray Analysis 18 (1975).
[8] R.P. McWhirter and A.G. Heran, Proc. Phys. Soc. London 82 (1963) 641.
[9] E.G. Goldman, Plasma Physics 15 (1973) 289; and University of Rochester, LLE Report #16 (1974) (unpubshed).
[10] U. Feldman et al., J. Appl. Phys. 47 (1976) 1341.
[11] A.V. Vinogradov et al., Sov. J. Quantum Electron. 5 (1975) 630; a revised version in Preprint 121, Lebedev Institute (1977).
[12] R.D. Cowan, Los Alamos Scientific Lab., private communication.

Reprinted with permission from *Soviet Journal of Quantum Electronics,* Vol. 8(8), pp. 1009-1010 (August 1978).

Possibility of rapidly cooling a multiply charged laser plasma and using it as an active medium for generating short-wavelength radiation

V. A. Gaponov, G. A. Pasmanik, and A. A. Shilov

Institute of Applied Physics, Academy of Sciences of the USSR, Gorki

Kvantovaya Elektron. (Moscow) 5, 1780–1782 (August 1978)

In order to increase the rate of cooling of a laser-produced plasma, formed by the breakdown of a gas in a focused light beam, it is proposed to surround it with a plasma shell of substantially lower temperature, produced by means of an additional picosecond pulse. Electron heat conduction in the colder outer region causes the temperature at the center of the plasma to drop. The recombination flux in the central region can thereby be increased considerably at the expense of a relatively small reduction in the plasma density. Estimates show that under such conditions one can expect an appreciable inversion of short-wavelength transitions and lasing in the far vacuum ultraviolet.

1. It is well known that a population inversion can occur in short-wavelength transitions as a result of three-body recombination of a supercooled multiply charged plasma.[1,2] The main difficulties which arise in putting such schemes into practice are associated with the necessity of cooling a plasma sufficiently rapidly. In many experimental studies an adiabatic expansion of a plasma into vacuum was used for cooling.[3,4] The results of the experiments showed a population inversion to be possible in a freely expanding plasma, although the rapid reduction in its density during the expansion makes it difficult to obtain a high enough gain for lasing action to occur.

2. It is of interest to discuss schemes for rapidly cooling a multiply charged plasma without substantially reducing its density. Such schemes can, for example, be realized by "instantaneously" producing, around a multiply charged plasma in equilibrium, a colder plasma shell having a lower degree of ionization. When the size of the multiply charged plasma is sufficiently small, heat conduction by the electrons in the colder outer region leads to a marked drop in temperature in the center in a time less than the characteristic time for the ions to disperse. The schemes discussed can be set up experimentally using two synchronized laser pulses, focused into a gas target. The first pulse, which produces a hot multiply charged plasma, must be sharply focused and have a duration of $t_1 = 10^{-9}$ sec, enabling an ionization equilibrium to be achieved up to $Z \leqslant 6$-8 (Ref. 5); here, Z is the degree of equilibrium ionization at the center of the plasma. The dispersal of the ions during the time t_1 can be neglected if the transverse dimension of the hot plasma is $a \gtrsim 10^{-3}$ cm. After the end of the first pulse, the gas surrounding the hot plasma is ionized by an ultrashort pulse, of intensity $I_2 = 10^{13}$ W/cm^2 and duration $t_2 = 10^{-12}$ sec, the ionization process in this case being due to multiphoton absorption. At electron densities $n_e \lesssim 10^{18}$ cm^{-3} the electron temperature in the surrounding plasma shell is equal to the optical quantum energy. At higher densities, heating due to the inverse bremsstrahlung effect becomes considerable. Thus, for $n_e = 10^{20}$ cm^{-3} the electron temperature after the end of the pulse can reach 20 eV.

3. As an example, let us consider a mixture consisting of H_2 of density n and a heavy active gas whose concentration n_i is less than the order of n/Z. For a diffusive cooling mechanism ($n \gtrsim 10^{19}$ cm^{-3}), the electron temperature in the center drops, because of the flow of heat into the colder outer shell, according to the law[6]:

$$T = T_0/(1+t/\tau)^m,$$

where $m = 2/7$ or $2/9$, respectively, for cylindrical and plane geometries; T_0 is the initial electron temperature; $\tau = 10^{-20} n_e a^2/T_0^{5/2}$, where τ is in seconds and T_0 is in electron-volts; a is the size of the central region, expressed in centimeters.

4. In order to estimate the inversion and gain we shall assume that the entire recombination flux[6]

$$\dot{n} = 10^{-27} Z^3 n_i n_e^2 / T^{9/2}$$

where T is in electron volts, goes through the upper active level. The population of this level is then $n = \dot{n}/A_{eff}$, where A_{eff} is the rate at which the upper level empties. Assuming that the lower active level empties considerably faster than the upper one,[7] the gain Γ at time τ_i, when the density of the ions is beginning to drop because they are flying apart, can readily be estimated. For cylindrical geometry

$$\Gamma = 10^{-3} \frac{\lambda^2 A Z^3 n_i n_e^{3/4} \tau_i^{1.3}}{A_{eff} \Delta\omega T_0^{1.3} a^{2.5}},$$

where A is the spontaneous transition probability and $\Delta\omega$ is the line width.

The maximum possible density $n_e = n$ is limited by the condition $\tau \ll \tau_i$; for $a \approx 10^{-3}$ cm and $T_0 = 100$ eV this gives $n \ll 10^{22}$ cm^{-3}. As an example, when $n = 5\times 10^{20}$ cm^{-3}, $\tau_i = 10^{-9}$ sec, $n_i = n_e/Z$, $\Delta\omega = 6\times 10^{14}$ cm^{-1}, $A/A_{eff} = 0.1$, the gain, for the $3S$–$2P$ transition in the lithium-like ion of neon ($Z = 7$, $\lambda = 103$ Å), is $\Gamma = 25$ cm^{-1}. The overall gain for a plasma of length $L \approx 0.1$ cm is several units, i.e., a value sufficient for recording directional superradiance.

5. In addition to the hydrogen plasma with a small admixture of another gas, which is considered above and for which the cooling process can be estimated relatively easily, schemes are possible using only a heavy gas alone. If the degree of ionization at the center is substantially greater than that at the periphery, cooling of the multiply charged plasma in the central part can take place more efficiently by dissipation of the energy of the dispersing thermal fluxes in supplementary ionization of the outer region. Schemes in which the gas density is less than the values considered above are also of interest. For a density of $n_i = 10^{18}$ cm^{-3}, electron collisions in the central region may be unimportant, while in the outer region the diffusive heat transport mechanism is the controlling factor as before. At still lower densities ($n_i \lesssim 10^{16}$ cm^{-3}) the plasma is everywhere collisionless. In this case, however, despite the rapid cooling of the central part, the inversion density of the multiply charged ions may nevertheless fail to reach the value needed to obtain a high enough gain for short-wavelength transitions in the several hundred angstrom region. In some schemes when hot and cold plasmas mix, appreciable gains can be obtained even assuming that the ions fly apart. For example if a hot plasma, initially obtained in the form of fairly small bunches by sharply focusing multimode radiation, disperses in a region filled with a cold plasma, it may be cooled in a very short time. The dispersal of the ions at a relatively high density of the hot bunches does not result in any substantial fall in the density. The problem of the flow of a multiply charged plasma flux into a relatively cold plasma, having a low degree of ionization, is of special interest. In this case one can also expect intense three-body recombination accompanied by the creation of an inversion for short-wavelength transitions.

[1]L. I. Gudzenko and L. A. Shelepin, Dokl. Akad. Nauk SSR 160, 1296 (1965) [Sov. Phys. Dokl. 10, 147 (1965)].

[2]L. I. Gudzenko (Goodzenko), S. I. Yakovlenko, and V. V. Evstigneev (Yevstigneyev), Phys. Lett. A 48, 419 (1974)

[3]F. E. Irons and N. J. Peacock, J. Phys. B 7, 1109 (1974).

[4]R. J. Dewhurst, D. Jacoby, G. J. Pert, and S. A. Ramsden, Phys. Rev. Lett. 37, 1265 (1976).

[5]Yu. V. Afanas'ev, É. M. Belenov, O. N. Krokhin, and I. A. Poluéktov, Zh. Eksp. Teor. Fiz. 57, 580 (1969) [Sov. Phys. JETP 30, 318 (1970)].

[6]Ya. B. Zel'dovich and Yu. P. Raizer, Physics of Shock Waves and High-Temperature Hydrodynamic Phenomena, 2 vols., Academic Press, New York (1966, 1977).

[7]B. F. Gordiets, L. I. Gudzenko, and L. A. Shelepin, Zh. Eksp. Teor. Fiz. 55, 942 (1968) [Sov. Phys. JETP 28, 489 (1969)].

Translated by A. N. Dellis

Reprinted with permission from *Optics Communications*, Vol. 28(3), pp. 331-335 (March 1979).

TRANSIENT POPULATION INVERSION AT 18.2 nm IN A LASER PRODUCED CVI PLASMA

M.H. KEY *, C.L.S. LEWIS and M.J. LAMB

Department of Pure and Applied Physics, Queen's University, Belfast, Northern Ireland

Received 12 October 1978
Revised manuscript received 15 December 1978

Population inversion at 18.2 nm in plasma produced by 2J, 150 ps pulse irradiation of solid carbon targets is deduced from time and space resolved CV and CVI resonance emission spectra obtained with a VUV streak camera.

1. Introduction

Transient population inversion between excited states of atoms in a rapidly recombining plasma was first considered theoretically in 1965 [1].The idea was developed as a possible route to X-ray laser action in 1972 [2] with a proposal for laser pulse heating of an aluminium fibre to form a fully ionised plasma which would cool by adiabatic expansion, recombine and develop a transient population inversion between the $n = 3$ and $n = 2$ levels of the hydrogenic ion Al^{12+}.

Examination of the scaling of theoretical gain with atomic number led to the identification of feasible experiments with carbon targets [3,4] and initiated the present work which has shown the development of a transient population inversion by time and space resolved VUV spectroscopy [5]. Similar observations using simply space resolved spectroscopy have also shown evidence for population inversion with laser irradiation of solid [6] and fibre [7] carbon targets.

We report here the first direct recording of the time varying populations of the $n = 3$ and $n = 2$ levels of C^{5+} ions in a laser produced plasma using a novel VUV streak camera/spectrometer system [9] to time and space resolve the resonance line emission lines from the excited states of C^{5+} ions.

* Present address: Laser Division, SRC Rutherford Laboratory, Chilton, Didcot, Oxon

2. Experiment

The experimental apparatus is shown in fig. 1. Grazing incidence diffraction at 5° on a 1 m radius of curvature grating dispersed the VUV spectrum onto the gold photocathode of the streak camera at a glancing angle of 7°. Wavelengths between 2.7 nm and 3.5 nm could be registered in the field of view of the streak camera. In the normal mode of operation rather low spectral resolution ($\Delta\lambda \approx 0.04$ nm) was chosen by setting the vertical slit width at 70 μm. This maximised the intensity in the spectrum while preserving sufficient spectral resolution to separate the C^{5+} and C^{4+} resonance lines. In addition, this slit, in combination with the grating aperture, defined a 300 μm wide observation zone in the plasma, thus providing some spatial resolution normal to the target surface (see fig. 1). A horizontal slit 350 μm wide determined the minimum temporal resolution of 400 ps when using a streak speed of 2 ns/cm.

The absolute sensitivity of the system was determined from the measured [8] first order efficiency of the grating (5% at 3 nm) together with the streak camera sensitivity. The latter was measured by previously described methods [9] to be 300 × greater than would be obtained by substituting VUV film for the camera photocathode; ie with 2.3 × magnification from photocathode to recording film an exposure of 0.9D on 1 cm^2 of 1000 ASA recording film was obtained with 6.2×10^{-4} ergs of soft X rays from a laser produced plasma filtered through 2.5 μm of Al

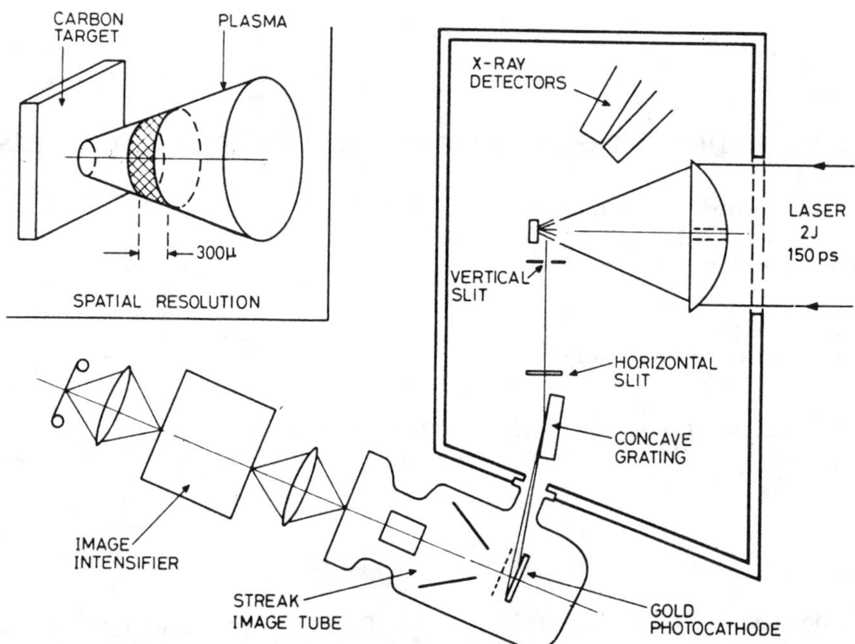

Fig. 1. Experimental apparatus. Below: the laser produced plasma and grazing incidence VUV spectrometer/streak camera system. Above (inset): schematic illustration of the spatial zone from which plasma emission was recorded.

and incident obliquely on the photocathode.

The Nd glass laser gave pulses of 150 ps half width and 2J energy which were focussed by an $f/1$ aspheric lens to either a 30 μm focal spot or, with the addition of a weak cylindrical lens, to a 0.6 mm × 30 μm line focus on solid carbon targets. Filtered X-ray continuum detectors monitored the time and space integrated plasma temperature [10].

Experimental observations of streaked VUV emission spectra were made for both point and line foci and for displacements of the plane of observation in fig. 1 varying from zero up to the limit of detectable C^{5+} line emission at about 2 mm from the target surface. Typical streaked spectra are shown in fig. 2a. In fig. 2a the plane of observation was at the target surface and the spectrum shows C^{5+} lines (Ly_α, Ly_β and Ly_γ), a C^{4+}line ($1s^2$–$1s3p$) and continuum. The continuum decays rapidly in less than the ~400 ps resolution, while the line radiation persists for ~1 ns. In fig. 2b the plane of observation was centred at 550 μm from the target surface and the streak record corresponds to the plasma emissivity at times $t \gtrsim 800$ ps after the laser pulse. A prominent feature of the emission is that it consists initially of the C^{5+} lines only with the C^{4+} line ($1s^2$–$1s3p$) developing about 1 ns later. It is this leading edge of the plasma plume with negligible C^{4+} emission which is shown below to develop population inversion. Table 1 lists line intensity data from fig. 2b and the discussion below concentrates on the data for 800 ps delay in table 1 which show the greatest inversion of population.

3. Discussion

The relative level population n_3^{5+}/n_2^{5+} in C^{5+} can be deduced from the intensity ratio I_α/I_β of the Ly_α and Ly_β lines since

$$\frac{I_\alpha}{I_\beta} = 7.09\,\frac{n_2^{5+}\,g(\tau_\alpha)}{n_3^{5+}\,g(\tau_\beta)}\,, \tag{1}$$

where $g(\tau)$ is the escape factor correction to the line intensity for a line centre opacity τ.

Since Doppler broadening dominates in the expanded plasma at densities of interest here,

$$\tau_\alpha/\tau_\beta = 6.22 \tag{2}$$

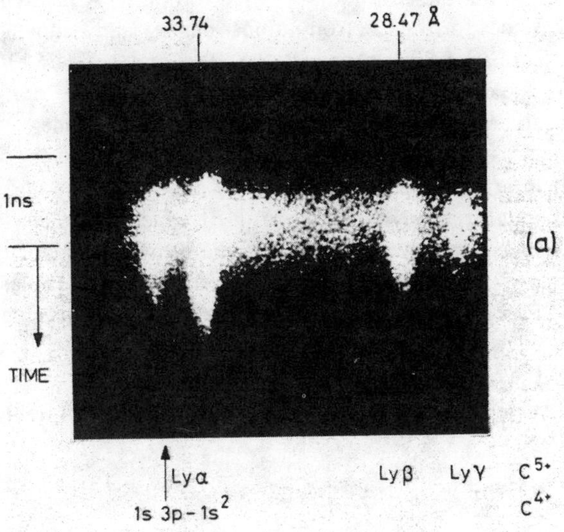

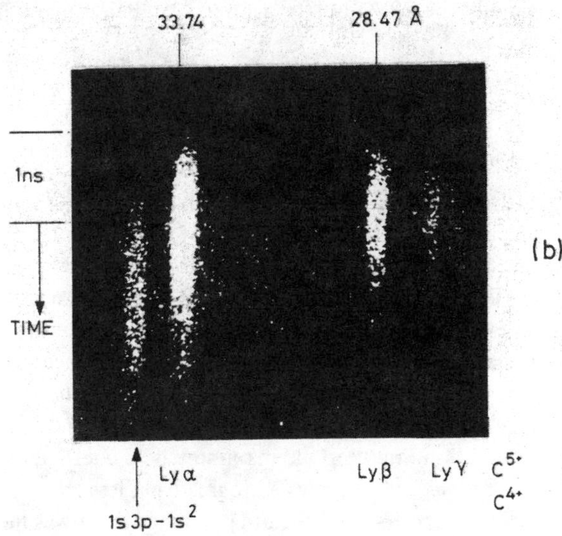

Fig. 2. Streak camera records of the spectrum (a) with the zone of observation centred at the target surface (b) with the zone of observation centred 550 μm from the target surface. Tabulated data from this shot are given in table 1.

and using expressions for $g(\tau)$ in a homogeneous plasma of the form,

$$g(\tau) = \exp(-\tau/1.6) \qquad 0 < \tau < 2.5$$
$$g(\tau) = \frac{1}{\tau(\pi \ln \tau)^{1/2}} \qquad \tau > 2.5 \tag{3}$$

Table 1
Line intensity ratios obtained by densitometer analysis of the streaked spectrum shown in fig. 2b. Laser energy 2.5J. Observed plasma zone centred 550 μm from the target surface. Laser focussed to a circa 50 μm diameter 'point' focus.

Time (ps)	$\frac{I_\alpha}{I_\beta}$	$\frac{I(C^{4+}, 1s^2 - 1s3p)}{I_\beta}$
800	1.4	<0.04
1200	2.4	0.2
2000	3.5	1.7

from ref. [11] and from an analytic fit to numerical calculations [12], it can be seen that the ratio $g(\tau_\alpha)/g(\tau_\beta)$ in eq. (1) has the limits 1.0 for $\tau \to 0$ and ≈ 0.1 for $\tau > 10$. Inversion of population is therefore present for sufficiently low opacity. The smallest experimental ratio I_α/I_β was in the leading edge of the expanding plasma after 800 ps delay and was 1.4 (see table 1). This is in the intermediate region where proof of inversion requires knowledge of opacity.

A determination of opacity was possible with the available experimental data. This involved a rather lengthy argument and procedure [13] but the essential steps were determinations of: (a) The fractional recombination ϵ (where $\epsilon/(1-\epsilon) = n^{5+}/n^{6+}$) from spectral line intensity ratios. (b) The absolute density of excited states n_3^{5+} from the absolute intensity I_β. (c) The electron number density N_e from n_3^{5+} and Saha's Equation, with a model for the plasma expansion normalized to the observed amount of recombination to eliminate T_e in Saha's Equation. (d) The ground state population density n_1^{5+} from N_e and ϵ. (e) The opacity from n_1^{5+} using a motional Doppler broadening model for the expanding plasma, [14].

Some details of the procedure may be simply presented. The opacity τ_α in the plasma with a flow velocity gradient along the line of observation ∇v and assuming Doppler broadening is

$$\tau_\alpha = (2.6 \times 10^{-2} f_{12}\lambda_0)\, n_1^{5+}/\nabla v$$
$$= 3.6 \times 10^{-9}\, n_1^{5+}/\nabla v\,. \tag{4}$$

∇v in fig. 2b was obtained from $\nabla v = 2v/R \sin\theta$. Space-resolved spectra showed the expansion from the point focus to be in cone of angle $2\theta \approx 50°$. The plasma front position R was at 550 μm and the front velocity, v, was 5×10^7 cms^{-1}. The front velocity was estimated from streak records in which the instrumental widths of the spectral lines were observed to increase with time as the plasma moved across to fill the field of view of the grating, ie the effective slit width of the instrument increased. It was also consistent with transformation of the initial thermal energy of the experimental initial temperature to the kinetic energy of spherical self similar expansion.

The density $n_1^{5+} = \epsilon N_e/Z$, where Z is the average charge of ions in the plasma, was obtained from the line intensity ratio $I(C^{4+}, 1s^2-1s3p)/I_\beta$ since,

$$\frac{I(C^{4+}, 1s^2-1s3p)}{I_\beta} = 0.24 \frac{n^{5+} r_0^{4+}(3)}{n^{6+} r_0^{5+}(3)} \exp\left(-\frac{16.9}{T_e \mathrm{eV}}\right) \quad (5)$$

in the limit of negligible opacity and where the $r_0(3)$ terms indicate departure from local thermodynamic equilibrium (LTE) for levels with $n = 3$ [15]. The recombination fraction ϵ was small in the case considered so that $\tau_\beta > \tau(1s^2-1s3p)$ and also $\tau_\beta \ll \tau_\alpha$ from eq. (2). It will be shown below that $\tau_\alpha \approx 1$ so that $\tau_\beta \ll 1$ and eq. (5) is valid in relation to opacity. The values deduced below for N_e and T_e are consistent with $r_0^{5+}(3) \approx 0.5$ [15]. Calculations of rate coefficients indicate that the $n = 3$ level in C^{4+} is 2 to 3 × more collision dominated than in C^{5+} so that the equivalent $r_0^{4+}(3) \geqslant 0.5$. As an upper limit on τ_α the ratio $r_0^{4+}(3)/r_0^{5+}(3)$ was taken as unity. Using the experimental intensity ratio at 800 ps from table 1 in eq. (5) the recombination is seen to be $\epsilon < 0.25$. The temperature dependence is weak at the experimental temperature (see below) of 35 eV. ($\epsilon = 0.25 \pm 0.05$ for $T_e = 35 \pm 15$ eV). From the experiment, with due allowance for the geometry and the space and time resolution, the absolute intensity $I_\beta = n_3^{5+} A_\beta h\nu_\beta$ gave $n_3^{5+} = 3 \times 10^{14}$ cm^{-3}. Saha's Equation is applicable in the form:

$$n_3^{5+} = 5 \times 10^{-22} \frac{N_e^2 r_0(3)}{T_e^{3/2}} (1-\epsilon) \exp\left(\frac{54.4}{T_e}\right), \quad (6)$$

where T_e is in eV. This gives N_e^2 in terms of n_3^{5+} and T_e with $r_0(3) = 0.5$.

A model of the conical geometry expansion of the plasma was used to eliminate T_e. The model assumed a self similar adiabatic expansion with a correction for recombination heating and an approximate analytic solution for recombination to C^{5+} [13]. The 800 ps time for the expansion, the 25% recombination and the value of n_3^{5+} were used to find self-consistent values for the electron number density and temperature after 800 ps, namely 8×10^{18} cm^{-3} and 35 eV. The corresponding initial conditions were 10^{21} cm^{-3} and 600 eV. The time and space averaging diodes measured an initial temperature of 300 eV and the inferred temperature of 600 eV arises from a computer hydrodynamic model [16] which shows the space–time averaging to bias the X-ray measurement of T_e to the higher density, lower temperature ablation front by about a factor 2 relative to the leading edge of the expanding plasma [13]. With above data the opacity τ_α was found from eq. (4) to be $\tau_\alpha \approx 1.2$ so that from eqs. (1), (2) and (3) the inversion ratio was

$$\frac{n_3^{5+}}{g_3} : \frac{n_2^{5+}}{g_2} = 1.4 : 1 \,. \quad (7)$$

Finally the 18.2 nm laser gain (α) can be estimated since

$$\alpha = 1.15 \times 10^{-8} f_{23} \lambda_{23} \times (M/T_e)^{1/2} (g_2 n_3^{5+}/g_3 - n_2^{5+}) \quad (8)$$

for a Doppler broadened line with M in amu., T_e in eV and λ in cm.The above values for T_e, population density n_3^{5+} and inversion ratio yield $\alpha = 0.2 \pm 0.1$ cm^{-1}

The above discussion refers to the particular case of expansion from a point focus > 800 ps after irradiation and ≈ 550 μm from the target surface. This was chosen because it was the earliest stage and therefore the highest plasma density showing inversion of population implying the maximum gain coefficient. At earlier times there was progressively less and eventually no inversion while at later times there was inversion but lower deduced gain due to the falling density. With the line focus the plasma density decreased less rapidly because of the cylindrical expansion geometry. Recombination was therefore stronger and no evidence of population inversion was recorded.

4. Conclusions

These observations on a non-ideal plane target carbon plasma confirm the occurrence of substantial population inversion and gain in accord with the basic concept of a CVI 18.2 nm laser [3,4] and are sufficiently encouraging to suggest a larger scale experiments aimed at direct measurement of gain.

Acknowledgments

Assistance with the experiments from J.G. Lunney and A.K. Roy is gratefully acknowledged. The work was supported by the Science Research Council.

References

[1] L.I. Gudzenko and L.A. Shelepin, Sov. Phys. Dokl. 10 (1965) 147.

[2] S. Slutz, G. Zimmerman, W. Lokke, G. Chapline and L. Wood, Bull. Am. Phys. Soc. 17 (1972) 972.

[3] M.H. Key, Gordon Conf. on Laser interaction with matter, Tilton USA (1973).

[4] G.J. Pert, J. Phys. B 9 (1976) 3301.

[5] M.H. Key, M.J. Lamb, C.L.S. Lewis and J.G. Lunney, Optics Comm. 18 (1976) 156.

[6] F.E. Irons and N.J. Peacock, J. Phys. B 7 (1974) 1109.

[7] R. J. Dewhurst, D. Jacoby, G.J. Pert and S.A. Ramsden, Phys. Rev. Letts. 37 (1976) 1265.

[8] R.J. Speer, J. Spectros. Soc. of Japan 23 (1974) 53.

[9] D.J. Bradley, et al. Optics Comm. 15 (1975) 231.

[10] T.P. Donaldson, R.J. Hutcheon and M.H. Key, J. Phys. B 6 (1973) 1525.

[11] T. Holstein, Phys. Rev. 72 (1947) 1212.

[12] R.P.W. McWhirter, in: Plasma diagnostic techniques, eds. R.M. Huddlestone and S.L. Leonard (Academics Press 1965) ch. 5.

[13] C.L.S. Lewis, PhD. Thesis, Queen's University Belfast, 1978.

[14] V.V. Sobolev, Theoretical astrophysics, ed. V.A. Ambartsumyan (London Pergammon 1958) p. 478.

[15] R.P.W. McWhirter and A.G. Hearn, Proc. Phys. Soc. 82 (1963) 641.

[16] J.P. Christiansen, D.E.T.F. Ashby and K.V. Roberts, Computer Phys. Comm. 7 (1974) 271.

Reprinted with permission from IEEE Journal of Quantum Electronics, Vol. QE-16(6), pp. 603-618 (June 1980). ©1980 IEEE.

Soft X-Ray Population Inversion in Laser Plasmas by Resonant Photoexcitation and Photon-Assisted Processes

V. A. BHAGAVATULA

(Invited Paper)

***Abstract*–In this paper, the results of studies on soft X-ray population inversion by the resonant photoexcitation process are presented. The experimental studies in highly ionized multicomponent plasmas produced by high power glass laser indicate large population inversion densities at wavelengths $\lesssim 130$ Å. Intensity inversions of resonance lines from the $n = 3$ and $n = 4$ levels of Mg^{11+} ions at electron densities as high as 10^{20} cm^{-3} have been observed, indicating that gains of ~ 5-10 cm^{-1} have been achieved. These results and other photon-assisted soft X-ray population inversion schemes in inhomogeneous plasmas are discussed.**

I. Introduction

LASER plasma is a rich source of high density and temperature charged particles. It is also an intense source of line and continuum X-rays. Under laser plasma conditions available with the present infrared laser systems [1], [2], various collisional and radiative processes with very high rates are possible. The high excitation rates possible with these processes can be used to meet the severe pumping requirements [2] for population inversion at X-ray wavelengths. For this reason numerous population inversion schemes on soft X-ray transitions have been proposed with laser produced plasma as the amplifying medium [2]. Some of the processes considered are electron collisional excitation, electron collisional and dielectronic recombinations, photoionization, etc. In addition to X-ray laser schemes with laser plasma as the amplifying medium, various frequency up-conversion techniques in rare gases and schemes involving the interaction of relativistic electron beams with periodic electric and magnetic fields have been suggested for coherent X-ray generation. A general survey of the X-ray laser schemes in laser plasmas and other medias has been done in a number of articles [2] and the reader is referred to these excellent reviews for details. The scope of this paper is limited to a study of soft X-ray population inversion by resonant photoexcitation and related processes in a laser plasma medium. In this paper, details on the theoretical studies, and in particular, the various experiments performed to verify the feasibility of the resonant photoexcitation scheme, are presented.

One of the promising mechanisms for creating significant population inversion in the soft X-ray region with laser plasma

Manuscript received June 14, 1979; revised January 28, 1980.

The author was with the Laboratory for Laser Energetics, University of Rochester, Rochester, NY 14623. He is now with the Department of Applied Physics, Corning Glass Works, Corning, NY 14830.

as an amplifying medium is resonant photoexcitation [3]. In resonant photoexcitation mechanisms, X-ray radiation, energetically coincident with a bound-bound transition of an ion, excites it from its lower state to a suitable upper state. Even though photoexcitation is quite common at infrared and visible wavelengths, its use at soft X-ray wavelengths has not been considered until recently. The reason for that has been the inability to find suitable intense X-ray line sources resonant with proper transitions in highly ionized ions. But using the systematic energy differences of helium-like and especially hydrogen-like ions produced in laser plasmas, it is possible to overcome the above problem [3], [4]. If the problem of a suitable X-ray source is overcome, resonant photoexcitation has many advantages over collisional processes in generating soft X-ray population inversion. Because of the resonance nature of this process, one can, in principle, selectively increase the population rate of an excited state without significant changes in other levels. A second advantage of this mechanism is its large cross section for allowed transitions. At soft X-ray wavelengths of ~100 Å with radiative coefficients of $A_{ki} \sim 10^{11}\ s^{-1}$, the photoexcitation cross section can be as high as 10^{-15}–10^{-16} cm^2. With such large cross sections and radiation densities available in high power glass laser plasmas, photoexcitation rates in the range of 10^{10}–$10^{12}\ s^{-1}$ are within reach.

Some of the resonant photoexcitation approaches we considered are discussed in Section II. Some target combinations that can be used in these schemes together with various parameters of interest like energy mismatch, linewidths, etc., are tabulated in Section II. In Section III, schemes that use intense line radiation to create conditions favorable for soft X-ray population inversion by other processes are presented. The excited state model and its application to a parametric study of the so-called two-step resonant photoexcitation scheme are given in Section IV. In the experimental Section V, a brief description of the laser system used in this study and details on the target design and X-ray diagnostics are given. In Section VI, results and an analysis of the results are presented. Axial profiles of the electron density, temperature, and inversion ratio are deduced from the experimental observations. The effect of opacity in evaluating these profiles from experimental observations is also considered in this section. The determination of the processes leading to the population inversion and finally an estimation of the gain coefficient achieved during this study are made in Section VI. The summary and the conclusions of this study on resonant photoexcitation and photon assisted schemes are given in Section VII.

II. Resonant Photoexcitation Schemes

A. *Principle*

As indicated in Section I, the main drawback of the resonant photoexcitation scheme is to find intense X-ray line sources resonant with a proper bound-bound transition of an ion. We considered two approaches to overcome this drawback. In one, the upper laser level in a suitable ion, referred to as the lasing ion (LI), is preferentially populated by enhanced photoexcitation using resonant radiation from another ion, the source ion (SI). In the other approach, the photoexcitation to the lower level of the LI, and hence its population, is suppressed by absorbing the radiation resonant with it. This is accomplished by a filtering ion (FI) that leaves the photoexcitation to the upper laser level relatively undisturbed. The proposed photoexcitation arrangements are shown in Fig. 1. The arrangement shown in Fig. 1(a) involves a two-step photoexcitation process. In the first step, the ion population is transferred very effectively from the ground state $n = 1$ (n is the principal quantum number) to the first excited state $n = 2$, by the combined electron collisional and radiative excitation processes. It will be shown in later sections that this radiative excitation process and the resonance line radiation at λ_{21} in the LI plays a dominant role in obtaining significant population inversions. The second step involves the preferential population transfer to the upper laser level $n = 4$ by resonant photoexcitation. The photoexcitation is by radiation from a source ion (SI) at λ_1, which is nearly coincident with λ_p, the wavelength of the transition from level $n = 2$ to $n = 4$ in the LI. Due to preferential excitation to level $n = 4$, population inversion can be expected between levels $n = 4$ and $n = 3$ with a transition wavelength λ_L. As a result of collisional mixing between the $n = 4$ level and higher levels, particularly the $n = 5$ level, inversion may also develop between these levels and the $n = 3$ level.

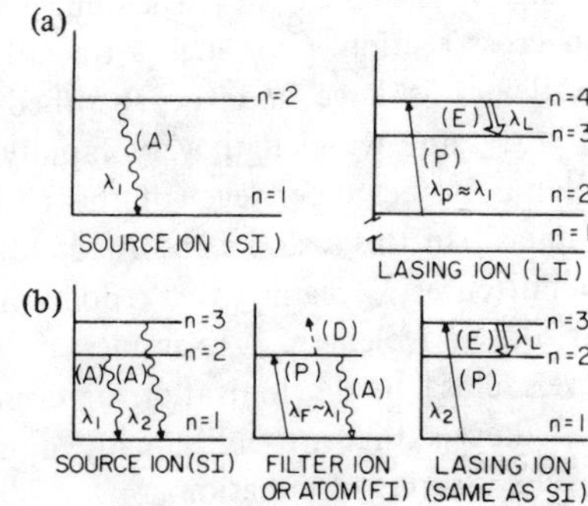

Fig. 1. Schematic diagram of the various resonant photoexcitation schemes: (a) two-step resonant photoexcitation scheme, and (b) filter-ion photoexcitation scheme.

In the above approach, the excitation rate to the upper laser level is enhanced by resonant photoexcitation. Alternately, similar results can be obtained if the excitation rate to the lower laser level is suppressed to well below its normal rate without disturbing the excitation rate to the upper laser level. One possible way to do it is shown in Fig. 1(b). In this approach, the excitation rate to the lower laser level is suppressed by filtering the radiation at λ_1 from the SI by selectively absorbing ions or atoms (FI) with absorbing wavelength at λ_F. The absorbing wavelength λ_F is nearly resonant with λ_1. The radiation by the SI at λ_2 passes through the filtering layer relatively undisturbed. The lasing ions (identical to the source ions) placed to receive the filtered radiation at λ_2 only are preferentially excited to the $n = 3$ level. Effectively, this approach is equivalent to an additional source of intense radiation at λ_2 selectively exciting the LI to the $n = 3$ level. Under suitable conditions, population inversion develops between the $n = 3$ and $n = 2$ levels with the transition wavelength λ_L. For the filtering ion approach to work, the filtering transition should satisfy certain conditions. For high absorption rates, the absorbing transition in the FI should have a high photoabsorption cross section. For such a transition, the radiative decay coefficient is large and the absorbed radiation is reemitted at the same wavelength very rapidly. This situation can be altered if the upper level of the FI has other faster decay channels. In this case the absorbed radiation at λ_1 does not get reemitted at λ_1 leading to a reduction in the radiation density at this wavelength. Examples of such transitions involve levels close to the ionization or even autoionization levels [5]. Levels that are collisionally dominated are also useful for such filtering of radiation.

B. Photoexcitation Ion Combinations

The motivation for proposing resonant photoexcitation schemes, especially the two-step photoexcitation process, came from the observation that the systematic scaling of the hydrogenic energy levels with atomic number can be used to satisfy the resonance conditions. For example, in the first approximation, the hydrogenic energy difference between levels with principal quantum numbers p and q can be expressed as follows:

$$\Delta E_{pq} \simeq 13.6\, Z^2 \left(\frac{1}{p^2} - \frac{1}{q^2}\right) \tag{1}$$

where Z is the atomic number of the hydrogenic ion. In this approximation the energy difference between levels $p = 1$ and $q = 2$ for a hydrogenic source ion Z_s is given by

$$\Delta E_{12}(Z_s) \simeq 13.6 \cdot Z_s^2 \cdot \tfrac{3}{4}. \tag{2}$$

Similarly, the energy difference between levels $p = 2$ and $q = 4$ for a hydrogenic lasing ion Z_L is given by

$$\Delta E_{24}(Z_L) \simeq 13.6 \cdot Z_L^2 \cdot \tfrac{3}{16}. \tag{3}$$

Hence, the required energy resonance between SI and LI transitions is possible when their atomic numbers are related as follows:

$$Z_L = 2Z_s. \tag{4}$$

Thus, the basic idea behind two-step resonant photoexcitation is that the intense $Ly\alpha$ radiation from an SI with atomic number Z can resonantly photoexcite the Balmer β transition of the LI with atomic number $2Z$. In addition to the hydrogenic combinations, other SI and LI combinations are possible especially with helium-like species. For this study, these species are of special interest because of their simple level structure, well-known atomic (ionic) cross sections, and especially their large population densities and spontaneous decay coefficients which allow very high intensity X-ray line emissions under laser plasma conditions.

As mentioned previously, the expression (1) for ΔE_{pq} is approximate. But the deviations from these values are quite small for low and medium Z ion species. Any energy mismatch between SI and LI species can be overcome by the line broadening [6] and line shifting mechanisms present in high density

TABLE I

HYDROGEN-LIKE SOURCE IONS (SI) [A)] AND THE CORRESPONDING HYDROGEN-LIKE AND HELIUM-LIKE LASING IONS (LI) FOR THE TWO-STEP RESONANT PHOTOEXCITATION. HELIUM-LIKE SI AND THE CORRESPONDING HYDROGEN-LIKE AND HELIUM-LIKE LI [B)]

A)

H-LIKE SI		H-LIKE LI					HE-LIKE LI	
Z_S	$\lambda_1(Ly\alpha)$	Z_L	λ_{24} (Balmer β)	λ_L	ΔE_M	$\Delta E_D + \Delta E_S$	Z_L	λ_{24}
4	75.928	8	75.890	293	0.07	0.87	9	75.512
5	48.587	10	48.55	188	0.16	0.96	11	----
6	33.736	12	33.70	130	0.3	1.1	13	33.94

B)

HE-LIKE SI		HE-LIKE LI					H-LIKE LI	
Z_S	W $(1s^2\text{-}1s2p)$	Z_L	λ_{24}	λ_L	ΔE_M	$\Delta E_D + \Delta E_S$	Z_L	λ_{24} (Balmer β)
4	100.255	8	100.253	385	2×10^{-3}	0.87	7	99.13
5	60.314	10	60.447	234	0.4	0.96	9	59.95
6	40.268	12	40.42	156	1.0	1.1	11	40.11

TABLE II

LASING ION (LI) (SAME AS SOURCE ION IN THIS SCHEME) AND FILTERING ION (FI) COMBINATIONS FOR FILTERING ION PHOTOEXCITATION SCHEME

LI	λ_1	FI	λ_F	λ_L	ΔE_M
BIV(2p-1s)	60.314	NaIX(4s-2p)	60.375	416	-0.17
BV (2 - 1)	48.587	NaIX(5p-2s)	48.553	262	0.14

and high temperature plasmas. The fine structure splitting present in hydrogenic species can also help in overcoming this problem.

Hydrogenic and helium-like SI and LI combinations suitable for the two-step photoexcitation scheme shown in Fig. 1(a) are given in Table I. In Table I-A), the $Ly\alpha$ radiation of the hydrogenic species is the source radiation. Hydrogen-like and helium-like ions with close ΔE_{24} energy resonances with the $Ly\alpha$ source radiation are listed. In Table I-B), the radiation from the transition $(1s^2\ {}^1S - 1s2p\ {}^1P)$ is the source radiation and the suitable lasing ions are listed. In Table II, some of the possible combinations for the filter ion scheme shown in Fig. 1(b) are presented. The wavelengths [7], [8] λ_1 of the source radiation, λ_p of the $(2 \rightarrow 4)$ transition in the LI, λ_F of the FI, and finally λ_L of the expected laser transition are all given in angstroms. In Table I, the resonance mismatch ΔE_M eV is the difference between source radiation energy and the $(2 \rightarrow 4)$ transition energy. In Table II, it is the difference between the energy radiation to be filtered and the filtering transition energy. Some typical values of the linewidth due to broadening mechanisms in laser plasmas are also given. The Doppler width [6] ΔE_D eV and the Stark width [6] ΔE_s eV are calculated at an ion temperature of 400 eV and ion density of 10^{20} cm^{-3}, respectively. It should also be pointed out that the Doppler shift due to streaming velocities of the ions can also help in overcoming the resonance mismatch. The total linewidth should be greater than the resonance mismatch for effective resonant photoexcitation. From the values tabulated in Tables I and II, we notice that the linewidths due to all the broadening mechanisms more than compensate for the resonance mismatch in most cases. Using this technique, coherent radiation at a number of wavelengths close to ~100 Å is possible provided the required plasma conditions can be generated. Some of the conditions that come to mind with regard to photoexcitation schemes are the following:

1) large population in the photoabsorbing level,
2) large photoabsorbing cross sections,
3) large source radiation density,
4) high degree of resonance between the source radiation and photoabsorbing transition,
5) close temporal and spatial matching of the SI and LI species (as well as the FI in the case of filtering ion scheme) in the plasma environment.

In principle, it is possible to satisfy all these conditions in a high intensity laser produced plasma using the target combinations indicated above. But in a plasma with high electron densities, various collisional processes are present and they may adversely affect the photoexcitation scheme even when all the above conditions are met. A detailed study of these effects has to be done using an excited state model. The details of this model are presented later on.

C. Comparison of Single- and Two-Step Photoexcitation

In the two-step photoexcitation scheme, the ion population has to be excited to the $p = 2$ level before it can be resonantly pumped by source radiation to the upper laser level. In the following, a simple estimate is made to show that in hydrogen-like and helium-like species such a two-step process can be quite effective as compared to direct photoexcitation to the $p = 4$ level. In this model where only photoexcitation and radiative decay are considered, the ion population in the $p = 4$ level by the two-step process can be expressed as follows:

$$\left.\frac{n_4}{n_1}\right|_{T\cdot S} \sim \frac{B_{12}B_{24}}{A_{21}\left(\sum_{i<4} A_{4i}\right)} P_\nu(2,4)P_\nu(1,2) \tag{5}$$

where A_{ki} and B_{ik} are the Einstein coefficients between levels i and k. Similarly, for direct photoexcitation, the ion population in the $p = 4$ level is given by the following expression:

$$\left.\frac{n_4}{n_1}\right|_{D} \sim \frac{B_{14}P_\nu(1,4)}{\sum_{i<4} A_{4i}}. \tag{6}$$

The ratio of the populations in the $p = 4$ level by the two-step and direct photoexcitation is given by the expression

$$\frac{n_4|_{T\cdot S}}{n_4|_D} \sim \frac{B_{12}B_{24}}{B_{14}A_{21}} \frac{P_\nu(2,4)P_\nu(1,2)}{P_\nu(1,4)}. \tag{7}$$

For example, substituting values corresponding to the hydrogenic magnesium case we get the following ratio:

$$\frac{n_4|_{T\cdot S}}{n_4|_D} \sim 2 \times 10^7 \, P_\nu(2,4). \tag{8}$$

Thus, for source radiation $P_\nu(2,4) > 10^{-7}$ erg/cm^3 · Hz, two-step photoexcitation is actually better than direct photoexcitation. This value of $P_\nu(2,4)$ is an easily achievable value in high intensity laser produced plasmas. As a matter of fact, radiation densities in the range of 10^{-6}–10^{-5} erg/cm^3 · Hz should be possible with focused laser intensities ~10^{14} W/cm^2.

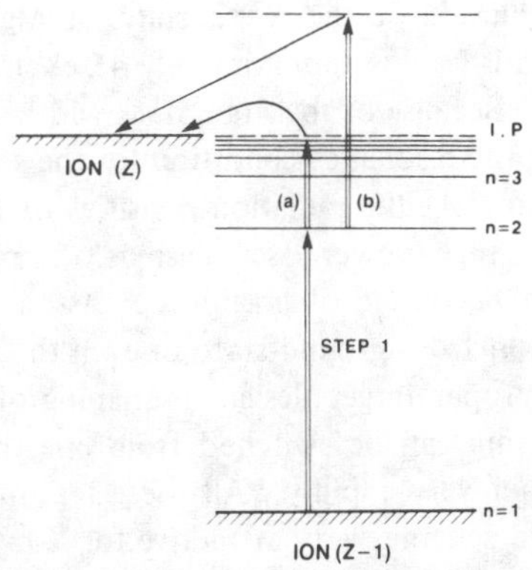

Fig. 2. Schematic diagram of photon assisted ionization process: (a) multistep photoexcitation is followed by collisional ionization, and (b) multistep excitation to levels in the continuum is followed by spontaneous (auto) ionization.

III. Photon Assisted Schemes

In addition to resonant photoexcitation schemes considered so far, intense X-ray line radiation generated in inhomogeneous laser plasmas may be used to create conditions favorable for soft X-ray population inversion by other mechanisms. For example, conditions favorable for soft X-ray population inversion by three-body recombination may be created using intense X-ray line radiation of a suitable wavelength. For the recombination scheme to work, one of the requirements is that a highly ionized plasma be generated at low enough electron temperatures and sufficiently high electron densities. These conditions can be obtained only in plasmas departing very severely from equilibrium ionization conditions. With intense X-ray line radiation, such highly nonequilibrant ionization conditions can be created in medium atomic number plasmas.

This technique involves a multistep photoexcitation of ionic species created in laser plasmas. By multistep photoexcitation, the ionic species can be excited to highly excited states close to the ionization potential or even possibly to the autoionization levels. The multistep photoexcitation is followed by a very rapid ionization. The principle of the photoassisted ionization scheme is shown schematically in Fig. 2. In step 1, the ion is excited to level $n = 2$ from the ground state as in the case of the two-step resonant photoexcitation scheme described previously. From the $n = 2$ level, the ion is excited to a level very close to the ionization potential or even to an autoionization level. From this level it can ionize spontaneously or by a low energy electron. Since only low electrons are required for the final ionization step, a highly ionized plasma can be generated even with low electron temperatures. Such conditions are quite favorable for soft X-ray population inversion by recombination.

Such a photon-assisted process may be possible with helium-like magnesium ions and intense $Ly\alpha$ radiation from carbon. For example, the $Ly\alpha$ radiation of carbon can be used to excite the sublevels of the $n = 2$ state of Mg^{10+} ion to the $n \sim 6$ level. This level is approximately 45 eV from the ionization potential. Because of the large Stark widths of such highly excited states, the resonance condition for the source radiation is not so severe. At the radiation densities of $Ly\alpha$ of carbon expected from high power laser plasmas, the photon assisted ionization can be orders of magnitude greater than the collisional ionization from ground state or even the $n = 2$ level. In addition, by proper target design or shaping of the radiation pulse, the plasma can be switched from one thermodynamic state to another very rapidly. All these features make X-ray photon-assisted schemes very attractive for X-ray laser studies.

IV. Modeling

A. *Excited State Model*

The population densities in the excited levels of an ion species can be estimated approximately from simple plasma models like Corona, Local Thermodynamic Equilibrium (LTE), etc. But these models are incapable of accurately modeling the population inversion schemes where excited state populations deviate greatly from equilibrium values. In this section a brief description of the excited state model developed to study the resonance photoexcitation scheme is given. This model is similar to the collisional radiative model of Bates [9], [10] except that here photoexcitation and induced transitions are included. This model is developed for hydrogenic species. The processes considered are the collisional excitation and deexcitation, spontaneous radiative decay, photoabsorption and induced emission, collisional ionization and three-body recombination, and finally radiative recombination among the various levels up to the level with principal quantum number $p = 5$. The processes like photoionization, dielectronic recombination which have marginal effects on levels of interest for the resonant photoexcitation scheme are neglected. In addition, the following assumptions are made in obtaining the excited level code.

1) Because of the near degeneracy of the sublevels of the hydrogenic ions, they are assumed to be statistically populated.

2) The population of the lower levels by cascading from levels with $p \geqslant 6$ (p = the principal quantum number) is neglected. As a result of their small populations, this assumption is justified.

3) The time scale for reaching steady state is orders of magnitude larger for the ground state compared to the excited states [9], [10]. Hence, the excited levels reach steady-state values long before the ground-state ion populations have a chance to change. This justifies the evaluation of the excited level populations in steady state.

In the case of hydrogenic ions, the energy levels and the atomic coefficients have a simple dependence on the atomic number Z of the ion. As a result, the atomic cross sections of any hydrogenic ion can be expressed in terms of the atomic hydrogen values, provided the electron temperature T_e, the electron density n_e, and the radiation density p_ν are expressed as reduced variables. The advantage in expressing the equations in terms of reduced variables is that from one set of solutions, the results for any hydrogenic ion having the same set of reduced variables can be obtained. The relations between the reduced values and the actual quantities for a hydrogenic ion with atomic number Z are as follows:

η, the reduced density $= n_e/Z^7$

θ, the reduced electron temperature $= T_e/Z^2$

P_ν, the reduced radiation density $= p_\nu/Z^6$.

With the assumptions and the transformation of the variables listed above, the steady-state excited level equations are

$$\begin{aligned} n_1[\eta c(1, p) + B(1, p)P_\nu(1, p)] &= -n_p\left[\eta\left(c(p, c) + \sum_{q \neq p} c(p, q)\right) + \sum_{q \neq p} B(p, q)P_\nu(p, q)\right. \\ &\left. + \sum_{q<p} A(p, q)\right] + \eta \sum_{q \neq p} n_q c(q, p) + \sum_{q>p} n_q A(q, p) \\ &+ \sum_{q \neq p} n_q B(q, p)P_\nu(q, p) + \eta n_E^{\text{red}}(p)c(p, c) \\ &+ \frac{\eta^2}{x_{\text{red}}}\beta(p) - \eta n_p c(p, 6)\delta_{5p} \end{aligned}$$

$$p, q = 2, 3, 4, \text{ and } 5 \tag{9}$$

where δ is the Kronecker delta; p and q are the principal quantum numbers of the excited levels with population densities n_p and n_q; $c(p, c)$, $c(p, q)$, $A(p, q)$, and $B(p, q)$ are the collisional ionization, collisional excitation (or deexcitation), and Einstein radiative coefficients from the corresponding levels for hydrogen, respectively; $x = n_e/n_{c \cdot s}$ and $n_E(p)$ is the Saha equilibrium population in level p. The Saha equilibrium population in level p is given by [9]

$$n_E(p) = \frac{n_e^2}{X} p^2 \left(\frac{h^2}{2mKT_e}\right)^{3/2} \exp\left(E(p, c)/KT_e\right). \tag{10}$$

To solve the above set of equations for the excited level populations, the values of θ, η, n_1, and finally the local radiation densities P_ν's have to be known. These quantities may be obtained self-consistently (for modeling purposes) for a given laser plasma experiment and target geometry, from the coupled hydrodynamic, ionization, and radiation transport codes. This is a very complex computational problem and at best only a theoretical estimate of the local radiation density and hence the usefulness of this complex exercise is at best limited. Instead, an easier approach where the results can be applied more directly to experimental observations is followed in this section. In this approach, a parametric study of the two-step resonant photoexcitation scheme is done, i.e., the performance of the inversion scheme for various electron and radiation temperatures and densities is evaluated. In later sections, the experimental profiles of the electron density and temperature, and the intensity and $T_{\text{radiation}}$, the black-body radiation temperature of the resonance lines are presented. These profiles allow the estimation of the local parameters; hence, the parametric study is more relevant than any complex computer simulation to determine the radiation coupling. This parametric study also helps in understanding the scaling properties of the inversion scheme.

B. Parametric Study

In this section, the results of the parametric study of the two-step resonant photoexcitation scheme are presented. In this two-step process, the parameters of interest are the electron density η, electron temperature θ, and radiation densities $P_\nu(1,2)$ and $P_\nu(2,4)$. The remaining radiation densities like $P_\nu(1,3)$ may be scaled from $P_\nu(1,2)$ by the Corona model. The range of values assumed for the reduced parameters are

$$
\begin{aligned}
&2.8 \cdot 10^4 \leqslant \theta \leqslant 5.2 \cdot 10^4 \text{ K} \\
&2.5 \cdot 10^{11} \leqslant \eta \leqslant 2.5 \cdot 10^{14} \text{ cm}^{-3} \\
&3 \cdot 10^{-14} \leqslant P_\nu(1,2) \leqslant 3 \cdot 10^{-11} \text{ erg/cm}^3 \cdot \text{Hz} \\
&3 \cdot 10^{-14} \leqslant P_\nu(2,4) \leqslant 3 \cdot 10^{-11} \text{ erg/cm}^3 \cdot \text{Hz}. \qquad (11)
\end{aligned}
$$

This range of parameter values includes the values expected in high temperature Mg and Al plasmas generated by an Nd^{3+}-glass laser system used in this study. For the range of values assumed above, the contribution of the recombination process to the levels of interest is marginal. In that case, the excited state populations can be expressed as fractions of ground-state density and hence the ionization state need not be known *a priori*. Some of the results of the parametric study on threshold radiation density for various electron densities were presented previously [3]. The variation of the fractional inversion density $\Delta n/n_1$ and the photoexcitation ratio $n_4 g_2/n_2 g_4$, etc., for various densities of source radiation $P_\nu(2,4)$ and electron density η were also presented. Apart from summarizing the previous results, additional results on optimization and scaling studies are presented here. Also curves that would be useful in interpreting the experimental results and in deriving the radiation densities, inversion densities, and gain coefficients present during the experiments are given. The previous study indicated the sensitivity of the threshold source radiation density with electron density. The study indicated that for sufficiently high radiation densities, a significant portion of the ground-state population can be excited to the upper laser level to get high inversion densities. The results applied to the case of a (C, Mg) combination [3] indicated that radiation densities in the range of 10^{-6}-10^{-5} erg/cm^3 · Hz are sufficient to lead to gain coefficients in the range of 10-100 cm^{-1} at $\lambda_{43} \sim 130$ Å. A number of detailed estimates of the conversion efficiencies of 1.06-μm laser radiation to X-rays in laser plasmas have been done [11], [12]. These studies indicated that large conversion efficiencies in the range of 5-30 percent of the absorbed energy are possible. The conversion efficiencies depend on the target material, pulsewidth, the focused intensity, etc. For medium atomic number elements ($Z \sim 10$) and at laser intensities $\sim 10^{14}$ W/cm^2, a large part of the X-rays generated are in the form of resonance line radiation of the hydrogenic and helium-like ions [11]. With such conversion efficiencies, the radiation densities in the range of 10^{-6}-10^{-5} erg/cm^3 · Hz can be obtained with laser systems delivering ~10 J of energy in 200-300 ps pulses. Later on some estimates of the experimental radiation densities are made from the film record of spectral line densities.

The study on fractional inversion density $\Delta n/n_1$ also indicated the importance of the radiation density $P_\nu(1,2)$ in obtaining large inversion densities with a two-step resonant photoexcitation scheme. But an increase in $P_\nu(1,2)$, which effectively excites the population to the photoabsorbing level $n = 2$, also increases the radiation density $P_\nu(1,3)$. The radiation at λ_{13} pumps the ions to the lower laser level and hence any increase in $P_\nu(1,3)$ affects the population inversion adversely. These competing effects can be optimized and the results of such optimization studies are indicated in Figs. 3 and 4. In Fig. 3 the normalized inversion density Δn (normalized) is plotted as a function of electron density with radiation densities $P_\nu(2,4)$ and $P_\nu(1,2)$ as parameters. The maxima of these curves give the optimum electron densities for a given set of radiation densities. Such optimization, done with respect to radiation density $P_\nu(1,2)$, is given in Fig. 4. The curves in Fig. 3 also indicate scaling potential of the two-step resonant photoexcitation with respect to electron density, etc. These curves indicate that higher population inversion is obtained with an increase in electron density until an optimum density is reached. Beyond that density any increase can be obtained only by increasing the radiation densities.

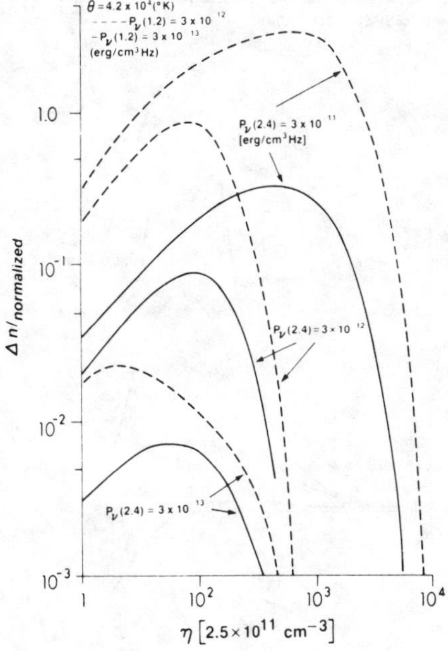

Fig. 3. Optimization of two-step resonant photoexcitation scheme with respect to reduced electron density η, with radiation densities $P_\nu(1,2)$ and $P_\nu(2,4)$ as parameters.

In Fig. 5, the reduced inversion ratio $(n_4 g_3/n_3 g_4)$ is plotted as a function of source radiation, with the reduced electron density η and radiation density $P_\nu(1,2)$ as parameters. These curves indicate that the inversion ratio scales rapidly with the source radiation density, at least for lower electron density range, and reaches saturation only at very high values. These curves also indicate that large reduced inversion ratios are possible and that under favorable conditions these ratios can be large enough to lead to even intensity inversion in the resonance transitions from the corresponding levels. Such intensity inversion is dramatically different from normal resonance line ratios and hence can be used as a population inversion diagnostic. Details on the application of Figs. 4 and 5 to determine the gain coefficient are given in later sections.

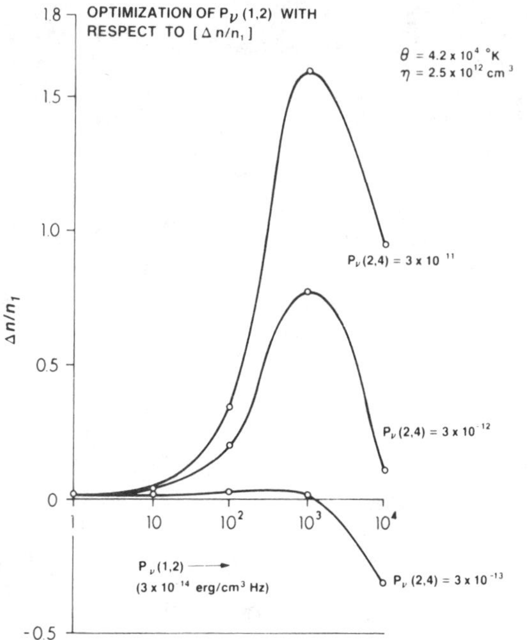

Fig. 4. Optimization of radiation density $P_\nu(1, 2)$ with respect to fractional inversion density $\Delta n/n_1$ with source radiation density $P_\nu(2, 4)$ as a parameter.

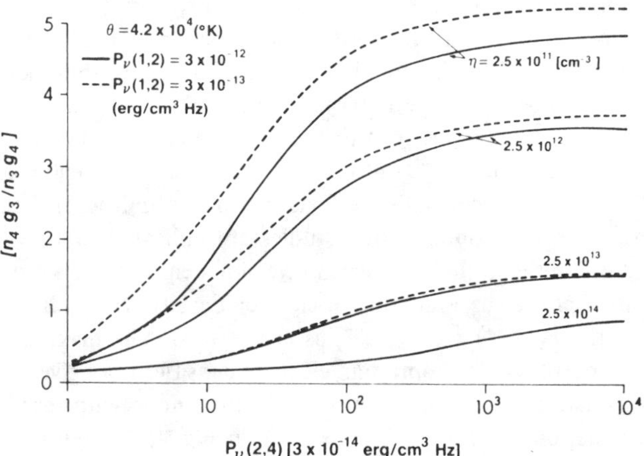

Fig. 5. Variation of inversion ratio $(n_4 g_3/n_3 g_4)$ as a function of source radiation $P_\nu(2, 4)$ with reduced electron density η and radiation density $P_\nu(1, 2)$ as parameters.

V. Experiment

A. Experimental System

The experiments have been conducted on a high power Nd^{3+}-glass laser system at a laser wavelength of 1.06 μm. The laser system consisted of a passively mode-locked *Q*-switched oscillator, a pulse switch-out network, and a chain of five rod amplifiers. A single switched-out pulse with a ~200 ps pulsewidth was amplified by the amplifier chain. By positioning a beam splitter, it was possible to generate a prepulse with 8 percent of the total energy 0.8-1.0 ns ahead of the pulse when necessary. The performance of the laser system was diagnosed by means of photodiodes placed to look at the energy reflected at the front surface of each amplifier stage. The total energy passing through the lens and entering the target chamber is deduced by calorimetric measurements. Typical energies obtained by the laser system were in the range of 5-10 J. The output was focused by an *f*/3.5 lens to the target. Focal spot sizes of approximately 100-200 μm were estimated. With the laser and focusing parameters indicated above, the nominal focused intensity obtained during these experiments was in the range of $\sim 10^{14}$ W/cm^2.

B. Target Selection

A large amount of computer simulation [13] and experimental data [14] is available to estimate the electron temperatures available for the system parameters quoted above. It can be assumed that under the operating conditions of the laser system described above, peak electron temperatures up to 1 keV at electron densities up to 10^{21} cm^{-3}, the critical density of the 1.06-μm laser, are easily obtainable. These conditions are quite adequate to obtain highly ionized ions of medium atomic number $(Z \sim 10)$ targets. In choosing the target combinations to experimentally verify the resonant photoexcitation scheme, the following factors have to be considered: 1) electron density and temperature, 2) radiation density, 3) energy resonance match, and 4) convenient availability of diagnostic instrumentation in the required spectral range. With an Nd^{3+}-glass laser system, the electron densities of interest for inversion schemes are in the range of 10^{19}–10^{21} cm^{-3}. As indicated in the section on parametric study, the electron density and radiation density requirements are related and they in turn depend on the atomic number of the lasing ion. The focused laser intensity roughly determines the electron temperatures possible in the plasma. The electron temperature determines whether a sufficiently high density of hydrogenic and helium-like ions can be generated. Considering these various factors, the target combination of (C, Mg) seems optimum. In this target combination, there are two possibilities for resonant photoexcitation. In one, the *Lyα* radiation from hydrogenic carbon can be used to photoexcite the transitions in hydrogenic magnesium. In the second variation, C^{4+} and Mg^{10+} are the source and lasing ions, respectively. From Table I, we notice that the nominal resonance match for the hydrogenic combination is much better than the match for the helium-like combination. For this reason, the photoexcitation effect is expected to be more pronounced for the hydrogenic case.

The next step is to determine how the (C, Mg) combination can be arranged to obtain the maximum observable photoexcitation effect and also population inversion. The results of the parametric study applied to the (C, Mg) combination indicated that the most effective photoexcitation takes place at electron densities of $\sim 10^{20}$ cm^{-3}. This conclusion follows the reasonable assumption that radiation densities around 10^{-6} erg/cm$^3 \cdot$ Hz are possible with the plasma parameters expected. At these electron and radiation densities, a large fraction of the ion population in the level $p = 2$ is transferred to the upper laser level $p = 4$ without significantly affecting the population in level $p = 3$. Hence, in the presence of resonant radiation of the magnitude $\sim 10^{-6}$ erg/cm$^3 \cdot$ Hz, the inversion ratios $(n_4 g_3/n_3 g_4)$ of Mg^{11+} ions differ significantly from its value in the absence of photoexcitation. Such large inversion ratios lead to anomolous intensities, possibly even "intensity inver-

TARGET CONFIGURATION	PURPOSE OF EXPERIMENT
a) Mg LASER	TO OBTAIN NORMALISED SPECTRA.
b) C Mg LASER	TO TEST RESONANT PHOTO-EXCITATION SCHEME. (NOTE: ENHANCED COOLING MAY HAVE IMPORTANT EFFECT IN THIS TARGET.)
c) Mg Al LASER	TO TEST RECOMBINATION SCHEME BY ENHANCED COOLING.
d) C Mg LASER	TO TEST RESONANT PHOTO-EXCITATION SCHEME. (NOTE: ENHANCED COOLING EFFECT IS NEGLIGIBLE IN THIS TARGET.)
e) Al Mg LASER	TO DOUBLE CHECK THAT ENHANCED COOLING IS NEGLIGIBLE IN THIS TARGET.

Fig. 6. Summary of targets for various experiments conducted in this study and the objective of each experiment.

sion" of the resonance lines from levels $p = 3$ and $p = 4$. Such intensity inversion is a nice diagnostic for verifying the photoexcitation scheme. For these reasons it would be advantageous to generate the source radiation close to the region of the lasing plasma with electron density $n_e \sim 10^{20}$ cm^{-3}. Computer simulations [15] indicate that for a glass laser system with the performance characteristics mentioned in Section V-A, electron densities $\lesssim 10^{20}$ cm^{-3} are expected at axial distances $\gtrsim 100$ μm from the original target surface. The computer simulations of flat targets also indicate that the maximum intensity of resonance lines of helium-like and hydrogen-like ions are generated very close to the original target surface with electron densities $\sim 10^{21}$ cm^{-3}. Thus, we notice a mismatch in the spatial locations of the region of intense source radiation and the region of lasing plasma where this radiation would be most effective. Such a mismatch may be avoided by choosing a target configuration shown in Fig. 6(b) and (c). In this configuration, referred to as "stepped target," the carbon electrode is axially displaced by approximately 100 μm from the magnesium surface. Hence, the moderately hot, high density plasma from the carbon target (where the most intense source radiation is emitted) lies next to the region of the lasing plasma with $n_e \sim 10^{20}$ cm^{-3} and substantial amounts of helium-like and hydrogen-like ions. This target configuration is expected to satisfy the essential requirements that the intense source radiation and substantial lasing ion population exist simultaneously and spatially as close as possible in spite of the differing atomic numbers of carbon and magnesium.

A possible source of problem for the stepped targets could be the geometry induced effects. The experiments on the (C, Mg) stepped targets gave some unexpected results which indicate that geometry induced effects could indeed be important. In order to clarify some of these results and also to verify the resonant photoexcitation scheme in greater detail, additional experiments were conducted. A summary of the target materials and configurations and the objectives of each of

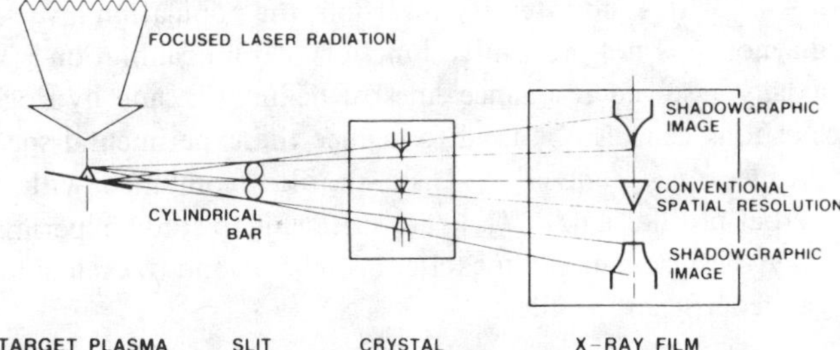

Fig. 7. Schematic diagram of the experimental setup with a fold out view of the spatially resolving spectrometer.

these experiments are shown in Fig. 6. The different target configurations can be classified basically into two types: 1) flat or segmented flat targets; and 2) stepped targets. The results and analysis of these experiments are presented later on.

C. Diagnostics–Spatially Resolved X-Ray Spectroscopy

In these experiments with path lengths of 100-200 μm and population inversion at $n_e \sim 10^{20}$ cm^{-3}, we expect the gain-length product "αl" to be less than 1. Under these circumstances, the comparison of the resonance line intensities is probably the best suited diagnostic. The resonance lines of helium-like and hydrogen-like ions of Mg and Al are in the spectral range 6-10 Å [7], [8]. There are a variety of crystals useful in this range whose reflection efficiencies have been studied [16]. A thallium acid phthalate (TAP) crystal with a $2d$ spacing of 25.9 Å is used to record the resonance lines. Beryllium foil of 1 ml thickness has good transmission characteristics for the wavelengths of interest [17] and was used as the window. Two types of films have been used to record the X-ray lines during this study: 1) Kodak No-Screen; and 2) Kodak RAR-2491. No-Screen X-ray film is more sensitive but the resolution and the signal-to-noise ratio of RAR-2491 has been shown to be superior [18].

The schematic diagram of the spatially resolving spectrometer is given in Fig. 7. This figure indicates how the spectral resolution and spatial resolution in the axial direction are possible. With this configuration, a magnified image with resolution in the axial direction is recorded. The magnification used in these experiments varied from 6 to 8. The possible spatial resolution is determined by the experimental conditions like the energy emitted in the X-ray line, collection efficiency of the instrument, the sensitivity of the recording medium, the magnification, etc. For this set of experiments, a long slit with a width of ~ 30 μm at a distance of 2-3 cm from the plasma source was used. For these values of slit dimensions and X-ray wavelengths involved in this experiment, the geometrical approximation is valid and the axial resolution available was between 37-50 μm. With such spatial resolution, the resonance line intensities emitted from the region of the lasing plasma with $n_e \sim 10^{20}$ cm^{-3} can be clearly separated from the X-ray emissions from regions near the critical surface. In the region of the lasing plasma with $n_e \sim 10^{20}$ cm^{-3}, inversion ratios $[n_4 g_3 / n_3 g_4] \gtrsim 2$ are expected when photoexcitation is present. With such inversion ratios, resonance line intensity ratios $[I_{41}/I_{31}] \gtrsim 1$ are possible, i.e., we can expect to see intensity inversion in the resonance lines from levels $n = 3$ and

$n = 4$. With such intensity inversion, the population inversion diagnostic is not a sensitive function of film calibration. The axially resolved resonance lines of helium-like and hydrogen-like ions can also be used to deduce the experimental spatial profiles of n_e and T_e. These profiles, combined with the spatial profile of $[I_{41}/I_{31}]$, are sufficient to study experimentally the resonant photoexcitation scheme and to evaluate the gain coefficient profiles.

VI. Results and Analysis

A. Spectral Data

The data in these experiments consisted of spatially resolved X-ray spectra of the helium-like and hydrogen-like ions of Al and Mg. The analysis of the data involved the determination of average plasma conditions present during the experiments. The results are averaged over time and also along the radial direction. The spatial resolution was available only in the axial direction. In particular, emphasis was placed in detecting any population inversion present and identifying the processes leading to inversion. In determining population inversion by the resonance line intensity ratios, one of the important factors to be considered is the opacity effect on the line ratios. In addition, the analysis of the data involved the evaluation of gain coefficient profiles present during the experiment.

Before presenting the data it is essential to mention that the targets can be classified into two types depending on their configurations: 1) flat (or segmented-flat) targets; or 2) stepped targets. The two categories of targets may have different hydrodynamic characteristics because of the different geometries. The various experiments indicated in Fig. 6 were conducted to distinguish the geometry induced effects from the photoexcitation induced effects.

The microdensitometer traces of the spatially resolved spectra for the different set of experiments are given in Figs. 8-12. In each spectra, the traces are taken at the various axial distances indicated. The different resonance lines of hydrogen-like and helium-like ions are identified. The optical density information for the different resonance lines in Figs. 8-12 can be converted to their exposure values from the film calibration curves. One such normalized profile is given in Fig. 13 for the $Ly\alpha$ line of the magnesium flat target. Also, the ratio of the intensities of resonance lines ($1s - 2p$) and ($1s^2 - 1s2p$) of hydrogen-like and helium-like ions, respectively, are given for flat and stepped targets. A comparison of the ratios for the two cases indicates that the presence of the second electrode in stepped targets noticeably affects the hydrogen-like resonance line. This is one of the indications of the geometry induced effects on the hydrodynamic expansion characteristics.

In the following sections, further analysis has been done using the intensity profiles of the resonance lines to obtain axial profiles of quantities like radiation density, n_e, T_e, inversion ratio, etc.

B. Plasma Dimension

One of the plasma parameters of interest in determining the opacity effects is the plasma length along the line of sight of the spectrometer. For the spectrometer configuration in this

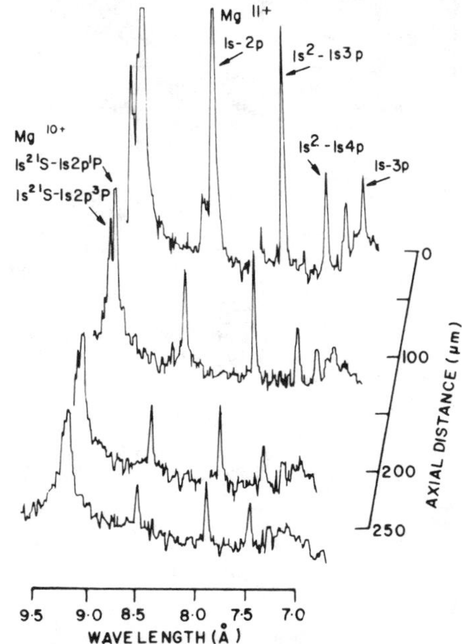

Fig. 8. Spectra from Mg flat target (target type (a) in Fig. 6) at various axial distances from the original target surface.

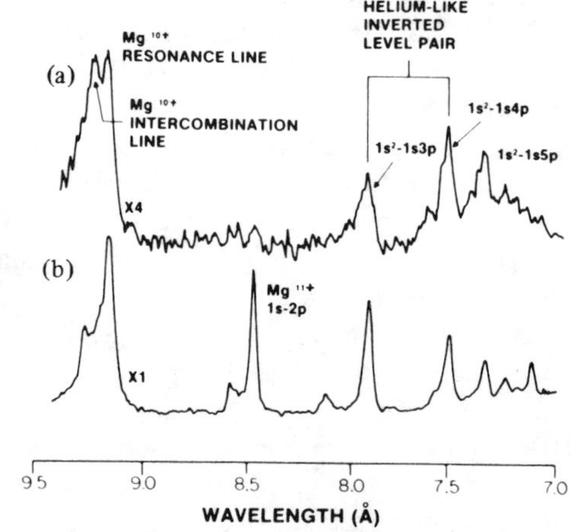

Fig. 9. Spectra from (C, Mg) stepped target (target type (b) in Fig. 6) at various axial distances.

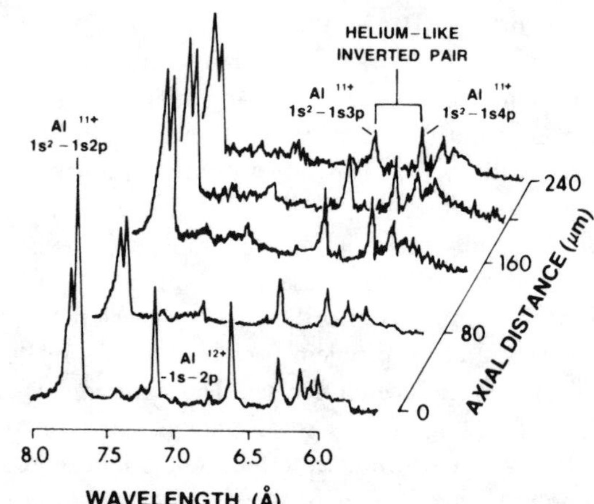

Fig. 10. Spectra from (Mg, Al) stepped target (target type (c) in Fig. 6) at various axial distances. The traces at axial distances ≥ 160 μm are taken with vertical scale sensitivity 2.5 times higher than the sensitivity for traces at axial distances < 160 μm.

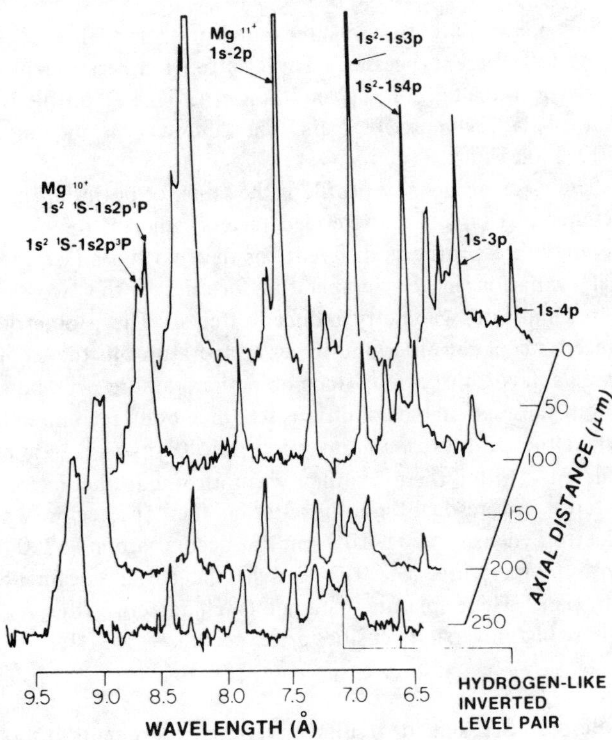

Fig. 11. Spectra from (C, Mg) flat segmented target (target type (d) in Fig. 6) at various axial distances. Intensity inversion is noticed in hydrogen-like lines ($1s-3p$) and ($1s-4p$), marked "hydrogen-like inverted level pair" at axial distances greater than 200 μm.

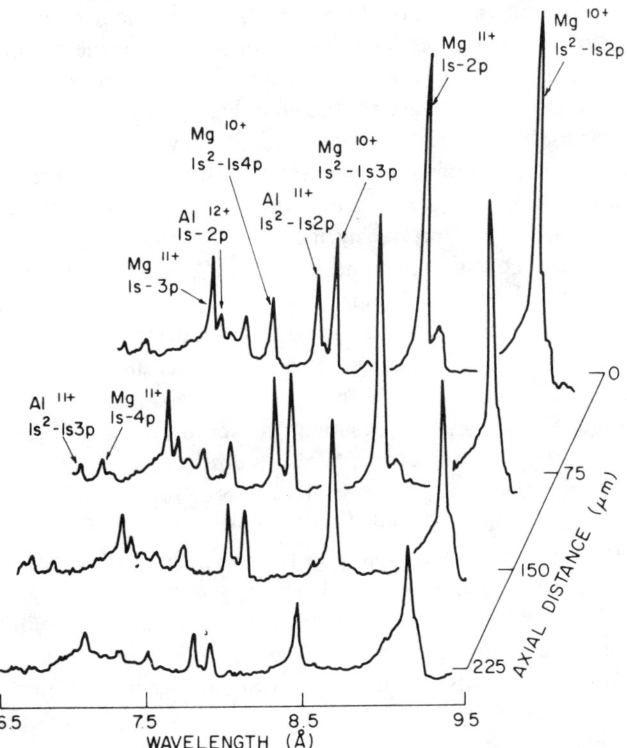

Fig. 12. Spectra from (Mg, Al) flat segmented target (target type (e) in Fig. 6) at various axial distances.

study, this dimension is the radial dimension of the plasma measured parallel to the original target surface. This dimension can be estimated from the widths of the resonance lines. For the geometry in these experiments, the half width of the resonance line is a combination of the spectral width and

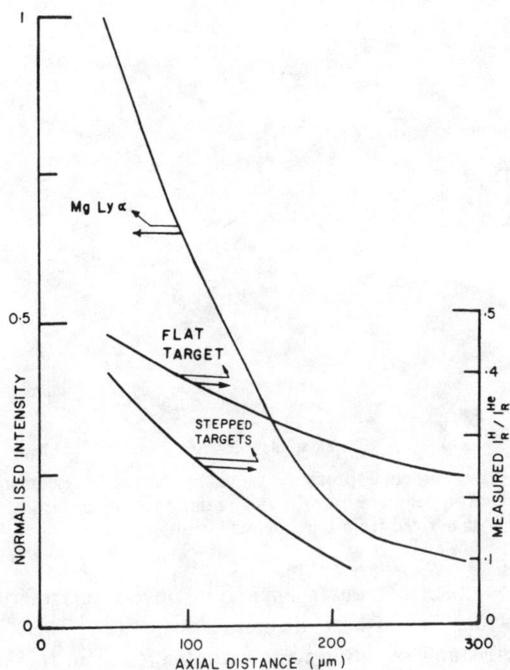

Fig. 13. Normalized intensity of Mg $Ly\alpha$ from a flat target. Also shown are the measured intensity ratios of $Ly\alpha$ and ($1s^2-1s2p$) lines of flat and stepped target types.

the plasma dimension in the radial direction. Thus, from these half widths, especially the half widths of the helium-like lines which exist for a wider range of plasma parameters, the plasma dimension along the line of sight of the X-ray spectrometer can be estimated. The radial plasma dimension measured in this manner is approximately ~200 μm. The plasma dimension does not vary much up to an axial distance of 300 μm [15]. The reason for the narrow expansion cone could be the large effective f-number of $f/4$ for the focusing lens.

C. Radiation Densities

One of the important quantities in the resonant photoexcitation scheme is the radiation density $P_\nu(1, 2)$ of the resonance line transition from level $n = 2$ to $n = 1$. An approximate estimate of the radiation density can be obtained from the exposure levels of the resonance lines. For example, in Fig. 13 the peak value of the exposure level is ~1.4 ergs/cm^2. The film plane is approximately 30 cm from the source. For the crystal reflectivity [16] $\Delta\theta \sim 5 \times 10^{-4}$ rad, the radiation emitted by the source in the resonance line is ~0.08 J. The peak radiation is emitted near the critical density in approximately 200 ps, the FWHM of the laser pulse. This experimental estimate indicates that X-ray line intensities ~8×10^{11} W/cm^2 · sr are possible. These values are comparable to the values predicted by various computer codes [11] and other recent experiments [12]. The radiation temperature values of Mg^{11+} $Ly\alpha$ line derived from the X-ray line intensities are given in Fig. 14. These X-ray line radiation densities fall in the range of 10^{-6}-10^{-5} erg/cm^3 · Hz. It should be pointed out that these profiles give only the values of local emission and that the actual local radiation densities can be higher than these emission values because of transport effects. The experimentally obtained values justify the parametric study of the photoexcitation scheme. The experimental radiation density values are more appropriate than the values that may be obtained

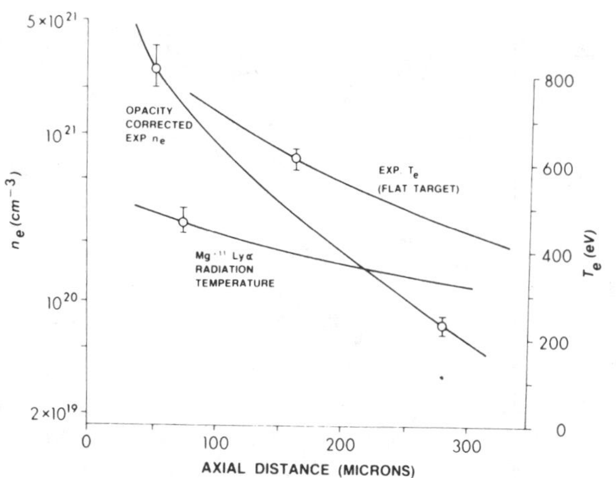

Fig. 14. Experimental profiles of opacity corrected electron density n_e, electron temperature T_e, and radiation temperature of the $Ly\alpha$ line of Mg derived from line intensity profiles.

from complex computer simulations involving radiation coupling which are, at best, theoretical estimates. The X-ray line intensities and radiation temperatures present in these experiments are more than sufficient to test the resonant photoexcitation scheme and to obtain sufficiently large inversion densities by this scheme.

D. Electron Density and Temperature Profiles

The determination of experimental electron density and temperature profiles is essential to characterize the region of inversion. A variety of methods have been developed to determine these plasma parameters [19]. In this study, the electron density is determined from the intensity ratio of the intercombination line ($1s^2\ {}^1S$ - $1s2p\ {}^3P$) and the resonance line ($1s^2\ {}^1S$ - $1s2p\ {}^1P$) of helium-like ions. The intensity ratio I_R/I_{IC} can be expressed as follows [20]:

$$\frac{I(1s^2\ {}^1S - 1s2p\ {}^1P)}{I(1s^2\ {}^1S - 1s2p\ {}^3P)} = R_1 + Pn_e \tag{12}$$

where n_e is the electron density; and R_1 and P are functions independent of n_e but slowly varying functions of electron temperature. Detailed calculations of this intensity ratio for various elements have been done [20] and these results have been used for density measurements in this study. The main problem with this technique is the opacity in the resonance line especially at high densities. The opacity of the resonance line leads to an underestimation of the electron density. The opacity corrected electron density profile is given in Fig. 13. These time averaged density profiles indicate that the region of the plasma with $n_e \sim 10^{20}$ cm^{-3} occurs at axial distances of ~200 μm.

As in the case of density measurement, there are a variety of models to determine electron temperatures [19]. For example, the temperatures may be deduced from the ratio of two resonance lines of hydrogenic or helium-like species, from the ratio of dielectronic satellite lines and the helium-like resonance line [21], etc. Since only some of the dominant atomic processes are taken into account, these models are applicable only in limited density and temperature ranges. In the density region of $n_e \sim 10^{20}$ cm^{-3}, various collisional and radiative processes have important effects. Hence, it is more appropriate to use an excited state model [10] that considers these processes. The electron temperature profile derived in this fashion is given in Fig. 14. This T_e profile is for flat (or flat segmented) targets. The values vary in the range of 400–800 eV.

The electron density profile is the same for both flat (or flat segmented) targets and stepped targets, whereas the electron temperature profile is different for the two types (see [15]). The variation in the temperature profiles in the two target types indicates geometry induced effects. The geometry induced steeper profiles and lower temperatures in the stepped targets favor three-body recombination. More will be said about these favorable conditions for three-body recombination when the profiles of the inversion ratio (n_4g_3/n_3g_4) are considered. From these profiles we notice that the region of interest for resonant photoexcitation (i.e., the region where electron density $n_e \sim 10^{20}$ cm^{-3}) occurs around 200 μm, with temperatures ~500 eV for the flat (or flat segmented) targets. These plasma parameters characterize the region where high inversion densities are expected.

E. Inversion Processes

Before discussing the results for various experiments, it should be reminded that the hydrogenic combination of (C, Mg) satisfies the resonance condition better than the helium-like combination. Under the conditions of the present experiments, hydrogenic source radiation from carbon can be expected to be more intense. For these reasons, the resonant photoexcitation is expected to work better for the hydrogenic combination. The hydrogen-like and helium-like lines of Mg from a (C, Mg) stepped target are shown in Fig. 9. We notice in these densitometer traces that the intensity inversion occurs in a helium-like combination whereas the hydrogenic lines fall off rather sharply in the axial direction. Based on these observations and other previously mentioned geometry induced effects, we conclude that the results in (C, Mg) stepped targets are influenced by additional processes apart from any resonant photoexcitation present. The rapid temperature drop along the axial direction compared to flat targets suggests that the additional process might be collisional recombination. The rapid cooling and the resultant enhanced recombination are caused by the geometry, where it is possible for the cool, high density plasma from the second electrode to act as a heat sink to remove the heat and thereby cool the hot underdense Mg lasing plasma quite rapidly. To verify this hypothesis, the experiments were conducted on stepped targets of (Mg, Al) as indicated in Fig. 6(c). In this case there are no energy resonances and hence no resonant photoexcitation possibilities. From the results of this experiment, the geometry induced effects can be studied. The results from the (Mg, Al) stepped targets, shown in Fig. 10, are very similar to those from (C, Mg) stepped targets. In (Mg, Al) stepped targets, we also notice intensity inversion in helium-like species proving that the results in stepped targets are mainly due to geometry induced rapid cooling and resultant enhanced recombination. This conclusion is substantiated by additional observations mentioned below. For example, in the case of (Mg, Al) targets, a strong K_α line of Mg appears as shown in Fig. 15. The K_α line is emitted when a K-shell electron is ejected from a neutral or

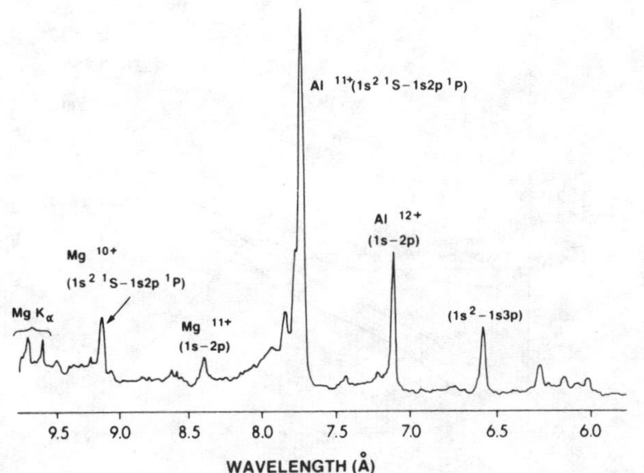

Fig. 15. Spectra from (Mg, Al) stepped targets indicating K_α lines from partially ionized Mg species.

partially ionized Mg plasma. Also a close examination of the spatially resolved helium-like resonance lines of Al indicates a break in the axial expansion of the Al plasma. This break in the expansion direction occurs at an axial distance very close to the location of the second electrode. These observations indicate that the hot Al plasma expands and collides with a cool, high density Mg plasma and is deflected by it. The deflection indicates that there is very little mixing between the two plasmas. Hence, the electrons from Mg plasma cannot directly contribute to the collisions in the lasing plasma. The same holds true for ions from Mg plasma. This eliminates the possibility of enhanced collisional excitation and charge exchange contributions to the observed intensity inversion in stepped targets. A more detailed discussion on the dynamics of rapid cooling and enhanced recombination in stepped targets leading to soft X-ray population inversion is given in [15].

The above discussion indicates the importance of the geometry induced cooling in stepped targets. That makes it difficult to identify the process leading to observed intensity inversion in (C, Mg) stepped targets. For that reason, experiments on segmented flat targets of (C, Mg) were conducted. As indicated before, the dynamics of segmented flat targets are similar to flat targets and hence the geometry induced cooling, etc., would be absent. In the (C^{5+}, Mg^{11+}) combination, no photon-assisted processes are expected. With this target, the results in the (C^{5+}, Mg^{11+}) combination can be attributed to resonant photoexcitation. The microdensitometer traces of the spectra for this target configuration are shown in Fig. 11. We notice that the results are better for the hydrogen-like ion pair compared to the helium-like pair. We see an intensity inversion in the hydrogenic pair for the resonance transitions from levels $n = 3$ and $n = 4$. Observations of these predicted results lead us to conclude that the inversion process in Mg^{11+} flat segmented (C, Mg) targets is indeed resonant photoexcitation. In the case of Mg^{10+} ions, in addition to the resonant photoexcitation, some amount of X-ray photon assisted ionization similar to the process indicated in Section III may be present. In this case, the $Ly\alpha$ radiation can resonantly excite the Mg^{10+} ions in the sublevels of the $n = 2$ state to level $n = 6$ or 7, which can then ionize very rapidly by collisions, etc. This process can lead to an anomalously high (Mg^{11+}/Mg^{10+}) ratio which favors population inversion by recombination.

Finally, in Fig. 12 the results from an (Mg, Al) flat segmented target are presented. In this case, no intensity inversion is seen either in hydrogen-like or helium-like lines from the $n = 3$ and $n = 4$ levels. This double checks the conclusion drawn previously that the hydrodynamics of the flat segmented target is similar to the flat target made of single material and that no geometry induced cooling effects are present. These results are consistent with the previous conclusions.

In summary, the following conclusions on the inversion processes have been drawn from the data presented so far.

1) In the (C, Mg) stepped targets, the intensity inversion in *helium-like* lines only is mainly due to geometry induced enhanced cooling even though some resonant photoexcitation and other photoassisted processes may be present because of the energy coincidences between C^{4+}, C^{5+}, and Mg^{10+} lines. [See Table I-B) and Section III.]

2) In the (C, Mg) stepped target, the geometry induced enhanced recombination of Mg^{11+} ions into Mg^{10+} levels leads to very low Mg^{11+} ion density and hence the disappearance of hydrogenic lines in the region of interest for resonant photoexcitation, i.e., the region where $n_e \sim 10^{20}$ cm^{-3}. This prevents any conclusion to be drawn about the resonant photoexcitation scheme in the (C^{5+}, Mg^{11+}) combination based on (C, Mg) stepped target results alone. Further experiments, where geometry induced enhanced cooling does not interfere with the photoexcitation process, are required to draw any conclusions regarding the resonant photoexcitation scheme.

3) In (Mg, Al) stepped targets, where no possibility for resonant photoexcitation or photon-assisted processes exists, the intensity inversion in helium-like lines is due to geometry induced effects only. This is further confirmed by the rapid disappearance of hydrogen-like lines.

4) In (C, Mg) flat segmented targets, there are no geometry induced effects. The very presence of hydrogenic lines in the region of interest (axial distance ~200 μm) verifies this. In addition, no photon-assisted processes are expected to contribute to Mg^{11+} lines. Thus, the intensity inversion in Mg^{11+} lines can be clearly attributed to resonant photoexcitation and this intensity inversion conclusively proves the feasibility of the photoexcitation scheme in the (C^{5+}, Mg^{11+}) combination. This is the primary conclusion of the experiments.

5) In (C, Mg) flat segmented targets, unlike the hydrogenic case, the process leading to inversion in the helium-like case is not so clear cut. As indicated in Section III, there may be some contribution from the photon-assisted process in the helium-like lines. Even with this contribution, the inversion is not as pronounced as in the hydrogenic species. This may be due to the larger mismatch in the (C^{4+}, Mg^{10+}) combination than in the (C^{5+}, Mg^{11+}) combination.

6) The results from (Mg, Al) flat segmented targets double check the conclusion drawn in (4) that geometry induced effects are not present in flat segmented type targets. These results give additional proof that the intensity inversion in the (C^{5+}, Mg^{11+}) combination in (C, Mg) flat segmented targets can be attributed to resonant photoexcitation only.

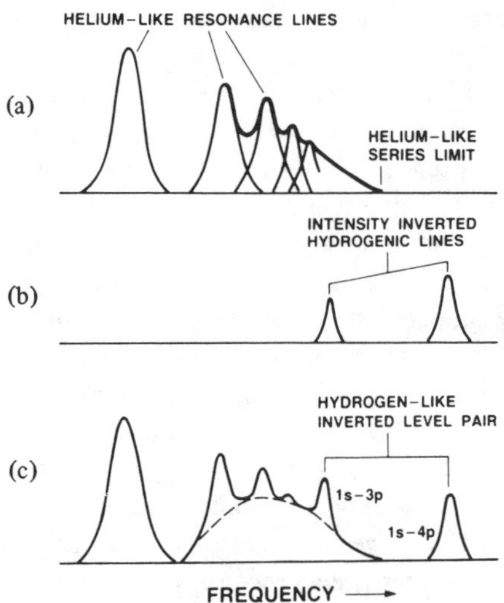

Fig. 16. (a) Helium-like structure due to overlapping lines near the series limit. (b) Intensity inverted hydrogen-like lines. (c) Superposition of the inverted hydrogen-like lines on the helium-like structure to give the total spectra.

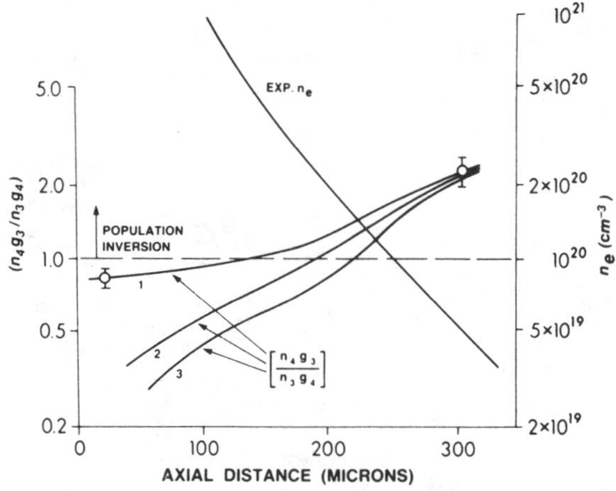

Fig. 17. Axial profiles of the population inversion ratio $(n_4 g_3/n_3 g_4)$ evaluated for various models on opacity corrections: curve 1 optically thin model, curve 2 absorber-emitter model, and curve 3 pure absorber model. The profiles are for Mg^{11+} ions in (C, Mg) flat-segmented targets.

F. Inversion Profiles

In this study, the diagnostic used for detecting inversion is the intensity ratio of the resonance lines from the levels of interest. From the experimental intensity ratio, the reduced population ratio $(n_k g_i/n_i g_k)$ can be deduced. In measuring the $Ly\beta$ line intensity from the traces, special care has to be taken. In the Mg spectra, the $Ly\beta$ line has a wavelength of 7.106 Å and Mg^{10+} has an ionization potential at ~7.037 Å. Because of its close proximity, the $Ly\beta$ line is affected by the helium-like structure near the continuum. This helium-like structure as indicated by the apparent shift of the base line is caused by the increasing overlap of the lines near the continuum. This overlap is due to larger widths of the helium-like lines compared to their separations on the recorded spectra. This effect is shown in Fig. 16. The helium-like linewidths are the result of spectral broadening and more importantly the source size broadening in our experimental setup. The experimental spectra at ~250 μm in Fig. 9 proves the hypothesis that the base line shift is due to helium-like lines near continuum. In this spectrum, because of the absence of hydrogenic lines, the base line shift can be attributed to the overlap of helium-like lines and possible to the free-bound continuum only. Hence, the $Ly\beta$ intensity has to be measured from the apparent base line. The spatial profile of the population density ratio $(n_4 g_3/n_3 g_4)$ determined in this manner is given in Fig. 17. These are the results from a (C, Mg) segmented flat target. The curves 1-3 represent the population density ratios evaluated from the line ratios under different assumptions regarding the opacity effects. It will be shown that the existence of intensity inversion proves population inversion conclusively for the density and path length parameters involved in these experiments.

G. Opacity Effects

One of the important factors to be determined in the detection of population inversion is the effect of opacity in resonance lines on the observed line ratios. The opacity effects can be considered under different assumptions. In Fig. 17, curve 1, the inversion ratio $(n_4 g_3/n_3 g_4)$ has been evaluated with the assumption that no opacity effects are present, i.e., under optically thin approximation. Under this assumption, the population inversion occurs at an axial distance of 120 μm and at electron densities as high as $n_e \sim 5 \times 10^{20}$ cm^{-3}. At these densities and the experimentally determined radial plasma path lengths of ~200 μm, optical thickness $\tau_{13} \sim 1$ is possible. Thus, at these densities, the optically thin approximation is not valid and is a best case approximation.

In curve 3, the inversion ratio has been estimated under the worst case approximation, i.e., the plasma behaves like a pure absorber with an average path length $\overline{D}$. In this approximation, it is assumed that whatever radiation absorbed on its way out of the plasma is completely lost and there is no reradiation. This assumption is valid only if the collisional rates from the $n = 3$ level are comparable or larger than the radiative decay coefficient A_{31} to the ground level. For hydrogen-like Mg, $A_{31} = 1.2 \times 10^{12}$ s^{-1} and the collisional rates are much smaller than A_{31} at $n_e \sim 10^{20}$ cm^{-3}. Thus, part of the absorbed radiation can be reemitted before it can be lost collisionally. Thus, the assumption that the plasma is a pure absorber is a worst case approximation. For the experimental conditions at axial distances $\gtrsim 100$ μm, the optical thickness τ_{13} is given by $\tau_{13} \lesssim 10^{-19}\, n_1$, where n_1 is the ground-state population in hydrogenic state. This assumes a linewidth $\Delta\nu(1, 3) \sim 2 \times 10^{14}$ Hz. Curve 3 represents the inversion ratio under the pure absorber approximation with the assumption that $n_1 \sim n_e/50$. Even under the worst case approximation, the observed line ratios indicate population inversion at axial distances $\gtrsim 200$ μm and at electron densities $n_e \sim 1.5 \times 10^{20}$ cm^{-3}. We also notice that at axial distances >250 μm and $n_e < 10^{20}$ cm^{-3}, the optical thickness is so small that the difference between the optically thin and pure absorber cases is negligible. These arguments indicate that the population inversion observed in these experiments is not dependent on the model.

As mentioned earlier, the pure absorber approximation is the worst case approximation. In general, plasma behaves both as

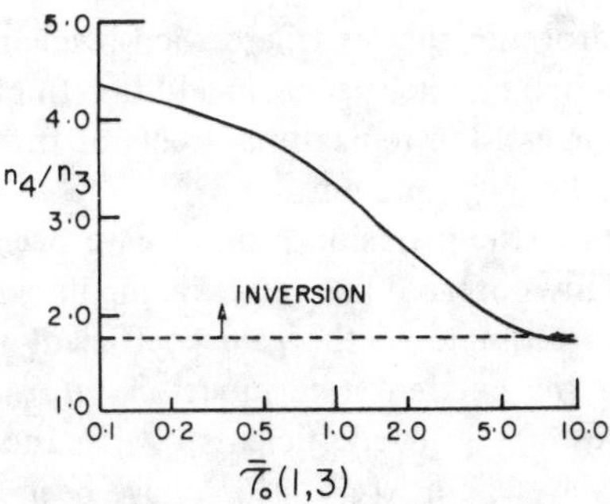

Fig. 18. Mg^{11+} ion population ratios that lead to an observed intensity ratio I_{41}/I_{31} = 1 for various optical thicknesses indicated.

an absorber and as an emitter. In a uniform plasma, for the case where the transport of the resonance lines from the $n = 3$ and $n = 4$ levels does not affect the population distribution, the line ratios can be written as follows:

$$\frac{I_{31}(\nu)}{I_{41}(\nu)} = \frac{n_3 A(3,1)B(1,4)}{n_4 A(4,1)B(1,3)} \frac{[1 - \exp(-\overline{\tau}_0^{13})]}{[1 - \exp(-\overline{\tau}_0^{14})]} \tag{13}$$

where $A(j,i)$ and $B(i,j)$ are the Einstein radiative coefficients from the indicated levels. $\overline{\tau}_0^{ij}$ is the optical thickness at the line center for the transition between levels i and j. For Doppler broadened transitions, the ratio of optical thicknesses for the resonance transitions from levels $n = 4$ and $n = 3$ can be written as follows:

$$\frac{\overline{\tau}_0^{14}}{\overline{\tau}_0^{13}} \sim \frac{B(1,4)}{B(1,3)} \sim 0.35. \tag{14}$$

The population ratios evaluated using (13) and (14) for various values of optical thicknesses of $\overline{\tau}_0^{13}$ are presented in Fig. 18 for the case of Mg^{11+} ions. We notice that as long as $\overline{\tau}_0(1,3)$ is less than 7 or 8, an intensity ratio of 1 implies population inversion. As a matter of fact, a ratio $(I_{41}/I_{31}) \gtrsim 1.14$ implies population inversion for any optical thickness with this model. This is the limit of the black body intensity ratio for the frequencies of interest for the case $KT_B \to \alpha$. This model assumes homogeneous plasma, whereas the experimental plasma has gradients. At any given axial location, in general, the plasma has a higher temperature on the axis with a gradual T_e drop-off in the radial direction. This could lead to more absorption than predicted by (13) provided a lower T_e off-axis leads to a lower off-axis ratio of (n_4/n_3) also [22]. Lower temperatures off-axis may lead to more recombination to higher levels, and thus, lower off-axis electron temperatures do not necessarily mean lower off-axis (n_4/n_3) ratios. Also off-axis ground-state density drops off rapidly and may not contribute much to the optical thickness. In any case, the results of the absorber-emitter model will be better than the extreme case of the pure absorber model. The absorber-emitter model represents the actual plasma more closely at the densities of interest. The population inversion ratios evaluated by the homogeneous absorber-emitter approximation are presented in curve 2. As expected, it falls in between the extreme cases of optically thin and pure absorber cases. In this approximation, the population inversion exists at axial distances $\gtrsim$180 μm and at

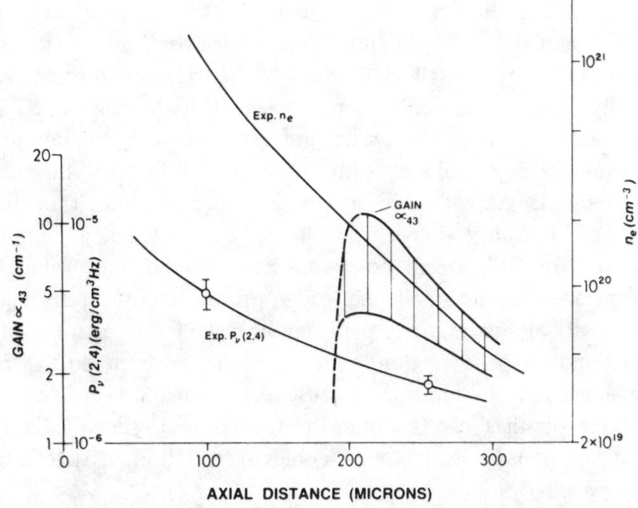

Fig. 19. Axial profiles of source radiation density $P_\nu(2,4)$ and gain coefficient α_{43} for Mg^{11+} ions in (C, Mg) flat segmented targets.

electron densities $n_e \sim 2.5 \times 10^{20}$ cm^{-3}. At axial distances $\gtrsim$220 μm, all three models indicate population inversion. These results conclusively prove population inversion at $n_e \sim 2 \times 10^{20}$. As indicated previously, the process leading to inversion in Mg^{11+} ions of the flat segmented (C, Mg) targets is resonant photoexcitation. From the values of n_e and inversion ratio $(n_4 g_3/n_3 g_4)$ evaluated so far, an estimate of the gain coefficient α_{43} is done in the following paragraphs.

H. Gain Coefficient

The gain coefficient on a bound-bound transition can be expressed as follows:

$$\alpha_{ki} \sim \frac{\Delta n_{ki} A_{ki} \lambda_{ki}^2}{40 \Delta \nu_{ki}} \tag{15}$$

Δn_{ki} cm^{-3}, A_{ki} s^{-1}, λ_{ki} cm, and $\Delta\nu_{ki}$ Hz are the population inversion, Einstein radiative coefficient, wavelength, and spectral width, respectively, of the transition of interest. The linewidth for Mg^{11+} ions can be estimated from the experimentally deduced electron densities and temperatures. In this study, the population inversion density Δn_{43} has been deduced with the help of the excited state model described in Section IV.

From n_e and $(n_4 g_3/n_3 g_4)$ profiles obtained previously and using graphs of the type indicated in Fig. 5, the radiation density profile of $P_\nu(2,4)$ can be obtained. In Fig. 19 the radiation density profile evaluated as indicated above is given for Mg^{11+} ions. We notice that the radiation density $P_\nu(2,4)$ has values in the range of $(10^{-6}$–$8 \cdot 10^{-6})$ erg/cm$^3 \cdot$ Hz. Again using the excited state model and the electron and radiation density profiles, the profile of fractional inversion density $(\Delta n/n_1)$ can be obtained. For the plasma parameters in the region of inversion it is reasonable to expect values of $(n_{Hy}/n_e) \sim (n_1/n_e) \sim 3 \times 10^{-2}$. Thus, from known values of n_e, (n_1/n_e) and $(\Delta n/n_1)$, the absolute inversion density can be estimated. The gain coefficients estimated in this manner are shown in Fig. 19. The upper range of values of gain coefficient are for radiation density values of $P_\nu(1,2) \sim 5 \times 10^{-6}$ erg/cm$^3 \cdot$ Hz;

whereas the lower bound is for $P_\nu(1,2) \sim 10^{-6}$ erg/cm$^3 \cdot$ Hz. The actual radiation densities and hence the gain coefficients are expected to fall in this range. The temporally and radially averaged gain coefficient has values in the range of $\alpha_{43} \sim$ 5-8 cm^{-1}. The peak values are expected to be higher than these averaged values. With these gain coefficients and radial plasma lengths of ~200 μm, the average gain on the transition $(4 \rightarrow 3)$ in Mg^{11+} ions has a value $(\alpha l)_{av} \sim 0.1$, i.e., an amplification of 10 percent per pass. Even though these values of average gain are small, the scaling prospects both in inversion density and particularly path lengths make the resonant photoexcitation scheme quite attractive for coherent soft X-ray generation. In addition, because of their high power densities, laser plasmas can be quite useful as amplifying media for high intensity, short pulse coherent radiation at soft X-ray wavelengths.

VII. Summary and Conclusions

In this paper, a two-step resonant photoexcitation process for soft X-ray population inversion has been studied in high density and temperature laser plasmas. This study indicates that the two-step photoexcitation process can be quite effective in pumping large populations to the excited states at the radiation densities available in laser plasmas. The experimental and theoretical results presented in this study indicated that resonant photoexcitation is a promising technique for obtaining large population inversions at ~100 Å. This technique can also be useful in a wide range of X-ray wavelengths.

With the help of an excited state model, a parametric study of the two-step resonant photoexcitation has been done. This study indicated that resonant photoexcitation can be effective enough to lead to intensity inversion in the resonance lines from the levels of interest. Such intensity inversion is significantly different from normal line ratios and can be used as a population inversion diagnostic. The scaling and optimization study indicates that two-step resonant photoexcitation can be scaled to higher densities. At any given radiation density, the absolute inversion density increases with electron density up to a certain optimum value. In scaling the system with respect to size, care has to be taken to eliminate radiation trapping. By making one of the transverse dimensions small, the radiation trapping problems may be eliminated. The scaling with respect to radiation densities indicated that saturation effects play a role only at very high radiation densities, which may not be relevant with present systems.

The two-step photoexcitation scheme was experimentally studied with a (C, Mg) combination with the so-called "stepped" and "segmented flat" target configurations. The experiments on stepped targets indicated some geometry induced effects. The experiments performed on various targets allowed the geometry induced and resonant photoexcitation induced effects to be distinguished. The dynamics of stepped targets lead to conditions quite suitable for three-body recombination, and hence can be used to an advantage in obtaining substantial population inversion by recombination. The results of (C, Mg) flat segmented targets indicate that significant population inversion can be obtained by two-step resonant photoexcitation in hydrogenic species where good resonance matching is possible. In helium-like species, in addition to photoexcitation, other photon-assisted ionization effects of the type described in Section III may be present.

In this study the inversion profiles have been reduced from experimentally observed line ratios taking into account opacity effects. An estimate of the gain coefficient was made with the help of the excited state model and n_e and $(n_4 g_3/n_3 g_4)$ profiles. Average gain coefficients α_{43} in the range of 5-10 cm^{-1} at a wavelength $\lambda_{43} \sim 130$ Å have been deduced in the present experiments. These and the results of the scaling study indicate that the two-step resonant photoexcitation process can lead to potentially high gain systems for X-ray amplification. Finally, it should be indicated that in addition to resonant photoexcitation, intense line radiation may be used to create conditions favorable for soft X-ray population inversion by other processes.

Acknowledgment

The author gratefully acknowledges the guidance and discussions with Prof. M. J. Lubin, Dr. B. Yaakobi, and Dr. J. Forsyth. The author wishes to thank the X-ray group members for their help with the experiments.

References

[1] M. J. Lubin, J. M. Soures, and L. M. Goldman, "Large-aperture Nd:Glass laser amplifier for high peak power application," *J. Appl. Phys.*, vol. 44, pp. 347-350, 1973.

[2] R. W. Waynant and R. C. Elton, "Review of short wavelength laser research," *Proc. IEEE*, vol. 64, pp. 1059-1092, 1976; J. M. Forsyth, T. C. Bristow, B. Yaakobi, and A. Hauer, "Soft x-ray amplification in a laser produced plasma: A review and prognosis," in *Laser Induced Fusion and X-ray Laser Studies*, S. F. Jacobs, M. O. Scully, M. Sargent III, and C. D. Cantrell, III, Eds. Reading, MA: Addison-Wesley, 1976, pp. 581-629; G. Chapline and L. Wood, "X-ray lasers," *Phys. Today*, pp. 40-48, June 1975.

[3] V. A. Bhagavatula, "Experimental evidence for soft x-ray population inversion by resonant photoexcitation in multicomponent laser plasmas," *Appl. Phys. Lett.*, vol. 33, pp. 726-728, 1978; ——, "Soft x-ray population inversion by resonant photoexcitation in multi-component laser plasmas," *J. Appl. Phys.*, vol. 47, pp. 4535-4537, 1976.

[4] A. V. Vinogradov, I. I. Sobel'man, and E. A. Yukov, "Possibility of constructing a far-ultraviolet laser utilizing transitions in multiply charged ions in an inhomogeneous plasma," *Sov. J. Quantum Electron.*, vol. 5, pp. 59-63, 1975; B. A. Norton and N. J. Peacock, "Population inversion in laser-produced plasmas by pumping with opacity broadened lines," *J. Phys. B: Atom. Molec. Phys.*, vol. 8, pp. 989-996, 1975; R. C. Elton, "Resonant photoexcitation pumping in hydrogenic ions," in *ARPA/NRL X-Ray Laser Program, NRL Memorandum*, 1977, pp. 92-114, Rep. 3482.

[5] A. Burgess, "Dielectronic recombination and the temperature of the solar corona," *Astrophys. J.*, vol. 139, pp. 776-780, 1964; A. H. Gabriel and T. M. Paget, "Measurement and interpretation of dielectronic recombination satellite line intensities," *J. Phys. B.*, vol. 5, pp. 673-685, 1972.

[6] G. Traving, "Interpretation of line broadening and line shift," in *Plasma Diagnostics*, W. Lochte-Holtgreven, Ed. Amsterdam, The Netherlands: North Holland, 1968, pp. 66-134.

[7] R. L. Kelly and L. J. Palumbo, "Atomic and ionic emission lines below 2000 Å," Naval Research Laboratories, 1973, Rep. 7599.

[8] W. Weise, M. Smith, and B. Miles, "Atomic transition probabilities," NBS Special Publication No. 22, U.S. GPO, Washington, DC, 1973.

[9] D. R. Bates, A. E. Kingston, and R. W. P. McWhirter, "Recombi-

nation between electrons and atomic ions in optically thin plasmas," *Proc. Roy. Soc. A*, vol. 267, pp. 297–312, 1962.

[10] R. W. P. McWhirter and A. G. Hearn, "A calculation of the instantaneous population densities of the excited levels of hydrogen-like ions in a plasma," *Proc. Phys. Soc.*, vol. 82, pp. 641–654, 1963.

[11] K. G. Whitney and J. Davis, "Hot-spot model of K-line emission from laser-heated plasmas," *J. Appl. Phys.*, vol. 44, pp. 5294–5302, 1974.

[12] H. D. Shay, R. A. Haas, W. L. Kruer, M. J. Boyle, D. W. Phillion, V. C. Rupert, H. N. Kornblum, F. Rainer, V. W. Shvinsky, L. N. Koppel, L. Richards, and K. G. Tirsell, "Interaction of 1.06 μm laser radiation with variable $\overline{Z}$ targets," *Phys. Fluids*, vol. 21, pp. 1634–1652, 1978.

[13] E. Goldman, "Numerical modeling of laser produced plasmas: Theory and documentation for Super," Univ. Rochester, Rochester, NY, 1974, LLE Rep. 16.

[14] V. A. Boiko, O. N. Krokhin, S. A. Pikuz, and A. Ya. Faenov, "Measurement of the intensity of the (2-10) Å radiation emitted by laser plasmas generated from targets with nuclear charges Z = 12-23 and determination of the plasma temperature," *Sov. J. Quantum Electron.*, vol. 4, pp. 1212–1215, 1975.

[15] V. A. Bhagavatula and B. Yaakobi, "Direct observation of population inversion between Al^{+11} levels in a laser-produced plasma," *Opt. Commun.*, vol. 24, pp. 331–335, 1978.

[16] B. L. Henke and M. A. Tester, "Techniques of low energy x-ray spectroscopy (0.1 to 2 keV region)," in *Advances in X-ray Analysis*, vol. 18, W. L. Pickles, C. S. Barrett, J. B. New Kirk, and C. O. Rudd, Eds. New York: Plenum, 1974, pp. 76–106.

[17] J. A. R. Samson, *Techniques of Vacuum Ultraviolet Spectroscopy*. New York: Wiley, 1967.

[18] R. F. Benjamin, P. B. Lyons, and R. H. Day, "X-ray calibration of RAR 2490 film for application to laser plasma experiments," *Appl. Opt.*, vol. 16, pp. 393–397, 1977.

[19] W. Lochte-Holtgreven, "Evaluation of plasma parameters," in *Plasma Diagnostics*, W. Lochte-Holtgreven, Ed. Amsterdam, The Netherlands: North-Holland, 1968, pp. 135–213.

[20] A. V. Vinogradov, I. Ya. Skobelev, and E. A. Yukov, "Determination of plasma density from spectra of helium-like ions," *Sov. J. Quantum Electron.*, vol. 5, pp. 630–633, 1975.

[21] A. H. Gabriel, "Dielectronic satellite spectra for highly charged helium-like ion lines," *Mon. Notic. Roy. Astron. Soc.*, vol. 60, pp. 99–119, 1972.

[22] K. N. Koshelev and S. S. Churilov, "A possible interpretation of the observed superradiance in the spectra of Al IV ions in the plasma of laser jet," *Sov. J. Quantum, Electron.*, vol. 5, pp. 400–402, 1975.

V. A. Bhagavatula was born in Guntur, India, on August 14, 1950. He received the B. Tech. degree from Indian Institute of Technology, Madras, India, in 1972, and the M.S. and Ph.D. degrees from the University of Rochester, Rochester, NY, in 1973 and 1979, respectively.

While at the University of Rochester he worked on X-ray laser studies and X-ray diagnostics in laser plasmas. After holding a Consultant Position at University of Rochester, he joined Corning Glass Works, Corning, NY, in 1979, where he is working on fiber optics and in particular, single-mode waveguides.

Reprinted with permission from *Journal of Applied Physics,* Vol. 51(4), pp. 1922-1931 (April 1980). ©1980 American Institute of Physics.

Conditions for soft x-ray lasing action in a confined plasma column

S. Suckewer and H. Fishman
Princeton University, Plasma Physics Laboratory, Princeton, New Jersey 08544

The idea of using a multi-Z (e.g., carbon, oxygen) thin plasma column as a medium for soft x-ray lasing action is presented. A plasma confined by a strong magnetic field is first heated by a CO_2 laser, and then cools rapidly by radiation losses. This leads to a level population inversion of hydrogen-like carbon or oxygen ions. Two computational models are presented. One uses given electron temperature $T_e(t)$ evolutions. The other uses $T_e(t)$ calculated from an energy balance equation with CO_2 laser beam power as a parameter. According to calculations, a total gain of $G > 100$ is expected for $3\rightarrow2$ and $G > 10$ for $4\rightarrow2$ transitions ($\lambda = 182$ Å and $\lambda = 135$ Å, respectively) for C VI ions using a CO_2 laser beam with power $\sim 5\times10^{10}$ W for plasma column heating.

I. INTRODUCTION

Added interest in soft x-ray lasers in the last four to five years has rapidly increased the number of investigations concentrated mainly on obtaining a high degree of inversion of level populations for short wavelength transitions. The need for high inversion is dictated by the requirement for a relatively high total gain G of the lasing action,

$$G = \kappa l \geqslant 10 , \tag{1}$$

in order to avoid an optical resonant cavity.[1,2] In Eq. (1) κ is gain per unit length and l is the length of the lasing medium. Although there have been several proposals[3-5] for resonant cavities in the x-ray region, it seems improbable that any of them could be useful for soft x-ray lasers due to the very difficult technical problems.

There are a number of approaches for achieving the proper inversion, reviewed in Refs. 1, 2, 6, and 7. The main ones are through the use of (1) photo and collisional ionization of the inner shells of multi-Z atoms or ions;[8-14] (2) photo-excitation[15,16] and electron collisional excitation of ions;[17-25] and (3) collisional recombination of ions[26-43] and atom-ion resonance charge exchange.[44-47] There have also been some controversial experiments[48,49] which have been analyzed and strongly criticized in several papers[1,50-52], therefore we will not discuss them here.[53]

It seems to us that approach (3) is the most promising for obtaining soft x-ray lasers working in the regime of amplified spontaneous emission (ASE). The idea of using a recombining plasma to create a population inversion was first proposed by Gudzenko and Shelepin[26] and developed in a series of theoretical papers by Gudzenko *et al.*[27-29] and others.[30-38,42] The principle of this idea is that a plasma by cooling rapidly becomes strongly nonequilibrium and is dominated by electron-ion collisional-radiative recombination. The equilibrium electron density $N_{e(eq)}$ corresponding to this T_e drops very quickly. If N_e decreases much more slowly than $N_{e(eq)}$ the relaxation processes (collisions) cannot keep up with the changes at some intermediate level n^* and thus create the inversion near such n^*. To cool the plasma, Gudzenko *et al.*[26,27] proposed to use adiabatic decompression. However, in such a plasma N_e is also decreasing quite rapidly. But the main problem was with achieving a short cooling time in comparison to the relaxation time of radiative processes.

Strong support for approach (3) arose through experiments on the interaction of powerful lasers with solid targets. The plasma produced in this manner expands quickly into a low-density region (e.g., vacuum) and its temperature (and also its electron density) decreases rapidly by adiabatic decompression. In this way, Irons and Peacock[39] obtained one of the first population inversions for soft x-ray transitions. A plasma was formed by irradiating a polyethylene target with a pulsed neodymium-glass laser beam. They observed inversion in hydrogen-like carbon ions C VI between levels $n = 3,4,5$, and $m = 2$. However, total gain was very low, $G \simeq 10^{-6}$–10^{-5}, because l was of the order of μm. Dehurst *et al.*[40] later reported higher gain in a similar type of experiment, but total gain still did not exceed $G \simeq 10^{-2}$.

Also, calculations predict the possibility of obtaining an inversion in that kind of plasma with respect to the ground level ($m = 1$) for hydrogen-like ions.[32,33,37,38] Jones and Ali[32] predicted high inversion of $2\rightarrow1$ transitions of C VI ions by solving a set of rate equations for populations and assuming an instantaneous decrease in electron temperature. Green and Silfvast[33] performed similar work for HeII. In more extensive calculations, Pert[37] and Tallents,[38] used the time dependent change of temperature in an expanding plasma (Pert[37] also included heat return to electrons by recombination). However, in all these calculations it is assumed that the plasma in its initial condition (steady state) consists only of totally stripped ions and electrons, and when the temperature starts to decrease at $t = 0$, ions and electrons begin to recombine. This type of approach leads to seemingly optimistic results, since in the early stage of expansion there would be a tendency toward populating the higher levels more than the ground level. However, if one includes fast ionization of the plasma during heating, then the population of ground level hydrogen-like ions should be quite high when strong recombination starts (see Sec. V). This effect makes inversion with respect to the ground level much more difficult to achieve experimentally.

Vinogradov and Sobel'man[44] proposed using a charge-exchange process for generating a sufficiently high inversion in an expanding plasma. They analyzed the plasma produced by laser evaporation of a solid target (pellet) placed in a helium atmosphere. According to them, the charge-exchange cross section has a resonance character for a certain level n^*. This cross section can be as high as

$$\sigma_{c\text{-}ex} \simeq \pi a_0^2 Z^2 \simeq 10^{-16} Z^2 (\text{cm}^2) . \tag{2}$$

Thus, n^* will be preferentially populated and, in turn, will lead to its overpopulation in comparison to lower levels. For example, for carbon ($Z = 6$) the charge-exchange collisions

$$C^{6+} + C^0 \to (C^{5+})^* + C^+ + \Delta E \tag{3}$$

are resonant for the excited level $n^* = 4$ of the product ion $(C^{5+})^*$ according to Refs. 45 and 46, although Vinogradov and Sobel'man[44] suggested $n^* = 6$ should be preferentially populated. The energy ΔE is the difference between the binding energies of the initial and final state.[45]

Dixon and Elton[46] have performed experiments to show that the resonance charge-exchange process can be efficient for selective enhancement of populations leading to inversion. According to Dixon *et al.*[47] this process can even be a dominant cause of inversion in a plasma expanding into a buffer gas. The conclusion was made on the basis of numerical modeling of observed line intensity inversion in Lyman and Balmer spectra of C^{5+} ions. Calculations of level populations were done using steady-state approximations. This assumption may lead to wrong conclusions in the case of a rapidly expanding plasma. Time dependent calculations for modeling the results of Dixon *et al.*[46,47] as well as the influence of charge-exchange on population inversion in a plasma with $N_e \sim 5\times10^{18}$–5×10^{19} cm^{-3} will be discussed in Sec. VI of this paper.

The main purpose of this paper is to point out another scheme for obtaining inversion in a recombining plasma when particle confinement time τ_p is much longer than electron temperature decay time τ_E. It is based on calculations[42] and observations of population inversion for H I and He II in the Spherator *FM*-1.[43] The concept and proposed experiment are the subject of Sec. II. In Sec. III we will discuss the set of equations and the computer program. The results will be presented in Secs. IV–VII. A discussion of the results and the possibility of stimulating lasing action will appear in Sec. VIII.

II. INVERSION IN A CONFINED PLASMA COLUMN[54]

We suggest using a multi-Z plasma column with a large ratio of length to radius $r_0 (l/r_0 > 10^2)$ as a medium for lasing action. The plasma would be confined by a magnetic field (or the chamber wall) and surrounded by a relatively high-pressure neutral gas. In this case, the particle confinement time τ_p would be much longer than the electron temperature decay time τ_E. This difference is caused primarily by large radiation and charge-exchange losses. It is possible to achieve these conditions in a plasma column produced by CO_2 laser-induced breakdown of neutral gas with high initial pressure (10–50 Torr) of CH_4, CO_2, or CH_4 + Xe in a strong solenoidal magnetic field.[55-57] In such a plasma, density N_e is highest midway ($r \simeq \frac{1}{2} r_0$) between the axis and the side of the column[55,56] [$N_e = (1$–$2)\times10^{18}$ cm^{-3} for relatively low CO_2 laser power, $P_L \simeq 3\times10^8$ W] where electron temperature T_e = 10–20 eV. The electron temperature has a maximum (T_e = 100–200 eV) at the center of the column [$r = 0$, $N_e(0) = 5\times10^{17}$ cm^{-3}], and rapidly decreases toward the outside. In this case, totally stripped ions from the center of the column can recombine in the high-density and low-temperature region near the side, thereby providing better conditions for inversion. The particle confinement time τ_p is much longer than temperature decay time τ_E as can be deduced from Refs. 56 and 57. Decay time τ_E can be decreased by increasing radiative losses. This situation can be achieved easily by adding a few percent of a high-Z substance to the plasma (e.g., Xe). After the CO_2 laser pulse ends and while T_e is dropping, the electron density N_e is much higher than the equilibrium density $N_{e(\text{eq})}$. Hence, after the breakdown, along the plasma column the conditions for high inversion for soft x-ray transitions are suitable, as will be shown in Secs. IV and V.

The principal differences between the confined plasma column (CPC) and expanding plasma (EP) are (a) Particle confinement time in CPC is much longer than for EP. Since CPC has a much more slowly decreasing N_e there is the possibility of obtaining a higher gain κ. (b) In CPC the long column is beneficial for total laser gain G while the small radius is useful from the point of view of the pumping power requirement and inversion (the plasma can be optically thin in a radial direction). (c) In CPC the maximum inversion can be obtained in a region close to maximum plasma density.

There is some disadvantage of CPC compared to EP due to a lower probability of charge exchange in CPC caused by the lower interaction energy of A^{Z+} ions with neutral atoms A^0 along the side of the column. However, if in some way we can increase the velocity of neutrals so that they penetrate the plasma column fast enough, it would increase netural density as well as the charge-exchange cross section at $r = \frac{1}{2} r_0$.

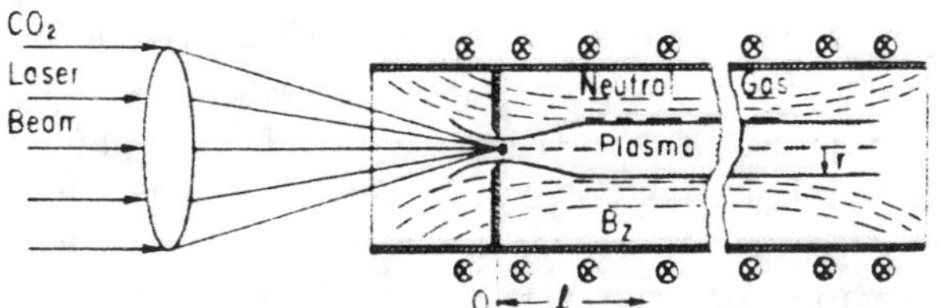

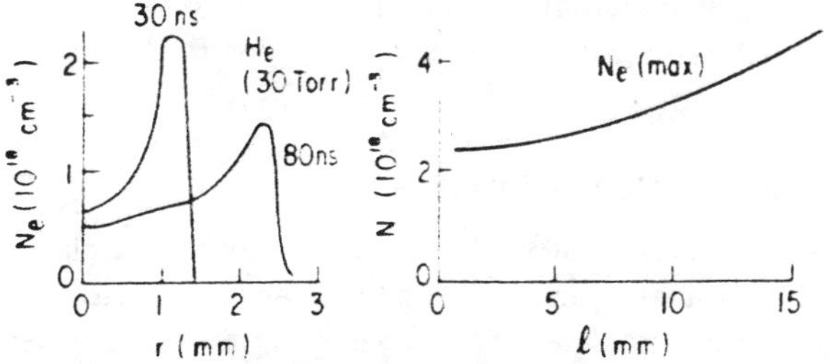

FIG. 1. Scheme of experiment for creating a level population inversion in a magnetically confined plasma column heated by CO_2 laser. Distributions of electron density N_e along the radius and column axis of the plasma heated by a relatively low-power CO_2 laser ($P_L \simeq 3\times10^8$ W) are taken from T.K. Chu and L.C. Johnson (see Ref. 55)

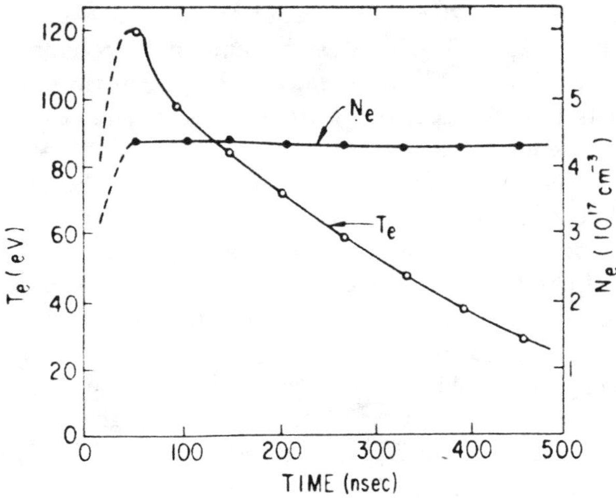

FIG. 2. Time evolution of N_e and T_e in a plasma column heated by a lower-power CO_2 laser ($P_L \approx 3\times 10^8$ W) (from Refs. 56 and 57).

A suggested scheme of experiment based on a CO_2 laser gas breakdown plasma[55-57] is presented in Fig. 1. It corresponds to a short plasma column ($l \approx 5$–10 cm) with $r_0 \approx 0.1$ cm and laser energy of order $W_L \approx 50$–100 J. A long plasma column ($l \approx 100$ cm) can be obtained with higher laser energy ($W_L \approx 500$–1000 J) by focusing it along the column using cylindrical lenses. In Fig. 1 the laser beam (a CO_2 or Nd glass laser could be used) is focused through an orifice onto a gas target in a strong magnetic field B_Z ($B_Z \approx 100$–150 kG). The B_Z is created by a low-inductance solenoid supplied by a condenser bank. Without B_Z the plasma would expand rapidly in a radial direction leading to a rapidly decreasing electron density.[59] (There is also the possibility of using a cylindrical chamber for plasma radial confinement[60]). In Fig. 1 the radial distribution of N_e is also shown and in Fig. 2 we see the temporal evolution of N_e and T_e in a CO_2 laser heated plasma[55-57] ($P_L \approx 10^9$ W cm^{-3}). Initially, we propose to use CH_4 and CH_4 + Xe as a gas target (working gas) in order to observe an inversion in H-like carbon C VI ions between levels $n = 3,4,5$ and $m = 2$ ($\lambda_{3,2} = 182$ Å, $\lambda_{4,2} = 135$ Å, and $\lambda_{5,2} = 120$ Å). By comparing experiments with different initial concentrations of Xe it is possible to predict the optimum efficiency of radiation cooling for given laser energy. The same scheme can be used for oxygen or atoms with higher Z in order to obtain inversion for shorter wavelength (in such a case the energy of the CO_2 laser should be higher for the same size plasma column). Using He + Ar or He + Xe mixtures it will be possible to obtain an inversion in He II for transitions with $\lambda = 1215$ Å and $\lambda = 1025$ Å.

III. COMPUTATIONAL MODEL

For about the first 30–70 ns after breakdown the plasma is heated by a laser beam leading to an increase in electron temperature T_e and density N_e. When the laser pulse is terminated, T_e decreases rapidly, primarily by radiation losses, while N_e changes only slightly. If the plasma consists almost exclusively of ions both fully stripped and hydrogen-like, the ratio of plasma energy to radiation losses by resonance lines gives an order of magnitude estimate of decay time as follows:

$$\tau_E \approx [N_e T_e(t)]/N_2 A_{21} h\nu_{21}\,. \tag{4}$$

For example, in a carbon plasma with $N_e = 5\times 10^{19}$ cm^{-3}, $T_e = 500$ eV ($T_i < T_e$), $N_2 \approx 5\times 10^{14}$ cm^{-3}, $A_{21} = 7\times 10^{11}$ sec^{-1}, and $h\nu_{21} \approx 370$ eV, we get $\tau_E \approx 4\times 10^{-8}$ sec. Taking into account radiation losses by ions in the lower ionization stages we may obtain an even shorter τ_E. A more accurate estimate of τ_E was obtained using self-consistent calculations for $T_e(t)$, $N_e(t)$, radiation W_{rad} and ionization W_{ioniz} losses all as a function of beam power P_L and neutral gas density N_0. The calculations presented in the last part of this section give a value for τ_E not far from the one above. In most of our calculations we use τ_E in the range 10^{-8}–10^{-7} sec for the time evolution of $T_e(t)$ if the energy balance equation is not used. $N_e(t)$, the level population densities $N_n^{Z-1}(t)$ of hydrogen-like ions and the ion densities for different stages of ionization $N_1^j(t)$ as a function of time were calculated from a set of rate equations for ionization, i.e.,

$$\begin{aligned}\frac{dN_1^j}{dt} &= (N_1^j S_1^{j-1} - N_1^j S_1^j)N_e + (\alpha_1^{j+1} + N_e\beta_1^{j+1})N_1^{j+1}N_e \\ &\quad - (\alpha_1^j + N_e\beta_1^j)N_1^j N_e + \delta_{j0}\psi^0 - \psi_1^j\,, \\ &j = 1, 2, \ldots, Z-1, Z\,, \\ &N_1^{j-1}, S_1^{j-1} \equiv 0 \text{ for } j = 0\,; \\ &N_1^{j+1}, S_1^j, \alpha_1^{j+1}, \beta_1^{j+1} \equiv 0 \text{ for } j = Z\end{aligned} \tag{5}$$

and for population:

$$\begin{aligned}\frac{dN_n^{Z-1}}{dt} &= N_e \sum_{\substack{k=1\\k\neq n}}^{k_{max}+m} (N_k^{Z-1}S_{kn}^{Z-1} - N_n^{Z-1}S_{nk}^{Z-1}) \\ &\quad - \sum_{k=1}^{n-1} N_n^{Z-1}A_{nk}^{Z-1}\gamma_{nk}^{Z-1} \\ &\quad + \sum_{k=n+1}^{k_{max}+m} N_k^{Z-1}(A_{kn}^{Z-1} + N_e S_{kn}^{Z-1}) \\ &\quad - N_e N_n^{Z-1}S_n^{Z-1} + N_1^Z N_e \\ &\quad \times(\alpha_n^Z + N_e\beta_n^Z) - \psi_n^{Z-1} \\ &\quad + \delta_{n^*n}\delta_{1s}N_1^0 N_1^Z R\,;\end{aligned} \tag{6}$$

$$n = 2, \ldots, k_{max}\,, \quad s = \frac{(t-t_0)}{|t-t_0|}\,,$$

and the plasma neutrality equation

$$N_e = \sum_{j=1}^{Z} jN_1^j\,, \tag{7}$$

where Z is the atomic number and δ_{jk} is Kronecker's delta $\delta_{jk} = 0$ for $j \neq k$ and $\delta_{jk} = 1$ for $j = k$. ψ^0 is the influx of neturals, ψ_n^j is the outflux (or influx) of ions in the state with quantum number n. The S_n^j, α_n^j, and β_n^j are the rate coefficients for ionization, photorecombination, and three-body recombination, respectively (to or from level n). S_{kn}^{Z-1} is the rate coefficient for collisional excitation ($k < n$) or de-excitation ($k > n$) of hyderogen-like ions ($j = Z-1$). A_{nk}^{Z-1} is the spontaneous transition probability. γ_{nk}^{Z-1} is the Biberman-Holstein radiation opacity coefficient,[62,63] which can be used in analytical form, presented in Ref. 64. For $n \to k$ transitions $\gamma_{nk} = 1$ for an optically thin plasma and $\gamma_{nk} = 0$ for an optically thick plasma. In most of our present calculations, we had $\gamma_{nK} = 1$, since the plasma was optically thin in a radial direction. For some calculations, where the density N_1^{Z-1} was high ($N_1^{Z-1} > 10^{18}$ cm^{-3}), we took into account the fact that $\gamma_{n1} < 1$, where γ_{n1} was calculated from analytical approximations.[64]

A resonance charge-exchange process with rate coefficient $R_0 = \langle \sigma_{c\text{-}ex} v_0 \rangle$ is included in Eq. (6) for $n = n^*$ and $t > t_0$. Time t_0 corresponds to a delay in the start of interaction between atoms and ions in the charge-exchange process. In R we used charge-exchange cross sections $\sigma_{c\text{-}ex}$ given by Vinogradov and Sobel'man[44] [Eq. (2)] or by Salop and Olson[65] and Salop[66] with relative particle velocity in the range $v = 10^6$–10^7 cm/sec. Most of the calculations were performed with $v \simeq 5 \times 10^6$ cm/sec. Spontaneous transition probabilities A^j_{nk} were taken from tables by Wiese *et al.*[67] Electron impact ionization and excitation rate coefficients were used in the form given by Drawin.[68] Rate coefficients for the reverse process (de-excitation and three-body recombination) were obtained from detailed balance relations. There are several other forms of cross section giving better agreement with experiment. However, Drawin's form scales with quantum number n quite well, which is important in finding optimum conditions for a maximum population inversion. Also, Drawin's cross sections are simple and can be used for atoms and ions with different Z (e.g., H, He, C, O). Seaton's approximation[68,69] was used for photorecombination. If the gas consisted of two kinds of atoms, e.g. carbon and hydrogen (CH_4), an additional equation was used for the ionization of hydrogen

$$\frac{dN_H}{dt} = -N_H N_e S_1^H + N_p(\alpha_1^r + N_e \beta_1^r);$$
$$\frac{dN_H}{dt} = -\frac{dN_p}{dt}, \tag{8}$$

and the proton density N_p was included in the right side of Eq. (7). The set of Eq. (5) gives the time evolution of ion density in ground state N_1^j for $j \neq Z-1$, whereas N_1^{Z-1} is obtained from Eq. (6). Except for hydrogen-like ions ($j = Z-1$), we neglected ionization from excited levels and recombination into these levels as being less important in determining N_1^j. This exclusion simplified the calculation.

Summation over k in Eq. (6) was ended at $k = k\max + m$ on the assumption that for levels with $k > k_{\max}$, Saha equilibrium with the ground state of the next stage of ionization is satisfied

$$\frac{N^{j-1}_{k_{\max}+m}}{N_1^j N_e} = \frac{g^{j-1}_{k_{\max}+m}}{2g_1^j}\left(\frac{2\pi m_e T_e}{h^2}\right)^{-3/2} \times \exp\left(\frac{E_1^j - E^{j-1}_{k_{\max}+m}}{T_e}\right). \tag{9}$$

E^j_n is the energy of level n of j ions in relation to the ground level, and its statistical weight is g^j_n. In most of the calculations we had $k_{\max} = 10$ and $m = 3$. As a check we used $k_{\max} = 20$ and $m = 5$. We found tht the difference is of the order of a few percent between the two calculations for levels $n = 1,2,\ldots,8$.

As initial conditions we used a steady state approximation for Eqs. (5) and (6) assuming that the plasma is ionized prior ($t<0$) to laser beam heating

$$\frac{dN^j_n}{dt} = 0 \text{ for all } j \text{ and } n, \tag{10}$$
$$T_e = T_{e0},$$

where $T_{e0} = 1$–10 eV with: (a) Constant fluxes: neutral influx $\psi_0^0 = N_0/\tau_0$, neutral outflux $\psi_1^0 = N_1^0/\tau_0^0$, and ion outflux $\psi_1^j = N_1^j/\tau^j$, where $\tau^j = l/v^j$, l is the characteristic length, and v^j is the velocity of the particles; or (b) Given atomic density at $t = 0$, $N_1^0 = C$ and $\psi^j_n = 0$ for all j and n. [In this case, the equation for N_1^0 in the set of Eq. (5) should be omitted at $t = 0$.] The initial values for N^j_n and N_e were found by iteration since N_e appears nonlinearly in Eqs. (5) and (6).

Integration of the set of differential Eqs. (5) and (6) was performed for two cases:

$$\frac{dN_1^j}{dt} \neq 0, \quad \frac{dN_n^{Z-1}}{dt} \neq 0 \quad (k_{\max} + Z \text{ differential equations}) \tag{11a}$$

$$\frac{dN_1^j}{dt} \neq 0, \quad \frac{dN_n^{Z-1}}{dt} = 0$$
$$\text{for } n \geqslant 2 \ (Z+1 \text{ differential equations}). \tag{11b}$$

Approximation (11b) is valid if relaxation times of the excited levels are much shorter than those of ground level. Indeed, C VI level populations calculated with approximation (11b) are very close to those calculated with all

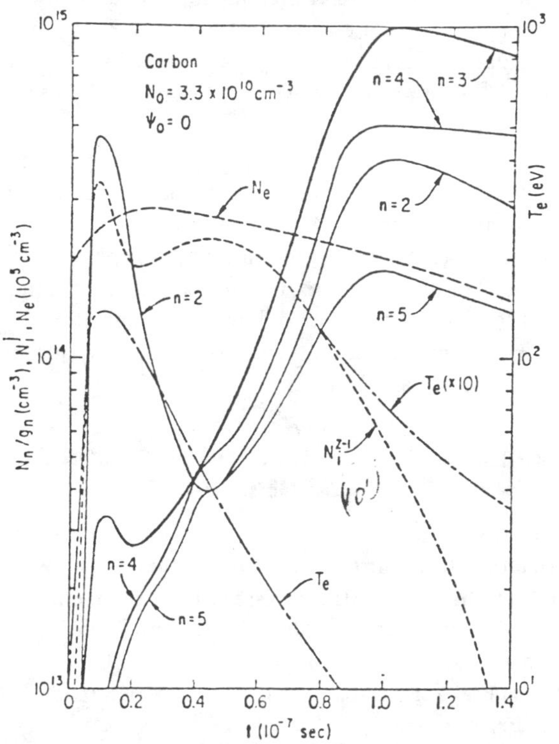

FIG. 3. Time evolution of relative level populations N_n/g_n for four levels ($n = 2,3,4,5$), population of ground level N_1^{Z-1} of C VI and electron density N_e calculated for given $T_e(t)$ profile.

$dN_n^{Z-1}/dt \neq 0$. Also the results were close for high N_e and rapidly changing T_e (beginning of evolution) unless $dT_e/dt < 10\text{–}20$ eV/nsec and $N_e < 10^{20}$ cm^{-3}. In all such cases we applied (11b) which shortened the computation time very much.

IV. POPULATION INVERSION [PRESCRIBED $T_e(t)$ PROFILES]

In Fig. 3 relative populations N_n/g_n of four levels ($n = 2,3,4,5$) and the population N_1^{Z-1} of the ground level of C VI are shown. The calculations were performed for the temperature evolution close to one expected experimentally[55-57] with maximum $T_{e(max)} = 140$ eV and cooling decay time $\tau_E \approx 4\times10^{-8}$ sec. The sets of Eqs. (5) and (6) are nonlinear in electron density N_e. Therefore N_e was calculated by iterating Eq. (7) together with the sets of Eqs. (5) and (6). The initial conditions (10b) were chosen. The neutral density, $N_1^0 = N_0 = 3.3\times10^{10}$ cm^{-3}, for $t = 0$ was found from the steady-state solution of Eqs. (5) and (6) with $T_e(0) = 10$ eV. With electron temperature dropping rapidly and electron density changing much more slowly, we can see a buildup of population inversion for levels $n = 3$ and $n = 4$ with relation to level $m = 2$ when T_e drops below 60 eV. The inversion $N_{inv} = N_n - N_m g_n/g_m$ reaches a maximum $N_{inv} \approx 1.1\times10^{16}$ cm^{-3} for $n = 3$ and $m = 2$ at $t \approx 1.0\times10^{-7}$ sec and $N_{inv} \approx 5\times10^{15}$ cm^{-3} for $n = 4$ and $m = 2$ at $t \approx 1.5\times10^{-7}$ sec.

For oxygen, the maximum temperature should be higher than for carbon in order to get the densities of totally stripped ions, hydrogen-like ions, and electrons high enough. However, increasing the temperature is not sufficient to obtain an inversion as high as that for carbon. To increase the inversion for oxygen, faster cooling is required.

The same results as in Fig. 3 were obtained with initial condition (10a) with $N_0^0 = N_0 = 5\times10^{17}$ cm^{-3} and $\nu_0 = \nu_0^0 = 5\times10^{23}$ cm^{-3} sec^{-1}.

From Fig. 3 it can be seen that an inversion appears at a time when the plasma parameters are changing much more slowly than at the beginning of laser heating. This can imply that by using a steady-state approximation it is possible to obtain similar results. However, the steady-state approximation gives results that are quite different although all the parameters are the same as in the time-dependent case (this will be discussed in Sec. VI).

V. CALCULATIONS OF POPULATION INVERSION WITH $T_e(t)$ FROM ENERGY BALANCE EQUATION

Before we describe the results of the calculations with $T_e(t)$ obtained from the energy balance equation, we will present an estimation for the necessary laser beam energy W'_L needed to maintain the balance with ionization W'_{ioniz}, radiation W'_{rad}, and thermal W'_{th} energies of CPC.

The energy for gas ionization was estimated from the Thomas-Fermi model

$$W'_{ioniz} = 16Z^{7/3} N_1^Z V \times 1.6\times10^{-19}(\mathrm{J}), \tag{12}$$

where V is the plasma volume. For totally ionized carbon with density $N_1^Z = 10^{18}$ cm^{-3} and short plasma column ($l = 10$ cm, $r_0 = 1$ mm) we have $W'_{ioniz} \approx 50$ J. In such a column with average $\bar{T}_e \approx 100$ eV and $\bar{N}_e \approx 10^{19}$ cm^{-3}, the thermal energy is

$$W'_{th} \approx \tfrac{3}{2} N_e T_e V \times 1.6\times10^{-19}(J) \approx 70\mathrm{J}, \tag{13}$$

where it is assumed that $\bar{T}_i \ll \bar{T}_e$ and $N_1^Z \ll N_e$. The main radiation losses W'_{rad} of this plasma can be expected for resonance transitions $2\to1$ of C VI and C V ($\lambda \approx 30$ Å).

$$W'_{rad} \approx N_2^{Z-1} A_{21} h\nu_{21} V \Delta t \times 1.6\times10^{-19}(\mathrm{J}). \tag{14}$$

For C VI the spontaneous transition probability is $A_{21} \approx 7\times10^{11}$ sec^{-1} for photons with energy $h\nu_{21} \approx 400$ eV. If average density $N_2^{Z-1} \approx 5\times10^{14}$ cm^{-3} exists during time $\Delta t \approx 10^{-8}$ sec, the radiation losses W'_{rad} will exceed ≈ 65 J. Taking into account the fact that resonance radiation losses for C V are similar to those for C VI and including nonresonance radiation losses (factor of 1.5) we get $W_{rad} \approx 3W'_{rad} \approx 200$ J. Hence the laser beam should balance the total energy $W_{rad} + W'_{ioniz} + W'_{th} \approx 320$ J. Assuming that the efficiency η of plasma hating by a CO_2 laser is about 50%, we come to the conclusion that laser beam energy should be of the order $W'_L \approx 600$ J, and its power should be $P_L \approx 10\text{–}20$ GW for heating during 30–50 nsec.

The laser beam energy W'_L or power P_L plays the role of an independent parameter in the energy balance equation which is sovled consistently with the set of Eqs. (5) and (6). This additional equation for energy rate is

$$\tfrac{3}{2}\frac{d}{dt}(N_e T_e) = \eta\frac{P_L}{V} - P_{rad} - P_{ioniz} + P_{rec} - P_{\Delta T}, \tag{15}$$

where laser beam power P_L is a constant parameter during time Δt. Radiation losses P_{rad} are included in the form

$$P_{rad} = F\sum_{n=2}^{k_{max}} N_n^{Z-1} A_{n1}^{Z-1} h\nu_{n1}^{Z-1}, \tag{16}$$

where the factor $F \approx 3$ takes into account the radiation losses of the lower stages of ionization. Terms for ionization P_{ioniz} and recombination P_{rec} have the forms

$$P_{ioniz} = \sum_{j=0}^{Z-1} N_e N_j S_j E_j, \tag{17}$$

$$P_{rec} = \sum_{j=1}^{Z} N_e N_j^{j-1} E_j^{j-1}(\alpha_j + N_e\beta_j), \tag{18}$$

and the rate of heat transfer $P_{\Delta T}$ from electrons (mass m_e) to ions (mass M) is

$$P_{\Delta T} = (2m_e/M)\nu_{el} N_e (T_e - T_i), \tag{19}$$

where ν_{el} is the frequency of elastic collisions of electrons with ions. In Eq. (19) we assumed that $T_i \ll T_e$, which is the usual condition in laser heating of a plasma column. Here, we used the same initial conditions as in Sec. IV.

In Fig. 4(a) the results of a calculation of T_e, N_e, and level populations N_n/g_n ($n = 2,3,4,5$) of C VI are shown for effective laser beam power $P_L = 1.5\times10^{10}$ W introduced into the plasma. We simulated heating of the plasma column ($l = 3$ cm, $r = 0.1$ cm) during the time interval from $t = 0$ to $t = 3\times10^{-8}$ sec. The populations of the ground states of C^{4+}, C^{5+}, and C^{6+} ions are shown in Fig. 4(b). In the calculations, the initial conditions (10a) were used with influx $\nu_0^0 = \nu_0 = 3\times10^{23}$ cm^{-3} sec^{-1} and density of neutrals N_0^0

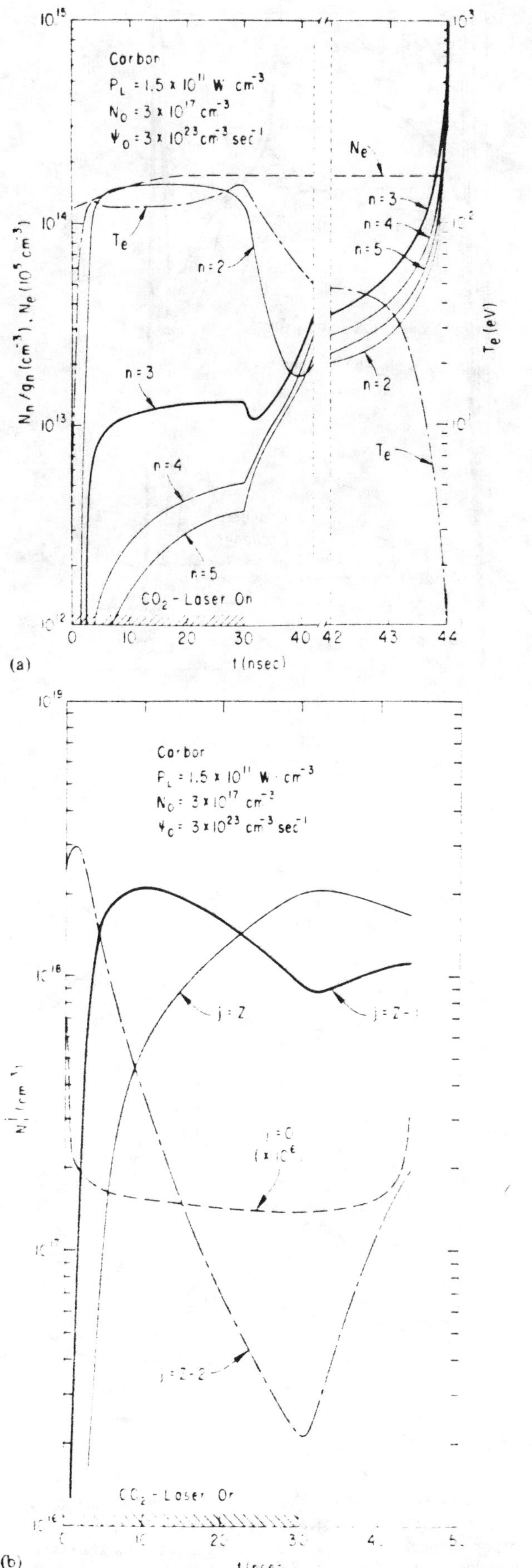

FIG. 4. (a) Time evolution of relative level populations of C VI with $T_e(t)$ calculated from energy balance equation. (b) Time evolution of ground state densities of C^{4+}, C^{5+}, and C^{6+} with $T_e(t)$ and $N_e(t)$ as in (a).

$= N_0 = 3 \times 10^{17}$ cm^{-3}. A temperature of $T_e \approx 120$ eV is reached in the first few nsec of heating and stays at this level until the end of CO_2 laser heating. Under these plasma conditions ionization and radiation losses do not allow a further increase in temperature for chosen CO_2 laser beam power. When heating is terminated, the temperature starts to drop due to radiation cooling in this relatively high density $[N_e \approx (1\text{-}1.5) \times 10^{19}$ cm$^{-3}]$ plasma column. While the temperature decreases, radiation losses increase as a result of population levels increasingly excited by collisonal (three-body) recombination of C^{6+}. This avalanche process produces a very rapidly decreasing T_e and a very rapidly increasing population inversion. Relative populations N_n/g_n for levels $n = 5,4,3,2$ reach values 1×10^{15}, 1.4×10^{15}, 1.7×10^{15}, and 8×10^{14} cm^{-3}, respectively, when T_e drops to 1 eV. If the maximum plasma temperature is higher (e.g when plasma density is lower for the same laser energy as in Fig. 4) then ionization results in a decrease in density of C VI which in turn causes lower radiation loss. This leads to a more slowly decreasing T_e after laser beam termination. Of course, when the temperature finally drops significantly, the processes of increasing inversion (radiation losses) and decreasing temperature again becomes fast. Unfortunately, in Fig. 4(a) the peak of the population density, its duration and its subsequent decrease are not shown because of an unresolved problem with our computer integration for a very rapidly dropping temperature near 1 eV and very large $\exp(\Delta E_{n1}/T_e)$. Therefore the results presented correspond only to the rising part of the buildup of the level population inversion, but not to its maximum.

In order to obtain a high $N_e (10^{19}\text{–}10^{20}$ cm$^{-3})$, with a correspondingly high inversion, the neutral gas density or influx should be high ($N_0 \approx 10^{17}\text{–}10^{18}$ cm^{-3}, $\Psi_0 = 10^{23}\text{–}10^{24}$ cm^{-3} sec^{-1}) and of course, laser beam power should be relatively high ($P_L \approx 10^{10}\text{–}10^{12}$ W) for a plasma column with $l \approx 1\text{–}10$ cm and $r_0 = 0.1\text{–}0.2$ cm.

VI. EFFECT OF CHARGE EXCHANGE ON LEVEL POPULATIONS

The papers of Vinogradov and Sobel'man[44] and Dixon *et al.*[46,47] stimulated our interest in the influence of charge exchange on level populations. We included the charge-exchange process (3) for carbon in Eq. (6) in the from N^{Z-1} $N_0 \langle \sigma_{c\text{-}ex} v \rangle$ for level $n = n^*$. Following Salop and Olson,[65] $n^* = 4$ was chosen for C VI. The same term was subtracted in Eq. (5) for the ground state of populations of C^{6+} and C^0 and added for the C^{5+} equation. In most of our calculations we used the Salop and Olson charge-exchange cross section. They suggest that for process (3) it should be similar to the one for the process

$$C^{6+} + H^0 \rightarrow (C^{5+})^* + H^+ + \Delta E \,, \quad (20)$$

with asymptotic value $\sigma_{c\text{-}ex} \approx 1.4 \times 10^{-16} Z^{3/2}$ (cm^2) for particles with relative velocity $v \gtrsim 5 \times 10^7$ cm/sec. For lower velocities, e.g. $v = 0.5$, 1.0, and 3×10^7 cm/sec, the corresponding cross sections[65,66] are $\sigma_{c\text{-}ex} \approx 1$, 5, and 20×10^{-16} cm^2, respectively. We used two values of the rate coefficient, $\langle \sigma_{c\text{-}ex} v \rangle = 5 \times 10^{-10}$ and 5×10^{-9} cm^3 sec^{-1}.

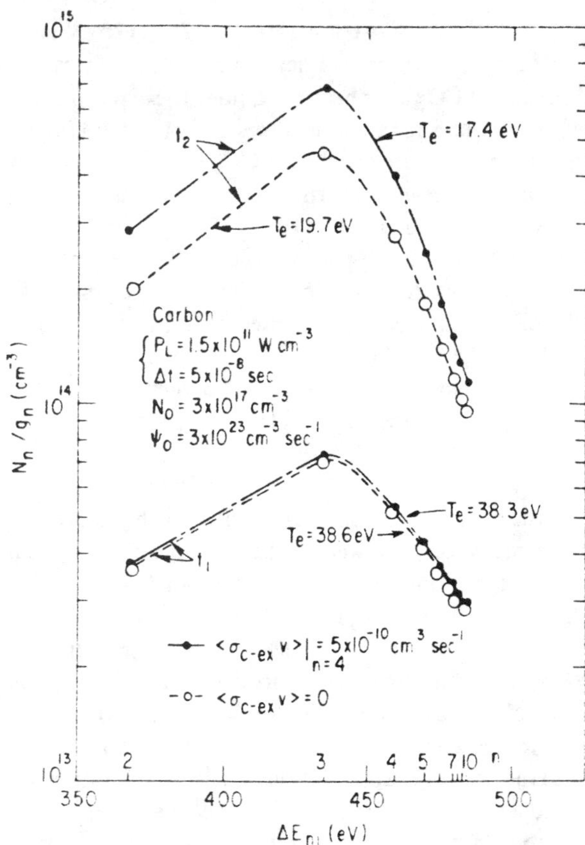

FIG. 5. Relative level populations of C VI calculated with and without charge exchange for times t_1 = 140 nsec and t_2 = 148 nsec from beginning of population evolution. Times t_1 and t_2 are chosen on the fast raising part of level populations.

The influence of the charge-exchange process on the formation of an inversion can be seen in Fig. 5 where results of calculations with ($\langle\sigma_{c\text{-}ex} v\rangle = 5\times10^{-10}$ cm^3 sec^{-1}) and without it are shown. The calculations for C VI level populations (n = 2–10) correspond to two different times of population evolution, t_1 = 140 nsec and t_2 = 148 nsec from the beginning of the simulation of plasma heating (they correspond to 90 and 98 nsec, respectively, from the end of plasma heating). These times were chosen to lie on the rapidly rising part of the curves. Electron temperature and density reached their maximum values, T_e = 490 eV and $N_e = 1.8\times10^{19}$ cm^{-3}, respectively, at the end of plasma heating. A plasma column (l = 10 cm, r_0 = 0.1 cm) was assumed to be heated by a CO_2 laser beam of power $P_L = 4.5\times10^{10}$ W during time Δt = 50 nsec. For this temperature evolution with a relatively high peak, radiation losses start to become large enough at t = 135 nsec to cool the plasma rapidly. From Fig. 5 it can be seen that for relatively high electron density, resonance charge exchange increases the population inversion. However, this process is enhanced more by the increased rate of plasma cooling as opposed to an increase in population of a certain level. In Fig. 5 neutral density N_1^0 increases rapidly between t_1 and t_2 changing the value of the charge-exchange term $N_1^0 N^{Z+}\langle\sigma_{c\text{-}ex} v\rangle$ from 10^3 cm^{-3} sec^{-1} at t_1 to 10^4 cm^{-3} sec^{-1} at t_2. (Please note that N_1^0 is not the same as N_0.

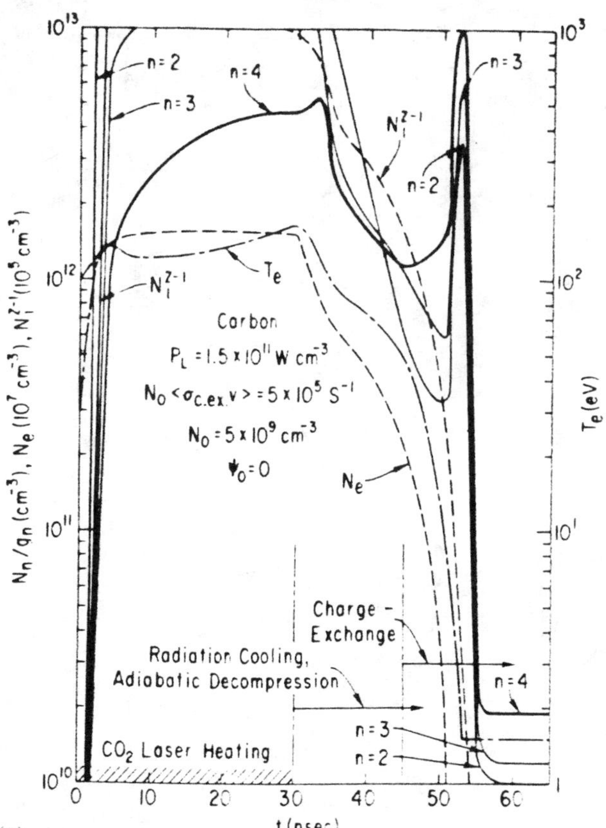

(a)

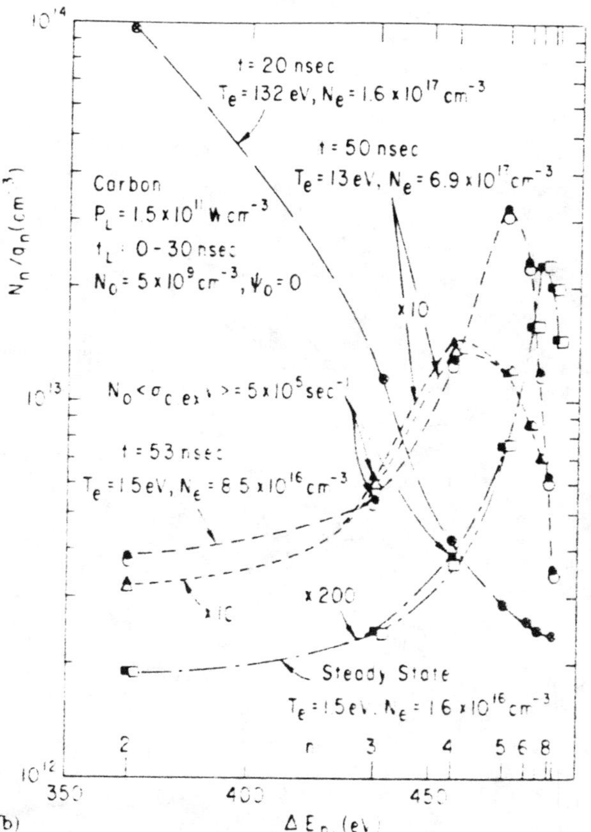

(b)

FIG. 6. (a) Time evolution of C VI level populations for laser heated, radiation cooled, and adiabatically decompressed plasma. For $t > 53$ nsec relaxation of population to steady-state conditions are shown. Charage-exchange term is included for $t \geq 45$ nsec. (b) Relative populations for levels with n = 2,3,....,9 at t_1 = 20 nsec, t_2 = 50 nsec, t_3 = 53 nsec, and for steady-state conditions with and without charge exchange taken into account (solid and open symbols, respectively).

The latter is related to the initial conditions.) The density of the totally stripped ions, $N^{6+} \simeq 2\times10^{18}\,\mathrm{cm}^{-3}$, does not change significantly. However, for a much larger charge-exchange term, the depopulation of C^{6+} by charge exchange can be strong enough to have a negative effect on the population inversion in this high-density plasma. Charge exchange increases the population of level n^*. Also, rapid relaxation processes (collisonal and radiative) increase the populations of levels $n < n^*$ when T_e is low. This is particularly true for level $n = 1$. In such a case, the decrease of the density of C^{6+} is faster than the increase of the population of level n^* of C^{5+}, which leads to a decreased time interval when a high degree of population inversion exists.

For a better understanding of the effect of charge exchange on population inversions as well as the results of Dixon *et al.*,[46,47] we provide calculations which model plasma heating in the first 30 nsec followed by radiation cooling and adiabatic decompositon. At $t_0 = 45$ nsec the charge-exchange term was "turned on" in the equations (a wait of time t_0 was used to simulate a delay in interaction between neutrals and ions). The charge-exchange term $N_0\langle\sigma_{c\text{-}ex}v\rangle = 5\times10^5\,\mathrm{sec}^{-1}$ was similar to the one reported by Dixon *et al.*[47] Figure 6(a) shows the time evolutions of T_e, N_e, N_1^{Z-1}, and N_n/g_n $(n = 2,3,4)$. When the temperature drops below 10 eV inversion increases rapidly. However, the rapid decrease of N_e causes the peak of the inversion to be short in time. At $t = 53$ nsec the temperature drops to 1.5 (similar to the temperature in Dixon *et al.*[47]). From this moment on we kept temperature constant, $T_e = 1.5$ eV, in order to observe the relaxation of populations to steady-state conditions. The level population plots in Fig. 6(b) are for certain times of interest chosen from the time evolutions in Fig. 6(a). At $t_1 = 20$ nsec ($N_1^Z = 1.3\times10^8\,\mathrm{cm}^{-3}$, $N_1^{Z-1} = 1.7\times10^{18}\,\mathrm{cm}^{-3}$), when collisional ionization and excitation processes dominate, inversion is not created. When the temperature has dropped to 13 eV at $t_2 = 50$ nsec ($N_1^Z = 8.6\times10^{16}\,\mathrm{cm}^{-3}$, $N_1^{Z-1} = 3.5\times10^{16}\,\mathrm{cm}^{-3}$), the highest population has level $n = 4$. However, only a small effect of charge exchange is noticeable (increasing the charge-exchange term 10^3 times higher produces only an increase of 10 times in populations of levels $n = 2,3$, and 4). At the peak of the inversion, $t_3 = 53$ nsec, where the population is approximately an order of magnitude higher than that at t_2, the influence of charge exchange is negligible. Even for a charge-exchange term 10^3 times higher there was practically no change in population distribution (at t_3 we have $N_1^Z = 6.2\times10^{15}\,\mathrm{cm}^{-3}$ and $N_1^{Z-1} = 2.5\times10^{15}\,\mathrm{cm}^{-3}$). In the steady state, the maximum population shifted toward $n = 7$ under the condition that the population density was 200 times lower than that for 53 nsec. A somewhat higher population of level $n = 4$ may be seen with charge exchange taken into account.

The charge-exchange process significantly modified the time evolution of the level populations in the plasma with $N_e < 10^{17}\,\mathrm{cm}^{-3}$. This can be seen by comparing population of level $n = 4$ with charge exchange and without charge exchange in Fig. 7. Calculations were performed in both cases with the other conditions the same. Temperature and density rise was calculated for lower laser beam power. Then, N_e

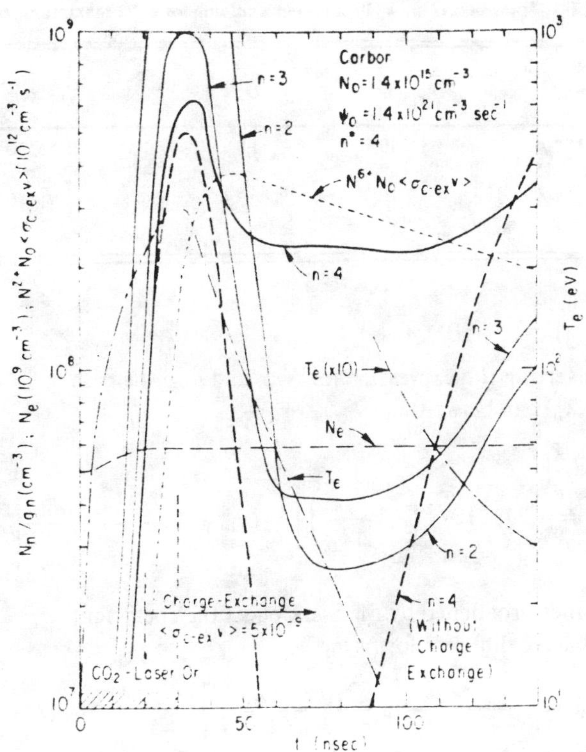

FIG. 7. (a) Time evolution of C VI level populations calculated with charge exchange term taken into account. Relatively low, constant electron density and rapidly decreasing electron temperature was assumed during cooling simulation. (b) Results of the same calculation as for (a) for $n = 4$ but without charge exchange. Calculated population of level $n = 4$ without charge exchange is shown for comparison.

was kept constant ($N_e \simeq 6\times10^{16}\,\mathrm{cm}^{-3}$) while T_e was made to decrease rapidly, somewhat arbitrarily. Charge exchange had a strong effect on the buildup of population inversion, but only for electron temperature $T_e > 20$ eV when three-body recombination was low. For $T_e < 5$ eV, the effect of charge exchange diminished and later reached a point where it had a negative effect on population inversions. Therefore, in order to make a judgment about the effect of charge exchange on population inversion in an experiment, the absolute densities of level populations as a function of time are required.

VII. GAINS

The crucial point of this paper is the value of the expected total gain $G = \int \kappa\, dx$ in a confined plasma column, where $\kappa(x,t,\lambda_0)$ is the gain per unit length at the center of line λ_0. In gain calculation, for $\kappa(x,t,\lambda_0)$ the following expression (e.g. Refs. 70 and 71) was used:

$$\kappa(x,t,\lambda_0) = \sigma_{nm}(\lambda_0)N_{\mathrm{inv}}(x,t)\,, \tag{21}$$

where $\sigma_{nm}(\lambda)$ is the cross section for stimulated emission. For the Gaussian profile of the line, $\sigma_{nm}(\lambda)$ has the form

$$\sigma_{nm}(\lambda) = \frac{\lambda^4}{8\pi c}\left(\frac{4\ln2}{\pi}\right)^{1/2}\frac{A_{nm}}{\Delta\lambda_D}\exp\left[-\left(\frac{\lambda-\lambda_0}{\Delta\lambda_D}\right)^2 4\ln2\right]. \tag{22}$$

TABLE I. Total gain G in $l = 10$ cm plasma column for C VI maximum level population inversions presented in Figs. 3, 4(a), and 5.

Wavelength, $n \rightarrow m$	Figure 3		Figure 4(a)		Figure 5	
	N_{inv} (cm^{-3})	G	N_{inv} (cm^{-3})	G	N_{inv} (cm^{-3})	G
$\lambda = 182$ Å $3 \rightarrow 2$	1.1×10^{16}	1.9×10^{2}	1.6×10^{16}	2.8×10^{2}	7.6×10^{15}	1.4×10^{2}
$\lambda = 135$ Å $4 \rightarrow 2$	5×10^{15}	3.6	1.9×10^{16}	1.3×10^{1}	3.8×10^{15}	2.8

By inserting the expression for N_{inv} and σ_{nm} the gain $\kappa(x,t,\lambda_0)$ can be written as

$$\kappa(x, t, \lambda_0) = 1.24 \times 10^{-12} \left(\lambda^4 \frac{A_{nm}}{\Delta\lambda_D}\right) \left[N_n(x, t) - \frac{N_m(x, t) g_n}{g_m}\right]. \tag{23}$$

For lines broadened by the Stark effect the coefficients σ_{nm} and κ have different forms, i.e.,

$$\sigma_{nm}(\lambda) = \frac{\lambda^4}{n\pi^2 c} \frac{A_{nm}}{\Delta\lambda_s} \left[1 + 4\left(\frac{\lambda - \lambda_0}{\Delta\lambda_s}\right)^2\right]^{-1}, \tag{24}$$

and

$$\kappa(x, t, \lambda_0) = 8.4 \times 10^{-13} \left(\frac{\lambda_0^4 A_{nm}}{\Delta\lambda_s}\right) N_{inv}(x, t), \tag{25}$$

where $\Delta\lambda_s$ is the half-intensity width of the line broadened by the Stark effect. In Eqs. (23) and (25) λ_0 and $\Delta\lambda$ are in cm, N_{inv} is in cm^{-3}, and κ is in cm^{-1}. If $\Delta\lambda_D$ and $\Delta\lambda_s$ have comparable values in formulas for $\sigma_{nm}(\lambda)$, the Voigt profile should be used. The Doppler width $\Delta\lambda_D$ has been calculated from the formula

$$\Delta\lambda_D = 7.6 \times 10^{-5} \lambda_0 (T_i/M)^{1/2}, \tag{26}$$

where ion temperature T_i is in eV, and M is the atomic weight of the ion. The widths of $\Delta\lambda_s$ for different λ_0 of hydrogen-like ions C VI (or O VIII) were estimated from formulas for the quasistatic linear Stark effect $\Delta\lambda_{s1}$ and the electron impact broadening $\Delta\lambda_{s2}$. $\Delta\lambda_s$ was chosen as the lesser of $\Delta\lambda_{s1}$ and $\Delta\lambda_{s2}$.[74] The $\Delta\lambda_{s1}$ and $\Delta\lambda_{s2}$ were calculated from the following formulas[74,75]

$$\Delta\lambda_{s1} \simeq (n^2 - m^2)\lambda_0^2 \frac{h}{\pi^2 cm} \frac{\bar{Z}_r}{Z} N_r^{2/3}, \tag{27}$$

and

$$\Delta\lambda_{s2} \simeq \frac{3n^4\lambda_0^2}{2\pi c} \frac{h}{mZ} \frac{N_e}{v_e}, \tag{28}$$

where Z is the ion charge and $\bar{Z}_r$ is the average perturbed charge of density N_r, n and m are the principal quantum numbers of the upper and lower levels of line λ_0, v_e is the electron velocity, which can be approximated by the electron thermal velocity. By comparing $\Delta\lambda_D$ and $\Delta\lambda_s$ from Eqs. (26)–(28) it can be seen that for $N_e > 10^{16}$ cm^{-3}, $\lambda_0 > 100$ Å and $T_i < 5$ eV the broadening of the lines is due mainly to the Stark effect.

In Table I the calculated total gain G in a plasma column $l = 10$ cm is given for maximum inversions from Figs. 3, 4(a), and 5. This very high gain for the $3 \rightarrow 2$ transition ($\lambda_0 = 182$ Å) indicates that even a shorter plasma column with an electron density one order of magnitude lower should be sufficient for obtaining strong lasing action. If the rate coefficients used were too favorable for calculating inversion (an uncertainty factor of 2–3 in rate coefficients may be expected) then the real gain κ would be lower. Experimentally, one can compensate for this uncertainty by simply modifying the length of the plasma column.

VIII. CONCLUSION

A new proposal for soft x-ray lasing in a confined plasma column was presented. Inversion was considered in carbon and oxygen columns without mirrors and with a small ratio of column radius to length. It was assumed that the plasma was heated by a CO_2 laser and terminated in the radial direction by a strong solenoidal magnetic field. This approach allowed for a slow decrease of $N_e(t)$ and a faster decrease of $T_e(t)$ by radiation losses which, in turn, provided good conditions for population inversion by recombination processes in the plasma column. Resonance charge exchange can lead to the increase of populations of selected levels in a plasma with electron density $N_e < 10^{17}$ cm^{-3}. For a higher electron density ($N_e \simeq 10^{19}$ cm^{-3}) the charge-exchange process stimulated an increased inversion through rapid decrease of $T_e(t)$ rather than by selective level population.

By extensive calculations of the time evolution of level populations it was shown that for a CO_2 laser beam with power $P_L \simeq 10^{10}$ W an inversion for C VI ions of order $N_{inv} \simeq 10^{14}$–10^{15} cm^{-3} can be obtained in the spectral range 100–200 Å. For a shorter wavelength ($\lambda_0 \simeq 27$ Å) the laser beam power should be about three orders of magnitude higher in order to reach $T_e \simeq 2000$ eV in a dense plasma column ($N_e \simeq 10^{20}$ cm^{-3}). This power would be necessary for strong depopulation by ionization of the ground state of C VI during plasma heating.

Calculated gain κ for different heating and plasma conditions indicates the possibility of obtaining strong lasing action ($G > 100$) in the amplified spontaneous emission regime (without mirrors) in the spectral range 100–200 Å. It is possible to obtain this G for a relatively short plasma column ($l \simeq 3$–10 cm) and moderate laser power.

ACKNOWLEDGMENTS

We are deeply indebted to Dr. T.K. Chu and Dr. L.C.

Johnson for providing us with all information about their CO_2 laser heated plasma experiments. Our appreciation is also extended to Dr. D. Dimock, Dr. H. Furth, Dr. E. Hinnov, Dr. T. Stix, and Dr. S. Yoshikawa for the fruitful discussions we shared. Also we would like to acknowledge Dr. K. Bol, Dr. E. Hinnov, and Dr. L.C. Johnson for very constructive comments on the manuscript. We are grateful for the continuing support of Dr. M. Gottlieb and Dr. H. Furth. This work was supported by the United States Department of Energy Contract No. EY-76-C-02-3073.

[1]R.W. Waynant and R.C. Elton, Proceedings of IEEE **64**, 1059 (1976).

[2]G. Chapline and L. Wood, Phys. Today **28**, 40 (1975).

[3]R.M.J. Cotterill, Appl. Phys. Lett. **12**, 403 (1968).

[4]A.V. Kolpakov, R.N. Kuzmin, and V.M. Ryaboy, J. Appl. Phys. **41**, 3549 (1970).

[5]W.L. Bond, M.A. Dugnay, and P.M. Rentzepis, Appl. Phys. Lett. **10**, 216 (1967).

[6]A.G. Molchanov, Sov. Phys.-Usp. **15**, 124 (1972).

[7]V.A. Bushuev and R.N. Kuzmin, Sov. Phys.-Usp. **17**, 942 (1975).

[8]M.A. Dugnay and P.M. Rentzepis, Appl. Phys. Lett. **10**, 350 (1967).

[9]Yu. L. Stankevich, Sov. Phys.-Dokl. **15**, 356 (1970).

[10]R.A. McCorkle, Phys. Rev. Lett. **29**, 982 (1972).

[11]W.W. Jones and A.W. Ali, Phys. Lett. **50A**, 101 (1974).

[12]E.J. McGuire, Phys. Rev. Lett. **35**, 844 (1975).

[13]R.C. Elton, Appl. Opt. **14**, 2243 (1975)

[14]T.S. Axelrod, Phys. Rev. A **13**, 376 (1976); A **15**, 1132 (1977).

[15]B.A. Norton and N.J. Peacock, J. Phys. B. **8**, 989 (1975).

[16]A.V. Vinogradov, I.I. Sobelman, and E.A. Yukov, Sov. J. Quantum Electron. **5**, 59 (1975).

[17]R.A. Andrews, in *Progress in Lasers and Laser Fusion*, edited by A. Perlmutter and S.M. Widmayer (Plenum, New York, 1975), p. 235.

[18]L.J. Palumbo, in *Proc. of Int'l. Conf. on the Physics of X-Ray Spectra* (Nat'l. Bureau of Standards, Gaithersburg, MD, 1976), p. 365.

[19]I.N. Knyazev and V.S. Letokhov, Opt. Commun. **3**, 332 (1971).

[20]T.C. Bristow, M.J. Lubin, J.M. Forsyth, E.B. Goldman, and J.M. Soures, Opt. Commun. **5**, 315 (1972).

[21]B. Lax and A.H. Guenther, Appl. Phys. Lett. **21**, 361 (1972).

[22]R.W. Waynant, Appl. Phys. Lett. **22**, 419 (1973).

[23]R.C. Elton, T.N. Lee, J. Davis, J.F. Reintjes, R.H. Dixon, R.C. Eckardt, K.G. Whitney, J.L. DeRosa, L.J. Palumbo, and R.A. Andrews, Phys. Fenn. Suppl. S1 **9**, 400 (1974)

[24]K.G. Whitney and J. Davis, J. Appl. Phys. **46**, 4103 (1975)

[25]J. Davis and K.G. Whitney, Appl. Phys. Lett. **29**, 419 (1976).

[26]L.I. Gudzenko and L.A. Shelepin, Sov. Phys. JETP **18**, 998 (1964), Sov. Phys.-Dokl. **10**, 147 (1965)

[27]B.F. Gordiets, L.I. Gudzenko, and L.A. Shelepin, Sov. Phys.-JETP **28**, 489 (1969)

[28]L.I. Gudzenko, Yu. K. Zemtsov, and S.I. Yakovlenko, Sov. Phys.-JETP Lett. **12**, 167 (1970)

[29]L.I. Gudzenko, L.A. Shelepin, and S.I. Yakovlenko, Sov. Phys.-Usp. **17**, 848 (1975).

[30]J. Peyraud and N. Peyraud, J. Appl. Phys. **43**, 2993 (1972)

[31]W.L. Bohn, Appl. Phys. Lett. **24**, 15 (1974)

[32]W.W. Jones and A.W. Ali, Appl. Phys. Lett. **26**, 450 (1975)

[33]J.M. Green and W.T. Silfvast, Appl. Phys. Lett. **28**, 253 (1976).

[34]T.S. Axelrod, G.F. Chapline, and L.L. Wood, University of California, Lawrence Livermore Lab., Report UCRL-76875 (1975).

[35]E. Ya. Konov and K.N. Koshelov, Sov. J.-Quantum Electron **4**, 1340 (1975).

[36]E. Ya. Konov, K.N. Koshelov, Yu. A. Levykin, Yu. V. Sidelnikov, and E.S. Churilov, Sov. J.-Quantum Electron **6**, 308 (1976).

[37]G.J. Pert, J. Phys. B **9**, 3301 (1976).

[38]G.J. Tallents, J. Phys. B **10**, 1769 (1977).

[39]F.E. Irons and N.J. Peacock, J. Phys. B **7**, 1109 (1974).

[40]R.J. Dewhurst, D. Jacoby, G.J. Pert, and S.A. Ramsden, Phys. Rev. Lett. **37**, 1265 (1976).

[41]K. Sato, M. Shiho, M. Hosokawa, H. Sugawara, T. Oda, and T. Sasaki, Phys. Rev. Lett. **39**, 1074 (1977).

[42]A. Skorupski and S. Suckewer, Phys. Lett. **46A**, 473 (1974).

[43]S. Suckewer, R.J. Hawryluk, M. Okabayashi, and J.A. Schmidt, Appl. Phys. Lett. **29**, 537 (1976).

[44]A.V. Vinogradov and I.I. Sobel'man, Zh. Eksp. Teor. Fiz. **63**, 2113 (1973); Sov. Phys. JETP **36**, 1115 (1973).

[45]H.J. Zwally and D.W. Koopman, Phys. Rev. A **2**, 1850 (1970).

[46]R.M. Dixon and R.C. Elton, Phys. Rev. Lett. **38**, 1072 (1977).

[47]R.M. Dixon, J.F. Seely, and R.C. Elton, Phys. Rev. Lett. **40**, 122 (1978)

[48]J.G. Kepros, E.M. Eyring, and F.W. Cagle, Jr., Proc. Acad. Sci. U.S. **69**, 1744 (1972); J.G. Kepros, Appl. Opt. **13**, 695 (1974).

[49]P. Jaegle, G. Jamelot, A. Carillon, A. Sureau, and D. Dhez, Phys. Rev. Lett. **33**, 1070 (1974); P. Jaegle, A. Carillon, D. Dhaz, G. Jamelot, A. Sureau, and M. Cukier, Phys. Lett. **36A**, 167 (1971).

[50]S. Slutz, G. Zimmerman, W. Lokke, G. Chaphine, and L. Wood, University of California, Lawrence Livermore Lab., Report UCID-16290 (1973).

[51]F.P.J. Valero, Appl. Phys. Lett. **25**, 64 (1974).

[52]W.T. Silfvast, J.M. Green, and O.R. Wood II, Phys. Rev. Lett. **35**, 435 (1975).

[53]Recent data by Jaegle *et al.*[76] supported their previous claim about negative absorption of AlIV 117 Å line.

[54]The idea and the experimental arrangement discussed here were presented by one of us (S.S.) at the Plasma Physics Laboratory in January 1976.

[55]L.C. Johnson and T.K. Chu, Phys. Rev. Lett. **32**, 517 (1974); also *7th Europ. Conf. on Controlled Fusion and Plasma Physics*, Lausanne, Switzerland, 1975.

[56]T.K. Chu and L.C. Johnson, Phys. Fluids **18**, 1460 (1975).

[57]N.M. Burnett and A.A. Offenberger, J. Appl. Phys. **45**, 2155 (1974)

[58]T.K. Chu and L.C. Johnson (private communication).

[59]J. Schuss, T.K. Chu, and L.C. Johnson, Phys. Rev. Lett. **40**, 27 (1978)

[60]R.A. Gross, Nucl. Fusion **15**, 729 (1975)

[61]K. Ando, M. Okabayashi, S. Suckewer, V. Arunasalam, R.J. Hawryluk and J. Wilson, Nucl. Fusion **16**, 797 (1976).

[62]T. Holstein, Phys. Rev. **72**, 1212 (1947).

[63]L. Biberman, Zh. Exp. Theor. Fiz. **17**, 416 (1947).

[64]S. Suckewer and A. Kuszell, J.Quant. Spectrosc. Radiat. Transfer **16**, 53 (1976).

[65]A. Salop and R.E. Olson, Phys. Rev. A **13**, 1312 (1976)

[66]A. Salop, Phys. Rev. **A13**, 1321 (1976)

[67]W.L. Wiese, M.W. Smith, and B.M. Glennon, *Atomic Transition Probabilities*, (NBS, Washington, 1966)

[68]H.W. Drawin, Z. Physik **225**, 483 (1969)

[69]M.J. Seaton, Mon. Not. R. Astron. Soc. **119**, 81 (1959)

[70]R.W.P. McWhirter, in *Plasma Diagnostic Techniques*, edited by R.H. Huddlestone and S.L. Leonard (Academic, New York, 1965)

[71]H.R. Griem, *Plasma Spectroscopy* (McGraw-Hill, New York, 1964)

[72]L. Allen and D.G.C. Jones, *Principles of Gas Lasers* (Butterworths, London, 1967).

[73]A.V. Elickij, B.M. Smirnov, *Gas Lasers*-in Russian (Atomizdat, Moscow, 1971)

[74]H.R. Griem, *Spectral Line Broadening by Plasmas* (Academic, New York, 1974).

[75]V.A. Bhagavatula and B. Yaakobi, Opt. Commun. **24**; 331 (1978)

[76]P. Jaegle, G. Jamelot, A. Carillon, and A. Sureau, J. Phys. (Paris) **39**, C4-75 (1978)

Reprinted with permission from *IEEE Journal of Quantum Electronics,* Vol. QE-17(3), pp. 418-422 (March 1981).

XUV Lasers by Quartet to Doublet Energy Transfer in Alkali Atoms

JOSHUA E. ROTHENBERG AND STEPHEN E. HARRIS, FELLOW, IEEE

***Abstract*—The paper describes and compares several systems in neutral Li and K for constructing lasers in the XUV spectral region. The systems are based on population storage in metastable quartet levels, with subsequent laser transfer to doublet levels which are themselves stable against autoionization.**

RAPIDLY decreasing spontaneous emission times at shorter wavelengths make it likely that lasers in the spectral region below 1000 Å will operate by first storing population in a metastable level [1], [2]. An intense, short pulse tunable laser would then be used to rapidly transfer this population to the upper level of the lasing transition.

In a recent paper [3], it was proposed that the quartet levels of alkali atoms be used for storage, with subsequent transfer to a level in the doublet series. The doublet level will typically be chosen so that, to first order, it is coulombically stable against autoionization. Lasing would occur to a lower level in the doublet series. Energy level diagrams for the proposed technique as it applies to systems in lithium and potassium are shown in Fig. 1.

In both cases, the storage levels are pure quartets and lie at or near the bottom of the quartet manifold. The levels are populated by direct electron excitation (optical fluorescence within the quartet manifold of Li has been observed for many years [4]), and it is expected that they may also be populated by recombination and by charge transfer. Natural lifetimes of the Li $1s2s2p\,^4P^0_{5/2}$ and K $3p^5 4s4p\,^4D_{7/2}$ levels of 5.8 and 90 μs, respectively, have been measured by Feldman and Novick [5].

Radiative emission at 207 Å, originating from the even parity (upper laser) level in neutral Li has been seen in a beam foil experiment [6], and more recently in a microwave excited plasma [7].

A key reason for studying the quartet to doublet transfer systems of this paper, as opposed to triplet to singlet systems in the ion [1], [2] (for example, $Li^+ 1s2s\,^3S \rightarrow Li^+ 1s2p\,^1P \rightarrow Li^+ 1s^2$), is that the systems of this paper provide a lower laser level which is not the ground level of the species. This level may be emptied by the same laser used for the quartet to doublet transfer, or perhaps by a second laser tuned to a discrete level near to the lowest continuum.

The technique described here is based on at least a partial breakdown of LS coupling, thereby allowing transfer on the intercombination line connecting the quartet to the doublet series. For low levels of light atoms such as Li, the breakdown of LS coupling is small and laser power densities of about 10^{11} W/cm^2 are required for complete transfer in a time short compared to the spontaneous emission time. There are two ways to increase the breakdown of LS coupling and to thereby reduce the necessary laser power density for transfer. The first is to work in a heavier atom, such as K, which has a larger coulombic gradient and therefore a larger spin-orbit matrix element. The second is to use a storage level which is somewhat higher in the quartet manifold and to thereby make use of smaller energy denominators between appropriate levels in the quartet and doublet series.

Either of these approaches has several additional effects. Of most importance, the breakdown of LS coupling allows an admixing of terms within the doublet series. This, in turn, may allow autoionization of the upper laser level, thereby reducing the gain cross section, and requiring that the population transfer take place in a shorter time. Also, to the extent that long storage times are desired, one may only use those quartet levels which have the maximum value of J for a particular configuration. Irrespective of the breakdown of LS coupling, these levels are pure quartets and should not autoionize coulombically.

In the following sections of the paper we will give the results of calculations and estimates for several quartet-doublet transfer systems in K and Li, and will compare the results with those obtained earlier in Li. Additional systems in Na and Rb will be briefly discussed.

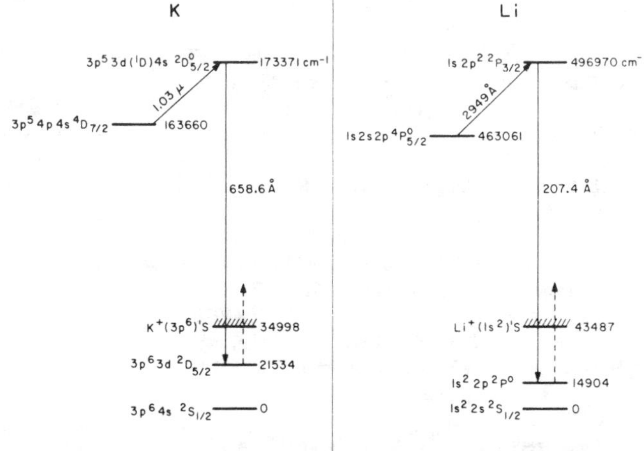

Fig. 1. Energy level diagrams for quartet to doublet transfer in Li and K. An incident laser is used to transfer population from a quartet storage level to a doublet (upper) laser level. The same laser, or a second laser, is used to deplete the lower laser level.

Manuscript received August 5, 1980; revised October 3, 1980. This work was supported by the U.S. Office of Naval Research. The work performed by J. E. Rothenberg was supported by the Fannie and John Hertz Foundation.

The authors are with the Edward L. Ginzton Laboratory, Stanford University, Stanford, CA 94305.

TABLE I

LS Coupled Basis States and Abbreviations for the $3p^5 3d4s$ $J = 5/2$ Configuration

$\lvert\Phi_i\rangle$	Abbreviation
$3p^5 3d(^1D)4s\ ^2D^o_{5/2}$	$(^1D)^2D$
$3p^5 3d(^3D)4s\ ^2D^o_{5/2}$	$(^3D)^2D$
$3p^5 3d(^1F)4s\ ^2F^o_{5/2}$	$(^1F)^2F$
$3p^5 3d(^3F)4s\ ^2F^o_{5/2}$	$(^3F)^2F$
$3p^5 3d(^3D)4s\ ^4D^o_{5/2}$	$(^3D)^4D$
$3p^5 3d(^3F)4s\ ^4F^o_{5/2}$	$(^3F)^4F$
$3p^5 3d(^3P)4s\ ^4P^o_{5/2}$	$(^3P)^4P$

TABLE II

Estimated Electrostatic and Spin-Orbit Parameters for the $3p^5 3d4s$ Configurations of Potassium

$F^2(pd)$	=	32116 cm^{-1}
$G^1(pd)$	=	37129
$G^3(pd)$	=	21598
$G^1(ps)$	=	2687
$G^2(sd)$	=	12577
φ_p	=	1391
φ_d	=	14

Potassium

A. Diagonalization of the Hamiltonian; Eigenfunctions

Much of the work in this section is based on the spectroscopic results and calculations of Mansfield and Ottley [8] and Mansfield [9]. The key step in the calculation is to find the $J = 5/2$ eigenfunctions of the $3p^5 3d4s$ configuration as components of an LS coupled basis set. Matrix elements of the (true) eigenfunctions are then obtained as sums of the products of mixing coefficients and matrix elements within the basis set. The basis states, along with the abbreviations we will use, are listed in Table I.

The eigenfunctions are found by diagonalizing the Hamiltonian matrix in this basis. Following Mansfield [9], the electrostatic matrix elements are found from Slater [10]. We used the formulas given for the $p^5 d$ configuration and used Van Vleck's theorem for the addition of the s electron. The Slater-Condon parameters were calculated by Mansfield in a single configuration Hartree-Fock calculation [9], and were subsequently modified by Mansfield and Ottley [8]. These parameters are shown in Table II. The spin-orbit matrix elements can be calculated directly from Roth [11] in terms of the radial parameters φ_p and φ_d. φ_p and φ_d were calculated in [9] and modified in [8], and they are also given in Table II. The parameter φ_d is much smaller than φ_p and we have neglected its contribution.

The results of the diagonalization of this matrix are given in Table III, where the eigenstates are named by their principal components and the eigenenergies are relative to that of the $(^1D)^2D$ eigenstate.

TABLE III

State Compositions and Their Positions for the Configuration $3p^5 3d4s$ with $J = 5/2$

Eigenstate	State Mixing Coefficients							Relative Position (cm^{-1})
	$C[(^1D)^2D]$	$C[(^3D)^2D]$	$C[(^3D)^4D]$	$C[(^1F)^2F]$	$C[(^3F)^2F]$	$C[(^3F)^4F]$	$C[(^3P)^4P]$	
$\lvert\psi_{(^1D)^2D}\rangle$	0.92	0.32	0.21	- 0.007	0.068	0.04	- 0.06	0
$\lvert\psi_{(^3D)^2D}\rangle$	- 0.32	0.92	0.005	0.17	- 0.13	0.01	- 0.008	4153
$\lvert\psi_{(^1F)^2F}\rangle$	0.12	- 0.17	- 0.11	0.91	- 0.34	0.05	0.005	646
$\lvert\psi_{(^3D)^4D}\rangle$	- 0.17	0.10	0.96	0.07	- 0.13	- 0.08	- 0.04	- 1363
$\lvert\psi_{(^3F)^2F}\rangle$	- 0.10	0.02	0.10	0.37	0.92	0.10	0.001	- 4764
$\lvert\psi_{(^3F)^4F}\rangle$	- 0.05	- 0.03	0.07	- 0.08	- 0.09	0.99	- 0.001	- 9283
$\lvert\psi_{(^3P)^4P}\rangle$	0.05	0.02	0.06	-9×10^{-5}	1×10^{-4}	6×10^{-4}	0.997	- 13919
where $\lvert\psi\rangle = \sum_i C(i)\lvert\Phi_i\rangle$								

B. Intercombination Line Oscillator Strength

Expanding in the LS basis, $\{\lvert\Phi_i\rangle\}$, the line strength of a transition, is given by

$$S_{if} = \lvert\langle\psi_i \Vert \vec{R} \Vert \psi_f\rangle\rvert^2$$

$$= \Big\lvert \sum_{jk} \langle\psi_i\lvert\Phi_j\rangle\langle\Phi_j \Vert \vec{R} \Vert \Phi_k\rangle\langle\Phi_k\lvert\psi_f\rangle\Big\rvert^2$$

$$\equiv \Big\lvert \sum_{jk} C_{ij}\cdot M_{jk}\cdot C_{kf}\Big\rvert^2. \tag{1}$$

The storage level $3p^5 4s4p\,^4D_{7/2}$ has the maximum angular momentum for this configuration and is a pure LS level. The incident (transfer) laser at $\lambda = 1.03\ \mu$ (see Fig. 1) couples this storage level to the $J = 5/2$ levels of the $3p^5 3d4s$ configuration, with weighting factors C_{ij} determined from Section A. For the intercombination transition $3p^5 4p4s\,^4D_{7/2} \rightarrow 3p^5 3d(^1D)4s\,^2D^0_{5/2}$, we must calculate the M_{jk} for $3p^5 4p4s\,^4D_{7/2} \rightarrow 3p^5 3d4s\,^4L^0_{5/2}$ where $L = P$, D, or F. Following the procedure of Shore and Menzel [12],

$$M = R_{\text{line}} \cdot R_{\text{mult}} \cdot \mathscr{I} \tag{2}$$

where R_{line} and R_{mult} are tabulated and $\mathscr{I}$ is the one electron matrix element $\mathscr{I} = \langle 4p \Vert \vec{r} \Vert 3d\rangle$. $\mathscr{I}$ was found from tabulated line strengths [13] of argon ($3p^5 4p \rightarrow 3p^5 3d$) and potassium ($3p^6 3d \rightarrow 3p^6 4p$). The calculated values of the M_{jk} (in atomic units) are given in Table IV. Summing over the components as per (1), we obtain $S = 1.95 \times 10^{-3}\ \mathscr{I}^2 = 0.16$, which corresponds to an oscillator strength for the intercombination transition $3p^5 4p4s\,^4D_{7/2} \rightarrow 3p^5 3d(^1D)4s\,^2D^0_{5/2}$ of $f = 6.0 \times 10^{-4}$.

C. Laser Transition

1) Oscillator Strength: The oscillator strength of the laser transition $3p^5 3d(^1D)4s\,^2D^0_{5/2} \rightarrow 3p^6 3d\,^2D_{5/2}$ is found in much the same way. The required M_{jk} are given in Table V. For this configuration, the multiplet factors are not given in Shore and Menzel and were calculated separately. $\mathscr{I}$ was obtained from tabulated line strengths [13] of Ar or Cl. Again, from (1) and Table V, we obtain $S = 1.95\ \mathscr{I}^2 = 0.63$, which

TABLE IV
LINE STRENGTH COMPONENTS FOR THE QUARTET TRANSFER
$3p^5 4p4s\ ^4D_{7/2} \longrightarrow 3p^5 3d4s\ ^4L^o_{5/2}$

Component	R_{LINE}	R_{MULT}	$\mathcal{J}(4p,3d)$	M_{jk}
$^4D_{7/2} \rightarrow {}^4P_{5/2}$	1.26	0.129	9.1	1.48
$^4D_{7/2} \rightarrow {}^4D_{5/2}$	- 0.478	- 0.5	9.1	2.17
$^4D_{7/2} \rightarrow {}^4F_{5/2}$	0.090	1.18	9.1	0.97

TABLE V
LINE STRENGTH COMPONENTS FOR THE LASER TRANSITION
$3p^5 3d(SL)4s\ ^2L^o_{5/2} \longrightarrow 3p^6 3d\ ^2D_{5/2}$

Component	R_{LINE}	R_{MULT}	$\mathcal{J}(4s,3p)$	M_{jk}
$(^1D)\ ^2D_{5/2} \rightarrow {}^2D_{5/2}$	1.06	- 0.913	0.570	- 0.567
$(^3D)\ ^2D_{5/2} \rightarrow {}^2D_{5/2}$	1.06	- 1.58	0.570	- 0.955
$(^1F)\ ^2F_{5/2} \rightarrow {}^2D_{5/2}$	0.239	1.08	0.570	0.147
$(^3F)\ ^2F_{5/2} \rightarrow {}^2D_{5/2}$	0.239	1.87	0.570	0.255

corresponds to an oscillator strength of the laser transition $3p^5 3d(^1D)4s^2D^o_{5/2} \rightarrow 3p^6 3d^2D_{5/2}$ of $f = 0.049$.

2) Linewidth: The autoionizing width of the upper laser level $3p^5 3d(^1D)4s^2D^o_{5/2}$ is not known and must be estimated. In pure LS coupling, coulombic autoionization is not allowed. This is because, due to parity, the only continua available to the $3p^5 3d4s$ configuration are ^2P and ^2F. However, as per Table III, the spin-orbit interaction mixes the ^2D state with ^2F states which do autoionize. If the ^2F states have an autoionizing rate of A_F, then the upper laser level would autoionize at a rate of about $(5 \times 10^{-3})A_F$. Since we do not know A_F, we will take it equal to the measured linewidth [14], [15] of the broad doublet states $3p^5 4s^2\ ^2P^o_{1/2,3/2}$. This ~60 cm^{-1} width implies $A_F \cong 1.2 \times 10^{13}\ s^{-1}$, corresponding to an autoionizing time and width of the upper laser level of 17 ps and 0.31 cm^{-1}, respectively. This is somewhat less than the Doppler width, at 400°C, of 0.45 cm^{-1}.

D. Laser Gain

The calculated oscillator strength of $f = 0.049$, a Voigt profile with a Doppler component of 0.45 cm^{-1}, and a Lorentzian component of 0.31 cm^{-1} yield a cross section for stimulated emission on the $3p^5 3d(^1D)4s^2D^o_{5/2} \rightarrow 3p^6 3d^2D_{5/2}$ transition at 658.6 Å of $\sigma_{gain} = 5.3 \times 10^{-14}\ cm^2$.

To calculate the steady-state gain we assume that the $3p^5 4p4s^4D_{7/2}$ storage level is undepleted by the transfer laser. The steady-state population of the upper laser level is then given by

$$N^* = \left[\frac{\sigma_{IC}(P/A)}{\hbar\omega}\right] \tau_{AI} N_{storage} \tag{3}$$

where σ_{IC} is the absorption cross section of the intercombination line, $\hbar\omega$ is the photon energy of the transfer laser, P/A is the intensity of the transfer laser, τ_{AI} is the estimated autoionizing time of the $3p^5 3d(^1D)4s^2D^o_{5/2}$ level, and $N_{storage}$ is the population of the storage level. The line shape of the intercombination transition is again a Voigt profile, but with a Doppler component of 0.03 cm^{-1}. Based on the calculated oscillator strength we have $\sigma_{IC} = 1.0 \times 10^{-15}\ cm^2$, and, with the previously estimated value of $\tau_{AI} = 17$ ps, we obtain

$$N^* = (8.3 \times 10^{-8}) \frac{P}{A} \cdot N_{storage} \tag{4}$$

where P/A is in units of W/cm^2. The steady-state laser gain is then

$$\text{gain} = N^* \sigma_{gain} = (4.5 \times 10^{-21}) \frac{P}{A}\ (W/cm^2) \cdot N_{storage}(cm^{-3})cm^{-1}. \tag{5}$$

As a consequence of the nondepletion assumption made, this formula only applies for an applied laser power density, at 1.03 μm, which is less than the saturation power density $(P/A)_{sat} = \hbar\omega/2\sigma_{IC}\tau_{AI} = 6 \times 10^6\ W/cm^2$. The results of the calculation are summarized in Table VI, column 1.

LITHIUM

In a recent paper, Nussbaumer [16] has calculated oscillator strengths and branching ratios for the 207 Å Li system proposed by Harris [3]. Based on these calculations, column II of Table VI gives revised numbers for this system. The cross sections of the transitions are based on Voigt line shapes with a natural component of 0.11 cm^{-1}. The Doppler components are based on an assumed temperature of 800°C. They are 4.3 and 0.3 cm^{-1} on the 207 and the 2949 Å transitions, respectively.

Fig. 2 shows another system in Li, with a laser transition at 200.3 Å. This system should have a larger intercombination line strength and should require less laser power density for transfer than does the 207 Å system. The transfer wavelength of 4671 Å is also somewhat more convenient. Here, energy is stored in the $1s2s4p^4P^o_{5/2}$ quartet level [17]. Although this level is metastable against autoionization, it may radiate to the $1s2s3s^4S_{3/2}$ level with an estimated lifetime of a few hundred nanoseconds. The upper laser level is that which Bunge [18] denotes as $[1s2p(^3P)4p - 1s2p(^1P)3p]^2P_{3/2}$. For the lasing transition at 200.3 Å, Bunge calculates an oscillator strength of 0.068 and a branching ratio of 0.93. Fluorescence at this wavelength was recently reported by Willison *et al.* [7].

The reason for the choice of this system is the near coincidence (401 cm^{-1}) of the $1s2p4p^4P_{3/2}$ level with the upper laser level. The dominant perturbation sequence for the calculation of the intercombination line strength is $1s2s4p^4P^o_{5/2} \rightarrow 1s2p4p^4P_{3/2} \rightarrow [1s2p(^3P)4p - 1s2p(^1P)3p]^2P_{3/2}$. As an approximation we assume that the radial portion of the spin-orbit matrix element for the second step of this sequence is the same as that calculated by Nussbaumer for the intermediate step $1s2p^2\ ^4P_{3/2} \rightarrow 1s2p^2\ ^2P_{3/2}$. The intercombination line oscillator strength of this system, as compared to the 207 Å system, then scales as the square of the energy denominators

TABLE VI
SUMMARY OF RESULTS

	K	Li	Li
Storage Level	$3p^5 4s4p\ ^4D_{7/2}$	$1s2s2p\ ^4P^o_{5/2}$	$1s2s4p\ ^4P^o_{5/2}$
Intercombination Transition	$3p^5 4s4p\ ^4D_{7/2} \rightarrow 3p^5 3d(^1D)4s\ ^2D^o_{5/2}$	$1s2s2p\ ^4P^o_{5/2} \rightarrow 1s2p^2\ ^2P_{3/2}$	$1s2s4p\ ^4P^o_{5/2} \rightarrow [1s2p(^3P)4p - 1s2p(^1P)3p]\ ^2P_{3/2}$
Laser Transition	$3p^5 3d(^1D)4s\ ^2D^o_{5/2} \rightarrow 3p^6 3d\ ^2D_{5/2}$	$1s2p^2\ ^2P_{3/2} \rightarrow 1s^2 2p\ ^2P^o$	$[1s2p(^3P)4p - 1s2p(^1P)3p]\ ^2P_{3/2} \rightarrow 1s^2 3p\ ^2P^o$
Laser Wavelength	658.6 Å	207.4 Å	200.3 Å
Intercombination Wavelength	1.03 μ	2949 Å	4671 Å
f_{laser} (emission)	0.049	0.129	0.068
f_{IC} (absorption)	6.0×10^{-4}	2.5×10^{-8}	7.4×10^{-7}
σ_{gain} (cm^2)	5.3×10^{-14}	2.4×10^{-14}	1.3×10^{-14}
σ_{IC} (cm^2)	1.0×10^{-15}	5.1×10^{-20}	2.4×10^{-18}
τ_{rad}	1.3 ns	49 ps	83 ps
τ_{AI}	17 ps	$> \tau_{rad}$	$> \tau_{rad}$
$(P/A)_{sat}$ (a)	6×10^6 W/cm^2	1.3×10^{11} W/cm^2	1.0×10^9 W/cm^2
Gain Coefficient κ (b)	4.5×10^{-21}	9.1×10^{-26}	6.0×10^{-24}

(a) $(P/A)_{sat} = \hbar\omega/(2\tau\sigma_{IC})$ is the laser power density which saturates the intercombination line. τ is the smaller of the autoionizing and radiative lifetimes.

(b) The gain coefficient κ is defined so that Gain = $\kappa N(cm^{-3})$ (P/A) (W/cm^2) cm^{-1}, where N is the population density of the storage level.

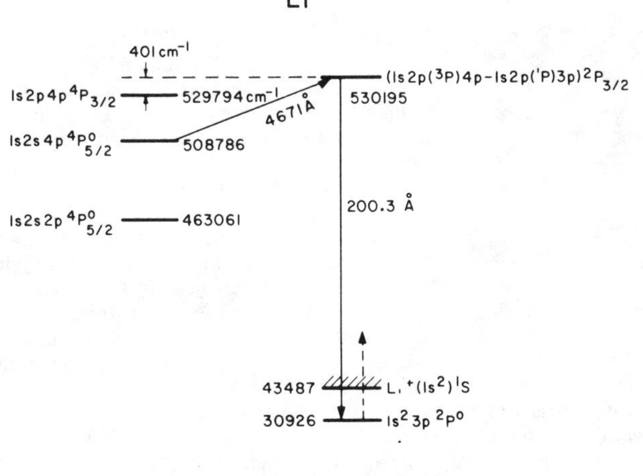

Fig. 2. Energy level diagram for a 200.3 Å system in Li.

$(6967/401)^2$ and as the square of the spin-orbit matrix element. The mixed final level and the fact that only one electron participates reduce the square of the spin-orbit matrix element by a factor of 7.9. Including the multiplet factor of 0.5 this yields an intercombination oscillator strength of $f = 7.4 \times 10^{-7}$. This estimate neglects spin-other-orbit and spin-spin contributions.

The remainder of the calculation proceeds as before. The natural and Doppler components of the 200.3 Å transition are 0.064 and 4.4 cm^{-1}, respectively. The intercombination transition at 4671 Å has a Doppler width of 0.19 cm^{-1}. The results are given in column III of Table VI.

TABLE VII
OTHER ALKALI SYSTEMS

Alkali Atom	Transition	Transfer Wavelength	Laser Wavelength
Na	$2p^5 3s3p\ ^4D_{7/2} \rightarrow 3p^5 3s(^3P)3d\ ^2D^o_{5/2} \rightarrow 3p^6 3d\ ^2D$	~ 3900 Å	~ 380 Å
Rb	$4p^5 5s5p\ ^4D_{7/2} \rightarrow 4p^5 4d(^1D)5s\ ^2D^o_{5/2} \rightarrow 4p^6 4d\ ^2D$	4721 Å	773.7 Å

OTHER ALKALI ATOMS

Table VII shows possible systems in Rb and Na. Level positions and identifications for Na and Rb were obtained from Weiss [19] and Mansfield [20], respectively. These systems are duals of the K system. In both cases the storage level is the lowest level in the quartet manifold. We have not calculated any of the other parameters.

SUMMARY

The increased breakdown of LS coupling as we proceed from Li to K has had two effects. 1) Due to the large mixing of the quartet and doublet series, the oscillator strength and absorption cross section of the intercombination line have been significantly increased, thereby reducing the necessary power density of the transfer laser. 2) As a result of level mixing, the lifetime of the upper laser level in K is determined by autoionization, instead of by spontaneous emission. Although this autoionization time is not known, we believe that we have established a reasonable lower bound.

A second potential laser system has been identified in Li. Here, a greater breakdown in LS coupling is achieved by selecting storage and target levels which are coupled by a near resonant intermediate level.

The results of the calculations on the two new systems, as well as revised calculations on the original 207 Å system in Li, are summarized in Table VI.

Possible laser systems are suggested in Na and Rb, and are summarized in Table VII.

Acknowledgment

The authors acknowledge helpful discussions with T. Lucatorto and A. Weiss of the National Bureau of Standards.

References

[1] H. Mahr and U. Roeder, "Use of metastable ions for a soft x-ray laser," *Opt. Commun.*, vol. 10, pp. 227-228, 1974.

[2] S. A. Mani, H. A. Hyman, and J. D. Daugherty, "Lithium-ion soft x-ray laser," *J. Appl. Phys.*, vol. 47, pp. 3099-3106, 1976.

[3] S. E. Harris, "Proposal for a 207Å laser in lithium," *Opt. Lett.*, vol. 5, pp. 1-3, 1980.

[4] G. Herzberg and H. R. Moore, "The spectrum of Li^+," *Can. J. Phys.*, vol. 37, pp. 1293-1313, 1959.

[5] P. Feldman and R. Novick, "Autoionizing states in the alkali atoms with microsecond lifetimes," *Phys. Rev.*, vol. 160, pp. 143-158, 1967.

[6] J. P. Buchet, M. C. Buchet-Poulizac, and H. G. Berry, "Classifications of some transitions in doubly excited Li I and Li II," *Phys. Rev. A*, vol. 7, pp. 922-924, 1973.

[7] J. R. Willison, R. W. Falcone, J. C. Wang, J. F. Young, and S. E. Harris, "Emission spectra of core-excited even parity ^2P states of neutral lithium," *Phys. Rev. Lett.*, vol. 44, pp. 1125-1128, 1980.

[8] M.W.D. Mansfield and T. W. Ottley, "The identification of low energy K and Ca^+ autoionizing levels observed in electron impact experiments," in *Proc. Roy. Soc. London A*, vol. 365, pp. 413-424, 1979.

[9] M.W.D. Mansfield, "The K I absorption spectrum in the vacuum ultraviolet: 3p-subshell excitation," in *Proc. Roy. Soc. London A*, vol. 346, pp. 539-553, 1975.

[10] J. C. Slater, *Quantum Theory of Atomic Structure*, vol. II. New York: McGraw-Hill, 1960, pp. 286-293.

[11] C. Roth, "Spin-orbit interactions of the configuration $l^{n-1}l'l''$," *J. Math. Phys.*, vol. 9, pp. 1832-1834, 1968.

[12] B. W. Shore and D. H. Menzel, *Principles of Atomic Spectra*. New York: Wiley, 1968, ch. 10.

[13] W. L. Wiese, M. W. Smith, and B. M. Miles, *Atomic Transition Probabilities*, U.S. Nat. Bureau Stand., Rep. NSRDS-NBS 22, vol. II, Washington, DC: U.S. Govt. Printing Office, 1969, pp. 194-195, 229, 192, and 159.

[14] R. D. Driver, "A measurement of the 3p subshell photoionization cross section of potassium," *J. Phys. B*, vol. 9, pp. 817-827, 1976.

[15] R. D. Hudson and V. L. Carter, "Experimental values of the atomic absorption cross section of potassium between 580 Å and 1000 Å," *J. Opt. Soc. Amer.*, vol. 57, pp. 1471-1474, 1967.

[16] H. Nussbaumer, "Atomic data for a Li I 207 Å laser," *Opt. Lett.*, vol. 5, pp. 222-224, 1980.

[17] C. F. Bunge and A. V. Bunge, "Absolute term values for the quartet states of neutral lithium," *Phys. Rev. A*, vol. 17, pp. 816-821, 1978.

[18] C. F. Bunge, "Accurate calculations for the even-parity core-excited ^2P states of neutral Li," *Phys. Rev. A*, vol. 19, pp. 936-942, 1979.

[19] A. W. Weiss, private communication.

[20] M.W.D. Mansfield, "A new interpretation of the Rb I 4p subshell excitation spectrum between 15 eV and 19 eV," *Proc. Roy. Soc. London A*, vol. 364, pp. 135-144, 1978.

Joshua E. Rothenberg was born in New York City, NY, on September 8, 1958. He received the B.S. degree in applied physics and the M.S. degree in electrical engineering from the California Institute of Technology, Pasadena.

In 1978 he was the recipient of a Hertz Foundation Fellowship to study at Stanford University, Stanford, CA, where he has been working in the area of XUV spectroscopy and lasers.

Mr. Rothenberg is a member of Tau Beta Pi.

Stephen E. Harris (S'59-M'64-F'72) was born in Brooklyn, NY, in November 1936. He received the B.S. degree from Rensselaer Polytechnic Institute, Troy, NY, in 1959 and the M.S. and Ph.D. degrees from Stanford University, Stanford, CA, in 1961 and 1963, respectively, all in electrical engineering.

Since 1963 he has been on the faculty of Stanford University where he is now a Professor of Electrical Engineering and Applied Physics. His research work has been in the fields of lasers, quantum electronics, nonlinear optics, and acoustooptics. His present research interests are in the areas of laser induced inelastic collisions and in the development of new techniques for generating vacuum ultraviolet and XUV radiation.

Prof. Harris was the recipient of the 1973 Curtis McGraw Research Award and the 1978 David Sarnoff Award. He is a Fellow of the Optical Society of America and the American Physical Society, and a member of the National Academy of Engineering.

Reprinted with permission from Optics Communications, Vol. 37(3), pp. 193-196 (May 1, 1981).

OBSERVATION OF GAIN IN A POSSIBLE EXTREME ULTRAVIOLET LASING SYSTEM

D. JACOBY, G.J. PERT, S.A. RAMSDEN, L.D. SHORROCK and G.J. TALLENTS
Department of Applied Physics, University of Hull, Hull HU6 7RX, UK

Received 21 January 1981

Measurements of gain by stimulated emission of the Balmer α line of the hydrogenic ion, C VI, at 182 Å are reported. The population inversion is generated by recombination in the expansion of a carbon fibre heated by a line focussed laser pulse. The gain is identified by observations using two calibrated spectrographs from the ratio of intensities, and by spectral line modification. Gain/length products of value up to 5 are deduced.

The development of a laser operating in the X-ray spectral regime represents a severe challenge to present day technology. Of particular interest are XUV schemes which in principle may be extrapolated into the X-ray region. To this end a large number of ingenious proposals have been made, although to date without any practical demonstration of gain sufficient to maintain laser action. A direct measurement of gain has been reported earlier by Jaegle et al. [1] on the $2p^5\,4d\,^3P_1 - 2p^6\,^1S$ intercombination line in Al^{3+} at 117 Å with a gain-length product, Gl, of 0.1. The mechanism producing the inversion remains unclear, however, and the interpretation of the results has been questioned by other workers. In this paper we report measurements of gain on the Balmer α transition in hydrogen like carbon, C^{5+}, at a wavelength of 182 Å. In contrast to earlier work the measured Gl values of up to 5 are sufficiently large for laser action to be demonstrated by a straightforward upgrading of the experiment.

In this work a population inversion is created between the $n = 3$ and $n = 2$ states of the hydrogen-like ion C VI resulting from recombination in a rapidly heated fully stripped carbon plasma. The basic difficulty in this scheme is to obtain sufficiently rapid expansion, and cooling, to enable the inversion to be achieved at a high enough density. Experiments involving laser heating of solid targets [2,3] have clearly shown evidence of inversion but the gains have been low. We have used thin carbon fibres as targets thereby restricting the dimensions of the plasma and increasing its expansion rate.

Preliminary studies reported earlier [4] of the population inversion in the expansion of laser heated fibres were in good agreement with computer simulation, and indicated that laser-fibre energy coupling of about 20% could be achieved. The inversion corresponded to a Gl product, of only about 10^{-2} due to the use of a small spot focus of 40 μm diameter. In order to achieve significantly large values of Gl line focussing along the fibre is necessary.

A detailed numerical study [5,6] of the gain produced by carbon fibres of 1–8 μm diameter irradiated uniformly along their axis showed that Gl values of order unity could be achieved by irradiating short lengths of small diameter fibres with laser energies of about 10 J. Further work [7] on axial non-uniformity of illumination indicated the detrimental effects of an absorbing end to the fibre associated with a decrease in the focussed intensity. The experiments reported in this paper broadly confirm the predictions of these numerical studies.

Carbon fibres of between 2.0 and 4.6 μm diameter [8] were mounted at the focus of the lens system shown in fig. 1 consisting of a 200 cm focal length cylindrical concave lens and a 10.4 cm focal length aspheric lens producing a line focus about 2 mm long and 40 μm wide. One vacuum spectrograph (Hilger and Watts type E580) [9] viewed the fibre directly along its axis whilst a second (A.R.U. rocket spectro-

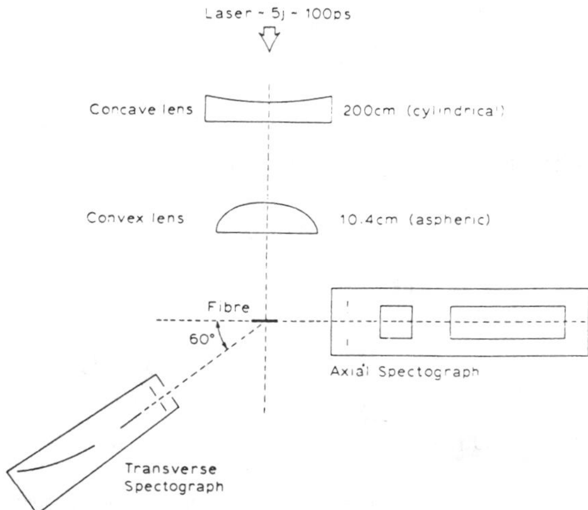

Fig. 1. Diagram showing the arrangement of the focusing system, fibre and spectrographs used in the experiment.

graph) [10] was arranged to look across the fibre, the field of view of both being sufficient to observe the complete illuminated length of the fibre. In order to avoid problems associated with non-uniform illumination the fibres are mounted with a free and pointing towards the first (axial) spectrograph, the fibre only filling $\frac{1}{2}$– $\frac{3}{4}$ of the focus.

The spectrographs were used with photographic recording; Kodak/Pathé type SC5 plates being used in the axial, and SC7 film in the transverse, spectrograph; the characteristics of both these emulsions having been carefully determined using multi-layer aluminium filters [11]. About six shots were required to obtain a satisfactory exposure of H_α. The two spectrographs were carefully calibrated against each other, principally for the line H_α, by simultaneously viewing plasmas formed by a vertical fibre (perpendicular to the normal horizontal mounting) irradiated by a spot focus under conditions in which both spectrographs viewed the same plasma from nearly opposite directions, and where H_α was expected to be optically thin. A linear plot of intensities over a range of laser/fibre conditions indicated that the calibration was satisfactory.

The laser was a standard Nd: glass system giving a maximum energy of 10 J in a single pulse of about 180 ps duration. Streak camera measurements showed that the pulse length was reproducible to ±40 ps, and that there were no spurious or satellite pulses. The single pulse extinction ratio was less than 10^{-4}. The laser energy was reproducible to within ±2 J (see table 1) on most shots; on the remaining shots there was an oscillator malfunction leading to a weak output pulse. The contribution of these weak pulses was less than 5% of the total H_α intensity, and was not significant.

As in our earlier experiments [4] a small pre-pulse of about 20% of the main laser pulse, and preceeding it by 200 ps was used to perform the plasma and improve the coupling from the Nd laser to the plasma. The maximum focal spot flux density did not exceed 10^{14} W/cm^2, a value sufficiently low to ensure that there were no adverse effects from flux limitation and hot electron production.

Gain has been identified in two distinct ways. The ratio of the intensities integrated over the complete line profile in the axial and transverse spectrographs gives a value for Gl, provided that H_α is optically thin across the plasma. Numerical checks from the computer code indicate that for the conditions of these experiments the transverse optical depth of H_α is less than 0.1. Since opacity effects will always be less significant across the plasma due to the smaller transverse dimensions and larger velocity, the net effect of opacity will be to underestimate the net gain or absorption along the axis. Detailed analysis of the plates

Table 1
Complete list of spectrograph plates obtained in these experiments, showing the experimental conditions and measured gain. The plates were obtained during two separate sets of runs, separated by the spectrograph calibration experiments, the alphabetic set being earlier, and the numeric later.

Plate	Laser energy (J)	Fibre diameter (μm)	$\overline{Gl}$
A	8.0 ± 1.2	4.1	5.0 ± 0.25
D	7.5 ± 2.0	4.5 & 6.0	3.5 ± 0.25
1	6.7 ± 0.6	2.9	2.5 ± 0.5
E	6.3 ± 1.8	3.3	2.6 ± 0.5
C	6.0 ± 1.3	3.3	3.5 ± 0.5
B	5.9 ± 2.3	2.2	3.0 ± 1.0
6	6.0 ± 2.2	4.0	0.1 ± 0.5
I	5.5 ± 2.5	6.2	0.1 ± 0.5
2	5.3 ± 1.0	2.5	0.7 ± 0.5
3	5.2 ± 1.8	4.2	–0.35 ± 0.5
4	4.9 ± 2.2	4.3	–1.3 ± 0.5
5	4.9 ± 2.6	4.6	–2.5 ± 0.5

showed the absence of any overlying impurity lines at 182 Å and indicated that the intensity of the co-incident seventh order L_ϵ line was less than 1% of that of H_α. The ratio of axial to transverse intensity is given by:

$$I_a/I_t = [\exp\{\bar{G}l\} - 1]/\bar{G}l$$

where $\bar{G}l$ is the mean value of gain length product, Gl, averaged over the line spectral profile.

The second method uses the detailed structure of the line H_α. As is well known this line has seven components which are grouped into two sets giving the appearance of a doublet. In the presence of gain each component is amplified with a gain coefficient dependent on its oscillator strength and the overlap of the neighbouring lines due to broadening. The ratio of the line intensities of the resolved components is a strong function of the gain but is also extremely sensitive to the assumption of statistical equilibrium between the levels [7]. In view of this sensitivity to the exact population distribution within the upper (and to a lesser extent lower) states any estimate of the gain coefficient thus obtained is likely to be inaccurate. None-the-less the method is a sensitive indicator of gain, in that the uniform enhancement of the peaks along a sequence for which the population distribution is expected to be similar, indicates a progressively increasing gain coefficient.

Spectrographic plates have been obtained over the range of experimental conditions listed in table 1. Fig. 2 shows microdensitometer traces of H_α for the plates A, 1, 2 and 6. Two features can immediately be observed. First the progressively increasing intensity H_α in the axial spectrograph despite a nearly constant value in the transverse one and secondly, the corresponding increase in the resolution of the doublet structure along the sequence. Indeed, at the lower energies the doublet structure is not resolved at all.

The values of $\bar{G}l$ deduced from the relative calibration, are given in table 1. These results are consistent with the spectral profiles provided a weak departure of less than 10% from the statistical distribution is assumed in each case and the plasma has a temperature of about 50 eV and diameter of about 200 μm at peak gain-values which are in good agreement with those predicted by the computer model.

Inspection of table 1 reveals two clear patterns. First, the gain is strongly dependent on laser energy;

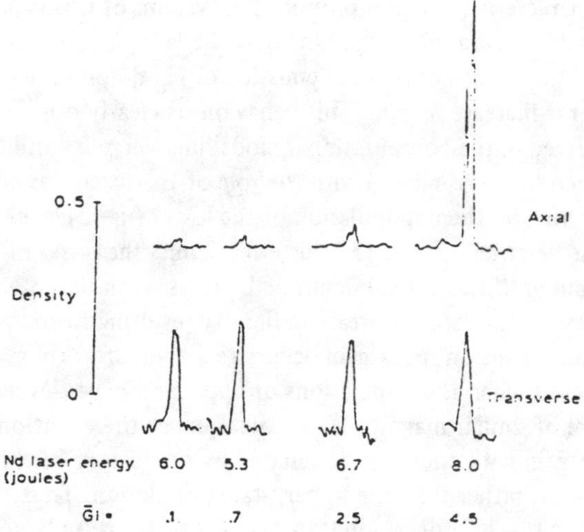

Fig. 2. Comparison of the microdensitometer traces of the line, H_α, for a series of plates 6, 2, 1 and A showing increasing gain. As can be seen the intensity of signals in the transverse spectrograph remains nearly constant, in contrast to the increase in the axial one, along the sequence. The increase in the doublet resolution is clearly apparent.

no gain is observed for laser energy less than 6 J. Secondly the gain varies only weakly with fibre diameter over the range 2–4 μm used. The first of these observations is in good agreement with the theoretical models discussed in refs. [5] and [6]. In these it is found that gain only occurs over a relatively narrow "window" in energy of about $\pm\frac{1}{2}$ the optimal value. The lack of variation with fibre diameter is, however, in contrast to the scaling laws derived in ref. [6], for a uniformly heated fibre, although this is readily explained once it is appreciated that the fibre may not be uniformly heated [7].

The uniformly heated model of ref. [6] shows that fibres of about 3 μm diameter are optimally heated by a laser pulse of about 40 J/cm when the experimentally measured coupling coefficient is taken into account. The optimal gain coefficient for these cases was calculated to be about 5 cm^{-1} compared with the value of about 20 cm^{-1} experimentally measured. Not too much weight should be ascribed to this discrepancy since, although the code is believed to be reliable in calculations of population densities, values of gain involving subtraction of two quantities of nearly equal magnitude are inherently sensitive to small errors in the atomic rates in the model.

An interesting and unexpected feature which is

characteristic of gain produced in systems of this type is demonstrated in fig. 2, namely the lack of variation of the total spontaneous emission of H_α despite the large increase in gain. This behaviour is clearly observed in the computational modelling where it can be seen to be associated with the role of L_α opacity as a switch on the depopulation of the lower ($n = 2$) level. As described in ref. [5] this effect limits the onset of gain until the optical depth of L_α is less than unity. Due to the rapid decrease in density resulting from the expansion, peak gain occurs very soon after the onset, when the populations of upper and lower levels are of similar magnitude. In consequence the variation of gain with energy is dominated by the history of the lower, rather than the upper, state population. Thus, as in ref. [5], delays in transparency of L_α cause large variations in gain, but with little change in the spontaneous emission.

In conclusion clear evidence of gain on the CVI Balmer α line at 182 Å has been observed. All the spectra thus far obtained fit into a sequence of increasing gain from negative values (absorption) to positive ones as the energy of the irradiating laser is increased. The largest gain-length product observed – $\bar{G}l = 5.0$ – indicates that scaling of the device to produce laser action in a spontaneous emission mode should be feasible provided a good quality line focus of about 1 cm length with energy density about 40 J/cm can be achieved.

This work was carried out as part of the XUV laser programme supported by the Science Research Council. One of the authors (GJT) was supported by a fellowship from U.K.A.E.A. The loan of the Rocket (transverse) spectrograph by the Astrophysical Research Unit is gratefully acknowledged.

References

[1] P. Jaegle, G. Jamelot, A. Carillon and A. Sureau, in: Laser interaction and related plasma phenomena, eds. H.J. Schwarz and H. Hora (Plenum Press, New York, 1977) Vol. 4a, p. 229.

[2] F. Irons and N.J. Peacock, J. Phys. B 7 (1974) 1109.

[3] M.H. Key, C.L.S. Lewis and M.J. Lamb, Optics Comm. 28 (1979) 331.

[4] R.J. Dewhurst, D. Jacoby, G.J. Pert and S.A. Ramsden, Phys. Rev. Lett. 37 (1976) 1265.

[5] G.J. Pert, J. Phys. B 9 (1976) 3301.

[6] G.J. Pert, J. Phys. B 12 (1979) 2067.

[7] G.J. Pert, Phil. Trans., to be published.

[8] D. Jacoby and L.D. Shorrock, J. Phys. E, to be published.

[9] A.H. Gabriel, J.R. Swain and W.A. Waller, J. Sci. Instrum. 42 (1965) 94.

[10] F.F. Freeman and B.B. Jones, Solar Phys. 15 (1970) 288.

[11] G.J. Tallents and L.D. Shorrock, J. Phys. E, to be published.

Reprinted with permission from *Soviet Technical Physics Letters,* Vol. 7(6), pp. 292-293 (June 1981). ©1981 American Institute of Physics.

Possibility of stimulated emission by channelled particles

A. V. Andreev, S. A. Akhmanov, and V. L. Kuznetsov

M. V. Lomonosov State University, Moscow

(Submitted March 11, 1981)

Pis'ma Zh. Tekh. Fiz. 7, 682–685 (June 12, 1981)

1. In this letter we discuss the possibility of arranging a population inversion between the transverse-motion levels of an electron channeled in a crystal. We propose a method for arranging an inversion which makes use of the difference between the dechannelling lengths of particles in different levels. We show that a gain of the order of 1 cm^{-1} can be achieved at electron current densities of the order of a kiloampere per square centimeter. This result shows that self-excitation is possible for a channelled-electron laser. We will discuss the possible use of the Borrmann effect and distributed feedback to substantially reduce the threshold conditions for x-ray emission, so that the mirror problem can be avoided and the absorption coefficient sharply reduced.

2. Radiation by channelled particles has attracted much interest in recent years.[1–5] The development of the theory for spontaneous emission by channelled particles has been accompanied by a discussion in the literature of the possibility of achieving stimulated emission during channelling.[6,7] That work, however, has been confined primarily to calculations of the gain for particle transitions between transverse-motion levels; there is still a need to discuss specific laser schemes.

The most promising system for achieving stimulated emission is a system of unequally spaced levels of the channelled electrons (transitions between such levels have been observed in spontaneous emission[2,8]). Consequently, a detailed discussion of the possibilities of arranging a population inversion for achieving coherent emission in the optical and x-ray ranges in a system of this type seems particularly worthwhile.

3. In the case of planar channelling the transverse motion of a channelled electron is described by the one-dimensional Schrödinger equation[6]

$$\frac{\hbar}{2m}\frac{d^2\varphi(x)}{dx^2} = \left[U(x) - E_\perp\right]\varphi(x), \tag{1}$$

where $m = m_0\gamma$, $\gamma = E/m_0c^2$ is the relativistic factor, and $E_\perp$ is the energy of the transverse motion. In a diamond-like lattice, the potential of planes of the type (001), (011), etc., is symmetric: $U(x) = U(-x)$ (x is reckoned from the atomic plane). Consequently, solutions of Eq. (1) are either even or odd functions of x. In particular, for the potential

$$U(x) = -U_0/\cosh^2\alpha x, \tag{2}$$

which is a good approximation of the actual potential of an atomic plane, the wave functions are expressed in terms of hypergeometric functions[9]:

$$\varphi_n(x) = \cosh^{n-s}\alpha x \cdot F\left(-n, n+2\varepsilon+1, \varepsilon+1, \frac{1-\tanh\alpha x}{2}\right), \tag{3}$$

where

$$s = \frac{1}{2}\left(-1+\sqrt{1+\frac{8mU_0}{\hbar^2\alpha^2}}\right), \quad \varepsilon = \sqrt{\frac{-2mE_\perp}{\hbar^2\alpha^2}}.$$

for example, the normalized wave functions of levels 0 and 1 are

$$\varphi_0(x) = \sqrt{\frac{\alpha}{\sqrt{\pi}}\frac{\Gamma(s+1/2)}{\Gamma(s)}}\cosh^{-s}\alpha x,$$
$$\varphi_1(x) = \sqrt{\frac{2\alpha}{\sqrt{\pi}}\frac{\Gamma(s+1/2)}{\Gamma(s)}}\,ch^{-s}\alpha x \cdot \sinh\alpha x, \tag{4}$$

where Γ(S) is the gamma function. Accordingly, while the wave functions of the odd states vanish at the atomic planes, those of the even states have local maxima there. For electrons in odd levels, therefore, there will be anomalous transmission, while electrons in even levels will interact strongly with the atomic lattice. Since the electron clouds of the atoms affect the scattering of relativistic particles only for scattering through very small angles (i.e., are important in channelling, while dechannelling, which is accompanied by scattering through large angles, occurs primarily at the unscreened nuclei), one can show that the partial electron dechannelling lengths ($lg^{(n)}$) are given by the following expression, which takes into account the thermal displacements of the atoms:

$$\ln\left\{\int_{-\infty}^{\infty}|\varphi_n(x)|^2\exp\left[-\frac{lg^{(n)}r_0^2}{a^2}\sqrt{\frac{2\pi}{\langle u^2\rangle}}e^{-\frac{x^2}{2\langle u^2\rangle}}\right]dx\right\} = -1, \tag{5}$$

where $\langle u^2\rangle$ is the mean square thermal displacement of the atoms, $\sigma_0 = \pi r_0^2$ is the effective cross section for an event in which an electron is scattered by a nucleus and thereby dechannelled, and a is the interatomic distance in the channelling plane. This expression shows that the partial dechannelling length depends strongly on the crystal temperature. For example, in the channelling of 56-MeV electrons in silicon in the (110) plane at a crystal temperature T = 543 K one would have $lg^{(1)}/lg^{(0)} \approx 3.5$. At T = 300 K this ratio increases to 9, and at absolute zero it reaches 130. If we choose a crystal thickness to satisfy $lg^{(0)} < L \sim lg^{(1)}$, then at a crystal depth greater than $lg^{(0)}$ we find a population inversion of the levels.[1)]

4. In the region of the crystal with the population inversion, the change in the intensity of a resonant light wave along its propagation direction is described by $I = I_0\exp[(\Gamma - \delta)\xi]$, where ξ is the running coordinate. The resonant gain Γ is given by

$$\Gamma = \frac{3\lambda^2}{4\pi}\frac{T_2}{T_1}\frac{1}{g}\frac{N_e}{V}\frac{1}{\gamma^2(1-\beta n\cos\theta)^2} = \frac{3\lambda_0^2}{4\pi}\frac{T_2}{T_1}\frac{1}{g}\frac{N_e}{V}, \tag{6}$$

where $1/T_2$ is the width of the transition line, T_1 is the radiative decay time, g is the number of levels in the channel, N_e/V is the electron density in the channel, θ is the angle between the radiation direction and the z axis, n is the refractive index, and Λ_0 is the wavelength of the radiation in the rest frame of the electron (refraction in the medium is taken into account). Let us examine some numerical estimates. In the optical frequency range, the typical absorption coefficient δ is 0.01 cm^{-1}. Setting γ = 10, and assuming channelling in the (110) plane of diamond, we then find that the following electron current density is required for a 10% gain per pass for a beam diameter d = 1 cm:

$$j = ec\frac{N_e}{V} = 10^3 \frac{A}{cm^2} \qquad (7)$$

5. We turn now to the possibility of x-ray emission with a wavelength of the order of several angstroms by a channelled beam. In this range, δ reaches values of the order of $10\text{-}10^2$ cm^{-1}, so that there is a substantial increase in the electron current density required. The situation is not hopeless, however, as we see by considering two factors which strongly affect the propagation of x rays in perfect crystals. First, the absorption may be sharply reduced by the Borrmann effect.[10] Second, a distributed feedback is created by dynamic scattering.[11] In a diamond-like lattice, the (220) planes, for example, are strongly reflecting planes. By arranging the appropriate orientation for a beam which is being channelled in the (010) plane we can always satisfy the Bragg diffraction conditions. An even greater increase in the mean free path is achieved in the case of multiwave diffraction (the anomalous Borrmann effect). Taking the Borrmann effect into account, we conclude that the characteristic values of δ in diamond and silicon are of the order of several reciprocal centimeters. Noting that the condition for laser self-excitation in a system with distributed feedback is[11] $\Gamma - \delta > 0$, we find the critical electron current density in this case to be j = 10^4 A/cm^2.

[1]M. A. Kumakhov, Dokl. Akad. Nauk SSSR 230, 1077 (1976) [Sov. Phys. Dokl. 21, 581 (1976)].

[2]R. H. Pantell and R. L. Swent, Appl. Phys. Lett. 35, 910 (1979).

[3]A. O. Agan'yants, Yu. A. Vartanov, G. A. Vartapetyan, M. A. Kumakhov, Kh. Trikalinos, and V. Ya. Yaramov, Pis'ma Zh. Eksp. Teor. Fiz. 29, 554 (1979) [JETP Lett. 29, 505 (1979)].

[4]S. A. Vorob'ev, V. I. Zabaev, B. I. Kalinin, V. V. Kaplin, and A. P. Potalitsyn, Pis'ma Zh. Eksp. Teor. Fiz. 29, 414 (1979) [JETP Lett. 29, 376 (1979)].

[5]I. I. Miroshnichenko, D. D. Merri, R. O. Avakyan, and T. Kh. Figut, Pis'ma Zh. Eksp. Teor. Riz. 29, 786 (1979) [JETP Lett. 29, 722 (1979)].

[6]V. V. Beloshchitskii and M. A. Kumakhov, Zh. Eksp. Teor. Fiz. 74, 1244 (1978) [Sov. Phys. JETP 47, 652 (1978)].

[7]G. V. Kovalev, Pis'ma Zh. Tekh. Fiz. 4, 592 (1978) [Sov. Tech. Phys. Lett. 4, 238 (1978)].

[8]J. U. Anderson and E. Laegsgaard, Phys. Rev. Lett. 44, 1079 (1980).

[9]L. D. Landau and E. M. Lifshitz, Quantum Mechanics: Non-Relativistic Theory, Pergamon Press, New York (1977).

[10]G. Borrmann, Z. Phys. 42, 157 (1941).

[11]R. A. Fisher, Appl. Phys. Lett. 24, 598 (1974); A. Yariv, Appl. Phys. Lett. 25, 105 (1974); S. A. Akhmanov and G. A. Lyakhov, Zh. Eksp. Teor. Fiz. 66, 96 (1974) [Sov. Phys. JETP 39, 43 (1974)].

Translated by Dave Parsons

Reprinted with permission from *Soviet Journal of Quantum Electronics,* Vol. 11(7), pp. 971-972 (July 1981). ©1981 American Institute of Physics.

Specification for pumping x-ray laser with ionizing radiation

F. V. Bunkin, V. I. Derzhiev, and S. I. Yakovlenko

P. N. Lebedev Physics Institute, Academy of Sciences of the USSR, Moscow
(Submitted May 28, 1981)
Kvantovaya Elektron. (Moscow) 8, 1606–1607 (July 1981)

It is shown that pumping of a medium with an atomic number $z \approx 30$ by short-wavelength ($\lambda_p \lesssim 0.1$ nm) electromagnetic radiation of $\sim 10^{15}$–10^{16} W/cm² intensity for a time $t_p \gtrsim 30$ nsec should, in principle, result in stimulated emission due to $n_i = 5, 4 \rightarrow n_f = 3$ transitions between the hydrogenic states of multiply ionized ions (giving rise to laser emission at $\lambda_l \sim 1$–2 nm). The active medium may be formed during irradiation from, for example, a copper or brass wire $l \sim 1$ m long with an initial radius $r_0 \lesssim 0.3$ mm.

Recombination nonequilibrium of a plasma can be maintained by an external ionizing source (for example, a beam of electrons or of short-wavelength electromagnetic radiation), as shown in §16 in Ref. 1. Conditions suitable for lasing may be established directly during the action of such an ionizing source. The situation is then basically similar to that discussed in the case of plasma lasers emitting visible radiation, but so far the discussions relating to the short-wavelength range (laser emission at $\lambda_l < 50$ nm) have been confined to pumping in which the energy deposition and cooling of electrons are separated significantly in time. This has been due to the absence of laboratory sources of ionizing radiation with a flux density sufficient to pump transitions in the short-wavelength range. We shall consider "exotic" sources[2] and estimate the requirements in respect of the flux of ionizing x rays needed to achieve laser emission at wavelengths of 1–2 nm.

We shall consider population inversion[1,3] of hydrogenic levels with c = 5, 4, and 3. Inversion as a result of $n_i = 5, 4 \rightarrow n_f = 3$ transitions appears because the final (lower) level n_f is depopulated more rapidly than the initial (upper) levels n_i. We cannot expect inversion relative to $n_f = 2$ because of reabsorption of the radiation due to the $2 \rightarrow 1$ transition when pumping with fast secondary electrons induces the $1 \rightarrow 2$ transition (see §16 in Ref. 1). The $n_i = 5, 4 \rightarrow n_f = 3$ transitions correspond to $\lambda_l \sim 1$–2 nm when the nuclear charge is $Z \approx 30$. For example, if $Z = 26$ (iron), we have $\lambda_{43} = 2.77$ nm and $\lambda_{53} = 1.9$ nm; in the case of $Z = 29$ (copper), we obtain $\lambda_{43} = 2.23$ nm and $\lambda_{53} = 1.52$ nm; if $Z = 30$ (zinc), we find that $\lambda_{43} = 2.08$ nm and $\lambda_{53} = 1.42$ nm. The ionization potentials $J_Z = 13.6Z^2$ (eV) of the H-like ions of these elements are $J_{Fe} = 9.2$ keV, $J_{Cu} = 11.4$ keV, and $J_{Zn} = 12.2$ keV. In the case of continuous pumping we have to ensure that the pump photon energy $\hbar\omega_p$ exceeds J_Z. This corresponds to a pump wavelength $\lambda_p \sim 0.1$ nm and to an effective source temperature $T_s \gtrsim 10$ keV.

Inversion as a result of the $n_i = 5, 4 \rightarrow n_f = 3$ transitions can be expected for relatively low values of the electron density and temperature in a plasma (see Figs. 5 and 3 in Ref. 1): $N_e \sim (5\text{–}10) \times 10^{11} Z^7$ cm^{-3} $\sim 10^{22}$ cm^{-3}, $T_e \sim (1-2)Z^2$ eV ~ 1–2 keV. If in the initial state the active medium is a solid (for example, a brass wire of $r_0 = 0.3$ mm radius), the reduction in the electron density by expansion from $N_{e0} \sim Z \times 10^{22}$ cm$^{-3} \approx 3 \times 10^{23}$ cm^{-3} to $N_e \sim 10^{22}$ cm^{-3} at a velocity $v_T \sim \sqrt{2T_e/Am_p} \sim \sqrt{T_e/m_p Z} \sim 0.5 \times 10^7$ cm/sec ($A \approx 2Z$, $m_p = 1.6 \times 10^{-24}$ g) takes place in a time $t_{exp} = r_0/v_T (N_{e0}/N_e) \sim 30$ nsec.

The duration of pumping t_p should exceed the time required for expansion to the appropriate electron density: $t_p > t_{exp}$). It should be noted that in the case of pumping by thermal ionization and subsequent cooling,[1] the pump time does not have a lower limit but an upper one ($t_p < t_{exp}$).

The threshold intensity of the ionizing radiation I_p in the case of equal numbers of ionization and recombination events is related to the threshold value of the gain $\varkappa_{th}$ by

$$\varkappa_{th} \approx (\lambda_l^2/16\Delta\omega)(N_{Z-1}\sigma_{ph} I_p/\hbar\omega_p),$$

where $\Delta\omega$ is the effective line width; σ_{ph} is the photoionization cross section of an ion with a charge $Z-1$; $N_{Z-1} \sim N_Z \sim N_e/Z \sim 3 \times 10^{20}$ cm^{-3}.

We shall assume that the wire length is $l \sim 1$ m and that $\varkappa_{th} \sim 10/l \sim 0.1$ cm^{-1}. Overestimating somewhat the Stark line width

$$\Delta\omega = 11 \frac{\hbar}{m_e}(n_f^2 - n_i^2)\left(\frac{N_e}{Z}\right)^{2/3} \sim \begin{cases} 5 \cdot 10^{13}\ \text{sec}^{-1} \text{ for } 4 \rightarrow 3, \\ 10^{14}\ \text{sec}^{-1} \text{ for } 5 \rightarrow 3, \end{cases}$$

we find that the conditions for the two transitions are

$$\sigma_{ph}\frac{I_p}{\hbar\omega_p} > \begin{cases} 5 \cdot 10_8\ \text{sec}^{-1} \text{ for } 4 \rightarrow 3\ (Z = 30), \\ 3 \cdot 10^9\ \text{sec}^{-1} \text{ for } 5 \rightarrow 3\ (Z = 30). \end{cases}$$

If $\sigma_{ph} \sim 10^{-21}$ cm², $\hbar\omega_p \sim 10$ keV $\approx 1.6 \times 10^{-15}$ J, we find that $I_p \sim 10^{15}$ W/cm² for the $4 \rightarrow 3$ transition and $I_p \sim 5 \times 10^{15}$ W/cm² for the $5 \rightarrow 3$ transition ($Z = 30$). At a distance of ~1 m from the pump source this intensity corresponds to the evolution of 10^{14} J in 50 nsec if the hard radiation carries more than 10% of the energy. The divergence of the laser beam should then be $\varphi = v_T t_{exp}/l \sim 10^{-3}$ rad.

It follows from the above estimates that laser emission at $\lambda_l \approx 1.4$ nm considered in Ref. 2 may indeed occur (the closest to this wavelength is the $5 \rightarrow 3$ transition in zinc, as discussed above). However, the information given in Ref. 2 is quite insufficient to judge the feasibility of the experiment itself and to interpret it more specifically. An analysis of the dynamics of forced expansion of the plasma under the action of high-power electromagnetic radiation, similar to that given in Refs. 4 and 5, becomes additionally interesting in connection with the above proposal.

[1]L. I. Gudzenko and S. I. Yakovlenko, Plasma Lasers [in Russian], Atomizdat, Moscow (1978).
[2]C. Robinson Jr, Aviat. Week Space Technol. 114, No. 8, 25 (1981).
[3]B. F. Gordiets, L. I. Gudzenko, and L. A. Shelepin, Zh. Prikl. Mekh. Tekh. Fiz. No. 5, 115 (1966).
[4]V. I. Derzhiev, V. S. Marchenko, and S. I. Yakovlenko, Pis'ma Zh. Tekh. Fiz. 6, 605 (1980) [Sov. Tech. Phys. Lett. 6, 262 (1980)].
[5]A. G. Zhidkov and V. S. Marchenko, Preprint No. IAÉ-3389 [in Russian], Kurchatov Institute of Atomic Energy, Moscow (1981).

Translated by A. Tybulewicz

Reprinted with permission from *Applied Physics Letters,* Vol. 39(3), pp. 212-214 (August 1, 1981). ©1981 American Institute of Physics.

Isoelectronic scaling of recombination lasers to higher ion stages and shorter wavelengths

W. T. Silfvast, L. H. Szeto, and O. R. Wood, II
Bell Telephone Laboratories, Holmdel, New Jersey 07733

Laser action in the visible and ultraviolet (at wavelengths as short as 298 nm) in the higher ionization stages of a number of metal vapors has been produced by a population inversion mechanism based on segmented plasma excitation and recombination. Many of the transitions have never been observed in laser action before by any excitation means and a number of the oscillating transitions in silver, cadmium, and indium form isoelectronic sequences.

The importance of electron-ion collisional recombination as a general laser excitation mechanism in an expanding plasma is clearly demonstrated for the first time by producing laser action in the ultraviolet (at wavelengths as short as 298 nm) in high-lying levels of In^{++} as a result of the recombination of ground state In^{+++}. In addition, ten recombination lasers have been observed in Cd^{+} and In^{+} at wavelengths as short as 468 nm. The extension of this recombination laser scheme from neutral atoms (producing recombination lasers with wavelengths in the IR)[1] to these new results in single and double ions (producing visible and ultraviolet lasers) was accomplished by following isoelectronic scaling sequences from known neutral laser transitions. All of the lasers reported in this letter were obtained in a simple segmented-plasma-excitation-recombination (SPER) laser.[1] Although it is felt that the visible and UV lasers reported here are important in their own right, the successful demonstration of scaling (i. e., selecting potential new laser transitions in higher ion stages and enhancing their gain using experimentally confirmed criteria and techniques) may prove to be a more important result if laser action ultimately can be extended into the VUV region of the spectrum with this technique.

The concept of a plasma recombination laser was first proposed[2] in H^{+} and was later theoretically shown[3] to offer the potential for high gain in the VUV and XUV in hydrogenlike ions ranging in Z from 2 to 8 (where Z is the charge on the recombining ion). Plasma recombination lasers have the potential for producing high small-signal gains because the excitation which occures over a broad spectrum of energies (via electron ionization) can, under the right conditions, be funneled to a single upper laser level (via collisional recombination). Important criteria and techniques recently shown experimentally to enhance the gain of these lasers include: (i) production of the plasma in a small volume followed by expansion into a larger volume where cooling takes place and consequently population inversions are established[4]; (ii) selection of potential laser transitions from among transitions that occur across the large gaps that are present in the energy spectra of many nonhydrogen-like ions[5] (taking advantage of the collisional decay bottleneck produced by such gaps); (iii) use of a low-pressure background gas (helium was found to provide the highest gains but other gases can and have been used)[6] to enhance electron cooling and to confine the recombining ions to a well-defined spatial region[6]; (iv) segmentation of the plasma to allow a more nearly three-dimensional (hemispherical) expansion and thus a more rapid cooling than can occur in the two dimensional expansion of a linear plasma[7]; (v) control of plasma expansion by shaping devices (such as parallel metallic plates) which can be used to guide the high-gain region of the plasma into a resonant cavity.[8] All of these criteria and techniques have been used to develop the lasers reported in this letter.

The experimental arrangement used in this work, to produce laser action in the higher ionization stages of a number of metal vapors, is a modification of one that was recently used to produce laser action in the neutral species of these elements.[1] The new device consists of 60–70 1-mm-thick by 2-mm-wide by 12-mm-long metal strips of the lasing species positioned end to end on an insulating substrate in such a way as to leave a 2-mm gap between each pair of strips. When 15-kV, 50–100 A, pulses of 2.5 μsec duration (with a rapidly falling trailing edge) are applied to the ends of this series of strips, high-density metal-vapor plasmas are formed in each gap. Once formed, these plasmas (consisting primarily of vaporized strip material) expand hemispherically away from the gaps and into a resonant cavity. The expansion velocity into helium gas at 2.5-3 Torr was measured to be $\sim 5 \times 10^5$ cm/sec. A 115-cm-long resonant cavity was formed by two 2-m radius of curvature dielectric mirrors having maximum reflectivity at the lasing wavelengths. The optical axis of this resonator was positioned parallel to and ~ 7 mm above the row of metal strips. The major differences between this experimental arrangement and that used in our earlier work are longer active length (64 versus 9 gaps), wider gaps (2 versus 1 mm), lower buffer gas pressure (2.5 versus 5 Torr), and excitation pulses with more rapidly falling trailing edges (0.16 versus 2.5 μsec).

With this experimental arrangement 23 additional metal-vapor recombination lasers in the ultraviolet, visible and near infrared at wavelengths between 2983 Å and 1.838 μm were observed. When taken together with our previous work,[1] we have now observed a total of 35 recombination laser in SPER-type devices. Some of the lasers observed in silver, cadmium, and indium are listed in Table I along with their transition assignments[9]. In every case the oscillating transitions occur between levels immediately above and below energy gaps in the excited states of the particular ion species.

TABLE I. Metal Vapor lasers produced by segmented plasma excitation and recombination.

Outer electronic configuration	Transition assignment	ISOELECTRONIC SCALING SEQUENCE Neutral species $\lambda(\mu m)$	Single ion $\lambda(\mu m)$	Double ion $\lambda(\mu m)$
$4d^{10}4f$-$4d^{10}5d$	${}^2F^o_{5/2}$-${}^2D_{3/2}$	AgI 1.832*	CdII 0.5337	InIII 0.2983*
$4d^{10}4f$-$4d^{10}5d$	${}^2F^o_{7/2}$-${}^2D_{5/2}$	AgI 1.838	CdII 0.5378	InIII 0.3008*
$4d^{10}6p$-$4d^{10}6s$	${}^2P^o_{3/2}$-${}^2S_{1/2}$	AgI 1.682*	CdII 0.8069	InIII 0.5249*
$4d^{10}6p$-$4d^{10}5d$	${}^2P^o_{3/2}$-${}^2D_{5/2}$	(Not allowed)	CdII 1.805*	InIII 0.5820*
$4d^{10}6p$-$4d^{10}6s$	${}^2P^o_{1/2}$-${}^2S_{1/2}$	AgI 1.742*	CdII 0.8533*	(Not observed)
$4d^{10}5f$-$4d^{10}6d$	${}^2F^o_{7/2}$-${}^2D_{5/2}$	(Not observed)	CdII 1.205*	InIII 0.7049*
$4d^{10}5s4f$-$4d^{10}5s5d$	${}^3F^o_4$-${}^3D_3$	CdI 1.650	InII 0.4680	
$4d^{10}5s6p$-$4d^{10}5s6s$	${}^3P^o_0$-${}^3S_1$	CdI 1.448	InII 0.7275*	
$4d^{10}5s6p$-$4d^{10}5s6s$	${}^3P^o_1$-${}^3S_1$	CdI 1.433	InII 0.7182*	
$4d^{10}5s6p$-$4d^{10}5s6s$	${}^3P^o_2$-${}^3S_1$	CdI 1.398	InII 0.6891*	

Of the 23 transitions listed, 14 have not been observed in laser action before (the new lines are designated with an asterisk). The infrared transitions occur primarily in the neutral atomic species as a result of recombination from the single ion, whereas, the visible and ultraviolet transitions occur in single- and double-ion species recombining from double and triple ions. The higher ionization stages tend to produce shorter wavelengths, since their ionization potentials are higher and consequently their energy levels are inherently more widely separated.

The results presented in Table I show that in a number of cases laser action has been observed on the same transition in Ag I, Cd II, and In III (see, for example, the $4f\,{}^2F$-$5d\,{}^2D$ transitions shown in Fig. 1). In the past, when attempting to produce laser action in higher ionization stages to obtain transitions between levels with larger energy separations and thus shorter wavelengths, it was often difficult to know which of the many thousands of possible transitions to study in detail. The concept of isoelectronic scaling of known visible and UV laser transitions has long been proposed[10] as a solution to this problem. Our experimental observation of isoelectronic scaling of lasers based on a population inversion mechanism as general as collisional recombination is thought to be important, since from a theoretical standpoint collisional recombination and decay pathways are expected to be similar in a scaling sequence as long as the relative energy level locations in the different ion stages are similar and the effects of scaling upon the recombination and radiative decay rates are properly taken into account. Our experimental results, shown in Table I and Fig. 1, clearly demonstrate the validity of this concept by scaling recombination laser action from the infrared (as a result of the recombination of Ag^+) through the visible (recombination of Cd^{++}) to the ultraviolet (recombination of In^{+++}) in expanding plasmas where the initial ionization energy is as high as 53 eV. In the future, these results may lead to the extension of laser action to even shorter wavelengths.

A second aspect of scaling with Z is illustrated in Fig. 2(a), where the temporal dependence of spontaneous emission from excited states of silver, cadmium, and indium is shown for double ions, single ions, and neutrals recombining from triple, double, and single ions, respectively. The delayed hump in the emission is characteristic of recombination radiation. The initial rise is a result of the increased recombination rate produced by the decrease in temperature, while the subsequent decay is determined primarily by the depletion of ions from the next higher ionization stage.

If one assumes that the delay times (from the termination of the current pulse to the peak in the recombination emission) for the various ionization stages shown in Fig. 2(a) are approximately proportional to the reciprocal of the recombination rate, uses the known Z^3 scaling law[11] for colli-

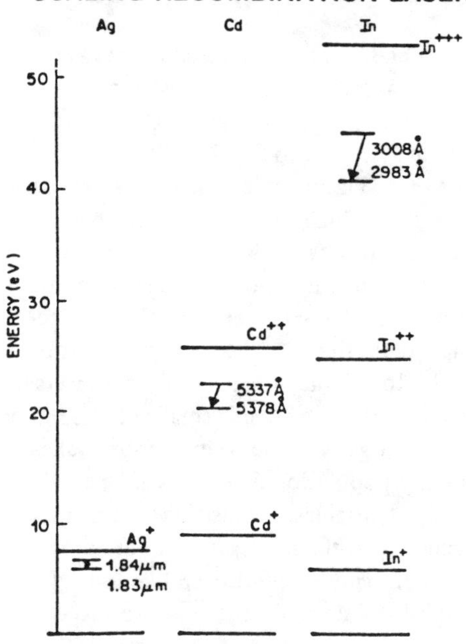

FIG. 1. Partial energy level diagrams illustrating one observed isoelectronic scaling sequence in silver, cadmium, and indium.

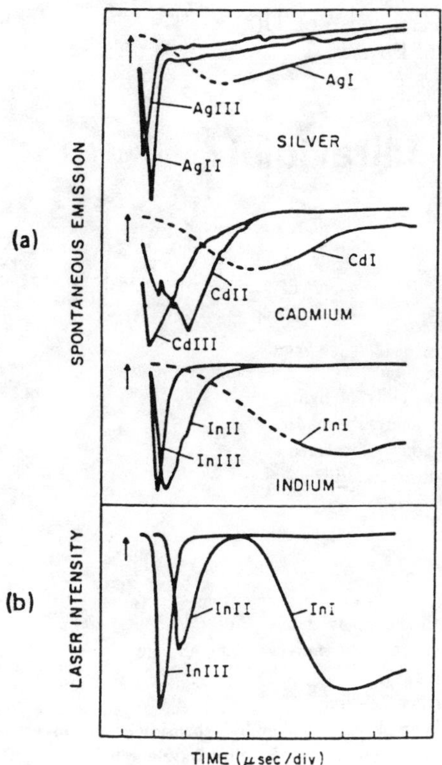

FIG. 2. Oscilloscope traces of the temporal dependence of (a) spontaneous emission from double ions, single ions, and neutrals recombining from triple, double, and single ions in metal vapor plasmas of silver, cadmium, and indium produced by segmented plasma excitation and recombination and (b) indium laser output for these three ion stages. Increasing intensity is in the downward direction. The emission wavelengths are as follows: Ag I–1.84 μm, Ag II–2277 Å, Ag III–2247 Å, Cd I–1.45 μm, Cd II–5378 Å, Cd III–2767 Å, In I–1.43 μm, In II–4680 Å, and In III–3008 Å.

sional recombination, defines a parameter, Z_{eff}, to take into account the actual ionization potentials of In^{+}, In^{++}, and In^{+++} (as compared to the corresponding hydrogenlike ion), and normalizes to the observed delay of the neutral emission (35 μsec), then one calculates a delay of 6.5 μsec to the peak of the single-ion emission and a delay of 3.5 μsec to the peak of the double-ion emission. These times compare favorably with the experimental values of 6.5 and 4.0 μsec shown in Fig. 2(a). This result may be somewhat fortuitous, since the $Z = 1$ recombination rate is known to be slightly lower than that obtained by simply scaling the recombination rate, but it nevertheless provides a qualitative explanation for the observed time dependence.

The corresponding temporal dependence of the laser output for the same three ion stages in indium is shown in Fig. 2(b). Just as in the case of the spontaneous emission on these lines, the time delay between the termination of the current pulse (indicated with an arrow in Fig. 3) and the peak of the indium laser pulse (as well as the duration of the indium laser pulse) was found to decrease with increasing Z. The slight delay between the peak of the spontaneous emission and the peak of the laser pulse is probably due to both the cavity buildup time and the disappearance of inhomogeneities produced in the plasmas during their formation. The maximum observed peak power output on the infrared transitions was about 5 W, and on the visible transitions was about 0.5 W. This suggests that the double- and triple-ion stages are not being as effectively populated during plasma formation. Experiments to optimize the production of higher ion stages are now in progress.

The spontaneous emission data presented in Fig. 2(a) also shows that, with this segmented plasma excitation and recombination scheme, the various stages of ionization always appear in the same temporal sequence; the highest ionization stage appears first and the neutral appears last. This means that the emission lines of an element can always be assigned unambiguously to the correct ionization stage of that element. This fact should be of use in the spectroscopy of elements in high stages of ionization. It could also be of use in determining transition assignments in future work on short wavelengths lasers.

We would like to acknowledge the technical assistance of C. R. Adams and several valuable discussions with W. L. Bohn and P. Wagli of the DFVLR–Institut fur Plasmadynamik, Stuttgart, Germany.

[1] W. T. Silfvast, L. H. Szeto, and O. R. Wood, II, Appl. Phys. Lett. 36, 615 (1980).
[2] L. I. Gudzenko and L. A. Shelepin, Zh. Eksp. Teor. Fiz. 45, 1445 (1963) [Sov. Phys. JETP 18, 998 (1964)].
[3] W. L. Bohn, Appl. Phys. Lett. 24, 151 (1974).
[4] W. T. Silfvast, L. H. Szeto, and O. R. Wood, II, Appl. Phys. Lett. 31, 334 (1977).
[5] V. V. Zhukov, E. I. Latush, V. S. Mikhalevskii, and M. F. Sem, Sov. J. Quantum Electron. 7, 704 (1977).
[6] W. T. Silfvast, L. H. Szeto, and O. R. Wood, II, Opt. Lett. 4, 271 (1979).
[7] W. T. Silfvast, L. H. Szeto, and O. R. Wood, II, Appl. Phys. Lett. 34, 213 (1979).
[8] J. F. Reintjes, R. H. Dixon, and R. C. Elton, Opt. Lett. 3, 40 (1978); W. T. Silfvast, L. H. Szeto, and O. R. Wood, II, Appl. Phys. Lett. 36, 500 (1980).
[9] C. E. Moore, *Atomic Energy Levels* (U. S. GPO, Washington, D. C. 1958), Vol. III.
[10] M. A. Duguay, Laser Focus 9, 45 (1973); R. C. Elton, Appl. Opt. 14, 97 (1975).
[11] See, for example, P. T. Rumsby, and J. W. M. Paul, Plasma Phys. 16, 247 (1974).

Reprinted with permission from *Soviet Journal of Quantum Electronics,* Vol. 11(8), pp. 981-997 (August 1981).

Prospects for light amplification in the far ultraviolet (review)

F. V. Bunkin, V. I. Derzhiev, and S. I. Yakovlenko

P. N. Lebedev Physics Institute, Academy of Sciences of the USSR, Moscow
(Submitted January 12, 1981)
Kvantovaya Elektron. (Moscow) **8**, 1621–1649 (August 1981)

A review is given of theoretical and experimental investigations concerned with the feasibility of light amplification in the far ultraviolet (3–50 nm) due to transitions in multiply charged ions. An analysis is made of the most advanced population inversion methods. Experiments in which population inversion was observed or amplification was achieved are examined. The feasibility of developing short-wavelength lasers utilizing recombination systems similar to those achieved for singly charged ions are discussed.

CONTENTS

INTRODUCTION

In the early seventies, the feasibility of amplifying radiation in the far ultraviolet, x-ray, and even gamma-ray ranges became the subject of extremely lively discussion. It could be said that there was a short-wavelength boom which reached a climax toward the middle of the last decade. The terms: raser (x-ray laser) and graser (gamma-ray laser) were proposed. At the Seventh Conference on Coherent and Nonlinear Optics (Tashkent, 1974) there was a discussion in which the participants were asked, on behalf of the organizing committee, as to how soon lasing would be achieved in the x-ray and gamma-ray ranges. The feasibility of amplification in the short-wavelength range was discussed repeatedly in the popular scientific literature.

The initiative came mainly from the theorists. The experimenters, on the other hand, had (with good reason) only taken seriously the discussions of the far ultraviolet.[1)] Many attempts had been made to obtain stimulated emission in this range. In some cases, reports of laser action were even published but the results of these investigations were either incorrect or irreproducible. However, population inversion in the far ultraviolet was nevertheless observed.

The short-wavelength boom has now begun to fade. Only in the popular literature are x-ray and gamma-ray lasers sometimes mentioned, the number of publications concerned with the far ultraviolet has dropped sharply, and some experimental groups which have been attempting to obtain amplification have curtailed their investigations. Clearly, the time has now come to make a calm assessment of the situation, i.e., to make a comparative analysis of the most carefully thought out proposals put forward, to discuss the most reliable experimental results, and to analyze the feasibility of making gradual purposeful progress in the short-wavelength range. These topics are the subject of the present review.

We shall not discuss the possible applications of far ultraviolet lasers, considering a detailed discussion of these topics to be premature. It is sufficient to note that any radical extension of coherent sources of electromagnetic waves to a new range must be accompanied by the observation of new physical effects and by their utilization. In addition, we shall not discuss problems associated with the development of feedback in the far ultraviolet. In this range, resonators are clearly not a feasible proposition so that to estimate the feasibility of obtaining stimulated emission, we shall take as the starting point the superradiance conditions (see Sec. 1.2). Moreover, we shall confine our analysis to the feasibility of amplification due to transitions in the outer shells of multiply charged ions. Thus, the main subject of our analysis is the population of the levels of multiply charged ions in plasmas having parameters attainable by existing technical means (laser breakdown, electron beams).[2)]

Almost all the main inversion methods proposed in the literature are described and analyzed critically in Part I. The analysis shows that the most promising methods involve recombination pumping of the upper active state with the principal quantum number $n=4$ by radiative depopulation of the $n=3$ lower active state. This method was first proposed by Gudzenko *et al.* in 1966 (Ref. 6) (see also Refs. 7–9).

Results of the experiments in which population inversion was achieved due to transitions in multiply charged ions are presented in Part II. Recombination pumping was used in all these experiments. Thus, also given are some results of the experiments on lasing due to transitions in singly charged ions where recombination pumping was also used. Taking these experiments as an example, the difficulties typical of recombination systems and methods of overcoming these are discussed.

The prospects for further research are analyzed briefly in Part III. Investigations are discussed in which it was shown that the main difficulties involved in advancing into the short-wavelength range are not associated with the requirements relating to the energy characteristics of the pump sources but with the need for accurate formation of the initial parameters of the medium. It is suggested that progress in the short-wavelength range should be made gradually, first using plasmas produced by laser breakdown in gases and then tackling laser action in hydrogen-like ions of increasingly high degrees of ionization.

I. INVERSION METHODS

1. General topics

1.1. *Open two-level model.* Relaxation of the populations N_m of the m levels of a certain ion may be described using rate equations determined by the kinetic (relaxation) matrix $K_{mm'}$, which gives the rates of $m' \to m$ transitions (for further details see, for example, Ref. 9). Generally, of the greatest interest are the populations of the $m = a, m' = b$ active states ($a < b$) used in attempts to achieve population inversion. In order to analyze this case, it is convenient to use an open two-level model:

$$\frac{dN_b}{dt} = K_{ba}N_a - K_bN_b + D_b; \tag{1a}$$

$$\frac{dN_a}{dt} = -K_aN_a + K_{ab}N_b + D_a, \tag{1b}$$

where the diagonal elements K_m ($m = a, b$) are the sum of the rates of transitions from a given state m to all other states; the values of

$$D_a = \sum_{m \neq a, b} K_{am}N_m; \quad D_b = \sum_{m \neq a, b} K_{bm}N_m \tag{2}$$

give the "fluxes" to the a and b states from other $m \neq a, b$ states, including the continuum. The existence of these fluxes distinguishes the open model from the closed model. The formulation of the rate equations as given by system (1) is convenient when the quantities (2) depend weakly on the population of the active states, which is generally the case.

In most of the problems under study, it is sufficient to allow only for spontaneous radiative transitions and collisions with plasma electrons (impact-radiative model). In this case, we have

$$\left.\begin{aligned} K_{mm'} &= A_{mm'} + V_{mm'}N_e; \\ K_m &= A_m + V_mN_e, \end{aligned}\right\} \tag{3}$$

where $A_{mm'}$ is the Einstein coefficient for the $m' \to m$ ($m' > m$) spontaneous transition; N_e is the electron density;

$$V_{mm'} = \int d\mathbf{v}_e f(\mathbf{v}_e)\, v_e \sigma^{(e)}_{mm'}(v_e) \equiv \langle \sigma^{(e)}_{mm'} v_e \rangle \tag{4}$$

is the rate of $m' \to m$ collisional transitions; $\sigma^{(e)}_{mm'}$ is the cross section of a transition as a result of an electron collision; $f(\mathbf{v}_e)$ is the electron distribution function in terms of the velocity $\mathbf{v}_e$.

In the far ultraviolet the probabilities of radiative transitions are extremely high ($A_b \gtrsim 10^{11}$ sec^{-1}). It is not generally realistic to expect a substantial change in the situation in a plasma consisting of multiply charged ions over times $\tau < A_b^{-1} \lesssim 10$ psec.[9] Thus, population inversion can only reasonably be expected in the quasisteady-state regime when it can be assumed that (for further details see Ref. 9):

$$\frac{dN_a}{dt} = \frac{dN_b}{dt} = 0; \; N_a, N_b \ll N_1, N_+, \tag{5}$$

where N_1 is the ground-state population of the ion under stucy; N_+ is the density of ions of the next degree of ionization.

The quasisteady-state conditions (5) imply that electrons in the a and b states are continuously replenished from the continuum or from the ground state and, as a result of decay of the a and b states, relax to the ground state. The pumping is governed by the quantities given by Eq. (2) and the decay is governed by the diagonal elements K_a and K_b.

We shall distinguish[7,9] between two thermodynamically opposite methods of pumping: in the excitation and recombination regimes. The specific implementation of the model (1) differs substantially in these regimes. In the first case, the flux D_b is mainly governed by excitation from the ground state of the ion, whereas in recombination pumping, it is governed by the relaxation flux from the continuum (Fig. 1). The qualitative difference between these two types of pumping is not only essential for the theory but is also decisive for the experimental implementation. For example, the different pumping conditions determine the choice of ions having different level structures. Moreover, a level configuration convenient for inversion in the excitation regime generally does not result in inversion in the recombination regime, and conversely. Moreover, an increase in the recombination flux when attempting to achieve the excitation regime and also an increase in the excitation flux when implementing the recombination regime generally result in quenching of the inversion. There are also significant differences in the conditions in the plasma when these two types of pumping are implemented successively. For example, pulsed excitation systems utilize the leading edge of the heating pulse whereas recombination systems utilize the afterglow. In the steady-state case, excitation systems require a high temperature to be sustained by an external source (so that radiative recombination predominates), whereas recombination systems require cooling of the free electrons.

Both general topics and specific theoretical methods of implementing the various pumping principles are analyzed in this section. However, before discussing specific topics, we shall analyze the general requirements for the pump intensity and energy input needed for lasing in the short-wavelength range.

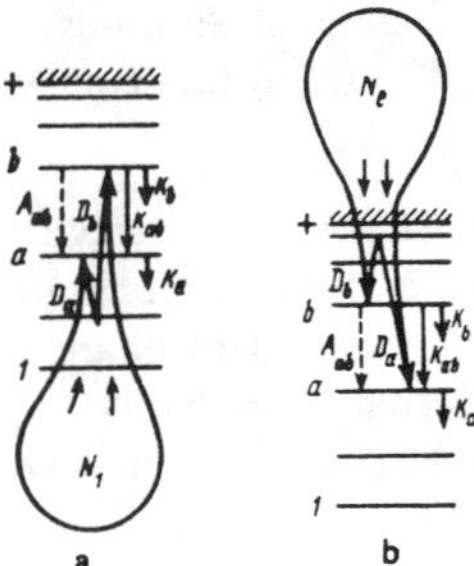

FIG. 1. Diagram showing pumping and depopulation of levels in the excitation (a) and recombination regimes (b).

1.2. *Threshold characteristics*. In order to assess the requirements for the pump sources, we shall, following the conventional procedure, assume that it is necessary to achieve populations N_b and N_a for which the gain

$$\varkappa = \frac{\lambda^2}{4} \frac{A_{ab}}{\Delta\omega} \Delta N, \quad \Delta N = N_b - \frac{g_b}{g_a} N_a, \tag{6}$$

exceeds a certain threshold value $\varkappa_{th}$. Here, λ and $\Delta\omega$ are the wavelength and effective line width of the $b \to a$ transition, respectively; ΔN is the active ion density; g_a and g_b are the statistical weights of the levels.

In order to achieve light amplification, the condition for population inversion of the lasing transition must be satisfied:

$$\Delta N \equiv N_b(1-\delta_{ab}) > 0 \quad \text{or} \quad \delta_{ab} \equiv g_b N_a/(g_a N_b) < 1. \tag{7}$$

The inversion condition (7) can be satisfied by selecting a particular pumping system and a specific ion having a level structure convenient for this system. The kinetics of the active levels will be analyzed in Secs. 2–5 and for the time being, assuming that the condition (7) is satisfied, we shall find the threshold pump flux from the requirement $\varkappa = \varkappa_{th}$ allowing for $\Delta N \leqslant D_b/A_b$

$$D_{th} = 4\Delta\omega\varkappa_{th}/\lambda^2. \tag{8}$$

Assuming, to be specific, a Doppler line profile $[\Delta\omega_D = 2\pi^{3/2}v_t/\lambda$, where $v_t = (2T/\mu)^{1/2}$ is the thermal velocity of ions of mass μ at a temperature T (Ref. 9)] and also bearing in mind that mirrors are not feasible in the far ultraviolet, we shall take as initial values the active length $L = 5$–10 cm and $\varkappa_{th} \approx 1\ \mathrm{cm}^{-1}$. We then have from Eq. (8)

$$D_{th} \approx 8\pi^{3/2}v_t\varkappa_{th}/\lambda^3 \sim 10^{29}/\lambda^3,\ \mathrm{cm}^3/\mathrm{sec}, \tag{9}$$

where $v_t = 10^6$ cm/sec. Here and subsequently in the "practical" equations the temperatures T and T_e and the transition energies $\varepsilon_{mm'}$ are measured in electron volts; the wavelength is in nanometers; the energy input and the specific energy input are in joules and joules per cubic centimeter, respectively; unless stated otherwise, the other quantities are measured in the cgs system.

We note that the radiation intensity needed to saturate the lasing transition is fairly high: $I_{sat} = 4\Delta\omega\hbar\omega/\lambda^2 \approx 0.5 \cdot 10^{14}\ \lambda^{-4}\ \mathrm{W/cm}^2$. This imposes additional constraints on the feasibility of using resonators.

We shall now analyze the requirements for the energy characteristics of the pump source. We shall assume that $\delta = \varepsilon_{ab}/\varepsilon_s$ is the ratio of the energy $\varepsilon_{ab} = \hbar\omega$ of the $b \to a$ transition to the average energy ε_s dissipated in the formation of a single ion in the upper active state b under the given plasma conditions. The threshold specific pump power $\dot W_{th}$ and the threshold source power $\dot E_{th}$ can then be estimated from

$$\dot W_{th} = \frac{\hbar\omega}{\delta} D_{th} = \frac{2\pi\hbar c}{\lambda\delta} D_{th}\ ;\ \dot E_{th} = \dot W_{th} LS, \tag{10}$$

where L and S are the length and transverse cross section of the active medium, respectively. Assuming that the plasma formed by a laser pulse focused using a cylindrical lens has the dimensions $L \approx 10$ cm and $S \approx 10^{-4}\ \mathrm{cm}^2$, we have

$$\dot W_{th} \sim 10^{13}/\delta\lambda^4,\ \mathrm{W/cm}^3;\quad I_{th} \approx \dot W_{th}\, S^{1/2} \sim 10^{11}/\delta\lambda^4,\ \mathrm{W/cm}^2;\quad \dot E_{th} \sim 10^{10}/\delta\lambda^4,\ \mathrm{W}, \tag{11}$$

where $I \approx WS^{1/2}$ is the laser radiation flux intensity.

It can be seen from Eq. (11) that the requirements for the pump power are not too stringent for $\lambda \approx 5$–10 nm. The main constraints are generally due to the threshold energy input. If the threshold ion density N_{th} needed for lasing is introduced, the specific and total threshold energy inputs can be estimated from

$$W_{th} \approx N_{th}\, 2\pi\hbar c/\lambda\delta \approx N_{th}\, 2\cdot 10^{-16}/\lambda\delta,\ \mathrm{J/cm}^3,\quad E_{th} \approx W_{th}\, SL \sim N_{th}\, (2\cdot 10^{-19}/\delta\lambda),\ \mathrm{J}. \tag{12}$$

In general, the values of N_{th} and δ cannot even be estimated without analyzing a specific pumping system. Assuming, for example, an efficiency of the order of the quantum efficiency $\delta \sim 0.1$ and a threshold density of the order of the solid-state value, $N_{th} \approx 10^{22}\ \mathrm{cm}^{-3}$, we obtain $E_{th} \approx 2$ kJ for $\lambda \approx 10$ nm. In particular, this implies that the energy must be deposited not in a solid but in a prepared medium (for further details see Secs. 9 and 10).

2. Charge transfer pumping

2.1. *Basic idea*. The idea of charge transfer pumping is based on the fact that as a reult of charge transfer between an ion of degree of ionization k of an element Z and an atom A, an ion of lower degree of ionization $k-1$ (or an atom) is formed preferentially in the excited state m:

$$Z^k(1) + A \to Z^{k-1}(m) + A^+. \tag{13}$$

Thus, by mixing fluxes of Z^k ions and A atoms, it is possible in principle to achieve a population inversion between a state m and one of the lower states. The level kinetics in charge transfer systems can be analyzed in approximately the same way as for recombination pumping (see Sec. 4) since in this case, the relaxation flux over the levels, generated by three-body recombination, is, as it were, replaced by a flux generated by the charge transfer events. In order to assess the potential of charge transfer pumping, it can be assumed that

$$D_b = \sigma_{ct}\, u N_A N_+ \tag{14}$$

and Eq. (9) can be used. Here, σ_{ct} is the cross section of the charge transfer reaction (13); u is the relative velocity of the fluxes of A particles and Z^k ions; N_A and N_+ are the appropriate densities. The charge transfer cross sections for ions of high degrees of ionization are fairly high [$\sigma_{ct} \sim 10^{-15} k$ cm^2 for $v \sim 10^7$–10^8 cm/sec (Refs. 10 and 11)]. This led many authors to assume that the charge transfer pumping mechanism is more efficient than three-body recombination. However, a careful analysis shows that the idea of mixing different gases to pump far ultraviolet lasers is hardly promising. Nevertheless, since charge transfer systems are extremely popular[3-5,12-15] and have even stimulated experiments (see Sec. 8), we shall discuss in greater detail the difficulties involved in implementing these systems.

2.2. *Charge transfer in beams*. The first charge transfer systems in the short-wavelength range were analyzed in Refs. 12 and 13. Smirnov[12] suggested passing an ion beam along a gas-filled tube and also amplifying radiation along the tube. The possibility of continuous tuning of the lasing frequency by using the Doppler effect was even discussed but no numerical estimates of the gain and length of the active medium were given. Presnyakov and Shevel'ko[13] discussed the possibility of lasing on the L_α (121.58 nm) atomic hydrogen line. It was suggested that the active medium could be produced by passing a proton beam ($N_+ \geqslant 5 \times 10^{13}$ cm^{-3}, $u = 10^8$ cm/sec) across an atomic cesium beam ($N_{Cs} \sim 10^{16}$–10^{17} cm^{-3}). In this case, a gain $\varkappa > 1$ cm^{-1} is achieved in a narrow layer of the order of the proton charge-transfer length ($l_{ct} \sim 10^{-2}$–10^{-1} cm) so that it is assumed that amplification is achieved in the transverse direction.

Before analyzing the proposals made in Refs. 12 and 13 and similar ones, we shall consider the general character of the constraints associated with the need to mix comparatively dense media. By selecting the product $N_A N_+$ in Eq. (14) to be fairly large, it is always possible in principle to achieve pumping giving a high gain. Constraints on the feasibility of implementing such a system are not so much due to the gain but to other factors. We shall discuss these.

The first constraint arises from the fact that the depth of the "charge transfer layer"

$$l_{ct} = (\sigma_{ct} N_A + \sigma_{ct} N_+)^{-1} \tag{15}$$

cannot be arbitrarily small since even transverse amplification is impossible if the layer is too narrow: the inevitable distortions have a harmful influence on the gain since, in this case, absorbing layers will be found in the optical path. Thus, having defined a certain minimum value ΔL_{min} of the transverse dimension of the active medium, we find that the condition $\Delta L_{min} \leqslant l_{ct}$ yields the constraint

$$N \leqslant (\Delta L_{min} \sigma_{ct})^{-1} \tag{16}$$

on the total density of the medium $N = N_A + N_+$. Subject to this constraint on the sum, the product has a maximum if $N_+ = N_A = N/2$ so that we have

$$D_b \leqslant \sigma_{ct}\, uN^2/4 \leqslant u/4\sigma_{ct} \cdot \Delta L^2_{min}. \tag{17}$$

We draw attention to an interesting fact that, as the charge transfer cross section increases, the maximum possible pumping D_b decreases. This is logical since in a layer of given depth, the atoms must not "obscure" each other. Thus, a large charge transfer cross section for multiply charged ions does not improve the situation, as is generally assumed, but causes a deterioration. Thus, the optimum charge transfer cross section for pumping is of the order of the transport cross section.

The second constraint arises from the fact that in a time interval $\sim l_{ct}/u$ a charged particle density comparable with the injected ion density accumulates in the charge transfer layer. As a result, the interaction between the beam and the medium begins to become essentially nonbinary. Instabilities develop, resulting in particular in strong deformation of the charge transfer layer and also in breakup of the beam. These topics have been investigated in comparatively great detail in connection with the thermonuclear problem. Charge transfer is used to produce a neutral beam which is then injected into a fusion plasma across magnetic fields. The condition for absence of instabilities gives rise to a stringent constraint on the product $N_A N_+$. In any event, for the reasons given above no neutral flux density j_n greater than $j_{max} < 3 \times 10^{18}$ cm$^{-2}\cdot$ sec^{-1} has been achieved up to now (see the literature cited in Ref. 16). On this basis, constraints on the feasibility of charge transfer pumping in the steady-state regime are readily derived for longitudinal amplification when $L = l_{ct}$. Assuming that

$$\varkappa L \approx \frac{\lambda^2}{4} \frac{A_{ab}}{\Delta\omega_D} \frac{\sigma_{ct}\, uN_A N_+}{A_{ab}} L > 1 \tag{18}$$

and bearing in mind

$$j_n = \sigma_{ct}\, uN_A N_+ L < j_{max}, \tag{19}$$

we obtain the following constraint on the wavelength attainable for laser action by charge transfer pumping in the steady-state regime:

$$\lambda > (8\pi^{3/2} v_t / j_{max})^{1/3} \approx 2\ \mu\ . \tag{20}$$

In this case, we find $l_{ct} \sim 10^2$ cm so that the attainment of transverse dimensions $L > l_{ct}$ cannot reasonably be expected.

It remains to consider the possibility of laser action within the time $\Delta t < l_{ct}/u$ when instabilities have not had time to develop. However, the amplification conditions cannot be produced instantaneously. For example, it is impossible to achieve sufficiently steep leading edges of the media undergoing mixing. This has the result that the flux D_b may reach the required value when instabilities have already developed. Thus, having defined the minimum time interval Δt_{min}, we obtain the second constraint:

$$l_{ct}/u > \Delta t_{min}. \tag{21}$$

On the basis of Eqs. (8), (17), and (21) we obtain a constraint on the wavelength attainable for laser action using pulsed pumping:

$$\lambda > (32\pi^{3/2} v_t \sigma_{ct}\ \Delta t_{min} \varkappa_{ct}\ \Delta L_{min})^{1/3}. \tag{22}$$

We shall now consider Refs. 12 and 13. For the case of longitudinal amplification discussed in Ref. 12 it must be assumed that $\varkappa_{ct}\Delta L_{min} \sim 1$ since ΔL_{min} is then the active amplification length. A heavy particle beam having a leading edge shorter than $\Delta t_{min} \sim 0.1$ μsec cannot realistically be expected. Thus, selecting typical parameters ($v_t = 10$ km/sec, $\sigma_{ct} \approx 3 \cdot 10^{-15}$ cm^2), we obtain the following condition from Eq. (22)

$$\lambda > (32\pi^3 \hbar v_t \sigma_{ct} \, \Delta t_{min})^{1/3} \approx 1 \; \mu \, . \tag{23}$$

In order to assess the possibilities for transverse amplification, we shall additionally assume that $\varkappa_{ct} \sim 1$ cm^{-1} and $\Delta L_{min} \sim 10^{-2}$ cm, in which case Eq. (22) yields

$$\lambda > 200 \, \text{nm} \, . \tag{24}$$

Approximately the same parameters were selected in Ref. 13 although the constraint (21) was neglected, so that the feasibility of amplification seemed realistic. However, in this case, the instability growth time is $l_{ct}/u \approx (10^{-2}-10^{-1})/10^8 \approx 10^{-10}-10^{-9}$ sec.

In the context of Ref. 13, we note another important factor: laser action due to transitions terminating in the ground state is generally only possible for an extremely short time, shorter than the time taken for decay of the upper active level. On the basis of an extremely simple system

$$\left. \begin{aligned} &\frac{dN_b}{dt} = D_b - K_b N_b; \quad \frac{dN_1}{dt} = K_b N_b; \quad N_b(0) = \frac{D_b}{K_b}; \\ &N_1(0) = 0; \quad D_b(t) = \text{const}, \end{aligned} \right\} \tag{25}$$

we have

$$\delta_{b1} \equiv \frac{g_b}{g_1} \frac{N_1}{N_b} = \frac{g_b}{g_1} K_b t, \tag{26}$$

i.e., for $t > g_1/g_b K_b$ the inversion is quenched. Longer-lived laser action is only possible if the ground state is depopulated as a result of fast reactions[9] or when $D_b(t)$ increases rapidly (over $t \gtrsim K_b^{-1}$). In general, laser action due to the $2 \to 1$ transition in atomic hydrogen is impossible for $t > 1/4A_{12} \approx 0.5$ nsec.

2.3. *Expansion of a plasma into a gas*. The constraints obtained above evidently also apply to systems in which a plasma is used in place of an ion beam. Moreover, the constraints become even more stringent because of the complex kinetics of the processes taking place when a hot plasma comes into contact with a cold gas. For example, the charge transfer layer should be preceded by an ionization wave produced by electrons escaping from the plasma to a distance of the order of the Debye radius. Thus, the possibility of mixing of a plasma and a cold gas or of different-temperature plasmas is even less promising than that for charge transfer systems using beams. In this context, we shall discuss the most frequently cited study by Vinogradov and Sobel'man.[14]

It was suggested in Ref. 14 that reaction (13) should be used to pump a lasing transition as a result of the expansion of a laser spark, formed at the surface of a solid target, into a cold comparatively dense gas (helium). An analysis was made of the feasibility of amplification in the $\lambda \approx 5-15$ nm wavelength range due to transitions between excited states ($4 \to 3, 5 \to 3$) of hydrogen-like ions ($k \sim 10$). The particle densities in the media being mixed were assumed to be: $N_{He} \approx 10^{18}$ cm^{-3}, $N_+ \approx 10^{17}$ cm^{-3}, and $N_e \approx kN_+ \approx 10^{18}$ cm^{-3}. The pumping was estimated from Eq. (14), where the plasma expansion velocity was assumed to be $u = 10^6-10^7$ cm/sec. The depth of the charge transfer layer was not estimated and constraints associated with the need for mixing were neglected. The authors of Ref. 14 assumed that during expansion almost all the ions are involved in the charge transfer process so that almost every ion generates a photon due to the lasing transition. It was noted in Refs. 14 and 15 that the most stringent constraints on the densities N_+ and N_{He} arise from the need to achieve a mixing zone of sufficiently large dimensions. However, no estimates were made of these dimensions.

In our view, the model studied in Ref. 14 inadequately describes the real situation. Under these conditions, the depth of the charge transfer layer is extremely small. At zero time when the ion density N_+ is close to the solid-state value, l_{ct} is of the order of the width of a monoatomic layer whereas after appreciable expansion (when $N_+ \ll N_{He} \approx 10^{18}$ cm^{-3}), we find $l_{ct} \approx 1$ μ. It is not reasonable to expect laser action in such a narrow clearly unstable layer and mixing of the plasma and the gas in a broader layer ($\Delta L \gg l_{ct}$) is extremely slow and diffusive. Even neglecting the premature ionization of the cold gas by plasma electrons, which was noted above, it is clear that a diffusion flux cannot provide high-intensity pumping in the far ultraviolet by virtue of conditions (22)–(24) and as a result of the low diffusion velocity u_{diff} compared with the hydrodynamic expansion velocity u.

Thus, it is deduced from this analysis that methods of charge transfer pumping based on mixing different media are unlikely to give successful results in the far ultraviolet. It is extremely difficult to use these methods in the visible range.[4] Almost the only possible method of using charge transfer pumping in the far ultraviolet would be to produce ions of the required degree of ionization using an external source (for example, an electron beam) directly in an active medium already containing atoms with a specially selected ionization potential. In this case, the charge transfer reaction could in principle speed up recombination. This method has been implemented in the visible and ultraviolet ranges, pumping being due to charge transfer with neutrals present in the active volume. However, the plasma needed for laser action in the far ultraviolet contains almost no neutrals. In this case, a recombination flux generated by three-body recombination is more likely.

3. Pumping by excitation from the ground state

3.1. *Inversion condition*. Methods of pumping by excitation from the ground state were considered for the first gas lasers utilizing electronic transitions.[17-19] These methods can either be used in the pulse leading edge of a heating field or even in a steady-state discharge when volume ionization is compensated by recombination at the periphery (for example, at the walls of the tube).

In a plasma containing multiply charged ions, it is also possible to achieve a situation when certain levels of a specific ion are mainly populated by excitation. This may be found under pulsed conditions if the electron temperature T_e increases sharply or under steady-state (with respect to N_e and T_e) conditions if the recombination flux bypasses the active levels. In order to achieve this, the electron temperature must be comparatively high and the density must be sufficiently low to ensure that radiative recombination, preferentially populating the ground state, predominates. The condition for predominance of radiative recombination may be expressed in the form[20]

$$N_e \ll 3 \cdot 10^{13}\, T_e^{3.75}/k, \tag{27}$$

where k is the degree of ionization of the recombining ion. For example, population of impurity ion levels in thermonuclear systems generally takes place as a result of excitation and this determines the appropriate diagnostic methods.[21]

The situation when the level populations are governed only by electron impact excitation from the ground state and by spontaneous radiative transitions is described as coronal equilibrium.[22,23] Under conditions of coronal equilibrium, instead of Eq. (1) we have

$$N_a A_a = S_a N_e N_1; \quad N_b A_b = S_b N_e N_1, \tag{28}$$

where $S_a = \sum_m a_{am} V_{m1}$, $S_b = \sum_m a_{bm} V_{m1}$ are the "excitation functions" of the a and b states; $a_{mm'}$ are elements of a matrix which is the inverse of the radiative transition matrix ($\|a_{mm'}\| = \|A_{mm'}\|^{-1}$); the element $a_{mm'}$ gives the probability of an electron in the m' state as a result of a cascade of radiative transitions. It can frequently be assumed to be an approximation that $S_a \approx V_{a1}$, $S_b \approx V_{b1}$.

The inversion condition (7) imposes the following constraint on the ratio of the transition rates for excitation from the ground state:

$$\delta_{ab} = \frac{A_b g_b}{A_a g_a} \frac{S_a}{S_b} < 1. \tag{29}$$

Since the a level is closer to the ground state than the b level, it is generally found that $S_a \gtrsim S_b$. Moreover, $A_b g_b \lesssim A_a g_a$ is generally true and the condition (29) is not satisfied. Nevertheless, for atoms and ions having a complex electronic configuration, the "interplay of the parameters" A_m and S_m for various m states is fairly fine and condition (29) can in principle be satisfied. We shall briefly discuss some systems of this type proposed in the literature.

3.2. *Helium-like ions*. In Ref. 24 an analysis was made of the feasibility of amplification due to $4^3 - 3^1$ and $3^3 - 2^1$ transitions between triplet and singlet states of helium-like ions. In the opinion of the authors of Ref. 24, inversion due to these transitions should occur for two reasons. The first is that the singlet states decay more rapidly than the triplet states. Secondly, at temperatures lower than or of the order of the excitation energy, the excitation cross sections for the singlet and triplet states are of the same order of magnitude. In particular, this reasoning suggests that a high population of the 2^3S lower metastable state [$N_{2^3S}/N_{1^1S} \sim 0.1$ (Ref. 24)] and thus additional excitation from this state could be expected. Calculated gains were $\varkappa \approx 0.45-24$ cm^{-1} at wavelengths $\lambda = 16-26$ nm (the spectroscopic symbol of the corresponding ions[5)] varied in the range $Z = 10-16$) for $N_e = (1.3-45) \cdot 10^{21}$ cm^{-3} and $T_e \approx 4-8.2$ $MK \approx 500$ eV. The analysis was made using the approximation of free escape of resonance radiation. Radiation trapping results in quenching of the inversion. Estimates made in Ref. 24 impose a stringent constraint on the ratio of the transverse dimension of the active medium ΔL to the length L: $\Delta L/L = 10^{-3}-10^{-4}$. The authors of Ref. 24 hope that illumination using additional laser radiation (see Sec. 5 below) in resonance with the triplet-singlet transitions may reduce the requirements for the ratio $\Delta L/L$. We note that the electron temperatures and densities required for inversion correspond to a specific energy input $W \gtrsim 3N_e T_e \sim 3 \cdot 10^5-10^7$ J/cm^3.

3.3. *Neon-like ions* (*Fig*. 2). In later investigations[25] similar calculations were made for neon-like ions ($Z \approx 7-15$).[6)] In this case, the feasibility of amplification due to the $2p^5 3p\,{}^1S_0 - 2p^5 3s\,{}^1P$ transition ($\lambda = 40-80$ nm) is analyzed. The rates of excitation and the radiative transition probabilities were calculated in the Coulomb-Born approximation and the LS coupling approximation, respectively. According to the calculations, the probability of radiative decay of the lower active state ($a = 2p^5 3s\,{}^1P_1$) to the ground state ($1 = 2p^6\,{}^1S_0$) was higher than the probability of decay of the $b = 2p^5 3p\,{}^1S_0$ state, whereas the rate of $1 \to a$ excitation was lower than the rate of $1 \to b$ excitation. This was responsible for the inversion obtained in the calculations made in Ref. 25a when analyzing a four-level system ($1 = 2p^6\,{}^1S_0$, $a = 2p^5 3s\,{}^1P_1$, $b = 2p^5 3p$, $c = 2p^5 3d\,{}^1P_1$). In the range of parameters $N_e \approx 10^{19}-10^{20}$ cm^{-3}, $T_e = 100-150$ eV high gains (up to 10^2 cm^{-1}) were predicted for an optically thin Ca XI plasma due to the $a \to 1$ transition. More detailed calculations[25b] gave lower values (~3-25 cm^{-1}). No numerical estimate of the maximum thickness of the active medium, for which reabsorption does not result in quenching of the inversion, was made in Ref. 25a. According to data given in Ref. 25b, the maximum layer thickness is $\Delta L \sim 10^{-2}-10^{-4}$ cm. In addition, the inversion is quenched for electron densities $N_e \gtrsim 10^{20}$ cm^{-3} when collisional transitions between excited levels become important.

3.4. *Degree of reliability of the excitation methods*. In our view, the inversion methods discussed above[24,25] are fairly difficult to implement in practice for the following reasons.

It has been noted that these methods are extremely sensitive to the reabsorption of resonance lines, which gives rise to stringent constraints on the transverse dimensions of the medium ($\Delta L \gtrsim 10^{-2}-10^{-4}$ cm). Since in those regions where reabsorption is substantial, the medium does not amplify but absorbs, the requirements for no distortion of such an extremely narrow strip of active medium become extremely stringent.

Methods of inversion by excitation from the ground state make it necessary to analyze ions having complex spectra. This has the result that both theoretical pre-

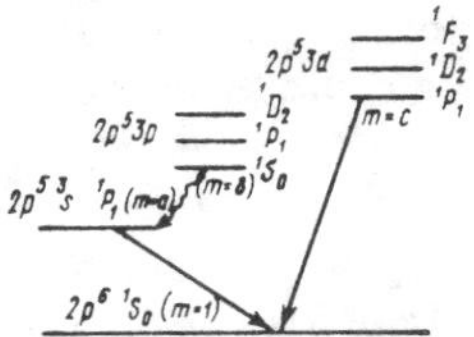

FIG. 2. Typical diagram showing $2p^53l$ singlet levels of a neon-like ion.

dictions and experimental investigations become less reliable. Theoretical analyses must be based on machine calculations of cross sections using approximations whose accuracy is not always clear. In experimental investigations, work with spectra of a set of complex ions in the x-ray range frequently makes it impossible to obtain a fairly clear picture of the relaxation kinetics.[7]

4. Recombination pumping

4.1. *Inversion condition.* Methods of recombination pumping are based on the fact that in almost any type of collisional recombination an electron is initially transferred to a highly excited state and only then, as a result of a chain of transitions which produce a recombination flux, is it transferred to the ground state. If one of the excited states decays more rapidly than a higher state, a population inversion occurs in the plasma and it exists as long as the parameters N_+, N_e, and T_e have the values necessary for the collisional recombination flux to predominate over ionization and excitation. Lasers utilizing this type of recombination-nonequilibrium (supercooled) plasma will be described as plasma lasers,[8] following Refs. 7 and 9. We note that for a dense plasma consisting of multiply charged ions, the supercooled state is natural; it occurs almost immediately after the action of the external source has ceased. On the other hand, the regime with a high temperature T_e needed for methods of excitation used as alternatives to recombination pumping cannot be sustained at high electron densities ($N_e \approx 10^{19}-10^{20}$ cm^{-3}). In particular, in order to achieve this it is necessary to prevent the plasma from expanding. Thus, the systems analyzed in Secs. 3.2–3.4 cannot be considered[15,24,25] to be steady-state, unlike recombination systems. Both systems are quasisteady-state in terms of the relaxation time of the populations which almost instantaneously acquire values corresponding to the given approximate parameters N_1, N_e, N_+, and T_e. On the other hand, the strongly nonequilibrium approximate parameters needed for amplification in the far ultraviolet cannot realistically be sustained under steady-state conditions either in excitation systems or in the recombination regime.

Plasma lasers utilizing transitions in atoms and atomic ions have now been developed in the infrared, visible, and near ultraviolet ranges (see Sec. 6 below). Their properties are in good agreement with the theoretical calculations. It is logical to expect that these inversion methods will be extended to shorter wavelengths.[8,9] There is reason to assume that the most reliable experimental observations of the population inversion in the short-wavelength range were made using recombination pumping (see Secs. 7 and 8 below).

We shall analyze the requirements for recombination pumping in the short-wavelength range. We shall first transform the equations from the open two-level model (1) to the recombination regime (for further details see Ref. 9, Secs. 2.2, 3.4, 5.3, and §13). In view of the diffusive character of collisional relaxation via the excited levels, population of the a lower active state "bypassing" the b state may be neglected (one-quantum approximation). On the other hand, assuming that the b state is below the "throat of the recombination sink," "upward" transitions can be neglected (preferential sink approximation). For the steady-state case the system (1) then takes the form:

$$K_bN_b=N_+/\tau_{\rm rec};\quad K_aN_a=K_{ab}N_b, \tag{30}$$

where $\tau_{\rm rec}$ is the recombination time of an ion of degree of ionization k, which is equal to $(\beta N_e^2)^{-1}$; β is the coefficient of impact radiative recombination. If the condition the opposite of condition (27) is satisfied when the three-body recombination predominates, it can be assumed that

$$\beta\approx 10^{-27}T_e^{-9/2}k^3, \tag{31}$$

where T_e is in electron volts. Data given in Ref. 28 may be used for more accurate calculations (see also Fig. 5.2 in Ref. 9).

The inversion condition is derived from the second equation (30):

$$\delta_{ab}=\frac{K_{ab}g_b}{K_ag_a}=\frac{g_b}{g_a}\,\frac{A_{ab}+V_{ab}N_e}{A_a+V_aN_e}<1 \tag{32}$$

[see Eq. (3)]. This implies that decay of the lower level as a result of collisional or radiative transitions should be faster than the $b-a$ transition. Condition (32) is satisfied considerably more frequently than condition (29) and for a simpler level structure. This is because the probabilities of collisional $V_{mm'}$ and radiative $A_{mm'}$ transitions have different dependences on the transition energy $\varepsilon_{mm'}$. For almost every ion it is possible to select active levels satisfying

$$A_{ab}g_b>A_ag_a;\quad V_{ab}g_b<V_ag_a, \tag{33a}$$

or conversely

$$A_{ab}g_b<A_ag_a;\quad V_{ab}g_b>V_ag_a. \tag{33b}$$

In the case of Eq. (33a), depopulation of the lower active level as a result of electron impact deexcitation may be expected. In this case, a fairly high electron density is required

$$N_e>A_ag_a/V_{ab}g_b. \tag{34a}$$

In the case (33b), radiative depopulation of the lower active level is possible. In this case, the free electron density should not be too high:

$$N_e<A_{ab}g_b/V_ag_a. \tag{34b}$$

There are many ions having an extremely simple level structure for which one or other mechanism of depopulation of the lower active level is quite suitable. For example, condition (33a) is usually satisfied for alkali-like ions, whereas condition (33b) is satisfied for any pair of hydrogen-like states $a=n, b=n+1$, where n is the principal quantum number. (For hydrogen-like states the decay rate decreases as n increases in accordance with $A_n \approx 1.6 \cdot 10^{-10} Z^4 n^{-9/2}$ sec^{-1}, $n \geqslant 2$.)

Before analyzing specific inversion systems, we shall briefly consider the constraints arising from the need for high-intensity pumping. In order to ensure that the value of N_+/τ_{rec} is higher than D_{th} given by Eq. (9), the plasma must be cooled fairly rapidly, i.e., within $\tau_c < \tau_{rec}$. Otherwise, the k ions recombine before the temperature decreases sufficiently to ensure a high recombination coefficient given by Eq. (31). Thus, Eqs. (9) and (30) yield constraints on the wavelength attainable for laser action using recombination pumping:

$$\lambda < \lambda_{lim} \approx (8\pi^{3/2} v_t \varkappa_{th} \tau_c / N_+)^{1/3}. \tag{35}$$

If cooling during expansion of a plasma cylinder is assumed, the cooling time can be estimated from $\tau_c \sim r_0/u$, where r_0 is the initial radius, u is the velocity of the boundary. For $r_0 \sim 10^{-2}$ cm and $u \sim 10^6-10^7$ cm/sec, we have $\tau_c \sim 1-10$ nsec. Specifying the parameters $\tau_c \sim 10$ nsec and $N_+ \sim 10^{21}$ cm^{-3}, we obtain from Eq. (35) $\lambda_{lim} \approx 1$ nm [compare with Eqs. (22)–(24)]. However, it will be shown that the feasibility of progressing to the range $\lambda \sim 1$ nm is limited not by the cooling time and not even by the pump power but by the necessary energy input. We shall now analyze some inversion methods.

4.2. *Pulsed regime*. The following inversion model can be envisaged theoretically. Initially, under the action of an external source, such a high-temperature plasma is formed that the ground-state population of the active (for simplicity, hydrogen-like) ions is almost zero. Rapid cooling then takes place and this is followed by population mainly of the excited states. Thus, as long as the ground state is not populated, a population inversion may occur.

In spite of its logical simplicity and the attractiveness of the high efficiency, this system is unrealistic.[8] This is because it would require cooling the free electrons within $\tau_c \ll A_{ab}^{-1} \sim 10^{-9} Z^{-2}$, which is at the present impossible for the case $Z \geqslant 2$ [see Eqs. (25) and (26)]. More detailed calculations (for example, Refs. 29–31) naturally give the same extremely short inversion lifetimes. Thus, an analysis is made of specific systems with depopulation of the lower active state for which inversion can be achieved in the quasisteady-state regime,[9)] i.e., over times for which the plasma parameters N_+, N_e, and T_e can be kept constant.

4.3. *Collisional depopulation. Lithium-like ions*. The feasibility of progressing into the short-wavelength range by using a collisional mechanism for depopulation of the lower active level was studied using lithium-like ions as an example.[8,32] In Ref. 8 an analysis was made of the feasibility of inversion due to the $3s \to 2p$ transition in Be II (177.6 nm), B III (75.8 nm), C IV (41.9 nm), and other ions up to F VII (13.5 nm). States with $n=2,3,4$ were included in the population balance. It was assumed that the whole recombination flux reaches the $n=4$ levels. Population balance equations were solved for the lower levels. Calculations showed that inversion is found for

$$T_e < 0.2 Z^{3/2} \text{ eV}, \quad N_e > 3 \cdot 10^{12} Z^7 \text{cm}^{-3}, \tag{36}$$

where $Z=k$ is the spectroscopic symbol of the ion under study and k is the degree of ionization of the recombining ion. The constraint on the temperature (36) arises mainly because the $2p$ lower active level is excited by collisions from the $2s$ ground state. The conditions (36) yield the constraint on the recombination time $\tau_{rec} < (N_e^2)^{-1} \approx 0.1 Z^{-11}$ (seconds), which corresponds, for example, to $\tau_{rec} < 10$ μsec for Be II, $\tau_{rec} < 2$ μsec for B III, and $\tau_{rec} < 0.6$ μsec for C IV. We note that these cooling conditions are more stringent than they appear at first glance. In this case, in contrast to the system discussed below, it is insufficient to reduce the temperature, say, by a factor of two for the recombination flux to predominate. Intensive supercooling in accordance with the conditions (36) is required. The wavelength range in which lasing may be achieved by collisional depopulation of the lower active level is clearly limited to $\lambda > 40$ nm (Ref. 8).

4.4. *Radiative depopulation. Hydrogen-like states*. Radiative depopulation of the lower active state is the most promising for amplification in the far ultraviolet. This is because when the spectroscopic symbol Z of the ion under study increases, the rates of radiative transitions increase as Z^4, whereas the rates of collisional transitions decrease as Z^{-3}. For many reasons it is best to discuss the $n=4 \to n'=3$ transition of hydrogen-like ions.[10)] Firstly, the characteristics of transitions for hydrogen-like ions are known more reliably. Secondly, for this transition an inversion is also possible by the reabsorption of lines in the Lyman series $n \to 1$. We shall analyze the feasibility of laser action due to these transitions.

The maximum inversion ΔN due to the $4 \to 3$ transition is achieved for[8]

$$T_e \approx Z^2, \text{ eV}, \quad N_e \approx 10^{12} Z^7, \text{ cm}^{-3}. \tag{37}$$

In this case, the throat of the sink is situated exactly between levels 5 and 4 (see Fig. 5.3 in Ref. 9). If the electron density is increased above $10^{12} Z^7$ cm^{-3}, condition (34b) is no longer satisfied and the $4 \to 3$ collisional transition begins to predominate. Substituting Eq. (37) into Eq. (31) and allowing for the relationship between the wavelength and the spectroscopic symbol Z ($\lambda = 1875 Z^{-2}$ nm), we obtain

$$\tau_{rec} \approx (\beta N_e^2)^{-1} = 10^3 Z^{-8} \approx 0.6 \cdot 10^{-10} \lambda^4, \text{ sec}. \tag{38}$$

If plasma cooling times of $\tau_c \sim 1-10$ nsec are assumed, laser action may be expected up to $\lambda \approx 2-3.5$ nm. However, we shall analyze the requirements for the energy input.

If condition (37) is satisfied, the gain due to the $4 \to 3$ transition may be expressed in the form

$$\varkappa = \frac{\lambda^3}{4} \frac{N_+}{\Delta\omega \tau_{rec}} \left(1 - \frac{g_4}{g_3} \frac{A_4}{A_{33}}\right) \approx \frac{\lambda^3 N_+}{16 \Delta\omega \tau_{rec}}. \tag{39}$$

In this case, one of the most stringent variants for inversion has been selected: the $3 \to 1$ transition is assumed to be completely reabsorbed whereas the $4 \to 1$ transition is transparent. For high densities of hydrogen-like ions, the broadening can be assumed to be of the Holtsmark type and it can be postulated that

$$\Delta\omega \approx \Delta\omega_H = (11\hbar/m)\,(n^2 - n'^2) N_+^{2/3} \approx 88 N_+^{2/3}, \ \text{sec}^{-1}. \tag{40}$$

The Holtsmark width predominates over the Doppler width $\Delta\omega_D \approx 2\pi^{3/2} v_t/\lambda \approx 5.5 \cdot 10^{10} Z^2$ for $N_+ > 10^{13} Z^3$ cm^{-3} or, allowing for condition (37), for $Z > 2$. Thus, it follows from Eq. (39) that

$$\left.\begin{aligned} &\varkappa_{43} \approx 0.7 \cdot 10^{-17} \lambda^2 N_+^{1/3}/\tau_{\text{rec}}; \quad N_{+,\text{th}} = (1.3 \cdot 10^{17} \tau_{\text{rec}})^3/\lambda^6; \\ &W_{\text{th}} \approx J_Z N_{+,\text{th}} \sim 2 \cdot 10^{10} (10^9 \tau_{\text{rec}})^3 \lambda^{-7}; \quad E_{\text{th}} \approx W_{\text{th}} LS \\ &\qquad \sim 2 \cdot 10^7 (10^{-9} \tau_{\text{rec}})^3 \lambda^{-7}, \end{aligned}\right\} \tag{41}$$

where J_Z is the ionization energy of the Z ion. The threshold characteristics are generally obtained from the condition $\varkappa \approx 1$ cm^{-1} and it is assumed that $SL \approx 10^{-3}$ cm^3.

The equations (41) impose fundamental constraints on the feasibility of laser action in the short-wavelength range. For example, assuming that $\lambda \approx 10$ nm and $\tau_{\text{rec}} \approx 10$ nsec, we obtain $N_{+,\text{th}} \approx 3 \cdot 10^{18}$ cm^{-3}, $W_{\text{th}} \approx 3$ kJ/cm^3, $\dot{E}_{\text{th}} \approx 0.3$ GW, and $E_{\text{th}} \approx 3$ J, i.e., very easy conditions. If it is assumed that $\lambda \approx 3$ nm and $\tau_{\text{rec}} \approx 1$ nsec, we obtain from Eq. (41) $N_{+,\text{th}} \approx 10^{22}$ cm^{-3}, $W_{\text{th}} \approx 0.3$ GJ/cm^3, $\dot{E} \approx 3 \cdot 10^5$ GW, and $E_{\text{th}} \approx 0.3$ MJ. Thus, laser action at wavelengths much shorter than $\lambda \approx 10$ nm is unrealistic using the system under study because of the enormous threshold energy input which would be required. For amplification in the range $\lambda \gtrsim 10$ nm, the requirements for the energy input and pump power are easy to satisfy. We note that the formation of a plasma with the necessary parameters is a complex task, which is discussed in Secs. 9 and 10.

We shall note also some other theoretical investigations of the feasibility of amplification due to transitions in multiply charged ions by radiative depopulation of the lower active level.

In Ref. 35, Kononov and Koshelev investigated the feasibility of amplification due to $4d-3p$ and $4f-3d$ transitions in the lithium-like ion Al XI. The inversion mechanism is the same as that for hydrogen-like ions since the $n = 3, 4$ states are almost hydrogen-like. Calculations were made of the populations of levels with $n < 5$. Levels with $n \geqslant 5$ were assumed to have equilibrium populations with a continuous spectrum. This is valid for fairly high electron temperatures $T_e \gtrsim 0.5 Z^2$ eV and electron densities $N_e \approx 3 \cdot 10^{11} Z^7$ cm^{-3}. An analysis was made of the mechanism of plasma cooling by electronic excitation and subsequent deexcitation of the $2p$ lower ($\Delta\varepsilon \sim T_e$) resonance states. Radiation trapping was neglected and its influence was not discussed. On the other hand, reabsorption of the $2p-2s$ lines and in particular $3-2p$ (since $N_{2p} \gtrsim 0.1 N_{2s}$ may possibly be found) may impose significant constraints on this system, although they are certainly weaker than those for excitation systems (see Secs. 3.2–3.4).

Bohn[36] made a numerical analysis of the possibility of inversion due to the $3-2$ transition in hydrogen-like ions. Reabsorption of radiation was neglected. In a later investigation[37] an analysis was made of plasma expansion into a gas which, in the opinion of the authors, should speed up cooling of the electrons. In Ref. 29, Pert analyzed kinetic equations for the populations of the $n = 1, 2, \ldots, 6$ states of the C VI hydrogen-like ion together with average one-dimensional equations for the plasma parameters. Scaling relationships were obtained for the energy input per particle and the gain due to the $3-2$ transition as a function of the initial parameters (radius and electron density).

In Ref. 38, it was suggested that a supercooled plasma could be formed at the center of a plasma bunch by the photoionization of ions in the inner layer of the plasma by radiation from the outer layers. Also proposed was selective pumping of a certain level of the peripheral ions by resonance radiation from the dense plasma core.

5. Methods with intermediate optical pumping

Almost all the amplification methods studied above have a fundamentally low efficiency. This fact could be ignored since far ultraviolet lasers are hardly likely to be used as commercial energy sources. However, an important factor is that the low efficiency makes it impossible to progress far into the short-wavelength range due to the high threshold energy inputs. Thus, attempts to study the possibility of inversion with respect to the ground state of the ions are essential.

The short radiative lifetimes of the excited states are responsible for stringent requirements in respect of their pulsed pumping which cannot be satisfied (see Sec. 4.2). Thus, only the metastable states can be taken into account. On the other hand, it is clear that amplification due to a strongly forbidden transition is unrealistic. In this situation, it is desirable to achieve a population inversion under pulsed conditions by lifting the forbiddenness for the metastable state, for example, by transferring electrons from the metastable state c to a certain other state b from which a transition to the ground state 1 is allowed (see Fig. 2).

In Refs. 39 and 40 it was suggested that electrons could be transferred from a metastable state to an upper active state using radiation from a comparatively long-wavelength laser. By way of a specific example, an analysis was made of transitions from the 2^3S metastable state of a helium-like ion to the 2^1P or 2^3P states (to initiate 2^1P-2^1S or 2^3P-2^1S). To achieve saturation of these transitions in the C V ion, illuminating laser fields of 50 kV/cm and 25 MV/cm, respectively, are required.[8]

The main difficulties involved in implementing these methods are that it is not quite clear how a population inversion and a sufficient density of metastables can be achieved. In Ref. 40 it was suggested that recombination pumping of metastables should be used. Calculations were made which showed that as a result of the expansion of a plasma, population inversion may occur, giving high gains. However, the calculations neglected three-body recombination of metastables which make it impossible to achieve inversion. In Ref. 39 it was proposed that metastable ion beams with a flux density of 3×10^{17} cm$^{-2}\cdot$sec^{-1}, obtained by bombardment of lithium vapor with helium ions, should be used. However, no quantitative estimates were made for this system.

Systems with illumination were also studied in Refs. 41–44. In Ref. 41 it was suggested that nonresonant stimulated Raman scattering due to the $2s-1s$ transition of the O VIII hydrogen-like ion should be used. In Ref. 42 a method with resonant pumping, similar to that proposed in Refs. 39 and 40, was suggested for laser action due to transitions in nuclei and multiply charged ions. Aspects involved in the formation of the population of metastables were not discussed in Refs. 41 and 42. In Ref. 44 an analysis was made of the feasibility of populating Li II metastable states under conditions of excitation in a plasma produced by a CO_2 laser. In this case, ionization of the metastables was neglected.

A metastable Li II ion beam produced in the recombination regime was obtained experimentally in Ref. 43, but at present there are no grounds to expect rapid progress in the attainment of high metastable ion densities.

II. EXPERIMENTS

6. Plasma lasers utilizing singly charged ions

The above comparative discussion of the inversion methods shows that the recombination methods are the most promising for the far ultraviolet. Thus, before examining experimental attempts at amplification in the far ultraviolet, we shall briefly discuss some experiments in which plasma lasers utilizing transitions in singly charged ions were developed and investigated.[11] This is because the main properties of the most promising inversion methods for the short-wavelength range can be fully checked using singly charged ions as an example. Moreover, from a discussion of the experimental difficulties overcome in the visible and ultraviolet ranges, it is possible to assess the feasibility of progressing into the far ultraviolet.

Laser action in a recombination-nonequilibrium rare-gas plasma containing metal vapor has now been obtained due to transitions in the following ions: Al II (747.1 nm), Ba II (1247.8 nm), Be II (467.4, 527.2, and 1210 nm), Ca II (370.6, 373.7, and 994 nm), Mg II (921.8 nm), Pb II (537.2, 1174.8, and 1322.1 nm), Sn II (558.8, 579.9, 1062, and 1074 nm), and Sr II (416.2, 430.5, 1087, and 1123 nm) and also in various other elements (in all, about 40 lines). It was noted in the review presented in Ref. 7 that, in principle, a population inversion in the recombination regime can be achieved for any atom and ion. Naturally, the transitions convenient for laser action are by no means sufficiently interesting in all cases. The difficulty involved in achieving laser action is to attain the plasma parameters for which the collisional or radiative mechanisms for depopulation of the lower level are possible (see Sec. 4). We shall illustrate the effect of these mechanisms using strontium and beryllium vapor lasers as an example (Fig. 3).

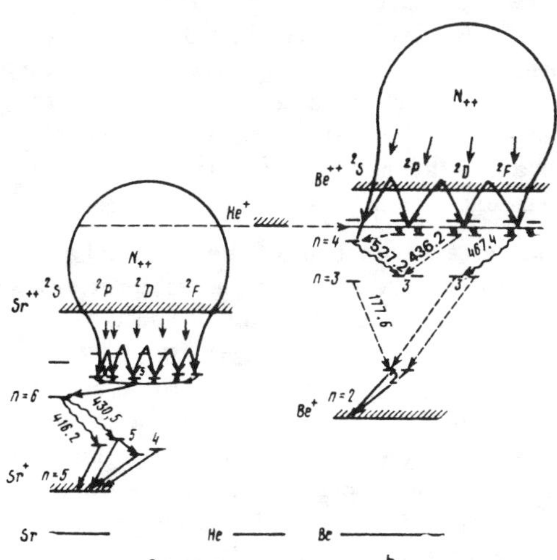

FIG. 3. Diagram of level pumping for He–Sr (a) and He–Be lasers (b). The continuous lines indicate collisional transitions, the dashed lines indicate radiative transitions, and the wavy lines indicate lasing transitions.

6.1. *Helium–strontium laser*. We shall briefly give some experimental results.[46,47] Of the greatest interest is laser action due to the $6S_{1/2}-5P_{3/2}$ (430.5 nm) and $6S_{1/2}-5P_{1/2}$ (416.5 nm) transitions. The plasma was produced in a positive column of a pulsed straight-through gas discharge. The current generator could deliver rectangular pulses of between 0.35 and 7 μsec duration. The pulse voltage and current could reach 17 kV and 150 A. The helium pressure was 5–550 Torr and the strontium pressure 5–10 Torr. Laser action occurred with a delay of 0.3–0.5 μsec relative to the end of the current pulse. The recombination character of the population of both the atomic and ionic levels was confirmed by experiments using pairs of current pulses. The second pulse, which was of the order of 1% of the first pulse in terms of power, was supplied after a delay of 0.5–5 μsec. This pulse not only quenched the laser action during its time of application but also results in a dip (by approximately an order of magnitude) in the emission intensity of the atomic and ionic lines.

It can be seen from the level structure of the Sr II ion that the depopulation of the $5^2P_{3/2,1/2}$ lower active levels is achieved by deexciting collisions with free electrons to the $4^2D_{3/2,5/2}$ states, and then to the $5S_{1/2}$ ground state. This is also confirmed by a qualitative analysis[9,46] and by recent detailed numerical calculations.[48,49] Good quantitative agreement was obtained between calculated and measured temporal characteristics of the afterglow and laser action. The results of calculations simulating experiments with pairs of current pulses also give good agreement with the experiment. Moreover, calculations show that nuclear pumping of an He–Sr laser is possible and that electron beam pumping is promising.[48] This is because, under steady-state pumping conditions, Sr III ions are produced rapidly as a result of a charge transfer reaction accompanied by ionization, which was first investigated in Ref. 50:

$$Sr+He^+ \to Sr^{++}+He+e \quad (\sigma\approx 10^{-15} cm^2).$$

6.2. *Helium–beryllium laser*. Experiments on the laser action and population of the Be II levels were carried out in Ref. 51 also using the afterglow of a positive column of a straight-through pulsed discharge.[12] Laser action was obtained by charge transfer to helium ions due to the $4F-3D$ (467.5 nm) transition. This was observed for small currents (the optimum was 5 A) and thus for low electron densities when the Be II ion lines above the ionization potential of helium gave a negligible afterglow. Laser action due to the $4s-3p$ transition (527.2 nm) was observed in the recombination regime of level population when the current (>30 A) and electron density were high so that the Be II lines above the ionization potential of helium gave high-intensity afterglow. No laser action was achieved[13] due to the $3S_{1/2}-2P_{1/2,3/2}$ transition probably because of the difficulties involved in obtaining a plasma with the necessary parameters in a straight-through discharge. Calculations show[32,51] that depopulation of the $3P_{1/2,3/2}$ lower active level is due to radiative decay of the $3S_{1/2}$ and $3D_{3/2,5/2}$ states with which the $3P_{1/2,3/2}$ levels are coupled by collisional transitions.

6.3. *Some conclusions*. On the whole, experimental and theoretical investigations of laser action on ionic lines of Sr II, Be II, and various other singly charged ions show that collisional and radiative depopulation of the lower active levels is efficient in the visible range. In principle, the same inversion mechanisms should be found at shorter wavelengths. The main difficulty involved in progressing into this range is to obtain a plasma with the required parameters N_+, N_e, and T_e.

In studying laser action for singly charged ions it has already been necessary to overcome various difficulties significantly different from those characteristic of gas lasers for which inversion is achieved during excitation from the ground state.[17-19] One of the main problems is the need to produce a rapidly decaying pulse containing no "tail" capable of heating electrons in the afterglow. (We note that even if the tail contains only approximately one hundredth of the main pulse power, this may be sufficient to quench the laser action.) Moreover, it is necessary to achieve fairly rapid cooling of the electrons in the afterglow. This may be achieved by breakdown in a comparatively dense gas so that the electrons are cooled by collisions with cold neutrals. There is reason to assume that the potential of a straight-through discharge for plasma lasers is almost exhausted but this by no means applies to the laser pumping systems themselves. In order to increase the radiation power further on transition to shorter wavelengths, it is necessary to change over to more progressive pumping methods. The most promising method of increasing the energy output is to use electron beams and various modifications of the transverse discharge (these methods are widely used in exciplex lasers, see the review presented in Ref. 52). On changing to shorter wavelengths, it will be natural to use high-power laser pulses or relativistic electron beams.

The problem of cooling the free electrons also becomes accentuated in the short-wavelength range. Since the electron thermal capacity in a multiply charged ion plasma is substantially higher than that of heavy particles, cooling as a result of elastic collisions cannot be expected. Cooling is only possible as a result of expansion, contact with a cold medium, and escape of radiation from the plasma. This imposes various constraints on the energy input conditions (see Sec. 9).

7. Population inversion in the short-wavelength range

Almost all reports of comparatively reliable observations of population inversion in the short-wavelength range refer either to hydrogen-like ions or to the $n = 3,4,5$ hydrogen-like states of multiply charged ions.[53-56]

The first experimental observation was made by Irons and Peacock[53] for populations of the C VI hydrogen-like ion. It was found that a population inversion $\Delta N \sim 10^{11}$ cm^{-3} corresponding to gains of ~$10^{-5}-10^{-6}$ cm^{-1} was achieved due to the $4\to3$ (52.08 nm), $3\to2$ (18.22 nm), and $4\to2$ (13.50 nm) transitions as a result of expansion of a plasma to a distance of 3 mm from a solid target. When determining[53] the gain, allowance was made for absorption in the plasma along the observation line. The experiment was carried out using a polyethylene target on which neodymium laser radiation was focused ($\lambda_0 = 1.6$ μ, $I = 0.3$ TW/cm^2, $\tau_1 \approx 1$ nsec, $E_1 \approx 6$ J). During the expansion process, measurements were made of the emission intensity of Lyman-series lines for the C VI ion at various distances from the target (1.0, 1.6, and 2.8 mm).

Higher gains for the $4\to3$ transitions of the C VI ion (up to $\varkappa \sim 6$ cm^{-1}) were achieved in experiments at the Institute of Spectroscopy of the Academy of Sciences of the USSR (Ref. 56). The apparatus and measuring technique were described in Ref. 57. The experiments were carried out by focusing laser radiation ($\lambda_0 = 1.06$ μ, $I = 10^5$ GW/cm^2, $\tau_1 \approx 0.25$ nsec) onto a laminar target which consisted of a KCl crystal substrate carrying a thin layer of vacuum grease (a substance containing a large amount of carbon). Most of the energy (~10 J) was supplied to the plasma by the second pulse after it had been prepared by a low-energy first pulse (~0.5 J). The observations were made along a "line" ($L \approx 1.5$ mm). For comparison, spectra were obtained for a pure carbon target and a target having a thick layer of grease. The highest-intensity $4\to3$ line was obtained for a thin layer of grease (~0.5 μ). The $4\to2$ transition was used for normalization.

A population inversion between the $n = 4,5$ and $n = 3$ levels of the lithium-like ion Al XI was achieved earlier by a group headed by Konov (Institute of Spectroscopy of the Academy of Sciences of the USSR).[54] Measured spatial distributions of the plasma parameters and level populations are shown in Fig. 4. It can be seen from Fig. 4 that the $4d$ and $5d$ levels are inverted relative to the $3d$ level throughout almost the whole measurement range. Estimates gave $\Delta N \sim 10^{15}$ cm^{-3}, $\varkappa \sim 0.1$ cm^{-1} for the $4f-3d$ line (~15.4 nm).

Observation of a population inversion between the $n = 4,5$ and $n = 3$ levels of the Al XII helium-like ion was reported in Ref. 55. The plasma, produced by a neodymium laser pulse, had parameters ($N_e \sim 10^{19}-10^{20}$

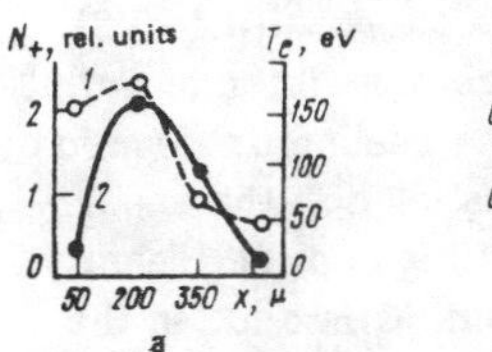
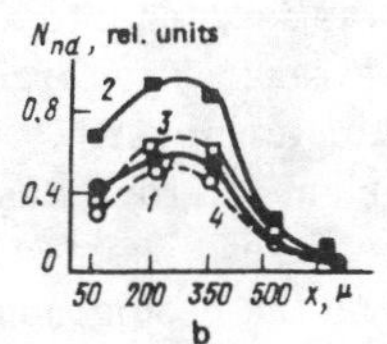

FIG. 4. Dependences of the number of Al XII ions in the ground state N_+ (1) and of the electron temperature T_e (2) (a) and also of the populations of the $n = 3$ (1), 4 (2), 5 (3), and 6 (4) levels of the Al XI ion on the distance from the target.[55]

cm^{-3}, $T_e = 100-800$ eV) similar to those achieved in the experiments reported in Ref. 54. A thin (~100 μ) magnesium foil was placed parallel to the target. The radiation was focused so that the plasma, expanding into a vacuum, came in contact with the foil. It was assumed that as a result of this contact, the plasma would be cooled more severely than as a result of simple expansion. The inversion was recorded from the ratio of the intensities of transitions from the $1s4p$ and $1s3p$ levels to the $1s^2$ ground state. When the point of observation was more than 300 μ from the surface of the target, the gain calculated from the experimental results for the $4^3F \to 3^2D$ transition (12.97 nm) was ~10 cm^{-1}. In the absence of the magnesium foil, inversion of these levels was also observed but the calculated gain was lower.

Emission intensities of the L_α, L_β, and L_γ lines of the C VI ion in a plasma jet at various distances from the surface of a target were studied in Ref. 57a. A neodymium laser ($E_1 \approx 0.5$ J, $\tau_1 \approx 140$ psec) was used. The target was a carbon fiber of 5.3 μ diameter. In order to improve the energy deposition, this was evaporated by a prepulse. The expansion was observed in the plane perpendicular to the axis of the fiber, with a radial resolution of ~100 μ. The results of the measurements were used to plot the emission intensity distribution of the lines in the direction of expansion. The measurements indicated that an inversion was due to the $n = 3 \to n = 2$ transition ($\lambda = 18.2$ nm). The experimental results agreed with calculations of the emission intensity using models describing the level kinetics in terms of average hydrodynamics, neglecting radiation trapping. According to the calculations, we have $\varkappa_{32}L \approx 2 \cdot 10^{-2}$ and this value decreases to 10^{-3} over ~1 nsec. The calculations also indicate that an inversion occurs 0.9 nsec after the end of the laser pulse at a distance of 150 μ from the fiber axis (in this case, we find $N_+ \approx 5 \cdot 10^{18}$ cm^{-3}).

A comparatively recent study[57b] was made of the emission of the L_α, L_β, and L_γ lines of the C VI ion and of lines of the $1s^2-1s3p$ transition in the C V ion and the continuum. A neodymium laser was used ($E_1 = 2$ J, $\tau_1 = 150$ psec). The radiation was focused on a carbon target in a spot of 30 μ diameter or a line (0.6 mm × 30 μ). Emission from the jet of the selected lines was resolved with respect to time from a given point in space and was recorded on photographic film. In the case of spherical expansion, no continuum was recorded at a distance of 500 μ from the target and only the C VI ion lines could be observed. Emission of the $1s^2-1s3p$ line of the C V ion began 1 nsec later (in this case, we have $N_e \approx 8 \cdot 10^{18}$ cm^{-3}, $T_e \approx 35$ eV). Allowing for radiation trapping, the ratio $\delta_{32} = N_3g_2/N_2g_3$ and $\varkappa_{32} = 0.2 \pm 0.1$ cm^{-1} was calculated for the C VI ion. No inversion occurred closer to the target and although it did occur further from the target, the gain was low. In experiments involving the formation of a line, no inversion was observed (it was assumed that as a result of the cylindrical expansion geometry, the plasma can recombine).

Spectra of C V, C VI, Al XI, Al XII, Al XIII, Mg XI, and Mg XII were also studied recently.[57c] In the experiments, neodymium laser radiation ($E_1 = 5-10$ J, $\tau_1 = 200$ psec, prepulse energy ~8% of E_1, delay relative to the main pulse 0.8–1 nsec) was focused in a spot of 100–200 μ diameter. Radiation from different points in the plasma jet was recorded using a spectrograph with a spatial resolution of ~50 μ. The targets were plates made of various materials: Mg + C, Al + Mg, and also "step" targets similar to those used in Ref. 55. It was observed that a distance of 100 μ from the target an inversion between the $n = 4 \to n = 3$ levels (Mg + C, Mg + Al) occurred when using step targets and an inversion between the same levels was observed for planar composite targets (Mg + C). It was suggested that an inversion occurred both as a result of recombination under intensified cooling conditions (using step targets) and as a result of resonance photoexcitation of the $2 \to 4$ transition in the Mg XII ion by the L_α line of the C VI ion. The gain was ~5–10 cm^{-1} and $\varkappa_{43}L \sim 0.1$. There is reason to assume that in the experiments discussed above a recombination pumping system combined with radiative depopulation of the lower active level was achieved (see Sec. 4). A similar inversion system was achieved in Ref. 58 for a laser utilizing the $4 \to 3$ atomic hydrogen transition and in the laser discussed above[51] utilizing $4S_{1/2}-3P_{1/2,3/2}$ transitions in the Be lithium-like ion.

Almost all the observations of population inversions must be treated with caution since errors may occur due to reabsorption of radiation and inhomogeneity of the plasma (see, for example, the discussion of Refs. 59–61 in Ref. 62).

8. Other experiments

In this section we shall analyze reports of various experiments in which either the interpretation of the results or the results themselves are doubtful.

Dixon and Elton[63] reported a population inversion between the $n = 5, 4$ and $n = 2$ levels in hydrogen-like C VI and helium-like C V carbon ions. Additional measurements indicating a population inversion between $n = 3-6$ states for the C VI ion were made in Ref. 64. In these experiments a plasma jet formed at the surface of a graphite target by a neodymium laser ($I_1 \approx 0.2$ TW/cm^2, $\tau_1 \approx 16$ nsec) expanded into a surrounding gas (helium, ($N_{He} \approx 3 \cdot 10^{16}$ cm^{-3}). Data on relative populations ($N_5/g_5 : N_4/g_4 : N_3/g_3 = 3.8 : 3.4 : 1$ for C V and 3.8 : 2.6 : 1 for C VI) were obtained by observing transitions to the ground state[63] and Balmer-series transitions[64] for distances of ~15–16 mm from the target surface. The authors attributed their results to charge transfer pumping as a result of reactions with carbon atoms

$$\mathrm{CVII+CI \rightarrow CVI}(n=4)\mathrm{+CII},$$
$$\mathrm{CVI+CI \rightarrow CV}(n=4)\mathrm{+CII},$$

and reported agreement between their calculations (allowing for charge transfer) and observations. Moreover, it was stated that the conventional recombination pumping mechanism only results in an inversion due to the 4 → 2, 3 → 2 transitions at extremely low temperatures: $T_e < 0.1$ eV (Ref. 64). This incorrect premise [see, for example, Eqs. (37), Secs. 4.2–4.4] was used as the main argument in favor of the charge exchange interpretation of the experiment. The density of C atoms was not measured and it was simply assumed that these are formed by the slowing of ions in helium (in the calculations it was assumed that $N_C \sim 10^{14}$ cm^{-3}).

We note that the inconsistency of the interpretation made in Refs. 63 and 64 is also indicated by the fact that it is impossible to explain a population inversion between $n = 5, 6$ levels situated above the charge transfer limit (compare with the experiments[51] discussed in Sec. 6). Judging by the data given in Refs. 63 and 64, it is logical to assume that these levels are populated in accordance with the impact-radiative recombination mechanism. We also note Ref. 65 in which it was shown that charge transfer under the conditions of Refs. 63 and 64 should result in a decrease in the inversion established under recombination conditions.

The authors of Ref. 66 reported the observation of appreciable amplification due to the 2 → 1 transition in hydrogen atoms ($\varkappa_{21} \approx 1.4$ cm^{-1}) as a result of charge exchange between a proton beam ($N_+ \sim 10^{14}$ cm^{-3}, $u = 7 \times 10^6$ cm/sec) and sodium atoms ($N_{Na} \sim 10^{14}$ cm^{-3}) over an extremely long time interval ($\tau_{am} \approx 80$ nsec). These results are doubtful for the following reasons. Firstly, in order to achieve such a high gain, a high pumping rate $D_1 > 8\pi^{3/2} u \varkappa_{21}/\lambda^3 \approx 2.4 \cdot 10^{23}$ cm$^{-3} \cdot$ sec^{-1} is required, whereas the experimental[66] value $D_2 \approx u\sigma_{ct} N_{Na} N_+ \sim 10^{20}$ cm$^{-3} \cdot$ sec^{-1} (for $\sigma_{ct} = 10^{-15}$ cm^2) was more than three orders of magnitude lower than the required value. Secondly, it was noted at the end of Sec. 2.2 that under these conditions, quasisteady-state amplification (with $\tau_{am} > 0.5$ nsec) is in principle impossible.

The authors of Ref. 56 reported anomalous intensities for lines in the 4.8–7.8 nm range when a KCl target was heated by two ultrashort pulses ($\tau_1 \approx 0.25$ nsec with an interval of ~1.5 nsec). The authors of Ref. 56 assigned these lines to transitions from autoionizing states of Cl VII which, it was assumed, should be populated by excitation from the Cl VII ground state. Subsequently, it was found[56] that the lines observed can be assigned to $4d$–$2p$ (5.8 nm), $3d$–$2p$ (7.0 nm), and $3p$–$2p$ (7.8 nm) transitions in Na IX lithium-like impurity ions. The reproducibility of the result was poor.

The authors of Ref. 67 reported results of experimental investigations to obtain laser action due to $2p^2 3p$–$2p^5 3s$ (~60 nm) transitions in the Ca XI neon-like ion (see Sec. 3) in a plasma produced by a neodymium laser pulse ($I_1 \approx 20$–75 GW/cm^2, $\tau_1 \approx 2.5$–5 nsec). The radiation flux was focused into a narrow [(0.4–0.8) × (10–40) mm] streak. The target consisted of a 0.03–0.125 mm thick calcium strip. A resonator formed by plane and spherical mirrors was used in the experiments. In some cases, spots of high optical density were observed on the photographic film and, in the opinion of the authors,[67] these indicate radiation of energy four orders of magnitude higher than the background thermal radiation. In the experiment reported in Ref. 67 there was no spectral diagnostics of the radiation due to the postulated lasing transition and, in particular, the lasing lines were not identified. The wavelength corresponding to the spots of high optical density (60–66 nm) was estimated on the basis of the relative positions of the resonator grating and the film.

III. PROSPECTS FOR FURTHER RESEARCH

9. Formation of an amplifying medium by expansion of a plasma

It is deduced from the previous analysis that on progressing into the short-wavelength range, transitions between hydrogen-like states with $n = 4, n' = 3$ can primarily be expected. A theoretical analysis of the feasibility of inversion due to the 4 → 3 transition has been used as a basis to obtain fairly reliable information on the probabilities of radiative transitions and on diffusion processes via excited levels under the influence of electron impact. Moreover, it may be considered that the theoretical assumptions have been verified in experiments on the development of plasma lasers utilizing the 4 → 3 hydrogen transition[59] and the 4 → 3 transition in the Be II lithium-like ion[51] (see Sec. 6). Finally, population inversion due to these transitions has been achieved in multiply charged ions. It would seem that laser action has not yet been achieved only because of the inadequate energy characteristics of the pump sources. Nevertheless, a more detailed analysis shows that the main reason is not this but the lack of sufficient attention to the creation of the necessary conditions in the plasma. We shall discuss this in greater detail on the basis of the results of Refs. 33 and 34.

In Part I, as in most of the literature cited, the plasma formation dynamics and associated requirements for the energy input were largely ignored. In practice, only estimates have been made of the energy input which is determined by the thermal capacity of the plasma and the threshold pump energy. If specific experimental systems with laser breakdown are considered, it is necessary to investigate the initial temperature and plasma density needed to satisfy the conditions for laser action to be achieved during expansion of the plasma jet. The initial plasma parameters define the energy input.

Such approximate calculations were made in Ref. 33 for a recombination amplification system utilizing the 4 → 3 transition in hydrogen-like ions and revealed the following important fact. It was found that the direct use of a solid target results in excessively stringent unrealistic requirements for the energy input. These requirements are due to the high initial electron density ($N_{e0} \sim 10^{22}$–10^{23} cm^{-3}) which arises from the fact that the target is solid. The electron density N_{e1} and temperature T_{e1} at the onset of lasing [see Eq. (37)] are related to the initial parameters N_{e0} and T_{e0} by $N_{e1}/N_{e0} = (t_0/t_1)^2$ and $T_{e1}/T_{e0} = (t_0/t_1)^{4/3}$, which are valid for slow-response cylindrical expansion found beginning from the time t_0. The initial temperature should be fairly high for the following reasons. Firstly, T_{e1} should not drop below $T_{id} = Z^2[N_{e1}/(3 \cdot 10^{20})]^{1/3}$ for which the plasma is ideal. Secondly, during cooling the plasma should not recombine appreciably ($t_1 < \tau_{rec}$). It is deduced from these estimates that an energy higher than 1 MJ must be deposited in a volume of 10^{-3} cm^3 within 1 nsec to obtain laser action in the range $\lambda \approx 20-10$ nm.

On the other hand, similar calculations showed that by selecting a comparatively low initial electron density, the requirements are reduced sharply. For example, in order to achieve a gain $\varkappa_{43} \approx 1$ cm^{-1} in the $\lambda = 20-10$ nm range for $N_{e0} \approx 10^{19}$ cm^{-3} it is sufficient to deposit several joules per nanosecond in the medium. As a result, it was suggested that a plasma having the necessary parameters could be produced by a prepulse before the main energy is supplied. An analysis was also made of the feasibility of reducing the energy input by using a solid target containing hydrogen with active-element impurities. By using this type of target, the threshold energy input can be reduced to several kilojoules at $\lambda = 20-3$ nm, which is of interest for $\lambda \approx 5-3$ nm, but for $\lambda \approx 20-10$ nm the energy input is too high.

In the context of this reasoning, it is extremely important to check the reliability of the qualitative analysis made in Ref. 33 by means of calculations based on a more detailed model. In particular, it is necessary to analyze spatial profiles of the plasma parameters and also the process of heating and ionization of the medium. Such calculations were made in Ref. 34 in which an analysis was made of the formation and expansion dynamics of a plasma produced by a CO_2 laser. An analysis was made of the feasibility of efficient amplification due to the $4 \to 3$ transition in the Na XI hydrogen-like ion (15.5 nm). A system of hydrodynamic equations for a cylinder symmetrically illuminated by a laser pulse was analyzed in terms of Lagrangian coordinates for thirty layers and included equations of motion and energy balance for the electrons and ions.[67,68] Allowance was made for the thermal conductivity, energy exchange between electrons and ions, energy losses due to ionization, and other factors. Absorption of laser radiation was described as follows. It was assumed that for an electron density $N_e < N_{cr} \approx 10^{19}$ cm^{-3} (where N_{cr} is determined from the plasma Langmuir frequency being equal to the CO_2 laser radiation frequency) absorption takes place only due to the inverse bremsstrahlung effect with a coefficient which allows for a decrease in the wave group velocity. In addition, it was assumed that, at the point where $N_e = N_{cr}$, all the incident optical energy is absorbed.

The possibility of inversion was analyzed and the gain was estimated on the basis of an approximate analysis of the recombination kinetics similar to that made in Secs. 4.2–4.4. The calculations were made for an initial cylinder radius $r_0 = 10^{-2}$ and the laser pulse profile was assumed to be Gaussian with a characteristic time $\tau_1 = 1$ nsec. The initial particle density was varied $N_0 = 10^{19}-10^{20}$ cm^{-3} and the energy input was $E_1 = 5-10$ J/cm.

The analysis showed that population inversion occurs almost at all times and at all points in space almost immediately after the end of the heating pulse. However, the peripheral layers have time to expand during heating so that the gain here is low due to the low value of N_e. In the variants studied, the width of the region where $\varkappa_{43} > 1$ cm^{-1}, situated near the cylinder axis, was $\Delta L = r(t)/3 \approx 3 \cdot 10^{-3}-10^{-2}$ cm. The amplification conditions ($\varkappa_{43} > 1$ cm^{-1}) remained favorable throughout the time interval studied (4 nsec) after the end of the pulse. The following variants were analyzed: $N_0 = 10^{19}$ cm^{-3}, $E_1 = 6$ J/cm ($\varkappa_{43} > 1$ cm^{-1}); $N_0 = 2 \cdot 10^{19}$ cm^{-3}, $E_1 = 9$ J/cm ($\varkappa_{43} > 1$ cm^{-1}); $N_0 = 2 \cdot 10^{19}$ cm^{-3}, $E_1 = 3$ J/cm ($\varkappa_{43} < 1$ cm^{-1}).

10. Feasibility of gradual progress in the short-wavelength range

This analysis has shown that the main difficulty in developing short-wavelength lasers does not lie in the energy characteristics of the pump sources but in initial parameters of the medium and the energy input conditions. This should strongly influence the organization of experimental programs. In particular, it is completely inadequate simply to supply high powers to a medium and observe the expansion of the plasma. In some way, it is necessary to deposit most of the energy in a medium of substantially lower density than that of a solid.

It follows from this, in particular, that in order to obtain laser action in the $\lambda = 20-10$ nm range, it is desirable to use a CO_2 laser for pumping. As a result of the low critical electron density ($N_{cr} = 10^{19}$ cm^{-3}), it is possible to deposit sufficient energy in a medium of low initial density by using a CO_2 laser. At the same time, estimates and calculations show that by selecting a low initial density $N_0 = 10^{19}-10^{20}$ cm^{-3}, it is possible to achieve efficient amplification for a low energy input. This clearly does not suggest that pumping using other lasers is not potentially useful.

In the energy deposition systems discussed in Sec. 9, it is most difficult to produce an initial homogeneous plasma for which the ratio of the width of the lasing zone $\Delta L \approx 3 \cdot 10^{-3}-10^{-2}$ cm to the length of the active medium $L \approx 3-10$ cm is small. However, this constraint is reduced substantially by the following two factors. Firstly, it follows from the calculations[34] that with a suitable choice of the initial plasma parameters, deeper layers less exposed to fluctuation deformations are most efficiently amplified. Secondly, in the peripheral regions amplification rather than absorption of light also takes place with $\varkappa_{43} < 1$ cm^{-1}. Thus, curvature of the irradiated strip does not result in quenching of the amplification, as in the systems described in Secs. 2 and 3, but only decreases the effective width of the active region. Nevertheless, experiments involving accurate formation of the initial plasma parameters are extremely difficult. Thus, we shall analyze the feasibility of preliminary investigations.

It is logical first to attempt to develop plasma lasers utilizing singly charged ions (similar to those analyzed in Sec. 6) and laser breakdown of a dense gas. Firstly, the experimental method may be adjusted for familiar lasing transitions (for example, in Sr II and Be II ions) and then attempts may be made to obtain laser action due to the $3s \to 2p$ Be II transition[32,33] and due to Balmer- and Paschen-series transitions in He II hydrogen-like ions. Laser action due to $n \to 2$ transitions in He II as a result of breakdown of dense helium ($N_{He} \sim 10^{19}$ -10^{20} cm^{-3}) is possible as a result of the Penning depopulation of the levels (see calculations made in Ref. 70). We note that a population inversion between the $n = 2, 3, 4, 5$ states in He II has already been observed.[71,72]

The main difficulty involved in these experiments is the need to avoid overheating of the medium. In particular, the initial electron density must not be too high. For example, calculations[50] show that laser action due to Sr II transitions for $N_{He} \lesssim 10^{20}$ cm^{-3} is only possible if $N_{e0} < 5 \cdot 10^{17}$ cm^{-3}, which corresponds to a specific energy input of $W \lesssim 1$ J/cm^3. In order to reduce the energy input for the breakdown of a gas, the laser radiation may be focused near the surface of a solid[73,74] or preionization may be used.[75] We note that experiments on the development of plasma lasers in an afterglow produced by laser breakdown have already been carried out.[75,76] The group headed by Silfvast achieved efficient laser action in the afterglow of a plasma produced by a CO_2 laser in dense (~1 atm) Ar (1.79 μ), Kr (3.07 μ), and Xe gases (2.03, 2.65, 3.43, and 3.65 μ).[14]

Systematic attempts to advance into the short-wavelength range are evidently best made using the $4 \to 3$ transition in a hydrogen-like ion plasma. We shall give the main advantages of this transition.

Firstly, the structure of hydrogen-like ions (unlike that of ions in other isoelectronic sequences) is extremely similar. This means that scaling relationships can be reliably used for the plasma parameters (see Secs. 4.2–4.4) and, on the basis of experimental data obtained for the previous ion, it is possible to predict the increase in difficulties on transition to the next ion. Secondly, a hydrogen-like ion plasma is appreciably less sensitive to excessive energy in the ionization pulse, since further ionization is impossible. Thirdly, the fact that the spectrum of a hydrogen-like ion plasma is simple and known in detail should make it substantially easier to investigate. In particular, there are no serious difficulties involved in identifying the spectral lines.

CONCLUSIONS

To sum up, it may be stated that in spite of the difficulties noted, the development of efficient sources of stimulated emission in the far ultraviolet is a completely realistic proposition. However, the requirements for the energy input increase rapidly as the wavelength decreases ($\sim\lambda^{-4}-\lambda^{-7}$, see Secs. 1.2, 4.2–4.4). Evidently, the systems studied here cannot be used to obtain emission at wavelengths substantially shorter than $\lambda = 10$ nm. On the other hand, there is reason to assume that in the x-ray and gamma-ray ranges, instead of hypothetical sources of stimulated emission, it is reasonable to expect emission from relativistic particles as a result of their interactions with various media and external fields. Firstly, emission from relativistic particles has a low angular divergence and, secondly, it can have a comparatively high density in certain frequency ranges. This is achieved by selecting conditions under which the particle emits coherently over a long path. Already in widespread use are electron storage rings which can produce high-power fluxes of narrow-band radiation in the $\lambda = 0.01$–10 nm range.[77] In the $\lambda \lesssim 0.01$ nm range, it is most promising to use radiation from channeled particles[78-80]

The commissioning of a nuclear-pumped x-ray laser ($\lambda \approx 1.4$ nm) was recently reported.[81] Our estimates show that it is possible to achieve quasisteady-state amplification in the $\lambda = 1$–2 nm range in a recombination-nonequilibrium plasma ($N_e \sim 3 \cdot 10^{21}-10^{22}$ cm^{-3}) of an element with $Z \approx 30$ (for example, the $5 \to 6$ transition in zinc with $\lambda \approx 1.42$ nm) produced by a high-power gamma-ray source ($\hbar\omega > J_Z \approx 10$ keV, $\lambda \lesssim 0.1$ nm, $q \sim 10^{15}-10^{16}$ W/cm^2). Unfortunately, the data given in Ref. 81 are quite inadequate both to assess the reliability of the experiment and for its interpretation.

Amplification due to the $3 \to 2$ ($\lambda_1 = 18.2$ nm) transition in the C VI hydrogen-like ion was obtained in Ref. 82. An inversion occurred as a result of recombination during expansion of a carbon wire of ~3–4 μ diameter heated by a laser pulse focused in a line of length $L \approx 0.2$ cm. The value $\varkappa_{32}L \approx 5$ was obtained. A population inversion between the levels of helium-like magnesium ions in a recombining laser plasma was reported in Ref. 83. The estimated gain for the $1s6h\,^1H_5 \to 1s5g\,^1G_4$ transition ($\lambda = 62.0$ nm) was $\varkappa_{65} \approx 750$ cm^{-1} and $\varkappa_{65}L \approx 15$ was obtained.

The authors are grateful to V. A. Bazylev for discussions of aspects mentioned in the conclusions. The authors are also grateful to A.V. Vinogradov and I.I. Sobel'man for familiarizing themselves with the manuscript and making various comments which helped to formulate a more accurate opinion on various topics discussed in the review.

1) Radiation in the λ = 3–50 nm range will be regarded as the far ultraviolet (compare with Ref. 1, Vol. 5, p. 245). In some cases, even comparatively long-wavelength $\lambda \lesssim 80$ nm radiation is assigned to the x-ray range (see Ref. 1, Vol. 4, p. 424).

2) A discussion of various aspects excluded from our analysis and appropriate literature may be found in Refs. 2-5.

3) Exceptions may be systems with optical pumping via an intermediate metastable level which are discussed in Sec. 5.

4) In order to avoid misunderstandings, we reemphasize that our discussions do not concern charge transfer systems in general but systems based on mixing of hydrodynamic streams.

[5)] We note that the spectroscopic ion symbol is a value one higher than the degree of ionization so that the spectroscopic symbol of the ion under study is equal to the degree of ionization of the next ion.

[6)] The feasibility of inversion due to transitions in neon-like ions was also studied in previous investigations.[2,26]

[7)] Similar difficulities are encountered in the diagnostics of impurity ions in fusion facilities.[21] Work in this direction has recently developed rapidly and considerable progress has been achieved in spectroscopic diagnostics (for literature, see Refs. 15 and 21). However, it is desirable to discuss the simplest possible spectra and thus there must be extremely strong reasons for changing to multielectron configurations.

[8)] These are sometimes called recombination lasers but this may result in confusion. This is because other types of lasers are also described as recombination: lasers utilizing vibrational transitions populated by association; lasers utilizing photoassociative transitions; and various semiconductor lasers.

[9)] In the literature it is incorrectly stated that for recombination pumping it is necessary to cool the plasma within a time of the order of the relaxation times of the excited states, which for multiply charged ions do not exceed 1-10 psec (see Ref. 15, p. 212 and also Ref. 31). In fact, in almost all investigations concerned with recombination pumping (including Refs. 6-9) quasisteady-state inversion methods are analyzed when the inversion is governed by the different rates of decay of the upper and lower active states (see Sec. 4.1). The lifetime of a quasisteady-state inversion for the far ultraviolet range is 1-10 nsec.

[10)] A population inversion between excited levels of multiply charged ions as a result of a higher rate of radiative decay of lower states was first noted as early as 1966 in Ref. 6. However, the feasibility of producing a plasma with the necessary parameters and threshold characteristics was not studied in Ref. 6. This line of research was developed later in Refs. 8, 33, and 34 (see also Sec. 9). We note that a population inversion in hydrogen-like ions also follows from calculations made by Bates *et al*. published in 1962 (for literature, see Ref. 9). However, the values tabulated there were normalized to the equilibrium populations which made the results less clear and a population inversion was not observed. Moreover, in Ref. 31 it is incorrectly stated that Bates' calculations indicate a lack of inversion in a quasisteady-state plasma.

[11)] The main credit for the experimental implementation of these lasers belongs to E. L. Latush, V. S. Mikhalevskiĭ and M. F. Sém of the Rostov State University. For discussions of a wider range of experiments in which plasma lasers were developed see Refs. 45, 46, and 9, Secs. 20 and 21.

[12)] Experiments with a hollow-cathode discharge were also carried out.

[13)] A population inversion due to $3s-2p$ and $4s-3p$ transitions was predicted in Ref. 32.

[14)] It would be interesting to attempt to develop exciplex lasers[52] using these devices.

---

[1]Encyclopedic Physics Dictionary [in Russian], Vols. 1-5, Sovetskaya Éntsiklopediya, Moscow (1960-1966).

[2]A. G. Molchanov, Usp. Fiz. Nauk **106**, 165 (1972) [Sov. Phys. Usp. **15**, 124 (1972)].

[3]V. A. Bushuev and R. N. Kuz'min, Usp. Fiz. Nauk **114**, 677 (1974) [Sov. Phys. Usp. **17**, 942 (1975)].

[4]G. Chapline and L. Wood, Phys. Today **28**, No. 6, 40 (1975).

[5]R. W. Waynant and R. C. Elton, Proc. IEEE **64**, 1059 (1976).

[6]B. F. Gordiets, L. I. Gudzenko, and L. A. Shelepin, Prikl. Mekh. Tekh. Fiz. **7**, No. 5, 115 (1966).

[7]L. I. Gudzenko, L. A. Shelepin, and S. I. Yakovlenko, Usp. Fiz. Nauk **114**, 457 (1974) [Sov. Phys. Usp. **17**, 848 (1975)]; Tr. Fiz. Inst. Akad. Nauk SSSR **83**, 100 (1975).

[8]L. I. Gudzenko, V. V. Evstigneev, and S. I. Yakovlenko, Tr. Fiz. Inst. Akad. Nauk SSSR **90**, 17 (1976).

[9]L. I. Gudzenko and S. I. Yakovlenko, Plasma Lasers [in Russian], Atomizdat, Moscow (1978).

[10]M. I. Chibisov, Pis'ma Zh. Eksp. Teor. Fiz. **24**, 56 (1976) [JETP Lett. **24**, 46 (1976)]; Preprint No. IAÉ-3232 [in Russian], I. V. Kurchatov Institute of Atomic Energy, Moscow (1980).

[11]A. Salop and R. E. Olson, Phys. Rev. A **16**, 1811 (1977); A **19**, 1921 (1979).

[12]B. M. Smirnov, Pis'ma Zh. Eksp. Teor. Fiz. **6**, 565 (1967) [JETP Lett. **6**, 78 (1967)].

[13]L. P. Presnyakov and V. P. Shevel'ko, Pis'ma Zh. Eksp. Teor. Fiz. **13**, 286 (1971) [JETP Lett. **13**, 203 (1971)].

[14]A. V. Vinogradov and I. I. Sobel'man, Zh. Eksp. Teor. Fiz. **63**, 2113 (1973) [Sov. Phys. JETP **36**, 1115 (1973)].

[15]V. A. Boĭko, A. V. Vinogradov, S. A. Pikuz, I. Yu. Skobelev, and A. Ya. Faenov, X-Ray Spectroscopy of Laser Plasmas [in Russian], VINITI, Moscow (1980).

[16]V. I. Pistunovich, Fiz. Plazmy **2**, 3 (1976) [Sov. J. Plasma Phys. **2**, 1 (1976)].

[17]W. R. Bennett Jr, Appl. Opt. **4**, Suppl. 2, 3 (1965).

[18]G. Gould, Appl. Opt. **4**, Suppl. 2, 59 (1965).

[19]G. G. Petrash, Usp. Fiz. Nauk **105**, 645 (1971) [Sov. Phys. Usp. **14**, 747 (1972)].

[20]Ya. B. Zel'dovich and Yu. P. Raizer, Physics of Shock Waves and High Temperature Hydrodynamic Phenomena, 2 vols., Academic Press, New York (1966, 1967).

[21]V. S. Marchenko and S. I. Yakovlenko, Preprint No. IAÉ-3147 [in Russian], I. V. Kurchatov Institute of Atomic Energy, Moscow (1979); in: Spectroscopy of Multiply Charged Ions [in Russian], Izd. Nauchnogo Soveta po Spectroskopii, Moscow (1980), p. 231.

[22]H. Griem, Plasma Spectroscopy, McGraw-Hill, New York (1964).

[23]R. H. Huddlestone and S. L. Leonard (eds.), Plasma Diagnostic Techniques, Academic Press, New York (1966).

[24]A. V. Vinogradov, I. Yu. Skobelev, I. I. Sobel'man, and E. A. Yukov, Kvantovaya Elektron. (Moscow) **2**, 2189 (1975) [Sov. J. Quantum Electron. **5**, 1192 (1975)].

[25]A. V. Vinogradov, I. I. Sobel'man, and E. A. Yukov, Kvantovaya Elektron. (Moscow) **4**, 63 (1977) [Sov. J. Quantum Electron. **7**, 32 (1977)]; A. V. Vinogradov and V. N. Shlyaptsev, Kvantovaya Elektron. (Moscow) **7**, 1319 (1980) [Sov. J. Quantum Electron. **10**, 754 (1980)].

[26]A. N. Zherikhin, K. N. Koshelev, and V. S. Letokhov, Kvantovaya Elektron. (Moscow) **3**, 152 (1976) [Sov. J. Quantum Electron. **6**, 82 (1976)].

[27]L. C. Johnson and E. Hinnov, J. Quant. Spectrosc. Radiat. Transfer **13**, 333 (1973).

[28]W. W. Jones and A. W. Ali, Appl. Phys. Lett. **26**, 450 (1975).

[29]G. J. Pert, J. Phys. B **9**, 3301 (1976).

[30]J. M. Green and W. T. Silfvast, Appl. Phys. Lett. **28**, 253 (1976).

[31]A. V. Vinogradov, I. I. Sobelman, and E. A. Yukov, J. Phys. (Paris) **39**, Colloq. 4, (4-61) (1978).

[32]L. I. Gudzenko and S. I. Yakovlenko, Kratk. Soobshch. Fiz. No. 7, 3 (1970); L. I. Gudzenko, V. V. Evstigneev, and S. I. Yakovlenko, Kratk. Soobshch. Fiz. No. 9, 23 (1973).

[33]L. I. Gudzenko, V. I. Derzhiev, V. V. Evstigneev, and S. I. Yakovlenko, Zh. Tekh. Fiz. **49**, 2408 (1979) [Sov. Phys. Tech. Phys. **24**, 1346 (1979)]; L. I. Gudzenko, V. I. Derzhiev, and S. I. Yakovlenko, Tr. Fiz. Inst. Akad. Nauk SSSR **120**, 68 (1980).

[34]E. V. Babarskov, V. I. Derzhiev, V. V. Evstigneev, and S. I. Yakovlenko, Preprint No. IAÉ-3361/6 [in Russian], I. V. Kurchatov Institute of Atomic Energy, Moscow (1980).

[35]É. Ya. Kononov and K. N. Koshelev, Kvantovaya Elektron. (Moscow) **1**, 2411 (1974) [Sov. J. Quantum Electron. **4**, 1340 (1975)].

[36]W. L. Bohn, Appl. Phys. Lett. **24**, 15 (1974).
[37]P. Wägli and W. L. Bohn, J. Appl. Phys. **51**, 3601 (1980).
[38]A.V. Vinogradov, I. I. Sobel'man, and E. A. Yukov, Kvantovaya Electron. (Moscow) **2**, 105 (1975) [Sov. J. Quantum Elektron. **5**, 59 (1975)].
[39]H. Mahr and U. Roeder, Opt. Commun. **10**, 227 (1974).
[40]L. I. Gudzenko, V. V. Evstigneev, and S. I. Yakovlenko, Kvantovaya Elektron. (Moscow) **1**, 2061 (1974) [Sov. J. Quantum Electron. **4**, 1148 (1975)]; L. I. Gudzenko (Goodzenko), S. I. Yakovlenko, and V. V. Evstigneev (Yevstigneyev), Phys. Lett. A **48**, 419 (1974).
[41]I. Freund, Appl. Phys. Lett. **24**, 13 (1974).
[42]E. V. Baklanov and V. P. Chebotaev, Pis'ma Zh. Eksp. Teor. Fiz. **21**, 286 (1975) [JETP Lett. **21**, 131 (1975)].
[43]A. A. Vekhov, V. N. Makhov, F. A. Nikoleav, and V. B. Rozanov, Kvantovaya Elektron. (Moscow) **2**, 1318 (1975) [Sov. J. Quantum Electron. **5**, 718 (1975)].
[44]S. A. Mani, H. A. Hyman, and J. D. Daugherty, J. Appl. Phys. **47**, 3099 (1976).
[45]V. V. Zhukov, E. L. Latush, V. S. Mikhalevskiĭ, and M. F. Sém, Kvantovaya Elektron. (Moscow) **4**, 1249 (1977) [Sov. J. Quantum Electron. **7**, 704 (1977)].
[46]V. V. Zhukov, V. S. Kucherov, E. L. Latush, and M. F. Sém, Kvantovaya Elektron. (Moscow) **4**, 1257 (1977) [Sov. J. Quantum Electron. **7**, 708 (1977)].
[47]E. L. Latush and M. F. Sém, Zh. Eksp. Teor. Fiz. **64**, 2017 (1973) [Sov. Phys. JETP **37**, 1017 (1973)].
[48]S. M. Babenko and S. I. Yakovlenko, Preprint No. IAÉ-3192 [in Russian], I. V. Kurchatov Institute of Atomic Energy, Moscow (1979); Phys. Lett. A **76**, 237 (1980).
[49]S. M. Babenko, I. S. Lakoba, and S. I. Yakovlenko, Kratk. Soobshch. Fiz. No. 12, 3 (1980).
[50]E. L. Latush and M. F. Sém, Pis'ma Zh. Eksp. Teor. Fiz. **15**, 645 (1972) [JETP Lett. **15**, 457 (1972)].
[51]V. V. Zhukov, V. G. Il'yushko, E. L. Latush, and M. F. Sém, Kvantovaya Elektron. (Moscow) **2**, 1409 (1975) [Sov. J. Quantum Electron. **5**, 757 (1975)].
[52]I. S. Lakoba and S. I. Yakovlenko, Kvantovaya Elektron. (Moscow) **7**, 677 (1980) [Sov. J. Quantum Electron. **10**, 389 (1980)].
[53]F. E. Irons and N. J. Peacock, J. Phys. B **7**, 1109, 2084 (1974).
[54]É. Ya. Konov, K. N. Koshelev, Yu. A. Levykin, Yu. V. Sidel'nikov, and S. S. Churilov, Kvantovaya Elektron. (Moscow) **3**, 576 (1976) [Sov. J. Quantum Electron. **6**, 308 (1976)].
[55]V. A. Bhagavatula and B. Yaakobi, Opt. Commun. **24**, 331 (1978).
[56]A. N. Zherikhin, K. N. Koshelev, P. G. Kryukov, V. S. Letokhov, and S. V. Chekalin, Kvantovaya Elektron. (Moscow) **8**, 88 (1981) [Sov. J. Quantum Electron. **11**, 48 (1981)].
[57a]A. N. Zherikhin, K. N. Koshelev, P. G. Kryukov, V. S. Letokhov, and S. V. Chekalin, Pis'ma Zh. Eksp. Teor. Fiz. **25**, 325 (1977) [JETP Lett. **25**, 300 (1977)];
[57b]R. J. Dewhurst, D. Jacoby, G. J. Pert, and S. A. Ramsden, Phys. Rev. Lett. **37**, 1265 (1976); M. H. Key,
[57c]C. L. S. Lewis, and M. J. Lamb, Opt. Commun. **28**, 331 (1979); V. A. Bhagavatula, IEEE J. Quantum Electron. **QE-16**, 603 (1980).
[58]V. S. Aleĭnikov and A. P. Shelepo, Opt. Spektrosk. **36**, 813 (1974) [Opt. Spectrosc. (USSR) **36**, 474 (1974)].
[59]P. Jaeglé, A. Carillon, P. Dhez, G. Jamelot, A. Sureau, and M. Cukier, Phys. Lett. A **36**, 167 (1971).
[60]P. Jaeglé, A. Carillon, G. Jamelot, and A. Sureau, Proc. Intern. Vavilov Conf. on Nonlinear Optics, Novosibirsk (1973).
[61]A. Carillon, These de Doctorat d'Etat, 08424, Paris (1973).
[62]K. N. Koshelev and S. S. Churilov, Kvantovaya Elektron. (Moscow) **2**, 723 (1975) [Sov. J. Quantum Electron. **5**, 400 (1975)].
[63]R. H. Dixon and R. C. Elton, Phys. Rev. Lett. **38**, 1072 (1977).
[64]R. H. Dixon, J. F. Seely, and R. C. Elton, Phys. Rev. Lett. **40**, 122 (1978).
[65]S. Suckewer and H. Fishman, J. Appl. Phys. **51**, 1922 (1980).
[66]R. Tkach, H. Mahr, C. L. Tang, and P. L. Hartman, Phys. Rev. Lett. **45**, 542 (1980).
[67]A. A. Ilyukhin, G. V. Peregudov, E. N. Ragozin, I. I. Sobel'man, and V. A. Chirkov, Pis'ma Zh. Eksp. Teor. Fiz. **25**, 569 (1977) [JETP Lett. **25**, 535 (1977)].
[68]A. A. Samarskiĭ and Yu. P. Popov, Gasdynamic Difference Schemes [in Russian], Nauka, Moscow (1975).
[69]E. V. Babarskov, V. I. Derzhiev, and A. Yu. Zakharov, Preprint No. 22 [in Russian], Institute of Applied Mathematics, Academy of Sciences of the USSR, Moscow (1980).
[70]L. I. Gudzenko, Yu. K. Zemtsov, and S. I. Yakovlenko, Pis'ma Zh. Eksp. Teor. Fiz. **12**, 244 (1970) [JETP Lett. **12**, 167 (1970)].
[71]K. Sato, M. Shiho, M. Hosokawa, H. Sugawara, T. Oda, and T. Sasaki, Phys. Rev. Lett. **39**, 1074 (1977).
[72]K. Sato, J. Phys. Soc. Jpn. **43**, 1027 (1977).
[73]V. P. Ageev, A. I. Barchukov, F. V. Bunkin, V. I. Konov, S. M. Metev, A. S. Silenok, and N. I. Chapliev, Izv. Vyssh. Uchebn. Zaved. Fiz. No. 11, 34 (1977).
[74]V. A. Boĭko, V. A. Danilychev, B. N. Duvanov, V. D. Zvorykin, and I. V. Kholin, Kvantovaya Elektron. (Moscow) **5**, 216 (1978) [Sov. J. Quantum Electron. **8**, 134 (1978)]; V. A. Boĭko, V. V. Vladimirov, V. A. Danilychev, B. N. Duvanov, V. D. Zvorykin, and I. V. Kholin, Pis'ma Zh. Tekh. Fiz. **4**, 1373 (1978) [Sov. Tech. Phys. Lett. **4**, 554 (1978)].
[75]L. I. Gudzenko, S. D. Kaitmazov, A. A. Medevedev, and E. I. Shklovskiĭ, Pis'ma Zh. Eksp. Teor. Fiz. **9**, 561 (1969) [JETP Lett. **9**, 341 (1969)].
[76]W. T. Silfvast, L. H. Szeto, and O. R. Wood II, Appl. Phys. Lett. **31**, 334 (1977); **34**, 213 (1979); **36**, 500 (1980).
[77]E. M. Rowe and J. H. Weaver, Scientific American **236**, No. 6, 32 (1977).
[78]M. A. Kumakhov, Dokl. Akad. Nauk SSSR **230**, 1077 (1976) [Sov. Phys. Dokl. **21**, 581 (1977)]; Zh. Eksp. Teor. Fiz. **72**, 1489 (1977) [Sov. Phys. JETP **45**, 781 (1977)].
[79]R. Wedell, Phys. Status Solidi B **99**, 11 (1980).
[80]V. A. Bazylev, V. V. Beloshitskiĭ, V. I. Glebov, N. K. Zhevago, V. A. Kumakhov, and Kh. Trikalinos, Zh. Eksp. Teor. Fiz. **80**, 608 (1981) [Sov. Phys. JETP **53**, 306 (1981)].
[81]C. A. Robinson Jr, Aviat. Week Space Technol. **114**, No. 8, 25 (1981).
[82]D. Jacoby, G. J. Pert, S. A. Ramsden, L. D. Shorrock, and G. J. Tallents, Opt. Commun. **37**, 193 (1981).
[83]V. A. Boĭko, B. A. Bryunetskin, B. I. Duvanov, V. M. Dyakin, S. A. Pikuz, I. Yu. Skobelev, A. Ya. Faenov, A. I. Fedosimov, and K. A. Shilov, Pis'ma Zh. Tekh. Fiz. **7**, 665 (1981) [Sov. Tech. Phys. Lett. **7**, (in press, 1981)].

Translated by R. M. Durham

Reprinted with permission from *Applied Physics Letters,* Vol. 41(2), pp. 121-123 (July 15, 1982).

Electron density and energy output limits of plasma-recombination lasers

O. R. Wood II and W. T. Silfvast
Bell Telephone Laboratories, Holmdel, New Jersey 07733

Theoretically estimated limiting electron densities for plasma-recombination lasers are shown to agree with experimentally measured values over a wavelength variation of nearly one decade. Radiation trapping is found not to restrict the electron densities in recombination lasers that operate at wavelengths longer than about 100 nm. For wavelengths shorter than 150 nm predicted specific output energies for plasma-recombination lasers may exceed those of excimer lasers.

Good agreement between calculated and measured limiting electron densities in plasma-recombination lasers has been found over a wide range of laser wavelengths. The measurements involve non-hydrogen-like recombination laser transitions in neutral and single ion species; yet, they agree with theoretical estimates based on hydrogenlike collisional rates. Restrictions on plasma volume due to radiation trapping effects are found to be significant only for recombination lasers operating at wavelengths less than 100 nm. The density limits verified in this letter predict that specific output energies (J/cm^3) for plasma-recombination lasers may exceed those of excimer lasers for wavelengths less than 150 nm.

Since the first suggestion by Gudzenko and Shelepin in 1963[1] that a population inversion could be produced during plasma recombination, recombination lasers have been operated at more than 100 wavelengths from the near UV to the mid IR. This success has led several groups to point out some of the potential advantages that lasers of this type might have,[2,3] namely, (1) applicability to a wide variety of laser systems and, hence, to devices with operating wavelengths from the infrared to the x-ray spectral region, (2) capability of either pulsed or cw operation, and (3) the possibility of developing more powerful and efficient laser devices in the future. The first advantage has already been confirmed experimentally, both by the variety of atoms and ions in which recombination laser action has been observed[4,5] and by the observation of the scaling of recombination lasers along isoelectronic sequences to higher ion stages and, thus shorter wavelengths.[6] The second advantage has also been confirmed, through the demonstration of quasisteady plasma-dynamic lasers in magnetoplasmadynamic (MPD) arcjets.[7,8] Attempts to confirm the third potential advantage have led to the electron density limits and to the specific energy limits reported in this letter.

It is well known that collisional recombination can result in a population inversion between two levels, q and p, if the electron density is low enough that the electron-collisional de-excitation rate from the upper level to the lower level does not dominate over the radiative rate.[9,10] An approximate expression for this limiting density in terms of laser wavelength and electron temperature can be derived by setting $n_e K(q,p) = A_{qp}$, where n_e is electron density (in cm^{-3}), $K(q,p)$ is the rate coefficient for collisional de-excitation (in cm^3/s), and A_{qp} is the radiative transition rate (in s^{-1}). Using the rate coefficient for collisional excitation of hydrogenic ions from Bates *et al.*,[11] together with the principle of detailed balance, the electron density above which inversions will begin to be reduced by electron collisions can be expressed as

$$n_e = 0.13(\sqrt{T_e})/\lambda^3, \qquad (1)$$

where T_e is electron temperature (in °K) and λ is the laser wavelength (in cm).

The electron temperature in a typical recombination laser, after the termination of the current pulse, is characterized by a rapid fall to a value in the range 2000–4000 °K governed primarily by the frequency of elastic collisions of electrons with atoms and ions followed by a monotonic slow decay determined by overall plasma cooling. A reasonable estimate for the quasisteady value of T_e during its slow decay in a discharge in 10 Torr of helium gas is 3000 °K.[5] The wavelength dependence of the limiting electron density [given by Eq. (1)] at this temperature is shown in Fig. 1 as the solid line. Also shown in Fig. 1 (as solid points) are limiting electron densities determined in experiments on recombination lasers operating at three different wavelengths.

The first two limiting values of electron density,

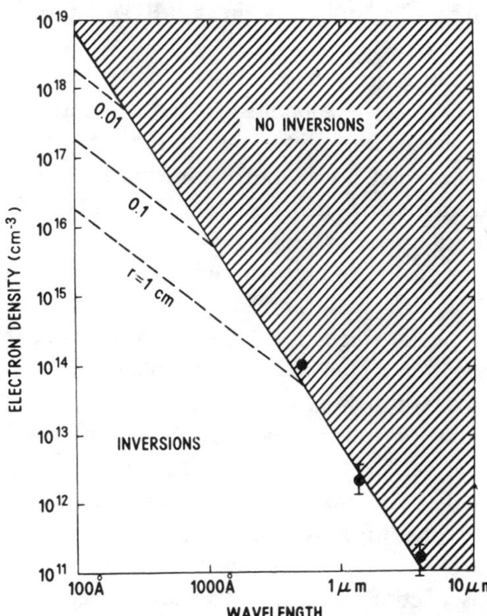

FIG. 1. Calculated upper limit on electron density in a plasma-recombination laser as a function of laser wavelength due to electron collisional de-excitation (solid line) and the trapping of resonance radiation (dashed curves for three plasma radii) together with experimentally determined limiting densities (solid points).

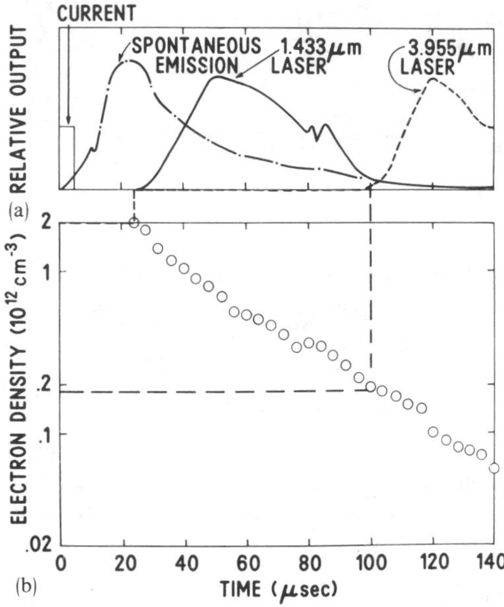

FIG. 2. Temporal behavior of (a) laser output (arbitrary units), spontaneous emission in Cd I (arbitrary units), discharge current (150-Å peak) and (b) electron density in Cd SPER laser (2.5 Torr helium).

1.8×10^{11} cm^{-3} at 3.955 μm and 2×10^{12} cm^{-3} at 1.433 μm, were obtained in a segmented-plasma-excitation-recombination (SPER) laser device under conditions similar to those described in Ref. 4. Both laser transitions occurred in expanding plasmas of neutral Cd produced by recombination of Cd^+ ions. Recombination emission from excited Cd neutral states [dot-dashed curve in Fig. 2(a)] was found to maximize approximately 20 μs after the excitation pulse terminated, whereas laser action at 1.433 μm on the Cd I $6p\,^3P_2^0$–$6s\,^3S_1$ transition [solid curve in Fig. 2(a)] did not begin until 24 μs after the excitation pulse terminated and laser action at 3.955 μm on the Cd I $7p\,^3P_1^0$–$7s\,^3S_1$ transition [dashed curve in Fig. 2(a)] did not begin until 100 μs after the excitation pulse terminated.

The two limiting electron densities for the above mentioned laser transitions were obtained from the variation of electron density versus time plot, shown in Fig. 2(b) (open points), at the times when laser action commenced. This plot was obtained from measurements of the Cd^+ ion density, N_{Cd^+}, via absorption measurements on the 226.5-nm resonance transition of Cd^+, and by assuming that $n_e = N_{Cd^+}$. This assumption is reasonable for the late times of these measurements since higher stages of Cd ionization would have long since decayed[6] and He ions and metastable atoms would have converted their energy to Cd^+ via charge exchange or Penning ionization. That these values are true density limits was verified by varying the excitation current magnitude and observing that the threshold for laser action moved to earlier times for lower currents and later times for higher currents, in such a way that the electron density at the threshold for laser action was always a constant. In contrast, the peak of the recombination emission was observed to move to earlier times for higher currents and later times for lower currents, consistent with a recombination mechanism.

The third limiting value of electron density, 1×10^{14} cm^{-3} at 488 nm was taken from an experiment on a plasma-dynamic Ar recombination laser operating on the Ar II $4p\,^2D_{5/2}^0$–$4s\,^2P_{3/2}$ transition in an MPD arc-jet.[2] This experiment demonstrated that the electron density shown in Fig. 1 at this wavelength was a true upper limit, i.e. one above which laser action did not occur.

Thus, over the range where experimental data are available (nearly one decade of wavelength), the agreement between calculated and experimental values of the limiting electron density illustrated in Fig. 1 is quite good. This good agreement is no doubt somewhat fortuitous since the calculation was based on an electron-collisional rate coefficient for hydrogenic ions whereas two of the experimental points came from recombination lasers operating on transitions in neutral atoms and none of the transitions were in hydrogenic ions. However, in the case of the two experiments involving neutral atoms, even when the coefficient for collisional excitation of neutral atomic hydrogen given in Bates *et al.*[11] is used, the agreement between calculation and experiment remains quite good.

In the derivation of Eq. (1) it was implicitly assumed that the plasma was optically thin for the 1–2 and 1–3 resonance lines. Under some plasma conditions, however, radiation trapping on these transitions could occur. For example, trapping on the 1–2 transition could reduce or eliminate an inversion on the 3–2 transition by reducing the radiative decay rate from level 2. Under these conditions, the radiative decay rate from level 2, A_{21}, becomes FA_{21}, where $F = 1.60/[k_0 r(\pi \ln k_0 r)^{1/2}]$ is the so-called escape factor ($F \leqslant 1$) for a Doppler-broadened transition in a cylindrical plasma,[12] k_0 is the absorption coefficient on the 1–2 transition (in cm^{-1}), and r is the plasma radius (in cm). Making the plausible assumption that the majority of the population is in the ground state of the ion stage under consideration [i.e., $N = n_e/Z$, where N is hydrogenic ground-state density, n_e is electron density, and Z is charge state of the recombining ion] and the reasonable assumption that $(M/T_i)^{1/2}$ is approximately equal to 10^{-2} for light atoms (where M is atomic mass and T_i is ion temperature), the electron density above which an inversion on the 3–2 transition in hydrogenlike ions will begin to be reduced by radiation trapping ($F = 0.5$) can be expressed as

$$n_e = 1.9\times10^7/r\lambda^{3/2}, \tag{2}$$

where r is plasma radius (in cm) and λ is wavelength (in cm).

The wavelength dependence of the electron density limit set by radiation trapping [given by Eq. (2)] is shown in Fig. 1 (as dashed lines for three values of plasma radius $r = 1$, 0.1, and 0.01 cm). The key assumption made in deriving Eq. (2) (that $N = n_e/Z$) almost certainly overestimates the value of N and therefore gives an electron density limit that is too low, but is not too different than the assumption made by others in the past, namely, that[13] $N = n_e/10$ for $Z = 5$ or[14] $N = n_e/(Z-1)$. Because nearly all recombination lasers to date operate on transitions between n states $\geqslant 3$, radiation trapping will probably not restrict the electron density to values less than those given by Eq. (1) for recombination lasers with wavelengths longer than about 100 nm.

Using the limiting electron density given in Eq. (1) and assuming that all of the ions in the next higher ion stage pass

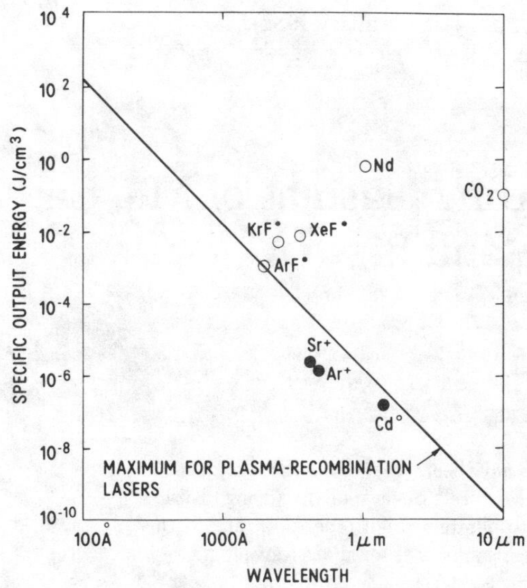

FIG. 3. Calculated specific output energy for plasma-recombination lasers as a function of wavelength (solid line) together with experimentally observed output energy densities for plasma-recombination lasers and other high-power lasers.

through the laser levels during recombination and contribute to the laser energy, the maximum specific output energy, E_{max} (in J/cm^3), for a plasma-recombination laser is approximately given by

$$E_{max} = n_e \times hc/\lambda = 2.5 \times 10^{-24} (\sqrt{T_e})/\lambda^4, \quad (3)$$

where T_e is electron temperature (in °K) and λ is wavelength (in cm). This wavelength dependence for a temperature of 3000 °K is shown in Fig. 3 as the solid line. Also shown in Fig. 3 (as solid points) are experimental values for the maximum observed specific output energy for plasma-recombination lasers in Sr II at 373.7 nm,[5] Ar II at 488 nm,[7] and Cd I at 1.433 μm.[4] The experimental point for the Cd SPER laser ($E_{max} = 1.5 \times 10^{-7}$ J/cm^3, $\lambda = 1.433$ μm) indicates that this device is providing nearly 50% of the maximum available specific output energy at this wavelength. Even so, the limiting value, 3.2×10^{-7} J/cm^3, is well below that achieved by many existing infrared lasers. For example, the specific output energy achieved by Nd lasers can be as high as 0.6 J/cm^3 at 1.06 μm (Ref. 15) and by high-pressure CO_2 lasers can be as high as 0.1 J/cm^3 at 10.6 μm.[16] These values are shown for comparison on Fig. 3 as open circles. In the near ultraviolet, performance of rare-gas halogen excimer lasers (open circles in Fig. 3) is also expected to outperform plasma-recombination lasers.[17] At still shorter wavelengths (150 nm and shorter), however, the performance of plasma-recombination lasers is expected to become equal to or exceed lasers based on all other population inversion mechanisms.

The authors would like to acknowledge several useful technical discussions with W. L. Bohn and the excellent assistance of J. J. Macklin.

[1]L. I. Gudzenko and L. A. Shelepin, Zh. Eksp. Teor. Fiz. **45**, 1445 (1963) [Sov. Phys. JETP **18**, 998 (1964)].

[2]E. M. Campbell, R. G. Jahn, W. F. von Jaskowsky, and K. E. Clark, J. Appl. Phys. **51**, 109 (1980).

[3]V. V. Zhukov, E. L. Latush, V. S. Mikhalevskii, and M. F. Sem, Sov. J. Quantum Electron. **7**, 704 (1977).

[4]W. T. Silfvast, L. H. Szeto, and O. R. Wood II, Appl. Phys. Lett. **36**, 615 (1980); W. T. Silfvast and O. R. Wood II, Opt. Lett. **7**, 34 (1982).

[5]V. V. Zhukov, V. S. Kucherov, E. L. Latush, and M. F. Sem, Sov. J. Quantum Electron. **7**, 708 (1977).

[6]W. T. Silfvast, L. H. Szeto, and O. R. Wood II, Appl. Phys. Lett. **39**, 212 (1981).

[7]E. M. Campbell, R. G. Jahn, W. F. von Jaskowsky, and K. E. Clark, Appl. Phys. Lett. **30**, 575 (1977).

[8]T. Hara, K. Kodera, M. Hamagaki, K. Matsunaga, M. Inutake, and T. Dote, Jpn. J. Appl. Phys. **19**, L606 (1980).

[9]R. C. Elton, in *Methods of Experimental Physics, Plasma Physics*, edited by H. R. Griem and R. H. Lovberg (Academic, New York, 1970), Vol. 9A, Chap. 4.

[10]H. R. Griem, *Plasma Spectroscopy* (McGraw–Hill, New York, 1964), p. 160.

[11]D. R. Bates, A. E. Kingston, and R. W. P. McWhirter, Proc. R. Soc. A **267**, 297 (1962).

[12]T. Holstein, Phys. Rev. **83**, 1159 (1951).

[13]R. C. Elton, Proc. SPIE Technical Symposium East '81, Washington, D. C. 1981, p. 279; NRL Memorandum Report 4525, Naval Research Laboratory, Washington, D. C. 1981.

[14]A. V. Vinogradov and V. V. Shlyaptsev, Sov. J. Quantum Electron. **10**, 754 (1980).

[15]W. E. Martin, J. B. Trenholm, G. J. Lunford, S. M. Yarena, and C. A. Hurley, IEEE J. Quantum Electron. **QE-17**, 744 (1981).

[16]O. R. Wood II, Proc. IEEE **62**, 355 (1974).

[17]C. A. Brau, in *Excimer Lasers*, edited by C. K. Rhodes (Springer, New York, 1979), Vol. 30, pp. 87–133.

Reprinted with permission from *Optics Letters*, Vol. 7(1), pp. 34-36 (January 1982).

Recombination laser transitions in expanding plasmas of Mg, Ca, Cu, Zn, Ag, Cd, In, Sn, Pb, and Bi

W. T. Silfvast and O. R. Wood II

Bell Laboratories, Holmdel, New Jersey 07733

Fifty new laser transitions in the visible and near infrared in ten metal vapors have been observed in the recombination phase of the expanding plasmas produced by a segmented-plasma laser device. Several of the strong visible transitions might be attractive for applications requiring simple lasers that operate at high repetition rates with pulse energies of the order of 0.1 mJ. All the transitions reported here suggest candidates for short-wavelength recombination lasers when isoelectronically scaled to higher ion stages.

Fifty new laser transitions in the vapors of Mg, Ca, Cu, Zn, Ag, Cd, In, Sn, Pb, and Bi have been observed in the recombination phase of expanding plasmas at wavelengths ranging from 4924 Å to 5.460 μm. The expanding plasmas in which these lasers were observed were generated in a simple room-temperature segmented-plasma-excitation recombination (SPER) laser device.[1] Thirty-three of the transitions have never to our knowledge been observed in laser action before with any type of excitation, and all are operating for the first time in the expanding-plasma recombination type of excitation. Devices based on some of the stronger transitions may be useful in applications in which simple laser devices with pulse powers of no more than 1 kW and pulse lengths in the range 10–200 μsec are required. The new midinfrared lasers (3–5 μm) may find use in range finding and target designation. All these new transitions provide an additional basis to scale recombination lasers isoelectronically to higher ionization stages and shorter wavelengths.[2]

The experimental arrangement used to produce these new laser transitions involves a newly developed SPER laser device described in some detail in Refs. 1 and 2. The electrode structure for this device consists of a series (typically numbering 30 to 60) of 1-mm-thick × 2-mm-wide × 12–20 mm-long metal strips (of the lasing material) positioned end to end on an insulating substrate in such a way as to leave a 1-mm gap between adjacent strips. When this electrode structure is electrically excited with a low-inductance pulser, providing 50–400-A current pulses of adjustable duration (3–6 μsec), a bright metal-vapor plasma is formed in each gap. A low-pressure background gas of He is present that provides a high initial electron temperature (increasing metal-vapor production in the gap region), controls the subsequent expansion of the vapor, and cools the recombining electrons, causing electron–ion recombination (and thus gain) to occur in the plasmas as they expand away from the gaps and into the region between the laser mirrors. The axis of the laser resonator is positioned parallel to and 7 mm above the row of gaps. Pairs of 2.54-cm-diameter dielectric mirrors (coated for maximum reflectivity at various visible wavelengths) with 3-m radii of curvature form 115-cm-long resonators for the visible transitions. Two 2.54-cm-diameter gold-coated mirrors (one had a centrally located 2-mm-diameter coupling hole) with 10-m radii of curvature form a 115-cm-long resonator for the near-infrared transitions.

The search for additional recombination lasers described in this Letter had two objectives. The first was to identify additional visible and UV laser transitions over a wide range of wavelengths for possible device applications. The second was to increase the total number of known recombination lasers to provide the basis on which isoelectronic scaling arguments can be used to determine those transitions in higher ionized species that might be attractive candidates for the future development of short-wavelength recombination lasers.

The first of these objectives was accomplished with the realization of several strong visible laser transitions (e.g., in Zn^+ at 4924 Å, in Pb^+ at 5372 Å, and in Sn^+ at 5799 Å) by using the simple SPER laser device just described. These transitions, when taken together with the previously reported strong Cd and In transitions in the visible and UV,[2] form the basis for a simple broad-spectrum laser. Such a device could be constructed by using resonator mirrors with a sufficiently broad bandwidth and a SPER-type electrode structure made either by alternately inserting strips of different metals or by grouping different metals on separate portions of the insulating substrate. As a specific example, one might include 25 metal segments each of In, Zn, Cd, and Sn to produce a laser operating simultaneously in the blue, blue-green, green, and yellow spectral regions. An alternative method, which would not produce a simultaneous output on all wavelengths but would produce more power at a given wavelength in a shorter device, would involve mounting four separate electrode assemblies (one for each metal) in the bore of a 15-mm-diameter glass or Lucite tube in such a way that each row of metal strips lies opposite a row of strips of one of the other metals. A high-voltage switch could

Table 1. Laser Transitions Obtained in Recombination Lasers of the SPER Type

Spectrum	Wavelength (μm)[a]	Transition Assignment
Magnesium		
Mg I	1.081*	$5f\ ^3F^\circ-3d\ ^3D$
Mg II	1.091	$4p\ ^2P^0_{3/2}-3d\ ^2D_{3/2}$
Calcium		
Ca I	1.905*	$3d^2\ ^3F_4-4p'\ ^3D^0_3$
Copper		
Cu I	1.257*	$5f\ ^2F^0_{7/2}-4d\ ^2D_{5/2}$
	1.815	$4f\ ^2F^0_{5/2}-4d\ ^2D_{3/2}$
	1.818	$4f\ ^2F^0_{7/2}-4d\ ^2D_{5/2}$
	3.089*	?
	3.726*	$4p'\ ^2P^0_{1/2}-5s\ ^2S_{1/2}$
	5.460*	$7d\ ^2D_{3/2}-7p\ ^2P^0_{1/2}$
Cu II	0.7807	$6s\ ^3D_3-5p\ ^3F^0_4$
	1.787*	?
Zinc		
Zn I	1.170*	$5f\ ^3F^0-4d\ ^3D$
	1.647*	$4f\ ^3F^0-4d\ ^3D$
	1.844*	$5d\ ^1D_2-5p\ ^1P^0_1$
	3.748*	$6p\ ^3P^0_2-6s\ ^3S_1$
	3.779*	$6p\ ^3P^0_1-6s\ ^3S_1$
Zn II	0.4924	$4f\ ^2F^0_{7/2}-4d\ ^2D_{5/2}$
	0.7757	$6s\ ^2S_{1/2}-5p\ ^2P^0_{3/2}$
	1.685*	$7s\ ^2S_{1/2}-6p\ ^2P^0_{3/2}$
Silver		
Ag II	1.646	$6p\ ^3P^0_1-5d\ ^3P_1$
	1.720	$6p\ ^3D^0_3-5d\ ^3D_3$
	1.735	$6p\ ^3F^0_4-5d\ ^3G_5$
Cadmium		
Cd I	3.955*	$7p\ ^3P^0_2-7s\ ^3S_1$
Indium		
In I	3.903*	$7p\ ^2P^0_{1/2}-7s\ ^2S_{1/2}$
In II	0.7685*	$7s\ ^3S_1-6p\ ^3P^0_2$
	0.7353*	$7s\ ^3S_1-6p\ ^3P^0_1$
Tin		
Sn I	1.121*	$6p\ ^1D_2-6s\ ^1P^0_1$
	1.176*	$6p\ ^3P_0-6s\ ^3P^0_1$
	1.196*	$6p\ ^3D_3-6s\ ^3P^0_2$
	1.305*	$6p\ ^3P_1-6s\ ^3P^0_0$
	1.347*	$6p\ ^3P_1-6s\ ^3P^0_1$
Sn II	0.5799	$4f\ ^2F^0_{7/2}-5d\ ^2D_{5/2}$
	1.063	$5f\ ^2F^0_{5/2}-6d\ ^2D_{3/2}$
	1.076	$5f\ ^2F^0_{7/2}-6d\ ^2D_{5/2}$
	1.239*	$7d\ ^2D_{5/2}-7p\ ^2P^0_{3/2}$
	1.363*	?
Lead		
Pb I	1.109*	$6f\ ^1F_3-6d\ ^3F^0_3$
	1.698*	$8p\ ^3D_2-6d\ ^3D^0_2$
	1.797*	$10d\ ^3F^0_3-8p\ ^3D_2$
	3.138*	$8p\ ^3D_1-8s\ ^3P^0_0$
	3.799*	$8p\ ^3P_1-8s\ ^3P^0_1$
Pb II	0.5372	$5f\ ^2F^0_{7/2}-6p^2\ ^4P_{5/2}$
	0.8396*	$8s\ ^2S_{1/2}-7p\ ^2P^0_{3/2}$
	1.166	$6f\ ^2F^0_{5/2}-7d\ ^2D_{3/2}$
	1.324	$6f\ ^2F^0_{7/2}-7d\ ^2D_{5/2}$
Bismuth		
Bi I	1.256*	$6p^27p-6p^3\ ^2P^0_{3/2}$
	1.286*	?
	3.107*	?
Bi III	0.7599	$6f\ ^2F^0_{5/2}-7d\ ^2D_{3/2}$
	0.8069	$6f\ ^2F^0_{7/2}-7d\ ^2D_{5/2}$

[a] Asterisks denote transitions never previously observed in laser action by any excitation means.

then be used to channel the electrical excitation selectively to each electrode assembly in turn and as a consequence obtain the desired emission wavelength.

The second objective of this study was accomplished with the observation of the large number of laser transitions shown in Table 1. Since each of these transitions[3,4] has now been observed in laser action in an expanding recombining plasma, it seems quite likely that the isoelectronic sequence of each laser transition might also suggest good laser candidates. The use of isoelectronic scaling to produce recombination lasers at higher ionization stages and shorter wavelengths has already been demonstrated.[2] Of the transitions shown in Table 1, one particular isoelectronic sequence is worth further emphasis: the observed single-ion transitions in Pb II occurring at 1.16 and 1.32 μm ($6f\ ^2F^\circ-7d\ ^2D$) isoelectronically scaled to the observed 7599- and 8069-Å transitions in Bi III. If the strong 5378-Å transition ($5f\ ^2F^\circ-6p^2\ ^4P$) in Pb II is also isoelectronically scaled to Bi, the evidence suggests that the transition at 2074 Å in Bi III should also have significant gain (as is indicated in the energy-level diagram of Fig. 1). Further scaling of this sequence to radioactive Po would of course not be practical, but a simple Bi SPER laser operating at 2074 Å might be attractive for some applications.

Of the 50 transitions reported in this Letter, 33 have never to our knowledge been observed in laser action with any type of excitation (designated with an asterisk in Table 1). This suggests both the versatility of the SPER laser device in easily producing a wide range of vapors from which laser action can be obtained and the uniqueness of the plasma-recombination process in producing excitation from above (recombination) rather

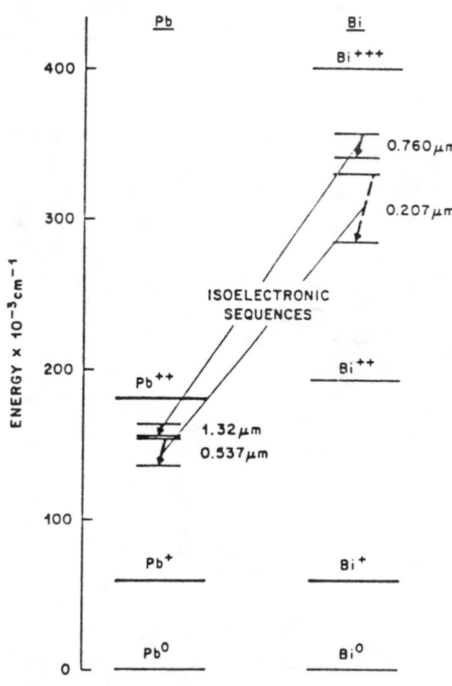

Fig. 1. Isoelectronic scaling sequence of known laser transitions (solid arrows) and potential laser transitions (dashed arrows) in Pb and Bi.

than from below (as in the more typical processes, such as electron collisional excitation and optical pumping). It is no coincidence that many of the strong transitions reported here have also been observed in laser action through charge-transfer processes since many charge-transfer lasers occur by excitation from above as a result of charge transfer followed by collisional decay to the upper laser level. One of the clearest examples of this is the 4924-Å transition in Zn II, which was shown by Green[5] to operate in this manner.

SPER lasers should be useful in applications that require a simple laser device that produces moderate peak-power outputs. Radiation trapping and electron thermalization place an upper limit of 10^{-4} J/plasma or 10^{-2} J/pulse on a 100-plasma-segment visible laser device. If the output from such a device occurred for a duration of 10 μsec, then the peak power could approach 1 kW/pulse. At a repetition rate of 1 kHz such a device could provide an average power of 10 W. Since each of the ions produced could potentially contribute a laser photon, these powers might be achieved in a device having efficiencies of the order of 1% or more.

We would like to acknowledge the excellent technical assistance of John J. Macklin.

References

1. W. T. Silfvast, L. H. Szeto, and O. R. Wood II, Appl. Phys. Lett. **36,** 615 (1980).
2. W. T. Silfvast, L. H. Szeto, and O. R. Wood II, Appl. Phys. Lett. **39,** 212 (1981).
3. C. E. Moore, *Atomic Energy Levels* (U.S. Government Printing Office, Washington, D.C., 1949), Vols. I–III.
4. S. Bashkin and J. O. Stoner, Jr., *Atomic Energy-Level and Grotrian Diagrams* (North-Holland, Amsterdam, 1975), Vols. I–II.
5. J. M. Green, G. J. Collins, and C. E. Webb, J. Phys. B **6,** 1545 (1973).

Reprinted with the permission of the American Institute of Physics from *Journal of Applied Physics,* Vol. 53(6), pp. 4020-4027 (June 1982).

Plasma conditions required for attainment of maximum gain in resonantly photo-pumped aluminum XII and neon IX

J. P. Apruzese, J. Davis, and K. G. Whitney[a]
Plasma Physics Division, Naval Research Laboratory, Washington, D. C. 20375

We present a detailed analysis of the plasma conditions required to optimize gain in two proposed x-ray lasing schemes using resonant photo-pumping. In one proposed configuration, the Si XIII line $1s^2$-$1s2p\,^1P$ at 6.650 Å pumps Al XII $1s^2 - 1s3p\,^1P$ at 6.635 Å, inverting the Al XII $n = 3$ and $n = 2$ levels which are separated by 44 Å. A similar approach which utilizes the Na X $1s^2$-$1s2p\,^1P$ line at 11.00 Å would invert the $n = 4$, 3, and 2 levels of Ne IX. Conditions in the pumped neon and aluminum plasmas, and in the pumping silicon plasma, are calculated using a multistage, multilevel atomic model with multifrequency radiation transport. For modeling the pumping sodium line we have inferred the intensity from a spectrum of a neon filled, laser-imploded glass microballoon containing sodium impurities obtained at Rochester. The pump line intensities calculated for Si and inferred for Na are equivalent to blackbodies of 252 and 227 eV, respectively. It is found that peak gain for the 3-2 lines of about 100 cm^{-1} occurs at ion densities of 10^{20} cm^{-3} and 4×10^{20} cm^{-3} in the pumped neon and aluminum plasmas, respectively. Temperatures required to maximize gain in the pumped plasmas are found to be 50 and 100 eV, for neon and aluminum, respectively. Finally, since the silicon and aluminum lines are slightly off resonance, we have investigated the effect of streaming the plasmas toward each other at various velocities to offset some or all of the wavelength difference. It is found that a streaming velocity of 6.8×10^7 cm sec^{-1}—fully offsetting the wavelength difference—will approximately triple the achieved gain compared to the zero velocity case. Lesser increases in gain occur with partial velocity offsets.

I. INTRODUCTION

It has been suggested[1–4] that population inversions in plasmas may be efficiently pumped by opacity broadened lines from different ionization stages of the same element or from different elements in a two component plasma. Experimental evidence[5,6] has been presented for inversions of the $n = 4$ and $n = 3$ levels in Mg XII and Mg XI, which were pumped by resonant $Ly\alpha$ and $1s^2$-$1s2p\,^1P$ radiation in C VI and C V. The above mentioned lasing transitions in Mg lie at ~130 and 156 Å for Mg XII and Mg XI, respectively. In this paper we present a detailed analysis of the plasma conditions which would be needed to optimally implement two promising lasing schemes utilizing resonant photoexcitation with considerably shorter lasing wavelengths (down to 44 Å). The radiation field—critical in a photoexcitation process—is modeled in detail. The pumped and pumping transitions—as well as other key optically thick lines—are calculated on a frequency grid allowing for accurate modeling of broadening processes and frequency-dependent absorption. Previous efforts at modeling short-wavelength resonantly photoexcited lasing processes have employed assumed linewidths,[1] line profiles arising from uniform source functions,[2] assumed power densities,[3,5] or probability-of-escape approximations.[4] In another study,[7] the pumped plasma was modeled with a fine frequency grid but the pumping spectrum was assumed to be a filtered Planckian. In Sec. II our atomic model is described along with the methodology for its employment for calculations for both the pumped and pumping plasmas. In Sec. III the equilibrium results are presented for optimum plasma densities, temperatures, and relative velocities and the relevant physical processes controlling these effects are analyzed. Finally, we summarize the work and present our basic conclusions in Sec. IV.

II. DESCRIPTION OF MODEL AND CALCULATIONS

A. Basic details of models

The photon pumping schemes to be analyzed are the following. Scheme 1 would employ the Si XIII $1s^2$-$1s2p\,^1P$ resonance line at 6.650 Å to pump the Al XII $1s^2$-$1s3p\,^1P$ resonance line at 6.635 Å, creating an inversion of the $n = 3$ and $n = 2$ levels of Al XII. Scheme 2 utilizes the Na X $1s^2$-$1s2p\,^1P$ line at 11.00 Å to pump the Ne IX $1s^2$-$1s4p\,^1P$ line at 11.001 Å, creating an inversion in the 3-2, 4-2, and 4-3 singlet lines of Ne IX. Scheme 1 results in stimulated emission at 44 Å and scheme 2 at 82 Å for the 3-2 inversion, 58 Å for the 4-2, and 230 Å for the 4-3 transitions. Ionic state and level densities as well as the radiation field are computed for Al using the model described in Ref. 7. For Si, a precisely analagous model to Al—the same level structure and transitions—is employed. The Ne atomic model is described in Ref. 8. This model possesses an extra degree of sophistication in that self-consistent Stark profiles[9] are used for the line opacity rather than the Voigt profiles employed for Al and Si. For Na, no atomic model is employed. Rather, the profile of the pumping line at 11.00 Å is utilized as it was experimentally measured from glass impurities in a laser implosion

[a]Optical Sciences Division.

experiment at the University of Rochester.[10] The multifrequency measured profile is modified within the pumped neon plasma by absorption and reemission in the Ne line and this phenomenology is computed in detail using the flux profile of the Na line as an input condition on the Ne plasma. Further details are given in Sec. II C. Results given below are calculated for collisional-radiative equilibrium (CRE).

B. Pumped plasma calculation

One of the major difficulties arising in resonant photoexcitation inversion mechanisms is the need to prevent overpopulation of the lower level by photon trapping. For Al XII, trapping in the strong resonance line $1s^2$-$1s2p\,^1P$ could spoil the 3→2 inversions by increasing the $n = 2$ populations well above their optically thin values. Similar considerations arise in the sodium-neon scheme. Hagelstein[11] has determined that optical depths greater than five in the principal resonance line will generally ruin the inversions. We find that the line center absorption coefficients for Al XII $1s^2$-$1s2p\,^1P$ and Ne IX $1s^2$-$1s2p\,^1P$ are approximately $1.2\times10^{-16}\,N_I$ and $1.6\times10^{-16}\,N_I$ (cm^{-1}), respectively. These approximate relationships for a total ion density N_I are obtained at optimally low plasma temperatures discussed below. Assuming for simplicity that $k = 1.4\times10^{-16}\,N_I$ for both Al and Ne, an optical depth $\tau\leqslant5$ implies that

$$r(\mu\text{m})\leqslant\frac{3.6\times10^{20}}{N_I}, \tag{1}$$

where r is the characteristic plasma radius in μm and N_I the total ion density. Satisfaction of Eq. (1) also guarantees sufficient penetration by the pump radiation whose characteristic opacity is lower than that of the $1s^2$-$1s2p\,^1P$ line. At ion densities $\sim10^{20}$, the total width of the pumped plasma must be $\leqslant10\ \mu$m, which rules out the use of a Z pinch at high density with present technology whose characteristic smallest structures are $\geqslant100\ \mu$m.[12] However, such spatial resolution and control has been achieved with laser plasmas at even higher density[10] and some success in resonant photoexcitation at lower densities[5] in laser plasma experiments has been reported. Of course a Z pinch may be employed at $N_I\leqslant10^{19}$ but there will still be a need for a high degree of control of the lasing medium geometry. Without minimizing these difficulties or the strong possibilities of future advances in experimental control of plasma geometries, we have performed the computations assuming that the lasing medium can be maintained small enough to prevent deleterious trapping. The radiation field is calculated in a planar plasma of infinite area with thickness small enough to insure an optically thin regime over a broad angular range of specific intensities. Our objectives—given an optically thin lasing medium—are to determine a range of temperatures, densities, and for scheme 1, streaming velocities in which maximum gain occurs and to determine some of the tradeoffs involved in establishing this maximum.

The pumped plasma is assumed to be bathed symmetrically in the pumping radiation which is calculated (for Si) or measured (for Na). The penetration of the pumping radiation into the pumped plasma is calculated in a straightforward manner. At the outer boundaries of the pumped plasma the inward specific intensity along each ray at each frequency I_ν^- is taken to be that emitted from the pumping plasma which is also assumed to be planar. The radiative transfer equation is then solved in the pumped plasma with this particular boundary condition for I_ν^- applied at each of the chosen rays at its outer boundaries. The calculation then proceeds by iteration until steady state conditions are obtained. Since fully coupled radiative transport and rate equations are solved in this model, the steady state obtained is a self-consistent collisional-radiative equilibrium. The quantity of primary interest here—the gain coefficient of the lasing transition—is obtained as a linear function of the computed densities of the upper and lower states. Finally, the temperature, density, and (for Al) velocity of the pumped plasma was varied in order to obtain the functional dependence of the gain coefficient on these quantities. We make no attempt to calculate the depletion of excited states by lasing, and thus are computing only the linear amplifier behavior (small signal gain).

C. Treatment of the pumping plasma

Since our principal objective is to determine the effect of varying conditions in the pumped plasma on the achieved gain, we selected only one set of pumping conditions for each of the Si and Na plasmas. Because the $1s^2$-$1s2p\,^1P$ Si XIII and $1s^2$-$1s3p\,^1P$ Al XII lines are off resonance by 0.015 Å, the profile of the $1s^2$-$1s2p\,^1P$ line must be wide enough to produce significant intensity at 0.015 Å (i.e., 13 Doppler widths at 400 eV) from line center. Thus, for a stationary plasma the line must be opacity broadened.[2] If the resonance line is very thick at line center, the Lorentz wings will still exceed optical depth unity many Doppler widths from line center, guaranteeing a wide profile. Such conditions can be obtained in a moderate energy Si plasma of 1.5 mm width, temperature 400 eV, and ion density 8×10^{19} cm^{-3}. Plasmas similar to this have been realized in the laboratory.[12] Most importantly, the CRE calculation for this plasma indicates that, depending on position, 62%–82% of the ions are in the active (helium-like) stage. Furthermore, the optical depth of the pumping resonance line $1s^2$-$1s2p\,^1P$ is ~500, which produces a very wide profile, as shown in Fig. 1. The maximum flux in this profile is 2.58×10^3 ergs/(cm^2 sec Hz), equivalent to a 252-eV blackbody. This pump brightness is quite reasonable considering that the kinetic temperature of the radiating plasma is 400 eV and it is quite optically thick. In addition to the calculated emission profile the intrinsic absorption profile for the $1s^2$-$1s3p\,^1P$ Al XII line is shown for typical conditions in the aluminum plasma. In this case, the Si resonance line is sufficiently broadened by opacity to overcome the resonance defect. Therefore, under the reasonable assumption that these equilibrium Si plasma conditions can be achieved, the Si/Al lasing scheme will be viable at least in the sense that the resonance defect can be overcome.

To obtain a radiation source to pump Ne, we have analyzed the spectrum of a laser-imploded neon filled glass microballoon obtained at Rochester.[10] One of the strongest lines appearing in this spectrum is the Na X $1s^2$-$1s2p\,^1P$—which arose from sodium impurities in the glass. Since we have been able to reproduce the observed spectrum with a

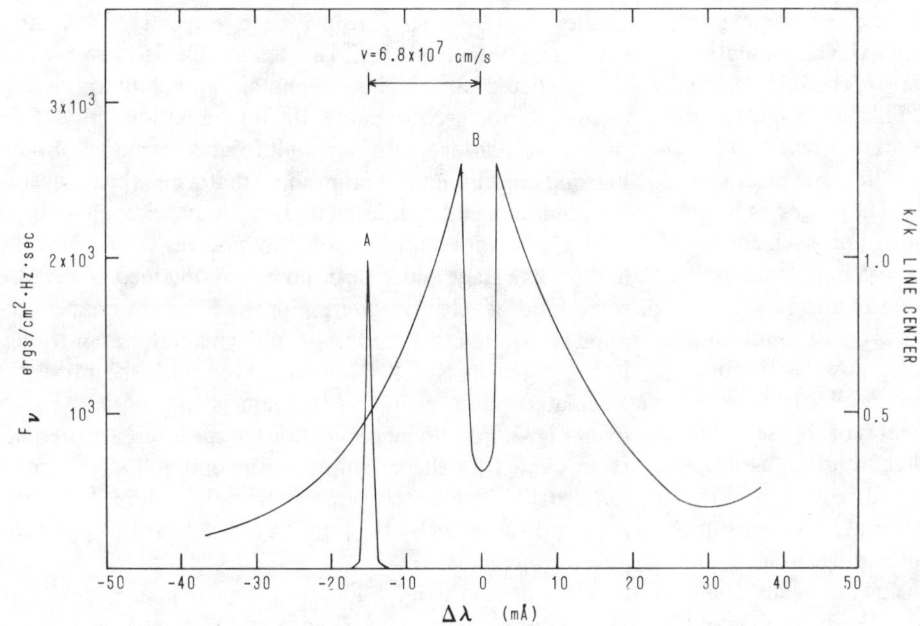

FIG. 1. Line profile of the Si pumping line (B) calculated to arise from the plasma conditions described in section II C is shown on the same wavelength scale as the intrinsic absorption profile of the pumped Al line (A). The left vertical scale applies to the flux of the emitted Si line; the right vertical scale applies to the absorption coefficient of the Al line.

first-principles non-LTE calculation of the line and continuum intensities,[8] the theoretical calculation which matches the observed spectrum also yields the absolute intensities of the lines—flux in ergs/(cm^2 sec Hz) at the outer surface of the pellet. Knowing the absolute intensities of the Ne lines, one may infer the Na line intensity profile from its measured value relative to the Ne lines. Its value at the central peak is 6.6×10^3 ergs/(cm^2 sec Hz). This is equivalent to a 227-eV blackbody flux, which is again quite reasonable from a dense, optically thick plasma of kinetic temperature 300–385 eV.[10] The actual intensity profile which we use as our pump source in the Na/Ne calculations is the one appearing in the published spectrum,[10] where experimental sources of broadening are relatively small. In any event deconvoluting any experimental broadening would result in a sharper central peak, which, since the lines are perfectly resonant, would give a better pump source.

In the next section it is shown that this experimentally observed Na X $1s^2$-$1s2p\,^1P$ intensity profile is sufficient to substantially invert the Ne X $n = 2$, 3, and 4 levels. This finding is significant in light of the fact that this radiation was merely a consequence of sodium impurities in the glass; i.e., no effort was made to increase its intensity in the experiment. We note that only the Na resonance line was used to irradiate Ne, whereas all of the calculated Si radiation, pumping plus other lines plus continuum, were included in the Al calculation.

III. RESULTS OF GAIN CALCULATIONS

A. Density dependence

A principal question related to the time varying conditions in the pumped plasma is: at what density is gain maximized? As has been often pointed out,[3,4,6,13] there exists for each lasing scheme contemplated a density above which no inversion is possible, due to the tendency of collisional processes to bring the state densities into LTE. In the opposite, low-density limit the plasma will be controlled entirely by radiative pumping and depletion. In this situation the medium may have its largest fractional inversion, although the gain may be reduced due to the smaller number of lasing ions in a given linear distance. In the limit that collisions are unimportant the ratio of the optically pumped level population (N_u) to the ground state population (N_g) is easily calculable from the equivalent blackbody temperature of the radiation T_B. If $B_\nu(T_B)$ is the pumping intensity, assumed flat across the normalized absorption profile ϕ_ν and the stimulated absorption and emission coefficients are denoted by B_{gu} and B_{ug}, the net pumping rate of the upper state is

$$\int_{\text{profile}} B_\nu(N_g B_{gu} - N_u B_{ug})\phi_\nu \, d\nu = B_\nu(N_g B_{gu} - N_u B_{ug}). \tag{2}$$

Setting this rate equal to the depletion rate $N_u A_{ug}$ in the collisionless limit one finds

$$\frac{N_u A_{ug}}{N_g B_{gu} - N_u B_{ug}} = B_\nu(T_B). \tag{3}$$

Substituting for $B_\nu(T_B)$ and utilizing the Einstein relations leads, as expected, to

$$\frac{N_u}{N_g} = \frac{g_u}{g_g} e^{-(h\nu/kT_B)}. \tag{4}$$

Thus, for a given ion density N_I the population density of the pumped level may be obtained from Eq. (4) in terms of T_B, the pump brightness temperature, and the fractional helium-like ion population f. Furthermore, the lower level of the lasing transition is negligibly populated at very low density and the gain coefficient is then a function only of N_u, i.e., of f, N_I, and T_B. For the Al XII $2p$-$3d$ line at 44 Å with an oscillator strength of 0.71, the gain coefficient in the low-density limit for a 100-eV Doppler profile is

$$k = 5.2\times10^{-15} f(\text{Al XII}) N_I e^{[-1864.4\ \text{eV}/T_B(\text{eV})]}\ \text{cm}^{-1}. \tag{5}$$

In Eq. (5) statistical equilibrium among the $n = 3$ singlet sublevels has been assumed. For a fractional Al XII population of 0.5 and our silicon pump $T_B = 252$ eV, the low density gain is ideally a linear function of N_I. This line is plotted in Fig. 2 along with the detailed computational results. Note that the CRE result approximately parallels the ideal gain until well past 10^{20} cm^{-3} where collisional processes begin to spoil the inversion. Computed results are given for the enforced statistical equilibrium of the $n = 3$ singlet sublevels as well as for a rate-by-rate calculation of the $3d$ and $3p$ populations. The assumption of statistical equilibrium leads to an overestimate of gain at low densities; however, for densities near the predicted peak gain, around 4×10^{20} cm^{-3}, the overestimate is very slight. This effect is of course due to the greater accuracy of the statistical equilibrium assumption at higher densities. The factor of ~ 3 reduction in the computed gain as opposed to the ideal case at lower densities is due almost entirely to the resonance mismatch of the pumped and pumping lines. As seen below, the gain would be very close to the ideal value if the resonance defect could be made up by streaming the plasmas toward each other at 6.8×10^{7} cm sec^{-1}. The chosen temperature of 100 eV corresponds approximately to maximum gain—this point is discussed further in the next section.

Finally, it is clear from Eq. (5) that the low-density gain coefficient will rapidly increase with T_B; indeed, if T_B is changed from 252 eV to 1 keV, the gain increases by a factor greater than 10^2. Thus, in principle, extremely high gains such as we obtained in Ref. 4 are achievable. However, when we predicted such gains, a photon probability-of-escape technique was used to model the line radiation only. More recent calculations with our multifrequency model of both line and continuum radiation show that when the Si plasma is hot enough and opaque enough to produce a 1-keV pump field, the continuum radiation photoionizes the Al past the helium-like stage and little or no gain is obtained. Therefore some kind of selective filtering of the Si nonresonant radiation is required to achieve gain of the magnitudes previously suggested in Ref. 4. However, even with the presently calculated pump radiation the gain is substantial as seen from Fig. 2. Fractional populations of the levels are presented in Table I for the maximum gain point at 4×10^{20} cm^{-3} ion density. The $3p/1s^2$ population ratio is 4.6×10^{-4}; the ideal ratio as given by Eq. (4) is 1.8×10^{-3}. At this point the gain coefficient is 10^2.

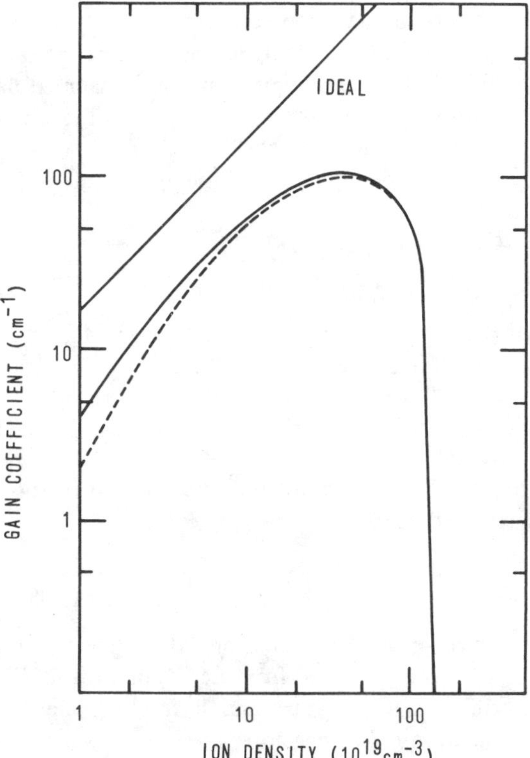

FIG. 2. Line center gain coefficient in the Al XII $2p\,^1P$-$3d\,^1D$ line is plotted vs Al plasma ion density, with an assumed pumped plasma temperature of 100 eV. Dual results for the assumption of collisional equilibrium between the $3p$-$3d$ states and for a general, rate-by-rate treatment of these states (dotted line) are displayed. Characteristics of the pumping Si plasma are discussed in the text. The line marked "ideal" describes the gain achievable for a purely radiative plasma, as described in the text.

For helium-like Ne IX the strongest lines where gain might be expected are $3d\,^1D$-$4f\,^1F$ at 230 Å with an absorption oscillator strength of 1.02, the $2p\,^1P$-$4d\,^1D$ line at 58 Å with an oscillator strength of 0.12, and the $2p\,^1P$-$3d\,^1D$ line at 82 Å with oscillator value 0.703. Figure 3 presents results for gain versus density for these three lines obtained from the detailed model as well as for an ideal, radiatively dominated system. In all cases statistical equilibrium among the singlet sublevels is assumed. For none of the three lines is the actual gain as close to that of the ideal case as was obtained for Al XII $2p$-$3d$. In this case, even though the pumping is closely resonant, the pumped $1s4p\,^1P$ level lies only 69 eV from the continuum and is easily collisionally ionized. This large ionization, whose rate is plotted in Fig. 4, prevents the $1s4p$ level from reaching its theoretically largest ratio, $(g(4p)/g(1s^2))e^{-h\nu/kT_B}$, with respect to the ground state. The fractional populations of Table II (at the temperature and ion density which approximately maximizes $2p$-$3d$ gain) demonstrate this; the ratio of $4p$ to $1s^2$ is 1.09×10^{-3}, whereas for a 227-eV sodium pump twenty times this ratio is expected in the absence of the extremely high collisional ionization rate at this density. Since the $3d$ population is also strongly coupled to the $4p$ level, this effect exists for all of the population inversions. The remainder of the deviation from ideality is due to the non-negligibie population of the lower levels. Even though gain is obtained for the widest range of densities for the $2p$-$3d$ line, the falloff at low density is quite sharp because collisions become increasingly ineffective in transferring population from the pumped $4p$ level to the $3d$. This necessity for collisional mixing between the $3d$ and $4p$ levels results in the $2p$-$3d$ gain reaching its maximum at the highest ion density of 10^{20} cm^{-3} of the 3 lasing lines. By

TABLE I. Al XII fractional populations.

$N_I = 4\times10^{20}$	$T = 100$ eV
$1s^2\,^1S$	5.4×10^{-1}
$1s2p\,^1P$	9.4×10^{-5}
$1s3p\,^1P$	2.5×10^{-4}
$1s3d\,^1D$	3.9×10^{-4}

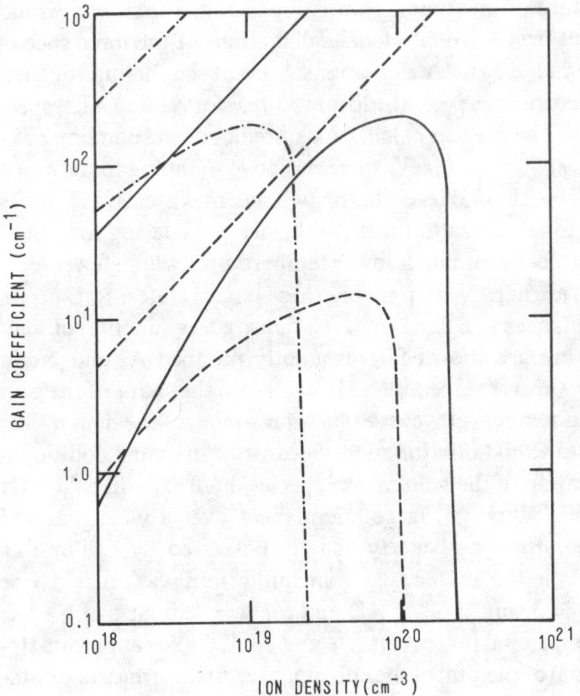

FIG. 3. Line center gain coefficients for the Ne IX $2p\,^1P$-$3d\,^1D$ (———), $2p\,^1P$-$4d\,^1D$ (-----), and $3d\,^1D$-$4f\,^1F$ (-·-·-·) lines are plotted against ion density. The corresponding overlying straight lines describe the gain achievable with an ideal radiatively dominant plasma, as described in the text. The assumed plasma temperature is 65 eV.

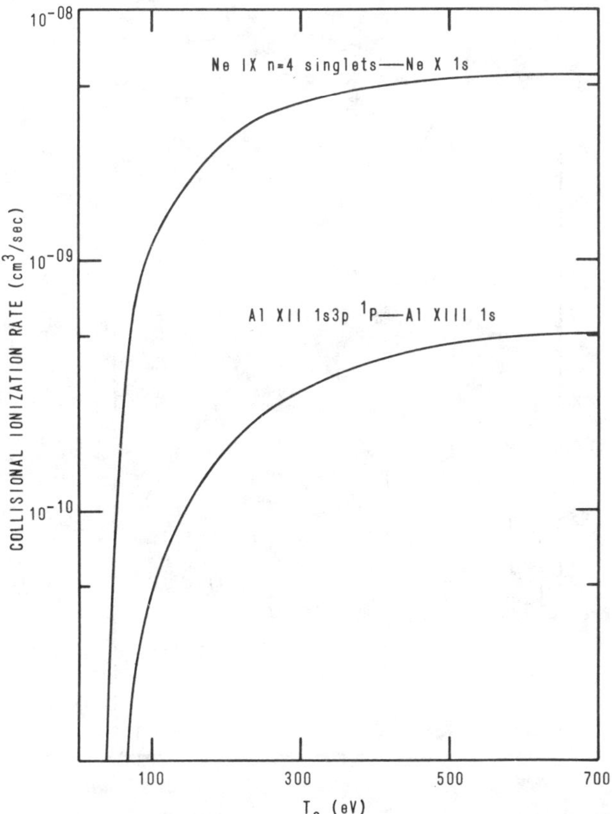

FIG. 4. Collisional ionization rates for Ne IX $n = 4$ singlets (assuming statistical population of the sublevels) and Al XII $1s3p\,^1P$ are shown as a function of electron temperature.

TABLE II. Ne IX fractional populations.

$N_I = 10^{20}$	$T = 65$ eV
$1s^2\,^1S$	6.4×10^{-1}
$1s2p\,^1P$	5.0×10^{-4}
$1s3p\,^1P$	1.1×10^{-3}
$1s3d\,^1D$	1.8×10^{-3}
$1s4p\,^1P$	7.0×10^{-4}
$1s4d\,^1D$	1.2×10^{-3}
$1s4f\,^1F$	1.7×10^{-3}

$3d$-$4f$ gain is maximized at $\sim10^{19}$ cm^{-3}; at higher densities collisional mixing already begins to spoil the inversion.

For Al, peak gain occurs at an ion (electron) density of 4×10^{20} (4.2×10^{21}) cm^{-3}, for Ne the corresponding numbers are 10^{20} (8.1×10^{20}) cm^{-3}. For hydrogenic lasing schemes, Bhagavatula[3,6] has presented reduced variable equations which demonstrate that the dependence of electron density at peak gain on Z is Z^7. We note with interest that the Z dependence of electron density at peak gain implied by the above numbers for our helium-like schemes is fairly similar, $Z^{6.3}$.

B. Temperature dependence

In Figs. 5 and 6 results for gain versus temperature are plotted for the 3-2 lines of the Si/Al and Na/Ne systems for fixed ion densities of 5×10^{19} and 10^{20} cm^{-3}, respectively. The gain dependence on temperature is similar to that on density in that a maximum is exhibited with a sharp falloff on one side caused by the variation of the active ion species' populations with temperature. Note, however, that the tem-

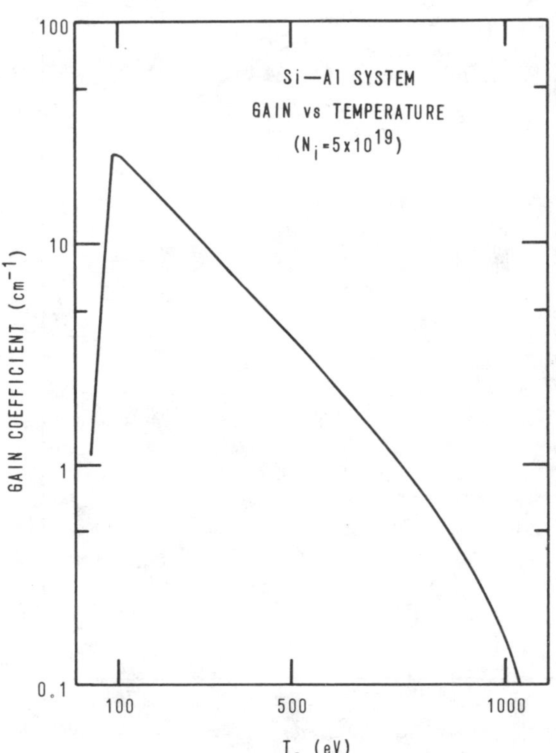

FIG. 5. Line center gain coefficient in the Al XII $2p\,^1P$-$3d\,^1D$ line is plotted vs Al plasma temperature for a fixed Al ion density of 5×10^{19} cm^{-3}.

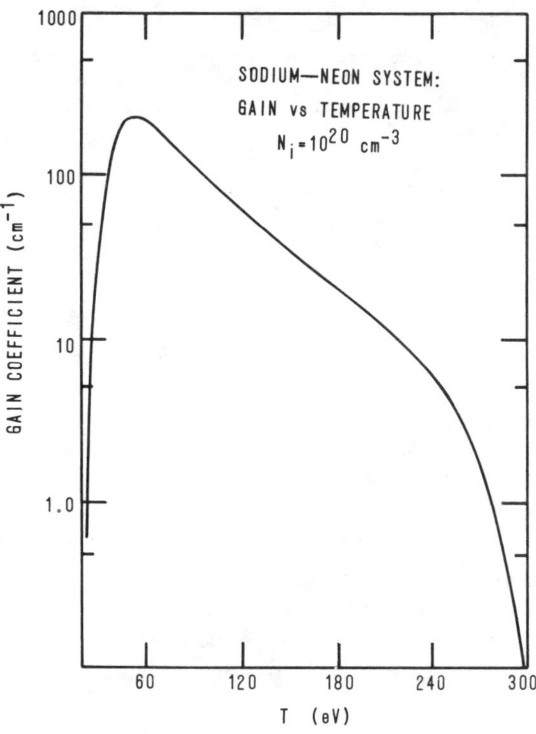

FIG. 6. Line center gain coefficient in the Ne IX $2p\,^1P$-$3d\,^1D$ line is plotted vs Ne plasma temperature for a fixed Ne ion density of 10^{20} cm^{-3}.

perature of maximum gain is much lower than one would expect from coronal model calculations of the ionic species abundances. Such calculations[14] reveal that helium-like ion concentrations peak at 120 and 330 eV for Ne and Al, respectively. The present calculations predict corresponding peak gains at 50 and 100 eV, since radiative pumping to the $n = 4$ and $n = 3$ bound levels in the two schemes greatly facilitates collisional ionization (Fig. 4). Hence peak lasing ion abundance occurs at much lower temperatures where fewer electrons are capable of ionizing these bound states. Ion species abundances at a fixed total ion density as a function of temperature are shown for resonantly pumped Al and Ne in Figs. 7 and 8, respectively. In each case the shape of the gain versus temperature curve is similar to that of the helium-like species abundance function. Because of the rapid collisional ionization of the helium-like species, hydrogen-like Al XIII and Ne X exhibit large abundances over a wide range of temperature, a property usually possessed by helium-like species in the absence of a nonequilibrium photon field. For the $n = 3$ singlet of Al XII and the $n = 4$ singlets of Ne IX, the collisional ionization rate at $T_e \sim 400$ eV is approximately equal to the sum of the collisional excitation and de-excitation rates to the other levels. Thus the pumped plasma must be kept cooler (50–100 eV) to preserve a substantial helium-like abundance. At still lower temperatures a sharp gain and abundance falloff occurs as the plasma assumes a more normal configuration when the "extra" ionization becomes small. In these two lasing systems, the strength of the pump-

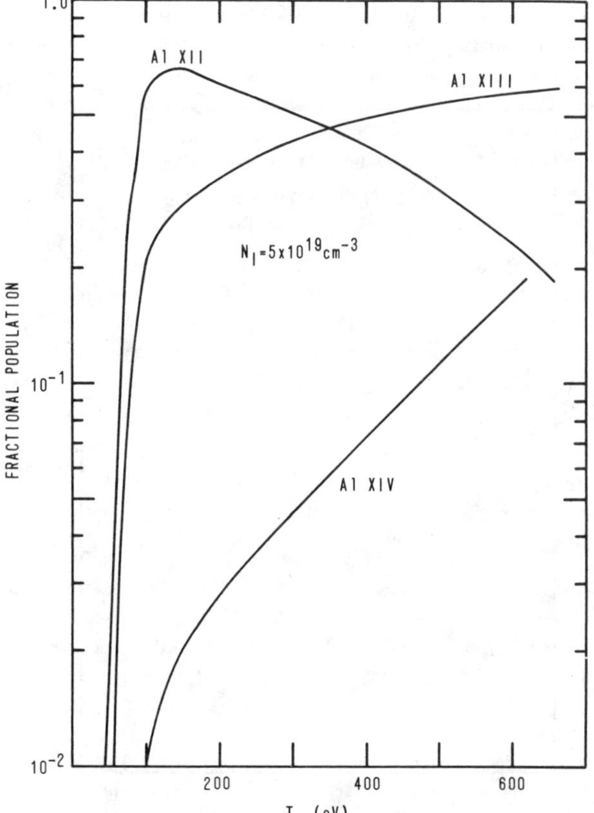

FIG. 7. Ionic species abundances for an optically thin Al plasma under the influence of the Si pump radiation of Fig. 1 are shown vs temperature at an ion density of 5×10^{19} cm^{-3}.

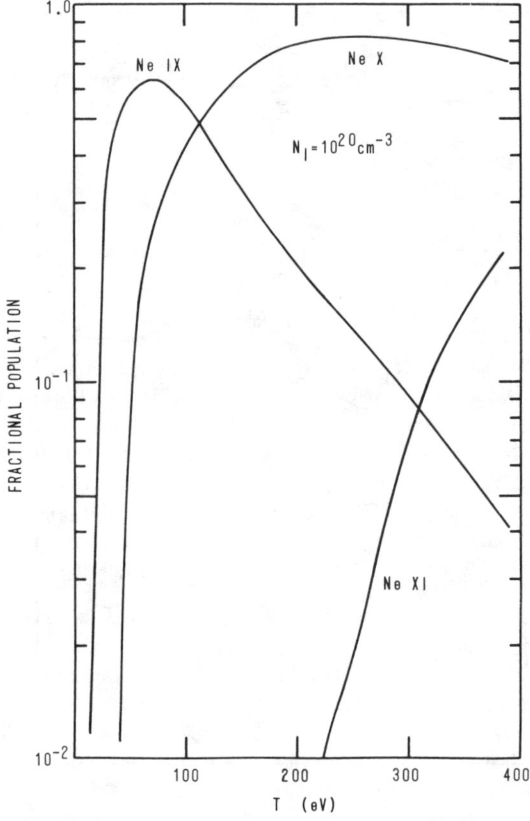

FIG. 8. Ionic species abundances for an optically thin Ne plasma under the influence of the Na pump radiation described in the text are shown vs temperature at an ion density of 10^{20} cm^{-3}.

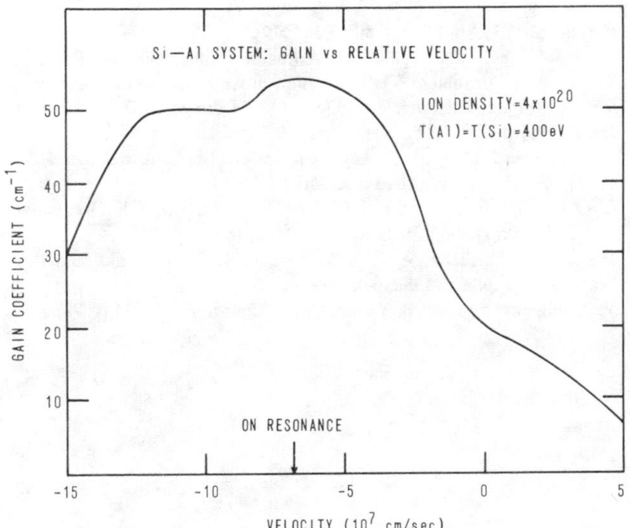

FIG. 9. Line center gain coefficient in the Al XII $2p\,^1P - 3d\,^1D$ line is plotted vs velocity of approach of the Si and Al plasmas. The Al ion density is 4×10^{20} cm^{-3} and its temperature (the same as that of the pumping Si plasma) is assumed to be 400 eV.

ing decisively affects the temperature at which the pumped plasma must be prepared for maximum gain to occur. Such effects have been noted elsewhere[6,7] in somewhat different contexts.

C. Velocity dependence

For the Na/Ne system, the pumped and pumping lines are within resonance to 1 part in 10^5, and thus there is no question as to the adequacy of the wavelength coincidence. For Si/Al, however, the wavelength difference of 0.015 Å amounts to 13 Doppler widths at 400 eV. For a photon traveling at normal incidence to the pumped plasma, this resonance defect could be made up if the two plasmas stream toward each other at 6.8×10^7 cm sec^{-1}. But given the wide opacity broadened pumping line profile (Fig. 1) the functional dependence of gain on plasma streaming velocity must be calculated; this result is presented in Fig. 9. In these calculations, the frequencies of the radiation incident on the pumped plasma were shifted angle by angle to reflect the streaming velocities indicated. Even though there is a substantial self-reversal at the center of the pumping line, peak gain does indeed occur for the matched streaming velocity of 6.8×10^7 cm sec^{-1}. This is due to the fact that most of the pumping radiation is not normally incident on the pumped plasma and therefore a range of velocity shifts are sampled (due to the cos θ effect) at any one physical streaming velocity. At the perfectly matched streaming velocity of 6.8×10^7, gain is $\simeq$3 times that of zero streaming velocity because the very highest pumping line intensities just outside the self-reversed core are sampled to the greatest degree. Such a velocity is somewhat higher than those experimentally produced to date, but not prohibitively so. Laser plasma ablation velocities of 3.3×10^7 cm sec^{-1} have been reported,[15] and Z-pinch implosion velocities of 2×10^7 cm sec^{-1} were deduced from spectroscopic evidence.[16] In any event, counter-streaming of the plasmas is helpful, but not essential to produce significant gain.

IV. FURTHER REMARKS AND CONCLUSIONS

We have determined, through a series of detailed calculations, the conditions under which significant gain at x-ray wavelengths, employing the Na/Ne and Si/Al plasmas for resonant photon pumping, should be attainable in the laboratory. Substantial gain at 58-230 Å and 44 Å for Na/Ne and Si/Al, respectively, is in principle achievable. However, the task of setting up the correct plasma conditions is not trivial for a number of reasons. First, there are the deleterious radiative trapping effects described in Sec. II. Also, for optimum employment of both schemes, the temperature of the pumped plasma should be maintained well below that of the pumping plasma to avoid excessive ionization in the lasing medium. This could perhaps be accomplished by keeping the two components as physically separate as possible to reduce conductive temperature equilibration. Similarly, the pumping plasma might be heated first, and then the pumped medium activated through use of a delayed heating pulse or laser beam to assure that the pumped plasma passes through the optimal temperature range while being exposed to the intense pumping radiation. Also, in previously successful experiments,[17] stepped targets using metal plates as heat sinks have allowed experimenters to tune the plasma temperature downward at certain distances from the initial plasma formation surface. Perhaps similar techniques could be employed for the present schemes. Even though a lower pumped plasma temperature is essential for optimum steady state gain, substantial gain is still achievable for equal pumped and pumping plasma temperatures (Fig. 9).

In the case of the Na/Ne system, pumping radiation was generated in an actual pellet implosion experiment at Rochester for which the ion density of the pellet has been diagnosed as 4.5×10^{21} cm^{-3}, which is more than an order of magnitude greater than the neon ion density required for maximum gain. In short, a very dense sodium plasma is desirable to obtain high pumping power, but a relatively tenuous neon medium is needed to prevent collisional processes from neutralizing the pumped inversion. Therefore, a configuration which is the reverse of a normal pellet suggests itself. One might compress a cylindrical glass rod (with a cylindrically focussed laser, perhaps) which has been heavily doped with sodium impurities. This rod would initially be encased in neon, which would form a more tenuous blowoff plasma. Or, alternatively two physically separate Na and Ne plasmas could be created with intensities and pulse widths tailored to produce optimum gain characteristics. This would certainly allow different densities to be produced in the separate components, and would minimize or eliminate conductive temperature equilibration.

ACKNOWLEDGMENT

This work was supported in part by the Office of Naval Research.

[1]A. V. Vinogradov, I. I. Sobelman, and E. A. Yukov, Kvant. Electron. (Moscow) **2**, 105 (1975) [Sov. J. Quantum Electron. **5**, 59 (1975)].
[2]B. A. Norton and N. J. Peacock, J. Phys. B **8**, 989 (1975).
[3]V. A. Bhagavatula, J. Appl. Phys. **47**, 4535 (1976).

[4]J. P. Apruzese, J. Davis, and K. G. Whitney, J. Phys. B **11**, L643 (1978).
[5]V. A. Bhagavatula, Appl. Phys. Lett. **33**, 726 (1978).
[6]V. A. Bhagavatula, IEEE J. Quantum Electron. **16**, 603 (1980).
[7]K. G. Whitney, J. Davis, and J. P. Apruzese, Phys. Rev. A **22**, 2196 (1980).
[8]J. P. Apruzese, P. C. Kepple, K. G. Whitney, J. Davis, and D. Duston, Phys. Rev. A **24**, 1001 (1981).
[9]H. R. Griem, M. Blaha, and P. C. Kepple, Phys. Rev. A **19**, 2421 (1979).
[10]B. Yaakobi, D. Steel, E. Thorsos, A. Hauer, and B. Perry, Phys. Rev. Lett. **39**, 1526 (1977).
[11]P. Hagelstein, "Physics of Short Wavelength Laser Design," Ph.D. thesis, Lawrence Livermore Laboratory, 1981 (unpublished).
[12]P. Burkhalter, J. Davis, J. Rauch, W. Clark, G. Dahlbacka, and R.Schneider, J. Appl. Phys. **50**, 705 (1979).
[13]K. G. Whitney, J. Davis, and J. P. Apruzese, "Some Effects of Radiation Trapping on Stimulated VUV Emission in Ar XIII," in *Cooperative Effects in Matter and Radiation*, edited by C. M. Bowden, D. W. Howgate, and H. R. Robl (Plenum, New York, 1977).
[14]V. L. Jacobs, J. Davis, J. E. Rogerson, and M. Blaha, Astrophys. J. **230**, 627 (1979); also unpublished calculations for Al.
[15]R. Decoste, S. E. Bodner, B. H. Ripin, E. A. McLean, S. P. Obenschain, and C. M. Armstrong, Phys. Rev. Lett. **42**, 1673 (1979).
[16]J. D. Perez, L. F. Chase, R. E. McDonald, L. Tannenwald, and B. A. Watson, J. Appl. Phys. **52**, 670 (1981).
[17]V. A. Bhagavatula and B. Yaakobi, Opt. Commun. **24**, 331 (1978).

Reprinted with permission from *Optics Letters*, Vol. 8(3), pp. 169-171 (March 1983).

Gain scaling of short-wavelength plasma-recombination lasers

W. T. Silfvast and O. R. Wood II

Bell Laboratories, Holmdel, New Jersey 07733

The theoretical $Z^{7.5}$ dependence of the small-signal gain of plasma-recombination lasers on the ionization stage Z of the laser species implies a straightforward development of short-wavelength lasers but appears to be significantly larger than the experimentally achieved gain scaling. A new analysis, which incorporates a simple experimental parameter representing the efficiency of populating the upper level at a given plasma electron density, results in a gain scaling with ionization state ($Z^{4.5}$) that is more consistent with experiments and also reveals a need for better experimental control of the ion-production and electron–ion-recombination processes when one attempts to make such lasers.

Plasma-recombination lasers have the potential for very high specific output energies ($>10^{-3}$J/cm^3) when operated at short wavelengths (<200 nm).[1] Pert has shown[2] that the small-signal gain of lasers resulting from recombination of the Zth ionization stage of H-like elements with the free electrons of the plasma should be $Z^{7.5}$ larger than the gain of a laser on the same transition in a recombining hydrogen plasma. This gain scaling suggests that the extension of laser action to higher ion stages and shorter wavelengths should be straightforward. Because such a strong gain scaling has not been experimentally observed, this problem has been reexamined. A dimensionless parameter r (the ratio of the upper laser level density to the plasma electron density) that should contribute a significant portion (Z^3) of the expected $Z^{7.5}$ gain scaling is instead found experimentally to be approximately constant over a wide range of Z. Measurements of this parameter can be used to identify specific physical processes that cause the lower-than-expected small-signal gain in a given experiment. Future experiments can then be designed to minimize the effects of such processes and thereby increase the chances for producing a plasma-recombination laser at short wavelengths.

The equation for the small-signal gain (in inverse centimeters) on a Doppler-broadened transition having upper level j and lower level k can be written as

$$G_{jk} = 1.74 \times 10^{-6}\lambda_{jk}{}^3 A_{jk} \sqrt{M/T}\, [N_j - (g_j/g_k)N_k], \quad (1)$$

where λ_{jk} is the wavelength (in centimeters), A_{jk} is the transition probability (in inverse seconds), M is the mass (in atomic mass units), T is the ion temperature (in kelvins), and N_j, g_j and N_k, g_k are the densities (in inverse cubic centimeters) and statistical weights of the upper and lower laser levels. A straightforward substitution of the well-known scaling laws for H-like ions[3] ($\lambda_{jk} = \lambda_{jk}{}^{\mathrm{H}}/Z^2$, $A_{jk} = A_{jk}{}^{\mathrm{H}}Z^4$, $M \cong 2M^{\mathrm{H}}Z$, $T = T^{\mathrm{H}}Z^2$, and $N_{j,k} = N_{j,k}{}^{\mathrm{H}}Z^{10}$) into Eq. (1) results in the following expression for the Z scaling of the small-signal gain in H-like ions ($Z > 1$):

$$G_{jk} = \sqrt{2}\, G_{jk}{}^{\mathrm{H}} Z^{7.5}, \quad (2)$$

where $G_{jk}{}^{\mathrm{H}} = 1.74 \times 10^{-6} (\lambda_{jk}{}^{\mathrm{H}})^3 A_{jk}{}^{\mathrm{H}} (M^{\mathrm{H}}/T^{\mathrm{H}})^{1/2}[N_j{}^{\mathrm{H}} - (g_j/g_k)N_k{}^{\mathrm{H}}]$ is the small-signal gain in hydrogen. The $\sqrt{2}$ factor in Eq. (2) results from the fact that there are approximately two nucleons per charge state for H-like ions but only one for the most common H isotope.

The rapid scaling of small-signal gain with Z given by Eq. (2) suggests that experimental studies at high Z and thus at short wavelengths could be advantageous. For example, according to Eq. (2), the small-signal gain coefficient on the 4–3 transitions in H I at 1.875 μm in a recombining H plasma produced by a magneto-plasma-dynamic arc jet (0.004 cm^{-1}) (Ref. 4) would scale to more than 3800 cm^{-1} on this same transition in C VI at 52 nm if fully stripped C ions were produced in sufficiently high abundance. This large gain coefficient should outweigh all the disadvantages of the short operating wavelength (such as the unavailability of highly reflecting resonator mirrors below 200 nm and the large energy input required to produce highly ionized plasmas), and amplified spontaneous emission at 52 nm should be readily observable. Since this is experimentally not the case for 4–3 H-like transitions in C VI (Ref. 5) and Al XII (Ref. 6) as well as for other H-like transitions in the extreme ultraviolet,[7,8] the predictions of Eq. (2) appear to be unrealistic.

Some of the scaling laws used to derive Eq. (2) are expected to lead to better estimates at high Z than others. For example, the Z scaling of λ_{jk} and A_{jk} is a straightforward derivation in atomic-structure theory and can be expected to be quite accurate. The scaling of N_j is less well founded and is the most sensitive to increases in Z (i.e., $N_j = N_j{}^{\mathrm{H}} Z^{10}$). Defining an experimentally measurable dimensionless parameter $r \equiv N_j/n_e$, where n_e is the electron density in inverse cubic centimeters, to remove N_j explicitly from the gain equation permits a comparison of the efficiency of populating the laser levels in different ion species at various values of Z as well as a simple comparison of the experimentally achieved gain to the maximum possible gain. By substituting rn_e for N_j and neglecting N_k (to permit an estimate of the largest possible gain), Eq. (1) can be rewritten as $G_{jk} = 1.74 \times 10^{-6} \lambda_{jk}{}^3 A_{jk}\sqrt{M/T}\, rn_e$.

A semiempirical formula for the maximum gain can then be obtained by using the expression $n_e{}^L = 0.13\sqrt{T_e}/\lambda_{jk}{}^3$ for the largest electron density at which an inversion can occur[1] (owing to electron collisional mixing of the upper and lower laser levels) by assuming that $T \cong T_e$ (not unreasonable for a recombining plasma) and by substituting the scaling laws for A_{jk} and M. This gives

$$G_{jk}{}^{\max} = 3.5 \times 10^{-7} A_{jk}{}^{H} r Z^{4.5}. \quad (3)$$

Theoretically, r should scale as Z^3 (since $N_j = N_j{}^H Z^{10}$ and $n_e = n_e{}^H Z^7$), and hence the Z scaling of Eqs. (2) and (3) agrees.

A similar gain-scaling expression can be derived for non-H-like (NHL) ions having ionization potential I_p by defining a parameter[9] $Z_{\text{eff}} = (I_p/I_p{}^H)^{1/2}$, where $I_p{}^H$ is the ionization potential of H. Since experimentally most recombination lasers in NHL species have been found to occur on 4–3 transitions[10] or on transitions that are similar to 4–3 H-like transitions, and because there are theoretical reasons for expecting recombination lasers most likely to occur on 4–3-like transitions,[11] the small-signal gain on 4–3-like transitions in NHL ions can be written (using Z_{eff} in place of Z and retaining the atomic mass) as

$$G_{43}{}^{\text{NHL}} = 2.9\sqrt{M} r Z_{\text{eff}}{}^4. \quad (4)$$

This expression will be most accurate for those NHL transitions for which the ratio of hc/λ_{jk} to I_p is ~0.05 (where h is Planck's constant and c is the velocity of light) and will underestimate the gain on transitions characterized by larger ratios because larger energy-level separations lead to larger limiting electron densities and hence to larger population inversions.

By using the results of a number of experiments that have reported the observation of population inversions and that have given enough information to obtain approximate values of r, the achieved scaling of r with Z can be studied, and the experimentally achieved gain can be compared with the maximum possible gain at various values of r and Z. Experimental values for r and for small-signal gain are listed in Table 1 along with the maximum gain values expected when Eqs. (2) and (3) are used. The values in H were obtained from an experiment on a recombining H plasma produced by a magneto-plasma-dynamic arc jet.[4] The values for neutral and singly ionized Cd were obtained from an expanding arc-plasma laser device.[12] The He^+ values were obtained from an experiment in a flowing He-plasma column interacting with neutral He gas.[13] The values from four experiments in C^{5+} were achieved in Nd-laser-produced C plasmas expanding into vacuum,[5,7,8,14] and the values for Al^{11+} were achieved in a Nd-laser-produced Al plasma.[6] A comparison of the small-signal gain values presented in Table 1 reveals that Eq. (2) predicts gains signficantly higher than the measured values at higher Z, whereas Eq. (3) gives gains in reasonable agreement with experiment.

The experimental values for r (Table 1) range from 10^{-3} to 1.5×10^{-3}, with the largest value (from two separate experiments) occurring at $Z = 1$. A plot of the experimental values for r at various Z is shown in Fig. 1 along with a solid curve illustrating the theoretically expected Z^3 dependence. It appears that, for $Z > 1$, $r \cong$ constant $\cong 6 \times 10^{-6}$ (dashed line) is a reasonable description of the experimental results to date and that, therefore, Eqs. (3) and (4) (with $r \cong 6 \times 10^{-6}$) can be used to obtain a reasonable estimate of the gain in experiments that use similar experimental techniques. For example, the small-signal gain on the 4–3 transition in H-like ions would be approximately given by $2 \times 10^{-?} Z^{4.5}$ (cm^{-1}). Because at $Z = 6$ this amounts to a gain of less than 0.1 cm^{-1} (i.e., not nearly high enough to produce detectable amplified spontaneous emission), if plasma-recombination lasers are to be successfully demonstrated at short wavelengths, the experimentally obtainable value of r at high Z must be increased.

The parameter $r = N_j/n_e$ represents the efficiency with which the plasma populates a specific energy level at a given electron density. It can be expressed as the product of two separate efficiency factors, r_r and r_p, by rewriting $N_j/n_e = \{r_r\}\{r_p\} = \{N_j/N(Z+)\}\{N(Z+)/n_e\}$, where $N(Z+)$ is the density of the ground state in the ion stage immediately above the laser levels. The efficiency factor for production, r_p, represents the efficiency with which ions in ion state $Z+$ (the source of population for the upper laser level) are made available for recombination at the time in the plasma-evolution process that the population inversion is established. If all the ions in a given volume element of the plasma are in ion state $Z+$ and no significant reduction in $N(Z+)$ owing to recombination or charge exchange processes occurs before the time that an inversion is established, then the maximum number of ions in the ion stage $Z+$

Table 1. Comparison of Measured and Calculated Small-Signal Gain in Recombining Plasma Containing H-like Ions in a Wide Range of Charge States Z

Species	Ref.	jk	λ_{jk} (nm)	Z	r	G (Exp.)	G [Eq. (2)]	G [Eq. (3)]
H	4	4–3	1875.0	1	1×10^{-3}	0.004	0.004	0.004
Cd	–	–	1433.0	0.81[a]	1×10^{-3}	0.01	–	0.01[b]
He^+	13	4–2	121.6	2	1.5×10^{-3}	–	1.0	1×10^{-6}
Cd^+	–	–	537.8	1.11[a]	3×10^{-6}	0.001	–	0.0001[b]
C^{5+}	5	3–2	18.2	6	1.3×10^{-6}	2×10^{-5}	4×10^3	0.06
C^{5+}	7	3–2	18.2	6	9×10^{-6}	0.7	4×10^3	0.4
C^{5+}	8	3–2	18.2	6	$<1 \times 10^{-5}$	0.2	4×10^3	0.5
C^{5+}	14	4–3	52.0	6	4×10^{-6}	0.02	4×10^3	0.04
Al^{11+}	6	4–3	13.0	12	6×10^{-6}	10	7×10^5	1.4

[a] Z_{eff}.
[b] G [Eq. (4)].

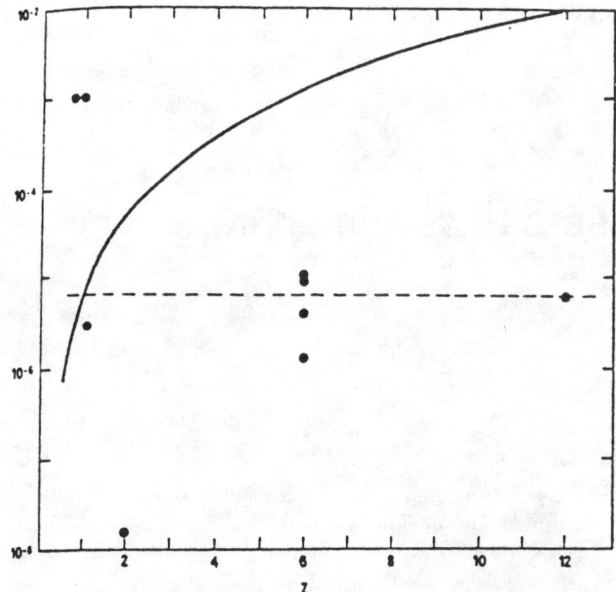

Fig. 1. Experimental values for r, the ratio of the upper level density to the electron density, plotted as a function of charge state Z (filled circles) together with the theoretically expected Z^3 dependence (solid curve).

at a given n_e is $N(Z+) = n_e/Z$ and the maximum value for this efficiency factor is $r_p^{max} = 1/Z$. Two effects tend to reduce r_p below this value. They will be referred to as ion dilution and early recombination. Ion dilution results when an inefficient plasma-heating process initially distributes the ion population among several ion stages. This effect is smallest for single and fully stripped ions and is largest for ion stages lying between these two extremes. The effect of ion dilution on r_p, for various ion stages in elements from H to Fe, can be computed from information given in Ref. 15. The second deleterious effect, early recombination, can occur when a plasma (such as a laser-produced plasma) is formed at an initial $n_e > n_e^L$. The high recombination rate at high n_e, which is due to the quadratic dependence of the recombination flux on n_e, can lead to an excessive depletion of $N(Z+)$ before the density is reduced to the point at which population inversion is established.

The efficiency factor for recombination, r_r, represents the efficiency of populating the upper laser level at the time in the plasma-evolution process that the population inversion is established. If it is assumed that, as a result of recombination, all the ions in ion stage $Z+$ pass through the upper laser level and that $n_e = n_e^L$ (the maximum electron density at which population inversions can occur), then (in a quasi-steady-state approximation) $r_r^{max} \cong \alpha(n_e^L)^2/A_j$, where α is the three-body recombination coefficient and A_j is the total decay rate of level j. Because α is extremely sensitive to temperature, an absolute upper limit on r_r^{max} cannot be given. However, when values for α from Bates *et al.* are used,[16] r_r^{max} for the 4–3 transition in H at two realistic temperatures is 1.3×10^{-5} at $T_e = 1000$ K and 5.5×10^{-3} at 500 K (probably a lower limit for T_e at $Z = 1$). Theoretically, these values for r_r^{max} should increase (in ions of higher Z) as Z^4. Processes that can lead to a reduction of r_r below this value include (1) radiative and collisional bypass of the upper laser level (e.g., a process such as radiative recombination that tends to favor lower quantum levels), (2) slow plasma cooling, leading to a low recombination rate and reduced upper-laser-level population, and (3) charge transfer to other species before population moves down to the upper laser level.

Experimental values for r_p and r_r are not generally available. However, in the Cd I experiment listed in Table 1, since the dominant ion species was Cd^+, $r_p \cong 1$, and therefore $r_r \cong 10^{-3}$ (i.e., near the maximum mentioned above). At higher Z, only the C VI (4–3) experiment[14] (listed in Table 1) provides a value of $N(Z+)$ during inversion and permits estimates of $r_p \cong 5 \times 10^{-3}$ and $r_r \cong 0.8 \times 10^{-3}$. In this experiment, since the plasma was initially fully stripped, r_p could potentially have been as high as 0.17 ($1/Z$ for $Z = 6$), but in practice apparently 97% of the C^{6+} ions were lost by recombination before the population inversion was established (i.e., early recombination). A comparison of the efficiency factors from these two experiments suggests that the largest loss in efficiency at high Z lies in the plasma production process before the time that the population inversion is established. Minimizing this effect by producing the plasma at a density closer to n_e^L or by modifying the cooling process should improve the gain scaling at higher Z and thereby increase the chances for producing plasma-recombination lasers at short wavelengths.

References

1. O. R. Wood II and W. T. Silfvast, Appl. Phys. Lett. 41, 121 (1982).
2. G. J. Pert, J. Phys. B 9, 3301 (1976).
3. See, e.g., R. W. McWhirter and A. G. Hearn, Proc. Phys. Soc. 81, 641 (1963). The parameters T^H and N^H were obtained from θ and $\eta(p)$ using $Z = 1$, and the Z scaling for N_j assumes fully stripped H-like ions.
4. T. Hara, K. Kodera, M. Hamagaki, K. Matsunaga, M. Inutake, and T. Dote, Jpn. J. Appl. Phys. 19, L606 (1980).
5. F. E. Irons and N. J. Peacock, J. Phys. B 7, 1109 (1974).
6. V. A. Bhagavatula and B. Yaakobi, Opt. Commun. 24, 331 (1978).
7. R. J. Dewhurst, D. J. Jacoby, G. J. Pert, and S. A. Ramsden, Phys. Rev. Lett. 37, 1265 (1976).
8. M. H. Key, C. L. S. Lewis, and M. J. Lamb, Opt. Commun. 28, 331 (1979).
9. W. L. Bohn, DFVLR-Institut für Plasmadynamik, Stuttgart, Federal Republic of Germany (personal communication).
10. W. T. Silfvast, L. H. Szeto, and O. R. Wood II, Appl. Phys. Lett. 36, 615 (1980); Opt. Lett. 7, 34 (1982).
11. F. V. Bunkin, V. I. Derzhiev, and S. I. Yakovelenko, Sov. J. Quantum Electron. 11, 981 (1981).
12. W. T. Silfvast, L. H. Szeto, and O. R. Wood II, Appl. Phys. Lett. 39, 212 (1981).
13. K. Sato, M. Shiho, M. Hosokawa, H. Sugawara, T. Oda, and T. Sasaki, Phys. Rev. Lett. 39, 1074 (1977).
14. R. C. Elton, J. F. Seely, and R. H. Dixon, in *Laser Techniques for Extreme Ultraviolet Spectroscopy*, T. J. McIlrath and R. R. Freeman, eds. (American Institute of Physics, New York, 1982), p. 277.
15. L. L. House, Astrophys. J. Suppl. 7, 307 (1964).
16. D. R. Bates, A. E. Kingston, and R. W. McWhirter, Proc. R. Soc. Lond. Ser. A 267, 297 (1962).

Reprinted with the permission of the Optical Society of America from *Applied Optics,* Vol. 22(9), pp. 1309-1312 (May 1, 1983).

Measured gain for XUV plasma lasers at varying pump intensities

R. H. Dixon, J. F. Seely, and R. C. Elton

Inverted population densities are measured in a laser-produced carbon plasma and interpreted in terms of absolute gain coefficients in the 1%/cm range for potential amplification in the XUV at 52-nm wavelength. Scaling to higher gain through increased ionization at higher pumping intensities is attempted, and a factor of 2 enhancement is indicated.

I. Introduction

The development of ion lasers for wavelengths in the XUV to x-ray spectral regions[1] requires an exceptionally high gain medium to compensate at decreasing wavelengths both for the decrease in cavity efficiency and for the explicit and implicit wavelength λ dependences of the gain coefficient, which is given below in Eq. (1). That a plasma is formed is made certain by the high pump power required[1] for the rapidly decaying high-energy transitions involved. This paper deals with measurement of gain on an absolute basis for the $4 \rightarrow 3$ transition (at a wavelength of 52 nm) in a one-electron hydrogenic carbon ion C^{5+}, where the gain coefficient G for single-pass amplification $\exp(GL)$ over a plasma length L is given by

$$G = N_4\sigma_{\text{ind}} - N_3\sigma_{\text{abs}} = \frac{\pi^2 r_0 c f (g_3/g_4)\lambda}{2}\left(\frac{M}{2\pi kT}\right)^{1/2} N_4 I, \qquad (1)$$

with $I = [1 - (N_3/g_3)/(N_4/g_4)]$ the inversion factor. This form of the gain equation is derived for a Doppler-broadened spectral line[2] at a plasma temperature T and ion mass M. The upper and lower state densities and statistical weights are represented by N_4,N_3 and g_4,g_3, respectively. Also the oscillator strength is denoted by f, r_0 is the classical electron radius, and σ_{ind},σ_{abs} represent the respective cross sections for induced emission and absorption.

From Eq. (1) it is clear that a positive gain coefficient may be determined in a plasma volume independent of the particular pumping method or geometry and even at levels normally considered to be too low for meaningful amplification, providing that the population density inversion I is measurably greater than zero and that the absolute upper state density N_4 and the line width (Doppler broadened here) can be determined. Hence such gain coefficient measurements may be used as a quantitative gauge for indicating the effect of parameter adjustments on increasing the gain toward significant amplification at very short wavelengths. In the present case, the ratio of population densities N_3/N_4 required for determining I is found from the relative intensities of the $3 \rightarrow 1$ and $4 \rightarrow 1$ Lymann resonance lines in the 3-nm wavelength x-ray region, for which the transition probabilities[3] are known. The temperature T is established from plasma diagnostics. The absolute upper state density N_4 is derived from the relation $N_4 = N_7(N_4/N_7)$, with the relative density ratio N_4/N_7 again obtained from Lyman-series lines and the density N_7 determined from the emission of the $7 \rightarrow 6$ transition line of known transition probability[3] at a wavelength of 343.4 nm in the UV region, conveniently accessible to instrumental calibration with a standard source. (This is analogous to a branching-ratio calibration of the x-ray spectrograph for a single wavelength.) An initial attempt to scale the measured gain coefficients with increased pump power density is also described, with measured results for the increased parameters.

The authors are with U.S. Naval Research Laboratory, Washington, D.C. 20375.

Received 26 January 1983.

II. Experiment

Most of the present absolute gain measurements were performed on a carbon plasma created by focusing an 8-J Nd:glass laser in a 10-nsec pulse to a 500-μm diam spot on a graphite target for an intensity of 4.1×10^{11} W/cm^2 (Fig. 1). For the scaling experiments at increased intensity, the laser was operated at an energy of 18 J, and the focal spot was reduced to 100-μm diam for a maximum intensity of 5.7×10^{12} W/cm^2; four lower intensity levels were also obtained from this with neutral density filtering.

Most of the spectroscopic measurements on the hydrogenic C^{5+} ion were performed at a distance of 3 mm from the target surface, where the electron density is reduced in the expansion to a value below 10^{18} cm^{-3}, and population inversions are observed to a measurable degree in grazing-incidence photographic spectra on

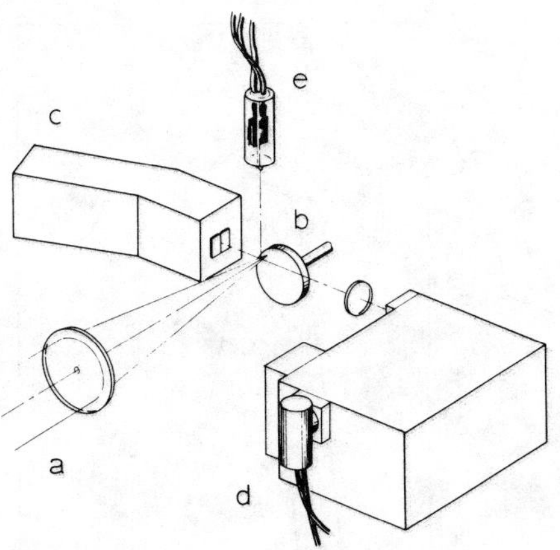

Fig. 1. Experiment schematic: *a*, Nd:glass laser pulse; *b*, graphite disk target; *c*, grazing incidence spectrograph; *d*, near UV-to-visible spectrometer; *e*, calibrated deuterium lamp.

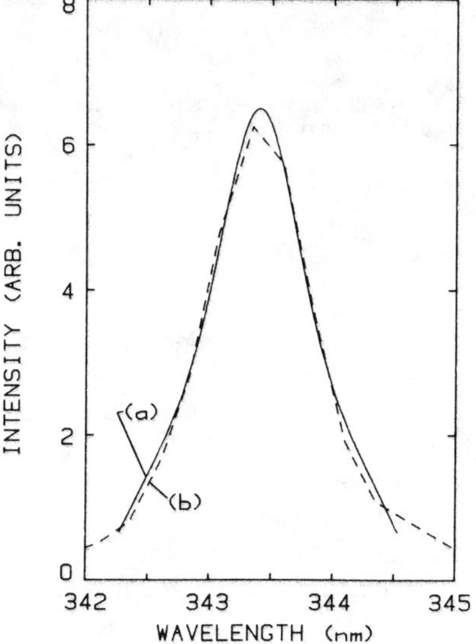

Fig. 2. (*a*) Convolved Stark profile and (*b*) observed profile.

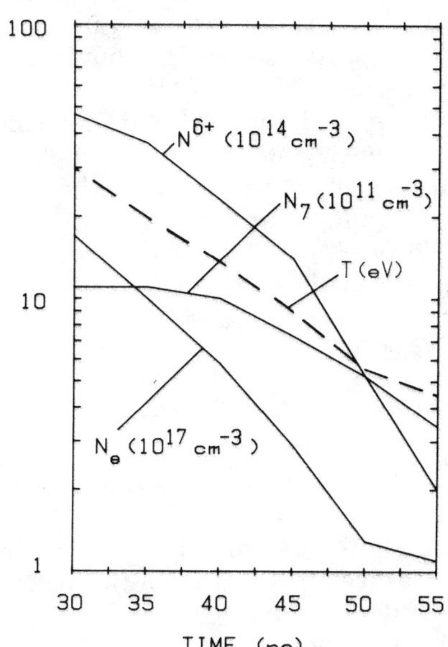

Fig. 3. Densities and temperature (dashed) at 3 mm from the target.

resonance lines in the one- and two-electron ionic species.[4,5] This distance is also consistent with simple analyses[6–9] for the upper bound on the density, which is imposed by electron collisional thermalization of energy level populations and by filling of the lower laser state by photon reabsorption (not a severe problem for the $n = 3$ level here).

The 343-nm wavelength spectral line from the C^{5+} $7 \rightarrow 6$ transition was measured with a Czerny-Turner mount spectrometer, fitted with a photomultiplier for time resolution and an aperture so that ±0.5 mm of plasma was resolved along the axis normal to the target surface. For electron density determinations, the profile of this line was measured by multiple-shot scanning. The absolute emission from this line was determined by calibrating[9,10] the spectrometer with a deuterium standard lamp *in situ* as indicated in Fig. 1.

III. Results

A. Plasma Conditions

The localized electron density N_e was determined by comparing (Fig. 2) the measured profile of the 343-nm line with a computed profile obtained by convolving a theoretical Stark line shape[11] with a Gaussian profile of 0.43-nm full width at half maximum. The latter represents constant instrumental broadening and some Doppler streaming effects measured for a point focus at distances of >5 mm from the target. Electron densities obtained in this manner at a distance of 3 mm from the target as a function of time during the pulse are included in Fig. 3. From a host of experimental data[12–17] on expanding laser-produced carbon plasmas summarized in Fig. 4, it is clear that the electron density and temperature in the free-expansion region beyond

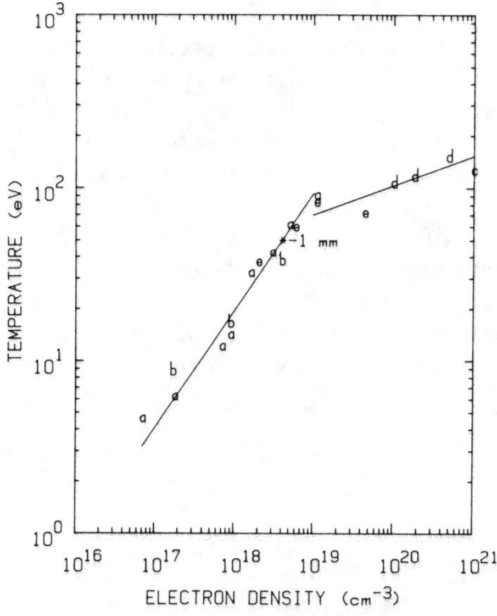

Fig. 4. Temperature as related to electron density through points from Refs. 12–16 as labeled *a–e*, respectively. An approximate distance of 1 mm in expansion toward lower parameters is indicated.

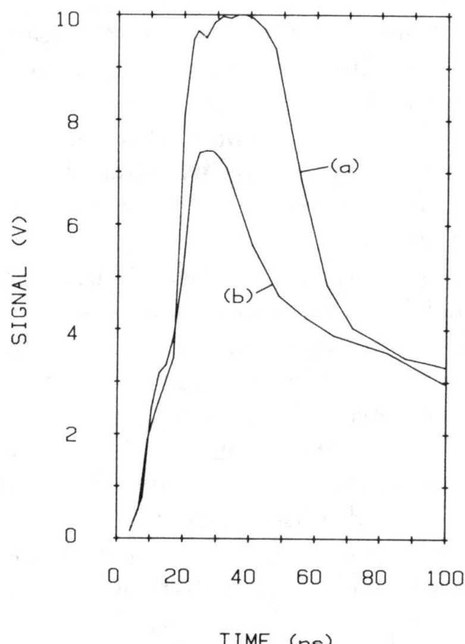

Fig. 5. (*a*) 343-nm line emission and (*b*) background emission at 3 mm.

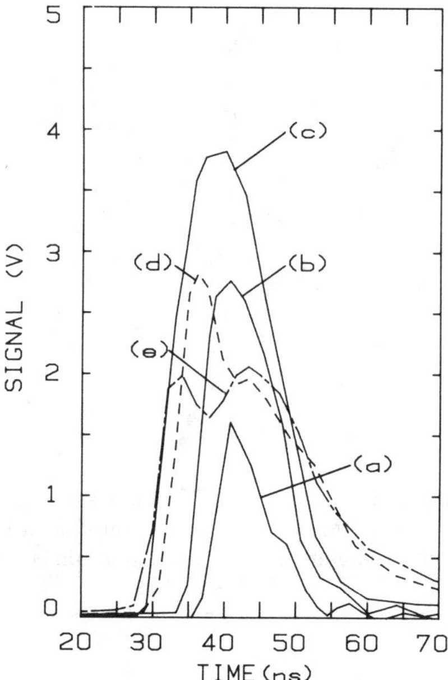

Fig. 6. 343-nm emission at irradiation intensities of (*a*) 0.34, (*b*) 0.63, (*c*) 1.5, (*d*) 2.9, and (*e*) 5.7×10^{12} W/cm^2.

~1 mm follow closely at $T \propto N^{2/3}$ adiabatic relation,[12] at least for pump power levels capable of creating a significant population of stripped carbon ions near the target. Hence the temperature shown in Fig. 3 is derived from Fig. 4 using the electron density as measured.

The time development of the 343-nm 7 → 6 spectral line signal is shown in Fig. 5 along with the underlying background emission. The density N_7 of the upper state as determined from absolute emission measurements is included in Fig. 3 as a function of time. Also included in Fig. 3 is the stripped-ion density N^{6+}, obtained assuming Saha equilibrium of the $n = 7$ level population with the ionized state for the corresponding densities and temperatures.

B. Absolute Gain Coefficient

The gain coefficient was deduced at a time of 45 nsec, while the bound state density represented by N_7 was still large and the relative ion stripping N^{6+}/N_e remained high, which is important for inversion-level pumping by free-electron capture into excited states followed by cascade.[6] From grazing-incidence spectroscopy,[5] the density ratios N_3/N_4 and N_4/N_7 were measured, and the quantities leading to an absolute gain of $G \approx 1\%$/cm at a distance of 3 mm and a time of 45 nsec for a pump intensity of 4×10^{11} W/cm^2 are collected in Table I. This value can be shown to be consistent with a simple physical mode based on free-electron capture pumping.[7,9]

Table I. Parameters and Gain at 4.1 × 10^{11}-W/cm^2 Pump Intensity

$N_e = 3 \times 10^{17}$ cm^{-3}
$T_e \approx 9$ eV
$N_7 = 7.3 \times 10^{11}$ cm^{-3}
$N_4/N_7 = 1.6$
$N_4 = 1.2 \times 10^{12}$ cm^{-3}
$N_3/N_4 = 0.4$
$I = 0.3$
$G \approx 1\%$/cm

Referring to Eq. (1), the uncertainty in the gain coefficient G is due primarily to uncertainties in the measured quantities I, T, and N_4. The inversion factor I depends on the excited state density ratio N_3/N_4, which is determined from the relative intensities of the Lyman series spectral lines on the photographic plates. The uncertainty in N_3/N_4, due to shot-to-shot variation and to the film calibration curve, is estimated to be 20%; and this also represents the uncertainty in the inversion factor I. The uncertainty in the value used for the temperature is estimated to be 50%, but its effect on the gain is less because of the $T^{-1/2}$ dependence. The density of the upper laser level N_4 is determined from measurements of the ratio N_4/N_7 and of N_7. The 7 → 1 Lyman line density is rather low on the photographic plate, which results in an uncertainty of 40% for the density ratio N_4/N_7. The accuracy of the absolute measurement of N_7 is estimated to be 30%. Thus the uncertainty in N_4 is ~50%; and the overall uncertainty in the gain G is 60%.

C. Gain Scaling with Pump Intensity

The 343-nm line signals for five levels of pump intensity are shown in Fig. 6, where a peak value is indicated for an intensity (*c*) of 1.5×10^{12} W/cm^2. The corresponding gain parameters deduced from measurements are given in Table II for this peak value and result, for similar resonance-line ratios, in a gain value increased by a factor of 2.1 at the increased pumping level, associated with the increased densities measured.

Table II. Parameters and Scaled Gain at 1.5 × 10^{12}-W/cm² Pump Intensity

$N_e = 6 \times 10^{17}$ cm^{-3}
$T_e \approx 14$ eV
$N_7 = 1.9 \times 10^{12}$ cm^{-3}
$N^{6+} = 1.1 \times 10^{16}$ cm^{-3}
$G \approx 2\%$/cm

IV. Conclusions

Gain coefficients in the %/cm range can be produced and measured directly from free-expanding and recombining laser-produced plasmas. Such gains over a 1-cm length of plasma would already be relevant for lasing in the XUV spectral region if cavities as efficient as for the visible region were available. At present, reflectances limited to ~40% for the 50-nm wavelength region require gain coefficients much higher, with 1 cm^{-1} being the goal. Increasing the ion population density to an apparent optimum level with an increase in pump intensity by a factor of 3.7 is shown here to lead to a factor of 2 increase in gain coefficient. Further pumping through free-electron capture will depend upon forced cooling of the plasma (recombination scales as T^{-2}) following ionization and expansion. Even a factor of 2 decrease in temperature could possibly create an order of magnitude improvement in inversion densities through exponentially increased and redistributed level populations favoring $n = 4$, for example.

It is a pleasure to acknowledge the expert technical assistance of J. L. Ford in all phases of the experiment described including laser operation. Appreciation is expressed to H. R. Griem for illuminating technical discussions and for his and P. C. Kepple's Stark broadening calculations for the 343-nm line.

References

1. R. W. Waynant and R. C. Elton, Proc. IEEE **64,** 1059 (1976).
2. For thermal Doppler broadening. Doppler spreading due to plasma streaming is not included here. Such additional broadening is not expected to exist in true elongated laser media [see, for example, J. F. Reintjes, R. H. Dixon, and R. C. Elton, Opt. Lett. **3,** 40 (1978) and G. V. Peregudov, M. E. Plotkin, and E. N. Ragozin, Sov. J. Quantum Electron. **9,** 1224 (1979)].
3. W. L. Wiese, M. W. Smith, and B. M. Glennon, "Atomic Transition Probabilities," NSRDS-NBS-4, Vol. 1 (U.S. GPO, Washington, D.C., 1966).
4. F. E. Irons and N. J. Peacock, J. Phys. B **7,** 1109 (1974).
5. R. C. Elton and R. H. Dixon, Phys. Rev. Lett. **38,** 1072 (1977); also R. H. Dixon, J. F. Seely, and R. C. Elton, Phys. Rev. Lett. **40,** 122 (1978); also R. C. Elton, T. N. Lee, R. H. Dixon, J. D. Hedden, and J. F. Seely, *Laser Interaction and Related Plasma Phenomena, Vol. 5*, H. J. Schwarz, H. Hora, M. Lubin, and B. Yaakobi, Eds. (Plenum, New York, 1981), p. 135.
6. R. C. Elton, Opt. Eng. **21,** 307 (1982).
7. R. C. Elton, J. F. Seely, and R. H. Dixon, in *Laser Techniques for Extreme Ultraviolet Spectroscopy*, T. J. McIlrath and R. R. Freeman, Eds., AIP Conf. Proc. 90, 277 (1982).
8. R. C. Elton, Comments At. Mol. Phys. (1983) (in press).
9. R. C. Elton, R. H. Dixon and J. F. Seely, *X-Ray and Atomic Inner-Shell Physics-1982*, B. Crasemann, Ed., AIP Conf. Proc. 94, 481 (1982).
10. R. H. Dixon, J. F. Seely, and R. C. Elton, in *Laser Techniques for Extreme Ultraviolet Spectroscopy*, T. J. McIlrath and R. R. Freeman, Eds., AIP Conf. Proc. 90, 305 (1982).
11. P. C. Kepple and H. R. Griem, Phys. Rev. A **26,** 484 (1982).
12. B. C. Boland, F. E. Irons, and R. W. P. McWhirter, J. Phys. B **1,** 1180 (1968).
13. F. E. Irons and N. J. Peacock, J. Phys. B **7,** 2084 (1974).
14. M. Galanti, N. J. Peacock, B. A. Norton, and J. Puric, in *Proceedings Fifth International Conference on Plasma Physics and Controlled Nuclear Fusion Research, Tokyo* (IAEA Report, Vienna, 1975).
15. M. Galanti and N. J. Peacock, J. Phys. B **8,** 2427 (1975).
16. A. M. Malvezzi, L. Garifo, E. Jannitti, P. Nicolosi, and G. Tondello, J. Phys. B **12,** 1437 (1979).
17. J. F. Seely, R. H. Dixon, and R. C. Elton, Phys. Rev. A **23,** 1437 (1981).

Reprinted with permission from *Soviet Journal of Quantum Electronics,* Vol. 13(11), pp. 1511-1515 (November 1983).

Amplification of ultraviolet radiation in a laser plasma

A. V. Vinogradov and V. N. Shlyaptsev

P. N. Lebedev Physics Institute, Academy of Sciences of the USSR, Moscow
(Submitted February 1, 1983)
Kvantovaya Elektron. (Moscow) **10**, 2325–2331 (November 1983)

An investigation is made of the possibility of using a laser plasma as an active medium in vacuum ultraviolet lasers. A theoretical model allows for the absorption of external radiation, heat transfer, cylindrical expansion of matter, electron–ion relaxation, and for detailed kinetics of the excitation, ionization, and recombination of ions. The optimal conditions for lasing in a medium consisting of Ne-like ions are found.

The main factor hindering the attainment of lasing in the far ultraviolet and soft x-ray ranges is the strong increase (compared with the visible range) in the pumping rate needed for population inversion.[1–3] Therefore, a laser plasma (because relatively simple means are sufficient to achieve an extremely high rate of energy deposition in such a plasma) has long been regarded as a potential active medium (for experimental results, see Refs. 4–13).

In the far ultraviolet and soft x-ray ranges the populations of levels of various multiply charged ions may be inverted. In particular, it is suggested in Ref. 14 that these may be neon-like ions with charges in the range $z \approx 7$–15. It has been shown that an inverted population with a gain $G \approx 10$–100 cm^{-1} may be achieved in the wavelength range $\lambda \approx 40$–80 nm simply by creating a plasma with an electron temperature $T_e \approx 100$–200 eV and an electron density $n_e \approx 10^{19}$–10^{20} cm^{-3}. Such inversion is not related to any fast transient (recombination or ionization) processes, but it occurs in a steady-state plasma when the optical thickness of resonance lines is small. A detailed analysis of the kinetics of filling levels of neon-like ions[15] carried out allowing for the real level structure of the configurations $2s^2 2p^5 3s$, $2s^2 2p^5 3p$, and $2s^2 2p^5 3d$ confirmed the main conclusions of Ref. 14. Next, a fuller model was analyzed,[16] where in addition to the populations of levels of neon-like ions, an allowance was made for ions with other degrees of ionization. This made it possible to determine finally the dependence of the gain in a steady-state and homogeneous plasma on the electron temperature and density, and also to identify the restrictions imposed on the transverse size by the trapping of resonance radiation.

The next stage has been to establish the relationship between the gain and the parameters of plasma-heating laser pulses. With this in mind we solved earlier[17] (as the first stage) the problem of determination of the charge composition of a laser plasma: in addition to the gasdynamic characteristics of the plasma (electron and ion densities and temperatures, expansion rate), we also found the ionic composition of the plasma and the dependence of this composition on the coordinates and time as a function of the laser radiation parameters.

In the present study we shall use the results of Refs. 16 and 17 to analyze the populations of excited levels and to determine the gain due to transitions in neon-like ions in the wavelength range 10–100 nm for an expanding laser plasma. We shall solve simultaneously the equations of gas dynamics and transient ionization, as well as steady-state rate equations governing the populations of excited levels of neon-like ions. We shall find the gain, the size of the region where it exists, and the power density and energy of laser radiation needed to create such an inverted medium. We shall give the results of specific calculations for sulfur, calcium, and iron targets.

CALCULATION METHOD

The inversion and gain for an inhomogeneous plasma formed by irradiation of a target made of a heavy element can be determined provided we know first of all the profiles of the electron and ion temperatures and densities, and also the distribution of ions in respect of the degree of ionization. They can be found by simultaneous solution of the equations of gas dynamics and of the ionization and recombination kinetics. Optimization of the external parameters—the power density and wavelength of laser radiation, size of the focusing spot of the laser radiation on a target, duration and shape of the pulses, etc.—can create conditions necessary, on the one hand, for the formation of a large number of ions of the required degree of ionization and, on the other, for the excitation of these ions and establishment of a population inversion. Characteristic times of the atomic processes of the excitation of levels and formation of a population inversion of multiply charged Ne-like ions are usually much shorter than the ionization and recombination times ($\sim 10^{-8}$–10^{11} sec) or the characteristic times of changes in the temperature and density of a plasma ($\sim 10^{-9}$–10^{-10} sec). Consequently, as soon as the required temperatures and densities are established in any particular region of an expanding plasma, the populations are then inverted and the inversion exists as long as these conditions are maintained. In particular, in the case of cylindrical and spherical expansion, which represents steady-state hydrodynamic conditions, the inversion lifetime is determined effectively by the energy deposition time. This lifts the restrictions on the duration of the leading edge of the pump pulses and makes it possible to employ a resonator.

The most effective method of finding the parameters of such a plasma is the following. The distribution of ions in respect of the degree of ionization is found from a complete system of transient equations for all the stages of ionization of an atom:

$$\frac{1}{n_e}\frac{d\alpha_z}{dt}=\alpha_{z-1}C^i_{z-1}-\alpha_z(C^i_z+C^r_z)+\alpha_{z+1}C^r_{z+1}, \quad (1)$$

where

$$z=0, 1, \ldots, z_N,$$

z_N is the nuclear charge; C^i_z and C^r_z are the rates of ionization and recombination of an ion carrying a charge z; N_z and $\alpha_z = N_z/\Sigma N_z$ are the absolute and relative concentrations of ions with the charge z; n_e is the electron density. The macroscopic parameters of the plasma (electron and ion temperatures and densities) occurring in the system (1) are then found by simultaneous solution of the equations of gas dynamics and of the ionization kinetics obtained using the average charge approximation.[17] It was shown in Ref. 17 that this approach ensures a high accuracy of the determination of the gasdynamic parameters of a plasma and at the same time makes it possible to allow correctly for the internal structure of the atoms and for the transient ionization effects.

The populations N_k of the excited levels of the required ions, which should be used as the active medium (in our case, Ne-like ions), are found in the quasisteady-state approximation, i.e., all the populations N_k are assumed to be determined by local (at any moment) values of the electron temperature, density, and ionic composition:

$$\frac{dN_k}{dt}=0=\Sigma N_i S_{ik}-N_k \Sigma S_{ki},$$

$$\sum_{i=0}^{36} N_i=\alpha_z \Sigma N_z, \quad (2)$$

where S_{ik} is the total probability of radiative and collisional population of a level k from a level i (Ref. 16). As pointed out earlier, this approach is justified because the characteristic relaxation times of the populations of levels in a laser plasma $[\sim(\Sigma_i S_{ki})^{-1}]$ are extremely short and they decrease on increase in the charge proportionally to z^4–z^5. Solution of the system (2) yields the population inversion ΔN and the gain G at the center of a Doppler-broadened line:

$$G=\lambda^2 A\,\Delta N/4\pi^{1/2}\Delta\omega_D, \quad (3)$$

where λ and A are the wavelength and probability of a radiative transition, respective; $\Delta\omega_D$ is the Doppler line width.

The relationships between the scales of the parameters in the corona of a laser plasma can readily be obtained for the case when the hydrodynamic plasma flow becomes steady state[18] and this can be done by equating the power density of laser radiation to the sum of the flux densities of the thermal, kinetic, and ionization energy of the evaporated matter and of the work done by the pressure forces[17]:

$$\begin{aligned} T_e&=6.24\cdot10^{-11}\,[q_L^2\lambda_L^2 R_0 M(3+1/3\gamma)^{-2}\exp(-2\tau)]^{2/9},\\ N&=(A_z\gamma)^{3/4}\tau^{1/2}(A_k R_0)^{-1/2},\\ v&=q_L^{1/3}(A_k R_0)^{1/6}(A_z\gamma)^{-1/4}[M(3+1/3\gamma)\exp(\tau)]^{-1/3},\\ z&=(T_e/A_z\gamma)^{1/2}, \end{aligned} \quad (4)$$

where T_e, N, v, and z are the temperature, density, velocity, and average charge of the plasma, respectively: M is the ionic mass; q_L is the power density of the incident laser radiation; R_0 is the characteristic size of a focusing spot (i.e., the initial target radius in the spherical and cylindrical cases); A_z is a coefficient of proportionality which appears in the process of approximation of the ionization potential I by a power law of the type $I = A_z z^2$ (A_z varies slowly within the limits of one electron shell of an ion); $A_k = 1.2\times10^{-46}\lambda_L^2$; λ_L is the wavelength of the external laser radiation. This model applies in the case of relatively low laser radiation power densities q_L of interest to us, when the position of the Jouguet point r_* relative to the point r_c with the critical density n_c is such that $r_* \gtrsim r_c$ (Ref. 1), the ionic composition differs only slightly from equilibrium so that $\gamma = T_e/I \approx 0.1$–$0.25$, and the inverse bremsstrahlung mechanism ensures practically complete absorption of the external laser radiation in the plasma corona. The optical thickness of the plasma up to the Jouguet point is then $\tau\approx0.5$–1.5 and the maximum electron temperature occurs near this point.

The expressions given in the system (4) are useful in estimating the contributions of the energies, temperatures, and densities necessary for the determination of the plasma conditions optimal for lasing. At shorter wavelengths one can use ions with larger charges. In the case of targets made of other elements, i.e., when the value of z for the Ne-like ions is altered, it is necessary to alter correspondingly the electron temperature of the plasma T_e, the electron density n_e, and the laser radiation power density q_L. Summarizing the results of Ref. 16 and of the present study, we obtain the following scaling relationship for z:

$$T_e\propto z_s^2;\; n_e\propto z_s^8;\; \lambda\propto z_s^{-1};\; G\propto z_s^{4.5};\; q_L\propto z^{4.5}\lambda_L^{-1}, \quad (5)$$

where $z_s = z + 1$ is the spectroscopic number of an ion.

We shall now consider the results of calculations of hydrodynamic quantities, ionic composition, and gains due to $2p^5 3p$–$2p^5 3s$ transitions in multiply charged Ne-like ions. The framework of one-dimensional transient two-liquid hydrodynamics and transient ionization kinetics was used to allow for the following principal physical processes governing the behavior of a plasma: inverse bremsstrahlung mechanism of absorption of the external laser radiation; work done by the pressure forces; electron thermal conductivity[19]; electron–ion relaxation of temperature; ionization; radiative, triple, and dielectronic recombination of matter, considered allowing for the influence of the electron density. The equations of state for an ideal gas were used. The maximum size of a focusing spot d, which governs (in the one-dimensional case) the initial expansion radius $R_0\approx d$, was selected in accordance with the restrictions imposed by trapping of radiation within the $2p^5 3s\rightarrow 2p^6$ resonance line so that the plasma was optically thin within the line ($R_0\leqslant 100$–$150\,\mu$ for sulfur and calcium and $R_0\lesssim 50\,\mu$ for iron[16]). In the direction of the normal a laser plasma was found to be always optically thin within a given spectral line, because the Doppler frequency shift in an inhomogeneous moving plasma amounting to one line width is known to occur in the region of strongest amplification at very short distances $L_{\Delta\omega}\approx v_t/(dv/dr)\approx 3$–$15\,\mu$ [$v_t\equiv(2T_i/M)^{1/2}$ is the thermal velocity of ions].

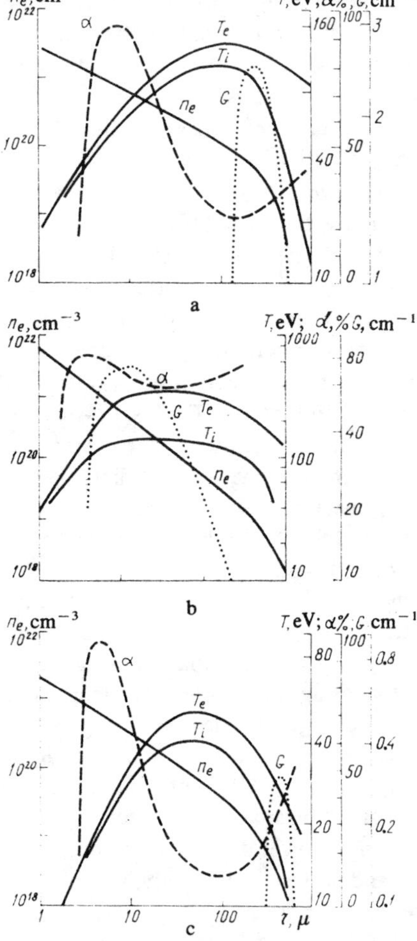

FIG. 1. Dependences of the electron temperature T_e, electron density n_e, ion temperature T_i, relative concentration of Ne-like ions α, and gain G on the distance r from a target in the case of cylindrical focusing: a) atomic number of the target $z_N = 20$ (calcium), absorbed power density of laser radiation $q_L = 1.5\times10^{11}$ W/cm², $R_0 = 100\,\mu$; b) $z_N = 26$ (iron), $q_L = 3\times10^{12}$ W/cm², $R_0 = 50\,\mu$; c) $z_N = 16$ (sulfur), $q_L = 5\times10^{10}$ W/cm², $R_0 = 50\,\mu$.

Figure 1 shows the dependences of the following quantities on the distance from the target: the gain, electron density, electron temperature, ion temperature, and relative concentration of Ne-like ions (expressed in percent of the total local concentration of ions) in a plasma of Ca, Fe, and S ions in the case of constant and near-optimal (from the point of view of attainment of the highest values of the gain G) power densities of the external laser radiation. It is assumed that the wavelength of the heating radiation $\lambda_L = 1.06\,\mu$ is that emitted by a Nd laser.

In the case of a plasma of calcium or iron ions (Figs. 1a and 1b) the profiles of the gasdynamic quantities are given for the moment of establishment of steady-state hydrodynamic flow in the region where G has its maximum ($t\approx 1$–3 nsec). In the case of sulfur ions in the same hydrodynamic flow regime ($t\gtrsim 5$ nsec) the optimal electron density of $\sim(4$–$8)\times10^{18}$ cm^{-3} is established not in the region of absorption of the heating radiation where the temperature is highest, but at a distance of 0.5–1 mm from the target. The temperature is insufficient for effective population of the excited states and the relative concentration of Ne-like ions does not exceed 10–15%. Consequently, the gain for sulfur is $G\lesssim 0.1$ cm^{-1}, but within a time interval $2\lesssim t\lesssim 4$ nsec required to reach steady-state flow conditions it rises to $G\approx 0.6$–0.7 cm^{-1}. This is due to the relatively high (for the selected laser pulse parameters) relative concentration of the investigated Ne-like ions ($\sim 50\%$) at the boundary of a laser jet (Fig. 1c).

As postulated in Refs. 14, 16, and 17, there is a wide range of temperatures in which Ne-like ions are the most representative of the species present in a plasma. However, in the case of a plasma composed of light elements (S, Ca), a favorable steady-state ionic composition is established at relatively low values $\gamma\approx\frac{1}{6}$–$\frac{1}{9}$, which reduces the population of the excited states; the gain is then small (0.1–0.7 and 2.5–3.5 cm^{-1}, respectively). The maximum gain due to multiply charged ions of the heavier iron (see Fig. 1b) reaches 70 cm^{-1} and the relative concentration of the active ions is $\sim 60\%$ and we have $\gamma\approx 0.25$.

Table I gives the optimized values of the laser radiation power density q_L and of the energy E_L of the radiation from a Nd laser arriving in 1 nsec on a focusing spot of $50\,\mu\times 1$ cm dimensions, together with the optimal steady-state values of the electron density and temperature,[16] and of the wavelengths of laser transitions and the maximum values of the gain.

The values of the gain C are similar for the three ions under consideration and are even somewhat higher than those calculated in Ref. 16 for a steady-state homogeneous plasma. This is due to a small lag of the ionization and ion temperatures behind the electron temperature. The former effect should, during the ionization time of Ne-like ions, maintain an electron temperature in a plasma slightly above the optimal steady-state value and this should result in a

TABLE I.

Ion	q_L, 10^{11} W/cm²	E_L, J/nsec	T_e, eV	n_e, 10^{19} cm^{-3}	λ, nm	G, cm^{-1}
S VII	0.3—0.5	0.15—0.25	40	0.5	61.38; 124	0.1—0.7
Ca XI	1—3	0,5—1	110—120	4—6	38; 57; 66	2,5—3.5
Fe XVII	10—30	5—15	300	30—70	25 20.3 10	70 20 10

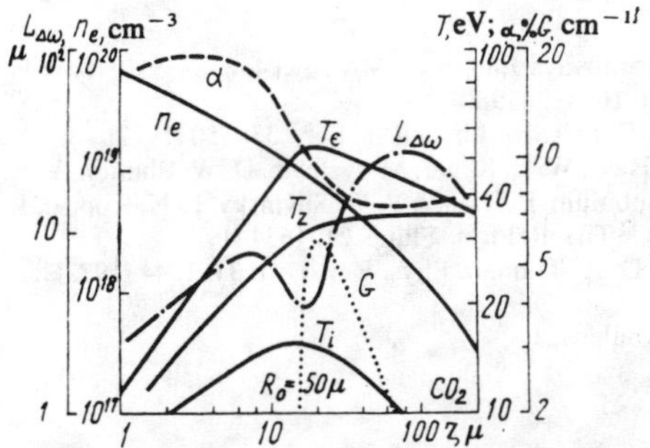

FIG. 2. The same as in Fig. 1c but for $q_L = 3$ GW/cm^2 and $\lambda_L = 10.6\,\mu$. In addition to the dependences in Fig. 1, this figure gives also the profiles of the average ionization temperature T_z and of the characteristic inhomogeneities $L_{\Delta\omega}$.

more effective filling of the active levels, because the excitation rate is given by $\langle v\sigma\rangle_{0k} \propto \exp(-E_k/T_e)$, where E_k is the energy of the k th level measured from the ground state. The lower value of the ion temperature increases G by a factor of $(T_e/T_i)^{1/2}$ compared with the equilibrium steady-state value of Ref. 16, because of the dependence $\Delta\omega_D \sim T_i^{1/2}$.

It should be pointed out that amplification and lasing in ions of elements with atomic numbers $z_N \lesssim 18$ (Ar, Cl, S, etc). can be achieved more readily using CO_2 laser radiation ($\lambda_L = 10.6\,\mu$, $n_c = 10^{19}$ cm^{-3}) because in this case the optimal electron densities are in the range $n_e \lesssim 10^{19}$ cm^{-3}. Moreover, in view of the lower plasma density and the longer ionization $\tau_i \approx (n_e\langle v\sigma\rangle^i_{\rm Ne})^{-1} \propto z^{-5}$ and electron–ion $\tau_{ei} \approx \tau_e M/2mz \sim z^{-4} - z^{-5}$ relaxation times, compared with the expansion time $\tau_r \approx R_0/v \propto z^{-1}$, we can expect a considerable increase in the gain compared with the equilibrium steady-state case if a plasma obeys the conditions $\tau_r < \tau_i, \tau_{ei}$ [here, $\langle v\sigma^i_{\rm Ne}\rangle$ is the rate of ionization of Ne-like ions; $\tau_e \equiv 3m^{1/2}T_e^{3/2}/[(2\pi)^{1/2}4e^4 n_e z\Lambda]$ is the characteristic elastic collision time[19]; Λ is the Coulomb logarithm}. Figure 2 shows the profiles of the same quantities as in Fig. 1c but for a plasma created by CO_2 laser radiation. Figure 2 includes also the average ionization temperature T_z which, in the average charge approximation, should be regarded as the temperature of a steady-state plasma with the same average charge as under given transient conditions. After $t \gtrsim 2$ nsec the gain is $G \approx 6$ cm^{-1}, which is over 50 times higher than that achieved using Nd laser radiation. Moreover, the required power density of the laser radiation is 10 times less [see Eq. (3)] and it now amounts to $q_L \approx (3\text{–}5)$ GW/cm^2, the corresponding energy delivered per unit time being $E_L \approx 15\text{–}25$ mJ/nsec. In the amplification region the relative concentration of Ne-like ions is then $\alpha \approx 40\%$. On attainment of steady-state hydrodynamic flow at the plasma boundary, where α is close to the maximum value of $\sim 96\%$ for sulfur, the maximum gain is $G = 20$ cm^{-1} ($0.2 \lesssim t \lesssim 0.5$ nsec). The estimates based on the system (4) obtained allowing for the nonequilibrium ionization regime, $\gamma \approx 1/5\text{–}1/6$, and a real optical thickness $\tau \approx 0.5$ of a plasma formed by heating with CO_2 laser radiation, and also assuming that $A_z \approx 1.24 \times 10^{-11}$ erg give $T_e \approx 53.4$ eV, $N \approx 1.59 \times 10^{18}$ cm^{-3}, $v \approx 31.9$ km/sec, whereas a numerical calculation (Fig. 2) gives $T_e \approx 53.6$ eV, $N \approx 1.55 \times 10^{18}$ cm^{-3}, and $v \approx 33$ km/sec.

We shall assume that heat transfer is due to the "classical" electron mechanism.[19] In recent papers there have been theoretical and experimental indications that in the case of a multiply charged plasma one may also encounter mechanisms which limit heat transfer.[20–22] These mechanisms may be ionic sound turbulence, magnetic and electric fields, etc. Preliminary calculations carried out allowing for limitations imposed on heat transfer have shown that the requirement in respect of the necessary pump energy can be reduced and the gain can increase severalfold under optimal conditions. In view of this, our results should be regarded as the lower limit of the expected gain.

The physical hydrodynamic model used above is, in our opinion, the "minimal" approach that can provide an adequate description of the behavior of a multiply charged laser plasma. We can use this model to allow for various physical effects and processes. In particular, the results are not greatly affected by corrections for the following: nonideal nature of the plasma, Coulomb interaction, electron gas degeneracy, ionic viscosity, and radiation losses (due to bremsstrahlung, photorecombination, and line emission of dielectronic satellites).

We have ignored the losses due to emission of radiation in the form of resonance lines. The total radiation losses from a multiply charged plasma have been estimated in various papers to be in the range $\sim$6–50% of the deposited energy.[22,23] An allowance for line emission from an inhomogeneous laser plasma under reabsorption conditions is very time-consuming. Inclusion of this allowance in the hydrodynamic model may reduce somewhat the plasma temperature and, consequently, increase the required rate of energy deposition. The influence of line radiation losses on the energetics and population inversion in a laser plasma requires a separate study.

The authors are grateful to A. Yu. Zakharov (Institute of Applied Mathematics, Academy of Sciences of the USSR) and the team operating the RDR-11 computer (Lebedev Physics Institute) for their help in this investigation.

[1]A. V. Vinogradov and I.I. Sobel'man, Zh. Eksp. Teor. Fiz. **63**, 2113 (1972) [Sov. Phys. JETP **36**, 1115 (1973)].
[2]R. W. Waynant and R. C. Elton, Proc. IEEE **64**, 1059 (1976).
[3]A. V. Vinogradov, I. I. Sobelman, and E. A. Yukov, J. Phys. (Paris) **39**, Colloq. 4, C4-61 (1978).
[4]P. Jaegle, A. Carillon, P. Dhez, G. Jamelot, A. Sureau, and M. Cukier, Phys. Lett. A **36**, 167 (1971).
[5]P. Jaegle, G. Jamelot, A. Carillon, A. Sureau, and P. Dhez, Phys. Rev. Lett. **33**, 1070 (1974).
[6]F. E. Irons and N. J. Peacock, J. Phys. B **7**, 1109 (1974).
[7]É. Ya. Kononov, K. N. Koshelev, Yu. A. Levykin, Yu. V. Sidel'nikov, and S. S. Churilov, Kvantovaya Elektron. (Moscow) **3**, 576 (1976) [Sov. J. Quantum Electron. **6**, 308 (1976)].
[8]R. H. Dixon, J. F. Seely, and R. C. Elton, Phys. Rev. Lett. **40**, 122 (1978).
[9]R. H. Dixon and R. C. Elton, Phys. Rev. Lett. **38**, 1072 (1977).
[10]V. A. Bhagavatula and B. Yaakobi, Opt. Commun. **24**, 331 (1978).
[11]V. A. Bhagavatula, Appl. Phys. Lett. **33**, 726 (1978).
[12]D. Jacoby, G. J. Pert, S. A. Ramsden, L. Shorrock, and G. J. Tallents, in: Lasers and Applications (Proc. Sergio Porto Memorial Symposium, Rio de Janeiro, Brasil, 1980, ed. by W. O. N. Guimaraes, C. T. Lin, and A. Mooradian), Springer Verlag, Berlin (1981), p. 228.
[13]A. A. Ilyukhin, G. V. Peregudov, E. N. Ragozin, I. I. Sobel'man, and V. A. Chirkov, Pis'ma Zh. Eksp. Teor. Fiz. **25**, 501 (1977) [JETP Lett. **25**, 535 (1977)].

[14]A. V. Vinogradov, I. I. Sobel'man, and E. A. Yukov, Kvantovaya Elektron. (Moscow) **4**, 63 (1977) [Sov. J. Quantum Electron. **7**, 32 (1977)].
[15]A. V. Vinogradov and V. N. Shlyaptsev, Kvantovaya Elektron. (Moscow) **6**, 1319 (1980) [Sov. J. Quantum Electron. **10**, 754 (1980)].
[16]A. V. Vinogradov and V. N. Shlyaptsev, Kvantovaya Elektron. (Moscow) **10**, 509 (1983) [Sov. J. Quantum Electron. **13**, 298 (1983)].
[17]A. V. Vinogradov and V. N. Shlyaptsev, Kvantovaya Elektron. (Moscow) **10**, 516 (1983) [Sov. J. Quantum Electron. **13**, 303 (1983)].
[18]I. V. Nemchinov, Prikl. Mat. Mekh. **31**, 300 (1967).
[19]S. I. Braginskii, in: Problems in Plasma Theory [in Russian], No. 1, Moscow (1963).
[20]E. N. Ragozin, Kvantovaya Elektron. (Moscow) **4**, 868 (1980) [Sov. J. Quantum Electron. **10**, 493 (1980)].
[21]B. Yaakobi and T. C. Bristow, Phys. Rev. Lett. **38**, 350 (1977).
[22]H. D. Shay, R. A. Haas, W. L. Kruer, M. J. Boyle, D. W. Phillion, V. C. Rupert, H. N. Kornbulum, F. Rainer, V. W. Slivinsky, L. N. Koppel, L. Richards, and K. G. Tirsell, Phys. Fluids **21**, 1634 (1978).
[23]N. K. Winsor and D. A. Tidman, Phys. Rev. Lett. **31**, 1044 (1973).

Translated by A. Tybulewicz

Reprinted with permission from *IEEE Journal of Quantum Electronics,* Vol. QE-19(12), pp. 1855-1860 (December 1983). ©1983 IEEE.

Population Inversion and Gain Measurements for Soft X-Ray Laser Development in a Magnetically Confined Plasma Column

SZYMON SUCKEWER, CHARLES H. SKINNER, DAVID R. VOORHEES, HOWARD M. MILCHBERG, CHRISTOPHER KEANE, AND A. SEMET

***Abstract*—We present population inversion and gain measurements from an experimental investigation of possibilities to obtain high gain and lasing action in the soft X-ray region. Our approach to soft X-ray laser development is based on rapid plasma cooling after the laser pulse by radiation losses, leading to fast recombination and collisional cascade into upper excited levels of CVI, for example, while the lower excited levels depopulate rapidly by radiative transitions, thus creating population inversions and gain. A ≈ 0.5 kJ CO_2 laser was focused onto a target of solid carbon or teflon; or CO_2, O_2, Ne gas, and the resulting plasma confined in a 50-90 kG magnetic field. Spectroscopic diagnostics with absolute intensity calibration were used to measure level populations. Population inversions were observed between the 4*d* and 3*d* levels in the lithium sequence ions: CIV, OVI, FVII, and NeVIII, and a gain of 0.1 (10 percent) was estimated for the OVI 4*f*-3*d* transition at 520 Å. In experiments with a solid carbon target, we observe relatively high CVI 182 Å emission in the axial direction compared to the transverse direction, which, if due to stimulated emission, would correspond to a gain of 4. Extension of these results to potential lasing transitions below 100 Å will be discussed.**

I. Introduction

Among the number of promising approaches toward the development of a soft X-ray laser (see [1]-[8], also review articles [9], [10]) is the idea of rapidly cooling a multi-Z high-density plasma to create a strongly nonequilibrium (recombination) regime. In such a plasma, rapid three-body recombination of totally stripped ions creates a high density of highly excited hydrogen-like ions. The lower levels are populated by collisional cascading processes and depopulated by radiative (spontaneous) transitions which are particularly fast for the first excited level. In this way, a population inversion can occur for levels $n = 3$ and 4 relative to level $m = 2$. Gudzenko *et al.* [11], [12], who first pointed out the possibility of using a recombining plasma as a medium for lasing action in the X-ray region, suggested cooling the plasma by rapid adiabatic expansion. Irons and Peacock [13] first observed a population inversion in 1974 in hydrogen-like CVI on a transition in the soft X-ray region. The plasma was created by a laser beam interaction with a solid target, and a population inversion was observed during plasma expansion into the vacuum with an estimated single pass gain $G \approx 10^{-5}$. Elton and Dixon [14] in a similar experiment with a carbon target, but with plasma expansion into a gas, observed a population inversion due mainly to a charge exchange process. Bhagavatula and Yaakobi [15] reported a population inversion in H-like AlXIII using a much more powerful laser. A significant gain in CVI at 182 Å was observed by Pert *et al.* [16], [17] during the free expansion of a carbon plasma created by the interaction of a laser beam with a 2 mm long 4 μm diameter carbon fiber. Of course, in a rapidly recombining plasma, a population inversion in the X-ray region can also be obtained in other ions, e.g., in Li-like ions between levels 4*f* or 5*f* and 3*d*, due to the fast radiative decay of level 3*d*, as was pointed out by Silfvast *et al.* [18], [19]. Recently, Jaeglé *et al.* [20] presented evidence for small single pass gain in Li-like AlXI at 105 Å (5*f*-3*d* transition). However, the free expansion makes it difficult to control the electron density and arrange optimum conditions for gain.

To avoid a rapidly decreasing plasma density and create a relatively uniform and long plasma column (single pass gain G is proportional to the length), it was proposed [21] to confine the plasma in a strong magnetic field and rely on radiation losses for fast cooling. In this proposal, the plasma dimensions are well suited to a practical laser with a large ratio of plasma length l to radius $r (l/r \geqslant 10^2)$. Calculations [21] have shown that for such a plasma column heated by a 0.5-1 kJ CO_2 laser (10-20 GW of power), CVI is the most suitable hydrogen-like ion to obtain lasing action in the soft X-ray region (to have the same gain in H-like oxygen, a more powerful laser is needed). A CO_2 laser operation wavelength of 10.6 μm is appropriate for our experiment from the point of view of the optimum electron density. For the maximum radiative cooling (a strong function of the recombination rate) one would like to have an electron density n_e as high as possible (three-body recombination rates are proportional to n_e^2). However, for each transition under consideration for lasing action, there is a limit for n_e above which collisional depopulation becomes faster than radiative decay. Above this limit, collisions "thermalize" the population inversion and prevent gain. For example, for the CVI 3 → 2 transition the electron density should not exceed 10^{19} cm^{-3} (see, e.g., [22]). This also corresponds to the critical density for a 10.6 μm laser (at which the plasma frequency equals the laser frequency).

The main purpose of this paper is a presentation of the experiments indicating the effectiveness of radiation losses for plasma cooling, preliminary results on the enhancement of the CVI 182 Å line intensity possibly due to stimulated emission, and an observation of population inversion in Li-like CIV, OVI, FVII, and NeVIII ions.

Manuscript received March 25, 1983; revised May 25, 1983. This work was supported by the U.S. Department of Energy, Advance Energy Projects.

The authors are with the Plasma Physics Laboratory, Princeton University, Princeton, NJ 08544.

II. Experimental Arrangement

The experimental setup is presented in Fig. 1. Four Lumonics 620 TEA CO_2 laser units in oscillator-amplifier configuration were used for plasma heating. The two oscillator units were operated broad band with a reduced N_2 component in the gas mix in order to remove the "tail" appearing in the laser output after the main pulse. A reflection from the output window of the last amplifier was focused to an intensity monitor (marked on Fig. 1 as Laser Beam Detector) consisting of a thermopile and a photon drag detector which provided a record of laser energy and power. The output energy could be varied in the $0.2 \rightarrow 0.7$ kJ range by operating with two, three, or four laser units. The output pulse was 75 ns FWHM duration. The laser beam was focused by a 2.84 m focal length NaCl lens to an evacuated target chamber inside a solenoidal magnet. The laser focal spot size was 1 mm in diameter with a corresponding intensity of $(0.3\text{-}1) \times 10^{12}$ W $\cdot$ cm^{-2}. A magnetic field of up to 90 kG was used to confine the plasma (maximum available magnetic field: 150 kG) and was essentially static over the plasma lifetime. For the case of gaseous targets, the gas was puffed into the target chamber by a fast valve. Gas puffing provides a decreasing pressure gradient in the backward direction with respect to the laser beam and prevents the formation of a backward going shock wave [23] which would decrease the efficiency of the laser-plasma coupling. The gas volume was limited by discs, one with a 2 mm orifice to decrease gas flow in the direction to the axial spectrometer (see Fig. 2) and the second one with a 10 or 15 mm orifice at a distance of $l \simeq 5$ or 10 cm upstream from the first one (towards the CO_2 laser) to provide a high gas pressure gradient near the laser focus. The gas density was monitored at different distances along the axis with a calibrated piezoelectric probe of rise time 2 μs. In Fig. 2 there is also shown a solid target with a 1 mm hole in the center. For this, a plasma column was created along the axis through the hole. With a magnetic field of $B \geqslant 50$ kG, the plasma column was well confined and the length of the column was $l \simeq 5$ cm as monitored by the streak camera.

Inverse bremsstrahlung is expected to be the main heating process for plasmas created from both gaseous and solid targets as was the case in a number of experiments related to the thermonuclear fusion program (e.g., [23]-[26]). In these experiments, peak electron temperatures in the range of 100-400 eV and electron densitites in the range of $(1\text{-}3) \times 10^{18}$ cm^{-3} were generated by a 200-300 J, 60-70 ns CO_2 laser in a plasma confined by a magnetic field [25], [26].

In the present experiment, mainly carbon targets have been used to date, although a few experiments were done with a teflon target (for observation of fluorine spectra, particularly Li-like FVII spectra) and an aluminum target (for Li-like AlXI). The primary plasma diagnostic instruments were an array of six spectrometers as shown in Fig. 1. A system of beam splitters was set up so that the grazing incidence VUV instruments and absolute intensity calibrated air monochromators viewed the same region of the plasma in order to facilitate "branching ratio" intensity calibration of the VUV instruments (Fig. 2). A grazing incidence glass "bent mirror" [27] was used to improve the sensitivity of the axial VUV instrument situated 3 m from the plasma. For the work reported here, the VUV data

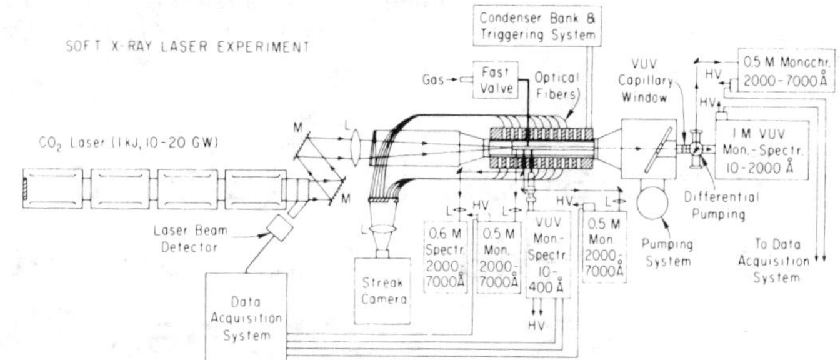

Fig. 1. Schematic of experimental arrangement.

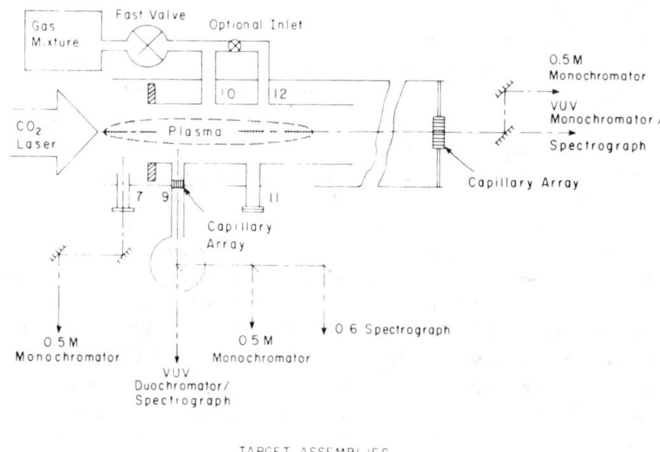

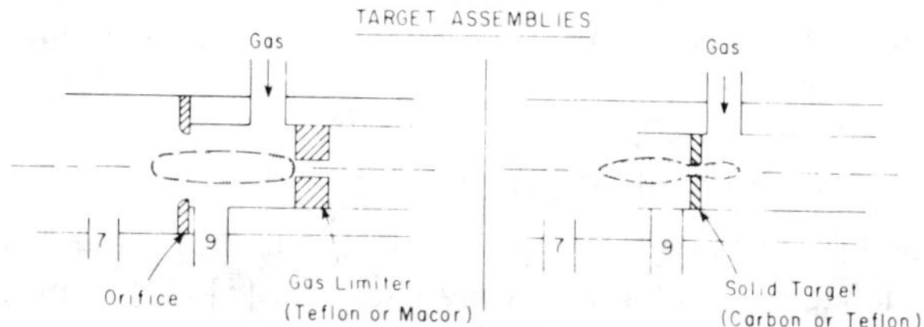

Fig. 2. The optical arrangement of the experiment and target assemblies.

were recorded on photographic plates with 1-20 laser shots per exposure. The 0.6 m air spectrograph provided spectral and spatial resolution across the plasma diameter. An absolute intensity calibration for the three 0.5 m air monochromators was performed using a standard tungsten strip lamp and an NBS mini-argon arc lamp (the arc lamp was used in the 2000-3000 Å region). The instrumental resolution was set at 1.9 Å and a wavelength calibration was performed before each data run using an Hg lamp.

A series of plastic light guides was set up, one leading from each viewport in the magnet to an array, with additional light guides for position calibration. This array was photographed by a streak camera on each laser shot and provided an overall view of the space and time development of the plasma as indicated by visible emissions.

The data were recorded by Tektronix 7912 and six LeCroy 2256 Transient Digitizers.

III. Effectiveness of Radiation Cooling

In the first series of experiments [28], an absolute intensity calibrated 0.5 m spectrometer and 0.6 m spectrometer (both for the 2000-7000 Å spectral range) were used for monitoring, respectively, the time evolution and space distribution of CVI emission lines from 7 → 6 (3434 Å) and 8 → 7 (5291 Å) transitions. Lines of carbon and oxygen ions of lower ionization stages were also recorded. In Fig. 3 are shown spectra near the CVI 3434 Å line for $B = 0$ and $B = 50$ kG for a gas (CO_2) target of pressure $p \approx 2$ torr. The vertical direction in the spectra represents a transverse section of the plasma near the CO_2 laser focus. It can be seen that the CVI is confined within a column radius $r \leqslant 1.2$ mm by the magnetic field at 50 kG. With such a magnetic field, the peak intensity of the CVI 3434 Å line increased three times in relation to $B = 0$ and the decay time decreased from 400 ns ($B = 0$) to 200 ns ($B = 50$ kG), as can be seen at the bottom of Fig. 3. This line emission peaked at 200 ns after the peak of the laser pulse during the plasma recombination stage. For a higher magnetic field ($B = 90$ kG, Fig. 4), the decay time becomes even shorter (100 ns) and the radius of the hot part of the plasma column becomes $r < 0.9$ mm. The data in Figs. 3 and 4 indicate that recombination in the high-density plasma confined by the magnetic field is much faster than the recombination in the zero field free expansion case. In the free expansion case, the electron density, and hence recombination rate and excited level populations are lower, leading to a reduced radiative cooling rate, and the difference is not compensated for by cooling due to adiabatic expansion. One caveat to this interpretation is the existence of a potential OVI emission line also at 3434 Å. In the VUV region of the spectrum the CVI and OVI lines are well separated and this problem will be eliminated in the near future when the VUV instruments are converted to the photoelectric mode.

IV. Measurements of Population Inversion and Gain

In the next series of experiments, we concentrated on measurements of line radiation in the soft X-ray region using the two vacuum ultraviolet (VUV) spectrometers. One spectrometer monitored line radiation from the plasma column along the axis (axial instrument) and the second one along the diameter of the column (transverse instrument). Two differential pumping stations isolate these instruments from the target chamber. A system of beam splitters enables absolute intensity calibrated 0.5 m air monochromators to view the same points of the plasma. In this way, we can calibrate the VUV instruments for absolute intensities by the method of branching ratios. The optical arrangement of the experiment and target assemblies were already presented in Fig. 2.

Population inversions were observed in Li-like spectra obtained by focusing the laser beam on gas or solid targets. The Li-like sequence has an energy structure similar to the one presented in Fig. 5 for OVI. In Fig. 6(a) is shown the OVI spectrum in the region 100-180 Å obtained by using a CO_2 gas target with a pressure $p \approx 3.5$ torr and magnetic field $B = 50$ kG. The effect of self-absorption on the line intensities was estimated by measurements of the intensity ratio of the fine structure components of the $3d$-$2p$ transition (172.934 Å, 173.082 Å), the strongest transition in the OVI spectrum. This ratio was close to the theoretical one for an optically thin plasma, and hence allowed us to neglect self-absorption

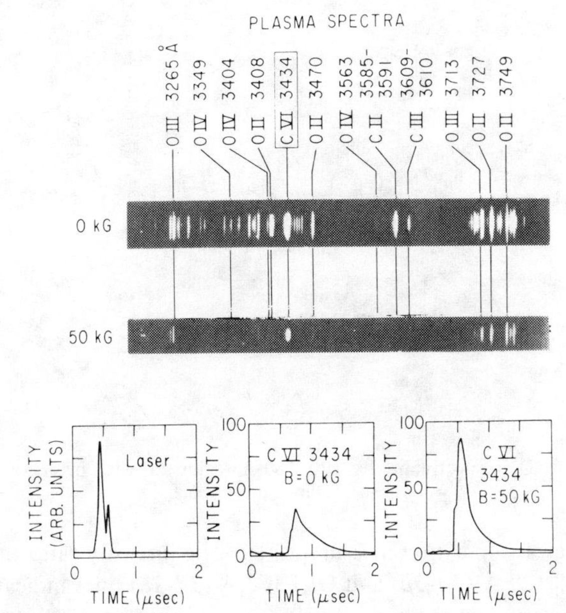

Fig. 3. Plasma spectrum near CVI 3434 Å line and time evolution of the intensities of this line for magnetic fields $B = 0$ and $B = 50$ kG.

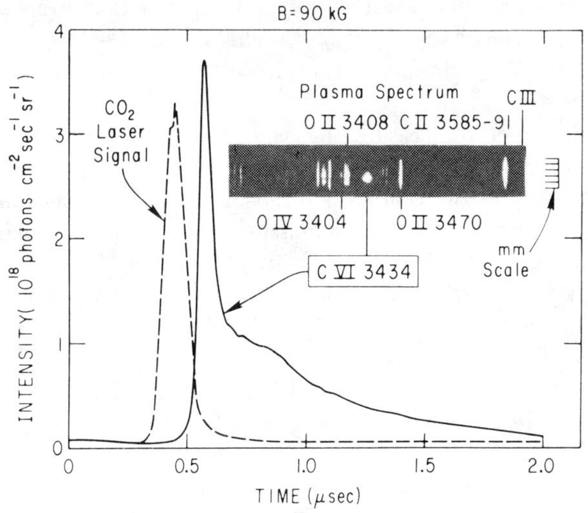

Fig. 4. Plasma spectrum near CVI 3434 Å line and its intensity evolution for $B = 90$ kG.

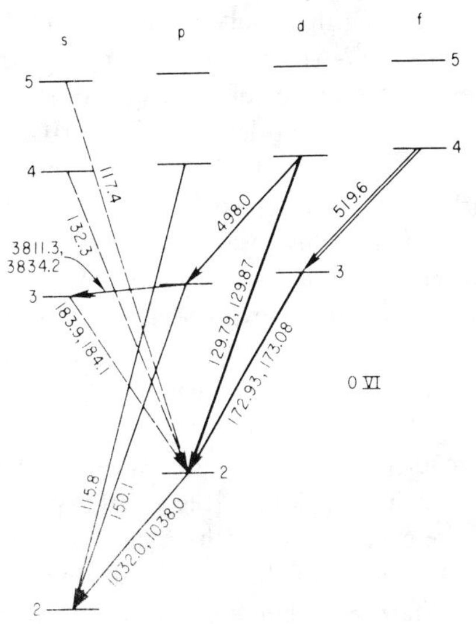

Fig. 5. Diagram of OVI levels.

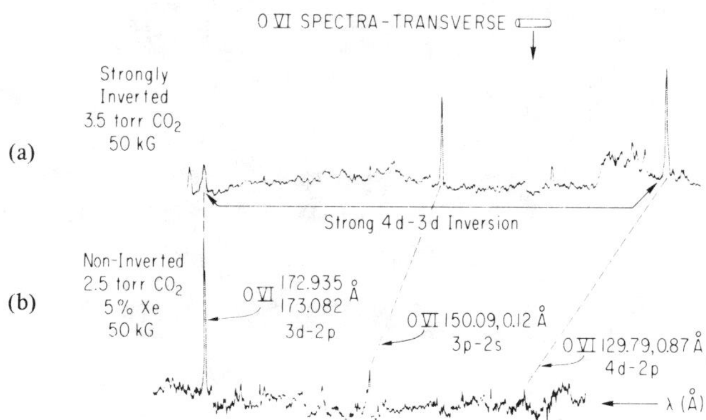

Fig. 6. OVI spectra in the 100–180 Å region (a) with inversion, and (b) without inversion.

in level population measurements. The intensity ratio of the OVI 129 Å (*4d-2p*) and OVI 173 Å (*3d-2p*) lines indicates a population-inversion for levels *4d* and *3d*. Also, a population inversion may be seen for levels *4p* and *3p* from the intensity ratio of the OVI 115 Å (*4p-2s*) and the OVI 150 Å (*3p-2s*) lines. Preliminary estimation of the population inversion for these levels was $n_{4d}/n_{3d} \approx 8$ and $n_{4p}/n_{3p} \approx 2$ ($n_k = N_k/g_k$ where N_k is the population density of level k and g_k is the statistical weight).

In order to measure the gain, the absolute population of OVI *3p* level was determined by measurements of the absolute intensity of the OVI 3811 Å (*3p-3s*) transition by a calibrated 0.5 m air spectrometer simultaneously with a VUV plate exposure. The 3811 Å intensity was $3.6 \times 10^{+19}$ photons $\cdot$ $cm^{-2} \cdot s^{-1} \cdot sr^{-1}$ corresponding to a *3p* sublevel population $n_{3p} = 2.2 \times 10^{12}$ cm^{-2}. The relative populations of the *3p*, *3d*, *4d* levels obtained from the OVI 150 Å, 173 Å, 129 Å emissions recorded on the VUV plate could thus be put on an absolute scale and the sublevel population difference $n_{4d} - n_{3s}$ was determined to be 5.5×10^{11} cm^{-2}. The *4d* and *4f* levels have a very small energy separation (0.02 eV) and we assume their sublevel populations to be equal. The Stark effect is expected to be the more dominant broadening mechanism for the OVI 520 Å line (*4f-3d* transition) and the line width was estimated by scaling the results of Kepple and Griem [26] for the CVI 3434 Å (7-6) transition by $n_l + \frac{1}{2}$ where n_l is the principal quantum number of the lower level of the transition. The result for an electron density of $n_e = 10^{18}$ cm^{-3} is 0.1 Å (FWHM). The gain of the OVI 520 Å transition based on a 0.1 Å Stark width is calculated to be $G \simeq 0.1$. We should emphasize here that this measurement was preliminary without any special attempt to maximize gain. The result is subject to some uncertainties with regard to the variation of the sensitivity of the VUV spectrograph with wavelength, but does represent a time integrated measurement. The peak gain at 520 Å is expected to be much higher. The inversion diminished when we cooled the plasma too much during the heating period by adding 5 percent Xe [Fig. 6(b)]. Such strong cooling prevented the creation of a high enough density of OVII ions which are the source of the OVI population inversion during the period of fast recombination. However, in the case of CIV ions, such additional cooling is not particularly negative during the heating period because the temperature of maximum abundance of CV is significantly lower than for OVII, and during the cooling period Xe increases the rate of radiative cooling. In Table I are shown the measured population inversions for Li-like ions from CIV to NeVIII with wavelengths λ of the potential lasing transitions in a plasma column confined by a 50 kG magnetic field.

Our most interesting results for soft X-ray laser development have been obtained in H-like CVI (Fig. 7). In this figure are presented axial and transverse emission spectra in the vicinity of the CVI 182 Å and CVI 33.7 Å lines from a carbon target with 1 mm hole and with applied magnetic field $B = 50$ kG. It can be seen that the CVI 182 Å line ($3 \rightarrow 2$ transition) intensity as compared to, e.g., the CVI 33.7 Å line ($2 \rightarrow 1$ transition) intensity is more than an order of magnitude stronger in the axial direction than in the transverse direction. If this enhancement of 182 Å line is by stimulated emission (which still needs to be proven in future experiments), it would correspond to a gain of $G \approx 4$. (This follows from the relationship between axial (stimulated, I_{stim}) and transverse (spontaneous, I_{spon}) line intensities

$$I_{stim}/I_{spon} = (e^G - 1)/G.)$$

Observation of the time evolution of the line intensities in the axial and transverse direction, modification of the plasma conditions to change the intensity ratio of the 182 Å and 33.7 Å lines, and measurements of the population of the CVI levels $n = 2$, 3, and 4 are planned for confirmation of this gain.

We are also planning to investigate conditions for X-ray laser development in the spectral region below 100 Å using hydrogen-like ions. Analysis of level populations in CVI, OVIII, and NeX versus plasma parameters should allow us to predict the conditions required for the creation of population inversions and high gain in the H-like isoelectronic sequence for higher Z elements in addition to the Li-like sequence discussed earlier.

V. Summary

The first series of experiments has shown that a magnetic field of order $B \approx 90$–100 kG can well confine highly ionized ions (e.g., CVI, OVI) within a radius of $r < 1$ mm in a column $l = 5$–10 cm long.

Preliminary measurements of line radiation using two vacuum ultraviolet (VUV) spectrometers have shown strong enhancement of CVI 182 Å line intensity emitted in the axial direction in comparison to the intensity of this line measured in the transverse direction (182 Å line intensity was measured relative to the CVI 33.7 Å $2 \rightarrow 1$ resonance transition). This enhancement suggested quite high single pass gain. A plasma column was created by focusing the laser beam on the edge of a 1 mm hole in a carbon disc target and the plasma extended through the hole along the magnetic field $B = 50$ kG.

In a separate experiment, observation of line radiation of Li-like ions in the VUV spectral region indicated population inversions between levels $n = 4$ and $m = 3$ for ions from CIV to NeVIII. Estimated average gain for OVI *4f-3d* transition (520 Å) was $\overline{G} \approx 0.1$, which suggested much higher peak gain,

TABLE I
POPULATION INVERSION IN Li-LIKE IONS

Conditions	B(kG)	Ion	Population $4d:3d$	λ(Å) $4f$-$3d$
2.4 torr CO_2 + 5 percent X_e	50	CIV	4.3:1	1168 Å
Carbon target	50	CIV	2.1:1	1168 Å
3.5 torr CO_2	50	OVI	8.3:1	519.6 Å
Teflon (CF_4)	50	FVII	1.2:1	381 Å
Neon	50	NeVII	3.7:1	292 Å

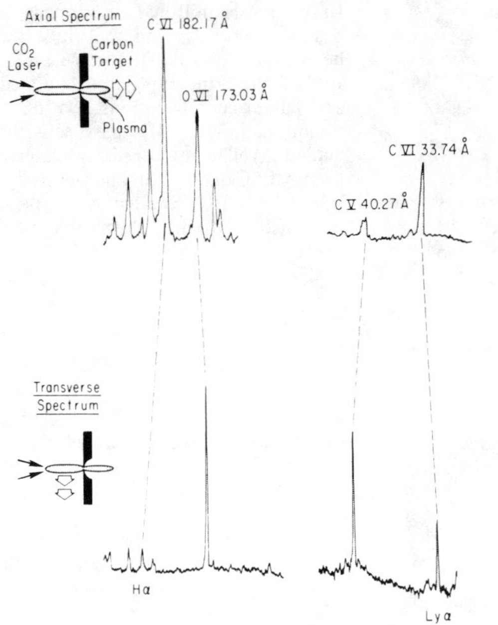

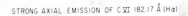

Fig. 7. Axial and transverse emission spectra in the vicinity of the CVI 182 Å and CVI 33 Å lines.

although no attempt has been made yet for the optimization of the population inversion for any of these Li-like ions.

ACKNOWLEDGMENT

The authors would like to express their gratitude to H. P. Furth for his encouragement and support. They would also like to thank J. L. Schwob for his interesting discussions and help in the operation of the VUV spectrometer. The authors highly appreciate the helpful technical assistance of G. Falo and D. DiCicco in the preparation of the experiments, and H. Fishman for his help in computer calculations.

REFERENCES

[1] M. A. Duguay and M. P. Rentzpis, "Some approaches to VUV and X-ray lasers," *Appl. Phys. Lett.*, vol. 10, pp. 350–352, 1967.

[2] R. A. McCorkle, "Practicable X-ray amplifier," *Phys. Rev. Lett.*, vol. 29, pp. 982–985, 1972.

[3] R. C. Elton, "Quasistationary population inversion on K_α transitions," *Appl. Opt.*, vol. 14, pp. 2243–2249, 1975.

[4] A. V. Vinogradov and I. I. Sobelman, "The problem of laser radiation sources in the far ultraviolet and X-ray regions," *Sov. Phys. JETP*, vol. 36, pp. 1115–1119, 1973.

[5] A. A. Ilyukhin, G. V. Peregudov, E. N. Rogozin, I. I. Sobelman, and V. A. Chirkov, "Concerning the problem of lasers for the far ultraviolet region $\lambda \sim 500$–700 Å," *Sov. Phys. JETP Lett.*, vol. 25, pp. 535–543, 1977.

[6] T. C. Bristow, M. J. Lubin, J. M. Forsyth, E. B. Goldman, and J. M. Soures, "High intensity X-ray spectra and stimulated emission from laser plasmas," *Opt. Commun.*, vol. 5, pp. 315–318, 1972.

[7] S. E. Harris, "Proposal for a 207 Å laser in lithium," vol. 5, pp. 1–3, 1980.

[8] E. Ya. Kononov, K. N. Koshelev, Yu. A. Levykin, Yu. V. Sidelnikov, and S. S. Churilov, "Population inversion of AlXI in a laser plasma," *Sov. J. Quantum Electron.*, vol. 6, pp. 308–311, 1976.

[9] R. W. Waynant and R. C. Elton, "Review of short wavelength laser research," *Proc. IEEE*, vol. 64, pp. 1059–1092, 1976.

[10] F. V. Bunkin, V. I. Derzhier, and S. I. Yakovlenko, "Prospects for light amplification in the far ultraviolet (review)," *Sov. J. Quantum Electron.*, vol. 11, pp. 981–997, 1981.

[11] L. I. Gudzenko and L. A. Shelepin, "Radiation enchancement in a recombining plasma," *Sov. Phys. Doklady*, vol. 10, pp. 147–149, 1965.

[12] L. I. Gudzenko, L. A. Shelepin, and S. I. Yakovlenko, "Amplification in recombining plasmas (plasma lasers)," *Sov. Phys. Usp.*, vol. 17, pp. 848–863, 1975.

[13] F. E. Irons and J. J. Peacock, "Experimental evidence for population inversion in C^{5+} in an expanding laser produced plasmas," *J. Phys. B*, vol. 7, pp. 1109–1112, 1974.

[14] R. H. Dixon and R. C. Elton, "Resonance charge transfer and population inversion following C^{5+} and C^{6+} interaction with carbon atoms in a laser generated plasma," *Phys. Rev. Lett.*, vol. 38, pp. 1072–1075, 1977.

[15] V. A. Bhagavatula and B. Yaakobi, "Direct observation of population inversion between Al^{11+} levels in a laser-produced plasma," *Opt. Commun.*, vol. 24, pp. 331–335, 1978.

[16] R. J. Dewhurst, D. Jacoby, G. J. Pert, and S. A. Ramsden, "Observation of a population inversion in a possible extreme ultraviolet lasing system," *Phys. Rev. Lett.*, vol. 37, pp. 1265–1268, 1976.

[17] D. Jacoby, G. J. Pert, S. A. Ramsden, L. D. Shorrock, and G. J. Tallents, "Observation of gain in a possible extreme ultraviolet lasing system," *Opt. Commun.*, vol. 37, pp. 193–196, 1981.

[18] W. T. Silfvast, L. M. Szeto, and O. R. Wood, II, "Isoelectronic scaling of recombination lasers to higher ion stages and shorter wavelengths," *Appl. Phys. Lett.*, vol. 39, pp. 212–214, 1981.

[19] W. T. Silfvast and O. R. Wood, II, "Recombination lasers in the VUV," in *Laser Technique for Extreme Ultraviolet Spectroscopy*, T. J. McIlrath and R. R. Freeman, Eds. New York: AIP, 1982, pp. 128–136.

[20] G. Jamelot, P. Jaeglé, A. Carillon, A. Bideau, C. Möller, H. Guennou, and A. Sureau, "Evidence of population inversion in Li-like aluminum ions in a laser produced plasma," in *Proc. Int. Conf. Lasers '81*, New Orleans, LA, Dec. 1981, pp. 178–183.

[21] S. Suckewer and H. Fishman, "Conditions for soft X-ray lasing action in a confined plasma column," *J. Appl. Phys.*, vol. 51, pp. 1922–1931, 1980.

[22] R. C. Elton, J. F. Seely, and R. H. Dixon, "Population density and VUV gain measurements in laser-produced plasmas," in *Laser Technique for Extreme Ultraviolet Spectroscopy*, T. J. McIlrath and R. R. Freeman, Eds. New York: AIP, 1982, pp. 277–286.

[23] T. K. Chu and L. C. Johnson, "Measurement of the development and evolution of shock waves in a laser-induced gas breakdown plasma," *Phys. Fluids*, vol. 18, pp. 1460–1466, 1975.

[24] A. L. Hoffman and E. A. Crawford, "Laser heating and ionization of magnetically confined plasmas in the presence of strong UV and X radiation," *J. Appl. Phys.*, vol. 49, pp. 3219–3228, 1978.

[25] W. Halverson, N. G. Loter, W. W. Ma, R. W. Morrison, and C. V. Karmendy, "CO_2 laser irradiation of solid targets in strong magnetic fields," *Appl. Phys. Lett.*, vol. 32, pp. 10–12, 1978.

[26] N. G. Loter, W. Halverson, and B. Lax, "Interaction of CO_2 laser pulses with solid targets in magnetic fields," *J. Appl. Phys.*, vol. 52, pp. 5014–5023, 1981.

[27] J. H. Underwood, "Generation of a parallel X-ray beam and its use for testing collimators," *Space Sci. Instrum.*, vol. 3, pp. 259–270, 1977.

[28] S. Suckewer, L. C. Johnson, K. Sato, A. Semet, C. H. Skinner, and D. Voorhees, "First results from a soft X-ray laser experiment in confined plasma column," Princeton Univ. Plasma Phys. Lab. Rep. PPPL-1896, pp. 1–27, Apr. 1982.

Szymon (Simon) Suckewer received the M.Sc. degree from Moscow University, the Ph.D. degree in 1966 from the Institute of Nuclear Research, Warsaw, and a higher degree–Habilitation–in 1971 from Warsaw University, all in physics.

In 1975 he joined the Plasma Physics Laboratory, Princeton University, Princeton, NJ where he holds the position of Principal Research Physicist and Head of the X-Ray Laser Laboratory. In Moscow he provided VUV spectroscopic measurements on *Z*-pinch. In Warsaw his interest was primarily in developing techniques for temperature and density measurements in low- and high-temperature plasmas, and in theoretical problems related to atomic processes, ionization equilibria, and radiation transport in plasmas. At Princeton his interest is in spectral line identification, development of spectroscopic techniques for plasma parameters, and ion transport measurements in tokamaks. His most recent interest is in the development of the X-ray laser.

Dr. Suckewer is the author of a number of theoretical and experimental publications and several patents. He is a Fellow of the American Physical Society.

Charles H. Skinner was born in Stone, England, on December 19, 1949. He received the B.Sc., A.R.C.S., D.I.C., and Ph.D. degrees from Imperial College, University of London, England.

Since 1974 he has conducted research at Harvard College Observatory, The Joint Institute for Laboratory Astrophysics (University of Colorado); and the Physikalisch-Technische Bundesanstalt-Berlin. Presently, his research interests include soft X-ray laser development and plasma diagnostics at the Plasma Physics Laboratory, Princeton University, Princeton, NJ.

Dr. Skinner is a member of the American Institute of Physics and the British Institute of Physics.

David R. Voorhees was born in Point Pleasant, NJ on June 26, 1951. He received the B.S. degree in physics from Rutgers College, New Brunswick, NJ, in 1973.

In 1974 he joined the cyclotron staff of Medi-Physics Inc., making radioisotopes for nuclear medicines. In 1978 he helped develop a combustion reactor at Aerochem Research Laboratories. Reaction rates for methane and oxygen were conducted over a wide range of temperatures and concentrations. At present, he is an Engineering Associate at the Plasma Physics Laboratory, Princeton University, Princeton, NJ. He is a part of a research team investigating approaches to X-ray lasers.

Mr. Voorhees is a member of the American Physical Society.

Howard M. Milchberg was born in Niagara Falls, NY on April 2, 1957. He received the bachelors degree in engineering physics from McMaster University, Hamilton, Ont., Canada, in 1979.

At Princeton University, Princeton, NJ where he is currently a Ph.D. degree candidate, he has studied the Princeton Large Torus edge plasma and has done calculations relating to recombination radiation. His past activities have included CANDU reactor safety analysis at Atomic Energy of Canada, Ltd. and the study of nuclear shape isomers at the McMaster University Tandem Accelerator.

Mr. Milchberg is a member of the American Physical Society.

Christopher Keane graduated from the University of Rochester, Rochester, NY, in 1980 with the B.S. degree in physics and the B.S. degree in engineering. He is currently a fourth year graduate student at Princeton University, Princeton, NJ where he is doing the Ph.D. degree thesis on short wavelength lasers.

Mr. Keane is a member of the American Physical Society, Tau Beta Pi, and Phi Beta Kappa.

A. Semet, photograph and biography not available at the time of publication.

Reprinted with permission from *Journal of Applied Physics*, Vol. 56(9), pp. 2475-2478 (November 1, 1984). ©1984 American Institute of Physics.

Scaling of collisionally pumped 3*s*-3*p* lasers in the neon isoelectronic sequence

U. Feldman and J. F. Seely
E. O. Hulburt Center for Space Research, Naval Research Laboratory, Washington, DC 20375

A. K. Bhatia
Laboratory for Astronomy and Solar Physics, Goddard Space Flight Center, Greenbelt, Maryland 20771

Population inversions between the 3*p* and 3*s* levels of neonlike ions with atomic numbers $Z = 14$, 18, 22, 26, 32, and 36 have been calculated. The population inversions result from the preferential population of the 3*p* level by electron collisional excitation from the ground configuration of the ion and occur over a wide range of electron temperature and electron density (from 10^{17} cm^{-3} for Si V to 10^{22} cm^{-3} for Kr XXVII). For all ions that are studied, the maximum value of the population inversion $(N_{3p}/g_{3p} - N_{3s}/g_{3s})$ for the transition $3p\ ^1S_0 - 3s\ ^uP_1$ (where *u* represents the upper of the singlet and triplet levels) is found to be approximately equal to $4\times10^{-3} N_I$, where N_I is the total density of neonlike ions. With the exception of Si V, laser gains greater than 1 cm^{-1} are possible for all the ions that are considered, and the gain increases with atomic number *Z*. For Si V and lower-*Z* ions, electron collisional mixing of the upper and lower laser levels restricts the electron density at which the population inversion occurs and limits the laser gain to values less than 1 cm^{-1}. The scaling of the laser gain and the plasma parameters with atomic number *Z* is presented. For an electron density of 10^{21} cm^{-3}, the optimum atomic number *Z* that results in the highest gain on the $3p\ ^1S_0 - 3s\ ^uP_1$ transition is $Z = 26$ (Fe XVII), and the gain is equal to 30 cm^{-1}.

I. INTRODUCTION

For ions in the neon isoelectronic sequence, the rates for electron collisional excitation from the $1s^22s^22p^6$ ground configuration to the $1s^22s^22p^53p$ configuration are greater than the rates for excitation from the ground configuration to the $1s^22s^22p^53s$ configuration (see Fig. 1). The radiative decay of the 3*p* levels to the ground level is forbidden, while the 3*s* levels decay very rapidly to the ground level. For electron densities and electron temperatures that are typical of laboratory high-density plasma sources such as laser-produced plasmas, it is possible to create a quasistationary population inversion between the 3*p* and 3*s* levels. Calculations[1-8] have shown that under favorable conditions large laser gains for neonlike transitions in the VUV and soft x-ray regions of the spectrum can be achieved. Experimental results for Ca XI at a wavelength of 600 Å have been reported.[9]

In this paper, we consider the scaling of the calculated population inversion and the plasma parameters with atomic number *Z*. The electron collision strengths and the radiative decay rates for the neonlike ions with $Z = 14$, 18, 22, 26, 32, and 36 have recently been calculated.[10] Using these atomic data, the rate equations are solved for the populations of the 27 levels belonging to the configurations $1s^22s^22p^6$, $1s^22s^22p^53s$, $1s^22s^22p^53p$, and $1s^22s^22p^53d$. The level populations are calculated as functions of the electron density and the electron temperature, and it is found that population inversions occur for transitions of the type 3*p*-3*s* over a wide range of electron density and temperature. The *Z* scaling of the plasma parameters is determined.

It is found that the highest gain occurs for the transition from the $3p\ ^1S_0$ level to the $3s\ ^1P_1$ level or the $3s\ ^3P_1$ level, whichever is higher in energy from the ground state. This level is designated $^1P_1$ in lower-*Z* ions and $^3P_1$ in higher-*Z* ions. Due to configuration mixing, the designation of this level changes from $^1P_1$ to $^3P_1$ with increasing *Z*. We shall refer to the lower laser level that gives the highest gain as $3s\ ^uP_1$.

II. CALCULATION OF LEVEL POPULATIONS

The computational model has been discussed in detail in Ref. 7. The level populations N_j are calculated by solving the 27 coupled rate equations

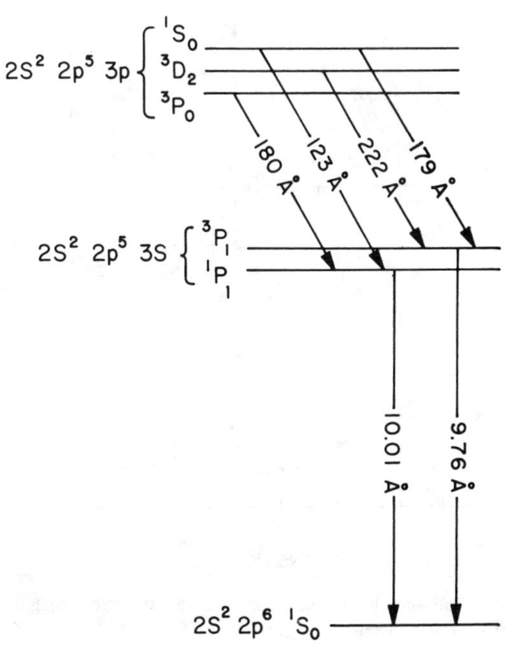

FIG. 1. A schematic diagram of some of the energy levels of Ge XXIII.

$$N_j\left[\sum_{i<j}A_{ji}+n_e\left(\sum_{i<j}C^d_{ji}+\sum_{i>j}C^e_{ji}\right)\right]$$
$$=n_e\left(\sum_{i<j}N_iC^e_{ij}+\sum_{i>j}N_iC^d_{ij}\right)+\sum_{i>j}N_iA_{ij}. \qquad (1)$$

C_{ij} represents the electron collisional rate coefficients and the superscripts e and d refer to excitation and deexcitation. We take into account spontaneous radiative decay and electron collisional processes between all level, but we neglect stimulated emission and photoabsorption processes. The effect of reabsorption of the resonance line radiation is to increase the populations of the $3s$ levels, which tends to reduce the $3p$-$3s$ population inversions, and to increase the populations of the $3d$ levels which decay to the $3p$ levels. This latter effect tends to enhance the population inversions. In the case of Kr XXVII,[7] including the reabsorption of resonance line radiation in the calculation had a small effect on the population inversion. For lower-Z ions, the effect of reabsorption is smaller because the population inversions occur at a much lower density than for Kr XXVII.

The fractional reduced populations $N_j'=N_j/g_jN_I$, where N_j is the level population, g_j is the statistical weight, and N_I is the total density for all levels of the neonlike ion, are presented in Fig. 2 as functions of electron density and at an electron temperature equal to 1/2 the ionization potential. Calculations were also performed at electron temperatures equal to 1/3 and 3/4 the ionization potentials, and it was found that the fractional populations are approximately proportional to the electron temperature. The fractional populations for Fe XVII and Ge XXIII and for the three values of electron temperature (1/3, 1/2, and 3/4 the ionization potential) are presented in Tables I and II.

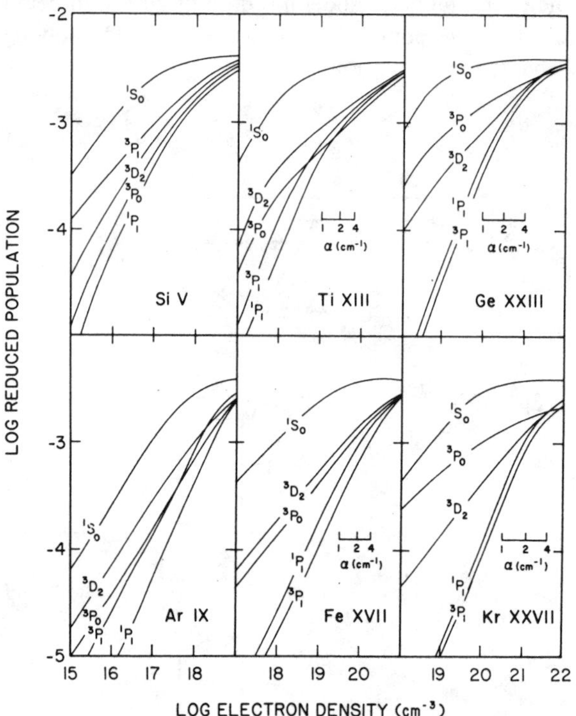

FIG. 2. Calculated fractional level populations per unit statistical weight (N_j/g_jN_I) for Si V (at an electron temperature of 9.6×10^5 K), Ar IX (2.4×10^6 K) Ti XIII (4.5×10^6 K), Fe XVII (7.3×10^6 K), Ge XXIII (1.3×10^7 K), and Kr XXVII (1.7×10^7 K).

TABLE I. Fractional level populations per unit statistical weight (N_j/g_jN_I) for Fe XVII.

Configuration	Term	Electron density (cm^{-3}) 10^{18}	10^{19}	10^{20}
$2s^22p^53s$	$^1P_1$	1.26-5[a]	9.53-5	7.43-4
		1.90-5[b]	1.40-4	1.05-3
		2.36-5[c]	1.69-4	1.22-3
	$^3P_1$	9.57-6	7.97-5	6.27-4
		1.44-5	1.17-4	8.87-4
		1.78-5	1.41-4	1.04-3
$2s^22p^53p$	$^3P_0$	9.60-5	2.16-4	5.68-4
		1.53-4	3.53-4	8.49-4
		2.01-4	4.80-4	1.06-3
	$^3D_2$	9.42-5	3.02-4	8.20-4
		1.49-4	5.02-4	1.26-3
		1.91-4	6.86-4	1.60-3
	$^1S_0$	7.42-4	2.25-3	2.92-3
		1.16-3	3.77-3	4.82-3
		1.48-3	5.19-3	6.64-3

[a] For an electron temperature of 4.9×10^6 K.
[b] For an electron temperature of 7.3×10^6 K.
[c] For an electron temperature of 1.1×10^7 K.

The abundance of the neonlike ionization stage is expected to be highest for an electron temperature near 1/2 the ionization potential. This is consistent with recent observations of spectral lines from the Na I, Ne I, F I, O I, N I, and C I isoelectronic sequences of Zn, Ga, and Ge from a dense laser-produced plasma.[11] We present detailed results for the gain on the $3p$-$3s$ transitions only for an electron temperature equal to 1/2 the ionization potential. We also present detailed results only for those levels that indicate the largest gain.

As shown in Fig. 2, at low electron densities the fractional populations increase as functions of electron density. This is due to the increase in the collisional excitation rates with density. At higher electron densities, where the collisional excitation rates exceed the radiative decay rates, the

TABLE II. Fractional level populations per unit statistical weight (N_j/g_jN_I) for Ge XXIII.

Configuration	Term	Electron density (cm^{-3}) 10^{19}	10^{20}	10^{21}
$2s^22p^53s$	$^1P_1$	1.90-5[a]	1.59-4	1.19-3
		2.80-5[b]	2.23-4	1.63-3
		3.40-5[c]	2.59-4	1.87-3
	$^3P_1$	1.68-5	1.50-4	1.04-3
		2.47-5	2.13-4	1.45-3
		2.99-5	2.49-4	1.68-3
$2s^22p^53p$	$^3P_0$	3.76-4	5.97-4	1.13-3
		6.10-4	9.77-4	1.67-3
		8.13-4	1.33-3	2.08-3
	$^3D_2$	1.60-4	3.98-4	1.20-3
		2.58-4	6.48-4	1.76-3
		3.36-4	8.64-4	2.16-3
	$^1S_0$	1.42-3	2.45-3	2.85-3
		2.29-3	4.12-3	4.51-3
		3.00-3	5.69-3	5.99-3

[a] For an electron temperature of 8.5×10^6 K.
[b] For an electron temperature of 1.3×10^7 K.
[c] For an electron temperature of 1.9×10^7 K.

fractional reduced populations are independent of electron density and are approximately equal (except for a Boltzmann factor of order unity). The population inversion is largest where the electron collisional deexcitation rate for the upper level is comparable to the radiative decay rate for this level. For increasing atomic number Z, the population inversions occur at higher electron densities. As shown in the following section, this is due to the increase in the radiative decay rate with Z and the decrease in the collisional deexcitation rate coefficient with Z. We note in Fig. 2 that the maximum reduced fractional population inversion for the $3p\ ^1S_0$-$3s\ ^1P_1$ and $3p\ ^1S_0 - 3s\ ^3P_1$transitions is approximately equal to 4×10^{-3} for all ions and for an electron temperature equal to 1/2 the ionization potential.

For a Doppler broadened transition, the gain coefficient is

$$\alpha = (\lambda^3 A_{21}/8\pi)(M/2\pi kT_i)^{1/2} g_2(N_2/g_2 - N_1/g_1), \quad (2)$$

where the ion temperature T_i is set equal to the electron temperature. The level population is written

$$N_j = (N_j/N_I)(N_I/N_T)(N_T/n_e)n_e, \quad (3)$$

where N_j/N_I is the fractional level population calculated from Eq. (1), N_I/N_T is the ratio of the density of the neonlike ionization stage to the density of all ionization stages and is set equal to 1/4, and n_e/N_T is set equal to the number of electrons that are removed from the neutral atom to form the neonlike ion.

Combining Eqs. (2) and (3), the gain is a function of the fractional population N_j/N_I, the electron density n_e, and the atomic data. The largest gain occurs for the transition between the $3p\ ^1S_0$ level and the $3s\ ^uP_1$ level, where u represents the singlet or triplet level closer in energy to the $3p\ ^1S_0$ level. The calculated gain for this transition is indicated in Fig. 2.

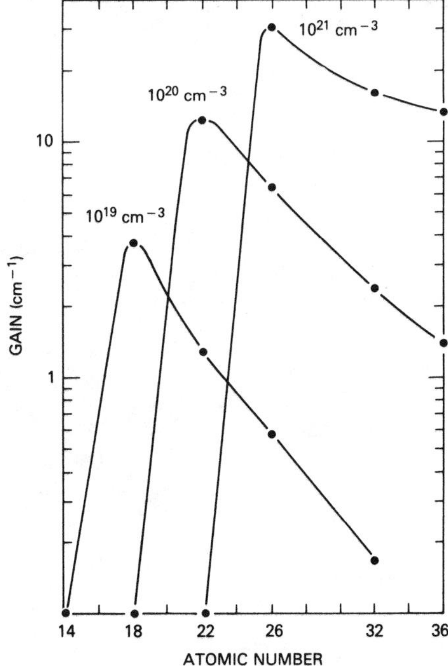

FIG. 3. Calculated gain for the $3p\ ^1S_0$-$3s\ ^uP_1$ transition for fixed values of electron density from 10^{19} to 10^{21} cm^{-3}. The data points are indicated, and a smooth curve has been drawn through the data points.

For Ti XIII, Fe XVII, Ge XXIII, and Kr XXVII, gains from 1 to 30 cm^{-1} are calculated for electron densities in the range 10^{19}–10^{21} cm^{-3}. The collisional mixing of the upper and lower laser levels prevents the gain from reaching higher values, and the maximum possible gain decreases for lower Z. For Ar IX, a gain of about 4 cm^{-1} is possible, while for Si V the gain is limited to values less than 1 cm^{-1}.

Shown in Fig. 3 is the gain for the $3p\ ^1S_0 - 3s\ ^uP_1$ transition as a function of atomic number Z and electron density. For given electron density, there exists an optimum value of atomic number Z that results in the highest gain. For example, at an electron density of 10^{21} cm^{-3}, the optimum ion is Fe XVII.

III. Z-SCALING RELATIONSHIPS

The level populations and gains shown in Figs. 2 and 3 are calculated by solving the 27 coupled rate equations indicated by Eq. (1). In this section, we shall consider the dominant collisional and radiative processes and derive the Z-scaling relationships for the plasma parameters. We are particularly interested in the population inversion between the $3p\ ^1S_0$ and $3s\ ^uP_1$ levels. The collisional and radiative rates for these two levels are listed in Table III, where the level designations are $2p^6\ ^1S_0$ (level 0), $2p^5 3s\ ^uP_1$ (level 1), and $2p^5 3p\ ^1S_0$ (level 2).

Referring to Fig. 2, for low electron densities the fractional populations increase linearly with electron density due to the increase in the collisional excitation rates. The fractional populations are independent of electron density for electron densities higher than the critical density at which the collisional deexcitation rate is comparable to the radiative decay rate. This critical electron density is lower for the $3p\ ^1S_0$ level, which has a higher collisional excitation rate coefficient and a lower radiative decay rate, than for the $3s\ ^uP_1$ level. The population inversion between these two levels reaches the maximum value at an electron density approximately equal to A_{21}/C^d_{21}, where C^d_{21} is the collisional deexcitation rate and A_{21} is the radiative decay rate for the $3p\ ^1S_0$-$3s\ ^uP_1$ transition. The upper and lower levels are collisionally mixed for electron densities exceeding A_{10}/C^d_{21}, where A_{10} is the radiative decay rate for the lower level. The values for A_{21}/C^d_{21} and A_{10}/C^d_{21} are listed in Table III and agree well with the computed results shown in Fig. 2.

TABLE III. Atomic data for the neon isoelectronic sequence.

	Ti XIII	Fe XVII	Ge XXIII
λ_{21} (Å)	328	255	180
A_{21} (sec^{-1})	1.2×10^{10}	1.5×10^{10}	2.0×10^{10}
A_{10} (sec^{-1})	4.3×10^{11}	8.4×10^{11}	2.1×10^{12}
T_e(K)	4.5×10^6	7.3×10^6	1.3×10^7
C^e_{01}(cm^3/sec)	5.0×10^{-12}	2.0×10^{-12}	7.5×10^{-13}
C^e_{02}(cm^3/sec)	8.3×10^{-11}	4.4×10^{-11}	1.9×10^{-11}
C^d_{21}(cm^3/sec)	2.1×10^{-9}	2.1×10^{-9}	1.2×10^{-10}
A_{21}/C^d_{21}(cm^{-3})	5.8×10^{18}	7.2×10^{18}	1.8×10^{19}
A_{10}/C^d_{21}(cm^{-3})	2.0×10^{20}	4.1×10^{20}	1.8×10^{21}
$r(\mu$m)	800	830	480

Since the fractional population inversion reaches the maximum value at an electron density of order A_{21}/C^d_{21} and is small for electron densities much greater than A_{10}/C^d_{21}, the optimum operating range lies between these two values of electron density. These two electron densities are 1×10^{17} and 1×10^{18} cm^{-3} for Si V and 2×10^{20} and 3×10^{22} cm^{-3} for Kr XXVII. Since A_{10} scales more strongly with Z than A_{21} (see Table III), the width of the electron density "window" increases with Z. The gain on the $3p\ ^1S_0$-$3s\ ^uP_1$ transition increases with Z as shown in Fig. 3. The gain increases with Z primarily because the favorable scaling of the electron density is stronger than the unfavorable scaling of the wavelength.

Also listed in Table III is the transverse dimension r, calculated at the electron density A_{21}/C^d_{21}, that results in an optical depth of unity for the $2s^22p^53s\ ^uP_1$-$2s^22p^6\ ^1S_0$ transition. As mentioned in Sec. II, the population inversion depends rather weakly on opacity, and the transverse dimension can in practice be larger than the values listed in Table III.

IV. CONCLUSIONS

Collision-pumped population inversions occur for several transitions in neonlike ions and over a wide range of atomic number Z, electron density, and electron temperature. The largest gain occurs for the $3p\ ^1S_0 - 3s\ ^uP_1$ transition. Due to the collisional mixing of these two levels, the gain is less than 1 cm^{-1} for Si V, but increases with Z and reaches values between 2 and 30 cm^{-1} for the ions Ti XIII through Ge XXIII. For a given value of electron density, there exists an optimum value of atomic number Z which results in the highest gain. For an electron density of 10^{21} cm^{-3}, the optimum ion is Fe XVII and the gain on the $3p\ ^1S_0$-$3s\ ^uP_1$ transition is 30 cm^{-1}.

ACKNOWLEDGMENT

This work was supported by the U. S. Department of Energy.

[1]A. N. Zherikhin, K. N. Koshelev, and V. S. Letokhov, Sov. J. Quantum Electron. **6**, 82 (1976).

[2]A. V. Vinogradov, I. I. Sobelman, and E. A. Yukov, Sov. J. Quantum Electron. **7**, 32 (1977).

[3]L. A. Vainshtein, A. V. Vinogradov, U. I. Safronova, and I. Yu. Skobelev, Sov. J. Quantum Electron. **8**, 239 (1978).

[4]A. V. Vinogradov and V. N. Shlyaptsev, Sov. J. Quantum Electron. **10**, 754 (1980).

[5]P. L. Hagelstein, Ph. D. thesis (Lawrence Livermore National Laboratory Report UCRL-53100, 1981).

[6]G. Dahlback, R. Dukart, R. Fortner, D. Dietrich, and S. Stewart, 1982 IEEE International Conference on Plasma Science, Carleton University, Ottawa, Canada, May 17–19, 1982.

[7]U. Feldman, A. K. Bhatia, and S. Suckewer, J. Appl. Phys. **54**, 2188 (1983).

[8]J. P. Apruzese and J. Davis, Phys. Rev. A **28**, 3686 (1983).

[9]A. A. Ilyukhin, G. V. Peregudov, E. N. Ragozin, I. I. Sobelman, and V. A. Chirkov, Sov. JETP Lett. **25**, 535 (1977).

[10]A. K. Bhatia, U. Feldman, and J. F. Seely, At. Data Nucl. Data Tables (to be published).

[11]W. E. Behring, J. F. Seely, Samuel Goldsmith, Leonard Cohen, M. Richardson, and U. Feldman, J. Opt. Soc. Am. B (to be published).

Reprinted with permission from *Optics Letters,* Vol. 10(3), pp. 122-124 (March 1985).

Stimulated emission in the ultraviolet by optical pumping from photoionization-produced inner-shell states in Cd^+

W. T. Silfvast, O. R. Wood II, H. Lundberg,* and J. J. Macklin

AT&T Bell Laboratories, Holmdel, New Jersey 07733

Stimulated emission on three UV transitions in Cd^+ has been observed by transferring population from inner-shell d-electron states, populated by photoionization, to outer-shell p-electron states using the output from a narrow-frequency dye laser. The use of similar techniques in other elements could eventually result in a number of new lasers in the UV and VUV.

Stimulated emission at 231.2, 257.3, and 274.8 nm in Cd^+ has been observed for the first reported time by transferring population from inner-shell (core-excited) d-electron states, populated by photoionization, to outer-shell p-electron states using the output from a narrow-frequency dye laser tuned to relatively weak core-linking transitions. Gain coefficients as high as 3 cm^{-1} at 274.8 nm have been observed. Population-inversion densities between the $4d^95s^2$ and $4d^{10}5p$ states of Cd^+ greater than 10^{14} cm^{-3} had been previously obtained by broadband soft-x-ray photoionization of Cd vapor with laser-produced plasmas,[1] and similar large population inversions were observed recently in Zn^+.[2] In this Letter we demonstrate that transfer of such populations to higher-lying states by optical pumping with tunable dye lasers can lead to shorter-wavelength lasers. This same pumping technique could also be applied to Hg and Zn as well as to other elements that have a similar inner-shell electronic configuration.

An energy-level diagram for transfer-pumped photoionization lasers in Cd^+ is shown in Fig. 1. The normal Cd^+ levels, identified in Fig. 1 as belonging to the $4d^{10}$ manifold,[3] involve a closed $4d^{10}$ subshell and a single outer electron. The core-excited Cd^+ levels, identified in Fig. 1 as belonging to the $4d^9$ manifold,[3] involve a partially filled d subshell and a closed $5s^2$ subshell. Optical coupling between these two manifolds is generally weak (e.g., the oscillator strength of the $4d^95s^2\ ^2D$–$4d^{10}5p\ ^2P^o$ laser transition at 441.6 nm is about 0.005)[4] because most transitions involve a change of two electrons. The population inversions reported in this Letter are the result of two steps of narrow-frequency optical transfer. The first step involved the transfer of population from inner-shell $4d^95s^2\ ^2D$ states to higher-lying core-filled $4d^{10}6p\ ^2P^o$ states using a dye laser that provided intensities well above the estimated saturation intensities (10–100 W/cm^2) for the core-linking transitions. When the dye laser was present, the transfer rate out far exceeded the photoionization rate in, thus precluding large population buildup in the $4d^9\ 5s^2$ level. The core-linking $4d^{10}6p\ ^2P_{3/2}$–$4d^95s^2\ ^2D_{5/2}$ transition at 382.6 nm had been observed previously in emission[5]; however, the core-linking $4d^{10}6p\ ^2P_{1/2}$–$4d^95s^2\ ^2D_{3/2}$ transition at 504.4 nm is so weak that it had not previously been reported in the spectroscopic literature. The second optical-pumping step involved the transfer of population from these $4d^{10}6p\ ^2P^o$ states to lower-lying $4d^{10}6s\ ^2S$ and $5d\ ^2D$ states by amplified spontaneous emission (ASE) produced within the pumping volume at 806.7, 853.0, and 2000 nm. This resulted in a population inversion between $4d^{10}6s\ ^2S$ and $5d\ ^2D$ states, which serve as the upper-laser levels for the ultraviolet lasers, and the lower-lying $5p\ ^2P^o$ states.

The experimental arrangement used to demonstrate stimulated emission in the UV by transfer pumping from inner-shell states in Cd^+ is similar to that used to produce soft-x-ray-pumped Li^+ metastable states[6] and to obtain photoionization lasers in Cd (Ref. 1) and Zn.[2] A 2.5-cm-diameter heat pipe in the form of a cross provided Cd vapor at pressures from 1 to 10 Torr. A 200-mJ, 10-nsec pulse from a Nd:YAG laser, focused

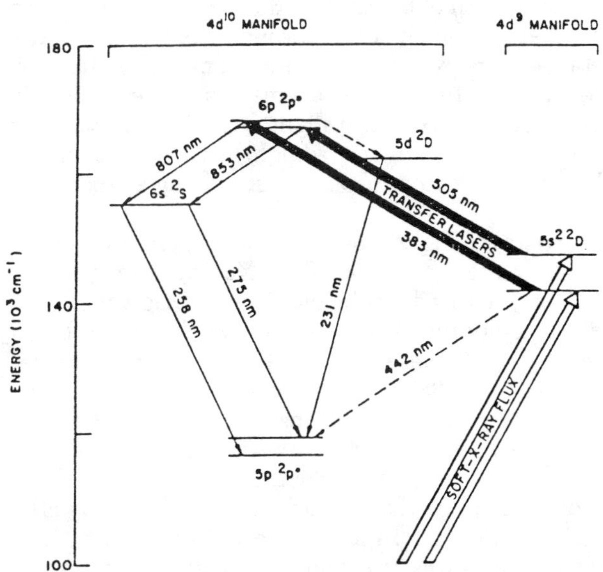

Fig. 1. Energy-level diagram for transfer-pumped Cd photoionization lasers.

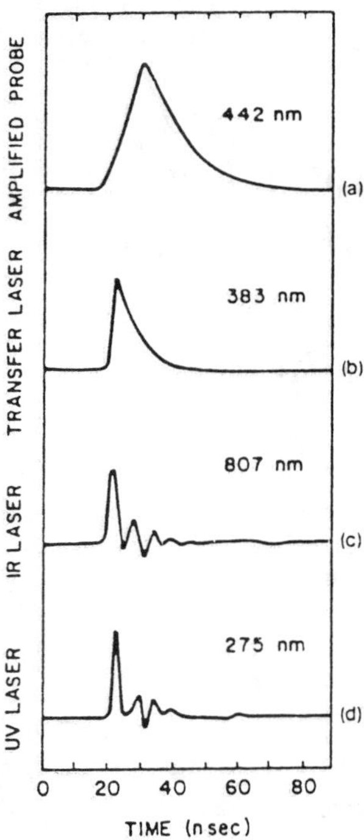

Fig. 2. Time dependence of (a) amplified cw probe laser at 441.6 nm, (b) dye laser used for transfer at 382.7 nm, (c) ASE at 806.7 nm, and (d) stimulated emission at 274.8 nm.

with a 25-cm focal-length lens through one arm of the cross to a 0.1-mm-diameter spot onto a W target inside the heat pipe, created a source of soft x rays at the target surface having an approximate 15-eV blackbody distribution. The resulting population in the core-excited inner d-electron states was monitored by passing a beam from a cw He–Cd probe laser, operating on the $4d^9 5s^2\ ^2D$–$4d^{10}5p\ ^2P$ transition at 441.6 nm, through the Cd vapor near the soft-x-ray source. Transfer of population from the $4d^9 5s^2$ states was accomplished by passing the unfocused output (beam diameter ~ 1 mm) from a dye laser that provided 1–10-mJ, 5-nsec pulses in a bandwidth of 0.3 cm^{-1} at 382.7 or 504.4 nm down the other axis of the cross through the Cd vapor at a distance approximately 5 mm from the soft-x-ray source. The resulting UV emission pulses from Cd vapor were observed at a slight angle to the dye-laser beam (to minimize scattered light) with a photomultiplier and oscilloscope arrangement having a 2-nsec rise time.

Curve (a) of Fig. 2 shows the time dependence of the small-signal gain on the $4d^9 5s^2$–$4d^{10}5p$ transition at 441.6 nm produced by photoionizing the Cd vapor with the soft-x-ray flux as measured with the probe beam from the He–Cd laser. Curve (b) shows the time dependence of the 382.7-nm dye-laser output used for the first transfer step. The transfer pulse from the dye laser was timed to occur early with respect to the soft-x-ray photoionizing pulse from the Nd:YAG laser. This was done to ensure that as much of the population in the $5s^2$ state as possible was transferred up to $6p$ rather than leaking downward to $5p$ by ASE at 441.6 nm since this process could reduce or destroy an inversion from $6s$ or $5d$. Curve (c) shows the temporal behavior of the resulting stimulated emission pulse at 806.7 nm observed in the forward direction (stimulated emission at 806.7 nm exhibited a 20 to 1 forward/backward intensity asymmetry) when the dye laser was tuned to 382.7 ± 0.3 nm. Curve (d) shows the temporal behavior of the emission at 274.8 nm when both steps of optical pumping were at maximum intensity. Increases in intensity of up to 2000 were observed on this transition when the transfer laser was present. The trace shown in curve (d) is typical of the emission observed at all three UV wavelengths. The duration of the stimulated-emission pulses at both wavelengths [curves (c) and (d)] is seen to be significantly shorter than the duration of the inversion between the $5s^2$ and $5p$ states [curve (a)]. In fact, when a detection system with a 300-psec rise time was used, the observed duration of the strong stimulated-emission pulse at 806.7 nm was found to be of the order of 400 psec. Thus the pulse ringing shown in curves (c) and (d) is an artifact of the detection circuit and is probably due to a relaxation oscillation of the detector when it is subjected to such short optical pulses.

Figure 3(a) is a plot of the infrared-emission intensity at 853.0 nm as a function of the 504.4-nm transfer laser intensity. Before the onset of stimulated emission, the emission at 853.0 nm increases linearly with transfer laser intensity. At this point [indicated by the arrow in Fig. 3(a)] the emission grows nonlinearly by 3 orders of magnitude and then resumes a saturated growth with increasing transfer laser intensity. The 1000-fold increase in intensity corresponds to a gain coefficient of a least 6.9 cm^{-1} at 853.0 nm. Figure 3(b) is a plot of the UV emission at 274.8 nm versus the intensity of the stimulated emission pulse at 806.7 nm that populates the upper laser level. Because the timing of the 806.7-nm pulse and the dye-laser pulse at 382.7 nm could not be independently adjusted, the emission at 274.8 could not be optimized. Even so, when taken together, the observed pulse shape [curve (d) of Fig. 2] and the nonlinear dependence of the UV emission intensity on the pumping intensity [Fig. 3(b)] are strong evidence that gain resulting from stimulated emission is present at 274.8 nm. The magnitude of the nonlinear growth of the emission shown in Fig. 3(b) corresponds to a gain coefficient at 274.8 nm as high as 2–3 cm^{-1}

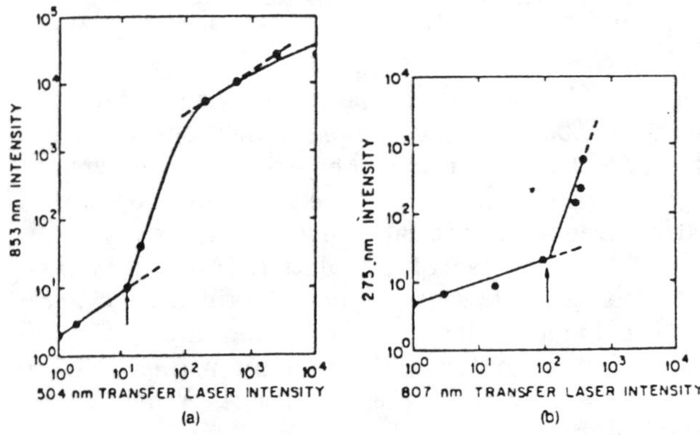

Fig. 3. Emission at (a) 853.0 nm as a function of 504.4-nm transfer laser intensity and (b) 274.8 nm as a function of 806.7-nm ASE intensity.

(similar values for gain were found at 257.8 and 231.2 nm). In addition, the emission at all three UV wavelengths exhibited the large intensity fluctuations that would be expected from stimulated emission with small fluctuations in the gain.

The 20-times-higher intensity of the 806.7-nm pulse in the direction of the 382.7-nm transfer laser than in the opposite direction could be explained either by ASE, through traveling-wave excitation, or by stimulated Raman emission, which can result in an asymmetric gain profile with respect to pump direction.[7] It is difficult to distinguish between these two effects when the pumping laser is at or near resonance.

In order to determine if the experimental results were consistent with ASE, a four-level rate-equation model was developed to predict the temporal behavior of the emission at 806.7 and 274.8 nm in response to a transfer laser beam at 382.7 nm. Values for the spontaneous-emission rates for the four levels (the $5p$, $5s^2$, $6s$, and $6p$ levels of Cd^+) were taken from the literature. Collisional rates were assumed to be small compared with spontaneous rates. Transition linewidths were taken equal to the Doppler widths except for transitions for which power broadening by the high-intensity transfer laser was large. The initial population in the $5s^2$ level was taken from a gain measurement at 441.6 nm. The initial population in the $5p$ level was determined from an absorption measurement at 274.8 nm. The initial populations in the other two levels were estimated from relative intensity measurements. The length of the medium was taken to be 1 cm (the gain length for the 441.6-nm photoionization laser).

According to this simple model, emission at 806.7 nm (and 274.8 nm) begins to grow nonlinearly if and only if the 382.7-nm dye laser transfers enough population from $5s^2$ to $6p$ to create a population inversion between $6p$ and $6s$. Because the stimulated-emission cross section on the $6p$–$6s$ transition is high (2×10^{-11} cm^2), when the transfer laser intensity at 382.7 nm is sufficiently high the small-signal gain on the $6p$–$6s$ transition at 806.7 nm rises rapidly. This rapidly rising gain results in an emission pulse at 806.7 nm that peaks 0.4 nsec after the start of the 382.7-nm dye-laser pulse and that consists of a 3-kW/cm^2 peak-power pulse of 200-psec duration followed by a 150-W/cm^2 tail lasting for several nanoseconds. The amplitude, duration, and timing of this pulse are consistent with the observations at 806.7 nm. The 20-to-1 forward/backward amplitude asymmetry could be accounted for by including the effects of swept gain in the model. The model predicts that the emission at 274.8 nm should rise 10 to 20 times above the spontaneous-emission level for fractions of a nanosecond and that it should be slightly delayed with respect to the 806.7-nm pulse. No sharp pulsing was indicated in the model in the absence of gain. The short duration of the gain, together with the length of the heat pipe, prevented the use of resonator mirrors.

The generation of the new VUV lasers may be possible in Cd^+ by using two-step transfer techniques. For example, in a process identical with that described above, population could be transferred from the inner-shell $4d^95s^2\,{}^2D$ state to the $4d^{10}7p\,{}^2P^\circ$ state by using a dye laser tuned to 266.8 nm, leading to ASE at 4571.3 nm and stimulated emission at 151.4 nm. Alternatively, a two-step process to reach the $4d^{10}6d$ state through an intermediate $4d^{10}6p$ state using dye lasers tuned to 382.7 and 673.0 nm could lead to stimulated emission at 157.2 nm.

The authors gratefully acknowledge helpful discussions with E. P. Ippen, R. W. Falcone, B. Wellegehausen, and R. G. Caro.

* Present address, Lund Institute of Technology, Lund, Sweden.

References

1. W. T. Silfvast, J. J. Macklin, and O. R. Wood II, Opt. Lett. **8**, 551 (1983).
2. H. Lundberg, J. J. Macklin, W. T. Silfvast, and O. R. Wood II, Appl. Phys. Lett. **45**, 335 (1984).
3. C. E. Moore, *Atomic Energy Levels* (U.S. Government Printing Office, Washington, D.C., 1958), Vol. III, p. 59.
4. Y. F. Verolainen and V. I. Privalov, Opt. Spectrosc. 48, 245 (1980).
5. A. G. Shenstone and J. T. Pittenger, J. Opt. Soc. Am. **39**, 219 (1949).
6. R. G. Caro, J. C. Wang, R. W. Falcone, J. R. Young, and S. E. Harris, Appl. Phys. Lett. **42**, 9 (1983).
7. N. Skribanowitz, M. Feld, R. E. Francke, M. J. Kelly, and A. Javan, Appl. Phys. Lett. **19**, 161 (1971).

Reprinted with permission from *Physical Review Letters,* Vol. 54(2), pp. 110-113 (January 14, 1985). ©1985 American Physical Society.

Demonstration of a Soft X-Ray Amplifier

D. L. Matthews, P. L. Hagelstein, M. D. Rosen, M. J. Eckart, N. M. Ceglio, A. U. Hazi, H. Medecki, B. J. MacGowan,[a] J. E. Trebes, B. L. Whitten, E. M. Campbell, C. W. Hatcher, A. M. Hawryluk, R. L. Kauffman, L. D. Pleasance, G. Rambach, J. H. Scofield, G. Stone, and T. A. Weaver

Lawrence Livermore National Laboratory, University of California, Livermore, California 94550

(Received 26 October 1984)

We report observations of amplified spontaneous emission at soft x-ray wavelengths. An optical laser ionized thin foils of selenium to produce a population inversion of the $2p^5 3p$ and $2p^5 3s$ levels of the neonlike ion. Using three time-resolved, spectroscopic measurements we demonstrated gain-length products up to 6.5 and gain coefficients of 5.5 ± 1.0 cm^{-1} for the $J=2$ to 1 lines at 206.3 and 209.6 Å. We also observed considerable amplification for the same transitions in yttrium at 155.0 and 157.1 Å.

For over a decade there has been an intense search for a way to produce amplification of XUV or soft x-ray radiation. Several recent papers[1,2] review the progress of the theoretical and experimental efforts. In general, the literature lacks a conclusive or unrefuted demonstration of such amplification.

One of the proposed methods of producing an XUV amplifier uses a high-power optical laser to directly heat a plasma. Using this technique, Zherikhin, Koshelev, and Letokhov[3] first described a mechanism for obtaining an inversion between $2p^5 3p$ and $2p^5 3s$ levels in neonlike ions. Vinagradov and co-workers[4] have subsequently written a series of papers refining the theoretical description. To produce the inversion, the $n=3$ excited levels are populated by electron impact excitation from the ground ($2p^6$) state of the neonlike ion, which is itself produced in the plasma heated by the optical laser. The population inversion between $2p^5 3p$ and $2p^5 3s$ levels develops because of the large difference between the radiative decay rates. Recent calculations[5-9] have extended this neonlike excitation scheme to ions in which the lasing wavelengths approach the soft x-ray regime.

The purpose of this Letter is to report the first results from new experiments on the neonlike collisional excitation scheme. We describe the first conclusive demonstration of a macroscopic-sized gain medium which exhibits substantial amplification of at least four $2p^5 3p$-$2p^5 3s$ transitions in selenium, with the largest being observed for the $J=2$ to 1 lines at 206.3 and 209.6 Å. The transition with the largest predicted gain,[4-9] the $J=0$ to 1 transition at approximately 183 Å, has not been uniquely identified. We base our conclusions on the results of over 100 separate laser-irradiated target experiments. We used a variety of spectroscopic instruments to measure the time-resolved absolute brightness of the amplified spontaneous emission (ASE), and to demonstrate the nonlinear increase of the emission with increased length of the gain medium. The anisotropy of the ASE was also verified by measurement of the relative intensity in the axial direction and in another direction far off that axis.

These x-ray laser experiments were conducted at the Novette laser-target irradiation facility. A simplified schematic representation of the experimental arrangement is shown in Fig. 1. The exploding-foil target design[10] is based on experience with long density-scale–length plasmas that are produced in inertial-confinement fusion research. Typically, the target was composed of a 750-Å layer of Se, vapor deposited on *one* side of a 1500-Å-thick Formvar substrate. The foil was nominally 1.1 cm long and was illuminated by green light ($\lambda = 0.532$ μm) along a line focus with dimensions of 0.02×1.12 cm. The nominal pulse length was 450 psec, and the typical incident intensity was 5×10^{13} W/cm^2. The targets were irradiated in two different geometries: "single-sided" in which a given segment of the foil was hit by only one laser beam, and "double-sided" in which opposing laser beams irradiated a common target area. Using the single-sided geometry we were able to illuminate targets up to 2.2-cm long by displacing the two beams axially.

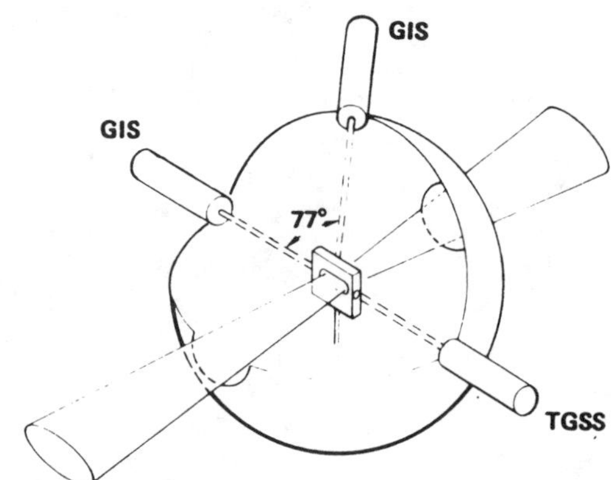

FIG. 1. Placement of primary diagnostics used in this experiment.

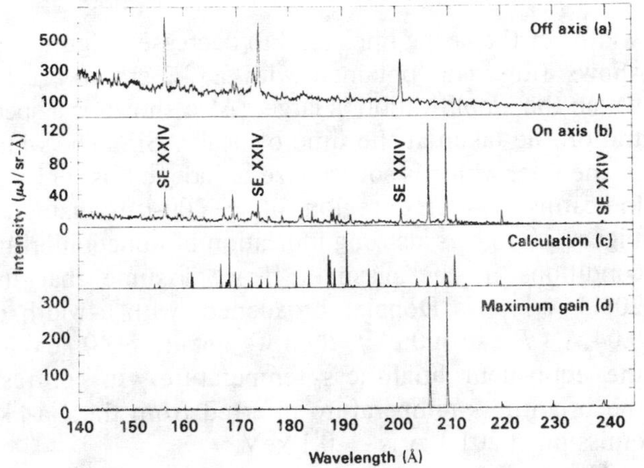

FIG. 2. (a) Grazing incidence spectrograph (GIS) data from off-axis line of sight. Data taken from beginning of radiative output until 500 psec after peak of pump laser. (b) On-axis GIS data from same time interval as (a). (c) Calculated spontaneous spectrum of neonlike selenium. (d) On-axis GIS data from maximum gain target.

X-ray emission in the two axial directions (see Fig. 1) was measured by use of a grazing incidence spectrograph (GIS) and a transmission grating spectrograph (TGSS). The GIS has high spectral resolution ($\lambda/d\lambda = 1800$) and a line-radiation-detection threshold of 6 erg/sr. It utilizes a microchannel plate contoured to the Rowland circle for detection of the x-ray spectra. Gating the microchannel plate detector by an Auston switch allowed viewing of the spectrum for a limited period of time (250–750 psec), thereby discriminating against emission occurring late in the experiment. The TGSS has a spectral resolution of $\lambda/d\lambda = 200$, detection threshold of 3.9 mW/Å (radiated into a solid angle of $\sim 1.1\times10^{-4}$ sr), and temporal resolution of 20–30 psec. The instrument incorporates an ellipsoidal collection optic, a 2000-Å period transmission grating, and a soft x-ray streak camera. In addition to the emission along the target's longitudinal axis, we recorded the spectrum at 77° off axis using another GIS which viewed the entire target.

In the course of the experiments we measured strong anisotropy of certain lines emitted from the exploding foils. Figures 2(a) and 2(b) illustrate spectral data monitored by the two GIS in the same time segment. Note the presence of Na-like resonance transitions (not expected to be amplified) both on and off axis, whereas the strong lines at 206.3 and 209.6 Å are *only* seen on axis. Based on *ab initio* calculations and isoelectronic extrapolation[11] from lower Z, these lines are positively identified as the $(2p_{3/2}3p_{3/2})_{J=2}$-$(2p_{3/2}3s)_{J=1}$ and $(2p_{1/2}3p_{3/2})_{J=2}$-$(2p_{1/2}3s)_{J=1}$ transitions of Ne-like Se, respectively. With the exception of the $3d_{3/2}$-$3p_{3/2}$ transition at 178.6 Å, the Na-like lines are optically thick and appear brighter off axis because the GIS views a larger surface area of the plasma in that direction.

In Fig. 2(c) we plot a theoretical *spontaneous*-emission spectrum of Ne-like transitions calculated under the assumption of an optically thin plasma in steady state at $T_e = 1.0$ keV and $N_e = 1\times10^{21}$ cm^{-3}. In the experimental spectra, the 206.3- and 209.6-Å lines

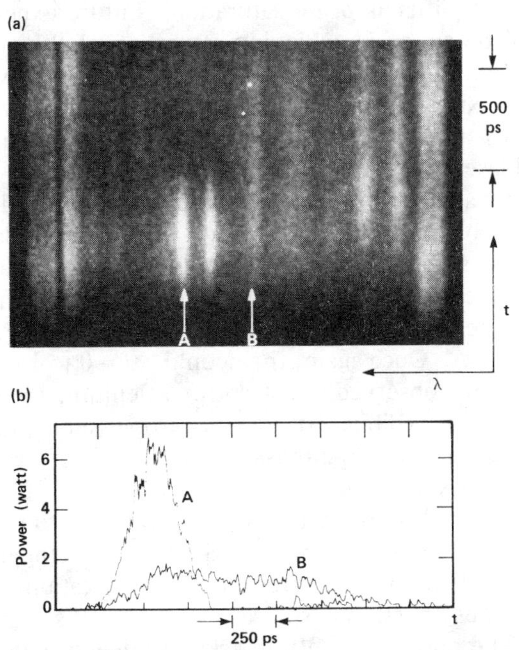

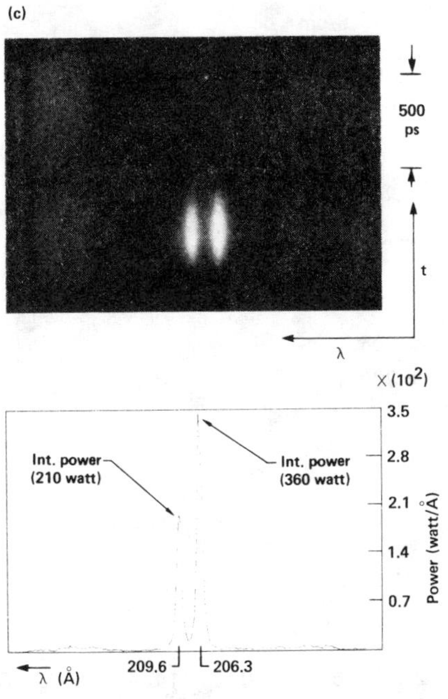

FIG. 3. (a) Film data from the TGSS for a moderate gain target. (b) Temporal profiles of the neonlike 209.6-Å lasing line (A) and the Na-like 201.1-Å line (B). (c) Film data from TGSS for a maximum gain target, and power vs wavelength.

are much stronger than all of the other nonlasing neonlike transitions which have larger gf values, e.g., the $2p^5 3d$-$2p^5 3p$ lines at 191.5, 188.4, and 169.2 Å (see Ref. 11). The dominance of the two $J=2$ to 1 lines in the spectrum was observed in approximately 100 laser shots.

Figure 2(d) illustrates the maximum amplification we obtained in these experiments. In this case the target was shot single sided at an incident intensity of 1×10^{14} W/cm^2, but with the beams displaced to give a total amplification length of 2.2 cm. It is important to note that we do not observe a strong line near 183 Å, the predicted position of the transition with the largest calculated[4-9] gain $[(2p_{1/2}3p_{1/2})_{J=0}$-$(2p_{1/2}3s)_{J=1}]$. If there were little or no amplification of this transition, it could not be seen because of its small gf value.[5,8,11]

Figure 3 illustrates the temporal behavior of the emission as recorded by the TGSS. Figure 3(a) shows film data obtained with a 1.0-cm target displaying moderate amplification. In Fig. 3(b) the temporal profile of the amplified line at 209.6 Å is compared with that of the spontaneous emission of the Na-like ion at 201.1 Å. Note that the time duration of the amplified emission is significantly shorter than that of the nearby spontaneous lines as well as the pulse width of the pump laser. With increased amplification, the pulse

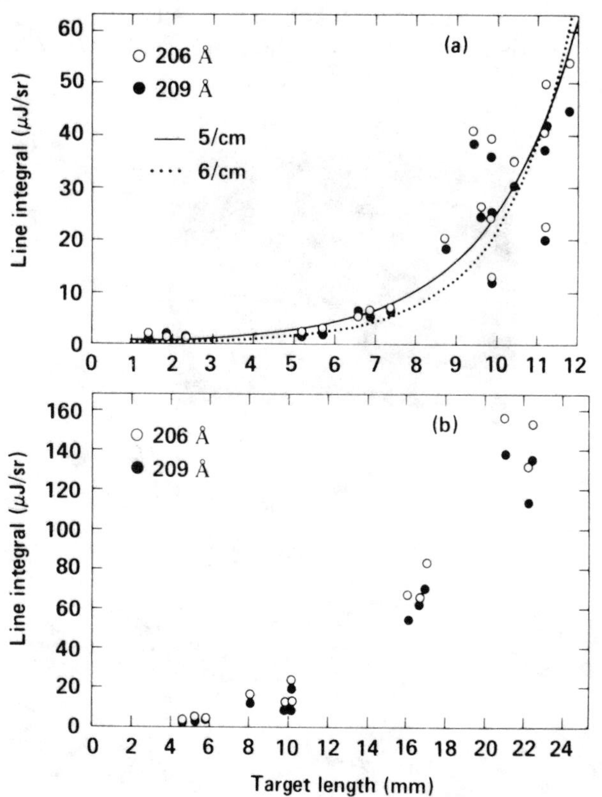

FIG. 4. Integrated line intensity of $J=2$ to 1 transitions vs amplifier length for (a) double-sided and (b) single-sided laser irradiation conditions.

widths of the lasing lines tend to decrease. Figure 3(c) shows film data obtained with a 2.2-cm target for which the amplification is large. Also shown is a spectral profile taken at the time of peak ASE. The width of the line, which is source-size broadened, is ~1.0 Å indicating a source region of ~200-μm diameter. Figure 3(c) gives a strong indication of nonequilibrium conditions in the plasma. If we assume that the 206.3-Å line is Doppler broadened, with a width of 0.04 Å ($T_{ion}\simeq 400$ eV), then we obtain ~40 keV for the equivalent brightness temperature. In contrast, the brightness temperature inferred from the Na-like emission at 201.1 Å is ~0.1 keV.

The most quantitative evidence for amplification is shown in Fig. 4. These results come from the axial GIS and are integrated over the linewidths of the 206.3- and 209.6-Å transitions. The data exhibit a nonlinear dependence on the length of the amplifier. The output intensity (integrated over frequency) emitted by a one-dimensional homogeneous gain medium of length L under steady-state conditions scales as $\exp(\alpha L)L^{-1/2}$, where α is the line-center gain coefficient. This scaling is valid when $\alpha L \gtrsim 2$. Fitting the data from double-sided shots with this expression yields a gain coefficient of $\alpha = 5.5 \pm 1.0$ cm^{-1} for both the 206.3- and 209.6-Å lines. Although the data obtained with single-sided irradiation demonstrates significant amplification, up to 700 times spontaneous levels, the complexity of both the target irradiation geometry and the radiation transport preclude simple modeling of the length dependence. Note also that the behavior of the data as a function of length indicates the amplifier is *below* saturation. Future experiments will be aimed at achieving saturation of the amplifier and improving the efficiency from the present value of approximately 10^{-10}. (Efficiency is the energy radiated by the lasing transition divided by the incident optical laser energy.)

In addition to the measurements described above, we have done preliminary experiments to produce amplification at shorter wavelengths. In particular, we irradiated yttrium foil targets and observed amplification of the $J=2$ to 1 neonlike transitions at 155.0 and 157.1 Å. Once again, the neonlike $J=0$ to 1 transition was not observed. Just as for selenium, the yttrium emission exhibited strong anisotropy, short time duration, and a brightness temperature of ~5 keV (155.0-Å line).

In conclusion, by using an optical laser to produce a population inversion in a simple exploding foil, we have demonstrated substantial amplification of spontaneous emission at soft x-ray wavelengths.

The authors gratefully acknowledge specific contributions from T. Barbee, B. Boyd, D. Christie, D. Dietrich, M. Gerassimenko, G. Heaton, S. Hildum, G. Howe, K. Manes, D. Nilson, G. Power, L. Seppala,

R. Stewart, S. Stribling, J. Tassano, A. Toor, J. Trenholme, G. Vayer, and J. Wiedwald. This work was performed under the auspices of the U. S. Department of Energy by the Lawrence Livermore National Laboratory under Contract No. W-7405-ENG-48.

[(a)]Permanent address: Blackett Laboratory, Imperial College, London, SW7 2AZ, England.

[1]R. C. Elton, in *Advances in X-Ray Analysis, Vol. 21,* edited by C. S. Barrett, D. E. Leyden, J. B. Newkirk, and C. O. Ruud (Plenum, New York, 1978), p. 1.

[2]F. V. Bunkin, V. I. Derzhiev, and S. I. Yakovlenko, Kvant. Elektron. (Moscow) **8**, 1621 (1981) [Sov. J. Quantum Electron. **11**, 981 (1981)].

[3]A. Zherikhin, K. Koshelev, and V. Letokhov, Sov. J. Quant. Mech. **6**, 82 (1976).

[4]A. V. Vinagradov and V. Shlyaptsev, Kvatn. Elektron. (Moscow) **10**, 2325 (1983) [Sov. J. Quantum Electron. **13**, 1511 (1983).

[5]U. Feldman, A. Bhatia, and S. Suckewer, J. Appl. Phys. **54**, 2188 (1983); U. Feldman, J. F. Seely, and A. K. Bhatia, J. Appl. Phys. **56**, 2475 (1984).

[6]J. P. Apruzese and J. Davis, Phys. Rev. A **28**, 3686 (1983).

[7]G. Dahlbacka, R. Dukart, R. Fortner, D. Dietrich, and R. Stewart, in *Proceedings of the IEEE International Conference on Plasma Science, Ottawa, Canada, 18–22 May 1982* (IEEE, New York, 1982), p. 39.

[8]R. Stewart, Ph.D. thesis, University of California, 1984 (unpublished).

[9]P. Hagelstein, Plasma Phys. **25**, 1345 (1983).

[10]M. D. Rosen *et al.*, preceding Letter [Phys. Rev. Lett. **54**, 106 (1985)].

[11]M. Eckart, J. Scofield, and A. Hazi, private communication.

Reprinted with permission from *Physical Review Letters,* Vol. 54(2), pp. 106-109 (January 14, 1985).

Exploding-Foil Technique for Achieving a Soft X-Ray Laser

M. D. Rosen, P. L. Hagelstein, D. L. Matthews, E. M. Campbell, A. U. Hazi, B. L. Whitten, B. MacGowan,[a] R. E. Turner, and R. W. Lee
Lawrence Livermore National Laboratory, University of California, Livermore, California 94550

and

G. Charatis, Gar. E. Busch, C. L. Shepard, and P. D. Rockett
KMS Fusion, Inc., Ann Arbor, Michigan 48106
(Received 26 October 1984)

We describe a design for producing a soft x-ray laser via $3p$-$3s$ transitions in Ne-like selenium (wavelength of about 200 Å). A 0.53-μm laser, focused in a 1.2×0.02-cm spot to $\sim 5\times 10^{13}$ W/cm^2, heats and burns through a thin foil of Se. Besides ionizing the Se to a Ne-like state, the laser explodes the foil, creating a region of uniform electron density. This allows propagation of the x rays down the 1-cm-long gain direction without debilitating refraction. Gains of 4 to 10 cm^{-1} are predicted for various transitions.

For ions in the neon isoelectronic sequence, the rates for electron collisional excitation from the $1s^22s^22p^6$ ground-state configuration to $1s^22s^22p^53p$ are greater than the rates for excitation from the ground state to $1s^22s^22p^53s$. Whereas the $2p^53p$ $J=0$ levels are populated by direct monopole excitation from the ground state, other $2p^53p$ levels such as $J=2$ are fed primarily by cascades from upper levels and recombination from F-like ions. Dipole radiative decay of the $2p^53p$ levels to the ground state is forbidden, while the $2p^53s$ $J=1$ levels radiatively decay very rapidly, leading to population inversion between the $3p$ and $3s$ levels. (See Fig. 1.) For electron densities and temperatures that are typical of laboratory laser-produced plasmas, calculations[1-6] have shown that under favorable conditions large soft x-ray laser gains and amplification can be achieved.

From theoretical considerations,[5] the most promising elements in which to implement this laser-driven electron-collisional-excitation scheme, occur near $Z=36$. Therefore solid Se ($Z=34$) was chosen as a candidate material. Elements much lower in Z tend to overionize, and those with higher Z have lower excitation rates for $n=2$ to $n=3$ transitions. Reference 5 describes the predicted high gains at 183 Å $[(2p^5_{1/2}3p_{1/2})_{J=0}$ to $(2p^5_{1/2}3s_{1/2})_{J=1}]$ when 0.53 μm light, line focused at an intensity of 10^{14} W/cm^2, illuminates solid Se. In that approach, the high-gain region occurs along the steep density gradient caused by the laser-heated blowoff from the Se surface. The lack of an observed signal in previous experiments[7] was attributed[5] to refraction (due to the steep gradient) which bends the x-rays out of the high-gain region (thus preventing significant amplification) and out of the line of sight of the diagnostic instruments.

In this paper we present a technique designed to minimize the refraction problem while still producing plasma conditions suitable for lasing. The target is a thin Se foil, typically 750 Å deposited on 1500 Å of Formvar (polyvinyl formal, $C_{11}H_{18}O_5$) for structural integrity. The 0.53-μm laser is focused by a cylindrical lens to a 1.2-cm-long by 0.02-cm-wide region of the foil. The foil explodes as the laser burns through it, creating a rather uniform electron density in the plasma that has expanded into a roughly cylindrical shape. The uniformity allows the x-ray laser beam to proceed straight down the long line focus direction, stay within the region of high gain, and propagate into the narrow angle of acceptance of the diagnostics. Exploding foils have previously been used[8] to create large-scale-length plasmas to study laser-driven parametric instabilities.

There are two main tools employed in the design of the foils. The two-dimensional (2D) code LASNEX[9] simulates the laser-foil interaction, including absorption, burnthrough, and hydrodynamic motion. It has been exercised with great success in dealing with other high-Z, non–local-thermodynamic-equilibrium laser-created plasmas.[10] Quantities such as the time-evolving electron and ion temperatures, densities, and flow fields are then fed into the 2D x-ray-laser code XRASER.[5] XRASER uses this input (along with detailed atomic data computed off-line) to calculate level populations and gain as a function of space and time. The atomic model includes in detail all the singly excited states of the Ne-like and Na-like ions with $n=3$ and 4 and F-like ions with $n=2$ and 3. Simpler models were used for the other sequences and levels. For the $n=2$ to 3,4 transitions, collisional excitation cross sections were computed by use of a multiconfiguration, relativistic, distorted-wave code.[11] Line transfer is computed in 1D and 2D including the effects of partial redistributions and bulk Doppler shifts, with use of a modified S_n (ray) algorithm with a linearized convergence scheme for an equivalent two-level atom. In

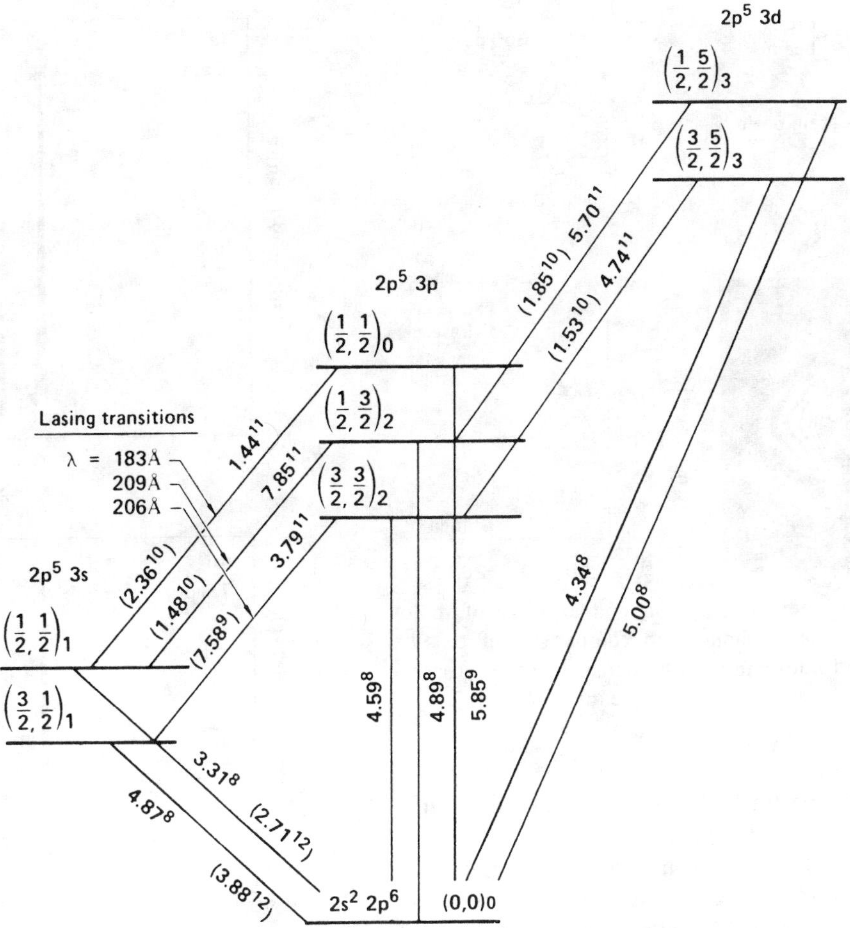

FIG. 1. Simplified energy-level diagram $[(j_1,j_2)_J$ notation] for Ne-like Se. (Hundreds of levels are included in the calculations.) Collisional excitation rates and radiative decay rates (in parentheses) for $n_e = 5\times10^{20}$ cm^{-3} and $T_e = 1$ keV are shown.

particular, trapping between the ground state and the 3*s* and 3*d* levels are included, as they can affect the predicted gain to a moderate degree. A postprocessor SPECTRE produces a predicted spectrum for any particular line of sight, including (in 1D) refraction effects, to facilitate direct comparison with experimental data.

The design goal is to produce a flat electron density (n_e) and temperature profile, with scale length L of at least 100 μm, to last at least 100 ps, with high enough n_e ($\sim 5\times10^{20}$ cm^{-3}) for appreciable density of neon-like ions and gain. These numbers are motivated by simple considerations. For a linear density gradient, $n_e = n_0[1-(y/L)]$, an x-ray propagating in the x direction has a trajectory $y = x^2 d/4L$, where $d = \omega_{p0}^2/\omega^2 = 1/2500$ for $n_0 = 10^{21}$ cm^{-3} and a 50-eV x ray. For a typical 10-mrad divergence and acceptance angle of the spectrograph, and an $x = 1$-cm line focus, $y = 0.01$ cm, which leads to the $L = 0.01$-cm requirement. The transit time for the x-rays down the 1.2 cm is about 40 ps, which leads to the requirement of a 100 ps or so duration of the plasma. A two-sided Novette laser illumination of the foil (1 beam per side) is employed in an attempt to compensate for random nonuniformities in any one beam that could lead to refractory density nonuniformities in the lasing medium. However, as will be shown below, even a 1-beam illumination is sufficient to explode the foil nearly symmetrically, so that with a sufficiently smooth beam profile it also would be an acceptable illumination scheme.

Experiments were performed at KMS Fusion, Inc., to test the LASNEX and XRASER modeling of the exploding foil, with use of a single beam of 0.53-μm laser light. A 0.26-μm probing laser of 20 ps duration produces holographic interferograms which can be inverted to indicate density profiles of the plasma.[12] In Fig. 2 we see the results from a 5×10^{13}-W/cm^2, 360-ps flat-topped illumination of a Se on Formvar foil, probed about 100 ps after the end of the pulse. The LASNEX simulation matches the data fairly well. Note the nearly symmetric profile despite the single-sided illumination, and the flat n_e profile over the requisite 100-μm distance. We have no data, however, on turbulence that may affect the density profile on the scale of 1 μm or shorter. The code's predictions track the profile data over large variations in intensity, pulse

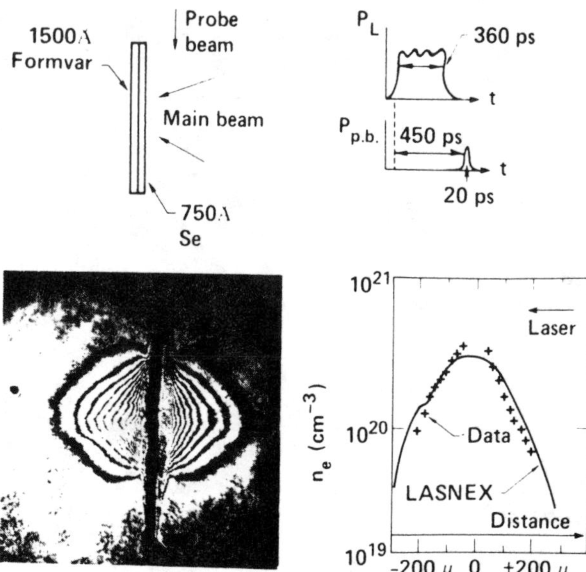

FIG. 2. Experimental setup for, and example of, holographic interferometry, along with comparison of LASNEX simulation (solid line) and electron density profile (crosses) inferred from the Abel inversion of the interferogram.

length, and probing times, leading to substantial confidence in this aspect of the modeling.

An inference of the electron temperature T_e can be made by observing the light scattered 135° from the incident laser's k vector at wavelengths between 0.53 and 1.06 μm. The detected spectrum is interpreted[13] in terms of stimulated Raman scatter (SRS). The short-wavelength cutoff of this SRS spectrum is usually quite sharp, and is attributed to Landau damping at $k_e \lambda_D = 0.3$, where k_e is the wave number of the electron-plasma wave, and λ_D is the Debye length. In the Novette experiments on the actual x-ray-laser thin-foil targets, most of the data show spectral cutoffs ranging from 0.67 to 0.70 μm, leading to estimates of peak T_e in the 700 to 1000 eV range. This is in rather close agreement to the predicted T_e of 900 eV. (The ion temperature is predicted to be about 400 eV). In addition, dot spectroscopy,[14] with use of the $Si^{13+}(Ly_\alpha)$-to-$Si^{12+}(He_\alpha)$ ratio as a T_e diagnostic, has been used to infer the plasma temperature in Se-disk experiments at KMS. Preliminary analysis indicates that the results agree with the predictions of LASNEX.

Given the densities and temperatures from LASNEX, XRASER predicts the fraction of Se in various ionization states. While most of the excitation and ionization rates and their inverses are calculated from first principles,[3, 11] dielectronic recombination is modeled in a crude way, albeit with plausible gross rates of $(1\text{-}5)\times 10^{-11}$ cm^3 sec^{-1}. In Fig. 3 a theoretical $3s$-$2p$ and $3d$-$2p$ spectrum is compared to one obtained from a KMS experiment. In this case the thin foil was illuminated with a 1-mm line focus at 5×10^{13} W/cm^2

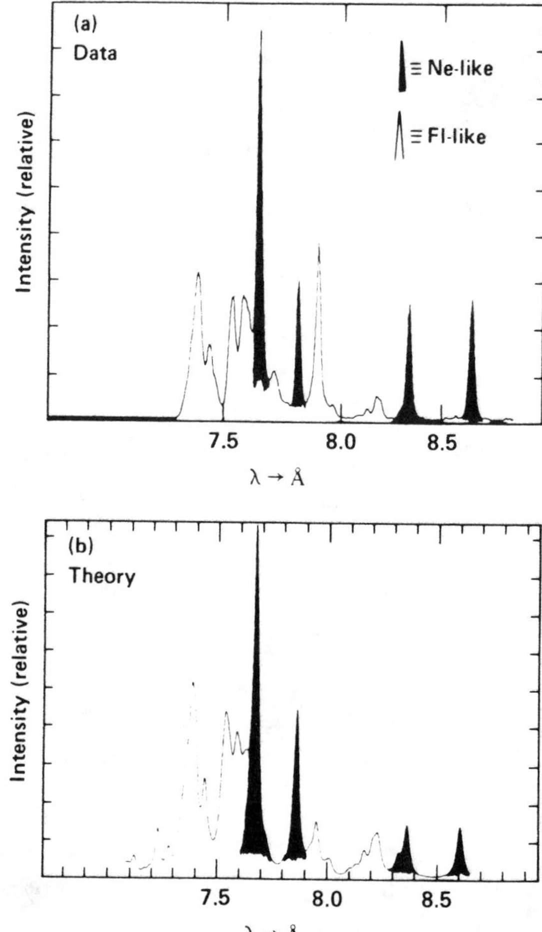

FIG. 3. Comparison of (a) experiment and (b) theory for the time resolved 3-2 spectra of Se. Darkened lines are Ne-like, and undarkened lines are F-like. Time is near the peak of the pulse. Lines above 8 Å are $3s$-$2p$, and below 8 Å are $3d$-$2p$.

and the data are time resolved, but spatially integrated over the exploding foil. Since the n_e and T_e profiles are quite uniform, the spatial integration does not severely compromise the data. The $3d$-$2p$ parts of the spectrum show rather good agreement with the theory, though the modeling perhaps overpredicts the F-like fraction by a moderate amount. The simulations predict about 30% of the Se to be the Ne-like, and about 40% F-like. The $3s$-$2p$ lines are quite a bit stronger than the theory's predictions.

The gains are predicted to be largest in the roughly 200-μm-diam, nearly cylindrical, uniform-density, central part of the exploding foil. This foil was irradiated at 4×10^{13} W/cm^2 for 450 ps. The predicted gain for the $J=0$ to 1 transition at 183 Å at the peak of the pulse is about 10 cm^{-1}. Before the peak of the optical-laser pulse, the foil has not burned through and refraction interferes with the x-ray propagation. By about 200 ps after the peak of the pulse the foil has expanded and cooled significantly. The lowered density contributes to a falling gain, as does the drop in monopole excitation rate due to the cooling. The predicted gain for a $J=2$ to 1 transition $[(2p_{1/2}^5 3p_{3/2})_{J=2}$ to $(2p_{1/2}^5 3s_{1/2})_{J=1}]$ at 209 Å is about 4 cm^{-1}. The gain stays slightly more constant in time for the $J=2$ lines, since those levels are fed by cascading from higher levels during the cooling phase. Similar gains are predicted for the $(2p_{3/2}^5 3p_{3/2})_{J=2}$ to $(2p_{3/2}^5 3s_{1/2})_{J=1}$ transition at 206 Å.

The measured gains are described in the companion paper.[15] While the $J=2$ to 1 transitions exhibit amplification with a gain coefficient of about 5 ± 1 cm^{-1}, within 50% of our predictions here, the $J=0$ to 1 transition is not observed to amplify to any great degree, and certainly not within an order of magnitude of the predicted 10 cm^{-1}. The time behavior of the $J=2$ to 1 lasing lines follows the theory rather closely, lending credence to the physical picture presented above. The agreement of the $J=2$ gain to within 50% of the theory is as good as we can reasonably expect, given our uncertainties in n_e, T_e, and in the fraction of the Se in the Ne-like state. It is of interest to note that the $J=2$ to 1 transitions at 206 and 209 Å are both calculated and measured to have nearly equal gains. This equality appears to be remarkable coincidence and should not necessarily be expected in other systems, as evidenced by the shorter-wavelength lasing results with a higher-Z element yttrium.[15] We believe that Ni-like states (which use higher-Z elements) can also lead to lasing[16] of the type discussed here, possibly with higher gain, and at shorter wavelengths.

There are many speculations as to the absence of the $J=0$ to 1 laser. The collisional-excitation rate directly into the state has been calculated by numerous authors[3,4,6,17] and all agree fairly closely. Extra recombinative processes may be feeding the lower ($3s$) levels as well as the $J=2$ $3p$ levels, thus maintaining the $J=2$ inversion while destroying the $J=0$ one. (This harkens back to the high $3s$-$2p$ emission discussed earlier.) Another way to destroy the $J=0$ inversion is to mix the $3p$ manifold such that all the sublevels are populated according to their statistical weights (the sublevels are less than 10-eV apart, and are in a 1-keV plasma). We have not identified the actual mechanisms to date. Varying Z did not produce the missing laser either, thus virtually ruling out coincidental absorption resonances. Another way to deplete the $J=0$ level may be electron capture. Consider a state with an electron already in the $3p$ $J=0$ level. Electron capture promotes another electron from the L shell into a higher-lying Rydberg level. The principal decay mode of this three-excited-electron state is the transfer of the $3p$ electron to the L shell (thus depleting $J=0$), release of the captured free electron, and the eventual cascade of the previously promoted L-shell electron back down to lower levels, quite possibly the $J=2$ levels.

In summary, data from holography, Si-dot and Raman spectroscopy, and 3-2 Se spectroscopy give us some confidence that the exploding foil plasma has been prepared in roughly the way the modeling would predict. To produce gain, amplification, and propagation we have created a flat n_e (5×10^{20} cm^{-3}) and T_e (1 keV) profile, with a substantial fraction of the Se in a Ne-like state. Gain predictions for the $J=2$ to 1 transitions are within 50% of the observations, but we can only speculate as to the fate of the missing $J=0$ to 1 transition.

We gratefully acknowledge the help and support of many colleagues in this effort. In particular, J. Nuckolls, T. Weaver, J. Lindl, R. London, and S. Maxon for target design; W. Kruer, K. Estabrook, and B. Lasinski for laser-plasma interactions; S. Morgan and J. Scofield for atomic physics; L. Minner, R. Jung, and M. Runyan for XRASER code support. This work was performed under the auspices of the U. S. Department of Energy under Contract No. W-7405-ENG-48.

---

[a]Permanent address: Blackett Laboratory, Imperial College, SW7 2AZ London, United Kingdom.

[1]A. N. Zherikhin, K. N. Koshelev, and V. S. Letokhov, Sov. J. Quantum Electron. **6**, 82 (1976).

[2]A. V. Vinogradov and V. N. Shylaptsev, Sov. J. Quantum Electron. **13**, 1511 (1983), and references therein.

[3]P. L. Hagelstein, Ph.D. thesis, Lawrence Livermore National Laboratory Report No. UCRL-53100, 1981 (unpublished).

[4]U. Feldman, A. K. Bhatia, and S. Suckewer, J. Appl. Phys. **54**, 2188 (1983).

[5]P. L. Hagelstein, Plasma Phys. **25**, 1345 (1983).

[6]U. Feldman, J. F. Seely, and A. K. Bhatia, J. Appl. Phys. **56**, 2475 (1984), and references therein.

[7]D. Matthews *et al.*, in Proceedings of the IEEE Second Topical Meeting on Laser Techniques in the Extreme Ultraviolet, Boulder, Colorado, March 1984 (to be published).

[8]D. W. Phillion, E. M. Campbell, K. G. Estabrook, G. E. Phillips, and F. Ze, Phys. Rev. Lett. **49**, 1405 (1982).

[9]G. B. Zimmerman, Lawrence Livermore National Laboratory Report No. UCRL-75881, 1974 (unpublished); G. B. Zimmerman and W. L. Kruer, Comments Plasma Phys. Controlled Fusion **2**, 85 (1975).

[10]M. D. Rosen *et al.*, Phys. Fluids **22**, 2020 (1979); W. C. Mead *et al.*, Phys. Fluids **26**, 2316 (1983).

[11]P. L. Hagelstein and R. Jung, unpublished.

[12]M. D. Rosen *et al.*, Bull. Am. Phys. Soc. **27**, 989 (1982); W. B. Fechner *et al.*, Phys. Fluids **27**, 1552 (1984).

[13]R. E. Turner *et al.*, to be published.

[14]M. J. Herbst *et al.*, Rev. Sci. Instrum. **53**, 1418 (1982).

[15]D. L. Matthews *et al.*, following Letter [Phys. Rev. Lett. **54**, 110 (1985)].

[16]S. Maxon, P. Hagelstein, K. Reed, and J. Scofield, J. Appl. Phys. (to be published).

[17]K. Reed and A. U. Hazi, Lawrence Livermore National Laboratory Report No. UCRL-87014 (unpublished).

Reprinted with permission from *Optics Letters,* Vol. 10(3), pp. 128-130 (March 1985).

Proposal for an extreme-ultraviolet selective autoionization laser in Zn III

A. J. Mendelsohn and S. E. Harris

Edward L. Ginzton Laboratory, Stanford University, Stanford, California 94305

A system is proposed whereby Zn atoms that are photoionized by soft x rays from a laser-produced plasma undergo selective super-Coster–Kronig decay leading to inversion and lasing on several XUV Zn III transitions. Calculations indicate that lasing will occur when a moderate-sized (~10-J) 1.06-μm pump laser is used.

It was recently demonstrated that soft x rays from laser plasmas produced by relatively small (<1-J) Nd:YAG lasers are capable of producing large densities of excited atomic species[1,2] and in certain cases of producing inversion and gain on visible and UV transitions.[3,4] In this Letter we propose a system based on this technology to produce population inversion and superfluorescent laser action on three transitions of Zn III with wavelengths of 133.2, 82.9, and 56.8 nm, respectively. X rays from a laser plasma are used to photoionize Zn vapor, producing Zn II $3p^5 3d^{10} 4s^2$ ions. These ions undergo MMM super-Coster–Kronig decay to the $3d^8 4s^2$ configuration of Zn III, which is thereby inverted with respect to the $3d^9 4s$ and $3d^9 4p$ configurations.

The use of Auger processes to create gain in the XUV region was first suggested by McGuire,[5] who proposed that (KLL) transitions in Na II would selectively populate levels in Na V, leading to gain at 410 nm. The required pump power for lasing for this system is large: 300 J in 1 nsec. Bokor *et al.*[6] have demonstrated a visible laser in Ba, which is pumped by a selective autoionization process. Recently, Krolik and Shapiro[7] proposed a scheme similar to McGuire's starting with O IV and using KLL Auger transitions to produce inversions in O VI with gain at 103.5 nm. They predict inversions of about 10%. The Zn system reported here has the following advantages: (1) The use of super-Coster–Kronig transitions leads to large inversions in the lasing species, (2) the initial species is neutral Zi vapor rather than a multiply charged ion, and (3) the laser power required for superfluorescent laser action in the XUV is moderate—about 10 J in 1 nsec. In the remainder of this Letter we discuss in detail the mechanism and necessary conditions for creating the population inversion.

Figures 1 and 2 show the levels and transitions relevant to the proposed scheme. The level positions are taken from the results of Dick.[8] The proposed experimental geometry is that used by Caro and Wang in Ref. 1. An intense 1.06-μm laser is focused through Zn vapor maintained in a heat-pipe oven onto a solid Ta target. The resultant plasma radiates soft x rays with an approximately blackbody distribution and photoionizes the surrounding vapor.

The key concept in this proposal is that $3p$ vacancies created by photoionization undergo rapid super-Coster–Kronig decay into the Zn III $3d^8 4s^2$ configuration, where they preferentially populate the $3d^8 4s^2\ ^1G_4$ level.[9–12] Nonsuper-Coster–Kronig transitions (i.e., decays to the $3d^9 4s$ and $3d^{10}$ configurations in Zn III) occur with only about 10% probability. Hence the super-Coster–Kronig process tends to leave the $^1G_4$ level inverted with respect to levels in the $3d^9 4s$ and $3d^9 4p$ configurations of Zn III. Population of the lower Zn III configurations by other processes (i.e., electron ionization and excitation) will be insignificant if the electron density is made sufficiently small by increasing the distance to the target of the lasing volume or if the pulse is made sufficiently short.

In Fig. 2 we show three systems utilizing the selective super-Coster–Kronig decay into $3d^8 4s^2\ ^1G_4$. Also

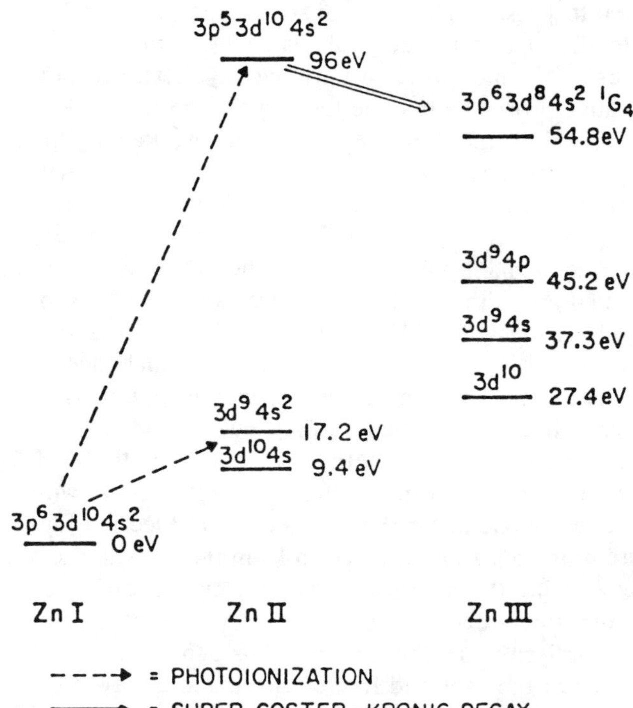

Fig. 1. Population of $3d^8 4s^2\ ^1G_4$ level by super-Coster-Kronig decay.

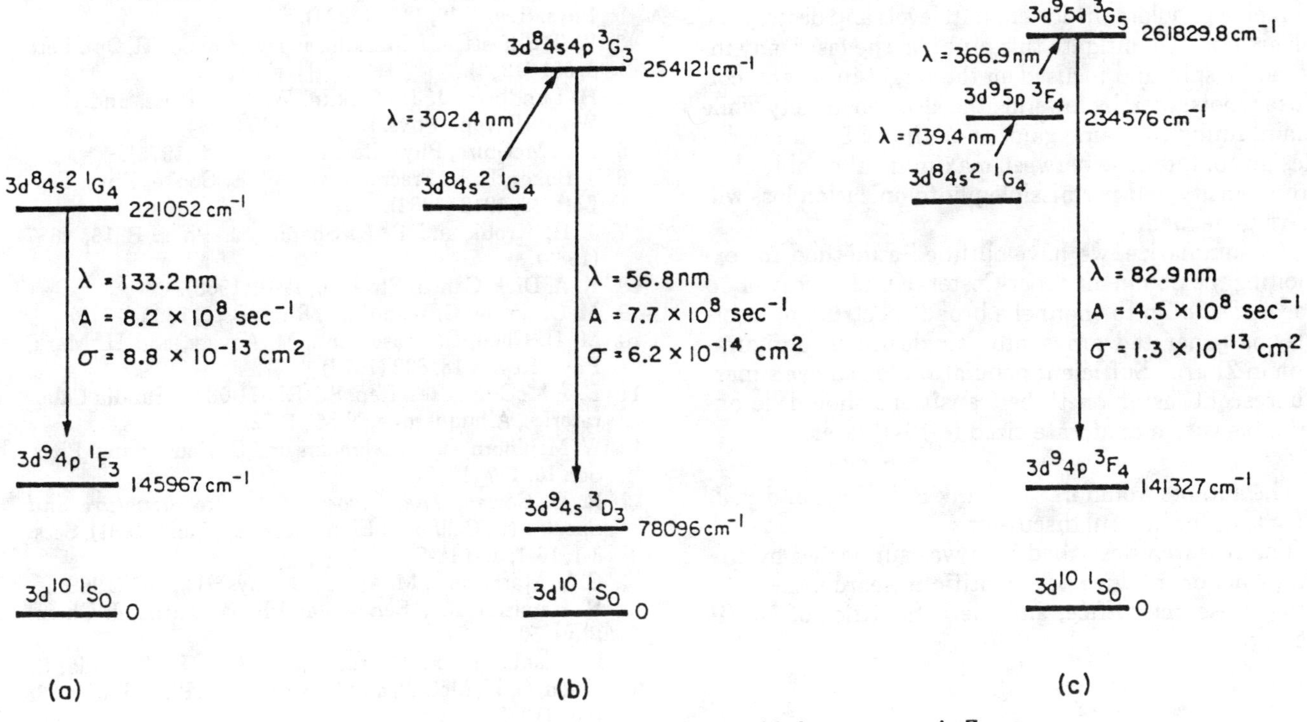

Fig. 2. Energy-level diagrams for three possible laser systems in Zn III.

shown are the Einstein *A* coefficients and the Doppler-broadened gain cross sections for each of the three laser transitions. These were calculated using the (RCN/RCG) Hartree–Fock code[13] with the effects of configuration interaction included. From the cross sections it is seen that a density–length (Nl) product of 6×10^{14} in the $^1G_4$ level at 221 052 cm^{-1} is sufficient to produce e^{20} gain and superfluorescent laser action in each of the three cases.

Figures 2(b) and 2(c) involve using tunable lasers to transfer the $^1G_4$ population to other Zn III levels. The oscillator strength for the $^1G_4$–$^3G_3$ intercombination line of Fig. 2(b) was calculated to be 7.3×10^{-5}, requiring about 1 mJ/cm^2 of 302.4-nm radiation to transfer the population completely. The oscillator strengths for the two steps of the transfer in Fig. 2(c) are 5×10^{-4} and 0.98, respectively, and require proportionately less laser energy to saturate these transitions.

Another key parameter to be considered is the Zn photoabsorption cross section at the proposed laser wavelengths. These cross sections have been measured by Marr and Austin[14] and are 2×10^{-20} cm^2 and 5×10^{-19} cm^2 at 133.2 and 829 nm, respectively, leading to insignificant loss at typical Zn ground-state densities of 10^{17} cm^{-3} and lengths of ~10 cm. However, the cross section at 56.8 nm was measured by Harrison *et al.*[15] and is 7×10^{-18} cm^2. At these densities this limits the length of the laser column to <1 cm.

The $^1G_4$ Nl product actually obtainable in a laser-plasma-pumped system can be calculated by estimating the number of $3p$ vacancies produced by photoionization and multiplying by the branching ratio for the $^1G_4$ super-Coster–Kronig process. The $3p$ density is determined by the method described in Ref. 2. Assuming a plasma radiation temperature of 50 eV and a conversion efficiency from 1.06-μm laser energy to blackbody radiation of 10%,[16] we calculate that 10 J of 1.06-μm energy focused on a target with an ambient Zn ground-state density of 2×10^{17} cm^{-3} produces a $N_{3p}l$ product of 3.4×10^{15} cm^{-2} at a distance of 11 mm from the target. In this calculation we have used the $3p$ and $3d$ photoionization cross sections calculated by Fliflet and Kelly[17] and the double-photoionization cross-section data of Holland *et al.*[18]

Next we consider the branching ratio for the super-Coster–Kronig process. Chen *et al.*[10] have calculated the Auger rates into each of the possible final terms using LS-coupled single-configuration final-state wave functions. Their results show that 57% of the decays lead to $^1G_4$ final states. The RCN/RCG code gives the composition of the $^1G_4$ level at 221 052 cm^{-1} as $3d^83s^2$ $^1G_4 = -(0.73)3d^84s^2\ ^1G_4 + (0.58)3d^94d\ ^1G_4 - (0.22)$ $3d^95d\ ^3F_4 - (0.29)3d^94d\ ^3G_4$. Hence as an approximation to the effect of configuration interaction we multiply the 57% branching ratio of Chen *et al.* by the fraction $(0.73)^2$ of the $^1G_4$ level that contains the $^1G_4$ basis-state wave function. This leads to a total branching ratio of 30% into the $^1G_4$ level.

The $N(^1G_4)l$ product is then $0.3 \times 3.4 \times 10^{15} = 1.0 \times 10^{15}$ cm^{-2}. Radiative decay of the upper level during a 1-nsec laser pulse reduces this value to 7×10^{14} cm^{-2}. This is sufficient to produce e^{20} gain on all three transitions of Fig. 2.

In the above discussion we have assumed that the incident 1.06-μm laser is focused on the Ta target in a single spot. This in turn leads to an initial photoelectron density of 4×10^{16} cm^{-3}. Depending on recombination rates, inelastic electron collisions and ionization may populate the lower Zn III levels and destroy the inversion. To mitigate this problem the laser may instead be split and focused on the target in several collinear spots, thereby lowering the electron density while maintaining the same gain. For the 56.8-nm laser, a design compromise between maximum allowable electron density and permissible photoionization loss will have to be made.

To summarize, we have outlined a method for exploiting the dominant super-Coster–Kronig decay of $3p$ vacancies in Zn to channel a broad spectrum of laser-plasma-generated x rays into a single upper configuration in Zn III. Sufficient population to achieve superfluorescent lasing on three transitions should be obtainable with a moderate-sized (~10-J) laser.

The authors would like to thank R. G. Caro and P. J. K. Wisoff for helpful discussions.

The research described here was supported by the U.S. Air Force Office of Scientific Research, the U.S. Army Research Office, and the U.S. Office of Naval Research.

References

1. R. G. Caro, J. C. Wang, R. W. Falcone, J. F. Young, and S. E. Harris, Appl. Phys. Lett. **42**, 9 (1983).
2. R. G. Caro, J. C. Wang, J. F. Young, and S. E. Harris, Phys. Rev. A **30**, 1407 (1984).
3. W. T. Silfvast, J. J. Macklin, and O. R. Wood II, Opt. Lett. **8**, 551 (1983).
4. H. Lundberg, J. J. Macklin, W. T. Silfvast, and O. R. Wood II, Appl. Phys. Lett. **45**, 335 (1984).
5. E. J. McGuire, Phys. Rev. Lett. **35**, 844 (1975).
6. J. Bokor, R. R. Freeman, and W. E. Cooke, Phys. Rev. Lett. **48**, 1242 (1982).
7. J. H. Krolik and P. R. Shapiro, J. Phys. B **16**, 4687 (1983).
8. K. A. Dick, Can. J. Phys. **46**, 1291 (1968).
9. M. Ohno and G. Wendin, J. Phys. B **12**, 1305 (1979).
10. M. H. Chen, B. Crasemann, M. Aoyagi, and H. Mark, Phys. Rev. A **18**, 802 (1978).
11. E. J. McGuire, Res. Rep. SC-RR-71 0835 (Sandia Laboratories, Albuquerque, N.M., 1972).
12. W. Mehlhorn, B. Breuckmann, and D. Hausamann, Phys. Scr. **16**, 177 (1977).
13. R. D. Cowan, *The Theory of Atomic Structure and Spectra* (U. California Press, Berkeley, Calif., 1981), Secs. 8-1, 16-1, and 18-7.
14. G. V. Marr and J. M. Austin, J. Phys. B **2**, 107 (1969).
15. H. Harrison, R. I. Schoen, and R. B. Cairns, J. Chem. Phys. **50**, 3930 (1969).
16. H. Nishimura, F. Matsuoka, M. Yagi, K. Yamada, S. Nakai, G. H. McCall, and C. Yamanaka, Phys. Fluids **26**, 1668 (1983).
17. A. W. Fliflet and H. P. Kelly, Phys. Rev. A **13**, 312 (1976).
18. D. M. P. Holland, K. Codling, and J. B. West, J. Phys. B **15**, 1473 (1982).

Reprinted with permission from *Optics Letters,* Vol. 11(7), pp. 425-427 (July 1986).

Identification and oscillator-strength measurement of the 109.1-nm transition in neutral Cs

K. D. Pedrotti,* D. P. Dimiduk, J. F. Young, and S. E. Harris

Edward L. Ginzton Laboratory, Stanford University, Stanford, California 94305

The 109.1-nm transition in neutral Cs is the prototype of a class of transitions that originate from doubly excited quasi-metastable quartet levels. In this Letter we describe experiments that use tunable VUV radiation to determine the identity of this transition, to measure its oscillator strength, and to estimate its hyperfine splitting.

In recent work[1] it was postulated that particular core-excited quartet levels of alkali and alkalilike ions should have radiative rates that are comparable with their autoionizing rates. This occurs since, by *LS* selection rules, these levels may couple only to doublet levels, which are themselves prohibited from autoionizing by angular momentum and parity considerations. Levels of this type have been termed quasi-metastable and are specified by the condition that $|J - L| = 3/2$ and that parity and angular momentum be both even or odd; they can occur even in heavy atoms.

The 109.1-nm transition in Cs (Fig. 1) is a prototype of the class of transitions that originate from levels of this type. The upper level of this transition is $Cs(5p^5 5d6s)^4P^{\circ}_{5/2}$ and is expected to radiate to the valence fine-structure levels $Cs(5p^6 5d)^2P_{5/2}$ and $Cs(5p^6 5d)^2P_{3/2}$. Holmgren *et al.*[2] recently observed intense emission at 109.1 nm using a pulsed hollow-cathode discharge and, on the basis of the fine-structure splitting and the intensity ratio of its fine-structure components, ascribed the radiation as originating from this transition. Somewhat earlier, Aleksakhin *et al.*[3] associated radiation at 108.5 nm with the same transition.

In this Letter we describe an experiment to confirm the identity of this transition through accurate measurements of the fine-structure splitting and from estimates of the oscillator strength and hyperfine splitting. A pulsed hollow cathode was used to populate the lower level of this transition, and tunable VUV radiation, generated by four-wave mixing, was used to make absorption measurements at near-Doppler-limited resolution.

Experiment

Tunable radiation near 109.1 nm was generated using two-photon resonant four-wave sum-frequency mixing (4WSFM) using a process in Zn similar to that of Jamroz *et al.*[4,5] The particular scheme, shown in Fig. 2(a), was chosen based on our desire to minimize the linewidth of the VUV source and to use 532-nm pumped dye lasers. Such dye lasers are able to generate only wavelengths longer than 540 nm; thus, in order to generate radiation near 109 nm by using only five dye photons, it was necessary to find a two-photon resonant level between 73 228 and 74 074 cm^{-1}. Referring to Fig. 2(a), the desired level was found by observing degenerate 4WSFM (tripling) through successive levels in the Zn $4sns\ ^1S_0$ Rydberg series. Based on a quantum-defect extrapolation from the (tabulated)[6] lower members of the series, we identify the level at 73 747.7 cm^{-1} as Zn $4s10s\ ^1S_0$. No other two-photon levels were observed within the necessary energy range.

A single *Q*-switched, frequency-doubled Nd:YAG laser was used to pump two dye-laser systems. The first was operated with an intracavity étalon to narrow the linewidth to 0.05 cm^{-1}, tuned to 542.2 nm, and frequency doubled to provide the two-photon resonant wave. The second dye laser was tuned around a small region near 558 nm and had a linewidth of 0.3 cm^{-1}. The two outputs were combined by using a dichroic mirror and focused into the Zn cell at a power density of about 2×10^{10} W cm^{-2}. The Zn cell consisted of a 2.5-cm-diameter stainless-steel tube (horizontal) with a 6-cm-long hot zone produced by an external (vertical) sodium heat pipe.[7] Typically, the cell was operated at a Zn density of about 10^{17} cm^{-3} along with 50 Torr of He to reduce the rate of Zn diffusion out of the hot zone. We estimate our generation efficiency as 10^{-8}. The source linewidth was measured (using the Xe 108.4-nm transition) at 0.7 cm^{-1}, resulting in a spectroscopic resolving power of 1.3×10^5.

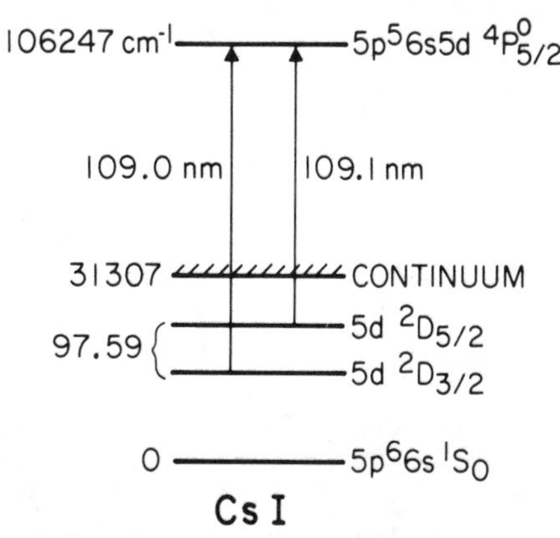

Fig. 1. Selected Cs I energy levels showing the transitions observed.

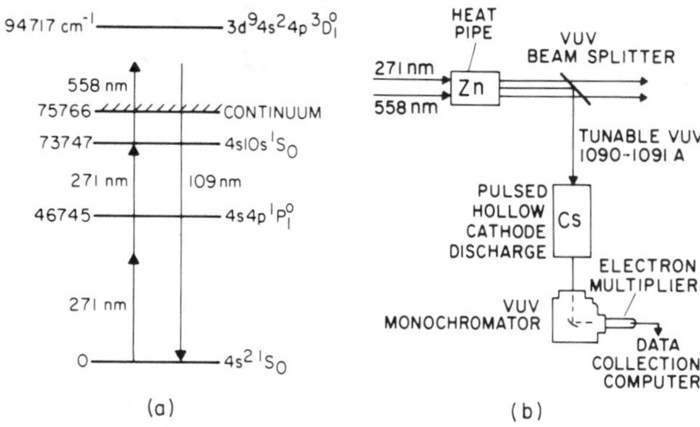

Fig. 2. (a) Energy levels for resonant VUV generation in Zn vapor; (b) simplified diagram of the experimental apparatus.

Because of a small residual sensitivity in our detector at 271 nm, it was necessary to filter 271 nm from the beam leaving the Zn cell. An uncoated quartz plate was put in the beam oriented at Brewster's angle for the 271-nm radiation, which thus passed through it. The orthogonally polarized 109.1-nm radiation, however, experienced a 30% reflection,[8] and the reflected beam was directed through the Cs absorption cell and into a 0.2-m VUV monochromator, which provided further discrimination. A schematic of the optical path is shown in Fig. 2(b); LiF windows were used to isolate the beam splitter, spectrometer, and detector volumes. Approximately 10^3 photons of 109.1-nm radiation per shot were incident upon the EMI D233 electron multiplier.

The Cs pulsed hollow cathode has been described in Ref. 9. The active region consists of a stainless-steel cathode 2 cm in diameter and 30 cm long operated at peak currents from 0.6 to 300 A with pulse lengths ranging from 20 to 1 μsec, respectively. For these measurements both the Cs vapor pressure and the He buffer-gas pressure were set at 1 Torr.

Results and Discussion

Figure 3 shows VUV absorption scans of the pulsed hollow-cathode discharge, both with the discharge on and with the discharge off. Absorption on both fine-structure components of the $5p^65d\ ^2D$–$5p^55d6s\ ^4P^\circ_{5/2}$ transition is clearly seen. The fine-structure splitting measured by us is 97.3 ± 0.3 cm^{-1} and is in agreement with the published value of 97.59 cm^{-1}.

Absolute calibration of the 109.1-nm wavelength was accomplished by comparing the wavelengths of the dye lasers used to generate the VUV radiation with emission lines of Kr and Hg. The result for the $^2D_{5/2}$ absorption is 109.111 ± 0.0035 nm. The uncertainty is due to errors introduced by the drive in the spectrometer used for the intercomparison.

The oscillator strength of each of the fine-structure components of the 109.1-nm transition was measured by using the curve-of-growth method.[10] For these measurements the hollow-cathode discharge current was reduced until each of the components was optically thin. In this regime the frequency-integrated VUV absorption depends on NfL, i.e., on the product of population, oscillator strength, and distance, and is insensitive to linewidths or hyperfine structures.

The density–length product NL of the $(6p^65d)^2D$ fine-structure levels was measured with a laser tuned between the $(5p^65d)^2D_{5/2}$ and $(5p^68f)^2F^\circ$ transition at 662.9 nm and the $(5p^65d)^2D_{3/2}$ and $(5p^68f)^2F^\circ_{5/2}$ transition at 658.6 nm. These transitions have oscillator strengths of 2.02×10^{-2} and 2.11×10^{-2}, respectively,[11] which are thought to be accurate to 10%. Under our operating conditions, i.e., an electron density of about 10^{14} electrons/cm^3, the chosen valence transitions are sufficiently Stark broadened that they do not become opaque at line center. This procedure resulted in measurement of NL of the valence-level atoms to an accuracy of about 20%.

The results of the VUV oscillator strength measurements are summarized in Table 1 and are compared with values that are calculated by using the RCN/RGG atomic-physics code.[12]

Figure 4 shows the measured equivalent width of the 109.1-nm absorption as a function of population in the lower state. The solid curve, denoted by B, is the calculated equivalent width based on the measured oscillator strength including both Doppler and Stark broadening. This curve does not fit the experimental data. To fit the data at the largest populations, a Stark width about 10 times larger than that which we calculate must be assumed, and the resulting curve deviates from intermediate experimental points.

We believe that this discrepancy results from neglecting the hyperfine splitting of the $(5p^55d6s)^4P^\circ_{5/2}$ level. The nuclear spin of $I = 7/2$ causes the transition to be split into nine components. (The hyperfine structure of the lower level of the 109.1-nm transition can be neglected.[13]) The relative frequency spacing is given by the Landé rule with a scale factor A. Curve A of Fig. 4 shows the calculated equivalent width assum-

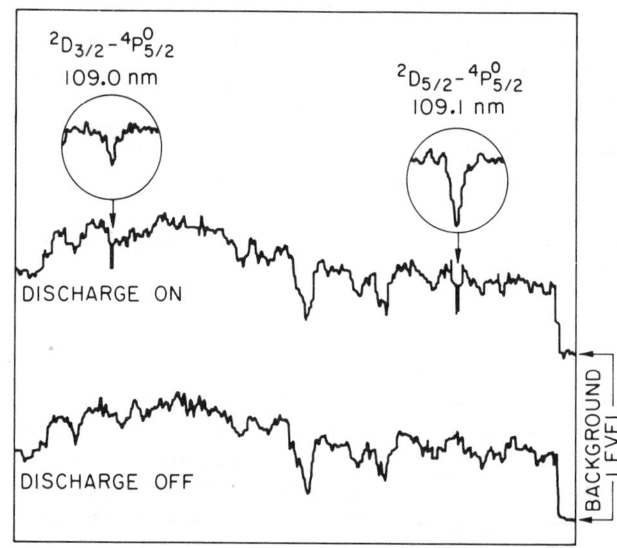

Fig. 3. VUV absorption scan showing the two fine-structure absorptions from Cs $(5d)^2D$. The data were taken with a lower-level population of 3×10^{13} cm^{-3}; the insets show the absorptions at full instrumental resolution.

Table 1. Summary of Results from Absorption Measurements on the 109-nm Transitions

Transition	λ (nm)	$f_{exp.}$	$f_{calc.}$[a]
$Cs(5p^6 5d)^2D_{5/2}$–$(5p^5 5d6s)^4P^{\circ}_{5/2}$	109.111	$(7.2 \pm 4) \times 10^{-3}$	6.95×10^{-3}
$Cs(5p^6 5d)^2D_{3/2}$–$(5p^5 5d6s)^4P^{\circ}_{5/2}$	108.998	$(6.5 \pm 2) \times 10^{-4}$	4.8×10^{-4}
Fine-structure splitting: 97.3 ± 0.3 cm^{-1}			
Hyperfine splitting constant: $A = 0.025$ cm^{-1}			

[a] Calculated using the RCN/RCG atomic-physics code.[12]

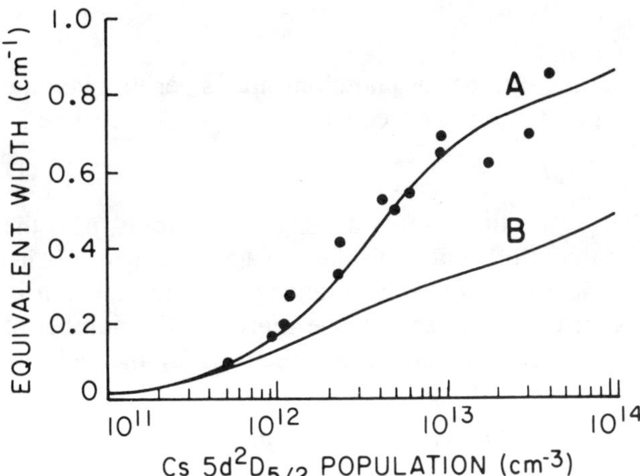

Fig. 4. Equivalent width versus lower-level population for the 109.1-nm absorption, assuming a 30-column length. The points are experimental data. The solid lines are calculated values from computer-modeled curves of growth assuming Doppler, Stark, and collision broadenings of 0.14, 1.3 × 10^{-3}, and 1.5 × 10^{-3} cm^{-1}, respectively. Curve A also includes hyperfine splitting with a constant of A = 0.025 cm^{-1}.

ing a scale factor of A = 0.025 cm^{-1} and Stark widths determined by the measured electron density.

As a theoretical estimate of the splitting,[14] we used RCN[12] to compute $|\psi 6s(0)|^2$ for Cs $5p^6 6s$ and Cs $5p^5 5d6s$. (The $5d$ electron and the $5p^5$ subshell contribute little to this hyperfine interaction.) If we use the known splitting constant for the Cs ground state of A_{ground} = 0.076 cm^{-1} and account for an angular-momentum factor of 1/5, this predicts $A_{quasi\text{-}metastable}$ = 0.021 cm^{-1}.

The hyperfine splitting reduces the gain cross section for lasers operating on the 109.1-nm transition. If hyperfine structure is neglected, the calculated cross section is 4.0 × 10^{-14} cm^2, based on our measured oscillator strength and assuming a Doppler width of 0.15 cm^{-1}. If, however, we assume that the upper level's population is distributed among its hyperfine components according to their degeneracies and sum the contributions of the various Doppler-broadened components, the peak value of the cross section is reduced to 1.2 × 10^{-14} cm^2. If the hyperfine splitting were much larger than the Doppler width, then the gain cross section on the largest component would be 1.08 × 10^{-14} cm^{-1}.

In summary, the 109.1-nm transition in Cs is an example of a transition that originates from slowly autoionizing, quasi-metastable levels of alkalilike atoms and ions. In this work we have confirmed the identity of this transition, measured its oscillator strength and fine-structure splitting, and estimated its hyperfine splitting.

This research was supported jointly by the U.S. Air Force Office of Scientific Research and the U.S. Army Research Office.

The authors acknowledge helpful discussions with A. J. Mendelsohn and J. K. Spong. D. P. Dimiduk acknowledges support from the U.S. Air Force Institute of Technology.

* Present address, Rockwell International Corporation, 1049 Camino Dos Rios, Thousand Oaks, California 91360.

References

1. S. E. Harris, D. J. Walker, R. G. Caro, A. J. Mendelsohn, and R. D. Cowan, Opt. Lett. **9,** 168 (1984).
2. D. E. Holmgren, D. J. Walker, and S. E. Harris, in *Laser Techniques in the Extreme Ultraviolet*, S. E. Harris and T. B. Lucatorto, eds. (American Institute of Physics, New York, 1984), p. 496.
3. I. S. Aleksakhin, G. G. Bogachev, I. P. Zapesochnyl, and S. Yu. Urgin, Sov. Phys. JETP **53,** 1140 (1981).
4. W. Jamroz, P. E. LaRocque, and B. P. Stoicheff, Opt. Lett. **7,** 617 (1982).
5. Initial 4WSFM experiments in Kr showed that the negative dispersion limit precludes generation of wavelengths shorter than 109.45 nm: K.D. Pedrotti, "Atomic spectroscopy for soft x-ray lasers," Ph.D. dissertation (Stanford University, Stanford, Calif. 94305).
6. C. E. Moore, *Atomic Energy Levels, Vol. II* (National Bureau of Standards, Washington, D.C., 1949).
7. H. Scheingraber and C. R. Vidal, Rev. Sci. Instrum. **52,** (1981).
8. R. W. Falcone and J. Bokor, Opt. Lett. **8,** 21 (1983).
9. R. W. Falcone and K. D. Pedrotti, Opt. Lett. **7,** 74 (1982); R. W. Falcone, D. E. Holmgren, and K. D. Pedrotti, AIP Conf. Proc. **90,** 287 (1982).
10. S. S. Penner and R. W. Kavanaugh, J. Opt. Soc. Am. **43,** 385 (1953).
11. M. Fabry and J. R. Cussenot, Can. J. Phys. **54,** 836 (1976).
12. R. D. Cowan, *The Theory of Atomic Structure and Spectra* (U. California Press, Berkeley, Calif., 1981); Mail Stop B212, Los Alamos National Laboratory, Los Alamos, New Mexico 87545 (personal communication).
13. K. Fredriksson, H. Lundberg, and S. Svanberg, Phys. Rev. A **21,** 241 (1980).
14. I. I. Sobel'man, *An Introduction to the Theory of Atomic Spectra* (Pergamon, Oxford, 1972), pp. 205–216.

Reprinted with permission from *Physical Review Letters,* Vol. 56(16), pp. 1687-1690 (April 21, 1986).

Gain on Free-Bound Transitions by Stimulated Radiative Recombination

Ernst E. Fill

Max-Planck-Institut für Quantenoptik, 8046 Garching, Federal Republic of Germany

(Received 16 October 1985)

This paper investigates the possibility of observing gain on a free-bound transition, i.e., by stimulated radiative recombination. The basic equations are derived from the Einstein-Milne relations for the continuum. Gain formulas for various plasma conditions are given. A continuously tunable short-wavelength laser seems to be possible.

The intensive search for new lasers and the challenge to extend the region of known laser lines into the uv and soft x-ray regime has led to the investigation of high-density plasmas as possible laser media. Plasma lasers emitting in the infrared, visible, and uv have been reported,[1-4] and recently, substantial gain in the soft x-ray region has been demonstrated in plasmas produced by high-power laser radiation.[5,6] All of these experiments involve generation of inversion between bound states of an ionized species in the plasma. The purpose of this Letter is to show that conditions can be found under which there is gain at a free-bound transition, i.e., a transition the upper level of which lies in the ionization continuum of the lasing species. The recombination continuum originating from transitions of this kind produces a large part of the continuum emission of high-density plasmas.[7] It is clear that to achieve gain at such a transition, the plasma must be far from Saha-Boltzmann equilibrium. As shown in the main part of the paper, several possibilities of such nonequilibrium exist, e.g., if the ions are highly overstripped or if the electron velocity distribution is non-Maxwellian.

Aside from its scientific interest, a free-bound laser could provide a number of advantagous features: The energy stored in the free-electron gas of a plasma would be directly extracted by the laser pulse, laser operation at rather short wavelengths would be possible, and, last but not least, such a laser would be tunable since the upper level is a continuum of states.

The principle of the laser involves stimulated transitions between two energy levels of a system. Except in the free-electron laser, such energy states are represented by discrete levels of an atom, ion, or molecule. The basic equations governing radiative transitions between such states are the Einstein relations which relate the coefficients of spontaneous emission, absorption, and stimulated emission to each other. To extend the laser principle to free-bound transitions, the basic relations between the rates of spontaneous radiative recombination, photoionization, and stimulated radiative recombination must be applied. They can be derived by analogy with the Einstein radiation theory and are known as the Einstein-Milne relations for the continuum.[8]

Let the number of photoionizations per unit volume in time dt and in the frequency range $(\nu, \nu + d\nu)$ be

$$N_0 p_\nu I_\nu \, d\nu \, dt, \tag{1}$$

where N_0 is the number density of the atoms, p_ν is the probability of photoionization of an atom per unit intensity, and $I_\nu \, d\nu$ is the intensity for the radiation in this frequency range. Furthermore, let the number of radiative recombination by electrons in the velocity range $(v, v+dv)$ be

$$N_1 n_e(v)[F(v)+G(v)I_\nu] v \, dv \, dt, \tag{2}$$

where N_1 is the number density of the ions, $n_e(v)$ is the distribution function of the electrons, and $F(v)$ and $G(v)$ are the coefficients for spontaneous and stimulated recombinations, respectively.

By postulating that the radiation of a system in Saha-Boltzmann equilibrium obeys the Planck radiation law, we obtain the Einstein-Milne relations, which relate $F(v)$, P_ν, and $G(v)$ to each other:

$$F(v) = (2h\nu^3/c^2)G(v), \tag{3}$$

$$p_\nu = (8\pi m^2 v^2 g_1/h^2 g_0)G(v), \tag{4}$$

where m is the electron mass and g_1 and g_0 are the degeneracies of the ion ground level and the final atom level. Equations (3) and (4) are the continuum analog of the Einstein relations for emission and absorption of radiation. They are valid even under nonequilibrium conditions and can be used to derive the absorption coefficient of a plasma by photoionization, corrected for stimulated emission. Using

$$h\nu = mv^2/2 + E_b, \tag{5}$$

where E_b is the binding energy of the lower level, one obtains

$$v \, dv = (h/m) d\nu \tag{6}$$

and, finally, for the absorption coefficient,

$$\kappa_\nu = -\frac{1}{I_\nu}\frac{dI_\nu}{dx} = p_\nu h_\nu \left(N_0 - \frac{N_1 n_e(v) hG(v)}{m p_\nu} \right). \tag{7}$$

There is gain instead of absorption if the second term in the bracket dominates. Reversing the order of the term and inserting for $G(v)$ from Eq. (4), one obtains for the gain

$$\alpha_\nu = \sigma_\nu \left[N_1 n_e(v) \frac{h^3}{8\pi m^3 v^2} \frac{g_0}{g_1} - N_0 \right], \tag{8}$$

where $p_\nu h_\nu$ has been replaced by σ_ν the photoionization cross section.

Equation (8) is the free-bound analog of the usual gain equation for a laser with the inversion replaced by the term in the bracket. Note that the lower level of the transition is not necessarily the ground state of the atom and therefore N_0 may be the number density of any level of the atom. Equation (8) is also valid for ionization stages higher than one. In this case N_1 is the number density of ions in, say, the ionization stage k, and N_0 the respective density in the ionization stage k-1. To simplify the terminology in the following, the two species will still be called ions and atoms.

For the gain to be positive, a situation very far from thermal equilibrium is required. The electron and ion densities must be high but the population of the lower level must be much smaller than in Saha-Boltzmann equilibrium. Depending on the distribution of the electron gas in phase space, three cases can be defined:

(a) *The electrons have a Maxwellian velocity distribution.*—In this case $n_e(v)/v^2$ is a maximum for $v=0$. The gain is maximized if the upper level is just the ionization limit of the atom and is given by

$$\alpha_\nu = \sigma_\nu \left[N_1 N_e \frac{h^3}{8\pi m^3 \pi^{1/2}(2kT_e/m)^{3/2}} \frac{g_0}{g_1} - N_0 \right], \tag{9}$$

where N_e is the number density of the electrons and T_e is the electron temperature. One has numerically in mixed units

$$\alpha_\nu = \sigma_\nu [1.66\times 10^{-22} N_1 N_e (kT_e)^{-3/2} g_0/g_1 - N_0], \tag{10}$$

where α_ν is in inverse centimeters, σ_ν is in centimeters squared, N_1, N_e, and N_0 are in inverse centimeters cubed, and kT_e is the electron temperature in electronvolts.

(b) *The electrons have a narrow velocity distribution around* v_0.—With the velocity distribution approximated by a "rectangular" one so that $n_e(v) = n_e$ for $v_0 - \Delta v/2 < v < v_0 + \Delta v/2$ and 0 elsewhere, the number density of free electrons is

$$N_e = n_e \Delta v. \tag{11}$$

Using the relations

$$E_{el} = m v_0^2/2 \text{ and } \Delta E_{el} = m v_0 \Delta v \tag{12}$$

for the energy and the energy spread of the electrons, respectively, one obtains for the gain

$$\alpha_\nu = \sigma_\nu \left[N_1 N_e \frac{h^3}{8(2\pi)^{1/2} m^{3/2} \Delta E_{el}^{1/2}} \frac{g_0}{g_1} - N_0 \right], \tag{13}$$

or with the same units as in Eq. (10),

$$\alpha_\nu = \sigma_\nu (1.26\times 10^{-22} N_1 N_e \Delta E_{el}^{-1} E_{el}^{-1/2} g_0/g_1 - N_0), \tag{14}$$

where E_{el} and ΔE_{el} are in electronvolts.

Equation (13) can also be derived directly by writing for the gain

$$\alpha_\nu = \sigma_\nu [N_e g_0/g_e - N_0], \tag{15}$$

where g_0 and g_e are the degeneracies of the lower (bound) level and of the electron gas, respectively. The degeneracy of an electron gas in the presence of ions with number density N_1 is given by[9]

$$g_e = \frac{4g_1}{N_1} \left(\frac{E_{el}}{\pi} \right)^{1/2} \left(\frac{m}{2\pi\hbar} \right)^{3/2} \Delta E_{el}. \tag{16}$$

In this expression a factor of 2 is included, which takes care of the two opposite directions of propagation of an electron with respect to the photon propagation vector. Inserting Eq. (16) into Eq. (15) leads to the gain formula of Eq. (13), as required.

(c) *The electrons not only have a narrow velocity distribution but also have high directionality.*—This occurs, for example, in an electron beam. In this case the electron distribution is highly peaked in phase space and their degeneracy g_e is very low. The smallest possible value of g_e is unity, and therefore the highest possible gain is given by

$$\alpha_\nu = \sigma_\nu (g_0 N_e - N_0). \tag{17}$$

The condition of unity degeneracy determines from Eq. (16) how narrow the distribution of electron velocities and directions for a given electron energy and ion density has to be.

Consider a plasma consisting of completely stripped ions of charge Z and density N_1 in an electron gas of density ZN_1. The electrons are assumed to have a Maxwellian velocity distribution and therefore maximum gain occurs from the ionization limit into a hydrogenlike state of quantum number n. The lowering of the ionization limit in a plasma is neglected for this estimate and the frequency of the emitted radiation is given by

$$h\nu = \mathcal{R} Z^2/n^2, \tag{18}$$

where $\mathcal{R}$ is the Rydberg constant. An approximate value of the photoionization cross section can be obtained from the Kramers formula with unity Gaunt factor[10]:

$$\sigma_\nu = 2.76\times 10^{29} Z^4/\nu^3 n^5 = 7.76\times 10^{-18} n/Z^2. \tag{19}$$

Inserting this into Eq. (10), with $g_0/g_1 = 2\, n^2$ for hydrogenlike ions, one obtains for the gain

$$\alpha_\nu = 1.29\times 10^{-39}(N_1^2/Z^4)(kT_e/Z^2)^{-3/2}2n^3 - 7.76\times 10^{-18}N_0 n/Z^2. \qquad (20)$$

Taking $Z=1$, $kT_e=5$ eV, $n=1$, and $N_1=10^{20}$ cm^{-3}, one has gain for $N_0 < 2.96\times 10^{17}$ cm^{-3}. If N_0 is negligible compared with that number, a gain of 2.3 cm^{-1} is achieved at a wavelength of 91.2 nm.

To evaluate the pumping requirements for the realization of such plasma conditions, the loss of "inversion" by recombination has to be taken into account. Any ionizing radiation can be used for pumping. The necessary pump power absorbed by the medium is given by the recombination rate R_{rec} multiplied by the average energy for reionization of an atom. One obtains

$$P = R_{rec}(\mathscr{R} + kT_e)1.6\times 10^{-19}\ \text{W/cm}^3. \qquad (21)$$

Taking the recombination rate from Bates, Kingston, and McWhirter,[11] one obtains in an optically thin plasma

$$P = 8.6\times 10^{12}\ \text{W/cm}^3. \qquad (22)$$

A free-bound laser would be an interesting way of generating coherent radiation in the uv and x-ray regions of the spectrum. Since the upper level is in the continuum, a given atom would lase at a much shorter wavelength than for a bound-bound transition. A major advantage would be the possibility of continuous tunability. It turns out, however, from the gain formulas of the preceding discussion that the requirements on a medium for it to exhibit reasonable free-bound gain are rather severe. Typically, electron and ion densities greater than 10^{20} cm^{-3} are required with a population of the lower level of less than 10^{18} cm^{-3} (see the previous example).

The situation easiest to verify experimentally is case (a), which only requires that the population of the bound level be much lower than given according to the Saha equilibrium. The Saha equation yields

$$N_0^{Saha} = 1.66\times 10^{-22}N_1 N_e(kT_e)^{-3/2}(g_0/g_1) \times \exp(E_b/kT_e), \qquad (23)$$

from which and Eq. (10) it follows that there is gain if

$$N_0 < N_0^{Saha}\exp(-E_b/kT_e). \qquad (24)$$

Gain to an excited level of the atom is therefore achieved if the temperature of the atom, as determined by the population of its bound levels, is much lower than the electron temperature determining the degree of ionization.

A disadvantage of case (a) is that the gain is maximum at the ionization limit (unless σ_ν has a distinct maximum in the continuum), and therefore such a laser would only marginally be a free-bound laser.

In case (b) lasing from well within the continuum is achievable. Because of the high self-relaxation rate of the electrons, the required narrow velocity distribution can probably be maintained only for a very short period of time and traveling-wave excitation would be necessary. However, if the energy spread of the electrons can be made sufficiently small, considerably higher gain than in case (a) could be obtained.

Case (c) could be verified by crossing an electron beam and an ion beam. The population of the lower level would be zero in this case, making the gain in any case positive. For its magnitude to be experimentally measurable, the current densities of existing electron beam generators would have to be considerably increased.

Under high-density plasma conditions the gain will be reduced by scattering and absorption. The total cross section of an electron for scattering a photon is[12]

$$\sigma_e = 6.65\times 10^{-25}\ \text{cm}^2, \qquad (25)$$

and so scattering can safely be ignored. The main photon-loss mechanism is free-free absorption by the electron gas, given by[12]

$$\beta_{ff} = 3.4\times 10^6 Z^2 N_1^2(kT_e/Z^2)^{-1/2}\nu^{-3} \times (1-e^{-h\nu/kTe})\ \text{cm}^{-1}. \qquad (26)$$

Under the conditions of the example this results in

$$\beta_{ff} = 0.4\ \text{cm}^{-1} \qquad (27)$$

and the gain is reduced by 17%.

It is interesting to discuss the effects which determine the gain profile of a free-bound laser. The contribution of the lower (bound) level to the linewidth will be negligible in most cases and the gain profile will be controlled by the term $[n_e(v)/v^2]\sigma_\nu(\nu)$ in Eq. (8), i.e., by the electron velocity distribution and the variation of the photoionization cross section with frequency. If the electron velocity distribution is narrow, as in cases (b) and (c), $\sigma_\nu(\nu)$ can be considered as constant and the gain bandwidth is given by the electron energy spread. In the case of a Maxwellian electron velocity distribution [case (a)], however, the variation of $\sigma_\nu(\nu)$ with frequency has to be taken into account. For lasing into hydrogenic states one obtains, by use of Eq. (21), for the functional form of the gain profile ($\nu \geqslant \nu_c$)

$$\alpha_\nu(\nu) = \alpha_0\exp[-(\nu-\nu_0)/kT_e](\nu_0^3/\nu^3), \qquad (28)$$

where α_0 is the gain at the maximum, given by Eq. (10), and ν_0 is the frequency at maximum gain, given by $h\nu_0 = \mathscr{R}Z^2/n^2$. For the previous example the gain is reduced to half of its maximum value within a bandwidth of $\Delta\nu/\nu_0 = 0.125$.

It is clear that the emission bandwidth of a laser operating on a free-bound transition will be much smaller than the gain bandwidth, since gain narrowing and possible cavity effects will reduce the spectral width of the emission. However, such radiation would still extract energy from all of the electrons since self-relaxation would quickly restore any holes burnt into the electron velocity distribution. In other words, the transition can be considered as homogeneously broadened down to a pulse duration given by the self-relaxation time of the electrons.

In summary, by analogy with the situation at a bound-bound transition, an "inversion" can be defined for a free-bound transition which leads to gain by stimulated radiative recombination. Gain formulas for three cases have been derived, the first being characterized by a Maxwellian electron velocity distribution, the second by a velocity distribution approaching a delta function, and the third by further restriction of the electrons in phase space by directionality.

Though difficult to achieve, gain on a free-bound transition would certainly be an effect of high interest, possibly leading to a tunable short-wavelength laser. A more detailed discussion concerning pumping requirements and competing processes will be left to a further publication.

This work was supported in part by the Commission of the European Communities in the framework of the Euratom/Institute for Plasma Physics Association.

---

[1]W. T. Silfvast, L. H. Szeto, and O. R. Wood, II, Appl. Phys. Lett. **36**, 500 (1980).

[2]W. T. Silfvast, L. H. Szeto, and O. R. Wood, II, Appl. Phys. Lett. **39**, 212 (1981).

[3]W. T. Silfvast and O. R. Wood, II, Opt. Lett. **7**, 34 (1981).

[4]J. J. Macklin, O. R. Wood, II, and W. T. Silfvast, IEEE J. Quantum Electron. **18**, 1832 (1982).

[5]D. L. Matthews *et al.*, Phys. Rev. Lett. **54**, 110 (1985).

[6]S. Suckewer, C. H. Skinner, H. Milchberg, C. Keane, and D. Voorhees, Phys. Rev. Lett. **55**, 1753 (1985).

[7]J. D. Kilkenny, D. W. Lee, M. H. Key, and J. G. Lunney, Phys. Rev. A **22**, 2746 (1980).

[8]See, for example, D. Mihalas, *Stellar Atmospheres* (Freeman, San Francisco, 1978), 2nd ed., p. 94.

[9]H. R. Griem, *Plasma Spectroscopy* (McGraw-Hill, New York, 1964), p. 136.

[10]G. V. Marr, *Photoionization Processes in Gases* (Academic, New York, 1967), p. 31 ff.

[11]D. R. Bates, A. E. Kingston, and R. W. P. McWhirter, Proc. Roy. Soc. London, Ser. A **267**, 297 (1962).

[12]L. Spitzer, Jr., *Physics of Fully Ionized Gases* (Interscience, New York, 1956), p. 89.

Reprinted with permission from *Physical Review Letters*, Vol. 57(23), pp. 2939-2942 (December 8, 1986).

Observation of a Short-Wavelength Laser Pumped by Auger Decay

H. C. Kapteyn,[(1)] R. W. Lee,[(2)] and R. W. Falcone[(1)]

[(1)]*Department of Physics, University of California, Berkeley, California 94720*

[(2)]*Lawrence Livermore National Laboratory, University of California, Livermore, California 94550*

(Received 15 September 1986)

We report the observation of gain in a new type of short-wavelength laser system at 108.9 nm. Soft x rays from a laser-produced plasma photoeject an inner-shell electron from xenon, and a population inversion is created by subsequent Auger decay to particular excited states. A model for this system is described, spectroscopic data are presented, and gain limitations due to parasitic amplified spontaneous emission are discussed. A maximum gain of 0.8 cm^{-1} over a length of 9 cm is reported.

Interest in the development of new short-wavelength lasers has resulted in recent demonstrations[1,2] of stimulated emission in the region of 10–20 nm. The techniques used to produce population inversions in those experiments involved collisional ionization and excitation by energetic electrons in dense laser-produced plasmas,[1] and recombination of ionized species in magnetically confined laser-produced plasmas.[2]

In this Letter we report the demonstration of a new class of short-wavelength lasers pumped by photoionization followed by Auger decay. As shown in Fig. 1, soft x-ray emission from a high-temperature laser-produced plasma causes photoejection of an inner-shell $4d$ electron from neutral xenon. The resulting ion, Xe II $4d^9 5s^2 5p^6\,{}^2D_{3/2,5/2}$, rapidly undergoes Auger decay, producing various excited states of Xe III. The branching of the Auger decay results in a population inversion between the levels Xe III $5s^0 5p^6\,{}^1S_0$ and Xe III $5s^1 5p^5\,{}^1P_1$. Gain is observed at the transition wavelength of 108.9 nm.

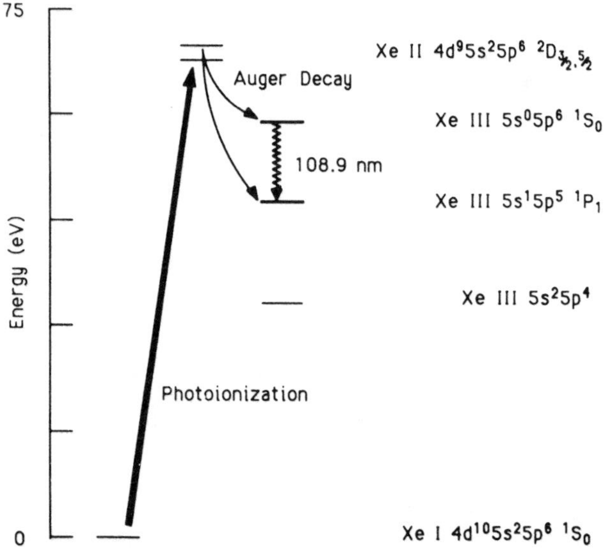

FIG. 1. Energy levels of xenon showing pumping of Xe III levels by photoionization followed by Auger decay. The lasing transition is at 108.9 nm.

The production of a population inversion by core-electron photoejection followed by selective Auger decay was originally proposed by McGuire[3] and recently discussed by Mendelsohn and Harris.[4] An advantage of this type of short-wavelength laser scheme over others[1,2] is that the population inversion is produced by a flux of photons, which results in low ion and electron densities in the lasing region, thus circumventing complex collisional pumping kinetics. This allows simpler modeling of population dynamics and results in smaller plasma refractive-index gradients. Large excited-state populations can be produced in this scheme since laser-produced plasmas are intense and efficient soft x-ray sources, and inner-shell photoionization cross sections and Auger branching ratios can be favorable.[4] Importantly, this scheme should be scalable to shorter wavelengths with existing technology.

The original proposal for photoionization pumping of short-wavelength lasers was made by Duguay and Rentzepis.[5] More recently, several related pumping schemes produced population inversions on longer-wavelength transitions; tunable lasers have been used to populate states which were selectively photoionized[6] or which selectively autoionized[7] into particular final states. Caro *et al.* have shown that soft x rays from laser-produced plasmas can create high densities of excited-state species by photoionization pumping.[8] Plasma-produced soft x rays have also been used to pump lasing states directly.[9]

A diagram of the experiment is shown in Fig. 2. A Nd-doped glass laser pulse with an energy of 55 J and a pulse width of 1 nsec is directed into a target cell containing 1 Torr of xenon gas. The laser is focused to a 50-μm × 9-cm line on a solid tantalum target at a power density of 10^{12} W/cm^2. Broad-band soft x rays radiate into a large solid angle from the resulting plasma. A 3×3-mm^2×9-cm-long channel faces the plasma and is 2 cm away from and parallel to it. The channel defines a long and narrow region which is viewed by the detection system. The xenon-filled target chamber is isolated from

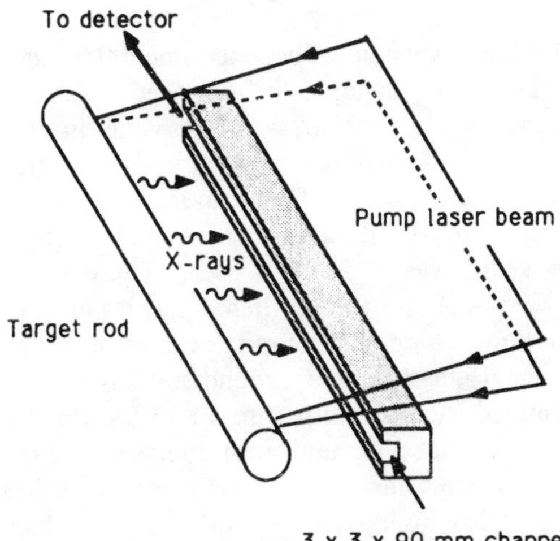

FIG. 2. Target cell design showing the line focus of the Nd-doped glass laser on the tantalum target rod and emission of x rays from the resulting plasma. The channel confines the observed region of excited xenon.

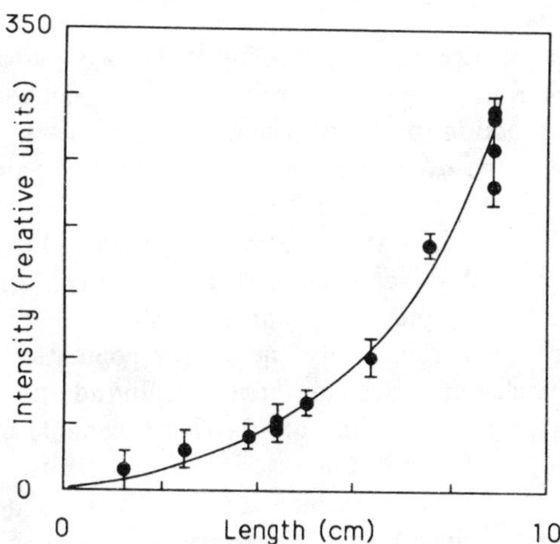

FIG. 3. 108.9-nm emission intensity as a function of illuminated channel length with the use of a normal mixture of xenon isotopes. The data are fitted by a function describing emission from a Doppler-broadened transition, yielding the gain coefficient $\alpha = 0.4\ \text{cm}^{-1}$.

a 0.5-m vacuum spectrometer by a 1-mm-thick lithium fluoride window. Fluorescence from the ionized xenon is dispersed by the spectrometer and detected with the use of an x-ray streak camera, which records the emission intensity as a function of time and wavelength for each laser shot. The streak camera was modified[10] for high soft x-ray sensitivity by replacement of the normal photocathode with a microchannel plate with adjustable gain. In our experiments data were taken with a wavelength resolution of 1.5 nm and a time resolution of 150 psec. The information was recorded on calibrated film and analyzed by use of an optical scanning digitizer.

The fluorescence intensity at 108.9 nm is determined as a function of length of the pumped region by the shadowing of varying portions of the channel from the x-ray source. This technique maintains constant plasma–light-source characteristics and constant electron and ion densities along the length of the channel, except at the ends. Apertures limit the collection solid angle of the detector so that the field of view is confined inside the channel. The detection efficiency is approximately constant along the length of the channel. This was verified by the observation of approximately equal signal intensity from each half-length of the channel. Most data were taken with the illuminated lengths centered along the slot to minimize end effects.

As shown in Figs. 3 and 4, we found that the emission intensity increased nonlinearly with illuminated length. Each datum point indicates the peak intensity of the 108.9-nm emission for one laser shot, and error bars indicate the noise level of the digitized film data. The Nd-doped glass pumping-laser energy was within $\pm 10\%$ of the nominal value for all points. The data were fitted by a spectrally integrated brightness function (shown as the solid line) generated by the consideration of the narrow angular and spectrally unresolved emission from an inhomogeneously broadened line source, with the assumption of uniform gain along its length. The two-parameter fit involves an overall intensity constant and the gain coefficient. Although the indicated curve is a numerical integration, the function reduces to $\exp(\alpha l)/(\alpha l)^{1/2}$ when $\alpha l > 2$, where α is the gain coefficient per unit length at line center and l is the length.[1]

The results shown in Fig. 3 are from an experiment in which normal xenon (an isotopic mixture with the largest component 27% ^{132}Xe) was used. No significant difference was observed with use of isotopically enriched xenon (84% ^{136}Xe). Figure 4 shows the results with use of the isotopically enriched xenon, when a 150-nm-thick parylene filter was placed over the open side of the channel facing the plasma. Parylene with this thickness will

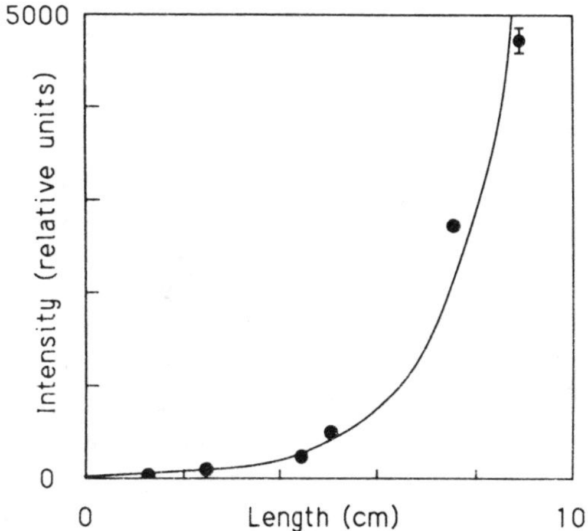

FIG. 4. Same as Fig. 3 except with the use of isotopically enriched xenon and 150-nm-thick parylene to filter the pump soft x rays. Note that the relative intensity units are the same as in Fig. 3. The fit to the data yields a gain coefficient of $\alpha = 0.8\ \text{cm}^{-1}$.

transmit 60% of the pumping soft x rays, but is opaque to photons below 50 eV energy. We expect that the filtering action of the parylene will increase the observed gain in the experiment by eliminating two gain-limiting effects. First, intense parasitic amplified spontaneous emission (ASE) at the lasing transition (11.4 eV), generated in the xenon-filled region between the plasma light source and the channel, results in a photon flux which could radiatively quench the population inversion in the channel. Second, intense pump radiation from the laser-produced plasma at 12–67 eV, capable of ejecting a Xe $5s$ electron but not a $4d$ electron, results in a higher density of electrons which could collisionally quench the population inversion. We observed a gain coefficient of 0.4 cm^{-1} with normal xenon and without the parylene filter, and 0.8 cm^{-1} with the isotopically enriched xenon and the filter. This corresponds to an output 50 times larger with the 9-cm length in the latter case and is perhaps the most dramatic indication of stimulated emission.

A calculation of the expected gain was made with the assumption that the laser plasma source radiated with a spectral distribution corresponding to a blackbody temperature of 30 eV, with an assumed conversion efficiency of 7% from laser energy to total radiated energy.[11] Photoionization cross sections are known[12] and estimates were made of the Auger branching rates from electron-spectroscopy data,[13-15] a multiconfiguration Dirac-Fock code,[16] and fluorescence measurements.[17] The inversion density is thus calculated to be approximately 2% of the total Xe II ions initially produced by $4d$ electron photoionziation. We measured[17] the lifetime of the upper laser level to be 4.75 ± 0.15 nsec, in good agreement with calculations[16] which also indicate that the primary decay of Xe III $5s^0 5p^5 {}^1S_0$ is the 108.9-nm transition. The resultant gain cross section, calculated with the assumption of Doppler broadening of a single line, is 3×10^{-13} cm^2. At a pressure of 1 Torr and 2 cm from the plasma target, the peak gain coefficient is thus estimated to be 2 cm^{-1} in the absence of quenching. The effects of isotope shifts and hyperfine splittings on the gain are difficult to predict since their magnitudes are calculated[18] to be on the order of the Doppler linewidth. However, we expect the gain for the normal xenon isotopic mixture to be 2–3 times smaller than the single-line gain predicted above for isotopically enriched ^{136}Xe.

In the absence of the parylene filter, parasitic ASE could act to limit the gain to a maximum value. However, the actual effect of the filter is difficult to predict. In addition to eliminating the inversion quenching effects of parasitic ASE, the filter is expected to reduce the pumping flux, and, thus, the inversion density, by 40% while decreasing the total electron density by a factor of 2. The reduction in the electron density could be significant in determination of the observable gain if collisional quenching (by recombination or deexcitation) limits the population inversion. The experimental observation is that both the isotopically enriched xenon and the parylene filter are required to observe an increase in the gain over the normal-xenon, unfiltered case. Neither improvement alone was sufficient to increase the gain significantly. For the data in Figs. 3 and 4, the emission pulse width was about 600 psec. These results imply that both ASE (in the unfiltered case) and electron collisional quenching act to limit the gain in our geometry. Collisional quenching by ground-state xenon atoms was determined[17] to be unimportant at a pressure of 1 Torr.

Evidence that photoionization followed by rapid Auger decay is the primary pumping mechanism in this system was provided by a separate experiment,[17] which used a plasma produced by a lower-energy, high-repetition-rate, short-pulse laser as a soft x-ray light source to excite the xenon. We observed that the ratio of fluorescence intensities from the upper and lower laser levels was in good agreement with predictions of the Auger branching ratio from both the electron spectroscopy data[13-15] and the code calculation.[16] We also observed that the start of the fluorescence decay from the upper laser level was simultaneous with the several-hundred-picosecond–long soft x-ray pulse from the plasma source, indicating a rapid pumping process.

The gain-limiting effect of parasitic ASE must be considered in the design of photopumped laser schemes. In a first approximation, an atom at the center of a uniformly excited spherical region of radius r, with a radial gain-length product ar, will have an effective lifetime reduced by a factor of approximately $\exp(ar)$. In real systems this problem is manifested as a nonlocal, geometrically determined, gain-limiting depletion rate. A related observation is that high gains transverse to the observation axis of a laser make it difficult, if not impossible, to observe exponential increases in emission intensity with increasing length if the inversion lifetime is on the order of the transit time through the region. This problem is especially important for photon-pumped short-wavelength laser schemes involving plasma x-ray sources which radiate into large solid angles. The solution to this problem is to restrict gain in all but one direction. In our experiment this was accomplished with use of the narrow channel and the parylene filter to limit the gain transverse to the observed volume.

In conclusion, we have demonstrated gain in a new type of short-wavelength laser system. Excited-state ions are produced by Auger decay into selected levels following photoejection of an inner-shell electron by broadband soft x rays from a laser-produced plasma. We expect that this type of laser system will be scaled to shorter wavelengths with the use of more intense laser-produced–plasma x-ray sources and efficient x-ray focusing optics.

We thank M. H. Chen, M. J. Eckart, S. E. Harris, G. Kolbe, and J. H. Scofield for useful discussions. This work was supported by the National Science Foundation under Grant No. PHY 83-51689 and by the University of California Lawrence Livermore National Laboratory Institutional Research and Development Program. We also acknowledge the generous support of AT&T Bell Laboratories. One of us (R.W.F.) is a National Science Foundation Presidential Young Investigator.

---

[1]D. L. Mathews, P. L. Hagelstein, M. D. Rosen, M. J. Eckart, N. M. Ceglio, A. U. Hazi, H. Medecki, B. J. MacGowan, J. E. Trebes, B. L. Whitten, E. M. Campbell, C. W. Hatcher, A. M. Hawryluk, R. L. Kauffman, L. D. Pleasance, G. Rambach, J. H. Scofield, G. Stone, and T. A. Weaver, Phys. Rev. Lett. **54**, 110 (1985).

[2]S. Suckewer, C. H. Skinner, H. Milchberg, C. Keane, and D. Voorhees, Phys. Rev. Lett. **55**, 1753 (1985).

[3]E. J. McGuire, Phys. Rev. Lett. **35**, 844 (1975).

[4]A. J. Mendelsohn and S. E. Harris, Opt. Lett. **10**, 128 (1985).

[5]M. A. Duguay and P. M. Rentzepis, Appl. Phys. Lett. **10**, 350 (1967).

[6]W. R. Green and R. W. Falcone, Opt. Lett. **2**, 115 (1978).

[7]J. Boker, R. R. Freeman, and W. E. Cooke, Phys. Rev. Lett. **48**, 1242 (1982).

[8]R. G. Caro, J. C. Wang, J. F. Young, and S. E. Harris, Phys. Rev. A **30**, 1407 (1984).

[9]W. T. Silfvast, J. J. Macklin, and O. R. Wood, Opt. Lett. **8**, 551 (19883).

[10]R. W. Falcone, H. C. Kapteyn, and R. W. Lee, to be published.

[11]R. G. Caro, J. C. Wang, R. W. Falcone, J. F. Young, and S. E. Harris, Appl. Phys. Lett. **42**, 9 (1983).

[12]J. Berkowitz, *Photoabsorption, Photoionization and Photoelectron Spectroscopy* (Academic, New York, 1979).

[13]L. O. Werme, T. Bergmark, and K. Siegbahn, Phys. Scr. **6**, 141 (1972).

[14]H. Aksela, S. Aksela, and H. Pulkkinen, Phys. Rev. A **30**, 865 (1984).

[15]S. Southworth, U. Becker, C. Truesdale, P. Kobrin, D. Lindle, S. Owaki, and D. A. Shirley, Phys. Rev. A **28**, 261 (1983).

[16]M. H. Chen, private communication.

[17]H. C. Kapteyn, M. M. Murnane, R. W. Falcone, G. Kolbe, and R. W. Lee, to be published.

[18]J. H. Scofield, private communication.

Reprinted with permission from *Physical Review Letters*, Vol. 59(11), pp. 1185-1188 (September 14, 1987).

Soft X-Ray Lasing in Neonlike Germanium and Copper Plasmas

T. N. Lee, E. A. McLean, and R. C. Elton

Laser Plasma Branch, Plasma Physics Division, Naval Research Laboratory, Washington, D.C., 20375

(Received 27 March 1987; revised manuscript received 22 June 1987)

Soft x-ray $3p \rightarrow 3s$ lasing in neonlike germanium (Ge^{22+}) and copper (Cu^{19+}) in the wavelength interval of 195 to 285 Å is observed for the first time, with gain coefficients ranging from 1.7 to 4.1 cm^{-1}, the higher gain with germanium. The lasing plasmas are produced by the focusing of a driving laser beam ($\lambda = 1.05$ μm, 2-ns FWHM) into an 18-mm-long line onto thin films and slab targets. The measured $J=0$ to 1 gain coefficients are comparable to those of the $J=2$ to 1 transitions. The measured wavelengths of the six lasing lines compare favorably with recent calculations.

Significant $3p \rightarrow 3s$ amplification of soft x rays in neonlike selenium with a gain coefficient of $\simeq 5$ cm^{-1} was recently demonstrated[1] in experiments at the Lawrence Livermore National Laboratory (LLNL) using laser-vaporized ultrathin foils.[2] As successful as these initial experiments were, certain puzzling aspects arose from the data analyses[1-3] that deserve further investigation. There was surprisingly low emission on the transition originating on the $2p^5_{1/2}3p_{1/2}$ $J=0$ level (for molybdenum as well as selenium). The gain for this transition is predicted to be $\simeq 1-2$ times larger than that for the $2p^5_{1/2}3p_{3/2}$ and $2p^5_{3/2}3p_{3/2}$ $J=2$ levels.[3,4] In fact, it was first undetected[1] and later found[3] to have a factor-of-5 lower gain coefficient (<1 cm^{-1}). An understanding of this anomaly could be important. It is also worth investigating target designs other than thin foils in order to understand more fully the hydrodynamic conditions[2,5] for optimum laser output. Finally, high-precision wavelength measurements for the lasing lines are needed for comparison with theoretical predictions and atomic physics models.

The present experimental investigation using time-integrated diagnostics addresses these issues, in elements of lower Z (Ge and Cu) than those used at LLNL. These elements are compatible[4] with our lower-power driving laser. To our knowledge, the successful results reported here represent the first measurements of gain in Ge and Cu in the extreme-ultraviolet spectral region, and, furthermore, the first demonstration of gain for neonlike ions with use of slab targets (rather than thin exploding films). In addition, we report here the first evidence of gain on a transition from a $J=0$ level being comparable to that from a $J=2$ level, in reasonable agreement with calculations.[3]

The experimental setup is described as follows, with further details given by Elton and co-workers.[6] A single beam of the Pharos III Nd-doped glass laser was operated at 1.05-μm wavelength over an energy range of 350–480 J in a 2-ns-FWHM pulse. A 200-μm-wide, 18-mm-long line focus was produced with use of a combination cylindrical-spherical lens system. This gave a target irradiance of about 6×10^{12} W/cm^2. The length of the target was always less than that of the line focus by at least 2 mm at the viewing end. The germanium targets were all slabs about 3 mm thick. Most Cu targets consisted of a Formvar ($C_{11}H_{18}O_5$) substrate of 1200 Å nominal thickness, with a copper overcoating of 1000 Å; the driving laser irradiated the copper side. Thicker (1.3 μm) copper foils as well as 3.2-mm-thick copper slab targets also were tested successfully.

The extreme-ultraviolet data (time integrated) in the 40–580-Å region were recorded on Kodak type-101 film with a 1-m grazing-incidence spectrograph, which was positioned to view the plasma axially. With a 5-μm entrance slit, the instrumental spectral resolution was $\simeq 0.04$ Å, which is comparable to the expected Doppler width of optically thin lines. A 1200-Å-thick aluminum filter was used to reject most higher-order radiation with wavelengths extending from approximately 70 Å to the 170-Å L edge. The spectrograph entrance slit was positioned close (4 cm from the center of the line focus) to the plasma and was oriented parallel to the driving laser beam, in order to collect refracted radiation[3,7] in the corresponding plane. The spectrograph thus accepted radiation refracted through an angle as large as ± 9 mrad, and also viewed plasma extending as far as 3 mm from the target in the direction of the incoming driver laser beam. In addition, a bent-mica-crystal x-ray spectrograph set to view the plasma transversely was used to monitor resonance lines in the 6–17-Å spectral region from various ions. An x-ray pinhole camera, filtered to detect x rays of energy 1 keV, photographed the hot plasma in both the axial and the transverse directions. According to the x-ray pinhole photographs[6] taken in the transverse direction, the plasmas created were of good uniformity.

Amplified spontaneous emission was recorded for the three $3p \rightarrow 3s$ Ge XXIII lines (from neonlike Ge^{22+} ions) as indicated in Fig. 1, where the spectra for 4- and 15-mm target lengths are shown. A rapid increase in intensity with length is very apparent. Two of these originate on transitions from the $J=2$ levels and one from the

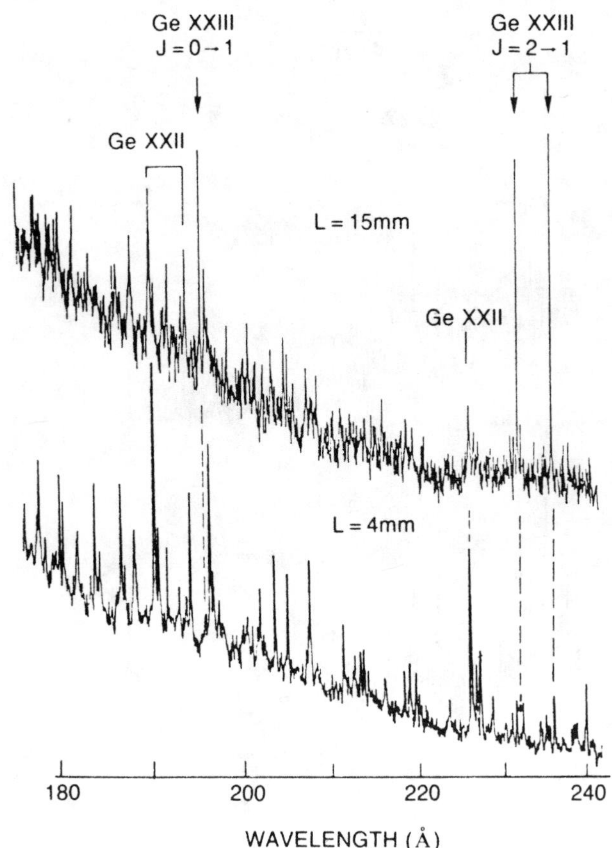

FIG. 1. Microdensitometer traces of second-order spectra obtained for plasma lengths of 4 and 15 mm, showing the neonlike Ge XXIII (Ge^{22+} ion) lasing lines at 236.26 and 232.24 Å ($J=2$ to 1) and 196.06 Å ($J=0$ to 1) increasing with length. Sodiumlike Ge XXII lines shown arise from 3 → 3 transitions.

$J=0$ level with line emissions at 236.26, 232.24, and 196.06 Å (±0.04 Å), respectively (see Table I). Unfortunately, the line at 236.26 Å is a blend with another spectral line and we did not determine the gain for this line. The other two lines are relatively free of overlapping lines.

Relative line intensities were derived from photographic densities with a density versus exposure curve, obtained with multiple exposures, and similar to that of Henke *et al.*[11] Exponentiation of the resulting intensities of the Ge lines with increasing target length is shown in Fig. 2(a) for the $J=2$ to 1 line. The solid line in this figure represents a best fit of the gain scaling relation[12] $[\exp(aL)-1]^{3/2}/[aL\exp(aL)]^{1/2}$ for amplified spontaneous emission through a plasma of length L, with a gain coefficient at line center of $a=4.1\pm0.3$ cm^{-1}. Similar data for the Ge XXIII $J=0$ to 1 line are plotted in Fig. 2(b), where a best fit is obtained with a gain coefficient at line center of $a=3.1\pm0.3$ cm^{-1}. For the multiple-shot data obtained at each length, the shot-to-shot variations shown are more significant than relative-intensity uncertainties (approximately ±10%).

Amplification was also recorded for the three $3p\rightarrow3s$ Cu XX lines (from neonlike Cu^{19+} ions), as indicated in Fig. 3, with wavelengths (±0.04 Å) for $J=2$ to 1 transitions of 284.67 and 279.31 Å, and for $J=0$ to 1 transitions of 221.11 Å (see Table I). The 284.67-Å lasing line nearly coincides with the longer-wavelength component of the sixth order of the $4f\rightarrow3d$ Cu XIX doublet in sodiumlike Cu^{18+} ions at 47.442 Å.[13] The net contribution due to the lasing line can be determined by our subtracting the intensity of the nonoverlapping doublet component, because both lines of the doublet are about equal in intensity when there is negligible amplification of the neonlike Cu^{19+} ion lines (see the $L=6$-mm trace of Fig. 3). The resulting intensities of the two $J=2$ to 1 Cu XX lines were found to be approximately equal at all plasma lengths (as for Ge XXIII in Fig. 1). Likewise, the overall intensity of the $J=0$ to 1 Cu XX line was found to be comparable to that of the $J=2$ to 1 lines, as shown in Fig. 3. Exponentiations of the Cu XX line intensities are shown in Fig. 4, where a best-fit theoretical curve indicates gain coefficients of 1.7 ± 0.2 cm^{-1} for the two $J=2$ to 1 lines [Fig. 4(a)] and 2.0 ± 0.2 cm^{-1} for the $J=0$ to 1 line [Fig. 4(b)].

It is intriguing that comparable gain was obtained by

TABLE I. Predicted (Refs. 8–10) and measured wavelengths.

Transitions	Predicted values (Å) Ref. 8	Ref. 9	Ref. 10	Measured values (±0.04 Å) (Å)
		Cu XX		
$(2p^5_{1/2}3p_{1/2})_0\rightarrow(2p^5_{1/2}3s_{1/2})_1$	221.38	220.68		221.11
$(2p^5_{3/2}3p_{3/2})_2\rightarrow(2p^5_{3/2}3s_{1/2})_1$	279.22	279.37		279.31
$(2p^5_{1/2}3p_{3/2})_2\rightarrow(2p^5_{1/2}3s_{1/2})_1$	284.59	284.70	284.97	284.67
		Ge XXIII		
$(2p^5_{1/2}3p_{1/2})_0\rightarrow(2p^5_{1/2}3s_{1/2})_1$	196.38	195.44		196.06
$(2p^5_{3/2}3p_{3/2})_2\rightarrow(2p^5_{3/2}3s_{1/2})_1$	232.24	232.28		232.24
$(2p^5_{1/2}3p_{3/2})_2\rightarrow(2p^5_{1/2}3s_{1/2})_1$	236.27	236.27		236.26

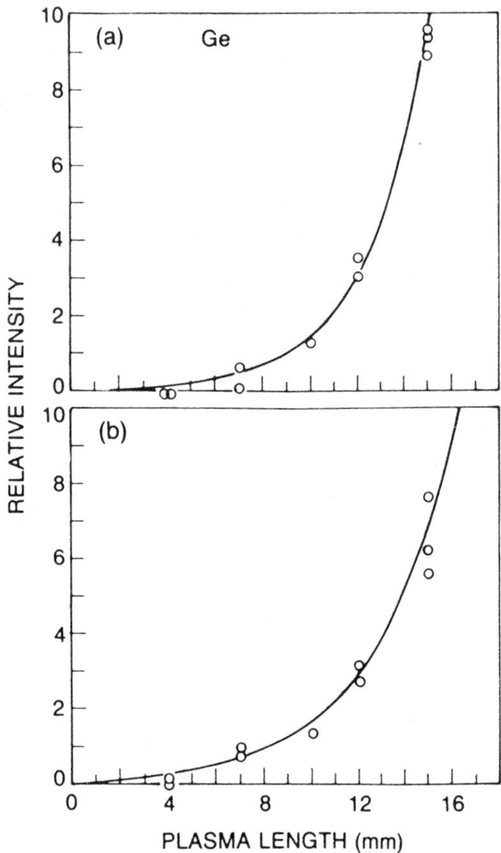

FIG. 2. Relative intensities vs plasma length for (a) 232.24 Å ($J=2$ to 1) and (b) 196.06 Å ($J=0$ to 1) lasing lines, along with calculated gain curves for gain coefficients of 4.1 and 3.1 cm^{-1}, respectively. Estimated uncertainties of $\pm 10\%$ in relative intensities are within the shot-to-shot spread.

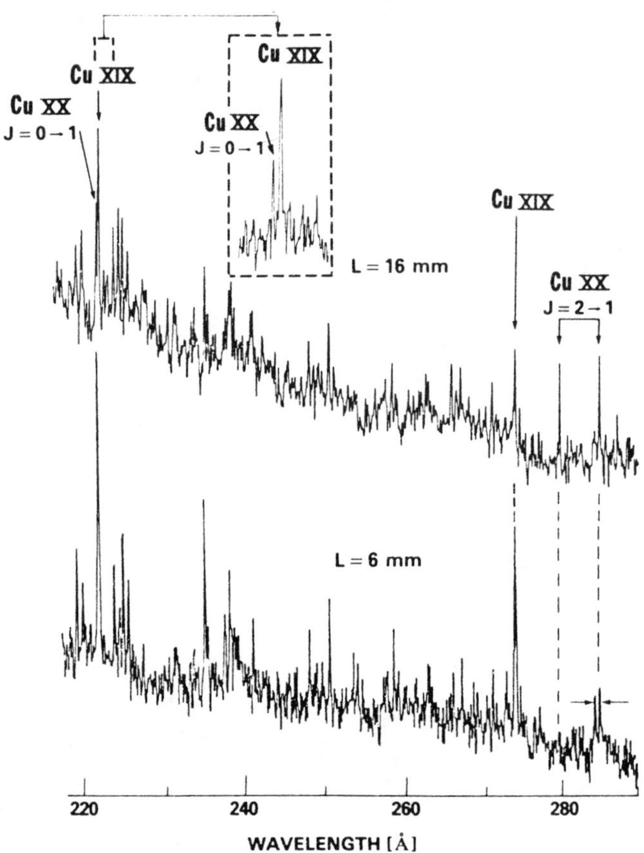

FIG. 3. Microdensitometer traces of first-order spectra obtained for plasma lengths of 6 and 16 mm, showing the neonlike Cu XX (Cu^{19+} ion) lasing lines at 279.31 and 284.67 Å ($J=2$ to 1) and 221.11 Å ($J=0$ to 1) increasing with length. The second order of the 221.11 Å ($J=0$ to 1) and the sodiumlike Cu XIX 221.37-Å lines are inserted on the expanded scale. Thin-film Cu-Formvar targets are used. The lines labeled as Cu XIX arise from $3\rightarrow 3$ transitions. The doublet (marked by two horizontal arrows) which appears near 284 Å for the $L=6$-mm case arises from the sixth-order $4f\rightarrow 3d$ line of Cu XIX.

the irradiation of thin and thick (1.3 μm) copper foils of various lengths, and that thick-slab germanium targets gave such a high gain. Also, 3.2-mm-thick solid copper slab targets produced the three gain lines. Such thick targets have been avoided previously because it was thought that nonuniformities and radial gradients in density and temperature could inhibit lasing.

The energy emitted in the Ge and Cu lasing lines was derived from the spectrographic data with use of a film calibration by Henke *et al.*[11] The magnitudes of the output from both ends of the 15-mm Ge and 16-mm Cu lasing plasmas were estimated to be $\simeq 3$ and 1 μJ, respectively. This is assumed to be emitted over a solid angle of $\simeq 10^{-4}$ sr, as defined by the source geometry. These energies correspond to a LLNL value for similar target lengths.[1] The data plotted in Figs. 2 and 4 represent 90% of the shots taken, indicating good reproducibility. It is important to note that no lines in the covered spectral region other than those from neonlike ions increase nonlinearly with length.

In addition to the three lasing lines, the end-on extreme-ultraviolet spectra showed resonance lines from the sodiumlike Cu^{18+} and Ge^{21+} ions (see Figs. 1 and 3), including the $3\rightarrow 3$ transition lines in the 220–304-Å region for Cu and 190–240-Å region for Ge, which served as reference wavelengths.[13] All of these lines were predicted to be highly optically thick, as evidenced by measured widths much greater than the Doppler width. Surprisingly, their intensities were found to be particularly weak for longer target lengths (see Figs. 1 and 3). This remains a problem for further investigation. According to the x-ray crystal-spectrograph data, plasma conditions are the same on most shots. On all shots, such time-integrated data showed relatively strong resonance-line emission from fluorinelike Cu^{20+} and somewhat weaker oxygenlike Cu^{21+} ions, in addition to the intense emission from the neonlike Cu^{19+} lasing ions. Essentially, similar spectral features are observed for germanium, except for somewhat fluorinelike Ge^{23+} and very weak oxygenlike Ge^{24+} ion lines for similar irradiances, as expected. These data indicate a peak electron

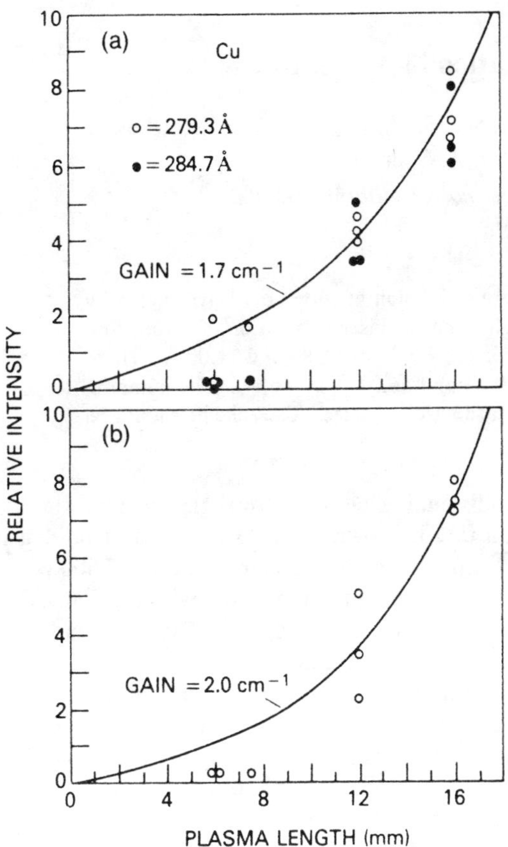

FIG. 4. Relative intensities vs plasma length for (a) the 279.31 and 284.67 Å ($J=2$ to 1) and (b) the 221.11 Å ($J=0$ to 1) lasing lines, along with calculated gain curves for gain coefficients of 1.7 and 2 cm^{-1}, respectively. Estimated uncertainties of $\pm 10\%$ in relative intensities are within the shot-to-shot spread. Data from thin-film Cu-Formvar targets were used.

temperature in the range of 400–700 eV.

End-on x-ray pinhole photographs obtained with thin-film targets indicate that the foil-plasma boundary remained intact as the plasma expanded towards the incoming laser beam, except for an occasional narrow jetting towards the rear. This suggests that the thin-film targets mainly ablated, rather than exploding symmetrically. This is consistent with the lasing from thicker Ge and Cu targets.

In summary, time-integrated gain coefficients for neonlike Cu^{19+} and Ge^{22+} ions have been measured for the first time. It is particularly interesting to notice that the $J=2$ to 1 gain coefficient of 4.1 cm^{-1} observed with a thick, plain slab of germanium under single-sided illumination is comparable to that obtained by the LLNL group with a selenium-film target which was illuminated from both sides. Also, for the first time, the copper $J=0$ to 1 line showed a gain coefficient comparable to that for the $J=2$ to 1 lines, in approximate agreement with recent calculations.[3,4] These results support electron-collisional excitation, where the cross section is known to favor the $J=0$ level. Because of the high spectral resolution possible with photographic detection and a very narrow (5 μm) entrance slit, we are able to make detailed comparisons of the measured wavelengths with theoretical calculations and extrapolations,[8-10] as shown in Table I. Our results should provide valuable input for future target designs and experiments with modest laser facilities.

The authors gratefully acknowledge the unwavering support of S. E. Bodner and B. H. Ripin and the many valuable contributions of H. R. Griem. We recall with appreciation numerous useful discussions with members of the LLNL group. Generous contributions at the U.S. Naval Research Laboratory were made by U. Feldman, J. F. Seely, C. M. Brown, J. O. Ekberg, J. E. Dahlburg, J. H. Gardner, J. A. Stamper, S. P. Obenschain, R. H. Lehmberg, A. Mostovych, J. Grun, C. K. Manka, K. Kearney, D. J. Michels, and W. A. Molander. Valuable technical support was provided by J. L. Ford, L. M. Shirey, and N. E. Nocerino. This research was supported by the U.S. Office of Naval Research, the Strategic Defense Initiative Office, and the U.S. Department of Energy.

Note added.—Since the submission of this paper, two more lasing lines in the neonlike Ge^{22+} ion have been identified. They are the $(2p^5_{3/2}3p_{3/2})_1$-$(2p^5_{3/2}3s_{1/2})_1$ and $(2p^5_{3/2}3p_{1/2})_2$-$(2p^5_{3/2}3s_{1/2})_1$ lines at 247.32 and 286.46 Å, respectively.

[1]D. L. Matthews *et al.*, Phys. Rev. Lett. **54**, 110 (1985).

[2]M. D. Rosen *et al.*, Phys. Rev. Lett. **54**, 106 (1985).

[3]D. L. Matthews *et al.*, J. Phys. (Paris) **47**, 1 (1986).

[4]U. Feldman, J. F. Seely, and G. A. Doschek, J. Phys. (Paris) **47**, 187 (1986).

[5]R. A. London and M. D. Rosen, Phys. Fluids **29**, 3813 (1986).

[6]R. C. Elton, T. N. Lee, and W. A. Molander, J. Opt. Soc. Am. B **4**, 539 (1987); T. N. Lee, W. A. Molander, J. L. Ford, and R. C. Elton, Rev. Sci. Instrum. **57**, 2052 (1986).

[7]V. A. Chirkov, Kvantovaya Elektron. (Moscow) **11**, 2253 (1984) [Sov. J. Quantum Electron. **14**, 1497 (1984)].

[8]J. H. Scofield (LLNL), private communication.

[9]J. A. Cogordan and S. Lunell, Phys. Scr. **33**, 406 (1986).

[10]R. R. Harr, L. J. Curtis, N. Reistad, C. Jupen, I. Martinson, B. M. Johnson, K. W. Jones, and M. Meron, Phys. Scr. **35**, 296 (1987).

[11]B. L. Henke, F. G. Fujiwara, M. A. Tester, C. H. Dittmore, and M. A. Palmer, J. Opt. Soc. Am. B **1**, 828 (1984).

[12]G. J. Linford, E. R. Peressini, W. R. Sooy, and M. L. Spaeth, Appl. Opt. **13**, 379 (1974); R. A. London, M. D. Rosen, and C. Cerjan (LLNL), private communication.

[13]J. Reader, V. Kaufman, J. Sugar, J. O. Ekberg, U. Feldman, C. M. Brown, J. F. Seely, and W. L. Rowan, J. Opt. Soc. Am. B (to be published).

Reprinted with permission from *Physical Review Letters,* Vol. 59(19), pp. 2157-2160 (November 9, 1987).

Demonstration of Soft–X-Ray Amplification in Nickel-like Ions

B. J. MacGowan, S. Maxon, P. L. Hagelstein,[a] C. J. Keane, R. A. London, D. L. Matthews, M. D. Rosen, J. H. Scofield, and D. A. Whelan

Lawrence Livermore National Laboratory, Livermore, California 94550

(Received 10 August 1987)

We report the first observation of amplification of spontaneous emission at soft x-ray wavelengths by ions in the nickel-like sequence. The ions are created by high-intensity laser irradiation of a thin foil. Gains of order 1 cm^{-1} are observed on $J=0$-1, $4d$-$4p$ transitions in Eu^{35+} at 65.83 and 71.00 Å. There is some evidence for amplification on the analogous lines at 50.26 and 56.09 Å in Yb^{42+}. The pumping mechanism is believed to be electron collisional excitation from the ground state. The scheme should be readily scalable to produce amplification in W^{46+} at 43.15 Å.

Since the demonstration of an extreme ultraviolet amplifier at 206.3 and 209.6 Å,[1,2] there has been much effort to develop an amplifier to produce significant power at wavelengths below the carbon K absorption edge at 43.76 Å. One motivation is to produce a coherent, monochromatic, high-brightness source suitable for holography of biological specimens in the "water window" between the K edges of carbon and oxygen.[3]

The work of Matthews *et al.*[1] achieved gain on $3p$-$3s$ transitions in neonlike selenium ions produced by intense irradiation of a thin Se foil. The explosion of the foil led to the creation of a plasma which served as the amplifier medium. The dominant line expected to be amplified was the $J=0$-1 transition at 182.4 Å, predicted to be pumped by electron collisional excitation from the ground state.[4] Reference 1 did not observe large gain on the $J=0$-1 line but instead saw gains of order 5 cm^{-1} on $J=2$-1 transitions. The population mechanisms for the $J=2$ levels are more complicated, including contributions by direct collisional excitation, recombination, and cascading from higher energy levels.

The Ne-like Se result has been extrapolated to higher-Z ions. Y^{29+} has shown gain at 155.0 and 157.1 Å while Mo^{32+} has produced a gain of 4 cm^{-1} at 131.0 and 132.7 Å.[5] However, the rapid scaling[6] of laser power required with increased target Z makes Ne-like schemes unsuitable for extrapolation to the water window. The increase in irradiance between Se and Mo was from 5×10^{13} to 4×10^{14} W cm^{-2}. To obtain gain below 43.76 Å would require producing Gd^{54+} with an estimated irradiance in excess of 10^{16} W cm^{-2}. This would be impossible to apply over a long plasma with currently available laser drivers.

The theory of a Ni-like analog to the Ne-like scheme has been discussed previously[7-9] but has lacked an experimental validation. The population inversion necessary for amplification is produced between the $4d$ and $4p$ levels which lie above a $3d^{10}$ closed shell. Figure 1 is a simplified level diagram for Eu^{35+} showing the four $4d$-$4p$ transitions most likely to be amplified. The dominant population mechanism for the $(3d^9_{3/2}4d_{3/2})_0$ level is electron collisional excitation from the ground state. The collision rate is shown in Fig. 1 for an electron density of 2×10^{20} cm^{-3} and electron temperature of 600 eV. This rate is calculated with the multiconfiguration, relativistic, distorted-wave code MCDW.[9] The $J=2$ and $J=1$ $4d$ levels are fed by collisions from the ground state but are also populated by recombination, cascading from higher n states, and feeding from the $4f$ levels. The $4d$-$4p$ population inversion is maintained by the fast $4p$-$3d$ radiative decay, and reduction of this decay rate by trapping will reduce the inversion. A 137-level, time-dependent model for Zn-like, Cu-like, Ni-like, and Co-like Gd has been incorporated in the XRASER kinetics code[10] and the two-dimensional hydrodynamics output from LASNEX[11] used as a basis to predict the expected gains on the four Eu^{35+} transitions shown in Fig. 1. A Gd atomic data file

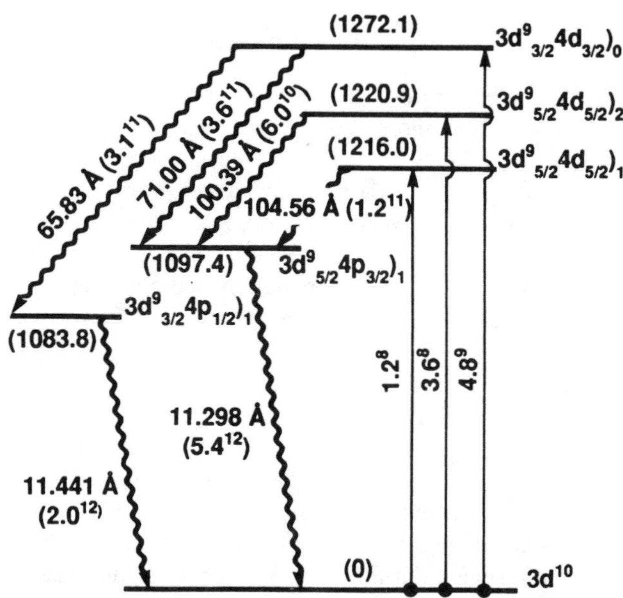

FIG. 1. Simplified level diagram for Eu^{35+} showing the transitions of interest. The collision rates are given for $n_e=2\times10^{20}$ cm^{-3} and $T_e=600$ eV. Level energies (in electronvolts) and spontaneous emission rates are in parentheses.

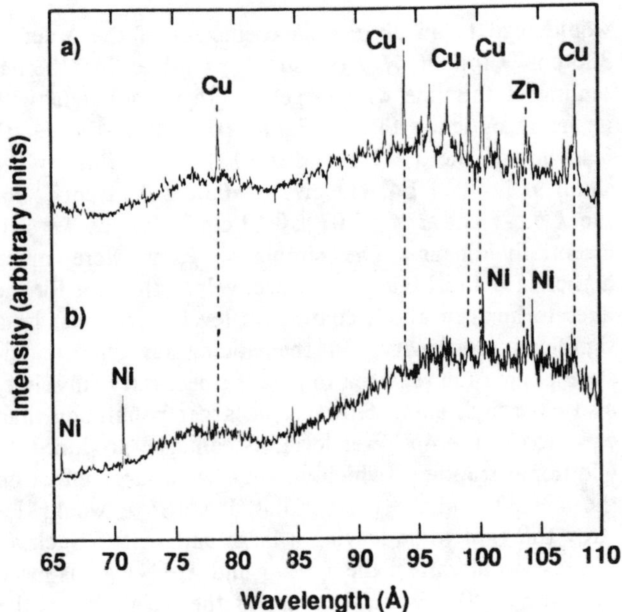

FIG. 2. $4l$-$4l'$ Eu spectra. (a) Off-axis observed spectrum. (b) On-axis observed spectrum.

was used to model Eu ($Z=63$) as early, unsuccessful attempts to fabricate thin-foil targets had centered on Gd ($Z=64$). The model included the effect of trapping of the $4p$-$3d$ transitions. Two types of target foils were used in the experiment, 50-μg-cm^{-2} EuF_2 on 10-μg-cm^{-2} CH and 90-μg-cm^{-2} EuF_2 on 10-μg-cm^{-2} CH. The targets were irradiated with a total of 7×10^{13} W cm^{-2} in two opposing line foci 200 μm wide with a pulse of 1 nsec duration. Simulations[12] of the experiments showed expected gains for both targets of order unity on the four Ni-like lines with the 65.83- and 71.00-Å $J=0$-1 lines predicted to have gains of 0.8 and 1.0 cm^{-1}, respectively. The gain was calculated to appear near the peak of the heating pulse when the electron temperature and density were expected to be 600 eV and 2×10^{20} cm^{-3}, respectively.

Two beams of the Nova laser were used for the experiment; the setup was similar to that described in Ref. 5. The principal diagnostics were grazing-incidence grating spectrometers with microchannel plate detectors capable of being gated in time. Two spectrometers were positioned so as to view the target along the axis of the line focus (the preferred direction for amplification), and a third viewed the target from 45° off axis. The signals from the spectrographs were integrated over time up to 500 ps after the peak of the 0.53-μm Nova pulse, then gated off. Figure 2 shows spectra from a 50-μg-cm^{-2} EuF_2 target. Figure 2(a) is an off-axis spectrum showing the bright optically thick emission from $4l$-$4l'$ transitions in Cu-like and Zn-like Eu which have been identified previously.[13] Figure 2(b) is an on-axis spectrum with Zn- and Cu-like emission but also showing bright emission at 65.83, 71.00, 100.39, and 104.56 Å, identified as previously unobserved $4d$-$4p$ transitions in Ni-like Eu. The line identifications are based on their proximity to calculated values and their behavior as the length of the target is increased. The predicted wavelengths[14] for the lines are shown in Table I. The disagreement with the measured wavelengths of the two shorter-wavelength lines arises from difficulty in calculating the energy of the $J=0$ state due to configuration-interaction contributions. As the two lines share the same upper state, the disagreements with the measured transition energies are similar (0.32 and 0.49 eV). A third, weaker $J=0$-1 transition from the same level (observed at 84.83 Å, on the longest targets) has a similar energy deviation.

Figure 3 shows sections of typical on-axis spectra from targets of different lengths. The $J=0$-1 lines show a nonlinear increase in intensity as the target length is increased, with the 71.00-Å line increasing more rapidly than the 65.83-Å line. Spectra were scanned by a digitizing densitometer and the resultant film density values converted to intensity with a calibration wedge, developed with the data. The intensity of an individual line was then measured by our subtracting out the background continuum level and integrating over the line profile. The results of these measurements are plotted in Fig. 4(a) for the two $J=0$-1 lines and for the $4f\,^2F_{5/2}$-$4d\,^2D_{3/2}$ Cu-like transition at 93.84 Å. The data shown are for the 50-μg-cm^{-2} EuF_2 targets. The $J=0$-1 data

TABLE I. Table of calculated and observed wavelength values in angstroms for Ni-like $4d$-$4p$ transitions. The Yb and W $j=0$-1 calculations have been adjusted on the basis of the observed Eu wavelengths.

	Eu^{35+}		Yb^{42+}		W^{46+}
Transition	Theory	Observed	Extrapolated theory	Observed	Extrapolated theory
$(3d^9_{3/2}4d_{3/2})_0$-$(3d^9_{3/2}4p_{1/2})_1$	65.72	65.83 ± 0.03	50.24	50.26 ± 0.05	43.15
$(3d^9_{3/2}4d_{3/2})_0$-$(3d^9_{5/2}4p_{3/2})_1$	70.80	71.00 ± 0.03	56.10	56.09 ± 0.05	49.34
$(3d^9_{3/2}4d_{3/2})_0$-$(3d^9_{3/2}4p_{3/2})_1$	84.62	84.83 ± 0.05	72.04	...	66.39
$(3d^9_{5/2}4d_{5/2})_2$-$(3d^9_{5/2}4p_{3/2})_1$	100.32	100.39 ± 0.03	81.03	...	72.27
$(3d^9_{5/2}4d_{5/2})_1$-$(3d^9_{5/2}4p_{3/2})_1$	104.56	104.56 ± 0.05	84.44	84.40 ± 0.05	75.29

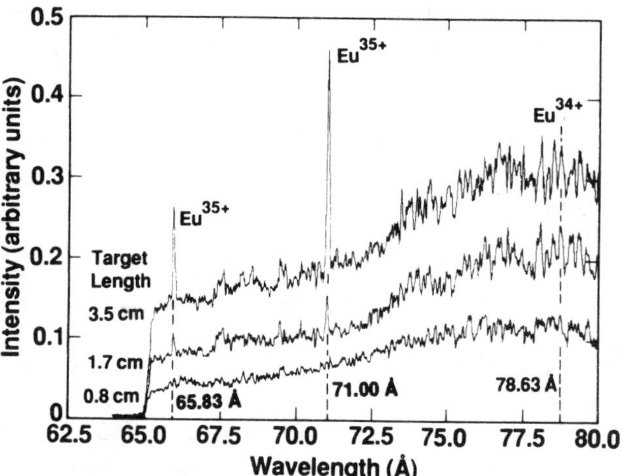

FIG. 3. Details from on-axis spectra in the region near the $J=0$-1 lines of Eu^{35+} for three different target lengths.

have been fitted by the formula

$$I \sim (e^{\alpha l}-1)^{3/2}(\alpha l e^{\alpha l})^{-1/2}, \quad (1)$$

for the output power of a Doppler-broadened, homogeneous, time-independent, distributed source of amplified spontaneous emission[15] of gain coefficient α and length l. The 71.00- and 65.83-Å data were fitted by gains of 1.11 ± 0.12 and 0.61 ± 0.14 cm^{-1}, respectively. The relative sizes of the gains are qualitatively consistent with the relative oscillator strengths[16] of the two lines. The uncertainties in the gains (68% confidence) are calculated on the assumption of an intrinsic error of (15–20)% in the intensity values. The expected plasma conditions would lead to an absorption coefficient of the order of 300 cm^{-1} for the $4f\,^2F_{5/2}$- $4d\,^2D_{3/2}$ Cu-like line; the flat scaling of this line with target length is consistent with its being optically thick. Figure 4(b) shows the length behavior of the $J=2$-1 and $J=1$-1 lines. Fits by the small-αl limit of Eq. (1) give $\alpha = 0.08 \pm 0.14$ cm^{-1} for the $J=2$-1 and $\alpha = -0.07 \pm 0.19$ cm^{-1} for the $J=1$-1, essentially linear. The simulated gains were much higher (1.6 and 1.0 cm^{-1}, respectively). In order for the lines to be seen above continuum level there must be a significant emissivity. In the calculation the excited-state population required to give the necessary emissivity also gave high gain. However, a larger population than expected in the $4p$ lower level, as could be produced by additional trapping (which already has a large effect on the $J=2$-1 and $J=1$-1 simulated gains[12]), would destroy the gain while leaving a large emissivity. Such an increase would affect the $J=2$-1 and $J=1$-1 gains more than the $J=0$-1 gains, because of the weighting of the lower-level population by the ratio of the statistical weights in the expression for population inversion. The gains could also be lower than calculated as a result of the difficulty in accurately modeling the multitude of $J=2$ and $J=1$ population mechanisms, or as a result of more refraction by plasma density gradients than is already included in the simulation.[12]

The optical depth of the bremsstrahlung continuum emission at 66 Å is calculated to be less than 0.2 for the longest target. The behavior of the continuum is shown in Fig. 4(b) to be linear, consistent with its being dominated by optically thin emission. The observation of the expected behavior of the continuum and the optically

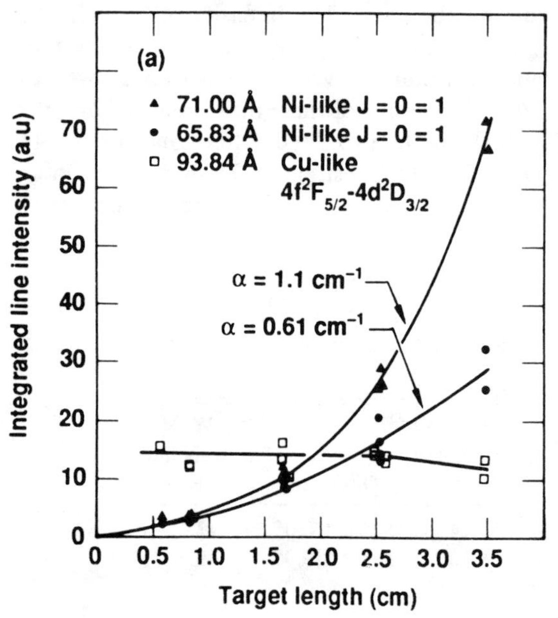

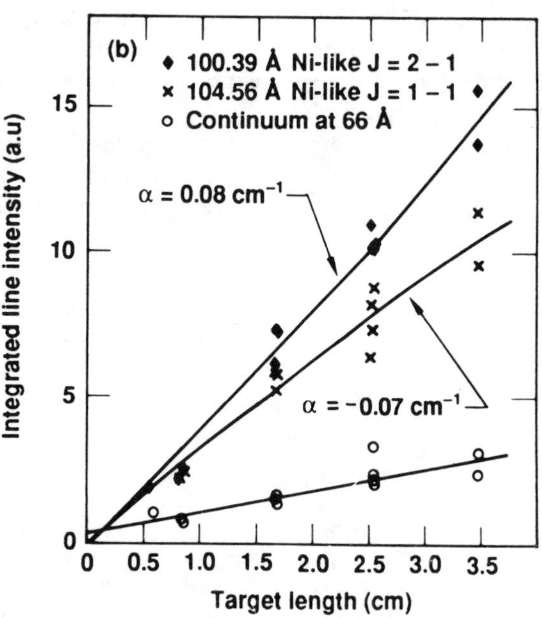

FIG. 4. Intensities as functions of length for five lines and the continuum at 66 Å from the on-axis spectra. The Ni-like line intensities are fitted by Eq. (1). The line through the 93.84-Å data is not a mathematical fit; the continuum is fitted by a straight line.

thick Cu-like line at 93.84 Å verifies that the spectrometers are providing a reliable measurement.

Data for the 90-μg-cm^{-2} EuF_2 targets, analyzed in a similar manner, resulted in gains of 0.60 ± 0.09, 0.24 ± 0.17, 0.01 ± 0.12, and -0.38 ± 0.16 cm^{-1} for the 71.00-, 65.83-, 100.39-, and 104.56-Å lines, respectively. Again the $J=2$-1 and $J=1$-1 gains disagree with calculation and the $J=0$-1 gains are now reduced. The thicker targets would be expected to be hotter, denser, and more ionized,[6] and also to suffer more from trapping of the $4p$-$3d$ transition. All of these changes would affect the gain coefficients.

The extrapolation of the Ni-like scheme to shorter wavelength was explored by our looking at Yb. The targets were 100-μg-cm^{-2} Yb on 10-μg-cm^{-2} CH irradiated at 1.4×10^{14} W cm^{-2} in a 1-ns pulse. Line emissions at 50.26 and 56.09 Å were identified as being the $J=0$-1 transitions in Yb^{42+}. The line at 50.26 Å increases nonlinearly with target length, consistent with its being amplified with a gain of the order of 1 cm^{-1}. The length behavior of the 56.09-Å line is closer to linear. The oscillator strengths are calculated[16] to be 0.075 and 0.061 for the 50.26- and 56.09-Å lines, respectively, and so the shorter-wavelength line would be expected to have slightly more gain. Table I shows the observed and calculated wavelengths of all the Ni-like lines seen to date. The calculated wavelengths for tungsten are also given, demonstrating the scaling of the shorter wavelength $J=0$-1 line to below the carbon K edge.

In conclusion, we have demonstrated that gain can be produced in a laser-heated exploding foil plasma of Ni-like ions. This demonstration now opens the way for extrapolation of present-day, relatively long-wavelength extreme ultraviolet lasers[1,5] to a domain where they are truly soft x rays. The scaling of the scheme to shorter wavelength is promising, as indicated by the results with Yb. We predict that an exploding-foil amplifier of tungsten will produce gain at 43.15 Å with heating pulse intensities of approximately 4×10^{14} W cm^{-2}.

The authors gratefully acknowledge contributions from P. Bell, S. Brown, A. Burnham, E. M. Campbell, J. Cox, G. Jameson, G. Hermes, D. Nilson, G. Powers, and L. Wettstein of Lawrence Livermore National Laboratory and G. Steele and W. Sharp of Luxel Corporation. This work was performed under the auspices of the U. S. Department of Energy by the Lawrence Livermore National Laboratory under Contract No. W-7405-ENG-48.

---

[a]Present address: Department of Electrical Engineering, Massachusetts Institute of Technology, Cambridge, MA 02139.

[1]D. L. Matthews *et al.*, Phys. Rev. Lett. **54**, 110 (1985).

[2]M. D. Rosen *et al.*, Phys. Rev. Lett. **54**, 106 (1985).

[3]B. L. Henke, in *Encyclopedia of Microscopy,* edited by G. L. Clark (Reinhold, New York, 1961), p. 675.

[4]A. N. Zherikhin *et al.*, Kvantovaya Elektron. (Moscow) **3**, 152 (1976) [Sov. J. Quantum Electron. **6**, 82 (1976)]; A. V. Vinogradov and V. N. Shylaptsev, Kvantovaya Elektron. (Moscow) **10**, 2325 (1983) [Sov. J. Quantum Electron. **13**, 1511 (1983)], and references therein; P. L. Hagelstein, Ph.D. thesis, University of California, Lawrence Livermore National Laboratory Report No. UCRL-53100, 1981 (unpublished); U. Feldman *et al.*, J. Appl. Phys. **54**, 2188 (1983), and **56**, 2475 (1984).

[5]B. J. MacGowan *et al.*, J. Appl. Phys. **61**, 5243 (1987).

[6]R. A. London and M. D. Rosen, Phys. Fluids **29**, 3813 (1986).

[7]S. Maxon *et al.*, J. Appl. Phys. **57**, 971 (1985).

[8]S. Maxon *et al.*, J. Appl. Phys. **59**, 239 (1986).

[9]P. L. Hagelstein, Phys. Rev. A **34**, 874 (1986).

[10]P. L. Hagelstein, Plasma Phys. **25**, 1345 (1983).

[11]G. B. Zimmerman and W. L. Kruer, Comments Plasma Phys. Controlled Fusion **2**, 85 (1975).

[12]S. Maxon *et al.*, to be published.

[13]J. Reader and G. Luther, Phys. Rev. Lett. **45**, 609 (1980); N. Acquista and J. Reader, J. Opt. Soc. Am. B **1**, 649 (1984); G. A. Doschek *et al.*, to be published.

[14]M. H. Chen and J. H. Scofield, private communication; calculation using Grant's MCDF code [I. P. Grant *et al.*, Comput. Phys. Commun. **21**, 207 (1980)].

[15]G. J. Linford *et al.*, Appl. Opt. **12**, 379 (1974).

[16]Oscillator strengths calculated from the relativistic configuration-interaction calculation YODA. P. L. Hagelstein and R. K. Jung, unpublished.

Reprinted with permission from *Physical Review Letters,* Vol. 59(19), pp. 2161-2164 (November 9, 1987).

Laser Amplification at 18.2 nm in Recombining Plasma from a Laser-Irradiated Carbon Fiber

C. Chenais-Popovics, R. Corbett, C. J. Hooker, M. H. Key, G. P. Kiehn, C. L. S. Lewis, G. J. Pert, C. Regan, S. J. Rose, S. Sadaat, R. Smith, T. Tomie, and O. Willi

Laboratoire de Physique des Milieux Ionisés, Ecole Polytechnique, F-91128 Palaiseau Cedex, France
Electrotechnical Laboratory, Sakura-Mura, Nihari-Gun, Ibaraki, Japan
University of Hull, Hull HU6 7RX, England
Imperial College of Science and Technology, London SW7 2BZ, England
Queens University, Belfast BT7 1NN, Northern Ireland
Rutherford Appleton Laboratory, Chilton, Didcot, Oxfordshire OX11 0QX, England

(Received 29 April 1987)

Extreme-ultraviolet laser amplification has been observed for the C VI Balmer-α transition at 18.2 nm, with use of a novel optical system to irradiate up to 1 cm length of carbon-fiber target. The measurements were time resolved and indicated peak single-transit amplification of about 30 times.

The development of extreme-ultraviolet (XUV) lasers is progressing rapidly through a variety of schemes that use laser-produced plasmas as the amplifying media.[1] Strong exponential behavior was first reported for $3p$-$3s$ transitions in Se XXV.[2] High gain on the C VI Balmer-α transition has been observed with a solid target in a strong magnetic field.[3] Smaller gain has been seen in Li-like Al XI with solid targets[4] and in C VI with thin-film targets.[5] Our work has concentrated on recombination to C VI,[6] including the use of short carbon-fiber targets.[7,8]

The present experiment was designed to produce significant amplification by the irradiation of longer fibers under optimized conditions. The laser used was a neodymium-glass system, Vulcan at the United Kingdom Science and Engineering Research Council Rutherford Appleton Laboratory, which can generate up to 10^{12} W in 70-ps, 0.53-μm pulses. A new six-beam target-irradiation facility was devised, combining focusing via $f/2.5$ aspheric doublet lenses with 13° off-axis reflection at $f/2.5$ spherical mirrors to produce 7-mm-long, 25-μm-wide aberration-free line foci.[9]

Carbon-fiber targets were supported horizontally at one end and positioned with $\simeq$5-μm spatial accuracy and 10^{-3}-rad angular accuracy.[9] The laser beams were focused in opposed pairs to a common line focus. One pair was used to irradiate lengths up to 5.5 mm. The free end of the fiber was placed in a fixed position close to one end of the line focus with an overlap to ensure its irradiation at high intensity. Masking of the two beams was used to produce a sharp cutoff in the irradiation pattern and thus to vary the irradiated length. For lengths between 5.5 and 9.5 mm, two pairs of beams were used to produce a longer line focus by the superposition of axially displaced overlapping foci. It was impractical to increase the irradiated length beyond 9.5 mm because of vibration and bending of the fibers.

A time-resolving XUV spectrometer observed the axial emission from the free end of the fiber.[10] The instrument used a variable-periodicity grazing-incidence diffraction grating to focus XUV spectrum to a flat field at the transmission photocathode of an XUV streak camera. Spectral resolution was 0.5 Å and the temporal resolution was 0.4 nsec. An XUV pinhole-camera image, filtered to $h\nu \simeq 500$ eV, recorded images of the plasma, and the absorbed energy was measured with plasma calorimeters.

Extensive analytic and numerical modeling was used to determine the optimum target and laser irradiation parameters. Practical constraints were included in the modeling in the form of a lower limit of 70 psec for the pulse duration from Vulcan and a lower limit of 7 μm for the fiber diameter due to the problems of bending and vibration referred to previously. A new analytical model combined earlier work, defining optimum energy input as a function of plasma mass and duration of heating,[6] with a more recent understanding of the process of ablation by laser irradiation which relates absorbed energy and pulse duration to plasma mass.[11] The model predicted higher gain for lower plasma mass and shorter heating time; thus 70-psec pulses and 7-μm fibers were chosen. The required absorbed energy was given as

$$E/(1\ \text{J cm}^{-1}) = 0.11[r/(1\ \mu\text{m})]^{2.4}\tau/(100\ \text{psec}),$$

in terms of fiber radius r and laser pulse duration τ, suggesting a requirement of 1.6 J cm^{-1}. Numerical modeling, discussed later, refined these conclusions and suggested that for an absorbed energy of 2 J cm^{-1}, a maximum gain coefficient of 15 cm^{-1} could be achieved. Experiments were conducted at incident energy levels of about 10 times the required absorbed energy because of the 10% absorption fraction for fiber targets.

The absolute and relative intensities of the Balmer lines were determined by calibration of the detector with synchrotron radiation. Line blending of H_β with $4\times Ly_\alpha$ was assessed by the recording of spectra showing simul-

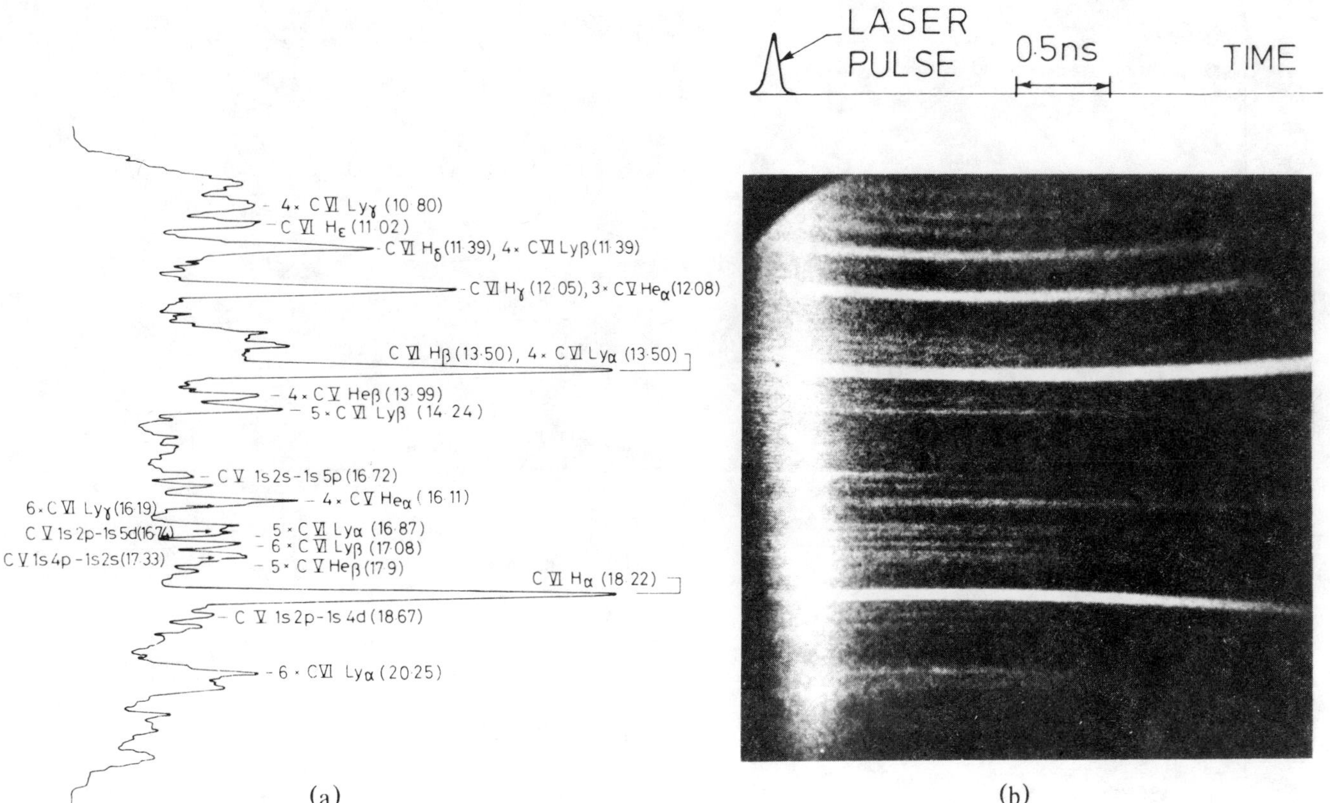

FIG. 1. (a) Streak-camera record of the emission spectrum along the axis of a 7-μm carbon-fiber target with 8 mm irradiated length and 2.5 J cm^{-1} absorbed energy. (b) Densitometry from (a) 975 psec after the peak of the laser pulse, with wavelengths labeled in nanometers.

taneously $H_\beta + 4 \times Ly_\alpha$ and $3 \times Ly_\alpha$, both with and without a 1000-Å Al filter to cut out the H_β component of the blended line. The results showed that the fraction of the observed intensity due to H_β was 75%. There was no blending for the H_α line. The detection sensitivity was 8 times higher for H_β relative to H_α.

An experimentally recorded streak spectrum is shown in Fig. 1. The main spectral feature is the C VI Balmer series. Weaker lines are C VI and C V resonance lines in higher orders and some C V $1s2l$ to $1snl$ transitions as indicated by the labeling.

Figure 2 shows H_α and H_β intensities for a range of lengths from 1.5 to 9.5 mm, 975 psec after the peak of the laser pulse. In Fig. 2 the exponentially increasing H_α intensities are fitted by the function $\exp(gl)-1$ (appropriate for small values of gl where gain narrowing of amplified spontaneous emission is not important). The method used was linear least-squares fitting for data points $\ln[I(l)/C+1]$, using C as a free parameter to obtain a fit passing through the origin, for which the slope g gave the gain. The resulting best fit is $g = 4.1 \pm 0.6$ cm^{-1} corresponding to a maximum single-transit gain of 49. Lengths l were taken from the x-ray pinhole-camera images of the irradiated fibers. The data have average absorbed energy per unit length E/l of 2.6 J cm^{-1} with rms variation ± 0.6 cm^{-1}. The incident energy was 10 times the absorbed energy. Least-squares fitting showed no systematic change in E/l with l.

The H_β data have a best-fit g value of 1.57 ± 0.17

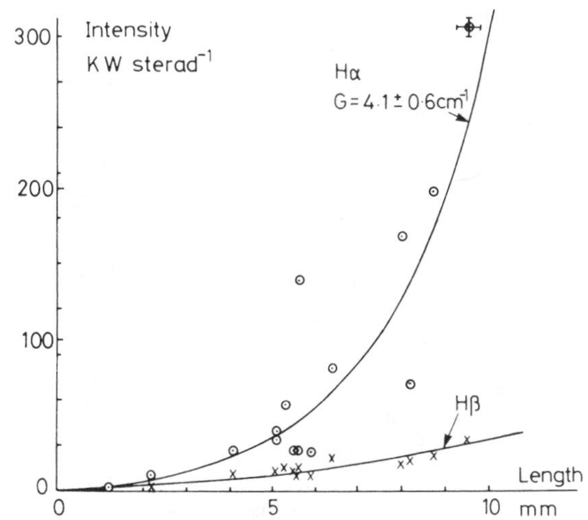

FIG. 2. Ordinate: absolute intensity of axial H_α and H_β emissions measured from streaked spectra 975 psec after the peak of the laser pulse. Abscissa: irradiated length. A typical measurement error bar is shown for H_α. Theoretical fits to the experimental data are also plotted.

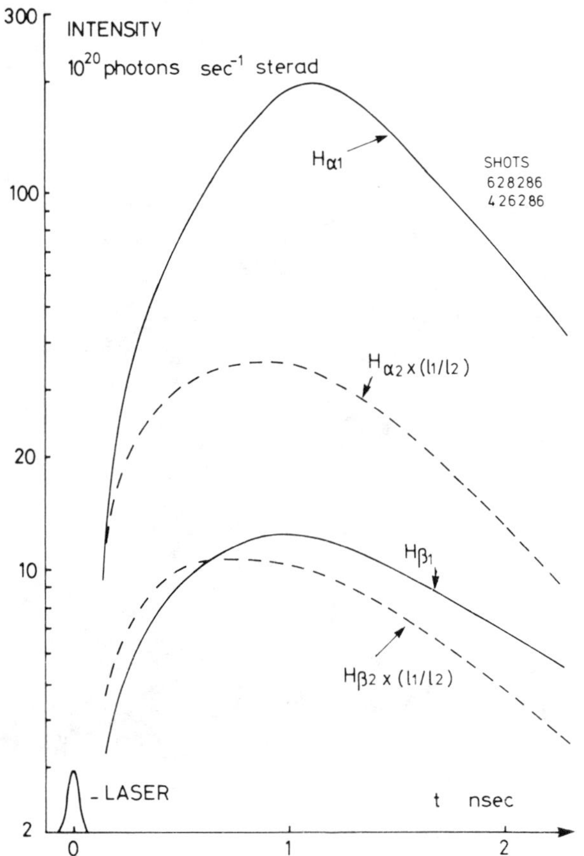

FIG. 3. Time history of the absolute intensities of H_α and H_β from two streak spectra. $H_{\alpha 1}$ and $H_{\beta 1}$ are for length $l_1=8$ mm and $H_{\alpha 2}$ and $H_{\beta 2}$ are for $l_2=2.2$ mm.

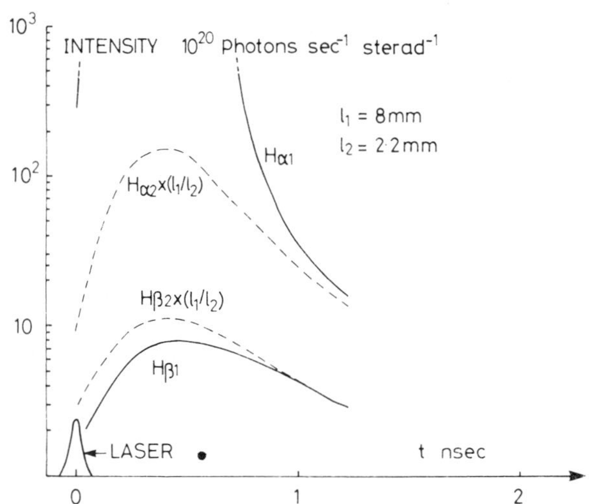

FIG. 4. Gain coefficient as a function of time deduced from Figs. 3 and 5 as explained in the text.

cm^{-1}. The H_β line is not expected to show gain and the small nonlinearity is attributed to systematic error in the data set, though there was no statistically significant variation in E/l with l, as noted earlier. To estimate the possible effect of this error on the gain coefficient deduced for H_α, the H_α data were scaled by a factor $gl/[\exp(gl)-1]$ with $g=1.57$, which gives zero gain if applied to the H_β data. The resulting g value for H_α is found to be $g=3\pm0.5$ cm^{-1} and represents a lower bound on the gain. The single-transit gain is therefore about 30 if we take the median of these two estimates.

The temporal variation of H_α and H_β is plotted in Fig. 3 for short (2.2 mm) and long (8 mm) plasmas. Line intensities can be measured from about 130 psec when the lines emerge from the continuum. The intensities for 2.2 mm have been scaled by the length ratio $l_1/l_2=8/2.2$, showing clearly that H_β has very similar pulse shapes for both lengths, with intensity scaling almost linearly with length at all times. The H_α pulse shape is similar to that of H_β for 2.2 mm, but for the 8-mm length the intensity rises rapidly relative to the other lines, with a ratio peaking after about 1 nsec.

The temporal variation of amplification was assessed by our measuring the time-dependent ratio of the H_α intensity for the two lengths. This ratio has the form $S_1[\exp(gl_1)-1]/S_2[\exp(gl_2)-1]$ enabling us to determine g provided that the ratio of the source function brightnesses S_1 and S_2 is known. In this case $S_1/S_2\approx 1$ as evidenced by the similarity of the scaled H_β intensities in Fig. 3.

Figure 4 presents the variation of gain with time. For times later than 1 nsec, a systematic error becomes important as the radius of the expanding short plasma becomes comparable with its length, leading to a spherical expansion and more rapid cooling. Some evidence of this is seen in Fig. 3 in the different late-time slopes of H_β emission for the two lengths. The estimated gain at late times therefore becomes systematically too high. At early times (<400 psec) the 400-psec temporal resolution in the streaks masks any sudden change of intensity ratio.

Various numerical simulations of the experiment were carried out. A one-dimensional Lagrangean hydrodynamic code was used, with a collision-radiative model for ionization and the Sobolev[12] approximation to describe the effect of Doppler decoupling on the trapping of C VI Lyman radiation. The results gave radial profiles of emission and gain as functions of radius and time, from which the total emission along the axis was computed as shown in Fig. 5. The computed values of absolute intensity of H_β for long and short plasma lengths agree well with the experimental values except that the peaks occur 300 psec earlier and decay more rapidly. The computed H_α emission for long lengths is much greater than is observed because the observed amplification is smaller. The H_α:H_β ratio at late times when gain is low is the same in both theory and experiment.

The apparent H_α gain in the numerical model was deduced by treatment of the computed intensities in the same manner used in analysis of the corresponding ex-

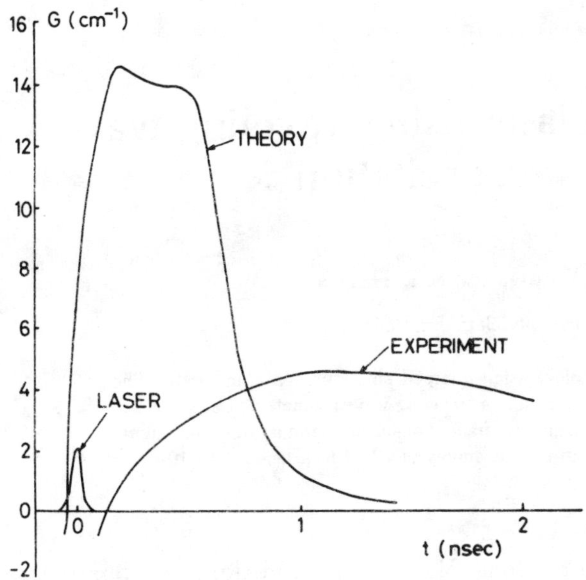

FIG. 5. Computed time history of absolute intensities of H_α and H_β for plasma lengths of 2.2 and 8 mm corresponding to the experimental data in Fig. 3.

perimental data. The finite (400 psec) temporal resolution of the streak camera was included in the simulation by a convolution procedure. Comparison of this apparent gain with experiment in Fig. 4 shows qualitative similarity. The calculated peak of 15 cm^{-1} is, however, much higher than the 4 cm^{-1} deduced from experiments and it decays more rapidly.

No satisfactory explanation has yet been obtained for the differences between experiment and theory, nor indeed for the lower value of gain coefficient relative to earlier experiments with shorter lengths of fiber, time-integrated diagnostics, and different irradiation conditions.[8]

In conclusion, we have successfully used new optical and diagnostic systems to measure moderately large laser gain on the 18.2-nm H_α transition of C VI.

We wish to acknowledge the technical and operational support given by the Central Laser Facility staff, including J. E. Boon, C. Brown, A. R. Damerell, P. Gottfeldt, D. A. Pepler, I. N. Ross, and P. T. Rumsby, and by the Sychrotron Radiation Facility staff, including J. West. Two of us (C.C.-P. and T.T.) received visiting fellowships from the Centre National de la Recherche Scientifique and Monbusho, respectively. The work is supported by the United Kingdom Science and Engineering Research Council.

---

[1]M. H. Key, Nature (London) **316**, 314 (1985).

[2]D. L. Matthews *et al.*, Phys. Rev. Lett. **54**, 110 (1985).

[3]S. Suckewer, C. H. Skinner, M. Milchberg, C. Keane, and D. Voorhees, Phys. Rev. Lett. **55**, 1753 (1985).

[4]G. Jamelot, A. Klisnick, R. Carillon, M. Guennou, A. Sureau, and P. Jaeglé, J. Phys. B **18**, 4647 (1985).

[5]J. F. Seely, C. M. Brown, U. Feldman, M. Richardson, B. Yaakobi, and W. E. Behring, Opt. Commun. **54**, 289 (1985).

[6]G. J. Pert, J. Phys. B **9**, 3301 (1976), and **12**, 2067 (1979); M. H. Key, C. L. S. Lewis, and M. J. Lamb, Opt. Commun. **28**, 331 (1979).

[7]R. J. Dewhurst, D. Jacoby, G. J. Pert, and S. A. Ramsden, Phys. Rev. Lett. **37**, 1265 (1976).

[8]D. Jacoby, G. J. Pert, S. A. Ramsden, L. D. Shorrock, and G. J. Tallents, Opt. Commun. **37**, 193 (1981).

[9]I. N. Ross *et al*, Appl. Opt. **26**, 1584 (1987).

[10]G. P. Kiehn, O. Willi, A. R. Damerell, and M. H. Key, Appl. Opt. **26**, 425 (1987).

[11]M. H. Key and G. J. Pert, Annual Report to the Laser Facility Committee, Rutherford Appleton Laboratory Report No. RAL-86-046, A5.38, 1986 (unpublished).

[12]V. V. Sobolev, in *Theoretical Astrophysics,* edited by V. A. Ambartsumyan (Pergamon, London, 1958), Chap. 29, p. 475.

Reprinted with permission from *Optics Letters*, Vol. 12(11), pp. 891-893 (November 1987).

Saturation of the Xe III 109-nm laser using traveling-wave laser-produced-plasma excitation

M. H. Sher, J. J. Macklin, J. F. Young, and S. E. Harris

Edward L. Ginzton Laboratory, Stanford University, Stanford, California 94305

We describe the construction and operation of a 109-nm, photoionization-pumped, single-pass laser in Xe III. The laser is pumped by soft x rays emitted from a laser-produced plasma in a traveling-wave geometry. Using a 3.5-J, 300-psec, 1064-nm laser pump pulse, we measure a small-signal gain coefficient of 4.4 cm^{-1} and a total small-signal gain of exp(40). The laser is fully saturated and produces an output energy of 20 μJ in a beam with 10-mrad divergence.

In this Letter we describe the construction and operation of a single-pass, 109-nm Xe III Auger laser.[1] The laser is pumped by soft x rays, which are emitted from a laser-produced plasma in a traveling-wave geometry. Using only 3.5 J of 1064-nm pump energy in a 300-psec pulse, we measure a small-signal gain coefficient of 4.4 cm^{-1} and a total small-signal gain of exp(40). The 109-nm laser is fully saturated over the second half of its length and produces an output energy of 20 μJ in a beam with 10-mrad divergence.

Population inversion of the 109-nm transition was proposed and demonstrated by Kapteyn *et al.*[1,2] The inversion mechanism, outlined in the energy-level diagram of Fig. 1, is inner-shell photoionization of a 4*d* electron, followed by Auger decay to Xe III. In this system, the Auger branching ratio is about 5% to both the upper and lower laser levels. The inversion results from the higher degeneracy of the lower level. Assuming only Doppler broadening, and ignoring hyperfine splitting, the gain cross section is 3×10^{-13} cm^2.

Proposals for photoionization pumping of short-wavelength lasers and for Auger-pumped short-wavelength lasers were made by Duguay[3] and by McGuire.[4] The possibility of constructing such lasers at low pumping energies was delineated by the work of Caro *et al.*,[5] Silfvast *et al.*,[6] and Mendelsohn and Harris.[7] Recently Yin *et al.*[8] showed that small-signal gain coefficients within a factor of 2 of those reported here could be produced with several joules of pump energy and, in addition, that the Xe III 109-nm gain can be limited by competing processes. Their work suggests that the most efficient use of pump energy requires a long, high-aspect-ratio geometry.

Figure 2 is a schematic diagram of the traveling-wave laser-produced-plasma excitation source. A 1064-nm laser is incident upon a cylindrical lens at θ = 68 deg from normal and is focused onto a target that is parallel to the lens. This oblique focusing geometry has several advantages over the normal-incidence arrangements used in previous work.[1,8] The large angle of incidence expands the length of the line focus by 1/cos θ; therefore our 3.3-cm-diameter beam produces a 9-cm-long plasma. In addition, the pump laser sweeps across the target, and the leading edge of the plasma travels at a speed, $c/\sin\theta$, only 8% greater than that of light. The emitted soft x rays thus provide nearly synchronous traveling-wave excitation of the ambient gaseous medium.

In order to reduce the pump energy lost to grazing-incidence reflection, grooves were cut into the target surface at a 45-deg angle, as shown in the inset of Fig. 2. The grooved surface decreases the local angle of incidence of the *p*-polarized pump laser from 68 to 23 deg and divides the input beam to form many small, separated plasmas rather than one continuous line. The combined length of these plasmas is only slightly greater than the input beam diameter. As a result, the extended gain length can be pumped with increased 1064-nm intensity and improved soft-x-ray conversion efficiency.

All the experiments described here were performed with a 3.5-J, 300-psec FWHM pump laser with a repetition rate of 1 shot every 5 min. The 3.3-cm-diameter, spatially uniform input beam was compressed (using normal-incidence cylindrical optics) to 1.7 cm in the focusing dimension to increase the *f*-number of the

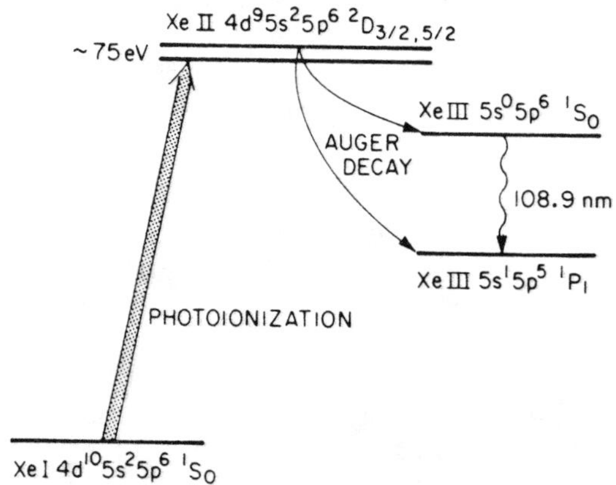

Fig. 1. Energy-level diagram of Xe showing the levels relevent to photoionization and to Auger pumping of Xe III.

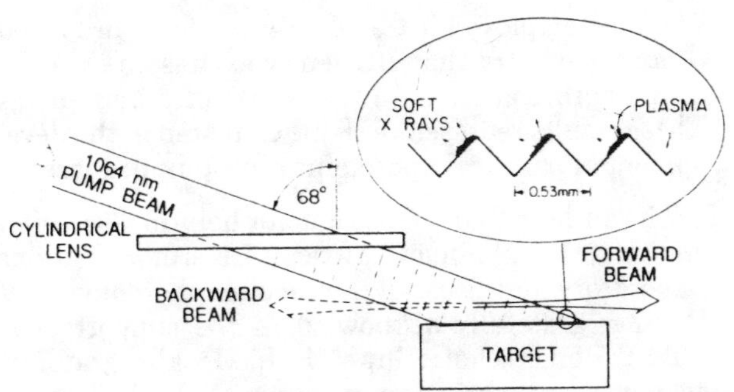

Fig. 2. Traveling-wave laser-produced-plasma soft-x-ray source.

lens and reduce aberrations. The focal length of the oblique cylindrical lens can be approximated by the sagittal focal length of a tilted spherical lens; for f_0 = 20 cm and θ = 68 deg, the focal length is 12 cm. A 2.5-cm-diameter stainless-steel rod, threaded at 19 grooves cm^{-1} and electroplated with gold, served as the target. This arrangement produced a focal line width of 200 μm and an intensity on target of about 2×10^{11} W cm^{-2}. The ambient Xe pressure was 4 Torr.

The observed excited volume was defined by two plates separated by 1.5 mm, through which the 1064-nm pump laser was focused, and by two 2-mm-diameter pinholes on an axis 1.5 mm above the target and located 2 cm from the ends of the line focus. We monitored the 109-nm emission in the forward and backward directions simultaneously, using two 0.2-m VUV monochrometers coupled to windowless channel electron multipliers. A 1-mm-thick LiF window isolated each of the monochrometers from the Xe cell. To avoid saturation of the electron multipliers, we used calibrated LiF and O_2 gas cell attenuators to achieve the 10^5 dynamic range required in these experiments.

The small-signal gain on the 109-nm transition was determined from measurements of time-integrated emission (the 109-nm pulses were shorter than the 700-psec response time of the detection system) as a function of length. The length of plasma on the target, and hence of the gain medium, was varied by masking the input laser beam. Figure 3 shows the increase in forward-propagating emission with length for three short sections of the target. A simple exponential fit to the data yields an average, time-integrated, small-signal gain coefficient of 4.4 cm^{-1}. This is a 70% improvement over the value obtained with a smooth, gold-plated target. Based on the measured, uniform small-signal gain coefficient, unsaturated amplification along the full 9 cm of length would provide a total gain of exp(40), or 170 dB.

The large-signal behavior of both the forward and backward 109-nm laser emission is shown in the semi-log and linear plots of Figs. 4(a) and 4(b), where each symbol represents the average of at least three data points. For short gain lengths, the slopes of the forward and backward energy versus length curves [on the log scale in Fig. 4(a)] are approximately the same. Beyond 4 cm of length, the forward beam grows linearly [Fig. 4(b)], while the backward emission remains constant. This behavior indicates that the forward beam is fully saturated and is extracting nearly all the stored energy from the second half of the length.

The vertical scale of Fig. 4 was calibrated in units of energy by replacing the monochrometer-based detection systems with a fast (350-psec), calibrated vacuum photodiode (Al_2O_3 photocathode) and a calibrated LiF window. The increase of energy with length was identical to that in the emission measurements made using

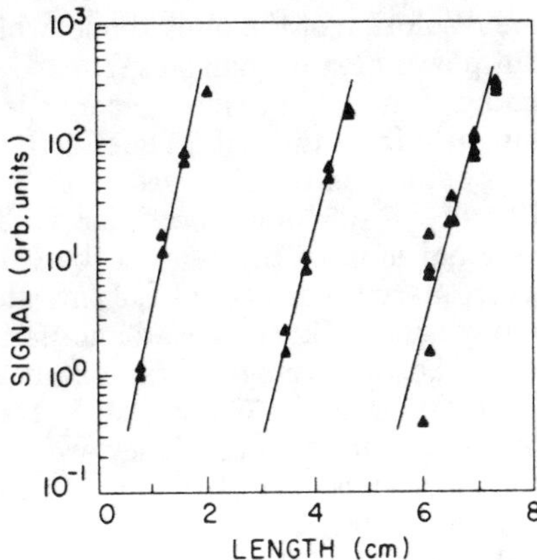

Fig. 3. 109-nm signal versus length for three different sections of the target. The average exponential gain coefficient is 4.4 cm^{-1}.

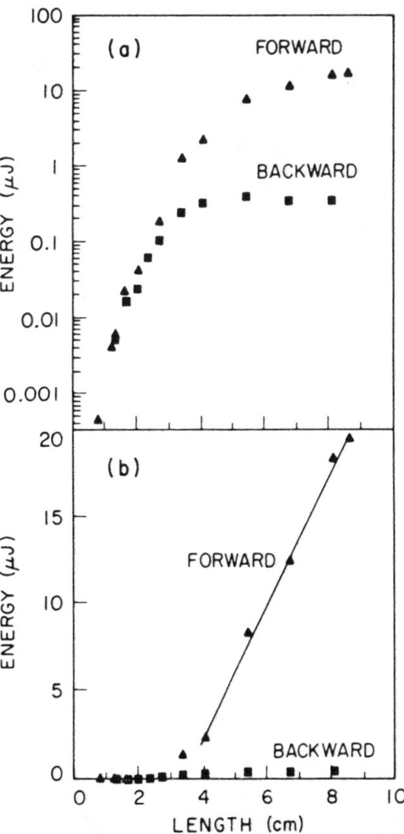

Fig. 4. 109-nm energy versus plasma length on (a) log scale, (b) linear scale showing saturated, linear growth of the forward beam.

the monochrometers. The maximum energy output was 20 μJ in the forward direction and 0.4 μJ in the backward direction, yielding a forward-to-backward emission ratio of 50:1.

By visual observation of fluorescence on a scintillator located 90 cm from the target, and by translation of the vacuum photodiode in this plane, we estimate a forward beam divergence of 10 mrad. This small divergence is consistent with the large aspect ratio (length/width ≈ 60) of the geometry. The pulse width of the 109-nm laser emission was less than the 350-psec time resolution of the photodiode, which implies an output power greater than 50 kW.

Assuming that the measured energy is extracted predominantly from the last 6 cm of gain length, the total energy stored in the observed volume is 30 μJ, or about 10^{-5} of the 1064-nm pump energy. Taking the cross-sectional area of the laser to be 0.03 cm^2, we calculate an energy density of 110 μJ cm^{-3} stored in the 109-nm inversion. Given the atomic parameters of the system,[2] i.e., an average 4*d* photoionization cross section of 15 Mb between 70 and 130 eV, the 5% Auger yield, and ~12% quantum efficiency, we can deduce a conversion efficiency of 1064-nm light to useful soft x rays of approximately 2%.

The relationship of the observed gain behavior to the measured stored energy is complicated by the transient nature of the population inversion. The spontaneous lifetime of the upper level is 4.75 nsec,[2] but the inversion lifetime and the pulse length are governed by stimulated decay and are on a scale with the transit time of the gain medium. The large forward-to-backward emission ratio imparted by the traveling-wave excitation can be explained in terms of competition between the two beams. Although the slopes of the forward and backward energy-versus-length curves in Fig. 4(a) are similar for the shorter lengths, the forward beam reaches saturation earlier and, therefore, dominates in the second half of the length.

In this research we have demonstrated single-pass gain saturation of a photoionization-pumped laser. We have employed a traveling-wave laser-produced-plasma geometry that efficiently excites an extended gain length using only a few joules of pump energy. These results represent a significant step in the development of practical photoionization-pumped lasers.

The authors thank G. Y. Yin for helpful discussions and H. N. Kornblum of Lawrence Livermore National Laboratory for the use of the vacuum photodiode. M. H. Sher gratefully acknowledges the support of an AT&T Ph.D. scholarship. J. J. Macklin gratefully acknowledges the support of an IBM Fellowship. This research was jointly supported by the U.S. Office of Naval Research, the U.S. Air Force Office of Scientific Research, the U.S. Army Research Office, the Strategic Defense Initiative Organization, and Lawrence Livermore National Laboratory.

Note added in proof: Recent streak-camera measurements indicate that the 109-nm pulse width is 50 ± 10 psec FWHM, which implies a peak power of 0.4 MW.

References

1. H. C. Kapteyn, R. W. Lee, and R. W. Falcone, Phys. Rev. Lett. **57,** 2939 (1986).
2. H. C. Kapteyn, M. M. Murnane, R. W. Falcone, G. Kolbe, and R. W. Lee, Proc. Soc. Photo-Opt. Instrum. Eng. **688,** 54 (1986).
3. M. A. Duguay, in *Laser Induced Fusion and X-Ray Laser Studies*, S. F. Jacobs, M. O. Scully, M. Sargent III, and C. D. Cantrell III, eds. (Addison-Wesley, Reading, Mass., 1976), p. 557.
4. E. J. McGuire, Phys. Rev. Lett. **35,** 844 (1975).
5. R. G. Caro, J. C. Wang, R. W. Falcone, J. F. Young, and S. E. Harris, Appl. Phys. Lett. **42,** 9 (1983).
6. W. T. Silfvast, J. J. Macklin, and O. R. Wood II, Opt. Lett. **8,** 551 (1983).
7. A. J. Mendelsohn and S. E. Harris, Opt. Lett. **10,** 128 (1985).
8. G.-Y. Yin, C. P. J. Barty, D. A. King, D. J. Walker, S. E. Harris, and J. F. Young, Opt. Lett. **12,** 331 (1987).

12.8-eV Laser in Neutral Cesium

C. P. J. Barty, D. A. King, G. Y. Yin, K. H. Hahn, J. E. Field, J. F. Young, and S. E. Harris
Edward L. Ginzton Laboratory, Stanford University, Stanford, California 94305
(Received 20 July 1988)

We report the operation of a saturated 96.9-nm laser in Cs vapor that has an extrapolated small-signal gain of exp(83) in a total length of 17 cm. We believe that lasing occurs from a core-excited level embedded in the continuum of the valence electron. The laser is pumped by soft x rays from a synchronous, traveling-wave, laser-produced (2.5 J, 20 ps, 1064 nm) plasma.

In this Letter we report the operation of what we believe is the first laser with its upper level embedded in the continuum of the valence electron.[1] The laser employs a grating-assisted traveling-wave geometry[2,3] that creates a ~20-ps-long pulse of laser-produced soft x rays traveling synchronously with the generated 96.9-nm (12.8-eV) radiation. The gain coefficient is 4.9 cm^{-1} over a 17-cm length, which results in a total extrapolated small-signal gain of exp(83). After about 4 cm, the output energy grows linearly with length, indicating that the laser transition is fully saturated.

Core-excited levels that are embedded within a continuum usually autoionize rapidly, making the accumulation of population difficult. But this need not be the case; recent work by Spong *et al.*[4,5] has shown, for example, that there are many levels in neutral Rb that have autoionizing lifetimes exceeding 10 ps, and several that exceed 100 ps. Such long lifetimes can result either from angular momentum selection rules that to first order prohibit autoionization, or from fortuitous radial matrix element cancellations. The possibility of using such levels to make extreme ultraviolet and soft x-ray lasers has been noted by several workers.[6-8] The existence of an inversion from an upper level embedded within a continuum has been inferred from fluorescence intensity measurements by Silfvast and Wood.[9]

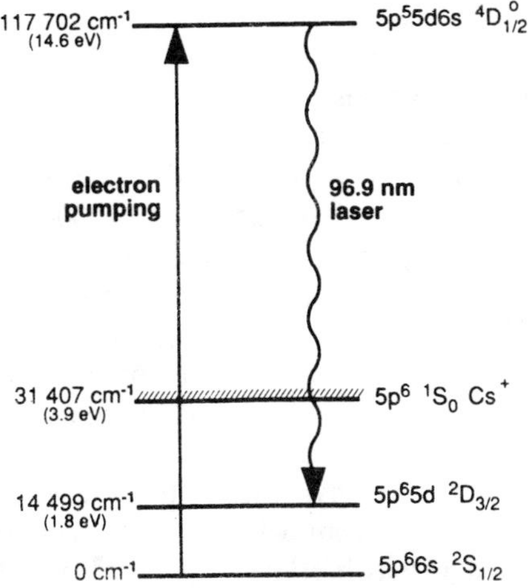

FIG. 1. Partial energy-level diagram for neutral Cs showing the laser transition.

Figure 1 is a partial energy-level diagram for the neutral Cs system showing the 96.9-nm laser transition. The 117702-cm^{-1} energy of the upper level has been measured by vacuum-ultraviolet absorption spectroscopy,[10,11] and the energy of the $5p^6 5d\,^2D_{3/2}$ lower level is well known.[11] The difference (96.897 nm) agrees with our measured emission wavelength of 96.86 ± 0.05 nm. Our identification of the upper level is based on a comparison of its characteristics as predicted by the multiconfigurational *RCN/RCG* atomic physics code of Cowan[12] with experimental measurements. Code-calculated oscillator strengths from the ground level are in good agreement with the absorption data of Connerade[10] and the ejected-electron data of Pejčev and Ross.[13] For simplicity, we have labeled the upper level $5p^5 5d6s\,^4D_{1/2}$ although it contains a large admixture of the $5d^2$ configuration. The code calculates a transition Einstein A rate of 2.3×10^7 s^{-1}, and an autoionizing rate of 1.6×10^{10} s^{-1}, yielding a radiative branching ratio of 0.0014. We calculate a Doppler-broadened stimulated emission cross section of 1.7×10^{-14} cm^2. Thus, it should be very difficult to observe spontaneous emission from this transition; significant outputs will occur only if the upper level is excited very rapidly and the stimulated emission rate exceeds the autoionizing rate. In our experiments rapid excitation is provided by the combination of a ~20-ps-long pumping pulse and a synchronous traveling-wave geometry.

The experimental geometry is a modification of that used by Sher *et al.*[2] for the Xe 108.9-nm Auger laser. As shown in Fig. 2, a 2.5-J, 15- to 20-ps-long 1064-nm pulse is incident upon a cylindrical lens at 65° from normal and is focused onto a target parallel to the lens. The width of the line focus is ~100 μm. The large angle of incidence expands the length of the line focus by $1/\cos 65 = 2.4$, producing a 17-cm-long plasma. By itself, this geometry would produce a plasma sweeping along the target at a speed of $c/\sin 65 = 1.1c$, resulting in a synchronism mismatch of 3.1 ps/cm of target length. In this experiment, however, the 20-ps-long pulse is formed

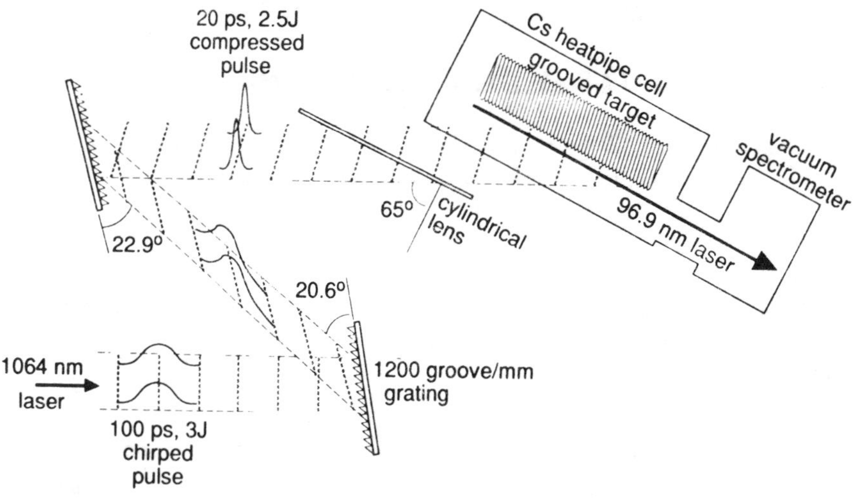

FIG. 2. Grating-assisted, traveling-wave geometry.

by chirping a mode-locked 1064-nm pulse in a fiber, amplifying it in Nd-doped yttrium-aluminum-garnet and Nd:glass stages, and compressing the resulting 120-ps pulse with a parallel grating pair.[14] The second grating of this pair is tilted off true parallelism by 2.3° so as to produce a tilted wave front[3] that exactly compensates for the group-velocity lead of the oblique geometry. The result is a plasma, and its associated pulse of soft x rays, which travels along the target at the speed of light. This correction is essential to produce the largest observed gains.

The target chamber is a Cs heat pipe operating at a density of 6.3×10^{16} cm^{-3}. The surface of the stainless-steel target rod is grooved[2] at a pitch of 43 cm^{-1} and during experiments is wet with liquid Cs. Heating of the target to remove the Cs reduced the observed signals by about 100. Radiation from a ~1-cm region in front of the target was collected by a 1-m normal-incidence spectrometer and detected by a microchannel plate having a 600-ps time resolution. Thin films of In and Al and LiF filters were used to check for possible grating second-order and ghost signals. For the wavelength measurements, the 96.9-nm laser beam was scattered from two ground glass plates before entering the spectrometer.

Gain coefficients were determined by our measuring the relative 96.9-nm energy as a function of plasma length for short sections of the target and fitting the data with the functional form for frequency-integrated superfluorescence output.[15] The length was varied by our masking the input plasma-producing beam. The gain measured at several sections along the 17-cm target was uniform, averaging 4.9 cm^{-1}, thus yielding a total extrapolated small-signal gain of exp(83). Figure 3 shows the dependence of the 96.9-nm output energy on plasma length. The linear increase after about 4 cm clearly indicates saturation. The absolute output energy, measured with an Al vacuum photodiode and a calibrated In filter, was 1.5 μJ.

The predicted poor radiative yield of this transition means that it should be very difficult to observe 96.9-nm spontaneous emission. Using a very short (0.6 cm) plasma in the same cell, we were unable to observe 96.9-nm radiation, and estimate that its intensity was at least a factor of 40 smaller than the 90.1-nm Cs II resonance line, a factor of 60 smaller than the 63.8-nm Cs III resonance line, and a factor of 40 smaller than the 87.5-nm Cs IV resonance line, all of which we observed. Emission at 96.9 nm may have been observed from a discharge in earlier work[16] at a signal level ~200 below the Cs II 90.1-nm resonance line.

Several experiments were performed to test the importance of synchronous traveling-wave pumping and of short-pulse excitation. The grating angle and target angle of incidence were changed to produce a group-velocity lead for the traveling excitation of 10 ps/cm of target length. For this condition, the output signal for a 2.4-cm plasma length was reduced by a factor of 525, and the gain was reduced to 1.8 cm^{-1} by the lack of synchronism. We also compared the 96.9-nm output from a 5.9-cm length of target using the normal 20-ps pumping pulse and an unchirped 220-ps pulse of the same energy. The output signal was ~2000 times weaker with the long pulse. The signal levels of the 90.1-nm Cs II resonance line and the 63.8-nm Cs III resonance line were unchanged for short- and long-pulse excitations, indicating that the laser-signal reduction with longer-pulse pumping should not be attributed to reduced x-ray conversion efficiency. Taken together, the above results strongly support the hypothesis that the 96.9-nm laser emission originates from a level with a very poor radiative yield and a short lifetime.

We believe that the upper laser level is pumped primarily by electrons produced by incoherent soft x rays emitted from the plasma. The expected gain can be es-

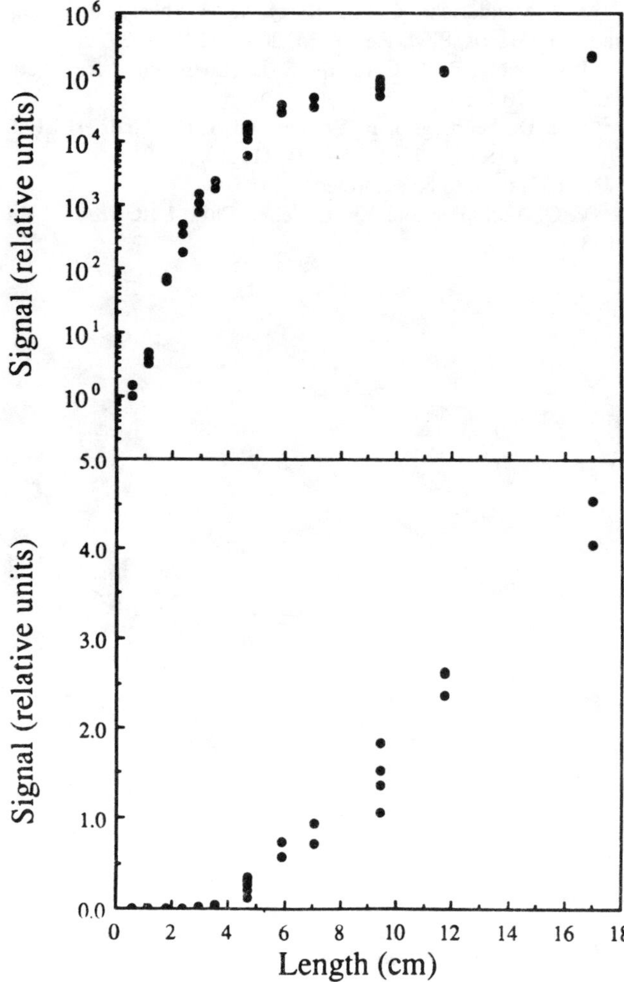

FIG. 3. Output energy at 96.9 nm as a function of plasma length; the same data are presented on both linear and logarithmic scales.

timated as follows. For our 1064-nm power density on target of 1.5×10^{12} W cm^{-2}, and with the assumption of a 25-eV effective blackbody plasma temperature, ~3% of the 1064-nm laser energy will be converted to soft x rays. At a distance of 1 mm from target this flux will create an electron density of about 10^{16} cm^{-3} with a temperature of ~30 eV. The *RCN/RCG* code calculates a temperature-averaged electron excitation cross section times velocity product for the upper laser level of 3.5×10^{-9} cm^3 s^{-1}. Use of the calculated upper level autoionizing lifetime of 62 ps as the effective pumping time yields an upper level population density of 1.4×10^{14} cm^{-3}. This value is consistent with experiments[17] demonstrating that laser-produced plasmas can produce populations in excess of 10^{14} cm^{-3} in metastable levels embedded within a continuum. This upper level population times the calculated gain cross section of 1.7×10^{-14} cm^2 gives a gain coefficient of 2.4 cm^{-1}, if we assume that the lower level is empty, as compared to our measured value of 4.9 cm^{-1}. The autoionizing lifetime and oscillator strength calculated by the *RCN/RCG* code can vary by about a factor of 2 depending on the relative energy spacing used between the $5d6s$, $5d^2$, and $6p^2$ configurations. Direct excitation by the soft x rays may also play a role in the production of upper level population.

The mechanism by which the population of the lower laser level is reduced below that of the upper level has not been determined and is critical to the understanding of this system. Calculations indicate that it is unlikely that electron collision alone can empty the level and produce the inversion. A 1064-nm two-photon transition to the continuum, with the $4f$ valence level as an intermediary, may play a role in this process. We also note that for levels embedded in a continuum, Fano-type interferences between autoionizing levels,[18,19] or in principle between a single level and the continuum,[20] may cause a cancellation of absorption and allow amplification without inversion.

In summary, we believe that this is the first observation of laser action on a transition having an upper level embedded within the continuum of an outer electron. Extremely large gains were produced with only 2.5 J of pumping energy. This fact bodes well for the extension of this concept to even shorter wavelengths.

The authors acknowledge many helpful discussions with A. Imamoḡlu, J. J. Macklin, M. H. Sher, and P. J. K. Wisoff, This work was jointly supported by the U.S. Office of Naval Research, the U.S. Air Force Office of Scientific Research, the U.S. Army Research Office, and the Strategic Defense Initiative Organization. K.H.H. acknowledges the support of the National Science Foundation.

---

[1]S. E. Harris and J. F. Young, J. Opt. Soc. Am. B **4**, 547–562 (1987).

[2]M. H. Sher, J. J. Macklin, J. F. Young, and S. E. Harris, Opt. Lett. **12**, 891–893 (1987).

[3]Zs. Bor, S. Szatmári, and Alexander Müller, Appl. Phys. B **32**, 101–104 (1983).

[4]J. K. Spong, J. D. Kmetec, S. C. Wallace, J. F. Young, and S. E. Harris, Phys. Rev. Lett. **58**, 2631–2634 (1987).

[5]J. K. Spong, A. Imamoḡlu, R. Buffa, and S. E. Harris, Phys. Rev. A (to be published).

[6]E. J. McGuire and M. A. Duguay, Appl. Opt. **16**, 83 (1977).

[7]S. E. Harris, Opt. Lett. **5**, 1–3 (1980).

[8]H. Egger, T. S. Luk, W. Müller, H. Pummer, and C. K. Rhodes, in *Laser Techniques for Extreme Ultraviolet Spectroscopy—1984*, edited by S. E. Harris and T. B. Lucatorto, AIP Conference Proceedings No. 119 (American Institute of Physics, New York, 1984), pp. 64–78.

[9]W. T. Silfvast and O. R. Wood, II, Opt. Soc. Am. B **4**, 609–618 (1987).

[10]J. P. Connerade, Astrophys. J. **159**, 685–694 (1970).

[11]C. E. Moore, *Atomic Energy Levels*, U.S. National Bureau of Standards, National Standards Reference Data Series—3

(U.S. GPO, Washington, DC, 1971), p. 124.

[12]R. D. Cowan, *The Theory of Atomic Structure and Spectra* (Univ. of California, Berkeley, 1981), Secs. 8-1, 16-1, and 18-7.

[13]V. Pejčev and K. J. Ross, J. Phys. B **10**, 2935–2941 (1977).

[14]D. Strickland and G. Mourou, Opt. Commun. **56**, 219–221 (1985).

[15]G. J. Linford, E. R. Peressini, W. R. Sooy, and M. L. Spaeth, Appl. Opt. **13**, 379–390 (1974).

[16]A. J. Mendelsohn, C. P. J. Barty, M. H. Sher, J. F. Young, and S. E. Harris, Phys. Rev. A **35**, 2095–2101 (1987).

[17]J. C. Wang, R. G. Caro, and S. E. Harris, Phys. Rev. Lett. **51**, 767–770 (1983).

[18]J. E. Rothenberg, J. F. Young, and S. E. Harris, IEEE J. Quantum. Electron. **19**, 1795–1804 (1983).

[19]S. E. Harris, to be published.

[20]V. G. Arkhipkin and Yu. I. Heller, Phys. Lett. **98A**, 12–14 (1983).

Reprinted with permission from *Physical Review A*, Vol. 38(6), pp. 3139-3142 (September 15, 1988). ©1988 American Physical Society.

Exploding-foil–photoionization x-ray laser

P. D. Morley
KMS Fusion, Inc., P.O. Box 1567, Ann Arbor, Michigan 48106

J. Sugar
Atomic and Plasma Radiation Division, National Bureau of Standards, Gaithersburg, Maryland 20899

(Received 26 February 1988; revised manuscript received 10 July 1988)

By combining the technique of exploding foils with inner-shell photoionization, we predict that lasing can occur for x rays below 50 Å in Cu-like ions. As an example, we work out the case for Cu-like iodine (I^{24+}) which should lase on the $3d^94s^2 \rightarrow 3d^{10}4p$ doublet calculated at 24.565 and 26.026 Å with integrated line energies comparable to the selenium x-ray laser.

Since the first demonstration[1] of soft-x-ray amplification in laser-exploded foils, there has been much effort to achieve shorter and shorter wavelengths.[2] In broad terms, an exploding foil lases due to collisional excitations. A different means to achieve inverted populations was suggested by Duguay and Rentzepis[3] who reasoned that inner-shell photoionization of atoms from broadband x rays will produce lasing transitions. This was subsequently proved experimentally, first in Cd vapor,[4] then in Zn vapor,[5] followed by In plasma.[6] We propose to combine these two procedures to produce lasing transitions which are unattainable by either method alone.

A combined technique experiment entails a double laser beam (see Fig. 1). The first beam explodes a foil while the second beam strikes a metal to create x rays which then impinge on the created plasma. As will be seen, judicious choice of the two materials to be irradiated should allow short wavelength (<50 Å) lasing transitions. We have investigated two particular inner-shell ionization schemes: Cd-like and Zn-like isoelectronic sequences. Both involve the photoionization of an inner d-shell electron, $4d$ and $3d$, respectively. For Cd itself, removal of a $4d$ electron from the $4d^{10}5s^2$ ground state results in Cd^+ $4d^95s^2\ ^2D$, which is an excited configuration of Ag-like Cd.[4] Lasing occurs to the $4d^{10}5p\ ^2P$ states which decay to the $4d^{10}5s$ ground state. However, as we go up to the

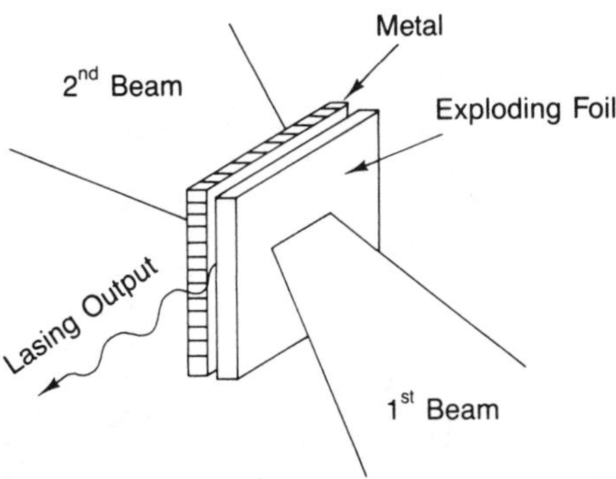

FIG. 1. Schematic representation of the exploding foil photoionization x-ray laser scheme. The metal foil is the source of the photoionizing x rays.

Ag-like isoelectronic sequence $4f$-shell collapse sets in. It has been shown[7] that the ground state of the Cd isoelectronic sequence becomes $4d^{10}4f^2$ at Sm^{15+}. Correspondingly, the excited state of the Ag isoelectronic sequence achieved by removing a $4d$ electron is $4d^94f^2$. The binding energy of this configuration increases with atomic number Z faster than $n=5$ orbits and eventually at $Z \simeq 80$ it becomes the lowest excited configuration.[8] The energy of $4d^{10}5p$ becomes equal to that of $4d^94f^2$ at $Z \cong 75$. Thus, we calculate that the promising lasing transition to $4d^{10}5p$ never achieves a wavelength below 100 Å.

Since these Cd-like transitions cannot do much better than present exploding foils alone,[9] we next investigated the Zn-isoelectronic sequence. Here the physics is very favorable. A Zn-like ion will be in the $3d^{10}4s^2$ ground state which then becomes the $3d^94s^2$ excited state of the Cu-like ion. This will lase to the $3d^{10}4p$ levels, which decay to the $3d^{10}4s$ ground state of the Cu-like ion. Unlike the Ag-like sequence no level crossings limit the maximum photon energy achievable for increasing Z. A particularly attractive element is iodine.

We have made energy-level and transition-probability calculations for this element using the Cowan Hartree-Fock (HFR) code which includes relativistic corrections.[10] Throughout, the HFR radial integral values for electrostatic interactions were reduced by 85%, while the spin-orbit integrals were left at their HFR values. This scaling is typical of what one finds in fitting the radial integrals to observed energy levels. All our calculations are made in the configuration-average approximation.

For I^{24+} we calculated the even configurations $3d^{10}4s$, $3d^{10}4d$, $3d^94s^2$, and $3d^94p^2$ with configuration interaction (CI) between them, and the odd configurations $3d^{10}4p$ and $3d^{10}4f$ each mixed with $3d^94s4p$. The largest effect of CI occurs between $3d^94s^2$ and $3d^94p^2$, which allows the lasing transition $3d^94s^2 \rightarrow 3d^{10}4p$ shown in Fig. 2. The population of the $3d^{10}4p$ term is rapidly depleted to the $3d^{10}4s$ ground state. The slight mixture of $3d^{10}4f$ with $3d^94s4p$ permits some branching of $3d^94s^2$ to $3d^{10}4f$, but this is 40 times weaker than the desired transition. Table I gives the HFR average energies of the configurations in question and the CI radial integrals between them. In Table II and Fig. 2 we show the calculat-

TABLE I. Hartree-Fock average energies of relevant configurations of I^{24+} and CI integrals between them.

Configuration	Energy (cm^{-1})	CI integrals (cm^{-1})	Interacting configurations
1 $3d^{10}4s$	0	$R^1(ds,pp) = -13400$	1–7
2 $3d^{10}4p$	499 700	$R^2(dd',ss') = -19600$	3–5
3 $3d^{10}4d$	1 227 900	$R^1(dd',pp) = -13900$	3–7
4 $3d^{10}4f$	1 948 800	$R^3(dd',pp') = -16400$	3–7
5 $3d^9 4s^2$	4 434 600	$R^1(ss,pp) = 175700$	5–7
6 $3d^9 4s4p$	4 902 500	$R^2(df,sp) = -31900$	4–6
7 $3d^9 4p^2$	5 426 800	$R^3(df,ps) = -30000$	4–6

ed electric dipole transitions, their transition rates and wavelengths. Since, in absence of configuration mixing, the $3d^9 4s^2 \rightarrow 3d^{10}4p$ transition disappears, we expect that the rate will be much slower than a normal dipole transition associated with a 25-Å line. Figure 2 shows this. Without this reduction of rate, it would be practically impossible to have an x-ray laser in this regime since an allowed electric dipole 25-Å line lives only ~ 2 ps.

The x-ray wavelength (λ) required to photoionize Zn-like iodine by the removal of a $3d$ electron was derived by calculating the difference in total energy between the configurations $3d^{10}4s^2$ and $3d^9 4s^2$. The corresponding wavelength is 9.4 Å.

To determine the conditions necessary to perform the double-beam iodine experiment, we have used the two-dimensional laser hydrodynamic code[11] HYRAD in nonlocal thermodynamic equilibrium. Iodine will be in the form of CsI which can be deposited very accurately on a substrate.[12] The design goal is to vary the CsI thickness and first beam intensity to produce a constant Zn-like iodine density profile for a maximum length of time and space. Calculations show that a 1000-Å layer on a substrate of 1500 Å metallic boron illuminated by 1 ns, 0.53 μm light of 5×10^{12} W/cm^2 intensity creates the desired

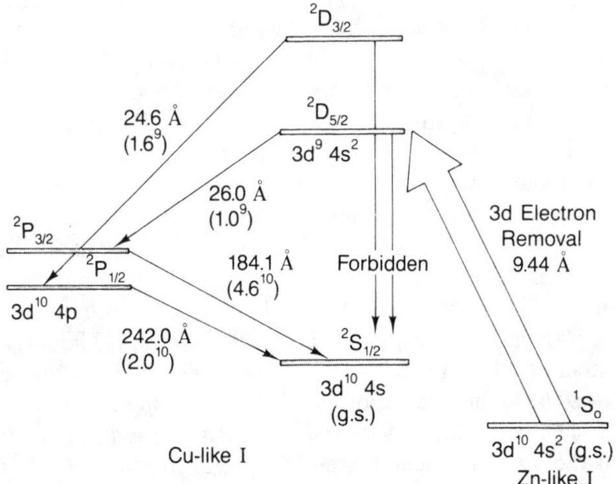

FIG. 2. Grotrian diagram for the lasing transitions. Numbers in parentheses are total radiative rates in reciprocal seconds. Notation $1.6^9 \equiv 1.6\times10^9$ is used. We do not show here the relatively weak $3d^9rs^2 \rightarrow 3d^{10}4f$ transitions.

characteristics;[13] see Table III. The electron temperature and density 0.5 ns into the pulse are about 0.14 keV and 9×10^{20} cm^{-3}, respectively.

The second beam and target material can be determined using the experimental results of Ref. 14, whose authors have experimentally measured the x-ray line emission of various metals upon laser irradiation. Now, the photoionization cross section of a $3d$ electron in Zn-like iodine near the absorption edge[15] is $\sigma_p \gtrsim 2$ Mb. For maximum efficiency, it is desirable that the ionizing photons be close to the 9.44 Å threshold. The K-shell $1s2p\ ^1P_1$-$1s^2\ ^1S_0$ transition in Mg XI, at $\lambda = 9.168$ Å was originally thought to be appropriate, but one also needs to remove the Cu-like iodine in its ground state. This is the ionic state which could quench the laser if allowed to accumulate. Unfortunately photoionizing Cu-like iodine requires a 9.14-Å photon and so the above K-shell Mg XI line is insufficient. The Al XII $1s2p \rightarrow 1s^2$ transition at 7.757 Å would do the job.[16] For large lasers of the KMS Chroma class about 0.5×10^{14} photons/J will be emitted[14] as K-shell line emission if the second beam hits Al metal with a wavelength 0.53 μm and intensity $\sim 10^{14}$ W/cm^2 and pulse width $\gtrsim 700$ ps. As an example, if 2-μm Al is hit with an intensity of 6×10^{14} W/cm^2, the electron temperature and density 0.5 ns into the pulse are 3.67 keV and 6.2×10^{18} cm^{-3} in the burn region. This will be a copious x-ray emitter. We now demonstrate that even if only a tiny fraction of the emitted photons eject $3d$ electrons, the integrated lasing energy will be comparable to the original[1] selenium laser.

The strongest integrated line energy flux of the original selenium laser was[1] about 160 μJ/sr at 206 Å. With a

TABLE II. Calculated transitions between levels active in the proposed laser scheme.

Transition		A (sec^{-1})	λ (Å)
$3d^9 4s^2 \rightarrow 3d^{10}4p$	$^2D_{3/2}$-$^2P_{1/2}$	1.6×10^9	24.56
	$^2D_{5/2}$-$^2P_{3/2}$	1.0×10^9	26.03
$3d^{10}4p \rightarrow 3d^{10}4s$	$^2P_{1/2}$-$^2S_{1/2}$	2.0×10^{10}	242.02
	$^2P_{3/2}$-$^2S_{1/2}$	4.6×10^{10}	184.11
$3d^9 4s^2 \rightarrow 3d^{10}4f$	$^2D_{3/2}$-$^2F_{5/2}$	4.2×10^7	39.40
	$^2D_{5/2}$-$^2F_{7/2}$	3.8×10^7	41.08

TABLE III. Time in picoseconds (ps) into the first pulse. L_T in microns is the transverse plasma scale length for the iodine density. The longitudinal scale length is the beam line focus.

Time (ps)	$\frac{N_{\text{Ga-like}}}{N_{\text{Zn-like}}}$	$\frac{N_{\text{Cu-like}}}{N_{\text{Zn-like}}}$	$N_{\text{Zn-like}}$ (10^{18} cm^{-3})	L_T (μm)
100	3.5	0.19	1.6	8
200	0.73	0.93	16.4	27
300	0.63	1.05	9.95	50
400	0.63	1.03	7.10	77
500	0.66	0.99	6.09	98
600	0.61	1.06	5.10	120
700	0.65	1.00	4.07	140
800	0.67	0.97	3.50	160
900	0.69	0.94	3.11	183
1000	0.71	0.91	2.75	204

10-mrad divergence, this gives 10^9 photons as the total signal radiated by one of the lines. [Since the original 1985 experiments a recent report (Ref. 9) gives higher output near saturation.] If the second pulse in a photoionization x-ray laser were $\sim$300 J (characteristic of large glass lasers) then the number of photoionization photons is $0.5\times10^{14}\times300=1.5\times10^{16}$. Thus to equal the original Se signal only a tiny fraction need be captured. From Table III the calculated mean free path for photoionization at 200 ps is $\lesssim$300 μm. Thus about 1 photon in 10 along the transverse direction will be captured at time 200 ps. Allowing for unknown losses, we expect that the integrated line energies of a photoionization x-ray laser should be comparable or even higher than a collisionally inverted x-ray laser.

The gain per unit length of the laser will be calculated from the formula[17]

$$g=\left[\frac{4\ln 2}{\pi}\right]^{1/2}\frac{1}{8\pi c}\frac{\lambda^4}{\Delta\lambda}A\left[N_U-\frac{g_U}{g_L}N_L\right], \quad (1)$$

where λ is the transition wavelength, $\Delta\lambda$ is the linewidth, A is the spontaneous transition rate and N, g are the number densities and statistical weights of the U (upper) and L (lower) lasing levels. Let ϕ be the photon flux/cm^2/ns and t the time. Then

$$N_U=\phi t\sigma_p N_{\text{Zn-like}}\le N_{\text{Zn-like}}. \quad (2)$$

The design of the experiment requires that

$$\phi t\sigma_p=1 \quad (3)$$

for maximum g at time t. $\Delta\lambda$ will be approximated by the Doppler broadening, $\Delta\lambda_D$,

$$\Delta\lambda\approx\Delta\lambda_D=(7.7\times10^{-5})\lambda\left[\frac{T}{M}\right]^{1/2}, \quad (4)$$

where the ion temperature T is in eV and M is the atomic weight. From the computer-simulation codes, Zn-like iodine has $(T/M)^{1/2}\approx1$. Thus, for example, the 26-Å line has a gain (in cm^{-1}) of

$$g_{26.0}=(2.86\times10^{-19})\left[N_U-\frac{g_U}{g_L}N_L\right]. \quad (5)$$

TABLE IV. Ground state (g.s.) and excited state of I^{23+}. $3d$ photoionization produces the corresponding states of I^{24+}. Only $3d^94p^2\rightarrow3d^{10}4p$ does not go through the lasing transition.

	I^{23+}	I^{24+}		Goes through lasing state
Third	$3d^{10}4s4d$	$3d^94s4d$	$\rightarrow3d^94s4p$	Yes
Second	$3d^{10}4p^2$	$3d^94p^2$	$\rightarrow3d^{10}4p$	No
			$\rightarrow3d^94s4p$	Yes
First	$3d^{10}4s4p$	$3d^94s4p$	$\rightarrow3d^94s^2$	Yes
g.s.	$3d^{10}4s^2$	$3d^94s^2$	$\rightarrow3d^{10}4p$	Yes

If there is little population in N_L, then from Table III, $N_U\sim7\times10^{18}$ for over half a nanosecond, so we would expect conservatively $g\sim2$ cm^{-1} if Eq. (3) is true. An important observation is that it does not matter how much of the Zn-like iodine is in its ground state versus its low excited states. Table IV shows that the excited states must go through the lasing transition, except for branching of the second excited state $3d^94p^2\rightarrow3d^{10}4p$. Because the excited transitions go much faster than the lasing one, essentially all the $N_{\text{Zn-like}}$ present is usable. Furthermore, Eq. (3) is very easily obtained. Let E_B be the energy in joules for the second beam and let r be the separation distance of the two foils. Then[18]

$$\phi\approx(0.5\times10^{14})E_B\frac{1}{4\pi r^2}\ (\text{cm}^{-2}\text{ns}^{-1}). \quad (6)$$

By requiring Eq. (3) to be valid at time $t=0.8$ ns, then $E_B\sim140$ J, with $r=300$ μm. Experimentally we expect some line trapping of the $3d^{10}4p\rightarrow3d^{10}4s$ radiation so the actual gain in green light will be less than the 2 cm^{-1} value. This line trapping may explain the surprising results of the Zn experiment[5] where the $^2D_{5/2}$-$^2P_{3/2}$ transition lased with a large $g=2.2$ cm^{-1}, but no lasing occurred at all on the $^2D_{3/2}$-$^2P_{1/2}$ line.

In conclusion, theoretical calculations predict that by combining two well-established experimental techniques, short-wavelength (<50 Å) transitions can be amplified. This method is expected to be more efficient than the exploding beam foil alone. We gave here the iodine example which should lase at 24.5 and 26.0 Å, but clearly one can go to shorter wavelengths than these. To maintain a respectable gain coefficient (say 2 cm^{-1}) as we go to shorter lasing wavelengths, we increase N_U by going to thicker targets. This requires that the pumping laser be shorter in wavelength in order to burn through the foil. If NOVA at Lawrence Livermore National Laboratory is operated in blue (0.351 μm) light or even quadrupled light (0.261 μm), a very high energy x-ray laser can be achieved based on this scheme. As an example, Tb^{36+} will have the lasing transitions $^2D_{3/2}\rightarrow{}^2P_{1/2}$ at 12 Å and $^2D_{5/2}\rightarrow{}^2P_{3/2}$ at 13 Å with respective rates 5×10^9 and 2×10^9. The required photoionizing photon is 1.6 keV. Lastly, refraction effects will be much less severe for these short wavelengths and saturation should be attained.

One of us (P.D.M.) would like to thank G. Charatis, Ed Gabl, B. MacGowan, and William Silfvast for helpful conversations and/or correspondence. The research at the

[1]D. L. Matthews *et al.*, Phys. Rev. Lett. **54**, 106 (1985); M. D. Rosen *et al.*, *ibid.* **54**, 110 (1985).
[2]B. J. MacGowan *et al.*, Phys. Rev. Lett. **59**, 2157 (1987).
[3]M. A. Duguay and P. M. Rentzepis, Appl. Phys. Lett. **10**, 350 (1967).
[4]William T. Silfvast, John J. Macklin, and Obert R. Wood, Opt. Lett. **8**, 551 (1983).
[5]H. Lundberg, J. J. Macklin, W. T. Silfvast, and Obert R. Wood, Appl. Phys. Lett. **45**, 335 (1984).
[6]R. A. Lacy, R. L. Byer, W. T. Silfvast, Obert W. Wood, and S. Svanberg, in *Short Wavelength Radiation: Generation and Applications,* edited by D. T. Attwood and J. Bokor (American Institute of Physics, New York, 1986), p. 96.
[7]J. Sugar and V. Kaufman, Phys. Rev. A **21**, 2096 (1980).
[8]K. Cheng and Y. Kim, J. Opt. Soc. Am. **69**, 125 (1979).
[9]D. Matthews *et al.*, J. Opt. Soc. Am. B **4**, 575 (1987).
[10]R. D. Cowan, *The Theory of Atomic Structure and Spectra* (Univ. of California Press, Berkeley, 1981).
[11]P. M. Campbell, KMS Fusion, Inc. 1987 Annual Technical Report (unpublished).
[12]The usual substrates which are plastic (Formvar, Mylar, etc.) cannot be used because C^{5+} has a 26-Å Lyman line.
[13]These are not unqiue parameters. 300-Å CsI on 1500-Å boron requires a nanosecond pulse of 3.0×10^{12} W/cm^2 intensity at 1.06-μm wavelength. Thinner targets will decrease the expected gain.
[14]D. L. Matthews *et al.*, J. Appl. Phys. **54**, 4260 (1983).
[15]Estimate based on the At. Data Tables **5**, 51 (1973).
[16]Another option is to use Au which produces a hard spectrum and which is an efficient converter of laser light to x rays.
[17]S. Suckewer and H. Fishman, J. Appl. Phys. **51**, 1922 (1980).
[18]The beam size of the pump laser would be pointlike for a small glass laser. However, for a large glass laser, the geometry will be parallel line focii and the scaling with distance will be a less severe r^{-1}.

Reprinted with the permission of the American Physical Society from *Physical Review A*, Vol. 38(10), pp. 5426-5429 (November 15, 1988).

Enhanced x-ray gain through photodepopulation

R. C. Elton
Naval Research Laboratory, Washington, D.C. 20375
(Received 7 March 1988)

Radiation trapping currently creates one of the major limitations on population inversion, gain, and size in x-ray lasers. The resulting increase in lower-level population may be reduced by photodepletion to higher energy levels. A natural energy match between hydrogenic lasing ions of nuclear charge Z, for $n=2$ to 4 or 6 excitation, and $Z/2$ radiating ions provides a scalable system for even-Z elements.

INTRODUCTION

Reaching the next short-wavelength plateau (<50 Å) in laboratory x-ray laser development could likely depend on $\Delta n=1$ transitions, because the successful $\Delta n=0$, $3p\rightarrow 3s$ neonlike ion transition[1] does not readily extrapolate that far, and the inherent multiplicity of the $n=4$ to 4 nickellike transitions limits the achievable gain.[2] For $\Delta n=1$ transitions, hydrogenic ions continue to be very attractive candidates, and there has been particular success[3] with the C^{5+} ion at 182 Å on the $n=3$ to 2 Balmer-α transition. The lasing wavelength for this transition extrapolates as simply Z^{-2} (Z being the nuclear charge), e.g., to 45 Å for Mg^{11+}. However, the size becomes micrometer in scale[4] because of the need to avoid radiative trapping on the 2*p*-1*s* Lyman-α resonance transition.

Electron-collisional recombination has proven to be a most promising pumping method for producing population inversions leading to amplified spontaneous emission in the xuv spectral region, with the gain scaling[4] hydrogenically as $\sim Z^{7.5}$. Maximum pumping is obtained in a high-density plasma consisting of totally stripped ions of the element of laser interest in which the electrons are suddenly cooled, leading to rapid collisional recombination and cascading. When the ion temperature is also low, an additional enhancement of the overall gain (scaling as $T^{-1/2}$) is obtained through reduced Doppler line broadening. Also, for a similar laser wavelength, present $\Delta n=1$ recombination-pumped devices operate at a lower electron density than do the electron-collision-pumped $\Delta n=0$ devices, with the added advantage of lower refraction losses through the amplifying line plasma.

Even with these obvious advantages, measured gain coefficients to date seem to be capped at about 3–6 cm^{-1}. This can be associated with a relative population inversion factor $1-N_2 g_3/N_3 g_2$ which just marginally exceeds zero, due to collisional mixing and radiative trapping at the high densities required for such high gain.[4,5] Hence, $N_3\approx N_2(g_3/g_2)$. [Here the upper- and lower-state densities are designated, respectively, by N_3 and N_2 and the statistical weights by $g_n=2n^2$ $(n=2,3)$ for the Balmer-α transition.]

Hence, to increase the population inversion and thereby the gain to saturation, to improve the overall efficiency, and to increase the plasma size for eventual multiple-oscillator plus amplifier operation, it is important to decrease the population density N_2.

CONCEPT

The density N_2 can be decreased by transferring $n=2$ electrons to the $n=4$ level through absorption of $n=2$ to 1 Lyman-α photons from a second $Z/2$ hydrogenic ion, where Z is the nuclear charge. This results in photoexcitation to the $n=4$ level in the lasing ion (see Fig. 1). From the Rydberg formula this Z, $Z/2$ is a natural match[6,7] which extrapolates readily for all even-Z elements. Also, a $n=3$ to 1 Lyman-β photon in the $Z/2$ plasma to a somewhat lesser degree can depopulate the $n=2$ level by photoexcitation to the $n=6$ level (shown with a dashed line in Fig. 1), followed by cascade to $n=3$

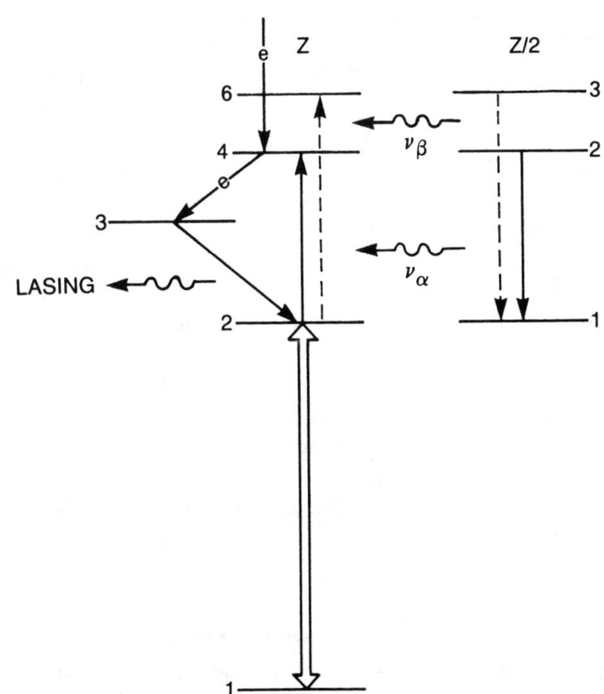

FIG. 1. Hydrogenic energy-level diagrams for $n=3$ to 2 lasing in ions of nuclear charge Z, with $n=2$ depopulated to $n=4$ or 6 by Lyman-α and Lyman-β (dashed) photons, respectively.

for further $n=3$ to 2 inversion and gain. A highly relevant combination is Mg^{11+} ($Z=10$) lasing on a 3-2 transition at 45 Å with $n=2$ depopulated to $n=4$ and 6 by C^{5+} Lyman-α and Lyman-β emission at 34 and 28 Å, respectively. Such $n=2$ to 4 photoexcitation in Mg^{12+} by C^{5+} Lyman-α emission may have been demonstrated[7] already for pumping fluorescence on a $n=4$ to 3 transition.
is C^{5+} ($Z=6$) currently lasing at 182 Å and irradiated by Li^{2+} Lyman-α emission at 135 Å. The following analysis is based primarily on the latter, i.e., creating a fully ionized carbon plasma at an electron kinetic temperature $kT \approx 150$ eV, rapidly cooling it to about 20 eV for recombination pumping, and irradiating it with a plasma designed for strong emission on the hydrogenic Li^{2+} Lyman-α line.

A less direct $n=2$ photodepopulation scheme that also could decrease N_2 involves matching only approximately the incident photon energy and the $n=1$ ground-state ionization potential. With sufficient irradiance, such a decrease in N_1 would result in less radiative trapping on the Lyman-α transition and hence a lower density N_2. This could also serve to reionize the lasing ion for additional pumping through the recombination with an overall potential increase in efficiency, an effect already demonstrated,[8] for C^{4+} $2p \rightarrow 1s$ irradiation of lithiumlike Na^{8+} ions. Short of a complete numerical analysis, including nonequilibrium radiative and thermal transport between the two plasmas, some validity can be ascertained by the following considerations.

LITHIUM-CARBON ANALYSIS

The wavelength matches for the Li^{2+}-C^{5+} combination are excellent. Most[9] ($\sim$65%) of the Li^{2+}-ion Lyman-α emission arises from the $J=3/2$ to 1/2 component at a wavelength[10] of 134.998 Å. For the C^{5+} lasant ion, approximately 63% of the total $n=2$ to 4 absorption occurs on the $2p \rightarrow 4d$ transitions,[11] about 75% (according to statistical weights) of which should occur on the $J=\frac{3}{2}$ to $\frac{5}{2}$ term at a wavelength[10] of 134.990 Å. The main coincidence, therefore, is within 0.008 Å. A convenient figure of merit here is the ratio $\Delta\lambda/\lambda = 0.59 \times 10^{-4}$, which is much less than a similar ratio of $\Delta\lambda/\lambda \sim 3 \times 10^{-4}$ for the Doppler spread[12] of the broader (pumping) line.

To be effective in reducing N_2, the $n=2$ to 4 volumetric photoexcitation pumping rate $N_2 P_{24}$ must at least exceed the $n=3$ to 2 spontaneous decay rate $N_3 A_{32}$ for populating the $n=2$ level (assuming that $\sum_{n>3} N_n A_{n2} \ll N_3 A_{32}$ and that the $n=3$ to 2 lasing is below saturation). Hence,

$$N_2 P_{24} \equiv N_2 N_\nu \sigma_{24} c \geq N_3 A_{32} \ , \tag{1}$$

where N_ν is the photon density at the lasing ion and σ_{24} is the peak $n=2$ to 4 photoexcitation cross section. The transition probability A_{42} is related by σ_{24} by

$$A_{42} = \frac{8\pi c}{\lambda_{24}^3} \frac{g_2}{g_4} \frac{\Delta\nu}{\nu} \sigma_{24} \ . \tag{2}$$

For threshold inversion, $N_3/g_3 = N_2/g_2$. Also, for Doppler broadening, the relative line width $\Delta\nu/\nu = \Delta\lambda/\lambda$ can again be taken as $\sim 3 \times 10^{-4}$, such that Eqs. (1) and (2) give

$$N_\nu = \frac{9\pi}{2} \frac{1}{\lambda_{24}^3} \frac{A_{32}}{A_{42}} \frac{\Delta_\nu}{\nu}$$

$$= 9 \times 10^{15} \text{ photons/cm}^3 \tag{3}$$

for the required flux at the lasing ion generated by Lyman-α emission from the $Z/2$ pumping-source ion. (The Lyman-β pumping will reduce this requirement further, but is not included in this simple analysis.)

The quantity N_ν in Eq. (3) may be used to estimate some pumping-plasma characteristics. Assuming a completely congruent plasma mixture, i.e., collection of photons over 4π steradians, the required flux generated by an optically thick Li^{2+} (primed quantities) Lyman-α line of wavelength $\lambda'_{21} = 135$ Å ($=\lambda_{24}$ for C^{5+}) is given by the blackbody formula:[6]

$$N'_\nu = \frac{4\pi}{\lambda_{24}^3} [\exp(hc/\lambda_{24} k T_B) - 1]^{-1} \frac{\Delta\nu}{\nu} \approx N_\nu \ . \tag{4}$$

Combining Eqs. (3) and (4) for matching line widths leads to the simple relation (independent of wavelength):

$$\exp(hc/\lambda_{24} k T_B) = 1 + \frac{16}{9} \frac{A_{42}}{A_{32}} = 1.3 \ , \tag{5}$$

for tabulated[11] hydrogenic transition probabilities. This leads to a required brightness temperature of

$$kT_B = 4 \times 10^4 / \lambda_{24} \text{ eV} \ , \tag{6}$$

for λ_{24} in Å. For the Li^{2+} Lyman-α line, this becomes

$$kT_B = 300 \text{ eV} \ . \tag{7}$$

Blackbody emission can be assured for an opacity[12]

$$\tau'_{21} = 5 \times 10^{-17} N'_i \lambda_{24} d (\mu / kT_B)^{1/2} \approx 100 \ , \tag{8}$$

where $\mu = 7$ is the atomic mass number, $\lambda_{24} = 135$ Å, and $kT = kT_B$ is in eV. This opacity can be achieved for a $d = 1$ mm dimension at an ion density of $N_i \approx 10^{18}$ cm^{-3}.

We can also relate[13] the required photon density N_ν in Eq. (3) to a measurable emitted power W'_P, again starting with congruent plasmas, by[13,14]

$$N_\nu = \frac{W'_P}{4\pi} \frac{\lambda_{24}}{hr^2 c^2} \ . \tag{9}$$

For a characteristic dimension $r = 100$ μm (200-μm diam), this gives

$$W'_P \approx 5 \text{ MW} \ . \tag{10}$$

This could be expected to increase by $\sim$3 times for dual plasmas separated by the same distance.[13,14] That this is in a reasonable range at least for laser-produced plasmas is evidenced by a measured[13] value of 25 MW emitted from a Na^{8+} pumping line in a plasma created by a high-power laser with an irradiance on target of 5×10^{14} W/cm^2.

Such a powerful emission, corresponding to a Li^{2+} plasma temperature of $kT \approx 300$ eV (the brightness temperature for the source), presents the possibility somewhat of overheating (e.g., by thermal conduction) the nearby C^{5+} lasing plasma, which must be cooled to ~ 20 eV for lasing. In this regard, it should be possible to generate initially a homogeneously mixed C^{6+}-Li^{3+} fully ionized plasma at an electron kinetic temperature $kT \approx 300$ eV. This is subsequently cooled to $kT \approx 20$ eV, such that the lower-Z Li^{2+} ions recombine at a lower ($\propto Z^4$) rate to provide the $2p$-$1s$ Lyman-α emission congruent with the carbon ions, which are recombining and lasing much more rapidly. For the sake of argument, suppose the Li^{3+} stripped ions are at such a density as to recombine within the mean C^{5+} Balmer-series decay time (lasing period) of $t_r \sim 100$ ps. For the Lyman-α photon energy of 92 eV, the required 5 MW of congruent power $(= N_i Vhc/\lambda_{42} t_r)$ could be produced by an ion density of $N_i = 10^{17}$ cm^{-3} in a laser-heated plasma of 500 μm radius. If operated at 10 times this density to assure a high opacity (see above), the emission would be more than adequate. (This recombination process is most likely the mechanism by which the 25 MW Na^{8+} power was produced.[13]) Hence, because this is a highly nonequilibrium situation, the Li^{2+} Lyman-α emission would not be limited to a brightness corresponding to the 20-eV C^{5+} plasma temperature.

CARBON-MAGNESIUM ANALYSIS

Similar parameters can be derived for the C^{5+}-Mg^{11+} combination (with possible further enhancement by Lyman-β pumping). The wavelength match[10] between the Mg^{11+}-ion $2P_{3/2} \rightarrow 4D_{5/2}$ main absorption transition at 33.733 Å and the $2P_{3/2}$-$1S_{1/2}$ dominant C^{5+} Lyman-α component at 33.734 Å, is 0.001 Å. Also, the figure of merit $\Delta\lambda/\lambda = 0.33 \times 10^{-4}$ is even better (compared to that for Doppler broadening) than was the case for the Li^{2+}-C^{5+} combination above. The carbon-magnesium plasma would have to be heated initially to $kT \approx 600$ eV and then be cooled to $kT \approx 80$ eV for recombination pumping, in analogy to the lithium-carbon scheme.

From Eq. (3), the required photon density N_ν scales as λ_{24}^{-3}, and therefore increases by a factor of $(\frac{135}{34})^3 = 63$, resulting in 7.0×10^{16} photons/cm^3 for Mg^{11+}. From Eq. (5) the blackbody brightness temperature is

$$kT_B = 1.2 \text{ keV} , \tag{11}$$

i.e., about 4 times that for the Li^{2+}-C^{5+} combination. From Eq. (8), an opacity of $\tau'_{21} = 100$ will be obtained at a C^{5+} ion density of 6×10^{18} cm^{-3}, for the same $d = 1$ mm depth.

From Eq. (9), the pump power W_P required scales as N_ν/λ_{24}, so that there is a total λ_{24}^{-4} scaling from Li^{2+} to C^{5+}. This results in an increase by a factor of 250 to 1.2 GW, which is high by present laser-produced plasma standards. It is, however, quite reasonable for large pulsed power devices, where 25 GW of power recently has been measured.[15] However, for nonequilibrium recombination from C^{6+} to C^{5+} in a period t_r reduced by a factor of λ^2, or $\frac{1}{16}$ the time of Li^{3+} to Li^{2+} (i.e., in ~ 6 ps), the ion density $N_i = W_P t_r \lambda_{24}/Vhc$ scales as λ^{-1} and increases only to $N_i \approx 4 \times 10^{17}$ cm^{-3} for C^{6+}.

SUMMARY

In summary, "naturally"-occurring hydrogenic line matches for Z and $Z/2$, $Z/3$ elements promise a reduction of $n = 2$ lower-level population and an associated increase in gain for the $n = 3$ to 2 Balmer-α line. The initial analysis is done for $Z = 6$ and 12. The required Lyman-α pumping-plasma conditions are reasonable for $Z' = Z/2 = 3$ and 6, respectively. The $Z = 6$, $Z' = 3$ example can be readily tested in present recombining C^{6+} to C^{5+} lasers with added lithium [or with lithium carbide (Li_4C_2)].

[1] D. Matthews, M. Rosen, S. Brown, N. Ceglio, D. Eder, A. Hawryluk, C. Keane, R. London, B. MacGowan, S. Maxon, D. Nilson, J. Scofield, and J. Trebes, J. Opt. Soc. Am. B **4**, 575 (1987); T. N. Lee, E. A. McLean, and R. C. Elton, Phys. Rev. Lett. **59**, 1185 (1987).

[2] B. J. MacGowan, S. Maxon, P. L. Hagelstein, C. J. Keane, R. A. London, D. L. Matthews, M. D. Rosen, J. H. Scofield, and D. A. Whelan, Phys. Rev. Lett. **59**, 2157 (1987).

[3] D. Jacoby, G. J. Pert, L. D. Shorrock, and G. J. Tallents, J. Phys. B **15**, 3557 (1982); S. Suckewer, C. H. Skinner, H. Milchberg, C. Keane, and D. Voorhees, Phys. Rev. Lett. **55**, 1753 (1985); J. F. Seely, C. M. Brown, U. Feldman, M. Richardson, B. Yaakobi, and W. E. Behring, Opt. Commun. **54**, 289 (1985); C. Chenais-Popovics, R. Corbett, C. J. Hooker, M. H. Key, G. P. Kiehn, L. S. Lewis, G. J. Pert, C. Regan, S. J. Rose, S. Sadaat, R. Smith, T. Tomie, and O. Willi, Phys. Rev. Lett. **59**, 2161 (1987).

[4] R. C. Elton, Opt. Eng. **21**, 307 (1982).

[5] R. C. Elton, Comments At. Mol. Phys. **13**, 59 (1983). (Printing errors of subscripts in this paper render it difficult to understand—contact the author for a revised version.)

[6] R. C. Elton, Appendix I, NRL Memorandum Report No. 3482, 1977 (unpublished), p. 92.

[7] V. A. Bhagavatula, Appl. Phys. Lett. **33**, 726 (1978).

[8] R. C. Elton and R. H. Dixon, Phys. Rev. A **28**, 1886 (1983).

[9] R. L. Kelly, J. Phys. Chem. Ref. Data **16**, Suppl. No. 1 (1987).

[10] G. W. Erickson, J. Phys. Chem. Ref. Data **6**, 831 (1977).

[11] W. L. Wiese, M. W. Smith, and B. M. Glennon, *Atomic Transition Probabilities: Hydrogen through Neon,* Natl. Bur. Stand. Ref. Data Ser., Natl. Bur. Stand. (U.S.) Circ. No. 4 (U.S. GPO, Washington, D.C., 1966), Vol. 1; W. L. Wiese, M. W. Smith, and B. M. Miles, *Sodium through Calcium,* Natl. Bur. Stand. Ref. Data Ser., Natl. Bur. Stand. (U.S.) Circ. No. 22 (U.S. GPO, Washington, D.C., 1969), Vol. 2.

[12] R. C. Elton, in *Methods of Experimental Physics, Plasma Physics,* edited by H. R. Griem and R. H. Lovberg (Academic, New York, 1970).

[13] R. C. Elton, T. N. Lee, and P. G. Burkhalter, Nucl. Instrum. Methods Phys. Res. **B9**, 753 (1985).

[14] R. C. Elton, T. N. Lee, and W. A. Molander, Phys. Rev. A **33**, 2817 (1986).

[15] F. C. Young, S. J. Stephanakis, V. E. Scherrer, B. L. Welch, G. Mehlman, P. G. Burkhalter, and J. P. Apruzese, Appl. Phys. Lett. **50**, 1053 (1987).

Reprinted with permission from *Journal de Physique*, Colloque C1, Suppl. 3, Vol. 49, pp. C1-135—C1-144 (March 1988).

XUV LASERS - A SURVEY OF PROGRESS

M.H. KEY

SERC Rutherford Appleton Laboratory, Chilton, GB-Didcot OX11 0QX, Great-Britain

RESUME

Le développment des lasers a rayonnement XUV est tellement avancé depuis 1985 qu'on peut parler d'une famille nouvelle de lasers dont la dureé d'impulsion est courte et la puissance est grande. Les characteristiques actuelles et potentielles de ces lasers et les resultats les plus importants sont presentés.

ABSTRACT

There has been an upsurge recently of both progress and interest in the development of XUV and X-ray lasers to such an extent that it is now possible to envisage the systematic development and application of a new family of powerful pulsed XUV lasers. The potential and actual characteristics of these lasers and the highlights of recent work will be reviewed.

Introduction

The physical concepts leading to XUV laser action in laser produced plasmas have been known for many years but detailed solutions to the practical and theoretical problems of demonstrating XUV lasers have been found only recently with the use of multiterawatt laser systems backed up by sophisticated computer modelling. Recent reviews detail the background and this paper sets out the main features of the sudden upsurge of progress in the last few years(1).

A basic characteristic of any plasma laser is the scaling with frequency of fluorescent power density and therefore of pumping power density. This shows a $\nu^{4.5}$ increase which imposes a requirement of immense fluorescent brightness for XUV lasers. With laser produced plasmas giving the most intense laboratory XUV brightness as shown in figure 1, it is not surprising to find them as the first XUV laser media, nor to find these lasers operating at the X-ray conversion efficiency peaks of ions with residual K L and M shell electrons(2).

Experiments have involved the use of line foci to create elongated cylindrical plasmas of small diameter from fibres, thin foils and solid targets as shown in figure 2. The amplification of spontaneous emission in a single transit along the plasma column gives an exponentially increasing intensity with increasing length which can be observed, for small exponents $g\ell$, in the axial/transverse intensity ratio $(\exp(g\ell)-1)/g\ell$ and for larger values of $g\ell$ in the obvious exponentiation with length. For $g\ell \geq 8$ the ASE has a narrow beam angle and for $g\ell > 15$ saturation occurs with stimulated emission becoming more probable than spontaneous emission, ie a saturated ASE laser.

The characteristics of a saturated single transit ASE(1) laser of beam aperture W and length L include high power and power density $P/1\text{MWatt} \sim (W^2/10^{-4}\ \text{cm}^2)\ (h\nu/1\text{MW})^{4.5}$, narrow bandwith $\Delta\nu/\nu \sim 2 \times 10^{-5}$, coherence length 500 μm x (λ/10 nm), spatial coherence distance W/n (where $n = W^2/L\lambda \sim 50$) and beam divergence $W/L \sim 10^{-2}$ to 10^{-3} rad. The spectral brightness is extreme and, as indicated in figure 1, exceeds by many orders of magnitude to that of any other source.

Ne-like 3p-3s

A major breakthrough in XUV lasers was a 1985 experiment using the world's most powerful laser (NOVA in the USA) which showed laser gain on 3p-3s transitions of Ne-like Se XXV(3). The mechanism is illustrated in figure 3 and relies on strong 3s-2p resonance emission to depopulate the 3s level. The 3p levels are populated both by collisional (monopole) excitation from 2p to 3p, by dielectronic recombination and by cascading from higher levels and have no allowed radiative decay to 2p. The

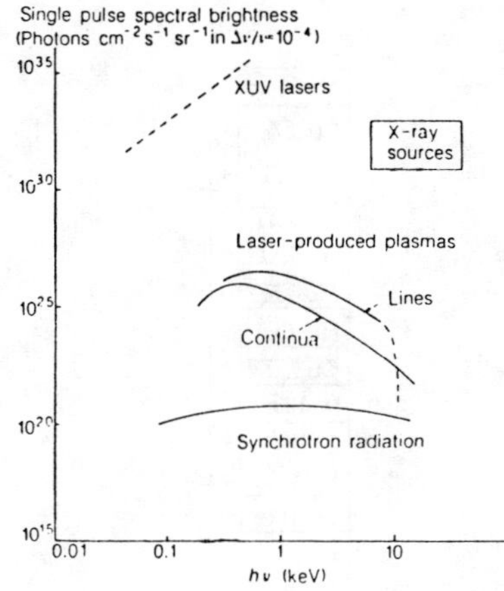

Fig. 1 Comparison of the absolute spectral brightness of XUV and X-ray sources. (Syndrotron data are from the SERC Syndrotron Radiation Source (SRS) and laser-produced plasma data are compiled for 10^{12} watt Nd glass lasers.)

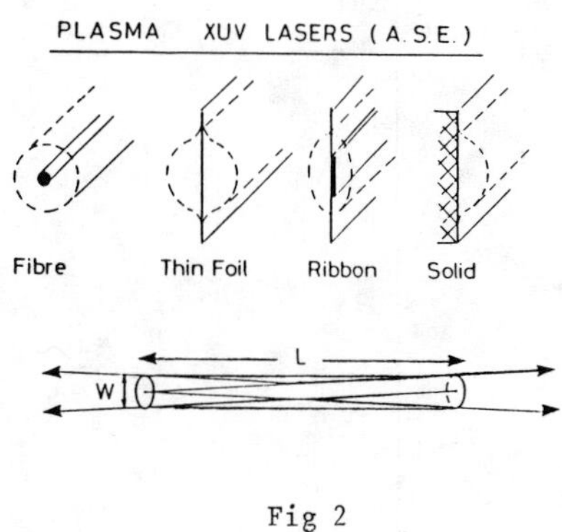

Fig 2

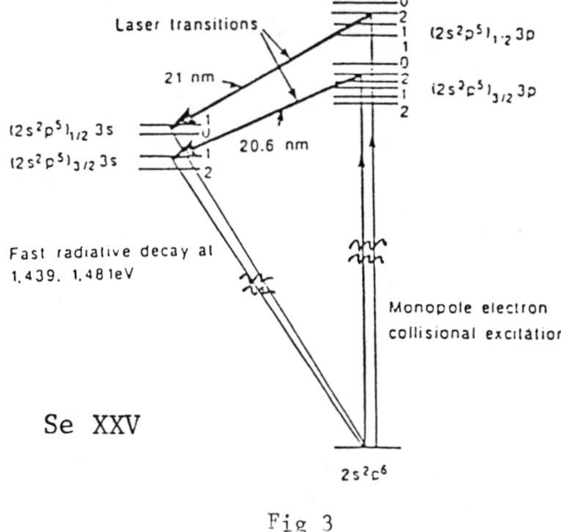

Fig 3

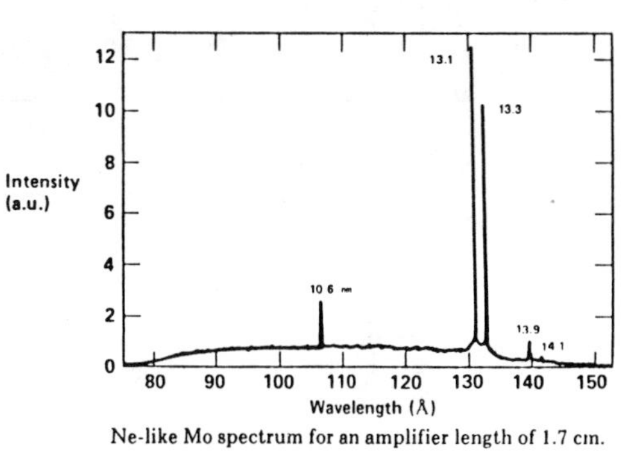

Ne-like Mo spectrum for an amplifier length of 1.7 cm.

Fig 4

temperature should be as high as possible to maximise collisional excitation without ionising the Ne-like ions and the density as high as possible but below the collisional thermalisation limit of the 3s and 3p levels (ie. LTE limit above n = 3).

The best conditions are kT = 1000 eV and $n_e \sim 5 \times 10^{20}$ cm^{-3} and the plasma must be small enough in lateral dimensions for resonance emission to escape without reabsorption. Both requirements have been achieved with a thin film target (750 Å of Se on 1500 Å of polymer) irradiated in a 200 μm wide line focus with 10^{12} Wcm^{-1} in a 500 psec pulse of 0.53 μm. A gain coefficient of 4 cm^{-1} on J = 2 to 1 transitions at 206 Å-209 Å has been observed with a maximum gain x length $g\ell \sim 14$ giving 10^6 single transit amplification! The output power is 10^6 W in a 200 psec pulse and the beam divergence 20 mrad. Refraction in the plasma begins to be a problem at the long (5 cm) length with the beam being deflected out of the region of gain[4].

Isoelectronic scaling to Mo XXXIII has been demonstrated[4][5] with 2×10^{12} Wcm^{-1} pumping and laser amplification at $g\ell$ up to 7 on transitions in the range 106-140 Å (figure 4).

Extrapolation to still shorter wavelength with the 3p-3s scheme is unpromising because of the rapidly falling ($g\ell$/pump power) summarised in figure 5. The underlying reason for this is illustrated in figure 6 which shows the small 3p-3s splitting relative to 2p-3p excitation energy in the Ne-like scheme.

A considerable increase in $g\ell/P$ has been achieved with 2 nsec 1.06 μm pump pulses and both solid and thin foil targets for transitions in

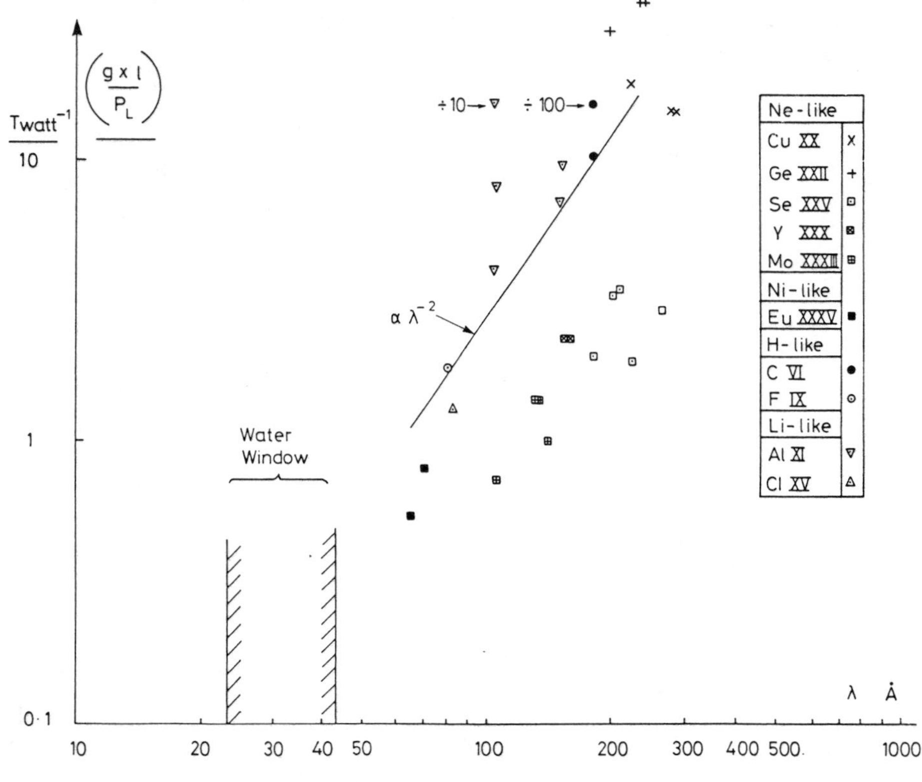

Fig 5

Cu XX and Ge XXII as shown in figure 5, though the reason for the better performance in these experiments with gℓ up to 6 and g up to 4 cm^{-1} is not yet understood(6).

Ni-like 4d-4p

Further progress to shorter wavelength has been achieved with an analogous scheme using 4d-4p transitions in Ni-like ions(7). The $3d^{10}$ closed shell of the Ni-like ion is very stable and the excitation energy of the 4d level is significantly smaller relative to the 4d-4p transition energy than in the analogous Ne-like scheme, as shown in figure 6. Ni-like Eu XXXVI has given gℓ $\sim$ 1.5 cm^{-1} and gℓ ≤ 3 at 66 and 71 Å as shown in figure 7, with 2 Twatt cm^{-1} pump power. Unpublished reports indicate successful isoelectronic extrapolation to Yb XXXX at 51 Å which is presently the shortest reported wavelength of laser amplification. The scheme clearly has some prospects for laser action in the water window using higher Z elements albeit requiring very high pump power as shown in figure 5.

H-like recombination

A quite different class of XUV lasers is based on transient production of population inversion in a rapidly recombining plasma. The initial state is a hot fully ionised plasma of bare nuclei and free electrons at high density produced by short duration laser pulse irradiation.

The hot surface layer of plasma explodes to form an expanding cylinder of plasma (see figure 8) and cools adiabatically to a density at which the LTE limit is at about n = 3 and the levels above n = 3 are in Saha Boltzmann equilibrium with the cool free electrons. The equilibriation above n = 2 is very rapid and there is no time lag relative to the cooling process. The n = 2 level has a lower than LTE population and is depopulated by Lyα radiative decay, for a sufficiently small cylindrical plasma with a strong radial velocity gradient giving a Doppler shift decoupling of the reabsorption of the Lyα transition in inner and outer regions. The n = 1 level is populated well below the equilibrium level because of the rather slow processes of recombination to n = 1. Population inversion and gain is thus established for the 3-2 Balmer α transition.

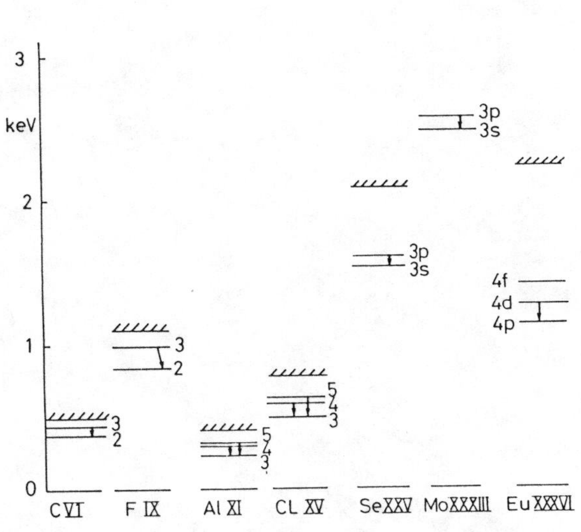

Fig 6

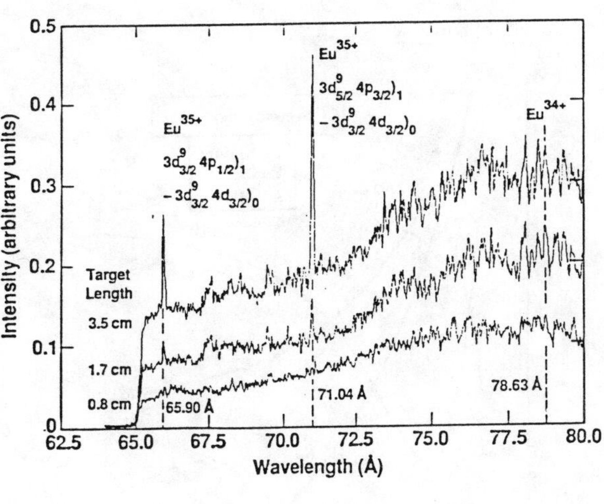

Fig 7

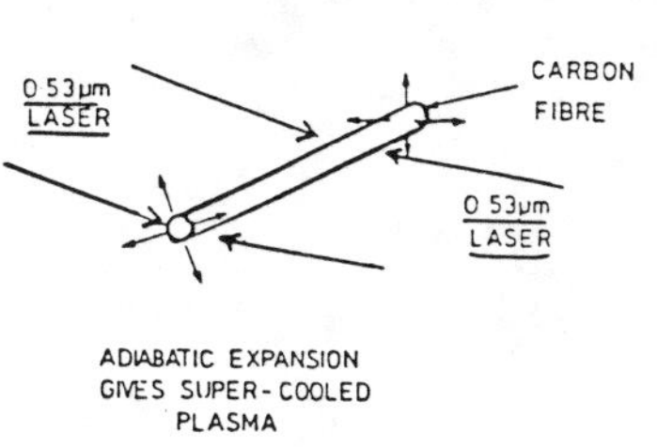

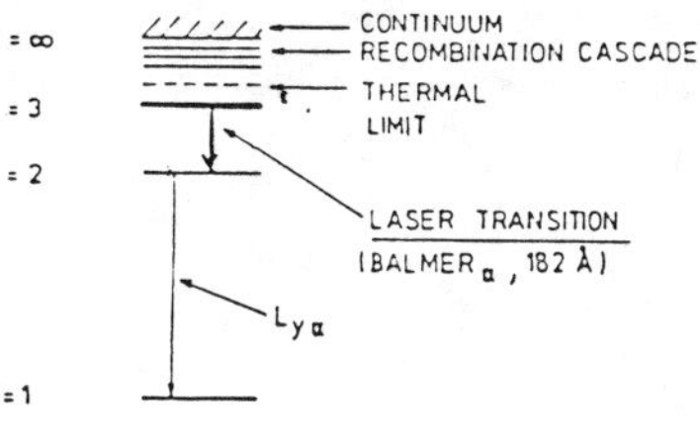

Fig 8

C VI RECOMBINATION LASER

This scheme has been studied in detail for C VI by numerical and analytical modelling(8), illustrated in figure 9 and leading to the conclusion that optimum conditions are obtained with a laser irradiated carbon fibre target in which the initial plasma is at 10^{21} cm^{-3} and 200 eV, requiring 70 psec pulse irradiation of a 7 µm diameter fibre at 0.3 TWatt cm^{-1}. The plasma expands to reach 30 eV at density of 2×10^{19} cm^{-3} in less than 1 nsec when significant gain (∿ $10 cm^{-1}$) is predicted.

A novel optical system producing aberration free line foci in a six beam configuration for irradiation of fibre targets has been developed(9), together with a new diagnostic system based on time resolved XUV spectrometers having a streak camera coupled to an aperiodic grazing incidence diffraction grating which disperses the spectrum into a perpendicular flat field instead of the usual Rowland circle(10). Gain of 4 cm^{-1} for length up to 1 cm giving 50 x single transit amplification has been recorded for C VI Hα at 182 Å with a carbon fibre irradiated as specified earlier (figure 10)(11).

Isoelectronic scaling has also been investigated(2) and modelling has shown a pump power requirement scaling as Z^4 with gain produced at higher final density scaling as Z^7 for which the LTE limit is around n = 3. A problem arises in that the initial plasma heating is at the fixed critical density whereas ideally it would also be at a density increasing as Z^7. This imposes a limit at which the density required for laser action is too close to the initial density to allow adequate adiabatic cooling.

Detailed calculations confirmed that the mechanism operates satisfactorily for F IX at 81 Å and a successful experiment gave the then shortest wavelength of laser action prior to the recent results with Ni-like ions.

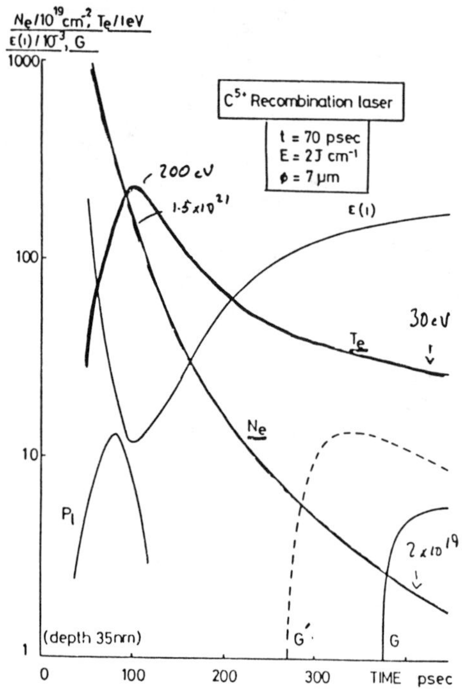

Fig 9

Computed time variation of plasma parameters. and gain.

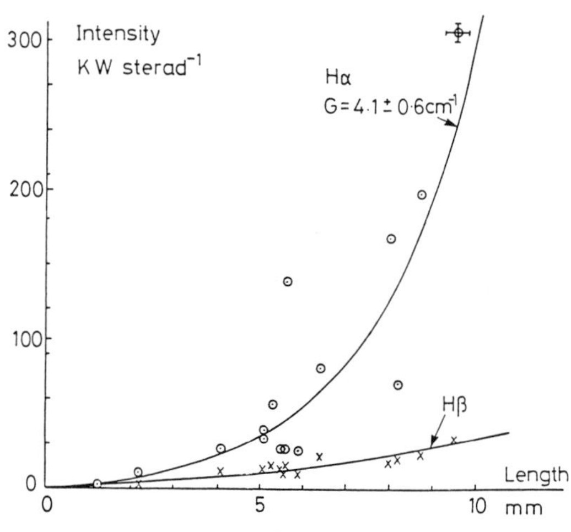

Fig 10 Variation of intensity with length for C VI H_α and H_β

Figure 11 illustrates a streaked spectrum[13] showing intense axial F IX Hα emission. The axial to transverse ratio shows the gain of 5.5 cm^{-1} for 1.7 Twatt/cm pumping (and absorption at lower pumping) in figure 12. The duration of the gain has been measured as ∿ 0.5 nsec.

An interesting feature of the recombination scheme in general is its better efficiency in terms of gℓ/P shown in figure 5. Fibre targets absorb only 10% of the incident power and the efficiency could therefore in principle be made higher with improved coupling.

A dramatically higher gℓ/P has been seen for C VI Hα laser action in a magnetically confined laser produced plasma with gℓ ∿ 6[14]. The cylindrical plasma is produced by a 4 x 10^9 W, 10.6 μm CO_2 laser pulse of 75 nsec duration focussed to a spot on a solid C target. An axial field of 9 Tesla confines the plasma flow to a narrow cylinder almost 1 cm long in which gain is produced in a cool boundary layer. The mechanism is not well understood and not readily scaled to shorter wavelength but the gℓ/P is almost 1000 x better than the other schemes illustrated in figure 5 and the long pulse duration favours the use of a resonator as discussed later.

Li-like recombination

The efficiency advantage of H-like recombination arises from the more favourable ratio of laser transition energy to ionisation energy of the laser ion and the situation is slightly more favourable again for recombination from the next lower stable ion configuration (He-like) to Li-like, as shown in figure 6.

This fact has been exploited in experiments with Aℓ XI in which gain was initially observed on the 103/106 Å 5f-3d transitions using a 6 x 10^9 W, 1 μm 20 nsec pump laser, to irradiate a solid Aℓ target[15]. gℓ values were low (∿ 2) and the gain coefficient was ≤ 2 cm^{-1} but the gℓ/P was very high (see figures 5 and 13). Isoelectronic scaing to S XIII has been examined and gain on the 5f-3d trnasition at 65.2 Å has been inferred indirectly[16].

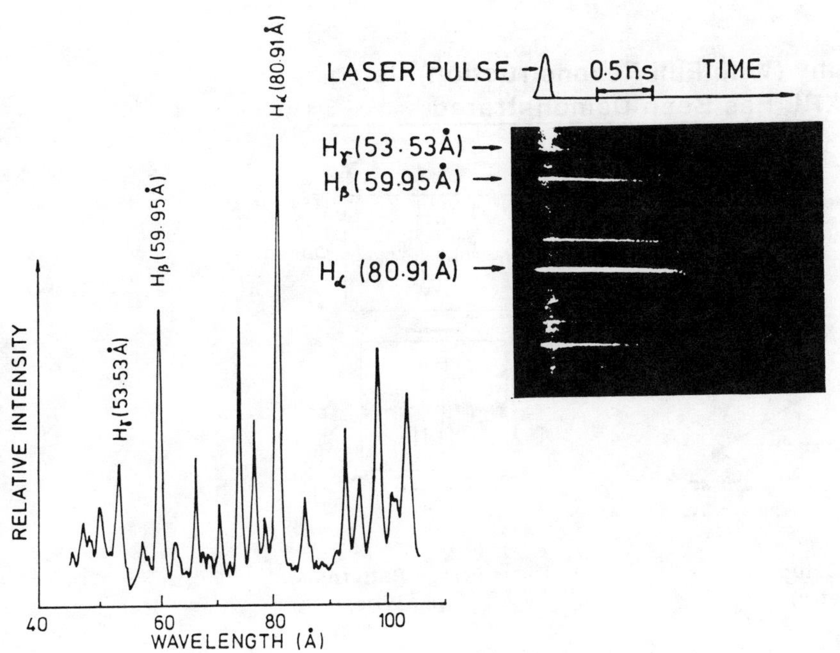

Fig 11

Streaked spectrum and densitometry at time of peak gain

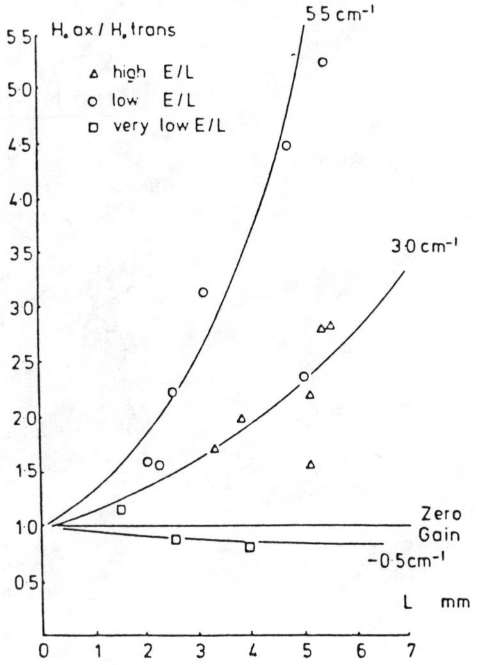

Fig 12

Gain coefficient from axial to transverse line ratio at different absorbed energies.
F IX

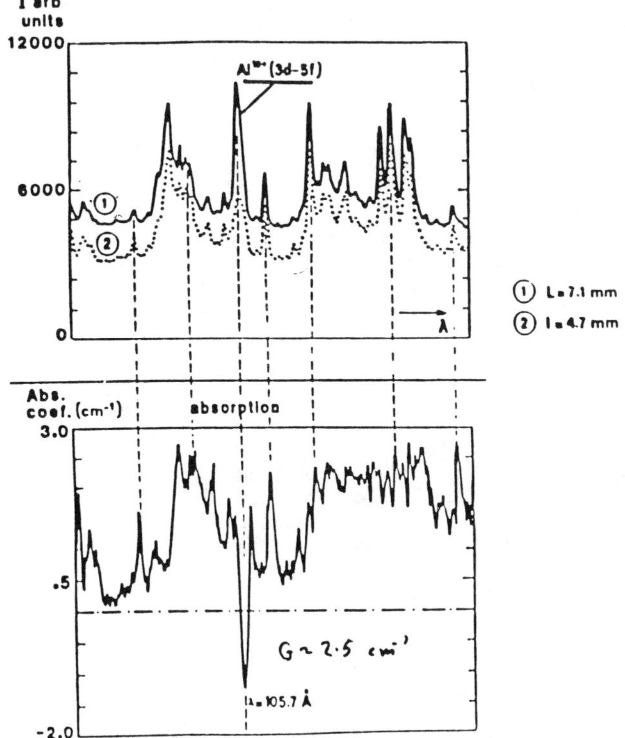

Fig 13
Axial spectra for 2 lengths and gain deduced from intensity ratios.

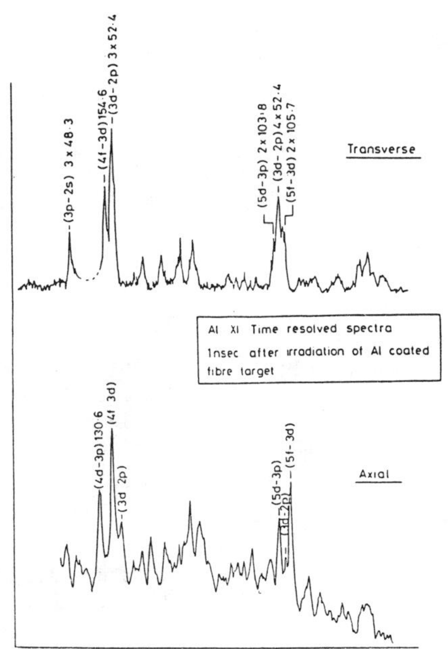

Fig 14

The scheme has also recently been tried with fibre targets for which the smaller plasma mass reduces optical trapping of the resonance radiation which depopulate the lower laser level. Higher gain ∿ 3 cm⁻¹ was observed on both the 5f-3d and 4f-3d transitions, the latter at 154 Å[17], see Fig 14. The high gain of 5f-3d relative to 4f-3d is unexplained at present.

X-Ray Holography (With Full Reconstruction) Using the Ne-like Se XRL Has Been Demonstrated

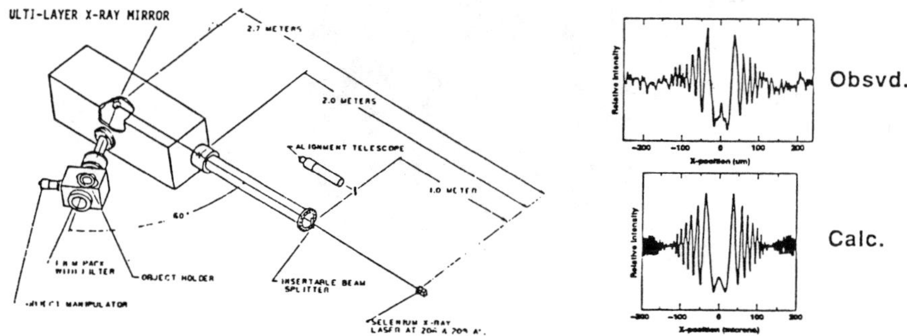

Experimental Setup
(Gabor Geometry)

Fringe Patterns
(8μ Wire)

Fig 15

Isoelectronic scaling has been demonstrated with g ∿ 3 cm^{-1} gain observed at 83 Å on the 4f-3d transition of Cℓ XV at a pump power level of 1.5 TW cm^{-1} in 70 psec pulses using NaCl coated 7 μm fibre targets(18).

The possibility of a further class of recombination laser using recombination from the stable Neon-like form to Na-like is currently under study with interest in the 5g-4f transition(19).

Future Developments

The future prospects for XUV laser research are exciting with expectation of laser action in the 'water window' soon, which will open up biological applications. Early work is already underway to develop resonators using the new XUV multilayer optics(4) and the first demonstration of laser produced XUV holograms has been made opening up the area of holography(20).

Acknowledgments

My review of this topic of XUV lasers is based on information from my colleagues from UK Universities and at the Rutherford Appleton Laboratory collaborating in the study of XUV lasers as well as on material supplied by others in research programmes elsewhere, to all of whom I owe many thanks.

References

1. M H Key, Nature 316, 314 (1985).
   D L Matthews, R R Freeman (Eds) J Opt Soc Am 4, 533 (1987).

2. K M Gilbert, J Anthes, M A Gusinov, H A Palmer, R R Whitlock, P J Nagel, JAP 51, 1449 (1980).

3. D L Matthews et al, Phys Rev Lett 543, 110 (1985).

4. D L Matthews et al, J Opt Soc Am 4, 575 (1987).

5. B J McGowan et al, JAP 61, 5243 (1987).

6. T N Lee, E A McLean, R L Elton, Phys Rev Lett 59, 1185 (1987).

7. B J McGowan, C J Keane, D L Matthews, UCRL Prepring 95971 (March 1987).

8. G J Pert, J Phys B 9, 3301 (1976), 12, 2067 (1979).
M H Key, G J Pert, Rutherford Appleton Lab Annual Rep to Laser Facility Committee RAL 86-046, pA5.38 (1986).

9. I N Ross et al, Appl Opt 26, 1585 (1987).

10. G P Kiehn et al, Appl Opt 26, 425 (1987).

11. C Chenais-Popovics et al, Phys Rev Lett, Nov 1987 (in press).

12. M H Key, Rutherford Appleton Lab Annual Rep to the Laser Facility Committee RAL 87-041, 100 (1987).

13. O Willi et al, Proc SPIE Mutlilayer structures and laboratory X-ray laser research, 688, 2 (1987).

14. S Suckewer et al, Phys Rev Let 55, 1753 (1985) and 57, 1004 (1986).

15. P Jaeglé et al, J Opt Soc Am 4, 563 (1987).
G Jamelot et al, J Phys B 18, 4647 (1985).

16. Reported by A Carrillon et al at 14th Int Conf on X-ray and Inner Shell Proesses, Paris September 1987.

17. A Carillon et al, Rutherford Appleton Lab Annual Rep to the Laser Facility Committee, RAL 87-041, B (1987).

18. Unpublished work at SERC Rutherford Appleton Lab in collaboration between UK groups and Univ Paris Orsay.

19. C M Brown et al JOSA 3, 701 (1986).
and unpublished collaborative experiments at the SERC Rutherford Appleton Laboratory with J Seely, (NRL) and M Richardson (LLE).

20. D L Matthews, (private communication).

Scaling of neonlike lasers using exploding foil targets

Barbara L. Whitten,* Richard A. London, and Rosemary S. Walling

Lawrence Livermore National Laboratory, University of California, Livermore, California 94550

Received June 13, 1988; accepted July 25, 1988

We present a set of calculations for laser-gain predictions in a neonlike collisional excitation scheme using laser-driven exploding foil targets. The calculation includes three steps: the ionization balance, the neonlike excited-state kinetics, and the hydrodynamics of the exploding foil target. The ionization-balance model solves steady-state rate equations, including excited states, using scaled hydrogenic atomic physics. The model for the neonlike excited-state kinetics is also steady state and includes the ground state and the 36 $n = 3$ excited states, with radiative and collisional transitions connecting these states. The plasma conditions in the exploding foil targets are calculated by using the similarity model of London and Rosen [Phys. Fluids **29,** 3813 (1986)]. For selected elements in the range $20 < Z < 56$, we predict the gain for the two most prominent $2p^53p$ to $2p^53s$ ($J = 2$–1) transitions seen in experiments, the plasma conditions necessary to maximize the gain, and the specifications for the laser driver and target required to reach those plasma conditions. Our predicted gains are larger than those measured in experiments, for reasons we discuss, but our calculations agree qualitatively with the observed trends; the gain peaks for elements around selenium and falls off for both lighter and heavier ions. Neglected effects, such as time-dependent kinetics and radiation trapping, are also discussed.

1. INTRODUCTION

Neonlike ions have long been recognized[1] as potential candidates for producing soft-x-ray lasers. The $2s^22p^53s$ excited states have a fast electric-dipole radiative transition to the $2s^22p^6$ ground state, whereas the $2s^22p^53p$ states can radiate to the ground state only by much slower electric-quadrupole transitions. A population inversion between the $2s^22p^53p$ and $2s^22p^53s$ excited states is natural and easy to create, provided that the correct plasma conditions can be obtained. A series of experiments using exploding foil targets driven by a high-powered laser have demonstrated amplified spontaneous emission in selenium,[2] yttrium,[2] molybdenum,[3] germanium,[4] and copper.[4]

In this paper we present model calculations of the behavior of the neonlike soft-x-ray laser for a series of elements between calcium and barium ($20 \leq Z \leq 56$). Table 1 lists some basic information about the neonlike ions of these elements. Our calculations predict the maximum gain to be expected from the collisionally pumped neonlike laser scheme, the plasma conditions under which this gain can be expected to occur, and the appropriate exploding foil target design and laser-driver parameters that will achieve these plasma conditions. We use a simple three-part model that first calculates the fraction of neonlike ions for a broad range of plasma conditions and then determines the inversion density of the laser transitions for the same set of plasma conditions. Combining these two sets of results gives us the maximum gain and the plasma conditions for which it is obtained. Finally, the similarity model for laser-driven exploding foil targets[5] is used to predict the target composition and thickness and the wavelength, intensity, and pulse length of the laser driver necessary to produce these plasma conditions.

The purpose of this simple model calculation is to suggest qualitative trends in the kinetics of neonlike ions and in the design of targets, as a function of Z. We have calculated gain coefficients for two $2s^22p^53p$ ($J = 2$) to $2s^22p^53s$ ($J = 1$) transitions (which occur at 206.4 and 209.8 Å in selenium) because these two transitions show the highest gain in most experiments and because the modeling is relatively straightforward. The $J = 0$–1 transition (at 182.4 Å in selenium) is difficult to model correctly, even when detailed atomic physics and hydrodynamical models are used,[6] and it is not useful to apply simple models to this problematic transition.

Our results show that the gain of the two $J = 2$–1 lines peaks near $Z = 34$ (selenium). It is small for lighter elements because of a mismatch between the plasma conditions required to maximize the fraction of neonlike ions and those conditions necessary to produce a large excited-state population. For heavier ions the gain falls off because of the rapid increase in radiative decay rates compared with collisional excitation rates, given the constraints on the maximum density.

Exploding foil targets designed to establish the plasma conditions giving maximum calculated gains are easy to find for lighter elements by using pumping lasers with wavelengths of 0.5 μm or longer. Suitable designs also exist for heavier elements, particularly when shorter-wavelength pump lasers are used to achieve high plasma densities; however, these designs appear to be somewhat inferior. The pump-laser energy required to produce optimal gain conditions increases sharply for heavy elements, making it difficult to produce extremely short-wavelength lasers by using this scheme, which is in agreement with Ref. 7.

Finally, we discuss the importance of effects that have been neglected in this model, such as time dependence of the ionization balance, population of the laser levels by recombination and ionization processes, and losses due to line trapping and other effects.

Table 1. **Basic Information about the Neonlike Ion for Various Elements**[a]

Element	Z	3–3 Transition Energy (eV)	3–3 Einstein A Coefficient (sec^{-1})	3–2 Transition Energy (eV)	3–2 Einstein A Coefficient (sec^{-1})
Calcium	20	22.6	1.46E9	348.5	1.49E11
Iron	26	36.4	3.28E9	727.1	9.11E11
Selenium	34	60.0	7.69E9	1438.	3.89E12
Molybdenum	42	94.5	1.81E10	2381.	1.08E13
Tin	50	147.	4.52E10	3549.	2.41E13
Barium	56	204.	9.24E10	4568.	4.05E13

[a] The 3–3 transition shown is the $2p^5_{3/2}3p_{3/2}$ (J = 2)–$2p^5_{3/2}3s_{1/2}$ (J = 1) laser transition. The 3–2 transition is the $2p^5_{3/2}3s_{1/2}$ (J = 1)–$2p^6$ (J = 0) resonance transition, which is the main depopulation mechanism of the lower laser level.

2. IONIZATION BALANCE

The problem of calculating kinetic factors that affect the gain falls into two parts: the ionization balance, which determines the fraction of neonlike ions, and the excited-state kinetics, which determines the excited-state populations of the neonlike ion and the inversion density of the x-ray-laser lines. These two parts are reasonably independent of each other. The ionization balance of the plasma depends mostly on the interactions between highly excited states and the next higher continuum. It is therefore important to include in the model a large number of highly excited states. However, because the excited electron is far from the core for these states, it is not necessary to use detailed atomic physics.

We have used the atomic physics code YTL,[8] which sets up a model including hydrogenic states as great as n = 10 (where n is the principal quantum number of the excited electron) for the ten most probable charge states. All other charge states are represented by the ground state only. Scaled hydrogenic rates for collisional excitation and ionization, three-body recombination, radiative recombination, and radiative decay connect all these levels. Dielectronic recombination is also included. For a given temperature and density, the code solves for the steady-state populations of all these states and sums them to calculate the fraction of ions in each charge state.

Results are shown in Figs. 1(a)–1(d), in which the fraction of neonlike ions (f_{Ne}) is plotted as a function of n_e for different elements and for several temperatures scaled to the neonlike ionization potential. f_{Ne} is large over a broad range of plasma conditions for low-Z elements. As Z gets larger, the maximum percentage of neonlike ions gets smaller.

It is also important to note that as Z rises the electron density required to maximize f_{Ne} also rises rapidly. This is because the collisional ionization rate falls as Z increases, whereas the dielectronic recombination rate is approximately constant with Z and radiative recombination rises. Therefore, for heavy ions, higher temperature and density are required for the neonlike charge state to be reached. This result agrees with the predictions derived by Apruzese *et al.*[9] and by Rosen *et al.*[7]

The scaled hydrogenic model should give qualitatively correct results for the ionization balance as a function of Z, n_e, and T_e, but it is important to recognize that it has some serious limitations. The most important is the assumption that the ionization balance is in the steady state; estimates indicate that the most important ionization and recombination rates are too slow to bring the ionization balance into the steady state during the lifetime of the plasma. We tested this by using a time-dependent version of YTL,[10] which uses the same atomic physics but solves time-dependent rate equations for an arbitrary temperature–density history. Using a constant temperature–density profile, we calculated the $1/e$ equilibration time of the ionization balance for several cases. For example, for selenium at T_e = 1268 eV (0.5 E_0) and $n_e = 10^{20}$ cm^{-3}, the plasma relaxes in 3 nsec. The time scales roughly with electron density; at n_e = 10^{22} cm^{-3}, equilibration requires 20 psec. For reasonable densities, these times are not short compared with the pulse length of high-powered lasers, so the assumption that the ionization balance is in the steady state is not a good one. This problem is particularly acute for light ions, for which maximum gain is achieved at low electron density.

A realistic time-dependent calculation of the ionization balance requires information about the temperature–density history of the plasma. There is little experimental information available; thus a temperature–density profile requires a computer simulation of the interaction between the laser driver and the exploding foil target. These simulations can be done (see, for example, Refs. 5, 6, and 11), but they shift the focus of the calculation to hydrodynamics. Because we are interested primarily in the kinetics of the laser plasma, we have considered only steady-state solutions. Berthier *et al.*[12] have compared steady-state to time-dependent solutions of the ionization balance for somewhat similar plasma conditions.

A second limitation on this model is the lack of detailed atomic physics; scaled hydrogenic rates tend to overestimate the fraction of ions in the neonlike charge state. This is because the ground state of the neonlike ion has a closed shell, and therefore the first excited state (n = 3) has many metastable levels. The scaled hydrogenic model, which permits no metastables, can underestimate the population of the first excited state. Because ionization rates out of excited states are much larger than those out of the ground state, the ionization from neonlike to fluorinelike ions will be too small, and the neonlike ionization fraction will be too large. The large gains predicted by this model (see Section 4) are due in part to this aspect of the ionization-balance calculation.

3. NEONLIKE EXCITED-STATE KINETICS

The second half of the kinetics problem is that of the neonlike excited states, which determines the inversion density of the laser transitions. We treat this problem as the complement of the ionization balance problem; we consider only the low-lying states of the neonlike ion but use detailed, high-quality atomic physics.

We calculate the kinetics of the neonlike excited states by using the steady-state code NELI.[13] This includes the neonlike ground state and the 36 $n = 3$ excited states, with radiative and collisional transitions among them. Energy levels and radiative decay rates are calculated by using fully relativistic configuration-interaction wave functions.[14] The ground-state–excited-state collision rates were calculated by using the distorted-wave approximation. Collision strengths were calculated for several ions by using the partially relativisitic codes DSW[15] and JAJOM[16] for low-Z ions and the fully relativistic code MCDW[17] for heavy ions ($Z > 36$). For intermediate ions the collision strengths (Ω) are scaled by using the dipole scaling law $Z^2\Omega$ = constant. Rates were then determined by averaging over a Maxwell–Boltzmann electron distribution for the appropriate temperature. For the dipole-allowed excited-state–excited-state collision rates, the oscillator strength approximation[18] is used. Nondipole-allowed excited-state–excited-state transitions are not included.

Using this model, we can calculate the fractional inversion density, which is related to the total inversion density by

$$(n_U - g_U n_L/g_L) = f_{\mathrm{Ne}} N_Z (y_U - g_U y_L/g_L), \qquad (1)$$

where $n_{L(U)}$ and $g_{L(U)}$ are the population and multiplicity, respectively, of the lower (upper) laser level, f_{Ne} is the fraction of neonlike ions, N_Z is the total density of all ions of the lasing element, and $(y_U - g_U y_L/g_L)$ is the fractional inversion density.

The results of our calculations are shown in Figs. 2(a)–2(c), in which the fractional inversion density for the $2p^5_{3/2}3p_{3/2}$ ($J = 2$)–$2p^5_{3/2}3s_{1/2}$ ($J = 1$) transition (the analog of the 206.4-Å transition in neonlike selenium) is plotted as a function of electron density for several temperatures and elements. Note that the electron temperature and density required to create a large fractional inversion density rise rapidly with Z because the collisional excitation rates that create the inversion get smaller. The absolute size of the fractional inversion density tends to rise with Z, creating the possibility of high gain for heavy ions.

Although collisional excitation from the neonlike ground state is the most important mechanism for populating the $2s^22p^53p$ ($J = 2$) upper laser states, we have neglected several other processes that more detailed calculations have shown to have an effect on the kinetics of neonlike selenium. Collisional cascade from higher states, for example, tends to populate the $J = 2$ upper laser states more than the $J = 1$ lower states. Including the $n = 4$ excited states in the kinetic model increases the inversion density of the $J = 2$–1 transitions by 15–20% in selenium.[19]

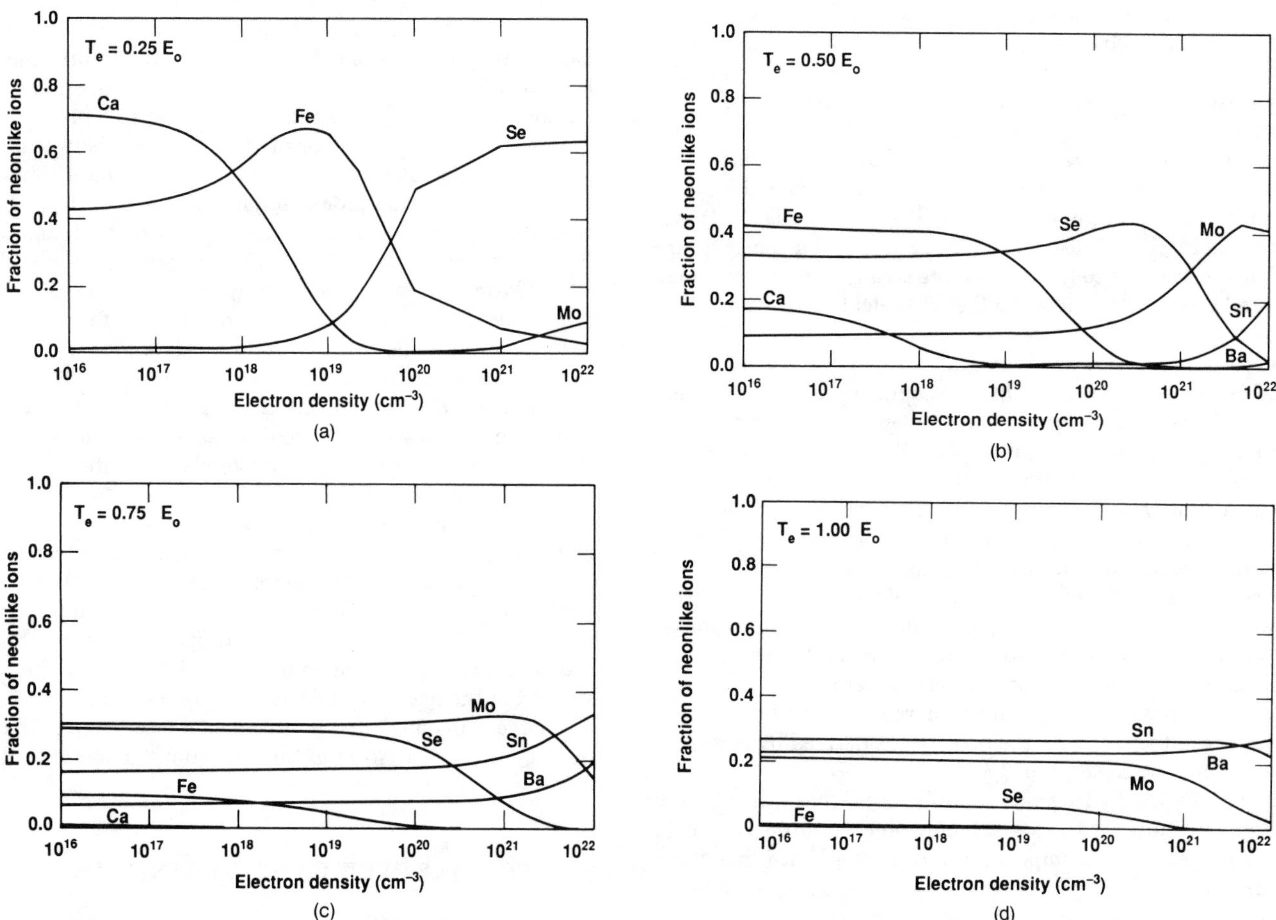

Fig. 1. Fraction of neonlike ions as a function of electron density for various ions: (a) $T_e = 0.25E_0$, where E_0 is the ionization potential of the neonlike ion; (b) $T_e = 0.50E_0$; (c) $T_e = 0.75E_0$; (d) $T_e = 1.00E_0$.

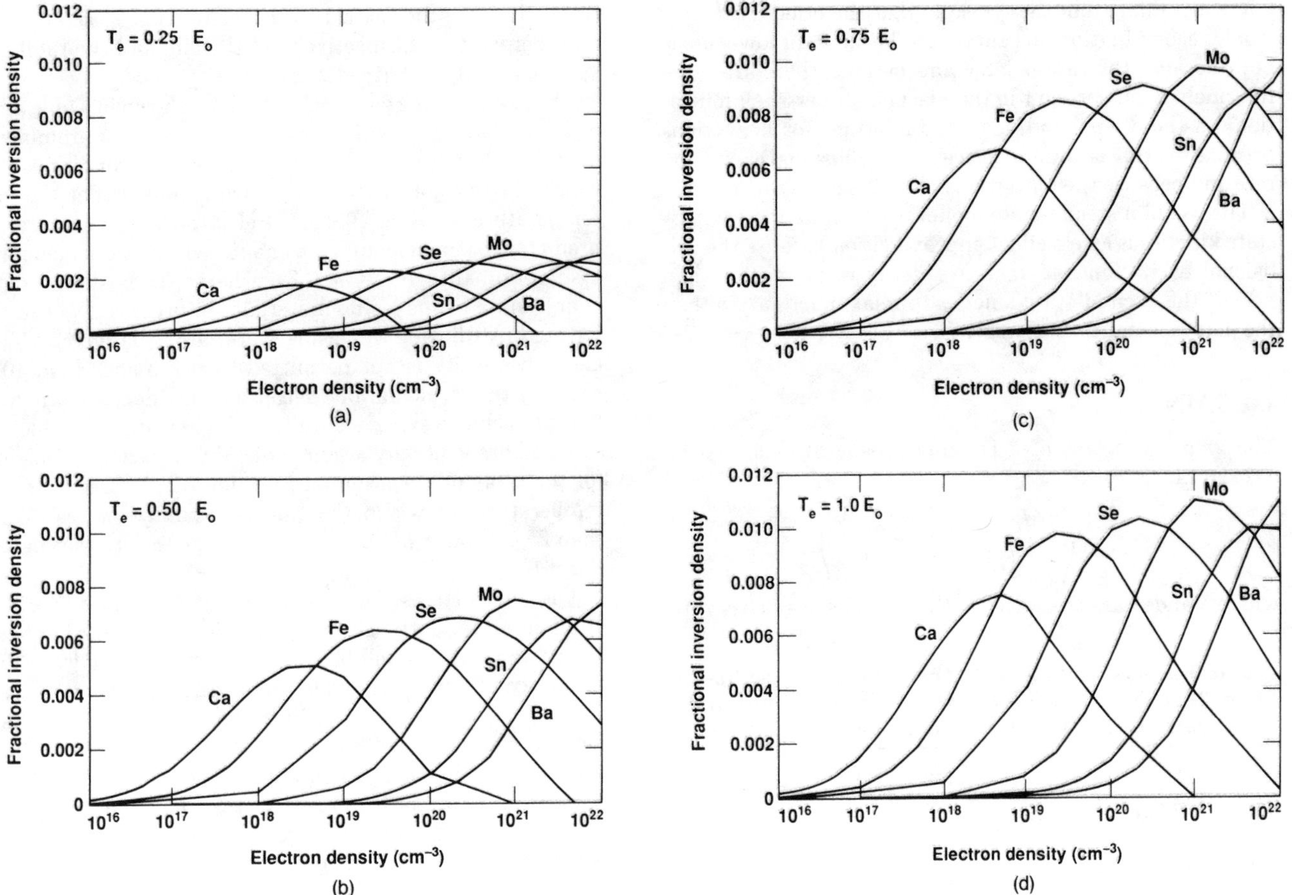

Fig. 2. Fractional inversion density of the $2p^5_{3/2}3p_{3/2}$ $(J = 2)$–$2p^5_{3/2}3s_{1/2}$ $(J = 1)$ laser transition as a function of electron density: (a) $T_e = 0.25E_0$, where E_0 is the ionization potential of the neonlike ion; (b) $T_e = 0.50E_0$; (c) $T_e = 0.75E_0$; (d) $T_e = 1.00E_0$.

Table 2. Comparison of Rates Populating the $2p^5_{3/2}3p_{3/2}$ $(J = 2)$ Upper Laser Level[a]

Z	Collisional Excitation Rate (cm^3/sec)	F/Ne Ratio	Dielectronic Recombination Rate (cm^3/sec)[b]	Na/Ne Ratio	Inner-shell Ionization Rate (cm^3/sec)
20	4.78E−12	1.93	4.50E−11	0.012	2.97E−12
26	1.25E−12	0.088	5.92E−11	0.613	7.66E−11
34	1.03E−12	0.906	4.55E−11	0.200	2.51E−12
42	6.23E−13	0.636	2.49E−11	0.569	2.31E−12
50	3.76E−13	0.699	–	0.662	1.67E−12
56	2.63E−13	0.536	–	1.12	1.11E−12

[a] Plasma conditions are those maximizing the gain (see Table 3).
[b] Total to *all* neonlike levels.

We have also neglected the effect of dielectronic recombination from fluorinelike ions[19,20] and of inner-shell ionization from sodiumlike ions,[21] both of which directly populate the neonlike excited states and can therefore affect the inversion density. These effects can be significant; in selenium more detailed calculations[19] have shown that, when the fluorinelike-to-neonlike ion ratio is taken to be 0.8, including dielectronic recombination increases the inversion density of the J = 2–1 transitions by 20–25%.

How much the inversion density of a particular transition is affected by these processes depends on the size of the rate relative to other population mechanisms, the ionization balance, and the inversion density (a smaller inversion density is more sensitive to small changes in the level populations). Some of this information is provided in Table 2 for the $2p^5_{3/2}3p_{3/2}$ $(J = 2)$–$2p^5_{3/2}3s_{1/2}$ $(J = 1)$ transition. Collisional excitation from the neonlike ground state[13] is the principal population mechanism in our model. The dielectronic recombination rates are interpolated from the calculations of Roszman.[22] Note that these are *total* dielectronic recombination rates into all neonlike states, not state-specific rates as in the other two cases. The inner-shell ionization rates are taken from the scaled Coulomb–Born calculation of Sampson and Zhang.[23] The ion ratios are calculated as described in Section 2. There is some variation in the ratios (most notably for iron) because of the finite scaled temperature grid, but on the whole the plasma is less ionized for heavy ions.

We can infer from these results that the effect of dielectronic recombination on gain should be large for low-Z ions, both because the rate is large and because there are more fluorinelike ions present in the plasma. Inner-shell ionization, on the other hand, is more important for heavy ions because the rate is larger relative to the collisional excitation rate and because the ionization balance is more favorable.

The use of a steady-state model to calculate the excited-state kinetics is an excellent approximation because the collisional excitation and radiative decay rates are fast and permit the excited-state kinetics to relax much faster than the plasma conditions change.[12]

4. GAIN

The gain coefficient of a Doppler-broadened line can be written as

$$\alpha = \frac{\lambda^3 A}{8\pi}\left(\frac{M_i}{2\pi k T_i}\right)^{1/2}\left(n_U - \frac{g_U n_L}{g_L}\right), \qquad (2)$$

where λ and A are the wavelength and radiative decay rate, respectively, of the lasing transition; M_i and T_i are the mass and temperature, respectively, of the ion; and the total inversion density is defined in Eq. (1).

The results of the gain calculation are shown in Table 3, in which we list the maximum gain of the two most prominent (J = 2–1) lasing transitions and the plasma conditions for which they are obtained. We have assumed that the ion temperature is always 40% of the electron temperature, as is predicted for the selenium plasma.[11] We have also made the assumption that $N_Z = n_e/\langle Z\rangle$, where $\langle Z\rangle$ is the average charge state of the lasing material. In practice, N_Z can be reduced by diluting the lasing material in the target. The electron density is not permitted to rise higher than 10^{21} cm^{-3} for these calculations because higher densities are difficult to achieve experimentally with currently available lasers and are generally accompanied by refractive problems for the x-ray propagation (see Section 5). We see that the temperature for which the gain is maximized rises faster than Z^2, although not as fast as the temperature that maximizes f_{Ne}.

The gain is largest for elements around selenium (Z = 34) and falls off for both lighter and heavier elements. For low-Z ions, the gain is small because of a mismatch between the plasma conditions required to produce a large inversion density and those needed to produce a large density of neonlike ions. A comparison of Figs. 1 and 2 shows that, for calcium, the most neonlike ions are produced when the electron temperature is one quarter or less of the ionization potential. The inversion density is largest at higher temperatures, when few neonlike ions are present. The match improves as Z increases; for barium the two conditions are met at approximately the same plasma conditions. This interplay between the ionization balance and inversion density was not taken into account by Feldman *et al.*,[24] who calculated only the inversion density and assumed a constant ionization balance. They predict much higher gain for low-Z ions.

For heavy ions, the gain falls off because the unfavorable scaling of collisional excitation and ionization rates make it harder to create neonlike ions and to produce a population inversion. This means that the density required to produce large gain grows rapidly with Z and quickly becomes unreachable experimentally.

Table 4 summarizes the results of experimental measurements of gain in neonlike ions. The results are qualitatively

Table 3. Maximum Gain of the Two Strongest 3*p*–3*s* (*J* = 2–1) Transitions for Several Neonlike Ions and the Plasma Conditions for Which They Are Obtained[a]

Z	T_e (eV)	n_e (cm^{-3})	Lambda (Å)[b]	Gain (cm^{-1})
20	147 ($0.25E_0$)	4.64×10^{18}	547.	0.54
			566.	0.56
26	315 ($0.25E_0$)	10^{20}	341.	9.9
			348.	6.7
34	1268 ($0.5E_0$)	10^{21}	206.3	38.
			209.6	24.
42	3189 ($0.75E_0$)	10^{21}	131.0	18.
			132.7	13.
50	6416 ($1.0E_0$)	10^{21}	84.3	3.5
			84.8	2.3
56	8332 ($1.0E_0$)	10^{21}	60.7	1.2
			62.0	0.5

[a] The electron temperature is chosen to be a multiple of one quarter of the ionization potential of the neonlike ion (E_0). The electron density is constrained to be no higher than 10^{21} cm^{-3}.

[b] For selenium and molybdenum, wavelengths are taken from Refs. 2 and 3, respectively; all others are calculated using fully relativistic configuration-interaction wave functions.[14]

Table 4. Summary of Experimental Results

Element	Z	Lambda (Å)	Gain (cm^{-1})	Target Design[a]	Laser Driver Frequency (μm)	Pulse Length (psec)
Copper[b]	29	279.31	1.7	1000-Å Foil	1.06	2000
		284.67	1.7			
Germanium[b]	32	232.24	4.1	Solid	1.06	2000
		236.26	–			
Selenium[c]	34	206.3	5	750-Å Foil	0.53	450
		209.6	5			
Yttrium[c]	39	155.0	(observed,	750-Å Foil	0.53	450
		157.1	not measured)			
Molybdenum[d]	42	131.0	4.1	1000-Å Foil	0.53	500
		132.7	4.2			

[a] All foils have a 1000–1500-Å CH substrate.

[b] From Ref. 4.

[c] From Ref. 2.

[d] From Ref. 3.

similar to our predictions, although the measured gains are much smaller. Measured gain declines from germanium ($Z = 32$) to copper ($Z = 29$) in similar experiments, as predicted. Experimental gain also declines in similar experiments for selenium, yttrium ($Z = 39$), and molybdenum ($Z = 42$), although it does so more slowly than is predicted by this calculation.

Although the calculated and measured gains show similar trends, the calculated gains are much larger. There are a number of reasons for this. First, the experimental gains were not maximized and, in particular, were measured in a lower-density plasma. The measured gains are space and time integrated over a range of plasma conditions. The steady-state hydrogenic ionization-balance model overestimates the fraction of neonlike ions, as discussed in Section 2. Finally, this simple model does not include any loss processes. Mixing between excited states, radiation trapping of the $2p^5 3s$–$2p^6$ radiative decay line, additional mechanisms for populating the $2p^5 3s$ lower laser levels, and refraction from density gradients will all tend to reduce the gain.

It is also interesting to note that, although the experiments measure nearly identical gains for the two lines in every case, our model predicts significantly larger gains for the shorter-wavelength $J = 2$–1 line. This is due mostly to the absence in this model of $3p$–$3p$ collisions, which have the effect of more evenly distributing population among the $2p^5 3p$ levels and thus tend to equalize the gain of the two lines. More-detailed calculations in selenium show that including these processes changes the ratio of the gains for these two lines from 1.5 to 0.95.

Reabsorption of the neonlike 3–2 resonance lines can alter the $3p$–$3s$ gains, mainly by repopulating the lower laser levels and thereby decreasing the inversion density [see Eq. (2)]. To study this effect, we use the escape probability method, in which each radiative decay rate used in the kinetics equations is multiplied by an escape probability in order to estimate how much reabsorption will occur in the plasma. For exploding foil plasmas the escape of 3–2 line radiation is dominated by the gradient in the flow velocity, which causes the line-absorption profile to Doppler shift in frequency across the plasma. It has been shown that the Sobolev escape probability theory[25] is an accurate approximation of the line-transfer problem in the limit of foils with large velocity gradients.[26]

In the examples discussed below, we use a formula for the escape probability in a plane-parallel slab with constant velocity gradient[27]:

$$P_e = (3\tau_s)^{-1}\{1 + \exp(-\tau_s)(2\tau_s - 1) + 2\pi\tau_s^{3/2}[\mathrm{erf}(\tau_s^{1/2}) - 1]\}, \tag{3}$$

where τ_s is the Sobolev optical depth:

$$\tau_s = \frac{\pi\epsilon^2}{mc} f_{osc}(n_L - g_L n_U/g_U)c \Big/ \nu\left(\frac{dv}{dx}\right), \tag{4}$$

where f_{osc} is the absorption oscillator strength for the transition, ν is the line frequency, and dv/dx is the velocity gradient in the plasma.

The Sobolev optical depth is approximately the optical depth of a distance in which the change in Doppler shift owing to the gradient in the flow velocity is equal to the intrinsic linewidth. It is typically an order of magnitude less than the optical depth would be if the plasma were not expanding. Therefore the degree of trapping is greatly reduced by the plasma expansion.

The effect of trapping on gain has been calculated for two examples: selenium at 1268 eV and tin at 6416 eV. We show the results in Figs. 3(a) and 3(b). The gains shown are for the $2p^5_{3/2}3p_{3/2}$ ($J = 2$)–$2p^5_{3/2}3s_{1/2}$ ($J = 1$) transition plotted versus the optical depth for the $2p^5_{3/2}3s_{1/2}$ ($J = 1$)–$2p^6$ ($J = 0$)

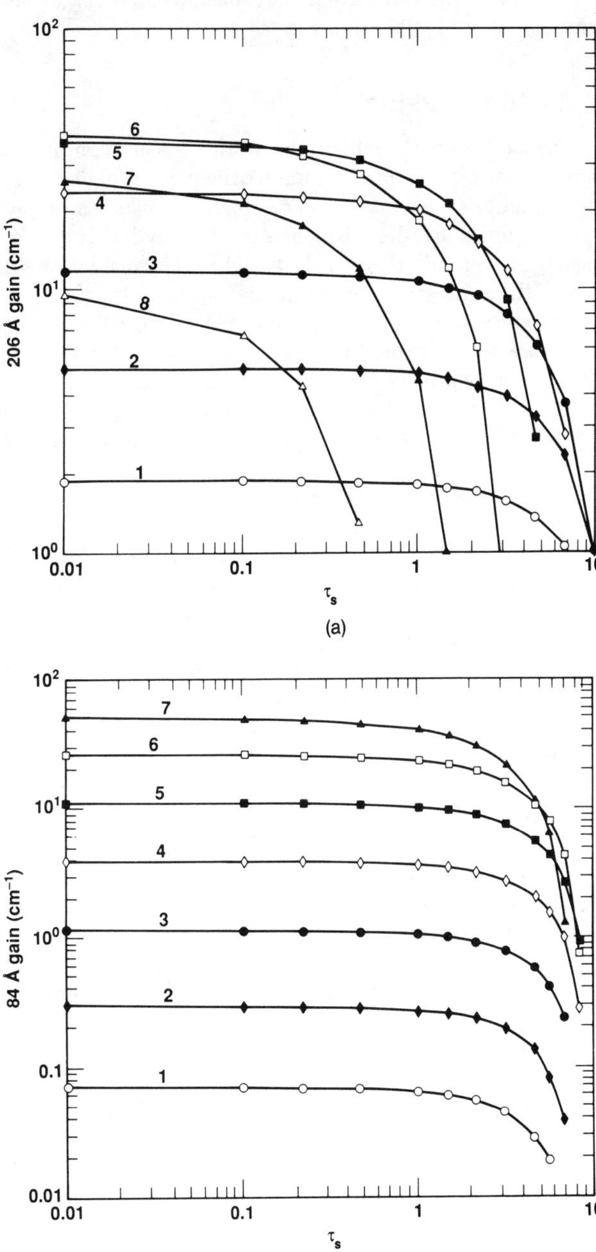

Fig. 3. Gain of the $2p^5_{3/2}3p_{3/2}$ ($J = 2$)–$2p^5_{3/2}3s_{1/2}$ ($J = 1$) laser transition versus optical depth of the $2p^5_{3/2}3s_{1/2}$ ($J = 1$)–$2p^6$ ($J = 0$) line, which connects the lower laser level to the ground state for several values of electron density. (a) Selenium at $T_e = 0.50E_0$ (=1268 eV). The laser transition is at 206 Å. The electron-density values (in cm^{-3}) are 1, 4.6×10^{19}; 2, 1.0×10^{20}; 3, 2.2×10^{20}; 4, 4.6×10^{20}; 5, 1.0×10^{21}; 6, 2.2×10^{21}; 7, 4.6×10^{21}; 8, 1.0×10^{22}. (b) Tin at $T_e = 1.00E_0$ (=6416 eV). The laser transition is at 84.2 Å. The electron-density values (in cm^{-3}) are 1, 1.0×10^{20}; 2, 2.2×10^{20}; 3, 4.6×10^{20}; 4, 1.0×10^{21}; 5, 2.2×10^{21}; 6, 4.6×10^{21}; 7, 1.0×10^{22}.

transition, which connects the lower laser state to the ground state. The optical depths of the other 3–2 lines are included in the calculation, in a manner proportional to the specified line. It is clear from the figures that optical depths of the order of unity are necessary to affect the gain. At fixed optical depth, trapping has a larger influence for higher densities. This is because at higher density $3s$–$3p$ collisions reduce the inversion density, making the gain more sensitive to the additional increase in lower-state population caused by trapping. The calculation of τ_s for particular target designs is discussed in Section 5.

5. TARGET DESIGN

Now we look at how to achieve the desired plasma conditions by using an exploding foil target driven by a high-power laser. Figure 4 shows a schematic diagram of such a target. The thin foil is irradiated by one or more cylindrically focused beams of pulsed optical laser light. The incident light is along the x direction, perpendicular to the foil surface. A plasma is created that is elongated in the z direction. The advantage of the exploding foil design is that the plasma produced is relatively homogeneous, with a gentle density profile.[11] The density and temperature of the plasma can be adjusted by varying the thickness of the target as well as the intensity and pulse length of the driver laser.

We use a simple model for the hydrodynamics of the exploding foil to determine the target and laser parameters required to achieve the temperature and density calculated in Part 4 to produce maximum gain. The model is based on a similar solution of the hydrodynamic equations and has been validated by comparisons with detailed numerical simulations using the LASNEX code. The details of the model are given in Ref. 5. Assumptions of the model are that the expansion is one dimensional (in the x direction perpendicular to the foil surface in Fig. 4), that the expansion velocity is a linear function of position, and that the plasma is spatially isothermal. With these assumptions, we find that the density has a Gaussian spatial profile and that the hydrodynamic equations can be reduced to time-dependent ordinary differential equations for the electron temperature, electron density, and scale length.

We use the analytical solutions for the mid-time period (after the foil becomes optically thin to the driver laser light but before the laser is turned off) for a constant intensity (flat-top) pulse. The following scaling laws for the electron temperature, the electron density, and the scale length L of the plasma are taken from Eqs. (16), (19a), and (19b) of Ref. 5:

$$T_e = (1.74\ \text{keV}) I^{1/3} \lambda^{2/3} m^{1/3} A^{-1/6} Q^{1/6}, \tag{5}$$

$$n_e = (1.78 \times 10^{20}\ \text{cm}^{-3}) I^{-1/3} \lambda^{-1/6} m^{7/6} A^{-17/24} Q^{5/8} t^{-5/4}, \tag{6}$$

$$L = (4.2 \times 10^{-2}\ \text{cm}) I^{1/3} \lambda^{1/3} m^{-1/6} A^{-7/24} Q^{3/8} t^{5/4}, \tag{7}$$

where I and λ are the flux and wavelength, respectively, of the driving laser, t is the time measured from the beginning of the driver laser pulse, m is the mass column density (thickness) of the target, and A and Q are the atomic mass number and ion charge, respectively, of the target element. These six quantities are scaled to a convenient set of values,

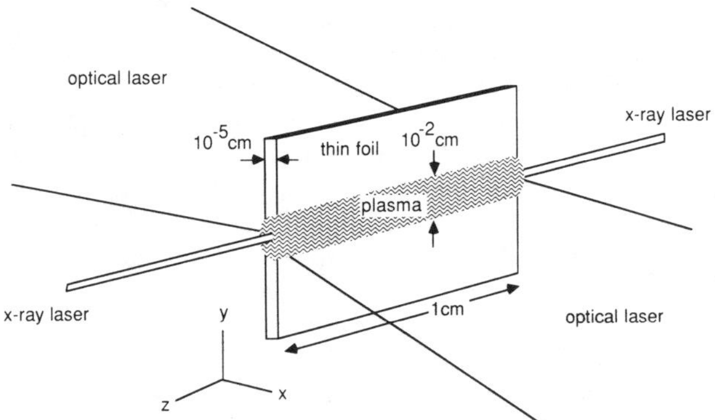

Fig. 4. Schematic diagram of an exploding foil target in which a plasma is created by optical laser heating using a cylindrically focused beam. Typical dimensions of the foil and laser focus are indicated. The foil is initially located in the y–z plane, with the optical laser beams incident along the x axis. The foil plasma expands mainly in the x direction, perpendicular to the foil surface.

Table 5. Normalizing Values for Scaled Variables

Physical Variable	Symbol	Normalizing Value
Time	t	1 nsec
Laser intensity	I	10^{14} W/cm^2
Laser wavelength	λ	0.53 μm
Foil Column density	m	10^{-4} g/cm^2
Ion charge	Q	25
Atomic mass	A	80
Laser focal spot width	W	200 μm
Electron density	n_e	10^{21} cm^{-3}
X-ray laser wavelength	λ_X	200 Å
Scale length	L	100 μm

listed in Table 5. In Eqs. (5)–(7) we have assumed a constant Coulomb logarithm of 5.

We would like to establish the desired temperature and density at the peak of the laser pulse, so we evaluate Eqs. (5)–(7) at $t = t_L/2$, where t_L is the duration (FWHM) of the laser pulse. For a laser with a different pulse shape, Eqs. (3)–(5) should give a reasonable estimate of the conditions at the peak of the pulse. For example, the errors for Gaussian pulses found by comparing numerical solutions of the similarity equations with the analytical solutions are less than 40%.

With this simple description of the hydrodynamics, we can design targets to achieve the desired temperature and density by inverting Eqs. (5) and (6). Treating the laser intensity and target thickness as dependent variables and leaving the other experimental parameters independent, we arrive at the following equations:

$$I = (8.69 \times 10^{12}\ \text{W cm}^{-2}) T_e^{7/3} n_e^{-2/3} A^{-1/2} Q^{-3/4} \lambda^{-5/3} t_L^{-5/6}, \tag{8}$$

$$m = (2.18 \times 10^{-4}\ \text{g cm}^{-2}) T_e^{2/3} n_e^{2/3} A^{7/12} Q^{-3/4} \lambda^{-1/3} t_L^{5/6}. \tag{9}$$

Therefore, for a fixed laser wavelength, a range of pulse lengths and corresponding laser intensities and target masses gives the desired density and temperature. We may also vary the laser wavelength somewhat, but there are only a few values at which high-powered lasers exist.

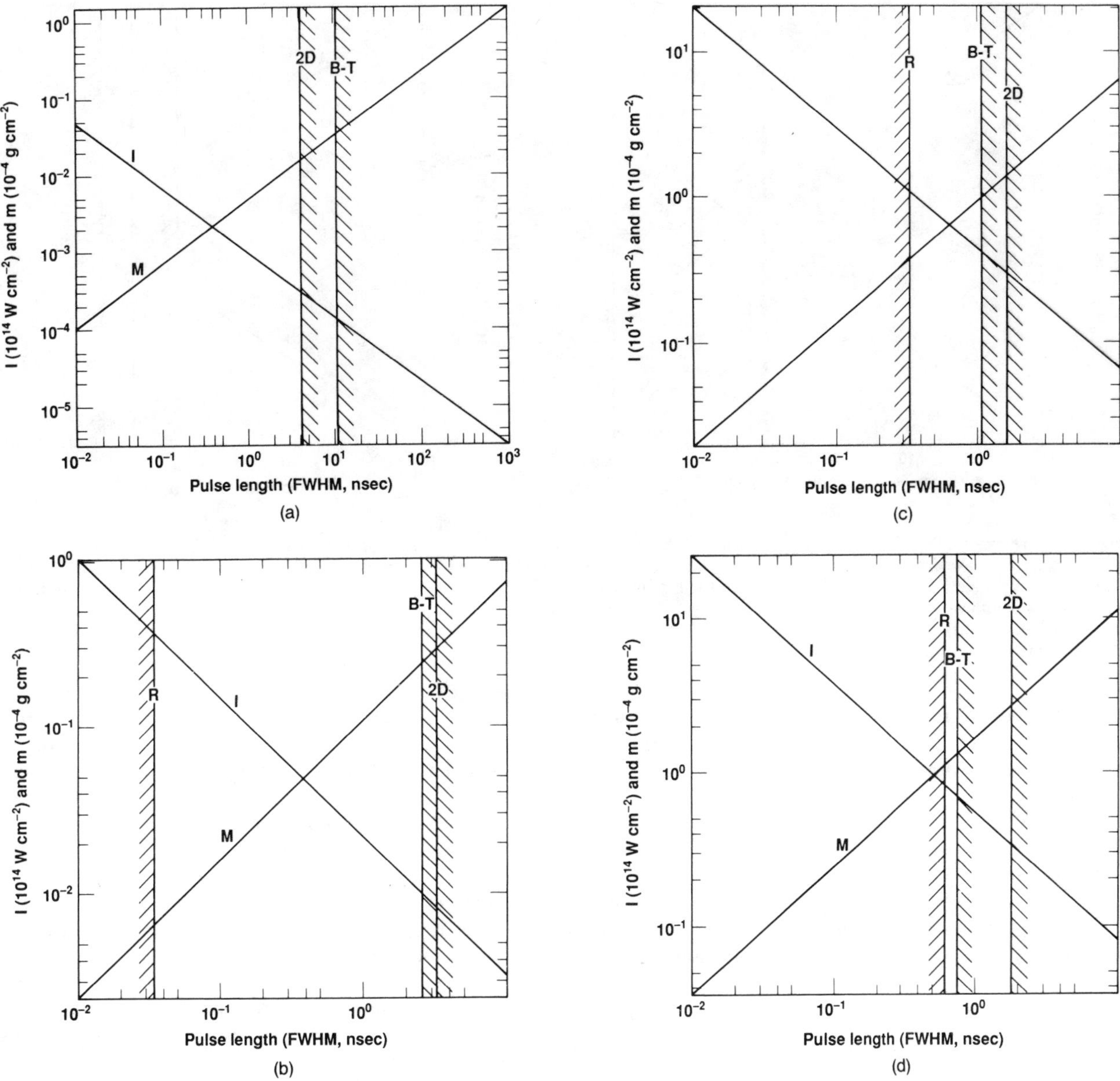

(a) (b) (c) (d)

(figure continued)

The range of allowed pulse lengths is further limited by several constraints, which are due to the conditions necessary for the validity of the simple hydrodynamical model and to requirements on the plasma to ensure x-ray-laser amplification and propagation. We describe each constraint briefly.

A. Burn-Through Constraint

The similarlity model is valid only after the laser heat front has burned through the foil. This condition is also desirable in order to produce a relatively uniform plasma conducive to laser amplification. We therefore require burn-through before the peak of the pulse. Using the estimate for burn-through time given by London and Rosen [Ref. 5, Eq. (21)] and substituting Eqs. (8) and (9) for I and m, we get the following constraint:

$$t_L < t_{bt} = (0.10 \text{ nsec}) T_e n_e^{-2} \lambda^{-2} A^{1/2} Q^{-3/2}. \qquad (10)$$

This constraint gives an *upper* limit on the pulse length because the burn-through time actually increases faster than linearly with the pulse length, given the dependences of intensity and mass on pulse length in Eqs. (8) and (9).

B. One-Dimensional Expansion Constraint

A second criterion for the validity of the model is that the expansion still be approximately one dimensional at the peak of the pulse. This requires the density scale length to be less than the transverse width (W) of the focal spot of the driving laser. Using Eq. (5) for L gives us another upper limit on the pulse length:

$$t_L < t_{1d} = (1.27 \text{ nsec}) T_e^{-4/5} n_e^{2/5} \lambda^{2/5} A^{1/2} Q^{-3/10} W^{3/2}. \qquad (11)$$

This constraint on the applicability of the model is also desirable because the density and temperature drop rapidly as the foil goes into two-dimensional expansion. Because we would like to achieve high density and temperature with

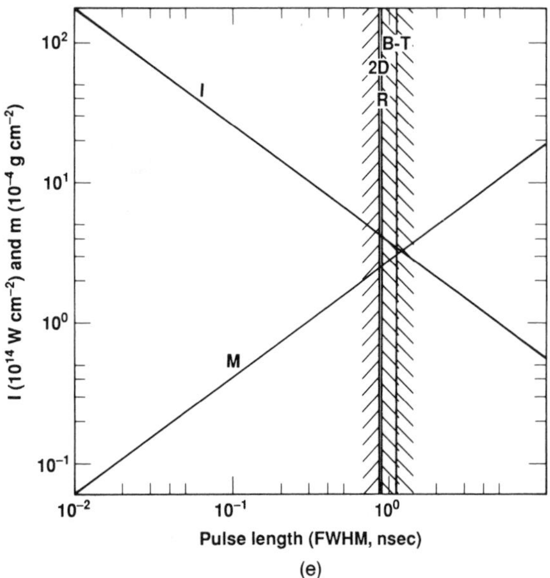

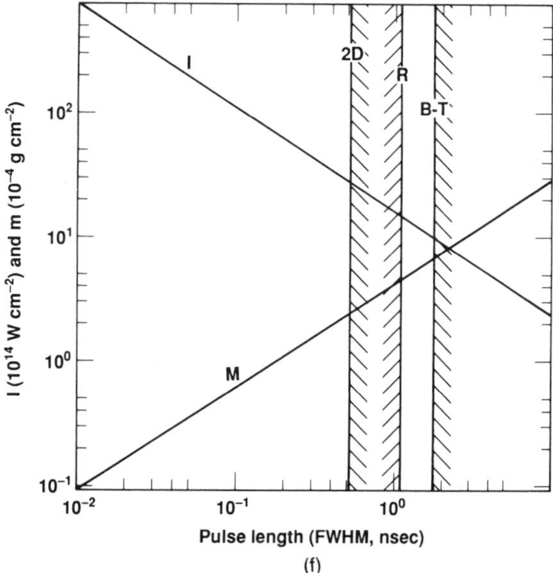

Fig. 5. Diagram of target design parameter space. We plot I, the required laser intensity, and m, target thickness, versus laser pulse length. Plasma conditions are from Table 3, chosen to create maximum gain, except where indicated. The constraints are labeled 2D for two-dimensional expansion, B-T for burn-through, and R for refraction. The half-space excluded by each constraint is indicated by the hatch marks. (a) Calcium with 10-μm laser illumination. (b) Iron with 1.06-μm laser illumination. (c) Selenium with 0.53-μm laser illumination for $n_e = 5 \times 10^{20}$ cm^{-3}. (d) Selenium with 0.35-μm laser illumination for $n_e = 10^{21}$ cm^{-3}. (e) Molybdenum with 0.35-μm laser illumination. (f) Tin with 0.35-μm laser illumination.

the least expenditure of driver energy, it would be best to avoid this regime. This can be done by making the spot width sufficiently large, with the penalty of requiring additional laser power.

C. Refraction Constraint

A third condition comes from the requirement that the lasing x rays be able to propagate the length of the target without being refracted out of the plasma by gradients in the electron density. We can estimate the maximum propagation length permitted by refraction (L_R) if we assume that the density profile has a linear gradient with scale length L:

$$L_R = (0.8 \text{ cm}) n_e L/\lambda_X, \tag{12}$$

where λ_X is the wavelength of the x-ray laser.

Requiring L_R to be larger than the length of the x-ray-laser target (L_Z) and using Eqs. (6) and (7), we get the following constraint:

$$t_L > t_R = (0.27 \text{ nsec}) T_e^{4/5} n_e \lambda^{2/5} A^{1/2} Q^{3/10} \lambda_X^{6/5} L_Z^{5/6}. \tag{13}$$

We can now apply this model to the design of targets for specific elements. We wish to achieve the plasma conditions (temperature, density, and ionization balance) that will maximize the gain, as listed in Table 3. The problem of target design may now be studied by plotting the range of intensity and target thickness versus pulse length, as specified by Eqs. (6) and (7), together with the constraints given by Eqs. (8)–(10). From such plots we can see whether an allowed region exists and, if so, what laser and target parameters are called for. We show in Figs. 5(a)–5(f) such plots for several elements and laser drivers of interest.

Figures 5(a) and 5(b) show that for low-Z materials it is easy to design a target that will be effective with long-wavelength lasers. The requirements become more severe for higher-Z materials, however. Figure 5(c) shows that an effective selenium target can be designed for a frequency-doubled neodymium:glass laser, although at a less than optimum density. To reach $n_e = 10^{21}$ cm^{-3}, the electron density predicted to produce maximum gain, it is necessary to use frequency-tripled light, as seen in Fig. 5(d). Using the same laser conditions to produce an appropriate plasma for molybdenum is barely possible; Fig. 5(e) shows only a small allowed region. For tin there is no allowed region at all. An effective tin target can be produced in several ways: by increasing the lateral size of the line focus (which further increases the power requirements of the driver laser), by decreasing the desired electron density (which reduces the gain), or by further decreasing the wavelength of the laser driver (which is difficult to do at high power). Clearly the design of high-gain targets using high-Z materials places extreme requirements on the power of the driver laser.

We have examined the degree to which trapping diminishes the gain for the target designs for selenium and tin shown in Figs. 5(d)–5(f). We require that the degree of trapping of the lower laser level decay line be small enough that the population inversion is not destroyed. We use the escape probability method to describe the radiative transfer for the trapped lines, as discussed in Section 4. For the velocity gradient we use the linear velocity assumption of the similarity model, noting that the characteristic velocities are of the order of the isothermal sound speed. We write

$$dv/dx = \mu C_s/L, \tag{14}$$

where $C_s = (kT_e Q/M_i)^{1/2}$ is the isothermal sound speed and $\mu = (C_s)^{-1}\, dL/dt$ is the Mach number of the expansion. Using Eq. (14) in Eq. (4) and assuming that $n_L \gg n_U$, we have

$$\tau_s = (57.1) m (AQT_e)^{-1/2} (\mu\nu)^{-1} y_1 f_{osc}, \tag{15}$$

where y_1 is the fraction of ions in the neonlike ground state and ν is in thousands of electron volts.

For the $n_e = 5 \times 10^{20}$ cm^{-3} selenium design [Fig. 5(c)], the optical depth is approximately 1 in the worst case, which is within the acceptable range of pulse lengths. From Fig. 3(a) we infer that the gain will be diminished by less than 15% as a result of trapping. For the higher-density ($n_e = 10^{21}$ cm^{-3}) case shown in Fig. 5(d), trapping lowers the gain by approximately 30%. In the case of tin [Fig. 5(f)] the optical depths are low, the maximum effect being a 4% decrease in gain, according to Fig. 3(b).

6. CONCLUSIONS

The philosophy of this paper is to use simple models to calculate the ionization balance, inversion density, and gain of the neonlike collisionally pumped soft-x-ray laser and to predict the laser and target parameters of a laser-driven exploding foil target. We do not expect such a simple model to produce quantitatively correct gains, but we do expect it to predict general trends. We see that the neonlike collisional excitation scheme is a robust scheme for producing gain over a broad range of plasma conditions, laser-driver parameters, and x-ray-laser wavelengths. The gain is predicted to be highest for elements near $Z = 34$ and to be smaller for both lighter and heavier ions. This trend is confirmed by experiments in elements ranging from copper ($Z = 29$) to molybdenum ($Z = 42$).

We have also attempted to address issues that are not included in this simple model but that we expect to have a significant effect on the performance of these lasers. Additional kinetic processes, line trapping, and time-dependent effects are all discussed and assessed regarding their effect on this laser.

A major goal of soft-x-ray laser research at present is to produce a laser at a wavelength of less than 44 Å. This is because of potential medical and biological applications; the contrast between the x-ray transmission of water and protein is largest just below the carbon K edge. Unfortunately, this research suggests that the collisionally pumped soft-x-ray laser scheme is unlikely to be useful below 44 Å for several reasons. Table 3 shows that the gain decreases significantly as Z increases because the collision rates that maintain the inversion grow smaller, and the plasma density required to optimize the gain grows rapidly with Z and quickly becomes experimentally unreachable. Even if these high densities were possible to reach, refraction would greatly decrease the gain predicted by this model.

We have also shown, in Fig. 5, that it is difficult to meet all the requirements of a desirable x-ray-laser target for a heavy ion. The designer must produce a plasma with less than optimal density, increase the lateral size of the line focus of the driver laser, or decrease the wavelength of the driver laser. The first of these choices further reduces the gain, and the other two place unrealistic demands on the power of the driver laser. We can therefore conclude that the neonlike scheme involving collisional excitation by thermal electrons is not a promising candidate for a sub-44-Å laser. This does not, however, preclude the possibility that a collisional excitation scheme involving suprathermal electrons will be more efficient. Such schemes have been proposed[28-30] and are showing experimental promise.[31]

ACKNOWLEDGMENTS

The authors are pleased to acknowledge useful conversations with M. D. Rosen, A. U. Hazi, D. L. Matthews, and B. J. MacGowan of Lawrence Livermore National Laboratory and with R. C. Elton and J. P. Apruzese of the Naval Research Laboratory. This research was performed under the auspices of the U.S. Department of Energy by Lawrence Livermore National Laboratory under contract W-7405-Eng-48.

* Present address, Department of Physics, Colorado College, Colorado Springs, Colorado 80903.

REFERENCES

1. A. N. Zherikhin, K. N. Koshelev, and V. S. Letokhov, Kvantovaya Elektron. (Moscow) **3,** 152 (1976) [Sov. J. Quantum Electron. **6,** 82 (1976)].
2. D. L. Matthews, P. L. Hagelstein, M. D. Rosen, M. J. Eckart, N. M. Ceglio, A. U. Hazi, H. Medecki, B. J. MacGowan, J. E. Trebes, B. L. Whitten, E. M. Campbell, C. W. Hatcher, A. M. Hawrylvk, R. L. Kauffman, L. D. Pleasance, G. Ramback, J. H. Scofield, G. Stone, and T. A. Weaver, Phys. Rev. Lett. **54,** 110 (1985).
3. B. J. MacGowan, M. D. Rosen, M. J. Eckart, P. L. Hagelstein, D. L. Matthews, D. G. Nilson, T. W. Phillips, J. H. Scofield, G. Shimkaveg, J. E. Trebes, R. S. Walling, B. L. Whitten, and J. G. Woodworth, J. Appl. Phys. **61,** 5243 (1987).
4. T. N. Lee, E. A. McLean, and R. C. Elton, Phys. Rev. Lett. **59,** 1185 (1987).
5. R. A. London and M. D. Rosen, Phys. Fluids **29,** 3813 (1986).
6. M. D. Rosen, R. A. London, P. L. Hagelstein, M. S. Maxon, D. C. Eder, B. L. Whitten, M. H. Chen, J. K. Nash, J. H. Scofield, A. U. Hazi, R. Minner, R. E. Stewart, T. W. Phillips, H. E. Dalhed, B. J. MacGowan, J. E. Trebes, C. J. Keane, and D. L. Matthews, in *Proceedings of 6th Conference on Atomic Processes in High Temperature Plasmas*, A. Hauer and A. Merts, eds. (American Institute of Physics, New York, 1988).
7. M. D. Rosen, R. A. London, and P. L. Hagelstein, Phys. Fluids **31,** 666 (1988).
8. Y. T. Lee, J. Quant. Spectrosc. Radiat. Transfer **38,** 131 (1987).
9. J. P. Apruzese, P. C. Kepple, and M. Blaha, J. Phys. (Paris) **47,** C6-15 (1986).
10. Y. T. Lee, G. B. Zimmerman, D. S. Bailey, D. Dickson, and D. Kim, in *Proceedings of the Third International Conference on Radiative Properties of Hot Dense Matter*, B. Rozsnyai, C. Hooper, R. Cauble, R. Lee, and J. Davis, eds. (World Scientific, Singapore, 1987).
11. M. D. Rosen, P. L. Hagelstein, D. L. Matthews, E. M. Campbell, R. E. Turner, R. W. Lee, G. Charatis, G. E. Busch, C. L. Shepard, and P. D. Rocket, Phys. Rev. Lett. **54,** 110 (1985).
12. E. Berthier, J.-F. Delpech, and M. Vuillemin, J. Phys. (Paris) **47,** C6-327 (1986).
13. R. S. Walling, Ph.D. dissertation (University of California, Davis, Davis, Calif., 1988)
14. J. H. Scofield, Lawrence Livermore National Laboratory, P.O. Box 5508, Livermore, California 94550 (personal communication).
15. W. Eissner and M. J. Seaton, J. Phys. B **5,** 2187 (1972).
16. H. E. Saraph, Comput. Phys. Commun. **1,** 232 (1970).
17. P. L. Hagelstein and R. K. Jung, At. Data Nucl. Data Tables **37,** 121 (1987).
18. H. van Regemorter, Astrophys. J. **136,** 906 (1962).
19. B. L. Whitten, A. U. Hazi, M. H. Chen, and P. L. Hagelstein, Phys. Rev. A **33,** 2171 (1986).
20. P. L. Hagelstein, M. D. Rosen, and V. L. Jacobs, Phys. Rev. A **34,** 1931 (1986).
21. W. H. Goldstein, B. L. Whitten, A. U. Hazi, and M. H. Chen, Phys. Rev. A **36,** 3607 (1987).
22. L. J. Roszman, Phys. Rev. A **35,** 2138 (1987); "Revised dielectronic-recombination coefficients for the fluorine isoelectronic sequence," submitted to Phys. Rev.

23. D. H. Sampson and H. Zhang, Phys. Rev. A **36,** 3590 (1987).
24. U. Feldman, J. F. Seely, and A. K. Bhatia, J. Appl. Phys. **56,** 2475 (1984).
25. V. Sobolev, *Moving Envelopes of Stars* (Harvard U. Press, Cambridge, Mass., 1960).
26. R. A. London, in *Laser Program Annual Report 86*, M. L. Rufer and P. W. Murphy, eds., Lawrence Livermore National Laboratory Rep. No. UCRL-50021-86 (National Technical Information Service, Springfield, Va., 1988).
27. D. G. Hummer and G. R. Rybicki, Astrophys. J. **254,** 767 (1982).
28. R. C. Carman and G. Chapline, in *Proceedings of the International Conference on Lasers '81* (STS, McLean, Va., 1982).
29. J. P. Apruzese and J. Davis, Phys. Rev. A **28,** 3686 (1983).
30. W. H. Goldstein and R. S. Walling, Phys. Rev. A **36,** 3482 (1987).
31. J. P. Apruzese, P. G. Burkhalter, J. E. Rogerson, J. Davis, J. F. Seely, C. M. Brown, D. A. Newman, R. W. Clark, J. P. Knauer, and D. K. Bradley, Bull. Am. Phys. Soc. **33,** 1998 (1988).

Reprinted with permission from *Journal of Applied Physics,* Vol. 64(3), pp. 1005-1014 (August 1, 1988).

Inversion and gain in hydrogenic ion levels induced by photoionization pumping

D. G. Goodwin and E. E. Fill
Max Planck Institut für Quantenoptik, D-8046 Garching, Federal Republic of Germany

If a low-Z plasma is subjected to ionizing radiation, stationary inversions on hydrogenic ion level populations occur. The plasma conditions and pumping requirements to achieve gain on the Lyman-α and Balmer-α lines are investigated by means of a collisional-radiative model. The calculations are carried out for two cases: first, for the case in which the electron temperature is determined solely by radiative cooling, and second, for the case in which additional electron cooling is provided. In the first case, measurable gain on the Balmer-α line is found, although the Lyman-α transition remains uninverted. In the second case, the Balmer-α gain is dramatically enhanced, and sizable Lyman-α gain is predicted.

I. INTRODUCTION

The challenge to develop new lasers at ever shorter wavelengths has led to several proposals and experiments at soft x-ray wavelengths, most of which have involved the generation of highly ionized species in a laser plasma. Notable successes have been achieved with the electron collisional pumping of Ne-like[1,2] or Ni-like[3] ions, with gain on $3s$-$3p$ or $4p$-$4d$ transitions, respectively, and with recombination pumping of hydrogenic ions, which led to the observation of gain on the Balmer-α transition.[4,5]

Various schemes to optically pump an x-ray laser have been proposed, most of which have involved matched-line pumping.[6,7] However, none of these have as of yet been successfully demonstrated. In this article, we present a study of an optical pumping scheme which has only occasionally appeared in the literature,[8-10] namely, pumping with ionizing radiation.

This excitation mechanism may be thought of as the x-ray analog of flashlamp pumping of, for example, a ruby or Neodymium laser where the pumping radiation (of relatively broad spectral composition) excites a continuum of levels, from which relaxation into the upper laser level occurs. Boiko *et al.*[9] noted using relatively simple analytic estimates that inversions between hydrogenic levels $n = 4$ and $n = 3$ should occur if ionizing radiation is applied to a low-Z plasma. We show in this article that it is also possible to achieve inversions between $n = 3$ and $n = 2$ (Balmer-α), and even between $n = 2$ and $n = 1$ (Lyman-α).

Such a scheme could be implemented by using the x-ray emission from a relatively high-Z laser plasma to pump a low-Z target plasma. Various configurations are conceptually possible: The two plasmas could be in contact with one another, which maximizes the geometric coupling but makes difficult the separate control of the density and temperature of the two plasmas. Alternatively, the two plasmas could be physically separate, with the x-ray emission from the pump plasma coupled to the target plasma with focusing x-ray multilayer mirrors. The target plasma could be created with a prepulse from the laser, allowing it to expand to the desired density and temperature before the x-ray pumping pulse arrives, or could be created directly by the x-ray pulse, since an intense x-ray pulse can fully strip a low-Z atom in a few hundred picoseconds or less. This second possibility is attractive for situations in which a high density is desired, since there is no limitation due to the laser critical density, as there is in a laser-created plasma.

This pumping scheme may have certain advantages in comparison to recombination pumping of hydrogenic ions. In the recombination scheme, very short laser pulses are required, and the conditions needed to achieve adequate hydrodynamic cooling can be quite severe, particularly as Z is increased. For example, Pert has calculated that optimum gain conditions for a recombining aluminum plasma require an initial density greater than solid density.[11] The present scheme is not subject to these constraints, and in addition has the possibility of achieving Lyman-α inversions, as well as Balmer-α inversions. On the other hand, an intense source of x rays is required, which can decrease the overall efficiency of the scheme, since losses are associated with the conversion of laser light to x rays and with the coupling of the x rays to the target.

In this work, we use a detailed collisional-radiative model to investigate the plasma conditions and pump intensities needed to obtain inversion on the Balmer-α ($3 \rightarrow 2$) and Lyman-α ($2 \rightarrow 1$) transitions, and the magnitude of the attainable gain coefficients. To concentrate on the underlying physics, we consider only the simplest possible case: a steady-state uniform plasma subjected to ionizing radiation. That this idealized situation is relevant to an actual experiment follows from consideration of the time scales involved: the relaxation times of the excited level populations ($\approx 10^{-12}$ s) are always much shorter than the time scale for hydrodynamic expansion ($\approx 10^{-9}$ s), and thus the excited state populations evolve in a quasistatic manner. Furthermore, the ground state also evolves quasistatically for sufficiently strong pumping, since its relaxation time is determined primarily by the photoionization rate.

Transient effects do come into play when the plasma temperature is considered. At steady state, the temperature is determined by the balance between the power absorbed from the pump and that radiated away into full solid angle. However, during the short duration of the pump pulse, this "power balance" temperature may not be attained. Furthermore, additional cooling due to hydrodynamic expansion or conduction may result in a temperature lower than that calculated for radiative cooling alone (see Appendix). Consequently, we consider both the case in which the temperature is given by power balance (i.e., radiative cooling alone) and that in which the temperature is below the power balance value.

We confine our attention to the case of monochromatic pump radiation with a photon energy greater than the ionization potential ($h\nu_p > 13.6Z^2$ eV). The opposite extreme of blackbody radiation has been shown previously to be less favorable for producing inversions.[10] Furthermore, the spectrum of a laser plasma is far from blackbody, and usually consists of strong line emission. The assumption of monochromaticity could be easily relaxed without changing any essential physics by integrating over the pump radiation spectrum (as long as bound-bound transitions are not pumped).

II. THEORY

A. Pumping rates

The ionizing radiation removes electrons from the various hydrogenic levels into the continuum. The ionization rate from level n may be written as

$$-\left(\frac{dB_n}{dt}\right)_{\text{pump}} = P_n B_n, \tag{1}$$

where B_n is the population density in level n (assuming the (l,j) sublevels are populated statistically). The ionization rate per ion P_n is given by

$$P_n = \sigma_n n_{\text{ph}}, \tag{2}$$

where σ_n is the cross section for photoionization from level n, and n_{ph} is the photon flux per cm^2 per second. The photoionization cross-section σ_n can be expressed by the Kramers formula as[12]

$$\sigma_n = 1.98\times 10^{-14} Z^4 G_{nf}/[(h\nu_p)^3 n^5] \quad \text{cm}^2, \tag{3}$$

where G_{nf} is the bound-free Gaunt factor of level n and $h\nu_p$ is the energy of the pump photons in eV. From Eqs. (2) and (3), the photoionization rate for level n is related to that for the ground level by

$$P_n = (P_1/n^5)(G_{nf}/G_{1f}). \tag{4}$$

Equation (1) is not valid at very high pump rates, as the stimulated emission from the continuum leads to a saturation which must be taken into account. The complete expression including stimulated emission is[13]

$$-\left(\frac{dB_n}{dt}\right)_{\text{pump}} = P_n\left[B_n - B_n^* \exp\left(-\frac{h\nu_p}{kT_e}\right)\right], \tag{5}$$

where B_n^* is the LTE value of the number density of ions in level n, given by

$$B_n^* = 1.66\times 10^{-22} g_n N_e N_1 (kT_e)^{-3/2} \times \exp(E_n/kT_e) \quad \text{cm}^{-3}. \tag{6}$$

Here g_n is the level degeneracy ($2n^2$), N_e is the electron density (cm^{-3}), N_1 is the density of bare nuclei (cm^{-3}), kT_e is the electron temperature (eV), and E_n is the ionization potential of level n, equal to $13.6Z^2/n^2$ eV.

The pumping rates, e.g., P_1, may be easily expressed in terms of the radiation intensity. From Eqs. (2) and (3) and using $I_p = h\nu_p\, n_{\text{ph}}$, one has for the intensity

$$I_p = 8.2\times 10^{-6} P_1 (h\nu_p)^4 Z^{-4} G_{1f}^{-1} \quad \text{W/cm}^2, \tag{7}$$

where $h\nu_p$ is in eV. It should be noted that the pump intensity needed to produce a given pumping rate P_1 is proportional to Z^4, since the required energy of the pumping photons ($> 13.6Z^2$) scales as Z^2.

B. Power balance

If the plasma is treated as an isolated system and hydrodynamic cooling is neglected, then in steady state the power absorbed from the pump must equal the power radiated into the full solid angle. This condition determines the steady-state temperature reached by the plasma.

Assuming the only ions present in the plasma to be bare nuclei with charge Z and hydrogenic ions with charge $Z-1$, the pump power absorbed by the bound-free transitions is given by

$$A_{bf} = h\nu_p \sum_n P_n\left[B_n - B_n^* \exp\left(-\frac{h\nu_p}{kT_e}\right)\right]. \tag{8}$$

The power absorbed in free-free transitions can be derived from the free-free absorption coefficient of Spitzer[12]:

$$\kappa_\nu = 3.69\times 10^8 \frac{\overline{z^2} N_e N_i}{T_e^{1/2}\nu^3}\left[1 - \exp\left(-\frac{h\nu}{kT_e}\right)\right] G_{ff} \quad \text{cm}^{-1}. \tag{9}$$

Here N_i is the total ion density, T_e is the electron temperature in K, G_{ff} is the free-free Gaunt factor, and $\overline{z^2}$ is the average value of the square of the ion charge, which, if most of the ions are fully stripped, is nearly equal to Z^2. The exponential in Eq. (9) accounts for stimulated emission from the electron gas with a Maxwellian velocity distribution. The absorbed power is given by $A_{ff} = n_{\text{ph}} h\nu_p \kappa_\nu$, which together with Eqs. (2), (3), and (9) results in the expression

$$A_{ff} = 1.2\times 10^{-23} P_1 \left(\frac{h\nu_p}{Z^2}\right)\left(\frac{\overline{z^2}}{Z^2}\right)\frac{N_e N_i}{\sqrt{kT_e}} \times [1 - \exp(-h\nu_p/kT_e)] G_{ff} \quad \text{eV/cm}^3\,\text{s}, \tag{10}$$

where kT_e is in eV.

The power radiated by the plasma consists of three contributions: bound-bound, free-bound, and free-free radiation. For bound-bound radiation, the emitted power is obtained by summing over all spontaneous decay channels

$$P_{bb} = \sum_n \sum_{n'<n} B_n A_{nn'} (E_n - E_{n'}), \tag{11}$$

where $A_{nn'}$ is the Einstein A coefficient for the transition $n \to n'$ ($n > n'$).

The power radiated in free-bound transitions can be obtained by summing over all final levels as

$$P_{fb} = N_e N_1 \sum_n \int_0^\infty h\nu \sigma_n(v) n_e(v) v\, dv, \tag{12}$$

where $n_e(v)$ is the normalized velocity distribution of the electrons, and $h\nu = m_e v^2/2 + E_n$. The quantity $\sigma_n(v)$ is the cross section for radiative recombination[12]

$$\sigma_n(v) = 2.11\times10^{-22}\frac{(E_n)^2}{h\nu(m_e v^2/2)}\frac{G_{fn}}{n^3}, \quad (13)$$

with all units in cgs. Here G_{fn} is the free-bound Gaunt factor. Assuming a Maxwellian velocity distribution for the electrons, the integration in Eq. (12) can be carried out and one obtains

$$P_{fb} = 2.61\times10^{-12}Z^4\frac{N_e N_1}{\sqrt{kT_e}}\sum_n\frac{G_{fn}}{n^3} \quad \text{eV/cm}^3\ \text{s}. \quad (14)$$

The free-free emission is given by[12]

$$P_{ff} = 9.56\times10^{-14}\ z^2\ (N_e N_i/\sqrt{kT_e})\ G_{ff} \quad \text{eV/cm}^3\ \text{s}. \quad (15)$$

The power balance condition then reads

$$P_{bb} + P_{fb} + P_{ff} = A_{bf} + A_{ff}. \quad (16)$$

Since each of these quantities is a function of temperature, either explicitly or implicitly through the level populations, the power balance temperature T_{pb} may be determined as that temperature which satisfies Eq. (16).

C. Fine-structure effects

The fine-structure splitting of the hydrogenic energy levels has two consequences which need to be considered. First, the splitting can be large enough that the electron-collisional transition rates between the various (l,j) sublevels with the same n are insufficient to maintain statistical equilibrium and thus their relative populations are no longer proportional to their degeneracies. In such cases, separate rate equations must be solved for each sublevel, rather than just for each energy level. Furthermore, the fine-structure splitting of the energy levels splits each spectral line into several components, which must be taken into account in computing the gain coefficient. The Lyman-α line is split into two and the Balmer-α line into seven fine-structure components. Under high-density, high-temperature conditions, however, only the structure relevant to level $n=2$ is resolved, resulting in an apparent doublet for both lines (although for very low Z, line broadening obscures the doublet structure).

Fortunately, it is only necessary to write separate rate equations for the sublevels of the first few energy levels, as the fine-structure splitting decreases with n as n^{-3}. Sampson[14] has given a criterion for statistical equilibration among sublevels which indicates that for the range of electron densities and temperatures of interest here, equilibration may be assumed for $n \geqslant 4$.

D. Line broadening

Since the gain depends sensitively on the linewidth, it is necessary to estimate the various broadening mechanisms with reasonable accuracy. Both Doppler and Stark broadening contribute to the width. If the ion temperature is taken to be equal to the electron temperature, then the thermal Doppler broadening is given by

$$\Delta\nu_D/\nu = 5.43\times10^{-5}(kT_e/Z)^{1/2}, \quad (17)$$

assuming the ion atomic weight $W = 2Z$.

The dominant Stark broadening contribution is the quasistatic ion broadening (Holtsmark broadening), the linewidth of which may be estimated as[15,16]

$$\Delta\nu_H = 2(n^2 - n'^2)N_i^{2/3} \quad \text{s}^{-1}. \quad (18)$$

This mechanism is only effective, however, for line components which exhibit a linear Stark shift. The Balmer-α and Lyman-α lines both contain unshifted components (2/3 of the total line strength for Lyman-α, and 1/3 of the line strength of the dominant $3D_{5/2} - 2P_{3/2}$ component of the Balmer-α line), which are unaffected by Holtsmark broadening, and are broadened only by Doppler and dynamic Stark broadening.

Both the electrons and the ions contribute to the dynamic Stark broadening. The electron broadening may be estimated using the formula given by Sobelman *et al.*,[15] which may be written in mixed units as

$$\Delta\nu_e = 6.8\times10^{-8}N_e(kT_e)^{-1/2} \times\left[\ln(kT_e/\sqrt{N_e I}) + 24.90\right]I \quad \text{s}^{-1}, \quad (19)$$

where $I = 27/Z^2$ for Balmer-α, and $17/(2Z^2)$ for Lyman-α.

There is, at present, no simple way to compute the broadening due to ion dynamic effects short of numerical simulation. However, Stamm *et al.*[17] have shown that the primary effect of ion dynamics is to cut off the dipole correlation function for times long compared to the inverse ion plasma frequency ω_{pi}^{-1}. Consequently, we have adopted the simple expedient of adding a contribution to the electron broadening equal to the ion plasma frequency to allow approximately for additional broadening due to ion dynamics. Thus, the full-width broadening due to ion dynamical effects may be estimated as

$$\Delta\nu_i = 297\sqrt{ZN_i} \quad \text{s}^{-1}. \quad (20)$$

The central component width computed in this manner $(\Delta\nu_e + \Delta\nu_i)$ agrees well with the width given by Oza, Greene, and Kelleher[18] for the Balmer-α line of C^{5+} at $T_e = 20$ eV (a typical temperature for x-ray laser experiments with hydrogenic carbon).

Putting typical parameter values into Eqs. (17)–(20), one finds that the Holtsmark broadening is generally far larger than the other widths, which leads to the conclusion that the Holtsmark-broadened components make little contribution to the gain. For example, if we take $N_e = 5\times10^{20}$ cm^{-3}, $T_e = 100$ eV, and $Z = 9$, then $\Delta\nu_D = 6\times10^{12}$ s^{-1}, $\Delta\nu_H = 1.4\times10^{14}$ s^{-1}, $\Delta\nu_e = 7.6\times10^{12}$ s^{-1}, and $\Delta\nu_i = 6.6\times10^{12}$ s^{-1}. The Doppler, electron impact, and ion dynamic widths are seen to be all of the same order of magnitude, and thus one may not, in general, assume that Doppler broadening is dominant in hydrogenic ions for conditions typical of x-ray laser experiments.

Taking all broadening mechanisms into account, the line shape can be approximately described as the sum of two profiles: a central "unshifted" component, broadened only by Doppler and dynamic Stark broadening, superimposed on a much broader profile, resulting from the Holtsmark-broadened components. The fractional area under the central component is 2/3 for Lyman-α, and 1/3 for Balmer-α $3D_{5/2} - 2P_{3/2}$.

III. NUMERICAL MODEL

A collisional-radiative code including the photoionization terms discussed above was used to calculate the steady-state populations of the various hydrogenic levels. The code allows for the presence of three ionization stages: bare nuclei, hydrogenic ions, and heliumlike ions, and considers the effects of the fine-structure splitting of the hydrogenic ion levels. The system of rate equations for the populations of each level for the hydrogenic and heliumlike ions is solved in the steady-state limit, accounting for all relevant collisional and radiative processes; namely (a) electron-collisional excitation, de-excitation, and ionization, (b) radiative decay, (c) radiative, three-body, and dielectronic recombination, and (d) photoionization due to the pump radiation, allowing also for stimulated recombination [Eq. (5)]. The plasma is assumed to be optically thin for all transitions.

The temperature may be either specified, or, for the power balance case, computed by solving the system of rate equations iteratively until the temperature is found which satisfies Eq. (16).

It should be noted that the expressions given to compute the pumping rates and power balance were written assuming the only ions present in the plasma are the hydrogenic and the completely stripped ions, and that the hydrogenic levels could be characterized by n alone. In the calculations, however, more complete versions of these expressions are employed, accounting where necessary for the (l,j) sublevels of the hydrogenic ions and for the presence of heliumlike ions.

The hydrogenic ion energy levels through $n=7$ are included in the model, with higher levels being lumped into the continuum.[19] The sublevels are considered individually for $n\leqslant 3$, while for $4\leqslant n\leqslant 7$ they are assumed to be populated statistically, so that only rate equations for the level populations as a whole need be solved.

The heliumlike ions are handled in an approximate manner, since in the present work they are of interest only as a sink term for the hydrogenic population. The He-like ions are treated in the high-Z (hydrogenic) limit, with an effective Z accounting for shielding. Levels up to $n=7$ are considered, with the (l,j) splitting neglected. Doubly excited states are likewise neglected.

The collisional and radiative rate coefficients are taken from the literature, and are derived assuming a Maxwellian electron velocity distribution. The collisional excitation coefficients of Golden *et al.*[20] and Clark *et al.*[21] are used for transitions $(nlj)\rightarrow(n'l'j')$, where $n,n'\leqslant 5$, and $n<n'$. The (j,j') dependence of the coefficients occurs only through an angular momentum coupling factor, given by[15]

$$Q_\kappa(lj,l'j')=(2l+1)(2j'+1)\begin{Bmatrix} l & j & 1/2 \\ j' & l' & \kappa \end{Bmatrix}^2. \tag{21}$$

Here κ is the multipole order for the transition, which is taken to be the lowest value for which Q_κ is nonzero, i.e., $\kappa=|l-l'|$. Where necessary, the coefficients are summed over (l',j') and/or averaged over (l,j). When summed over j', Q_κ reduces to 1.0, and when averaged over j, Q_κ reduces to the relative statistical weight of the final state $(2j'+1)/[2(2l'+1)]$. For transitions $(n)\rightarrow(n')$ and transitions $(nlj)\rightarrow(n')$ $(n'=6,7)$, the coefficients for $(n)\rightarrow(n')$ of Jacobs[19] are used, neglecting the l dependence in the case of $(nlj)\rightarrow(n')$ for $n'=6,7$. The coefficients for collisional de-excitation are computed from detailed balance.

The collisional ionization coefficients are taken from Jacobs.[19] The l dependence is included for $n=2$, but the l-averaged value (the only one given in Ref. 19) is used for $n=3$.

The coefficients for intralevel $(n=n')$ transitions among sublevels for $n=2,3$ are taken from Shevelko *et al.*[22] (It should be noted that the expression for λ^2 in Ref. 22 contains a misprint, which is corrected by Tallents.[23]) Due to the small transition energies for the intralevel transitions, the ions as well as the electrons are effective in causing transitions. The transition rate is thus calculated including the effects of both ion and electron collisions.

Tabulated Einstein coefficients are used for the radiative decay rates.[24,25] Only optically allowed, interlevel transitions are included. The (j,j') dependence is handled in the same manner as for the collisional coefficients, namely by multiplying the $(n'l')\rightarrow(nl)$ Einstein coefficients by the angular factor $Q_\kappa(l'j',lj)$ with $\kappa=1$, where necessary summed over (lj) and/or averaged over $(l'j')$.

The radiative recombination coefficient for the hydrogenic ions is computed using the expression[26]

$$A_{\infty n}=5.1\times10^{-14}Z\left(\frac{\beta}{n^2}\right)^{3/2}\exp\left(\frac{\beta}{n^2}\right)E_1\left(\frac{\beta}{n^2}\right)G_{nf}\quad \text{cm}^3/\text{s}, \tag{22}$$

where $\beta=13.6Z^2/kT_e$ and $E_1(x)$ is the exponential integral function

$$E_1(x)=\int_x^\infty\left(\frac{e^{-x}}{x}\right)dx. \tag{23}$$

Three-body recombination is calculated from detailed balance, as the inverse to collisional ionization. Dielectronic recombination from the hydrogenic to the heliumlike ions is calculated using the expression given by Sobelman *et al.*,[15] which is an empirical fit to the results of detailed calculations. This expression is valid in the low-density limit, and overestimates somewhat the dielectronic recombination coefficient at high densities, since it does not allow for the reionization due to electron collisions of the highly excited intermediate state. However, it is sufficient for the present purposes, as the numerical results show that for the conditions of interest dielectronic recombination has little effect on the results.

All Gaunt factors [i.e., G_{nf} in Eq. (3) and Eq. (22), G_{ff} in Eq. (9), and G_{fn} in Eq. (13)] are set to 1.0 in the calculations. This is a reasonable approximation, since the Gaunt factors do not usually differ greatly from 1.0.

For the gain calculations, the line profile is assumed to consist of two superimposed components, as discussed above, the first of which has a homogeneous width given by $\Delta\nu_1=\Delta\nu_e+\Delta\nu_i$, and the second of which has a homogeneous width $\Delta\nu_2=\Delta\nu_e+\Delta\nu_i+\Delta\nu_H$. Both profiles are assumed to be Voigt, with Doppler width $\Delta\nu_D$. The relative area ratio of the two components is 2:1 for Lyman-α, and 1:2 for Balmer-α $3D_{5/2}-2P_{3/2}$. The gain coefficient is calculated from the expression

$$G=(\lambda^2 A/8\pi)P(0)[N_u-(g_u/g_l)N_l],\qquad(24)$$

where $P(0)$ is the value of the normalized composite profile at line center.

IV. RESULTS

In this section, results for typical plasma characteristics, inversions, and gain coefficients are presented. Most of the Balmer-α gain results are given for a fluorine plasma, and most of the Lyman-α results for either a lithium or beryllium plasma. These results may be scaled to other elements using the well-known Z-scaling laws for hydrogenic ions[27] (although the scaling is only valid if the He-like population is negligible and all sublevels are populated statistically). For example, the gain coefficient varies with Z as

$$G\propto Z^p\times f(\eta_e,\theta_e,\overline{P_1},H),\qquad(25)$$

where $\eta_e=N_e/Z^7$, $\theta_e=T_e/Z^2$, $\overline{P_1}=P_1/Z^4$, and $H=h\nu/Z^2$. The exponent p is between 6 and 7.5, depending on the dominant broadening mechanism.

It may be shown that the power balance temperature exhibits a similar Z scaling. All of the terms in Eq. (16) have the same Z dependence, when expressed in terms of the reduced parameters η_e, θ_e, $\overline{P_1}$, and H, and thus the power balance temperature scales according to

$$T_{\rm pb}=Z^2\times f(\eta_e,\overline{P_1},H).\qquad(26)$$

The results shown were in all cases calculated for a photon energy of $15Z^2$ eV (i.e., approximately 10% higher than the ionization energy). This value was chosen somewhat arbitrarily. Ideally, the photon energy should be as close as possible to the ionization limit, both to maximize the coupling efficiency and to minimize the electron temperature (since the energy $h\nu-13.6Z^2$ eV is given up to the electrons in each ionization event). Some possible pump/lasant schemes could be expected to have a mean pump energy between $13.6Z^2$ and $15Z^2$ eV. For example, if H-like fluorine were pumped with $2\rightarrow1$ radiation from He-like Na, then $h\nu=1126.9$, or $13.91Z^2$ eV. Such schemes would then have somewhat better gains for a given intensity than the results given here. Conversely, if the mean pump energy were significantly larger than $15Z^2$ eV, then the results would be worse than those presented here.

In presenting the results, the electron density is taken to be a free parameter. In an actual situation, density gradients will exist in the plasma, in which case the inversion will be determined by the local value of the electron density. Also, the maximum achievable electron density will be determined by the critical density for the radiation used to create the plasma. For laser radiation at 0.65 μm, the critical density is 2.6×10^{21} cm^{-3}. If the plasma is created directly by x-ray radiation, however, then all densities up to solid density are possible, since the critical density for x rays is above solid density.

A. Plasma characteristics

Some typical characteristics of the steady-state plasmas produced by ionizing radiation are shown in Figs. 1–3. In Fig. 1, the fractional ion populations of the bare nuclei, H-like ions, and He-like ions are shown for a fluorine plasma versus electron density with and without ionizing radiation. The temperature is held at 150 eV, and the pump intensity is 5×10^{13} W/cm^2.

Without radiation, the plasma is dominated by the He-like ions. (The large He-like fraction indicates that lower ionization stages would also be present, if these had been included in the calculations.) In the presence of the ionizing radiation, however, the plasma is nearly fully stripped, with only a negligible He-like fraction for electron densities less than 10^{21} cm^{-3}. These results illustrate the point that the plasma may have a significantly higher ionization state in the presence of ionizing radiation than would normally be ex-

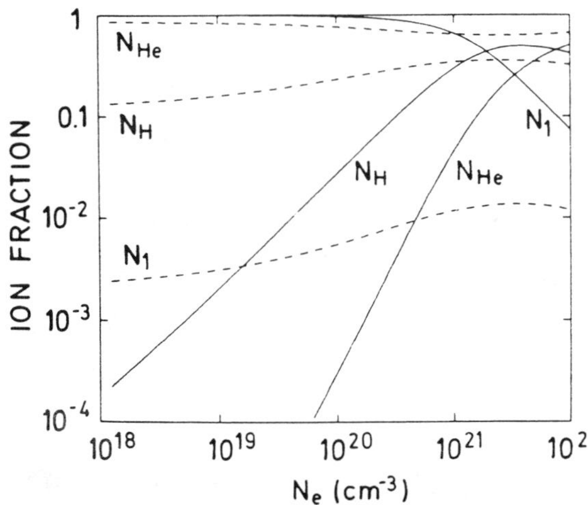

FIG. 1. Ion fractions for the bare nuclei N_1, H-like ions N_H, and He-like ions $N_{\rm He}$, without irradiation (dashed lines) and with irradiation (solid lines). $Z=9$, $T_e=150$ eV, $I_p=5\times10^{13}$ W/cm^2, and $h\nu_p=1215$ eV.

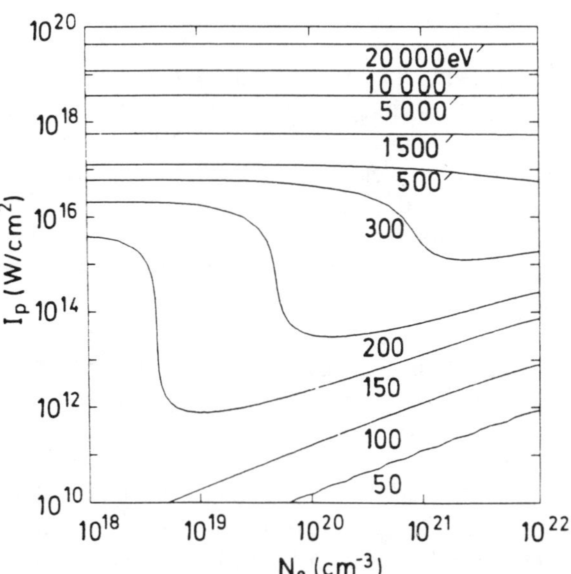

FIG. 2. Contours of power balance temperature (eV). I_p is the pump intensity, and N_e the electron density. $Z=9$, $h\nu_p=1215$ eV.

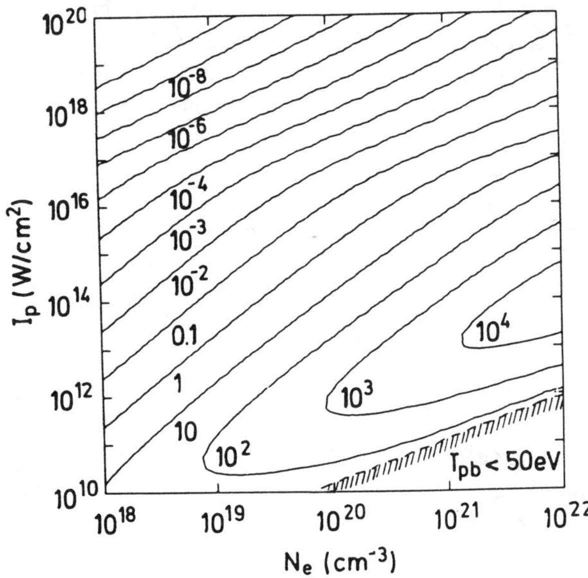

FIG. 3. Contours of Lyman-α line-center absorption coefficient (cm^{-1}) under power balance conditions. $Z = 9$, $h\nu_p = 1215$ eV. (Results where $T_{pb} < 50$ eV not shown.)

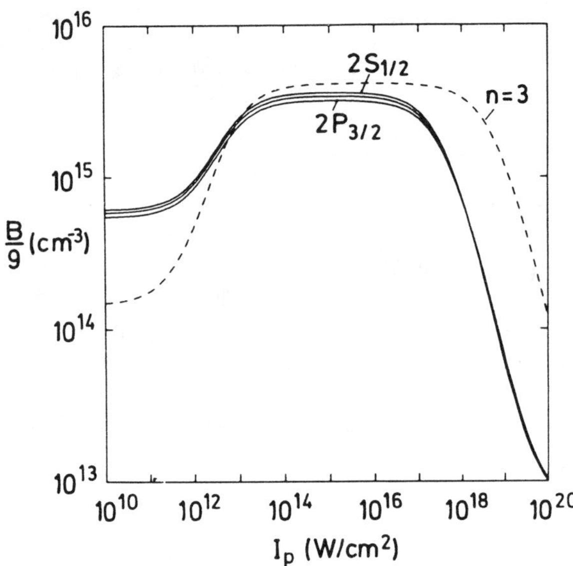

FIG. 4. Effect of pump radiation on level populations. The quantity B/g is the population density divided by the degeneracy. $Z = 9$, $N_e = 5 \times 10^{20}$ cm^{-3}, $T_e = 162$ eV.

pected for a given temperature, since the ionization balance is maintained by the external pump radiation, rather than by electron collisions.

In Fig. 2, a contour plot of the power balance temperature T_{pb} is shown for a fluorine plasma versus electron density and pump intensity. For moderate intensities (say, less than 10^{14} W/cm^2), the temperature reached is in the neighborhood of 0.5–2.5$\times Z^2$ eV. At very high intensities, the power balance temperature is independent of electron density. This results since the plasma is fully stripped, and the the only terms in Eq. (16) are A_{ff} and P_{ff}, which both have the same dependence on N_e and N_i.

A critical assumption in these calculations is that the plasma is optically thin. It is well known that optical trapping on the Lyman-α line can easily destroy Balmer-α inversions in hydrogenic ions. The effects of optical trapping may be accounted for in calculations by introducing escape probabilities, by which the Einstein coefficients are multiplied. For the escape probability for Lyman-α to be greater than $\approx$0.9, the optical depth at line center for Lyman-α should be kept less than one.[28]

In Fig. 3, the values of the line-center absorption coefficient κ_{12} of the Lyman-α line are shown, in units of cm^{-1}. These results indicate the maximum tolerable lateral dimension of the plasma for which optically thin results may be expected to apply. For example, on the contour where $\kappa_{12} = 10^3$ cm^{-1}, the transverse plasma dimension must be held to less than 10 μm for an optical depth less than one. It should be noted, however, that this does not take into account the bulk Doppler shifts due to strong velocity gradients within the plasma, which may relax the strict requirements on plasma size to some extent.

B. Inversions

The pumping effect of the ionizing radiation is illustrated in Figs. 4 and 5. In Fig. 4, the sublevel populations for $n = 2$ and $n = 3$ are shown (divided by their respective degeneracies) as a function of pump intensity for hydrogenic fluorine. The plasma temperature is held fixed at the value 162 eV ($= 2Z^2$ eV) and the electron density is 5×10^{20} cm^{-3}. For $n = 2$, all three sublevels are shown ($2S_{1/2}$, $2P_{1/2}$, and $2P_{3/2}$), while for $n = 3$ the sublevels are in statistical

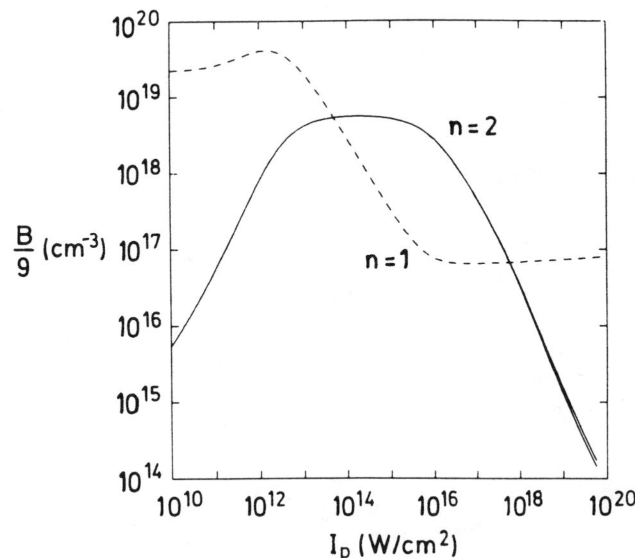

FIG. 5. Effect of pump radiation on level populations. $Z = 3$, $N_e = 5\times10^{20}$ cm^{-3}, $T_e = 9$ eV.

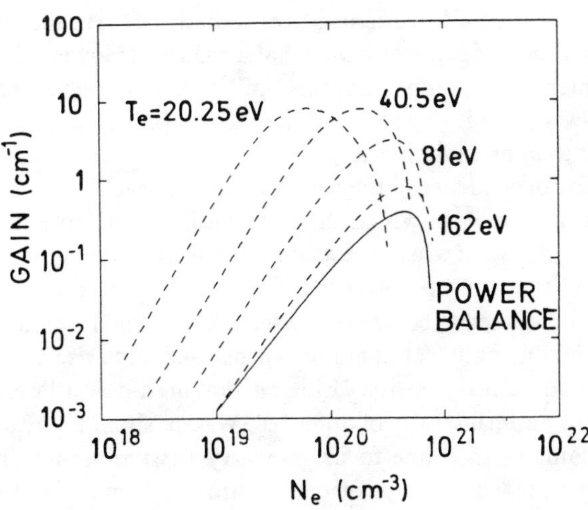

FIG. 6. Balmer-α gain vs electron density with the electron temperature as parameter. $Z = 9$, pump intensity 5×10^{13} W/cm^2. The temperatures are 0.25, 0.5, 1.0, and $2.0\times Z^2$. For the power balance case, the temperature varies along the curve within the range $2Z^2$ eV – $3Z^2$ eV.

equilibrium at this electron density, and thus have equal values of B/g.

At low intensities, the ionizing radiation has little effect, and the populations deviate only slightly from the values that they would have for $I_p = 0$. At approximately 10^{12} W/cm^2, the populations of all levels begin to increase, as the He-like ions are stripped to hydrogenic ions. At an intensity of 10^{13} W/cm^2, the $3D_{5/2} - 2P_{3/2}$ transition first becomes inverted. At much higher intensities ($>10^{17}$ W/cm^2), the populations decrease, as direct photoionization out of the $n = 2$ and $n = 3$ states becomes strong.

The lack of statistical equilibrium among the $n = 2$ substates has an appreciable effect on the calculated inversion density, even for this relatively large electron density. For example, at $I_p = 10^{14}$ W/cm^2, the inversion is twice as large for transitions ending on $2P_{3/2}$ as it is for those ending on $2S_{1/2}$.

In Fig. 5, the level populations for $n = 1$ and $n = 2$ for hydrogenic lithium ($Z = 3$) are shown, again at an electron density of 5×10^{20} cm^{-3}, for a pump photon energy of 135 eV. The electron temperature is held at 9 eV (2–3 times smaller than the power balance temperature). The threshold for positive inversion occurs at 5×10^{12} W/cm^2, beyond which large fractional inversions may be obtained.

C. Gain

The Balmer-α $3D_{5/2} - 2P_{3/2}$ gain coefficient for $Z = 9$ is shown in Fig. 6 as a function of electron density for a pump intensity of 5×10^{13} W/cm^2. The solid curve shows the gain obtained when the plasma temperature is determined by the power balance condition. The maximum gain for this case is approximately 0.4 cm^{-1}. The dashed curves show the gain coefficient obtained if the plasma temperature is reduced by means of additional cooling to values below that given by the power balance condition. These curves show that decreasing the electron temperature results in a dramatic increase in the gain coefficient. At too low an electron temperature, however, the pump is no longer strong enough to keep the plasma primarily in the hydrogenic ionization stage, and the gain again decreases.

The magnitude of the additional cooling obtainable due to hydrodynamic expansion and/or conduction is estimated to be sufficient to hold T_e to a value of Z^2 eV, which is less than half the power balance value (see Appendix). The primary requirement is to keep the transverse linear plasma dimension small—for the conditions assumed in the Appendix, less than approximately 50–70 μm. Since this constraint can be easily met, temperatures on the order of Z^2 eV appear to be realistic values, and thus substantially higher gain than that predicted at the power balance temperature should be possible.

Figures 7 and 8 give an overview of the parameter regions where gain occurs on the Balmer-α transition. Contours of equal Balmer-α gain are shown for a fluorine plasma, where the abscissa and ordinate are the electron density and pump intensity, respectively. The gain coefficients shown in Fig. 7 were computed assuming the temperature to be given by the power balance condition. In Fig. 8, the corresponding contour plot is shown for the case where the electron temperature is held at 81 eV.

In the regions below the dashed lines, more than 10% of the ions are in the He-like ionization stage. In these regions, the pumping radiation is not strong enough to hold the plasma in the hydrogenic ionization stage. It should be noted that the calculated results are only approximate where the He-like concentration is large, since lower ionization stages are not included.

The shapes of the contours in Figs. 7 and 8 may be easily understood physically. Increasing the pump power at fixed electron density, a threshold is first encountered, at which point the inversion first becomes positive. Raising the pump power beyond the threshold increases the gain strongly, as the total hydrogenic population increases, due to increased

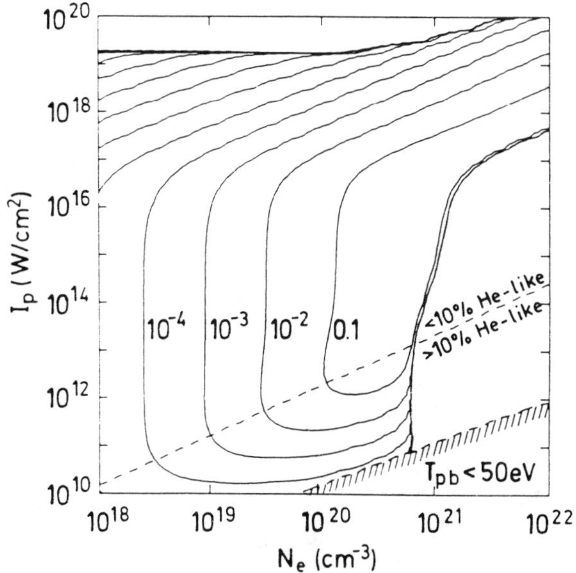

FIG. 7. Contours of equal Balmer-α gain under power balance conditions. $Z = 9$, $h\nu_p = 1215$ eV. (Results where $T_{pb} < 50$ eV not shown.)

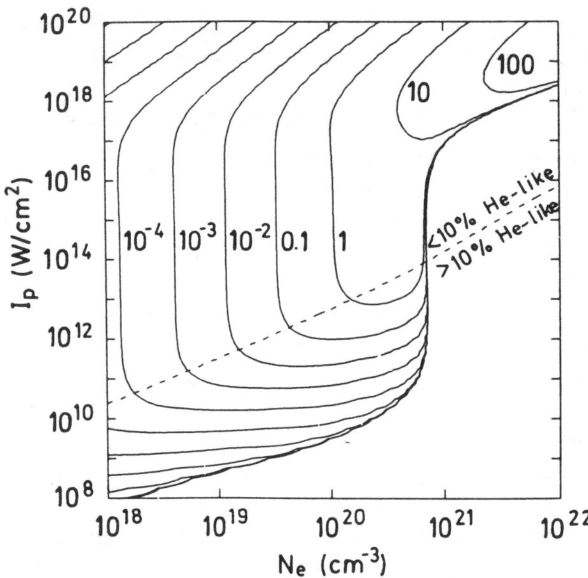

FIG. 8. Contours of equal Balmer-α gain with electron temperature fixed at 81 eV. $Z = 9$, $h\nu_p = 1215$ eV. (Note that additional cooling is needed to achieve this temperature.)

ionization of the He-like ions. Once the He-like population has become negligible, the gain flattens out, and then decreases at very high pump rates, as the hydrogenic ions are stripped to bare nuclei. At still higher intensities (not shown in Fig. 8), the gain becomes negative again. This can be understood by recalling that at high pumping rates, the populations of the levels approach their saturation values and the level populations are not inverted [Eq. (5)].

Keeping the pump power constant at a value in the range $10^{11} - 10^{17}$ W/cm^2, the gain increases approximately quadratically with electron density, until a high electron density limit is reached ($\approx 10^{14}Z^7$ cm^{-3}), at which point the inversion is strongly quenched, as the collision-induced transition rates begin to dominate over radiative decay, and the populations tend toward their Saha values. (However, at extremely high pump rates, this limit does not apply, since the lower level is depopulated directly by photoionization, rather than by radiative decay.)

The dependence of the peak gain on nuclear charge Z is shown in Fig. 9, in which the gain coefficient at optimum electron density (where the gain is maximized; see Fig. 6) is shown versus pump power for $Z = 6$ to $Z = 13$. The temperature is taken to be Z^2 eV. It is seen that the gain increases considerably with Z, but at the expense of a large rise in the threshold pump intensity. Using current high-power lasers, an x-ray pump intensity of order 10^{13} W/cm^2 should be readily attainable in a line focus geometry (assuming a 1 cm length, a 20% conversion efficiency into x rays, and a source plasma/target plasma separation of ≈ 200 μm). For this pump power level, $Z = 8$ and $Z = 9$ (with Balmer-α wavelengths of 103 and 81 Å, respectively) appear to offer the most promise.

Unlike the case for Balmer-α, the Lyman-α transition does not invert if the plasma temperature is given by the power balance condition. Thus, additional cooling beyond radiative cooling alone is necessary for Lyman-α gain. However, if this can be achieved then large gain coefficients may be obtained, as seen in Fig. 10, in which contours of equal gain for the Lyman-α transition are shown for $Z = 4$ and $kT_e = 16$ eV. The energy of the pump photons is 240 eV, and the wavelength of the laser is 75.9 Å. For the Lyman-α transition, there is no optimal electron density for the range shown here, as the gain continues to increase with increasing electron density.

Due to the high gain coefficients of the Lyman-α laser, a shorter line focus maybe used to obtain an acceptable gain-length product, with the double advantage that a higher x-ray pump intensity can be generated with a given pump laser

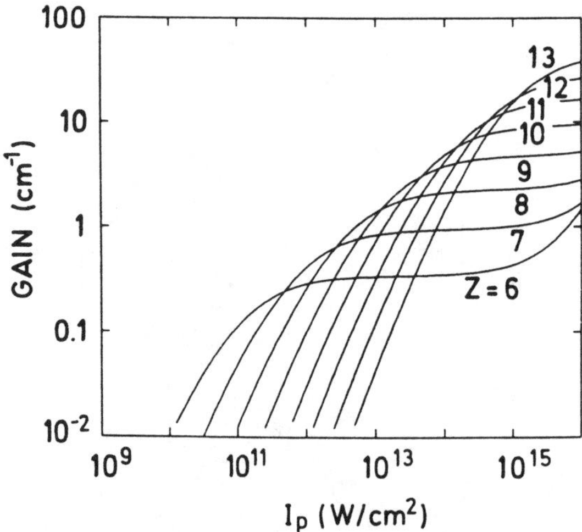

FIG. 9. Gain at optimum density vs pump intensity for various Z ($Z = 6$ to 13). Electron temperature = Z^2 eV, $h\nu_p = 15Z^2$ eV. (Note that additional cooling is needed to achieve this temperature.)

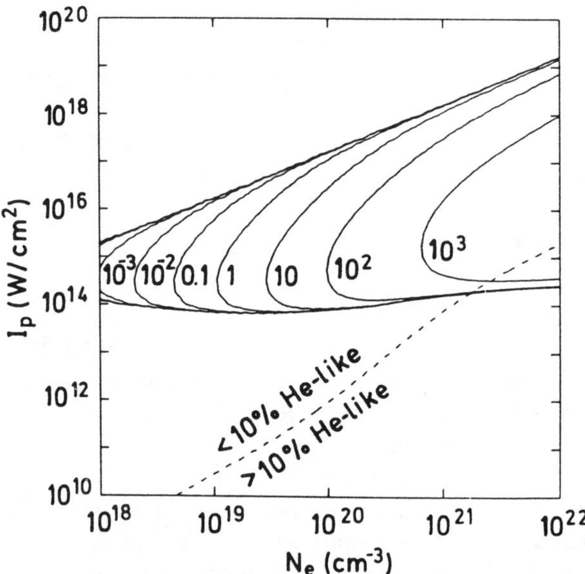

FIG. 10. Contours of equal Lyman-α gain. Electron temperature 16 eV, $Z = 4$, $h\nu_p = 240$ eV. (Note that additional cooling is needed to achieve this temperature.)

and beam refraction from electron density gradients is less problematic.

The Lyman-α gain coefficient is shown in Fig. 11 for Z values from 3 to 6 plotted against pump power at an electron density of 5×10^{20} cm^{-3}. The plasma temperature is Z^2 eV. These results show that the primary difficulty in achieving Lyman-α gain is in supplying enough pump power to overcome the high threshold values. By using a short line focus, however, the threshold values for $Z<5$ should be attainable.

V. CONCLUSIONS AND OUTLOOK

By means of numerical modeling, the conditions under which soft x-ray gain occurs in a hydrogenic plasma subjected to ionizing electromagnetic radiation have been investigated. It is found that powers available from current high power lasers are sufficient to produce gain on hydrogenic Balmer-α lines for $Z<10$, and on Lyman-α lines for $Z<5$. In the case of the Balmer-α line, small but measurable gain is predicted under conditions where the plasma temperature is determined solely by the radiative cooling of the plasma itself. If additional cooling is provided, the gain can be increased substantially. For the Lyman-α line, additional cooling of the electron gas is required to see any gain, but the gain coefficients become very large.

ACKNOWLEDGMENTS

This work was supported in part by the Commission of the European Communities in the framework of the Association Euratom/IPP.

APPENDIX

There are several ways to obtain a reduction of the electron temperature as required for higher gain, cooling by hydrodynamic expansion and heat conduction to a nearby cold surface being the most promising ones. We note that radiative cooling by seeding the plasma with a high-Z material[29] will most likely not work in this case since the high-Z ions would also strongly absorb the pump radiation and the net effect may be zero.

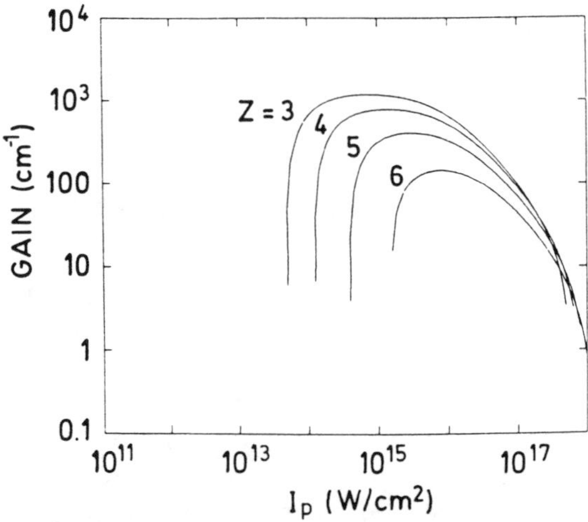

FIG. 11. Lyman-α gain vs pump intensity for $Z=3$ to $Z=6$. Electron temperature $=Z^2$ eV, electron density $=5\times10^{20}$ cm^{-3}, $h\nu_p=15Z^2$ eV. (Note that additional cooling is needed to achieve this temperature.)

We estimate the cooling effect to be expected from hydrodynamic expansion and heat conduction. Let the plasma cloud be a cylinder with radius r. The energy equation is[30]

$$\frac{3}{2}(N_e+N_i)\pi r^2\frac{dkT}{dt}=-2\pi rP\dot{r}+\pi r^2\Delta W, \tag{A1}$$

where the dot means differentiation with respect to time, P is the plasma pressure, and ΔW is the difference between the absorbed and emitted powers per cm^3 (i.e., $\Delta W=A_{bf}+A_{ff}-P_{bb}-P_{bf}-P_{ff}$). The quantity ΔW is strongly temperature dependent and becomes zero at the power balance temperature $T_{\rm pb}$. By inserting for the pressure

$$P=(N_e+N_i)kT, \tag{A2}$$

one obtains

$$\frac{dkT}{dt}=-\frac{4kT\dot{r}}{3r}+\frac{2\Delta W}{3(N_e+N_i)}. \tag{A3}$$

For expansion cooling to balance the heating by the pump radiation, we require that

$$\frac{4kT\dot{r}}{3r}=\frac{2\Delta W}{3(N_e+N_i)}. \tag{A4}$$

With $Z=9$, $kT=81$ eV, a pump intensity of 5×10^{13} W/cm^2 and $N_e=3\times10^{20}$ cm^{-3} (the density for maximum gain from Fig. 6), the computer code gives

$$\Delta W=7.6\times10^{12}\quad \text{W/cm}^3. \tag{A5}$$

Therefore from Eq. (A4)

$$r/\dot{r}=1.1\times10^{-9}\quad \text{s}. \tag{A6}$$

If we estimate the expansion velocity as equal to the ion thermal velocity at this temperature (3.3×10^6 cm/s) then $r=36\ \mu$m, which is a physically realistic value. As long as the cylinder radius is kept at or below this value, hydrodynamic cooling is sufficient to offset radiative heating and hold the plasma temperature to 81 eV or less.

To estimate the cooling by heat conduction, we neglect hydrodynamics and assume that only a small portion of the plasma is illuminated by the pump radiation, whereas the outer part is in contact with a cold material. We consider a cylindrical geometry, in which a small cylinder of radius r_0 is pumped, surrounded by a concentric cold cylinder of radius R. The heat flux is

$$Q=-\kappa\frac{dT}{dr}, \tag{A7}$$

with the thermal conductivity given by[12]

$$\kappa=4.67\times10^{-12}\frac{T^{5/2}\delta_T}{Z\ln\Lambda}\ \text{cal K}^{-1}\,\text{cm}^{-1}\,\text{s}^{-1}. \tag{A8}$$

In this equation $\ln\Lambda$ is the Coulomb logarithm and δ_T accounts for the non-Lorentzian nature of the gas. Taking $\ln\Lambda=5$, $Z=9$, and $\delta_T=0.7$ yields

$$\kappa=\kappa_0T^{5/2}, \tag{A9}$$

with

$$\kappa_0=3\times10^{-13}\ \text{J K}^{7/2}\,\text{cm}^{-1}\,\text{s}^{-1}. \tag{A10}$$

If the situation is stationary, the total heat flowing outward per second is constant at every radius, and thus

$$2\pi r Q(r) = \pi r_0^2 \Delta W = \text{const.} \tag{A11}$$

From Eqs. (A7), (A8), and (A11) with the boundary condition $T(R) = 0$, one obtains for the temperature

$$T = T_0[\ln(r/R)/\ln(r_0/R)]^{2/7}, \tag{A12}$$

where T_0 is the temperature at $r = r_0$. The power transported by heat conduction becomes

$$\pi r_0^2 \Delta W = \frac{4\pi\kappa_0 T_0^{7/2}}{7\ln(R/r_0)} \quad \text{W/cm.} \tag{A13}$$

Taking $R/r_0 = 10$ and again $kT_0 = 81$ eV, the power conducted to the outer cylinder per cm of axial length is

$$P = \pi r_0^2 \Delta W = = 1.9\times 10^8 \quad \text{W/cm.} \tag{A14}$$

With $\Delta W = 7.6\times 10^{12}$ W/cm^3 at 81 eV, one concludes that an irradiated inner cylinder with a maximum radius of $r_0 = 28\ \mu$m can be cooled to 81 eV by heat conduction.

[1]D. L. Matthews, P. L. Hagelstein, M. D. Rosen, M. J. Eckart, N. M. Ceglio, A. U. Hazi, H. Medecki, B. J. MacGowan, J. E. Trebes, B. L. Whitten, E. M. Campbell, C. W. Hatcher, A. M. Hawryluk, R. L. Kaufman, L. D. Pleasance, G. Rambach, J. Scofield, G. Stone, and T. A. Weaver, Phys. Rev. Lett. **54**, 110 (1985).

[2]B. J. MacGowan, M. D. Rosen, M. J. Eckart, P. L. Hagelstein, D. L. Matthews, D. G. Nilson, T. W. Phillips, J. H. Scofield, G. Shimkaveg, J. E. Trebes, R. S. Walling, B. L. Whitten, and J. G. Woodworth, J. Appl. Phys. **61**, 5243 (1987).

[3]B. J. MacGowan, S. Maxon, P. L. Hagelstein, C. J. Keane, R. A. London, D. L. Matthews, M. D. Rosen, J. H. Scofield, and D. A. Whelan, Phys. Rev. Lett. **59**, 2157 (1987).

[4]S. Suckewer, C. H. Skinner, H. Milchberg, C. Keane, and D. Vorhees, Phys. Rev. Lett. **55**, 1753 (1985).

[5]M. H. Key, J. E. Boon, C. Brown, C. Chenai-Popovics, R. Corbett, A. R. Damerell, P. Gottfeldt, C. J. Hooker, G. P. Kiehn, C. L. S. Lewis, D. A. Pepler, G. J. Pert, C. Reagan, S. J. Rose, I. N. Ross, P. T. Rumsby, S. Sadaat, R. Smith, T. Tomi, and O. Willi, J. Phys. (Paris) Colloq. **6**, 71 (1986).

[6]P. L. Hagelstein, Plasma Phys. **25**, 1345 (1983).

[7]R. H. Dixon and R. C. Elton, J. Opt. Soc. Am. B **1**, 232 (1984).

[8]F. V. Bunkin, V. I. Derzhiev, and S. I. Yakovlenko, Sov. J. Quantum Electron. **11**, 971 (1981).

[9]V. A. Boiko, F. V. Bunkin, V. I. Derzhiev, and S. I. Yakovlenko, IEEE J. Quantum Electron. **QE-20**, 206 (1984).

[10]E. E. Fill, J. Phys. (Paris) Colloq. **6**, 117 (1986).

[11]G. J. Pert, Plasma Phys. Contr. Fusion **27**, 1427 (1985).

[12]L. Spitzer, *Physics of Fully Ionized Gases* (Interscience, New York, 1956).

[13]D. Mihalas, *Stellar Atmospheres* (Freeman, San Francisco, 1978), p. 95.

[14]D. H. Sampson, J. Phys. B **10**, 749 (1977).

[15]I. I. Sobelman, L. A. Vainshtein, and E. A. Yukov, *Excitation of Atoms and Broadening of Spectral Lines* (Springer, Berlin, 1981).

[16]H. R. Griem, *Spectral Line Broadening by Plasmas* (Academic, New York, 1974), p. 8.

[17]R. Stamm, B. Talin, E. L. Pollack, and C. A. Iglesias, Phys. Rev. A **34**, 4144 (1986).

[18]D. H. Oza, R. L. Greene, and D. E. Kelleher, Phys. Rev. A **34**, 4519 (1986).

[19]A. Jacobs, J. Quant. Spectrosc. Radiat. Transfer **12**, 243 (1972).

[20]L. B. Golden, R. E. H. Clark, S. J. Goett, and D. H. Sampson, Astrophys. J. Suppl. Series **45**, 603 (1981).

[21]R. E. H. Clark, D. H. Sampson, and S. J. Goett, Astrophys. J. Suppl. Series **49**, 545 (1982).

[22]V. P. Shevelko, I. Yu. Skobelev, and A. V. Vinogradov, Phys. Scr. **16**, 123 (1977).

[23]G. J. Tallents, J. Phys. (Paris) Colloq. **6**, 151 (1986).

[24]W. L. Wiese, M. W. Smith, and B. M. Glennon, *Atomic Transition Probabilities*, Vol. 1 (National Bureau of Standards, Washington, DC, 1966).

[25]L. C. Green, P. P. Rush, and C. D. Chandler, Astrophys. J. Suppl. **3**, 37 (1957).

[26]M. J. Seaton, Mon. Not. Astron. Soc. **119**, 81 (1959).

[27]R. W. P. McWhirter and A. G. Hearn, Proc. Phys. Soc. **82**, 641 (1963).

[28]H. W. Drawin and F. Emard, Beitr. Plasma Phys. **13**, 143 (1973).

[29]J. P. Apruzese, J. Davis, P. C. Kepple, and M. Blaha, J. Phys. (Paris) Colloq. **6**, 15 (1986).

[30]K. M. Dawson, Phys. Fluids **7**, 981 (1964).

Soft x-ray laser source development and applications experiments at Lawrence Livermore National Laboratory

C J Keane, N M Ceglio, B J MacGowan, D L Matthews, D G Nilson, J E Trebes and D A Whelan

Lawrence Livermore National Laboratory, University of California, Livermore, CA 94550, USA

Abstract. Recent progress in experimental laboratory soft x-ray laser research at Lawrence Livermore National Laboratory (LLNL) is reviewed. Research at LLNL in this area has concentrated on further characterising and understanding neon-like x-ray laser plasmas, investigating soft x-ray amplification at shorter wavelengths, and demonstrating examples of x-ray laser applications. For the standard 200 Å neon-like selenium collisional excitation laser, the output source size as well as the beam time history, divergence, energy and spatial profile have been measured. Gain has been demonstrated at wavelengths as short as 50.3 Å in nickel-like ytterbium. Several recombination x-ray laser schemes have also been investigated. X-ray laser holography, cavity operation of an x-ray laser, and the capability to point and focus the output laser beam have been demonstrated.

1. Introduction

The development of laboratory soft x-ray lasers has been intensively pursued worldwide since the early 1970s. Interest in demonstrating soft x-ray laser emission has been spurred by both the technical challenges of source development and the promise of far reaching and novel applications for these radiation sources as they become available. A wide variety of schemes to demonstrate x-ray lasing have been investigated. These include systems pumped directly by relatively standard high power electrical discharge or laser devices, as well as schemes using more exotic pump sources such as laser-produced soft x-rays or picosecond lasers. In this paper we will review experimental x-ray laser research at Lawrence Livermore National Laboratory (LLNL), which has concentrated on the first of these two areas. (Theoretical work at LLNL on x-ray lasers is reviewed in the accompanying article (London *et al* 1989a, hereafter referred to as II).) Discussion of recent results from a number of groups using similar type pump devices has been given in reviews (Suckewer *et al* 1986b, Jaegle *et al* 1987, Lewis *et al* 1988). We will not discuss approaches using laser produced soft x-rays or picosecond lasers as pump sources except to note that considerable progress has recently been made with these schemes (Kapteyn *et al* 1986, Barty *et al* 1988).

In common with several other groups (Lee *et al* 1987, Jaegle *et al* 1987, Lewis *et al* 1988, Louis-Jacquet *et al* 1988, Kato *et al* 1989), Nd-glass lasers used for inertial confinement fusion (ICF) have provided the pump energy source for LLNL x-ray laser research. For x-ray laser work at LLNL, two beams of the Nova laser (Campbell *et al* 1986) operating at second harmonic ($\lambda = 0.53\ \mu$m) are normally used. Typical laser operating parameters include pulsewidths between 100 ps and a few ns, powers up to 5 TW and total focused intensities on target of up to 10^{15} W cm^{-2}. (High-power CO_2 lasers of $\sim$50 ns pulse duration have also been used in x-ray laser research (Suckewer *et al* 1986b).) The years 1984–1987 were a landmark period for x-ray laser development, with several groups succeeding in demonstrating gain for a variety of schemes using ICF type lasers as a pump source (Matthews *et al* 1985, Suckewer *et al* 1985, 1986a, Chenais-Popovics *et al* 1987). At LLNL, lasing was first demonstrated in electron collisionally pumped neon-like selenium.

In this paper, results of experiments characterising this first LLNL x-ray laser as well as other research since 1984 will be summarised. Recent x-ray laser research at LLNL has focused on three areas. The first of these is characterising and increasing our understanding of the high-gain neon-like x-ray laser systems, of which selenium is the standard example. In this work the physics of inversion, propagation and laser

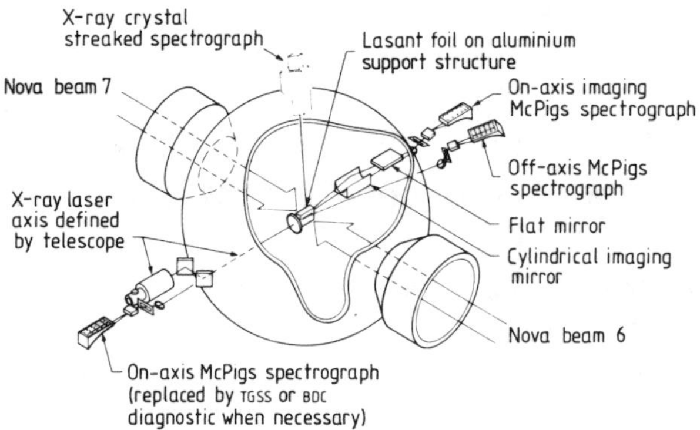

Figure 1. Experimental set-up at the Nova two-beam chamber, showing the x-ray laser axis and diagnostic orientation.

saturation has been studied. The goal in doing this is to attempt to resolve standing questions about neon-like lasing systems as well as to provide knowledge relevant to new x-ray laser schemes. These experiments have also yielded the highest reported gain–length products to date in the soft x-ray region. The second area of research is aimed at demonstrating soft x-ray amplification at shorter wavelengths. Recent work has indicated that x-ray lasers operating at wavelengths slightly on the long wavelength side of the carbon K edge at 43.7 Å are the most useful for a variety of applications (London *et al* 1989b). The goal of our work in this area is to demonstrate such an x-ray laser source, and more generally, to extend x-ray lasing to wavelengths as short as possible. A number of experiments along this line have been carried out and the results of this work will be discussed.

The goal of producing shorter wavelength lasers is motivated by and closely linked to our third major area of research, which is x-ray laser technology development and applications. The application experiments summarised in this paper demonstrated for the first time the two key concepts of (i) boosting total laser output using cavity geometries, and (ii) pointing, focusing and performing useful experiments (in this case, x-ray laser holography) with the x-ray laser output beam.

The remainder of this paper will be divided as follows. Section 2 will describe the experimental set-up. Next, § 3 will discuss results from characterisation of neon-like x-ray amplifiers. Section 4 will discuss results from experiments aimed at producing gain at shorter wavelengths, while § 5 will summarise efforts in x-ray laser technology development and applications experiments. Section 6 will summarise and conclude with an outlook for future research.

2. Experimental set-up

The work described in this paper was carried out at the Nova two-beam chamber, shown schematically in figure 1. Two of the ten beams of the Nova laser are diverted to a secondary vacuum chamber, converted to green light and line focused onto an x-ray laser target. Laser pulse widths ranging from 100 ps to a few ns and peak powers on target of up to 2.5 TW (per beam) at $\lambda = 0.53\ \mu m$ are available. A combination of one spherical and two cylindrical lenses in each beam allow a line focus up to 5 cm in length to be produced. The target foil (consisting of the lasant (selenium, molybdenum, etc) coated onto a plastic support foil) is positioned at chamber centre and aligned (MacGowan *et al* 1987b) with the x-ray laser axis using autocollimation techniques to within ±1.5 mrad. (The x-ray laser axis itself is defined using the on-axis McPigs spectrograph and its associated telescope, as shown in figure 2.) In an experiment the line-focused beams are superposed on the exploding-foil target; the resulting long, elongated plasma then serves as the x-ray amplifier, as shown in figure 2.

The plasma produced when the foil is irradiated is viewed by a variety of diagnostics. Two 'McPigs' soft x-ray spectrographs (Eckart and Matthews 1985) observe the plasma along the x-ray laser axis; the variation of line intensity with target length as seen by

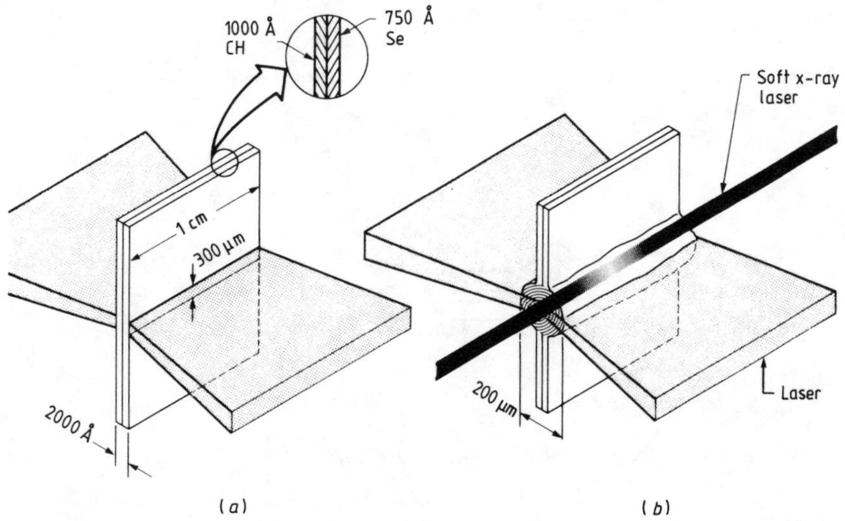

Figure 2. (a) Schematic of the exploding-foil target used in the neon-like selenium experiments. (b) Upon irradiation by the Nova laser, the target foil explodes, producing a long plasma of characteristic dimension 200 μm in the transverse direction. Nova laser (left): $I_{\text{total}} = 7 \times 10^{13}$ W cm^{-2}, $\lambda = 0.53$ μm. In the plasma (right): $n_e \simeq 4 \times 10^{20}$ cm^{-3}, $T_e \simeq$ 1 keV.

these spectrographs is used to measure gain. One of these spectrographs may be operated in imaged mode (Whelan *et al* 1987) where a spectrum spatially resolved in the horizontal plane of the incident laser beams (i.e. the plane perpendicular to the target foil) can be obtained; the spatial resolution in this case is 20 μm at the target. In non-imaging mode, the axial McPigs spectrographs have an acceptance angle of 11 mrad in the horizontal direction and 1.5 mrad in the vertical direction. In addition, a third McPigs (viewing the entire target foil) looks at off-axis emission from the cylindrical plasma. The McPigs instruments are 1 m, Rowland circle, grazing incidence reflection spectrometers; their spectral resolution was typically $\lambda/\Delta\lambda \sim 500$–$1000$ for the experiments discussed in this paper. They are equipped with microchannel plates which can be gated off using Auston switch technology at a specified time after the start of the Nova 0.53 μm pulse to afford a measure of time resolution (Christie *et al* 1985, Wiedwald 1985).

Certain experiments require a different set of on-axis diagnostics to those shown in figure 1. For experiments where the time evolution of soft x-ray lasing lines is measured, an on-axis McPigs is replaced by a transmission grating streaked spectrograph (TGSS) (Ceglio and Medecki 1987). This instrument has a time resolution of 40 ps and a spectral resolution $\lambda/\Delta\lambda \sim 200$. Similarly, when measurements of the beam output spatial profile and divergence are required, a 'beam divergence camera' (BDC) (MacGowan *et al* 1986) is installed on-axis. The plasma is also observed by time-integrated and time-resolved x-ray spectrographs which monitor the 4–10 Å region; the observed x-ray line spectra are used to estimate the ionisation balance. A set of pinhole cameras filtered to look at radiation near 1.5 keV completes the diagnostic suite.

The 'exploding-foil' type target used in these experiments is shown in detail in figure 2. These targets are designed so as to minimise the effects of x-ray refraction on laser beam propagation as well as to provide a homogeneous plasma gain medium (Rosen *et al* 1985). Upon irradiation by the pump laser these targets explode and produce a long uniform plasma of roughly constant temperature. The resulting relatively flat transverse density profile (of characteristic scale length $L_n \sim 100$ μm) allows x-rays to propagate down the entire length of the amplifier. A detailed discussion of the hydrodynamics of these targets has been given elsewhere (Rosen *et al* 1985, London and Rosen 1986).

3. Neon-like ion amplifier physics

Recent work at LLNL on neon-like x-ray laser schemes has concentrated on characterising the neon-like selenium x-ray laser (Matthews *et al* 1987, MacGowan *et al* 1986)

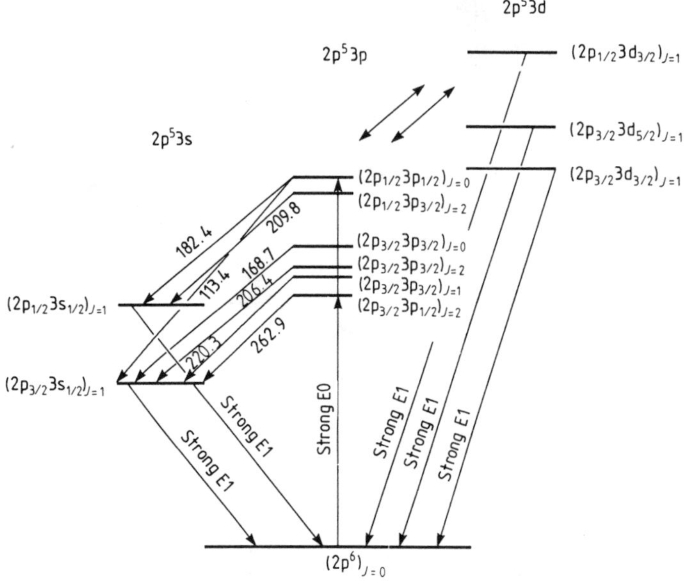

Figure 3. Grotian diagram for neon-like selenium. The strong $J = 2$–1 lasing lines at 206.4 and 209.8 Å are shown, as well as other $J = 0$–1, $J = 1$–1 and $J = 2$–1 transitions of interest. The levels shown in the $2p^5 3d$ manifold are the upper levels for the 3C, 3D and 3E transitions (Gordon *et al* 1980, Hutcheon *et al* 1980). Energy intervals between excited states are drawn to scale, while the position of the ground state is not.

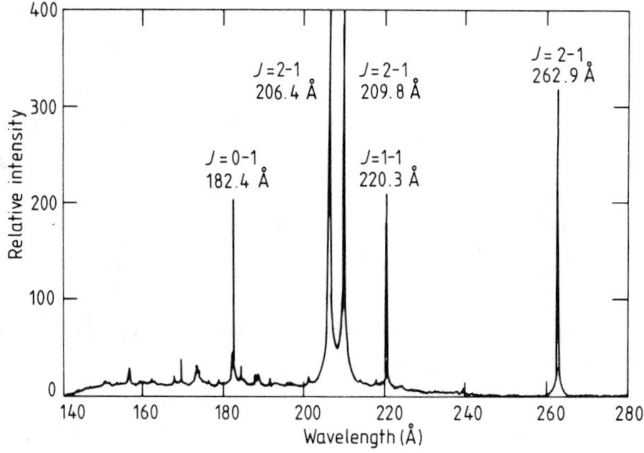

Figure 4. Axial spectra of a neon-like selenium exploding foil target obtained with the McPigs spectrograph. The target length was 2.0 cm. The 206.4 and 209.6 Å lines are over exposed in order to allow weaker transitions to be clearly seen.

and extrapolating these systems to higher Z (shorter wavelength) (MacGowan *et al* 1987a, Keane *et al* 1989a, b). Figures 3 and 4 show a neon-like selenium Grotrian diagram and a selenium spectrum taken from a 2 cm long target, respectively. The $J = 2$–1 lasing lines at 206.4 and 209.8 Å are overexposed in figure 4 in order to allow the weaker $J = 0$–1 and $J = 1$–1 lasing transitions to be clearly seen. With targets up to 4 cm in length, the emission from the $J = 2$–1 lines has been amplified by over a factor of 10^5, as shown in figure 5. In this figure the spectrally integrated intensity of the lines as a function of target length has been fitted to the following formula (Linford *et al* 1974):

$$I = (E/g)(e^{gL} - 1)^{3/2}(gL\, e^{gL})^{-1/2} \tag{1}$$

where g is the small signal gain coefficient, L is the amplifier length, and E is proportional to the emissivity.

The best fit to the data using this formula yields a small signal gain coefficient of $4\ \mathrm{cm}^{-1}$ for both the 206.4 and 209.8 Å lines. This implies that 17 gain lengths have been demonstrated in neon-like selenium; this is close to the gain-length product for a saturated system. Both Novette (Matthews *et al* 1985) and Nova two-beam (Mac-

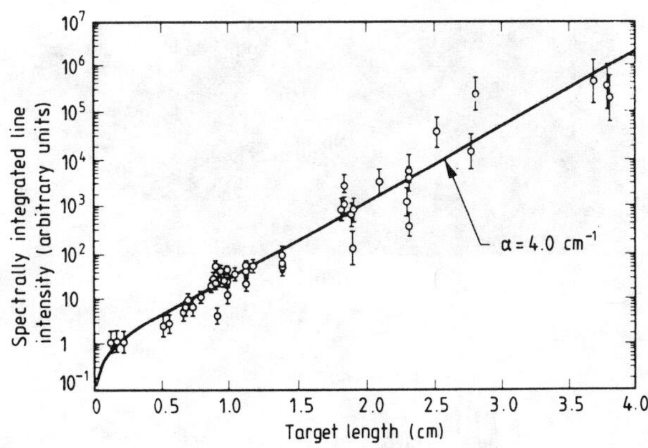

Figure 5. Intensity of the Se 206.4 Å $J=2$–1 line plotted target length for 45 μg cm^{-2} areal density selenium targets irradiated at 7×10^{13} W cm^{-2} (the 'nominal' selenium case).

Gowan *et al* 1986) data are shown in figure 5. The small signal gain of 4 cm^{-1} for the 206.4 Å line shown in figure 5 is lower than the previously reported value of 5.5 cm^{-1} for Novette data (Matthews *et al* 1985) due to the more accurate equation (1) being used to compute the gain.

The 209.8, 220.3 and 262.9 Å lines have measured gains of 3.8, 2.3 and 3.5 cm^{-1}, respectively (MacGowan *et al* 1986). Reanalysis of the length behaviour of the 182.4 Å $J=0$–1 line for longer targets has shown that this line has a gain of about 2 cm^{-1} (MacGowan 1989). The $J=0$–1 transition at 113.4 Å has also been observed (Eckart *et al* 1988), but no systematic attempts to measure its gain have been made. The 168.7 Å transition in figure 2 has not been definitely identified due to the presence of a nearby sodium-like selenium line (Scofield 1989). A detailed listing of the 3-3 selenium lines observed to date has been given by Eckart *et al* (1988).

The gains quoted above were all measured for the 'nominal' selenium case. The 'nominal' conditions are: (i) target: 35 μg cm^{-2} (750 Å) of selenium on 10 μg cm^{-2} (1000 Å) of CH (plastic); (ii) laser: 0.53 μm wavelength, $I=3.5\times10^{13}$ W cm^{-2} (per beam), 500 ps FWHM pulse, 300 μm wide line focus on target foil. It should be emphasised that little systematic attempt has been made to investigate the behaviour of gain as a function of irradiance. By varying the target design or driving laser wavelength it may be possible to demonstrate lasing at total intensities less than 7×10^{13} W cm^{-2}.

With the gain coefficients determined, further experiments were carried out to characterise the laser output beam. In particular the beam pointing and divergence (or, equivalently, the beam profile) and time history were measured. In addition, the beam energy as well as the spatial extent of the x-ray lasing region in the plasma were determined. These will be considered each in turn. Further details regarding this work are available in the literature (MacGowan *et al* 1986, Matthews *et al* 1987).

The beam output profile was measured using the BDC diagnostic mentioned in § 2. This diagnostic uses a piece of x-ray sensitive Kodak 101 film placed 130 cm from the chamber centre to take a photograph of the beam 'footprint'. A combination of a grazing incidence mirror and aluminium filter is used to limit the spectral coverage of this diagnostic to a band near the 206.4 and 209.8 Å lines. A time-integrated photograph for a 3 cm target taken from this diagnostic is shown in figure 6.

The main beam is seen to exhibit an angular divergence of 11 mrad with an offset from the laser axis of 8 mrad. A weaker lobe is present on the opposite side and is displaced 4 mrad from the x-ray laser axis. The higher intensity lobe is on the side that corresponds to the selenium-coated side of the exploding-foil target. The beam profile is symmetric in the vertical direction, and a vertical divergence of 20 mrad has been measured. The vertical divergence is thus greater than the geometrical divergence of 10 mrad appropriate for a 3 cm long plasma of 300 μm lateral dimension. In the horizontal direction, each of the two beamlets displays a geometrical divergence. The shift of each beamlet from the x-ray laser axis in the horizontal direction is consistent with refraction being present (MacGowan *et al* 1986, London 1988, London *et al* 1989b).

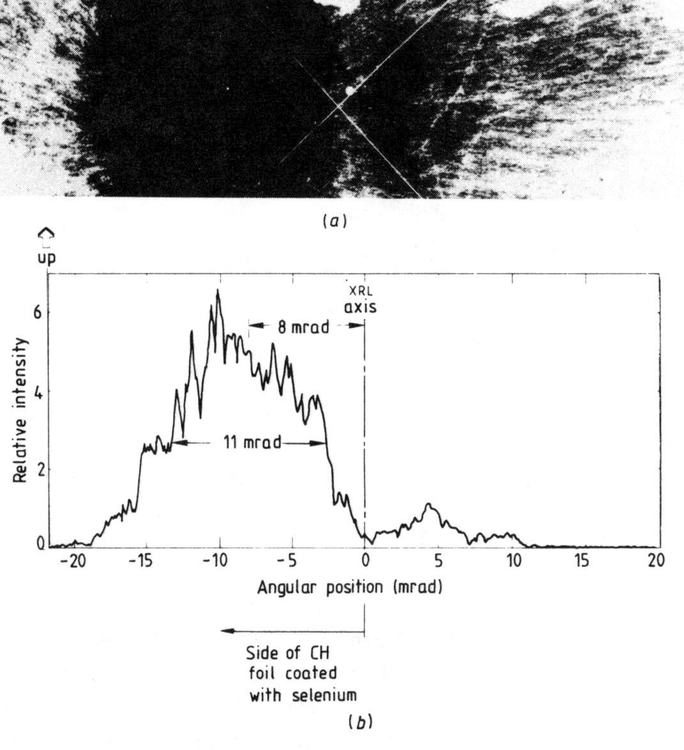

Figure 6. (*a*) Photo of neon-like selenium x-ray laser beam taken at a distance of 130 cm from a 3 cm long target. (*b*) Lineout through the horizontal axis of the picture showing the two-lobe structure of the beam as well as the angular divergence.

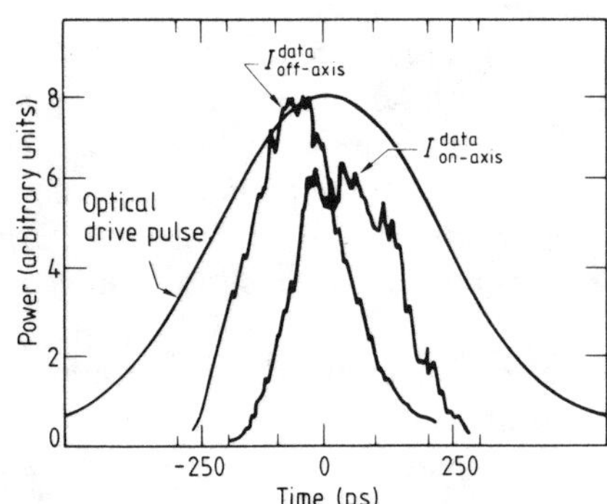

Figure 7. Temporal profiles of the laser 0.53 μm Nova laser pulse and the on- and off-axis 206.4 Å neon-like selenium x-ray laser emission. The TGSS instrument was offset 7 mrad from the x-ray laser axis for the off-axis case.

More specifically, in travelling along the x-ray laser axis, x-rays will tend to be refracted towards the low-density region and out of the amplifier. Note that the distance travelled before a ray refracts out of a tube of length L approximating the amplifier is given by $L_R \sim (L)\ (2N_c/N_0)^{1/2}$, where L is the transverse density gradient scale length, N_c is the critical density at the x-ray laser wavelength and N_0 is the peak on-axis electron density. For 200 Å x-rays, $L = 100\ \mu$m and $N_0 = 5 \times 10^{20}\ \text{cm}^{-3}$ (typical for an exploding-foil amplifier), we find $L_R \sim 1$ cm. Refraction can then be expected to be an observable effect for the 1–4 cm amplifiers used in these experiments. The expected effect of refraction is to shift the beam off the x-ray laser axis in the horizontal direction, and this is evident in figure 6. These output beam patterns have been extensively modelled using x-ray tracing techniques and are consistent with one-dimensional refraction effects, as discussed in II and in previous work (London 1988, London *et al* 1989b).

Figure 7 shows a measurement of the 206.4 Å line time history from the TGSS

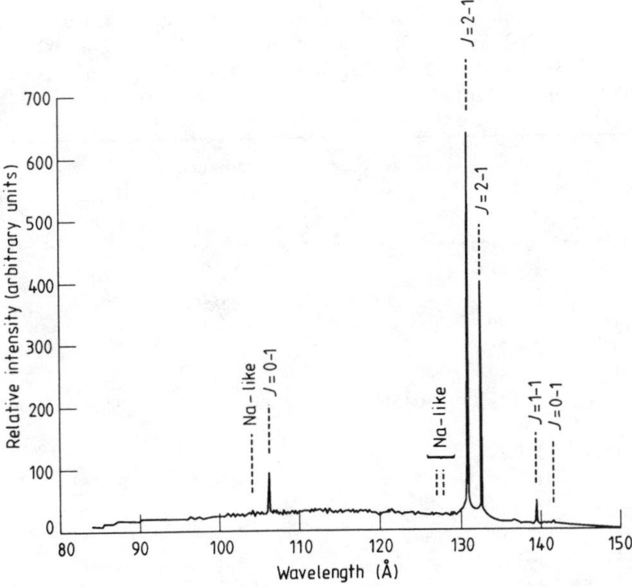

Figure 8. Axial spectrum from a 1.71 cm long pure molybdenum foil. Note the bright $J=2$–1 transitions and the $J=0$–1 line at 106.4 Å.

instrument measured along the x-ray laser axis as well as 7 mrad off-axis. Note the different time histories of the on- and off-axis emission. (These results and their implications for x-ray laser kinetics have been discussed elsewhere (Rosen *et al* 1987).) This is consistent with the refraction effects described above: at early time, before the foil has burned through, the x-ray emission is strongly diverted off axis; at later times, as the density gradient relaxes, the laser emission shifts back to the nominal x-ray laser axis. Similar conclusions regarding the time behaviour of the beam output profile were drawn from time-resolved BDC data (MacGowan *et al* 1986).

An estimate can be made of the combined energy in the 206.4 and 209.8 Å lines for the longest targets examined (4.7 cm) based on the total integrated exposure of the BDC film. Present estimates indicate that the order of 500 μJ is detected by the BDC (MacGowan *et al* 1986). The power in the 170 ps pulse of x-rays is thus of the order of 1 MW per line.

The source size of the lasing region has also been measured using the imaging McPigs spectrograph (Whelan *et al* 1987) shown in figure 1. The source size is smaller for longer targets, and varies between 50 and 250 μm. (Further analysis of these data to determine a more precise value for the source size is underway.) In addition, the emitting region is located near the centre of the plasma, in qualitative agreement with other measurements indicating that lasing occurs during the driving laser pulse when the plasma is relatively hot and dense.

In addition to these gain length and laser characterisation studies in selenium, progress has been made in isoelectronically scaling neon-like x-ray laser schemes to higher Z and thus shorter wavelengths. In particular, detailed experiments have been carried out for yttrium ($Z=39$) (Matthews *et al* 1985), molybdenum ($Z=42$) (MacGowan *et al* 1987b), and strontium ($Z=38$) (Keane *et al* 1989a, b). As an example of this work, figure 8 shows a time-integrated spectra taken from a 1.71 cm long pure molybdenum exploding foil target. (The actual target material used for gain measurements was 90% molybdenum by weight, with various compounds composed of molybdenum and nitrogen also present; this is referred to in table 1 as Mo_2N.) Note again the relatively low intensity of the $J=0$–1 transition at 141.6 Å. As discussed in II, a major unresolved issue regarding neon-like x-ray lasers is the difference between the large theoretical gain and low measured gain on this $J=0$–1 transition. One especially interesting feature to note in molybdenum is the presence of gain on the 106.4 Å $J=0$–1 line, which is the analogue of the 168.7 Å Ne-like Se transition shown in figure 2. Efforts are continuing to understand the physics underlying the behaviour of these $J=0$–1 transitions. Table 1 summarises the neon-like x-ray laser lines observed to date at LLNL and their measured gains.

Table 1. Summary of LLNL achievements to date with neon-like schemes. Transitions A(2–1), $(2p^5_{3/2}3p_{3/2})_2$–$(2p^5_{3/2}3s)_1$; B(2–1), $(2p^5_{1/2}3p_{3/2})_2$–$(2p^5_{1/2}3s)_1$; C(2–1), $(2p^5_{3/2}3p_{1/2})_2$–$(2p^5_{3/2}3s)_1$; D(1–1), $(2p^5_{3/2}3p_{3/2})_1$–$(2p^5_{3/2}3s)_1$; E(0–1), $(2p^5_{1/2}3p_{1/2})_0$–$(2p^5_{1/2}3s)_1$; F(0–1), $(2p^5_{3/2}3p_{3/2})_0$–$(2p^5_{3/2}3s)_1$.

Ion	Transition	λ (Å)†	Target areal density (μg cm^{-2})	Irradiance (pulse length) (W cm^{-2})	λ_{pump} (μm)	Gain (cm^{-1})	Gain length
Se^{24+}	A(2–1)	206.38‡	45	7×10^{13}	0.53	4.0	16.0
	B(2–1)	209.78‡		(0.5 ns)		3.8	15.2
	C(2–1)	262.94				3.5	11.8
	D(1–1)	220.28				2.2	9.2
	E(0–1)	182.43				2.4	9.6
Sr^{28+}	A(2–1)	164.1§	90 (SrF_2)	1.4×10^{14}	0.53	4.4 ± 0.4	9.7
	B(2–1)	166.5§		(0.5 ns)		4.0 ± 0.4	8.8
	E(0–1)	159.8§				Blend	Blend
Y^{29+}	A(2–1)	155.0	47	1.4×10^{14}	0.53	~4	~11
	+E(0–1)			(0.5 ns)			
	B(2–1)	157.1				~4	~11
Mo^{32+}	A(2–1)	131.0	88 (Mo_2N)	4×10^{14}	0.53	4.1	7.1
	B(2–1)	132.7		(0.5 ns)		4.2	7.3
	D(1–1)	139.4				2.9	5.0
	E(0–1)	141.6				0	0
	F(0–1)	106.4				2.2	3.8

† All wavelengths are measured. Errors are as follows: Se, ±0.02 Å; Sr, ±0.1 Å; Y, ±0.1 Å; Mo, ±0.07 Å.
‡ Neon-like selenium x-ray laser output parameters: energy, 250 μJ/line; power = 1 MW/line; divergence, 11 mrad × 20 mrad.
§ Experiments performed at and in collaboration with the Centre d'Etudes de Limeil-Valenton, Villeneuve St Georges, France.

The molybdenum studies discussed above were our first step towards producing shorter wavelength x-ray lasers. It was realised shortly after the demonstration of lasing in neon-like ions in 1984 that scaling neon-like schemes to the 44 Å region would require laser powers in excess of 100 TW, corresponding to line focus intensities in excess of 10^{16} W cm^{-2} (Rosen *et al* 1988). As this is currently not possible with available drivers (i.e. on one Nova two beam, the highest power (irradiance) attainable over 1 cm with 0.53 μm light is 5 TW (5×10^{14} W cm^{-2})), efforts have focused on alternative approaches to producing gain at short wavelengths. In the next section we discuss results from experiments using specific schemes designed to produce amplification at shorter x-ray wavelengths near the carbon K edge.

4. Progress toward demonstration of x-ray amplification at shorter wavelengths

Recent x-ray laser experiments on Nova have focused on producing x-ray amplification at shorter wavelengths with the goal of building a high brightness laser operating near the carbon K edge at 43.7 Å. This push to shorter wavelengths is closely related to our efforts to demonstrate significant applications; as mentioned previously, the utility of techniques such as x-ray laser holography is enhanced at shorter wavelengths (London *et al* 1989b). To date two types of inversion schemes to attain this goal have been explored: collisional excitation of nickel-like ions and recombination pumped systems in hydrogen-like, helium like and lithium-like ions. We will discuss each of these schemes in detail below.

4.1. Measurements of amplification in nickel-like ions

The nickel-like analogue of the neon-like scheme has been described by a number of authors (Maxon *et al* 1985, 1986, 1988, Hagelstein 1986, MacGowan *et al* 1987a, 1989). In the spirit of the neon-like scheme, population inversion is produced between the 4d and 4p levels of a nickel-like ion as a consequence of strong collisional pumping of the 4d level from the closed shell $3d^{10}$ nickel-like ground state coupled with fast

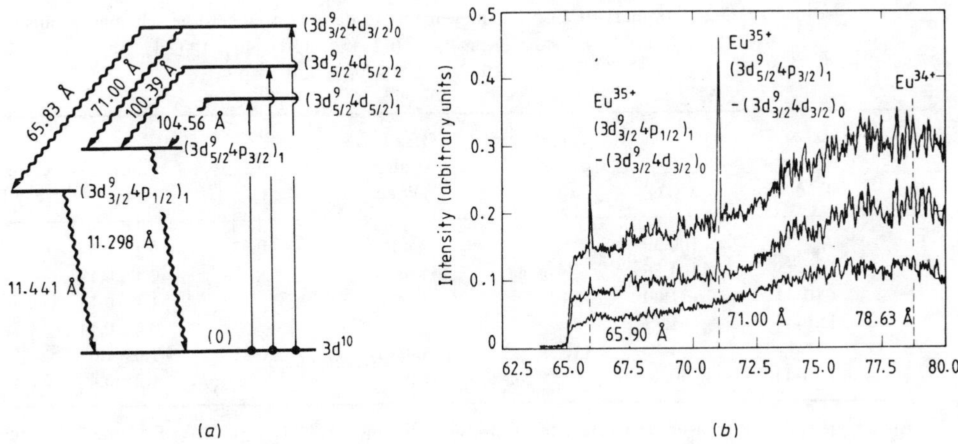

Figure 9. (*a*) Simplified Grotrian diagram for nickel-like europium, showing transitions of interest. (*b*) Details from the on-axis spectra in the region near the $J = 0$–1 line of Eu^{35+}. Spectra are shown for three different target lengths: A, 3.5 cm; B, 1.7 cm; C, 0.8 cm. The target thickness was 60 μg cm^{-2}.

radiative decay of the 4p lower laser level. Initial experiments with this approach focused on the nickel-like stage of europium ($Z = 63$) (MacGowan *et al* 1987a), for which a simplified Grotrian diagram is shown in figure 9(*a*). In this work exploding-foil targets, consisting of 50 μg cm^{-2} EuF_2 on 10 μg cm^{-2} CH or 90 μg cm^{-2} EuF_2 on 10 μg cm^{-2} CH, were irradiated with 1 ns Gaussian pulses at an intensity of 7×10^{13} W cm^{-2}. Gains of order unity were expected from theory for the lines shown in figure 9(*a*).

The results of these experiments are illustrated by the typical on-axis McPigs spectra shown in figure 9(*b*); here spectra from three different target lengths are superposed, demonstrating the exponentiation of the $J = 0$–1 lines with target length. In this work, the signals from the McPigs spectrograph were time integrated up to 500 ps after the peak of the 0.53 μm Nova pulse, then gated off. With 50 μg cm^{-2} EuF_2 targets, the $J = 0$–1 transitions at 65.8 and 71.0 Å were observed to have gains of 0.6 ± 0.14 cm^{-1} and 1.1 ± 0.12 cm^{-1}, respectively. The ratio of the gains is consistent with the relative oscillator strengths of the two lines; note that these two $J = 0$–1 transitions share the same upper state. The gain was found to be lower in the 90 μg cm^{-2} EuF_2 targets (0.6 and 0.24 cm^{-1}, for the 65.8 and 71.0 Å lines, respectively). For both target thicknesses, no apparent gain was measured on the $J = 2$–1 and $J = 1$–1 transitions, although the lines were observed.

The most attractive feature of the nickel-like scheme is the relative ease by which it may be scaled to the 44 Å region. Extrapolation of the nickel-like scheme to higher Z has been demonstrated using ytterbium ($Z = 70$) (MacGowan *et al* 1988) where a gain of 1.2 cm^{-1} has been observed at 50.3 Å, which is the line analogous to the 65.8 Å Eu^{35+} $J = 0$–1 transition. The target foils (consisting of 100 μg cm^{-2} of Yb on 10 μg cm^{-2} of CH) were indicated with 0.53 μm light at a total intensity of 1.4×10^{14} W cm^{-2}. Table 2 summarises the Ni-like lasing lines observed to date and their respective gains. Figure 10 shows the path whereby these nickel-like schemes may be extrapolated to shorter wavelength. Note that the wavelength of the $J = 0$–1 transition drops below 43.7 Å for tungsten ($Z = 74$). Thus, scaling the europium and ytterbium results to tantalum ($Z = 73$) or tungsten would represent demonstration of a short wavelength source ideal for x-ray laser holography experiments. Extrapolating from the Eu and Yb data, a 1 ns Gaussian pulse with intensity between 2–4×10^{14} W cm^{-2} should be sufficient to produce a demonstration of amplification on the $J = 0$–1 transition in these elements (Maxon *et al* 1989).

In summary, demonstration of gain in nickel-like europium and ytterbium has shown the feasibility of scaling this scheme to shorter wavelength. Experiments in the near future will attempt to both optimise the gain in ytterbium and demonstrate amplification in nickel-like tantalum and tungsten at 45.5 and 43.2 Å, respectively.

Table 2. Summary of LLNL achievements to date with nickel-like schemes. Transitions: A(2–1), $(3d^9_{5/2}4d_{5/2})_2$–$(3d^9_{5/2}4p_{3/2})_1$; B(1–1), $(3d^9_{5/2}4d_{5/2})_1$–$(3d^9_{5/2}4p_{3/2})_1$; C(0–1), $(3d^9_{3/2}4d_{3/2})_0$–$(3d^9_{5/2}4p_{3/2})_1$; D(0–1), $(3d^9_{3/2}4d_{3/2})_0$–$(3d^9_{3/2}4p_{1/2})_1$.

Ion	Transition	λ (Å)†	Target areal density (μg cm^{-2})	Irradiance (pulse length) (W cm^{-2})	λ_{pump} (μm)	Gain (cm^{-1})	Gain length
Eu^{35+}	A(2–1)	100.39	6.0	7×10^{13}	0.53	0.1 ± 0.14	—
	B(1–1)	104.56		(1 ns)		-0.1 ± 0.19	—
	C(0–1)	71.00				1.1 ± 0.12	3.8
	D(0–1)	65.83				0.6 ± 0.14	2.1
Yb^{42+}	B(1–1)	84.40	110	1.4×10^{14}	0.53	-1.0 ± 1.0	—
	D(0–1)	50.26		(1 ns)		1.2 ± 0.4	2.0

† All wavelengths are measured. Errors are as follows: Eu (lines A, C, D), ±0.03 Å; Eu (line B), ±0.05 Å; Yb, ±0.05 Å.

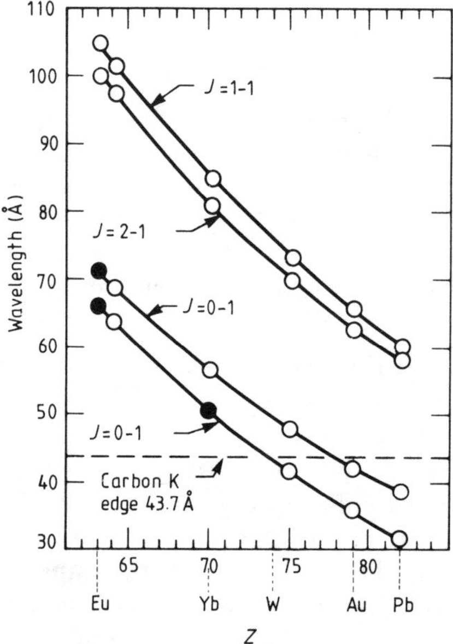

Figure 10. Nickel-like $J = 0$–1 lasing line wavelength plotted against Z (nuclear charge). Transitions for which gain has been observed are indicated by a full circle. The location of the carbon K edge at 43.76 Å is shown.

Tantalum is of special interest due to recent work (London *et al* 1989b) showing that x-ray lasers operating close to but just on the *long* wavelength side of the carbon K edge are optimal for x-ray laser holography of biological microstructures. Finally, it should be noted that the gain length products (and thus laser intensities) achieved to date (four gain lengths at 71.0 Å, two gain lengths at 50.3 Å) can be enhanced by (among other possibilities) multipass amplification using x-ray mirrors. 'Proof of principle' experiments for such x-ray laser cavities will be discussed in § 5 of this paper.

4.2. Recombination x-ray laser experiments

Recombination systems have long been attractive for short wavelength x-ray lasers due to their rapid scaling to shorter wavelengths with nuclear charge Z. The most commonly investigated lasing schemes involve 3–2 inversions in hydrogen-like ions (Suckewer *et al* 1986a, b, Chenais-Popovics *et al* 1987, Lewis *et al* 1988, Kato *et al* 1989) and 4f–3d and 5f–3d inversions in lithium-like ions (Jaegle *et al* 1987, Lewis *et al* 1988). In the past year, recombination experiments at Nova have looked at candidate lasing transitions in hydrogen-, helium- and lithium-like aluminium as well as lithium-like chromium

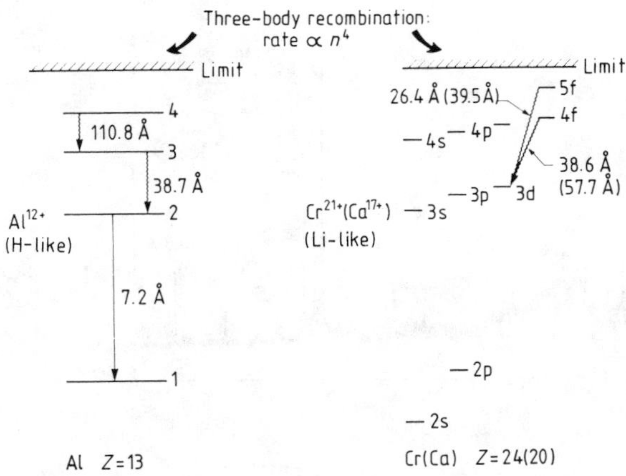

Figure 11. Grotrian diagrams for hydrogen-like aluminium and lithium-like calcium and chromium recombination schemes.

and calcium (Keane *et al* 1988). These ions were each chosen because they offer possible lasing transitions near 43.7 Å. Population inversions at longer wavelengths in helium- and lithium-like aluminium have also been investigated. Figure 11 shows Grotrian diagrams for the recombination experiments discussed in this paper.

The design for the targets used in these experiments is an outgrowth of earlier work investigating recombination pumped inversions in hydrogen-like magnesium (Eder *et al* 1987). The targets consist of thin strips of aluminium, 100 μm high and varying in thickness from 1000 to 4000 Å, sandwiched between 500 Å thick foils of Lexan. These targets (which varied in length from 0.5 to 2 cm) were irradiated in the Nova two-beam chamber by line-focused light with intensities ranging from 10^{14} to 10^{15} W cm^{-2}. The pulse width used was 100 ps. The targets were designed to ionise quickly while the laser is on and then cool rapidly by adiabatic expansion. Gain is expected to occur on the 3–2 and 4–3 transitions in hydrogen-like aluminium approximately 500 ps after the peak of the driving laser pulse.

The focus of initial efforts was to search for evidence for amplification of the 38.7 Å 3–2 transition in hydrogen-like aluminium. This requires complete stripping of the aluminium ions in the plasma during the heating phase in order to drive three-body recombination in hydrogen-like aluminium as the plasma cools. Data indicated, however, that the hydrogen-like emission is primarily due to collisional excitation (Keane *et al* 1988). This implies that the bulk of the plasma is ionising not to fully stripped but to hydrogen-like aluminium. It appears that the peak temperature in these plasmas is lower than required to produce fully stripped aluminium. This condition is supported by recent measurements at KMS Fusion, Inc., where peak electron temperatures of 550 eV were measured for aluminium foil plasmas irradiated at 5×10^{14} W cm^{-2} (Whitten *et al* 1987, Young *et al* 1988).

The ionisation balance data discussed above suggests that conditions are more appropriate for recombination pumped inversions in helium-like and lithium-like aluminium. This possibility was examined by looking for non-linear behaviour of 4–3, 5–3 and 5–4 lines seen in McPigs soft x-ray spectra. Figure 12 shows a typical aluminium soft x-ray spectrum. Note the presence of the 3–2 and 4–3 hydrogen-like lines at 38.7 and 110.8 Å, as well as the helium- and lithium-like 5f–3d lines at 88.9 and 105.7 Å. Experiments with 1000 Å thick aluminium strip targets of various lengths at an intensity of 2.5×10^{14} W cm^{-2} showed evidence for weak non-linear behaviour of the 88.9, 102.43 and 105.7 Å lines. The detailed behaviour of these transitions with variation in target length is currently being investigated.

Spectroscopy experiments to investigate the lithium-like ions of calcium and chromium (using similar type CaF_2 and Cr targets) have also been carried out (Keane *et al* 1988). These experiments led to the identification of the candidate 4f–3d lasing lines in chromium (38.6 Å) and calcium (57.7 Å), as well as the 5f–3d transition in calcium (39.5 Å). No definitive amplification of these lines was observed in this work.

Future work on recombination will include the elements mentioned previously as well as hydrogen-like magnesium ($\lambda_{3\text{-}2}=45.5$ Å), lithium-like potassium ($\lambda_{5f\text{-}3d}=$

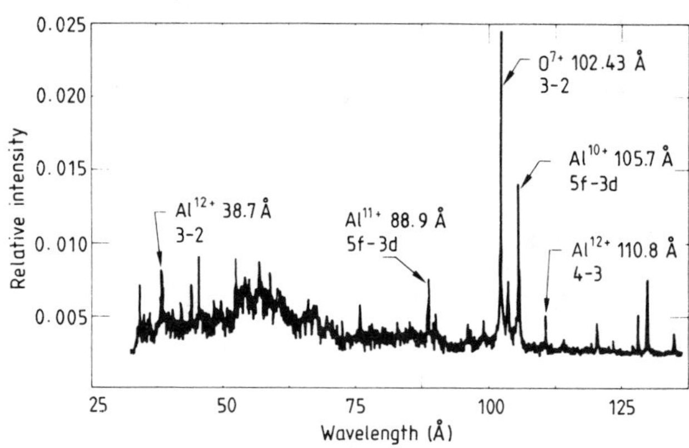

Figure 12. Axial McPigs spectra from a 2 cm long aluminium strip irradiated at $I = 2.5 \times 10^{14}$ W cm^{-2}. The aluminium thickness and laser pulsewidth were 1000 Å and 100 ps, respectively. The spectra shown are time integrated up to 2.2 ns after the laser pulse.

44.3 Å) and lithium-like titanium ($\lambda_{4f-3d} = 46.7$ Å). These ions possess candidate lasing lines on the long wavelength side of the carbon K edge. Future experimental work will also focus on using shorter driving laser pulses ($\tau \leq 20$ ps) and obtaining time-resolved spectra. The shorter pulse used in these experiments should result in a higher electron density during the plasma recombination phase and thus higher gain. These short pulses should thus provide more favourable conditions for both producing and measuring amplification.

5. X-ray laser applications experiments

Our desire to demonstrate x-ray laser applications has led us to investigate multilayer x-ray optics to both directionally control and increase the output of shorter wavelength soft x-ray lasers. We have made progress along these lines in three areas of x-ray laser applications experiments described below. In each instance, successful 'proof of principle' experiments have been carried out at wavelengths of 206.4 and 209.8 Å using the neon-like selenium x-ray laser. The three areas of research described here are: (i) x-ray laser cavity experiments, (ii) x-ray laser output beam pointing and focusing, and (iii) x-ray laser holography.

Double-pass amplification of x-rays has been demonstrated in the past few years by several research groups (Suckewer *et al* 1985, Keane *et al* 1986, Ceglio *et al* 1988a, 1989). At LLNL, double pass amplification was first observed at 206.4 and 209.8 Å in selenium (Ceglio *et al* 1988a) and later at 131.0 and 132.7 Å in molybdenum (Ceglio *et al* 1989). (A detailed discussion of the expected versus the observed enhancement of the laser emission for the double-pass case has been presented (Ceglio *et al* 1988a).) In recent experiments at LLNL, true multipass 'cavity-like' amplification has been demonstrated (Ceglio *et al* 1988b). In this work, a simple cavity consisting of a molybdenum/silicon miltilayer mirror and beamsplitter placed at opposing ends of a neon-like selenium x-ray laser was constructed. Experiments of this type have been made possible by advances in multilayer x-ray optics technology; in the past few years, relatively efficient normal incidence mirrors and beamsplitters covering a spectral range from 125–250 Å have been successfully fabricated (Stearns *et al* 1986, Hawryluk *et al* 1988, Ceglio 1988, 1989).

Figure 13(a) shows the set-up for an experiment where a multilayer mirror/beam-splitter combination was used to demonstrate multipass amplification of soft x-rays. In this work a spherical mirror with a 12 cm radius of curvature was placed 3.5 cm from one end of the selenium exploding-foil amplifier. A flat beamsplitter was placed 3.0 cm from the opposite end (for double-pass-only work the beamsplitter was removed). The normal incidence reflectivities near 206.4 and 209.8 Å for the mirror and beamsplitter were 20% and 15%, respectively; the beamsplitter had a transmission of 5%.

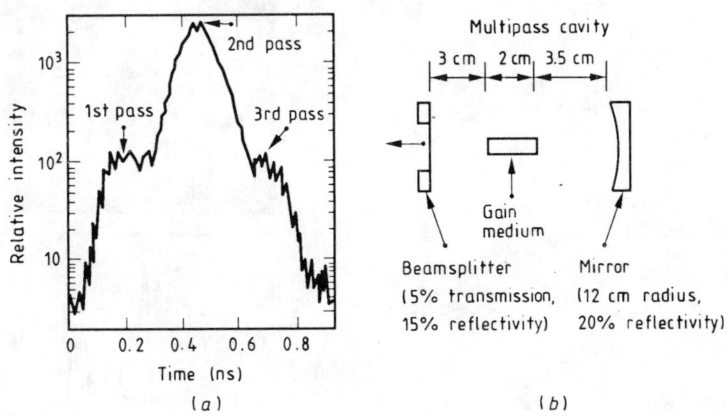

Figure 13. (*a*) Time-resolved multipass cavity output at 206.4 Å for the cavity shown in (*b*). The nominal selenium target and irradiance conditions as discussed in the text were used in this experiment.

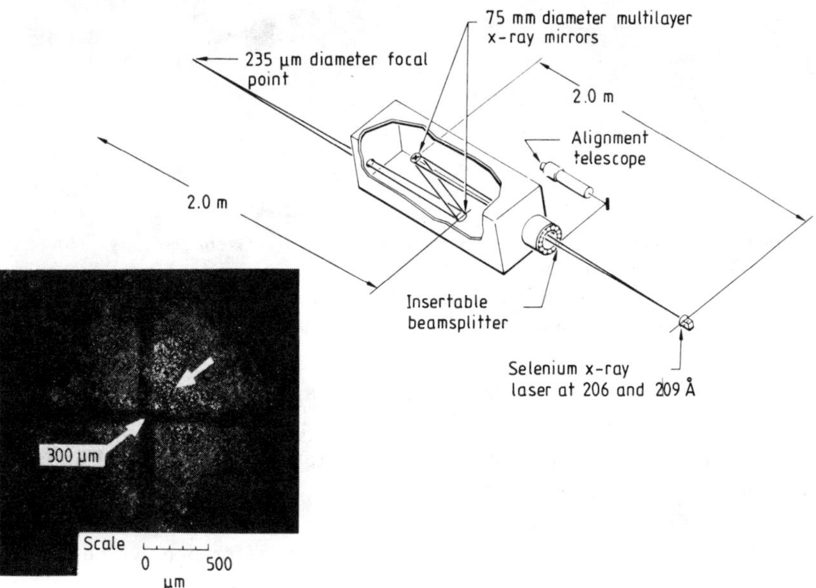

Figure 14. Experimental arrangement for x-ray laser pointing and focusing experiments. A photograph of the focused spot is also shown. The shadow of the crosshair in the photograph marks the position where the focused x-ray beam was pointed.

A transmission grating streaked spectrograph observed the 206.4 and 209.8 Å emission with time and a typical time history of the 206.4 Å line from this diagnostic for the multipass experiment is shown in figure 13(*a*). The three output bumps correspond to single-pass, double-pass and triple-pass x-ray amplification (in a standard 'no cavity' experiment only the first of these three peaks is seen). The data are consistent with a rapidly rising and falling profile in time of the amplifier gain. A key point to note here is that the total x-ray laser output in the second pass was enhanced by 22 times over the first pass value. Thus, the use of cavities has a high potential for reducing the driving laser power requirements, assuming a gain medium of longer time duration can be produced. Extension of this technique to wavelengths near the carbon K edge will also obviously be important in providing a high brightness short wavelength laser necessary for applications.

In addition to increasing x-ray laser brightness the capability to point and focus the x-ray laser output beam is important. Our second major effort in the applications area was to demonstrate this capability for the neon-like selenium x-ray laser (Nilson *et al* 1988a). Figure 14 shows a diagram of the experimental set-up used in this work.

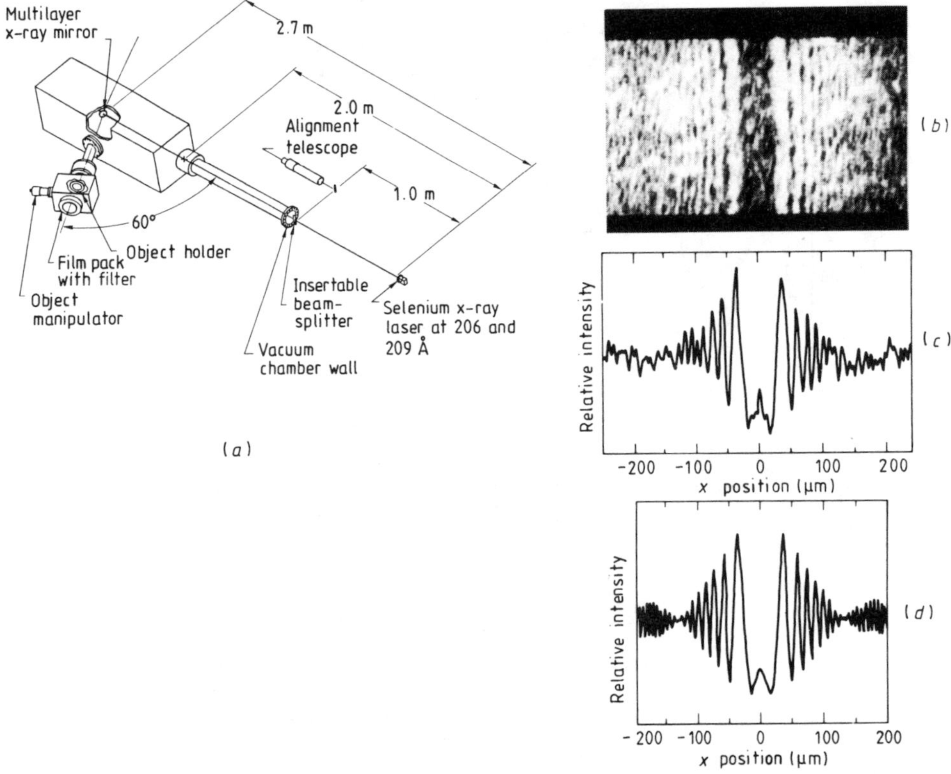

Figure 15. (*a*) Experimental set-up for x-ray laser holography (Gabor geometry). (*b*)–(*d*) X-ray hologram of an 8 μm diameter carbon wire: (*b*) fringes obtained in the hologram on the x-ray film; (*c*) the measured linear x-ray exposure as a function of relative position in the x-ray hologram; (*d*) the predicted linear x-ray exposure as a function of position in the hologram.

A pair of 76 mm diameter multilayer mirrors (once again optimised to reflect the two selenium $J=2$ transitions at 206.4 and 209.8 Å) were used to relay the x-ray laser output beam to a point focus 4 m away from the x-ray laser target. A thin aluminium filter was used to ensure that only x-rays near 200 Å were detected by the x-ray film.

In these experiments spot sizes as small as 235 μm in diameter were obtained. These spots were centred within 300 μm of the pointing reference, which corresponds to a ± 75 μrad pointing error for the beam. In this work the beam spot on the film was defocused in order to make it easier to see and detect; experiments will be performed in the future to determine the spot size at best focus. This pointing and focusing system was actually used in a first applications experiment to photoionise argon gas in a cell at an optical distance of 4.6 m (Nilson *et al* 1988b). A variant of this technique will also be used in future experiments to produce plasmas from x-rays point focused on a target.

Our third major application was the first demonstration of an x-ray laser-produced hologram (Trebes *et al* 1987). In this experiment a modified Gabor holography geometry (figure 15) was used, in which interference at the film plane between an object beam (light scattered forward from the object) and a reference beam (light that passes around the object) creates the hologram. To ensure that only 206.4 and 209.8 Å emission strikes the object, a flat spectrally discriminating x-ray multilayer mirror was used to relay the x-ray laser output beam to the test object. In order to keep the x-rays from losing coherency upon reflection, the multilayer mirror must be flat to better than a tenth of the wavelength over a region approximately 150 μm across. A mirror that exceeded this specification, having a flatness of a hundredth of the x-ray laser wavelength (i.e. 2 Å) was actually obtained and used in the experiment.

Figure 15 shows the fringe pattern observed in the hologram of an 8 μm diameter carbon fibre. Six fringes are clearly visible. The fringe pattern is in good agreement with that calculated assuming Fraunhofer diffraction including the effects of a partially coherent source. The spatial resolution obtained in these holograms is 5 μm and is limited by the film used to record the image. In addition to this fibre, holograms were successfully made of a number of three-dimensional test objects. These results clearly illustrate the potential for x-ray holography to obtain images of very small objects.

Part of our future work will be to examine more advanced holography geometries for use with shorter wavelength x-ray lasers. These geometries, to be made possible by the future development of high-quality x-ray laser optics and coherent x-ray lasers, should offer higher resolution and better signal-to-noise ratios and should make possible holography of live biological specimens. In addition to holography, we will also be investigating other applications experiments such as x-ray interferometry and plasma formation by x-rays.

6. Summary

In this paper progress in experimental x-ray laser research at Lawrence Livermore National Laboratory has been summarised. Significant progress has been made in: (i) understanding neon-like x-ray lasers and scaling them to shorter wavelengths, (ii) observing soft x-ray amplification near the carbon K edge, and (iii) demonstrating x-ray laser applications. Particular highlights include: (i) isoelectronic scaling of neon-like systems to wavelengths as short as 106.4 Å, (ii) observation of x-ray amplification at wavelengths as short as 50.3 Å, and (iii) demonstrating for the first time multipass amplification of soft x-rays, x-ray laser pointing and focusing and x-ray laser holography.

In the future our plans call for a concerted effort to make a high-brightness short-wavelength laser and use it in a variety of applications. In particular, we are working toward producing holograms of live biological cell components. To these ends efforts will continue to produce short-wavelength x-ray lasers and to enhance their output by using cavities, or, more simply, by finding schemes that yield a higher single-pass gain. In addition to holography, we hope that in the future this work will lead to techniques such as plasma probing and/or production by x-rays as well as a host of as yet unforeseen applications.

Acknowledgments

We would like to thank the many people involved in obtaining the results summarised in this paper, including: D Y Al-Salameh, T Harvey, P J Maloney, W Silfvast and O R Wood II (AT&T); G Charatis and G Busch (KMS Fusion, Inc.); S Brown, E M Campbell, J Cox, M Eckart, D Eder, D Gaines, P Hagelstein, A Hawryluk, A Hazi, R London, S Maxon, T Phillips, M Rosen, J Scofield, G Shimkaveg, D Stearns, R Stewart, G Stone, B Whitten and J Woodworth (LLNL); and P Hagelstein (MIT). In addition, we would like to acknowledge Nova operations for their assistance in carrying out these experiments. The neon-like strontium data presented in table 1 were acquired at the Centre d'Etudes de Limeil Valenton, Villeneuve St Georges, France in collaboration with J L Bourgade, P Combis, G Nierat, M Louis-Jacquet, D Naccache and G Thiell, and we acknowledge the assistance of the Phebus laser operations staff in obtaining these results. The support of the Inertial Confinement Fusion Program at LLNL and the assistance of C Molkenbuhr in preparing the manuscript is appreciated. This research was performed under the auspices of the US Department of Energy by the Lawrence Livermore National Laboratory under contract W-7405-ENG-48.

References

Barty C P J, King D A, Yin G Y, Hahn K H, Field J E, Young J F and Harris S E 1988 *Phys. Rev. Lett.* **61** 2201

Campbell E M, Hunt J T, Bliss E S, Spedk D R and Drake R P 1986 *Rev. Sci. Instrum.* **57** 2101

Ceglio N M 1988 *X-ray Microscopy II* ed D Sayre *et al* (New York: Springer) p 130
—— 1989 *OSA Proc. on Short Wavelength Coherent Radiation: Generation and Applications* vol 2, ed R Falcone and J Kirz (Washington, DC: Optical Society of America) pp 357–70
Ceglio N M, Gaines D P, Stearns D G and Hawryluk A M 1989 *Opt. Commun.* **69** 285
Ceglio N M, Gaines D P, Trebes J E, London R A and Stearns D G 1988a *Appl. Opt.* **27** 5022
Ceglio N M and Medecki H 1987 *Multilayer Structures and Laboratory X-ray Laser Research* ed N M Ceglio and P Dhez (*Proc. Soc. Phot. Opt. Inst. Eng.* **688**) p 26
Ceglio N M, Stearns D G, Gaines D P, Hawryluk A M and Trebes J E 1988b *Opt. Lett.* **13** 108
Chenais-Popovics C *et al* 1987 *Phys. Rev. Lett.* **59** 2161
Christie D J, Nilson D G, Wiedwald J D and Wilcox R B 1985 *Rev. Sci. Instrum.* **56** 818
Eckart M J and Matthews D L 1985 *Energy and Technology Review* (Livermore, CA: Lawrence Livermore National Laboratory) p 25
Eckart M J, Scofield J H and Hazi A U 1988 *J. Physique Coll.* C1 **49** 361
Eder D C, Rosen M D, Lee R W, Trebes J E, Ceglio N M, Eckart, M J Kauffman R L, MacGowan B J and Matthews D L 1987 *J. Opt. Soc. Am.* B **4** 1949
Gordon H, Hobby M G and Peacock N J 1980 *J. Phys. B: At. Mol. Phys.* **13** 1985
Hagelstein P L 1986 *Phys. Rev.* A **34** 874
Hawryluk A M, Ceglio N M and Stearns D G 1988 *J. Vac. Sci. Technol.* B **6** 2153
Hutcheon R J, Cooke L, Key M H, Lewis C L S and Bromage G E 1980 *Phys. Scr.* **21** 89
Jaegle P, Jamelot G, Carillon A, Klisnick A, Sureau A and Guennou H 1987 *J. Opt. Soc. Am.* B **4** 563
Kapteyn H C, Lee R W and Falcone R W 1986 *Phys. Rev. Lett.* **57** 2939
Kato Y *et al* 1989 *OSA Proc. on Short Wavelength Coherent Radiation: Generation and Applications* vol 2, ed R Falcone and J Kirz (Washington, DC: Optical Society of America) pp 47–51
Keane C J, MacGowan B J, Matthews D L and Whelan D A 1988 *High Intensity Laser Matter Interactions* ed E M Campbell and H Baldis (*Proc. Soc. Phot. Opt. Inst. Eng.* **913**) p 105
Keane C J, Nam C H, Meixler L, Milchberg H, Skinner C H, Suckewer S and Voorhees D 1986 *Rev. Sci. Instrum.* **57** 1296
Keane C J *et al* 1989a *OSA Proc. on Short Wavelength Coherent Radiation: Generation and Applications* vol 2, ed R Falcone and J Kirz (Washington, DC: Optical Society of America) pp 93–8
—— 1989b Soft x-ray amplification in a laser-produced strontium plasma, submitted for publication
Lee T N, McLean E A and Elton R C 1987 *Phys. Rev. Lett.* **59** 1185
Lewis C L S *et al* 1988 *Plasma Phys. Controlled Fusion* **30** 35
Linford G L, Peressini E R, Sooy W R and Spaeth M L 1974 *Appl. Opt.* **13** 379
London R A 1988 *Phys. Fluids* **31** 184
London R A and Rosen M D 1986 *Phys. Fluids* **29** 3813
London R A, Rosen M D, Maxon S, Eder D C and Hagelstein P L 1989a *J. Phys. B: At. Mol. Opt. Phys.* **22**
London R A, Rosen M D and Trebes J E 1989b *Appl. Opt.* **28**
Louis-Jacquet M, Bourgade J L, Combis P, Jacquemot S, Le Breton J P, Naccache D, Perinne J P and Peyrusse O 1988 *C.R. Acad. Sci. Paris* **306** 867
MacGowan B J 1989 Private communication
MacGowan B J, Maxon S, Hagelstein P L, Keane C J, London R A, Matthews D L, Rosen M D, Scofield J H and Whelan D A 1987a *Phys. Rev. Lett.* **59** 2157
MacGowan B J, Maxon S, Keane C J, London R A, Matthews D L and Whelan D A 1988 *J. Opt. Soc. Am.* B **5** 1958
MacGowan B J *et al* 1986 *Multilayer Structures and Laboratory X-ray Laser Research* ed N M Ceglio and P Dhez (*Proc. Soc. Phot. Opt. Inst. Eng.* **688**) p 36
MacGowan B J *et al* 1987b *J. Appl. Phys.* **61** 5243
—— 1989 *OSA Proc. on Short Wavelength Coherent Radiation: Generation and Applications* vol 2 ed R W Falcone and J Kirz (Washington, DC: Optical Society of America) pp 2–10
Matthews D L *et al* 1985 *Phys. Rev. Lett.* **54** 110
—— 1987 *J. Opt. Soc. Am.* B **4** 575
Maxon S, Dalhed S, Hagelstein P L, London R A, MacGowan B J, Rosen M D, Charatis G and Busch G 1989 *Phys. Rev. Lett.* **63** 236
Maxon S, Hagelstein P, MacGowan B J, London R, Rosen M, Scofield J, Dalhed S and Chen M 1988 *Phys. Rev.* A **37** 2227
Maxon S, Hagelstein P, Reed K and Scofield J 1985 *J. Appl. Phys.* **57** 971
Maxon S, Hagelstein P, Scofield J and Lee Y 1986 *J. Appl. Phys.* **59** 293
Nilson D G, Brown S B, Keane C J, MacGowan B J, Matthews D L and Trebes J E 1988a *Lasers Particle Beams* **6** 751
Nilson D G *et al* 1988b *Appl. Phys. Lett.* **54** 786
Rosen M D, London R A and Hagelstein P L 1988 *Phys. Fluids* **31** 666
Rosen *et al* 1985 *Phys. Rev. Lett.* **54** 106
—— 1987 *Phys. Rev. Lett.* **59** 2283
Scofield J H 1989 Private communication
Stearns D G, Ceglio N M, Hawryluk A M, Stearns M B, Retford-Long A K, Chang C H, Danzmann K, Kyhne M, Muller P and Wende B 1986 *Multilayer Structures and Laboratory X-ray Laser Research* ed N M Ceglio and P Dhez (*Proc. Soc. Phot. Opt. Inst. Eng.* **688**) p 91
Suckewer S, Skinner C H, Kim D, Valeo E, Voorhees D and Wouters A 1986a *Phys. Rev. Lett.* **57** 1004
—— 1986b *J. Physique Coll.* C6 **47** 23

Suckewer S, Skinner C H, Milchberg H, Keane C and Voorhees D 1985 *Phys. Rev. Lett.* **55** 1753

Trebes J E, Brown S B, Campbell E M, Matthews D L, Nilson D G, Stone G F and Whelan D A 1987 *Science* **238** 517

Whelan D A, Keane C J, MacGowan B J, Matthews D L, Trebes J E and Eckart M J 1987 *X-rays from Laser Plasmas* ed M Richardson (*Proc. Soc. Phot. Opt. Inst. Eng.* **831**) p 275

Whitten B L, Hazi A U, Keane C J, London R A, MacGowan B J, Matthews D L, Phillips T W, Rosen M D and Whelan D A 1987 *Lawrence Livermore National Laboratory Internal Report* No UCID-21152

Wiedwald J D 1985 *EE Technical Review* (Livermore, CA: Lawrence Livermore National Laboratory) Report no UCRL-50025-85-1

Young B K F, Stewart R E, Cerjan C J, Charatis G and Busch G E 1988 *Phys. Rev. Lett.* **61** 2851

Reprinted with permission from *Physical Review Letters*, Vol. 65(4), pp. 420-423 (July 23, 1990). ©1990 American Physical Society.

Demonstration of X-Ray Amplifiers near the Carbon K Edge

B. J. MacGowan, S. Maxon, L. B. Da Silva, D. J. Fields, C. J. Keane, D. L. Matthews, A. L. Osterheld, J. H. Scofield, G. Shimkaveg, and G. F. Stone

Lawrence Livermore National Laboratory, University of California, P.O. Box 5508, Livermore, California 94550

(Received 30 April 1990)

The Ni-like $4d$-$4p$ laser scheme has been extended to wavelengths near the K absorption edge of carbon. A gain of 2.3 cm^{-1} with a duration of 250 psec was observed in Ni-like Ta at 44.83 Å (a wavelength close to optimal for holographic imaging of live cells). Ni-like W produced a gain of 2.6 cm^{-1} with a total of 7 gainlengths of amplification at 43.18 Å. This is the first demonstration of an x-ray amplifier on the short-wavelength side of the carbon K edge, within the "water window." Both lasers should be scalable to coherent power sufficient for holographic imaging and other applications.

Since 1984 when extreme ultraviolet (XUV) amplification was demonstrated[1,2] near 200 Å, there has been much effort to develop an amplifier to produce significant power at wavelengths below the carbon K absorption ege at 43.76 Å.[3] One motivation was to produce a coherent, high brightness source suitable for holography of biological specimens within the "water window" between the K edges of carbon and oxygen.[4] More recently, a study of the power requirements specific to x-ray holographic imaging by London, Rosen, and Trebes[5] has shown that while for x-ray microscopy it can be advantageous to be inside the water window, for x-ray holography[4,6] the dosage received by a cell is minimized for a given image resolution if the illumination wavelength is slightly to the long-wavelength side of the carbon K edge.

Nickel-like x-ray lasers[7-11] were first demonstrated in a laser-produced plasma of Eu in 1987.[8] Four gainlengths of amplification were observed at 71.0 Å in Ni-like Eu. Subsequently, the scheme was isoelectronically extrapolated to 50.26 Å in Ni-like Yb.[10] The result reported here extrapolates the system further to the edge of the water window, at 44.83 Å, and provides the basis for the design of an x-ray laser source that should fulfill some of the requirements for holography of living cells.[5,6] Also reported here is the further extrapolation of the scheme to 43.18 Å, within the water window, a wavelength more suited perhaps, to short-pulse x-ray microscopy.

Collisionally pumped Ni-like x-ray lasers are $4d$-$4p$ transitions in high-Z Ni-like ions. The $4d$ levels are populated through a combination of direct collisional excitation from the ground state and cascading from upper levels. The $4d$-$4p$ population inversion is maintained by fast radiative decay from the $4p$ levels to the $3d^{10}$ Ni-like ground state while the $4d$ levels are metastable to radiative decay to the ground state. The largest gain is expected on the $J=0$-1 transition $(\underline{3d}_{3/2}4d_{3/2})_0$-$(\underline{3d}_{3/2}4p_{1/2})_1$, at 44.83 Å in Ta^{45+}, where $\underline{3d}_{3/2}$ denotes a vacancy in an otherwise full $\underline{3d}$ shell. The upper state of this transition is populated mainly by collisional excitation from the ground state. The same upper state has another $J=0$-1 lasing transition, to the $(\underline{3d}_{5/2}4p_{3/2})_1$ level (at 50.97 Å in Ta^{45+}). This second, longer-wavelength transition has more gain in lower-Z ions[8] but in higher-Z ions its stimulated emission cross section is smaller than that of its shorter-wavelength partner.[12] For Ta the stimulated emission cross sections of the two transitions are in the ratio 1.3:1.

The Ni-like amplifier is produced by irradiating a thin foil of Ta with a high-intensity optical laser such as the Nova laser at LLNL. The heated foil then becomes a plasma that expands to form a large, uniform gain medium.[2] The plasma needs to be uniform as steep transverse electron-density gradients will cause the x rays to refract out of the plasma before traveling its length.[2] At a density of 10^{21}, transverse scale lengths larger than 50 μm are needed for a 44.83-Å x ray to propagate the length of a 3-cm amplifier. The plasma, at an electron temperature of order 1 keV, and density of order 10^{21} cm^{-3}, should have a significant Ni-like population. The gain in the amplifier may be influenced by trapping, i.e., self-absorption of the $4p$-$3p$ dump lines. The typical line-center optical depth of these lines is $\sim$3–6 with the $(\underline{3d}_{5/2}4p_{3/2})_1$-$3d^{10}$ having almost twice the opacity of the other dump line; hence the 50.97-Å $J=0$-1 line should be more sensitive to trapping. Doppler shifts due to velocity gradients in the explosion of the foil lead to a reduction of the opacity of both dump lines in the direction perpendicular to the original foil surface; hence radiation should escape in this direction. Calculations utilizing the LASNEX, XRASER, and SPECTRE, hydrodynamics, time-dependent kinetics, and line-transfer models[11] predict that the two $J=0$-1 lines should have similar gains (see Table I).

The target used in the Ta experiment was a foil of 127 $\mu g\,cm^{-2}$ Ta on a 24-$\mu g\,cm^{-2}$ Lexan substrate irradiated simultaneously with two of Nova's beams, superposed with a total irradiance of 4.6×10^{14} $W\,cm^{-2}$ in a 120-μm-wide line focus up to 2 cm in length. A total of 5.5

TABLE I. Wavelengths (in angstroms) and gains of the Ni-like Ta and W lines. The estimated uncertainties are given in parentheses. Wavelengths are calibrated against known wavelengths for the Cu-like Ta (Ref. 14) and W (Ref. 19) resonance lines.

		Wavelength (Å)		Gain (cm^{-1})			
	Transition	Theory[a]	Observed	SFFS (Peak)	MCPIGS	SFFS (Int.)	XRASER
Ta^{45+}	$(\underline{3d}_{3/2}4d_{3/2})_0$-$(\underline{3d}_{3/2}4p_{1/2})_1$	44.76	44.83(0.02)	2.3(0.2)	1.4(0.3)	1.6(0.2)	2.6
	$(\underline{3d}_{3/2}4d_{3/2})_0$-$(\underline{3d}_{5/2}4p_{3/2})_1$	50.84	50.97(0.02)	0.5(0.4)	−1(1)	−0.9(1)	2.0
	$(\underline{3d}_{5/2}4d_{5/2})_2$-$(\underline{3d}_{5/2}4p_{3/2})_1$	74.31	74.42(0.02)		−1(1)		3.9
	$(\underline{3d}_{5/2}4d_{5/2})_1$-$(\underline{3d}_{5/2}4p_{3/2})_1$	77.40	77.47(0.02)		1.3(0.4)		1.8
W^{46+}	$(\underline{3d}_{3/2}4d_{3/2})_0$-$(\underline{3d}_{3/2}4p_{1/2})_1$	43.08	43.185(0.01)		2.6(0.2)		5.5
	$(\underline{3d}_{3/2}4d_{3/2})_0$-$(\underline{3d}_{5/2}4p_{3/2})_1$	49.24	Not observed				4.2
	$(\underline{3d}_{5/2}4d_{5/2})_2$-$(\underline{3d}_{5/2}4p_{3/2})_1$	72.25	72.40(0.015)		−0.6(1)		4.9
	$(\underline{3d}_{5/2}4d_{5/2})_1$-$(\underline{3d}_{5/2}4p_{3/2})_1$	75.23	75.35(0.015)		0.8(0.3)		2.2

[a]Reference 15.

kJ of 2ω was used in a 500-psec (full width at half power) Gaussian pulse. The foil was set up in a target chamber vacuum vessel with a large number of XUV and x-ray spectrometers and imaging diagnostics. In particular, the foil was viewed from one end of its axis (the preferred axis for stimulated emission) by a gated grazing incidence XUV spectrometer with a microchannel plate detector (the MCPIGS). Another MCPIGS spectrometer viewed the plasma from an off-axis direction while various time-resolved and time-integrated x-ray spectrometers recorded the x-ray transitions near 2 keV as a signature of the ionization state of the plasma.

Time-integrated spectra from the off-axis MCPIGS spectrometer showed optically thick Cu-like 4-4 resonance lines that have been previously observed and their wavelengths well documented.[13,14] The on-axis spectra were dominated by strong line emission at 44.83 Å; weaker Ni-like emission was visible at 50.97, 74.42, and 77.47 Å. These last two lines are $J=2$-1 and 1-1 transitions which are expected to have gain and share the same lower state as the 50.97-Å $J=0$-1 line. The wavelengths both calculated and measured (using the Cu-like wavelengths as fiducials from Ref. 14) are given in Table I. The calculations are Grant's multiconfigurational Dirac-Fock code with an optimized level scheme.[15]

Figure 1 shows spectra from the other on-axis diagnostic, the streaked flat-field spectrometer (SFFS) which is a grating spectrometer coupled to an x-ray streak camera with 70-psec continuous time resolution. Spectra at one instant in time are shown from two different length foils. Figure 1 illustrates the nonlinear growth of the line intensity with foil length. The spectrometer viewed second, third, and fourth order to obtain good dispersion. The aluminized Mylar filter bandpass restricted its spectral range to the region between the carbon K edge and slightly to the long-wavelength side of the 50.97-Å $J=0$-1 line.

The line intensities from the SFFS are plotted in Fig. 2(a) as a function of foil length. They are fitted with the formula for the axial emission from a distributed source of amplified spontaneous emission from Linford *et al.*[16] The data shown are for the time of peak gain. The time-resolved values of the gains on the two Ni-like $J=0$-1 lines are shown in Fig. 2(b) illustrating the 250-psec duration of the 44.83-Å gain. The time-integrated MCPIGS line intensities were fitted in the same way; the results are summarized in Table I. The SFFS data for the 44.83-Å line peak at a gain of 2.3 ± 0.2 cm^{-1} while the MCPIGS gain is 1.4 ± 0.3 cm^{-1}. The value of the gain obtained by integrating the SFFS data in time is 1.6 ± 0.2 cm^{-1} which is consistent with the MCPIGS value and, as expected, shows that our time-integrated gain measurements may underestimate the peak gain.

To extrapolate this scheme to shorter wavelengths and try and demonstrate a higher gainlength product, tungsten foils of thickness 89 $\mu g\,cm^{-2}$ on 20-$\mu g\,cm^{-2}$ Lexan up to 3 cm in length were irradiated with a total of 3.1×10^{14} $W\,cm^{-2}$ of 2ω light. The Ta experiment

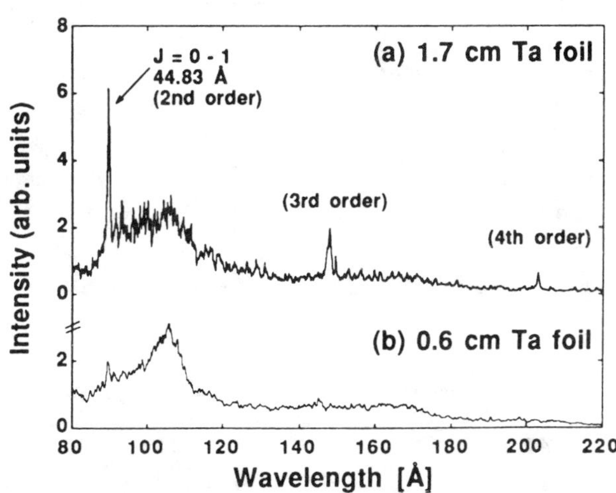

FIG. 1. On-axis spectra from the SFFS streaked spectrometer from (a) 1.7- and (b) 0.6-cm-long Ta foils. Data obtained at the peak of the 44.83-Å gain.

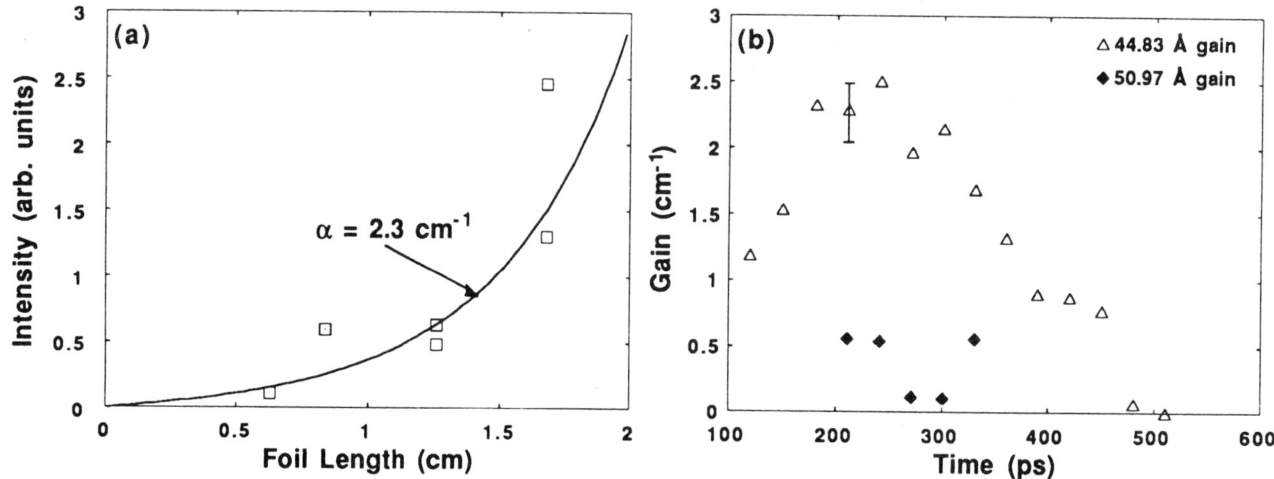

FIG. 2. (a) Line intensity as a function of foil length from SFFS at the peak of the gain. The fit is with the equation $I=(\varepsilon/\alpha)(e^{\alpha l}-1)^{1.5}/(\alpha l e^{\alpha l})^{1/2}$ for a distributed source with emissivity ε, small signal gain α, and length l (Ref. 16). (b) The time history of the gain deduced from the SFFS data.

had shown significant amounts of (Co-like) Ta^{46+} 4-3 and 5-3 x-ray emission indicating that we could reduce the irradiance and still ionize to Ni-like. Figure 3(a) shows on-axis MCPIGS spectra from 2.5- and 1.7-cm-long W foils with the $J=0$-1 laser line at 43.185 Å in first and second order and weaker $J=2$-1 and $J=1$-1 Ni-like lines at 72.40 and 75.35 Å, respectively. In Fig. 3(b) the intensity of the 43.185-Å line is plotted as a function of foil length from the MCPIGS spectrograph. The time-integrated gain from the fit with the same formula as before is 2.6 cm^{-1} with a maximum gainlength of 7 recorded. Time-resolved XUV spectra were not obtained from the W shots but the peak gain may be higher than the time-averaged MCPIGS value. The other $J=0$-1 line (predicted to be at 49.24 Å) was not observed. The gains on the $J=1$-1 and 2-1 lines were qualitatively the same as for Ta and are summarized in Table I.

Table I also shows calculated (time-integrated) gains from simulations similar to those of Ref. 11. Note that there is qualitative agreement (a factor of 2) between the theoretical and measured (time-integrated) gains on the 44.83- and 43.185-Å lines and also their respective $J=1$-1 lines (at 77.47 and 75.35 Å). The calculated gains on the other lines terminating on the $(\underline{3d}_{5/2}4p_{3/2})_1$ level are inconsistent. In particular, the model predicts more gain on the $J=2$-1 line at 74.42 Å (72.40) than the $J=1$-1 line at 77.47 Å (75.35) while the experiment shows no gain on the $J=2$-1. (In Ref. 8 a low gain was seen on the 2-1 and 1-1 lines of Eu^{35+}, in disagreement with calculation.) The ratio of the gains on the two $J=0$-1 lines is predicted to be the same as the ratio of

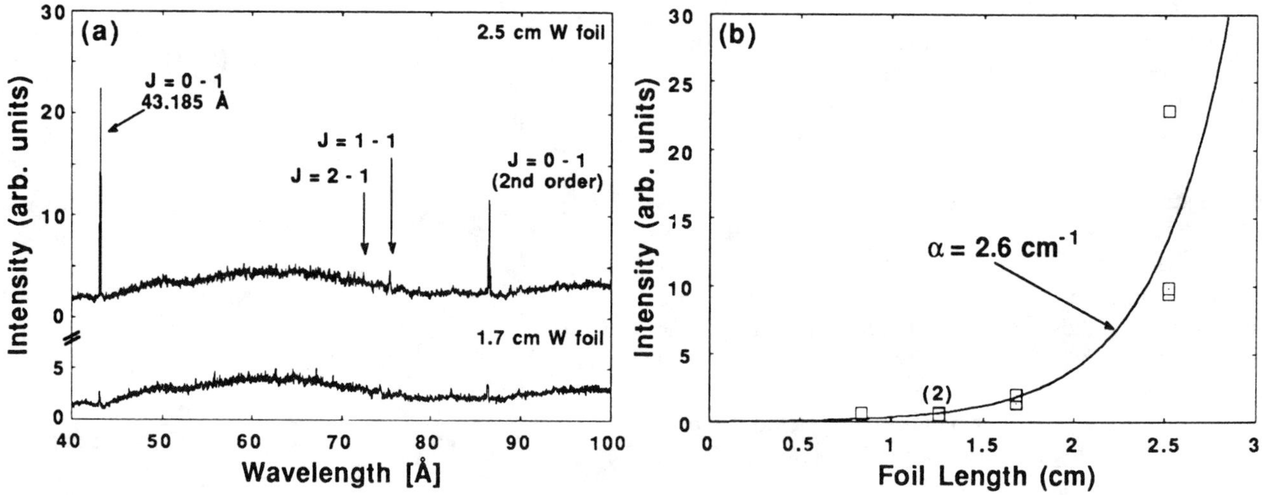

FIG. 3. (a) On-axis spectra (MCPIGS) from 2.5- and 1.7-cm-long W foils. The 2.5-cm foil had a gainlength product of 7 on the 43.18-Å $J=0$-1 laser line. (b) Intensity of the 43.18-Å transition of Ni-like W as a function of foil length, from the MCPIGS spectrometer.

their stimulated emission cross sections, while the Ta $J=0\text{-}1$ at 50.97 Å has little or no gain and the analogous line in W was not even observed. These observations may be explained by errors in the population mechanisms for the $(\underline{3d}_{5/2}4p_{3/2})_1$ level, either through an underestimate of the significance of trapping on the $4p$-$3d$ dump lines, or through an error in the coupling of the $4p$ levels to other levels such as the $4s$ states. Postulating a reduced electron temperature in the plasma (which might explain the lower than expected short-wavelength $J=0\text{-}1$ gains) does not account for the ratio of the $J=0\text{-}1$ gains. This inconsistency of the gains of two $J=0\text{-}1$ lines, which share the same upper state, points to a shortcoming in our modeling of Ni-like lasers.

Although we have not yet measured the energy output of these amplifiers, we estimate (using the expected divergence and source size of the amplifier) that the 7 gainlengths of the brightest W laser gave an energy of order 20 μJ at 43.18 Å. The gain duration of order 250 psec is long enough to allow the use of normal incidence multilayer x-ray mirrors to double pass the gain medium.[17] Using a 5% reflectivity mirror a net amplification equivalent to 11 gainlengths should be possible by double passing a 3-cm foil. This amplifier would have an energy output of order 1 mJ. Optimization of the gain in the target through varying its thickness could increase this output further. The saturation flux of a Ni-like Ta x-ray laser (XRL) is estimated to be of order 10^{11} W cm^{-2} which would occur at 12 to 16 gainlengths (depending on the amplifier's divergence) and an energy of 4 mJ. If the divergence is restricted due to the geometry of the target or through use of apertures in combination with the mirror, the amplifier will saturate at a similar energy but higher gainlength product. Estimates of the x-ray laser intensity needed for holography vary. For single-frame holography of a cell with resolution of 300 Å an energy of 300 μJ has been estimated in Ref. 5 while more sophisticated experiments have been proposed using as little as 10 μJ.[18] This energy should be in one transverse mode of the laser. The number of modes emitted by the 44.83-Å x-ray laser will be studied experimentally now that we have passed the initial hurdle of generating gain and significant energy. A worst-case estimate for a 3-cm Ta amplifier is of order 10^4 modes, but this may be overly pessimistic as it ignores any coherence in the beam beyond that expected from its geometric divergence and source size. Now that we have produced gains of order 2.5 cm^{-1} at 43.18 and 44.83 Å, the optimization of that gain may allow the saturation of a Ta laser with gainlength greater than 12, using two beams of Nova, and provide enough energy per mode to perform holography experiments. Possibilities exist to increase the efficiency of the Ta XRL such that pump sources smaller than Nova may be usable. The use of 1ω light would save energy currently lost in the conversion process to 2ω. It may also be possible[20] to use a low-energy, long-pulse ($\sim$1 nsec) laser, to produce a uniform plasma amplifier, then a short pulse ($\sim$20 psec) to heat and ionize it to Ni-like, hence saving the energy that is conducted or radiated away from the hot plasma while it is expanding.

In conclusion, we have demonstrated a working x-ray laser operating at an optimum wavelength for producing holographic images of living cellular material. In addition, we observed seven gainlengths at 43.185 Å in Ni-like tungsten in the first demonstration of an x-ray amplifier operating within the "water window." It remains to enhance output power and characterize and improve coherence in order to have an x-ray laser source, at 44.83 Å, suitable for holography.

We acknowledge the support of the Nova Experiments Group in the performance of these experiments and would like to thank J. Cox, D. Leibeskind, and R. Wing for their contributions and Luxel Inc., of Seattle, Washington, who fabricated the target foils. We would like to acknowledge helpful discussions with R. London and M. Rosen. This work was performed under the auspices of the U.S. Department of Energy by the Lawrence Livermore National Laboratory under Contract No. W-7405-ENG-48.

---

[1]D. L. Matthews *et al.*, Phys. Rev. Lett. **54**, 110 (1985).

[2]M. D. Rosen *et al.*, Phys. Rev. Lett. **54**, 106 (1985).

[3]R. C. Elton, *X-Ray Lasers* (Academic, New York, 1990), and references therein.

[4]J. C. Solem and G. C. Baldwin, Science **218**, 229 (1982); J. C. Solem and G. F. Chapline, Opt. Eng. **23**, 193 (1984).

[5]R. A. London, M. D. Rosen, and J. E. Trebes, Appl. Opt. **28**, 3397 (1989).

[6]J. E. Trebes *et al.*, Science **238**, 517 (1987).

[7]S. Maxon *et al.*, J. Appl. Phys. **57**, 971 (1985); **59**, 239 (1986).

[8]B. J. MacGowan *et al.*, Phys. Rev. Lett. **59**, 2157 (1987).

[9]S. Maxon *et al.*, Phys. Rev. A **37**, 2227 (1988).

[10]B. J. MacGowan *et al.*, J. Opt. Soc. Am. B **5**, 1858 (1988).

[11]S. Maxon *et al.*, Phys. Rev. Lett. **63**, 236 (1989).

[12]P. L. Hagelstein and S. Dalhed, Phys. Rev. A **37**, 1357 (1988).

[13]J. Reader and G. Luther, Phys. Scr. **24**, 732 (1981).

[14]D. R. Kania *et al.*, J. Opt. Soc. Am. B (to be published).

[15]I. P. Grant *et al.*, Comput. Phys. Commun. **21**, 207 (1980).

[16]G. J. Linford, E. R. Peressini, W. R. Sooy, and M. L. Spaeth, Appl. Opt. **13**, 379 (1974).

[17]N. M. Ceglio, D. P. Gaines, D. G. Stearns, and A. M. Hawryluk, Opt. Commun. **69**, 285 (1989).

[18]J. E. Trebes and J. W. Gray (private communication).

[19]J. F. Seely, C. M. Brown, and W. E. Behring, J. Opt. Soc. Am. B **6**, 3 (1989).

[20]M. D. Rosen and D. L. Matthews, Bull. Am. Phys. Soc. **33**, 2042 (1988); L. B. Da Silva *et al.*, in *Femtosecond to Nanosecond High Intensity Lasers and Applications, 1990*, edited by E. M. Campbell, SPIE Proceedings No. 1229 (SPIE, Bellingham, WA, 1990), p. 128.

Section Six

Gamma Ray Lasers

To extend the laser idea beyond the x-ray region requires a summation of the problems that can be foreseen. Two courageous leaders in this field have been George Baldwin and the late Rem Khokhlov. The inclusion of their mid-1970s paper is to summarize problems that still exist, as well as to express the hope that the current group of gamma ray laser workers will soon make significant progress in that field.

Prospects for a gamma-ray laser

Lasers generating wavelengths shorter than one angstrom unit would have many important applications. Ever since the discovery of the Mössbauer effect it has been realized that we would be able to stimulate nuclear transitions suitable for lasers in this range if we could prepare the population inversion on which lasers depend, and it has also long been known that some nuclear isomers are producible in a state of population inversion. Why then do we not yet have any operating gamma-ray lasers?

We propose here to consider this question and to show that, although these two phenomena have not yet been achieved with the same transition, this may yet prove to be possible. Such a development would be an extremely difficult and challenging task, but we believe that it is possible and that it is worthwhile.

G. C. Baldwin is a professor of nuclear engineering and science at Rensselaer Polytechnic Institute, Troy, N.Y.; R. V. Khokhlov is a professor of physics at Moscow State University as well as being Rector of the University.

The trend toward short wavelengths has been an outstanding feature of the development of quantum electronic devices. Initially, only microwave radiation could be stimulated; today, lasers operate over a frequency range extending into the vacuum ultraviolet. (See figure 1.) Soft x-ray lasers, which a decade ago were generally conceded to be impossible, are now under active development. The appeal of new important applications continues to attract efforts to surmount the ever-greater challenge of higher frequencies, which is inherent in the λ^3-dependence of the ratio of Einstein's A and B coefficients.[1]

Although no absolute limit is predicted by Einstein's ratio, it has occasionally been suggested that a practical upper limit may exist to the frequency that can be generated by stimulated emission. For example, an authoritative text on electrodynamics,[2] published in the middle 1950's, remarks in a footnote that ". . . . stimulated emission is unimportant at all temperatures less than [*the photon energy*] . . . . It may become important for radio waves." Several years later, in a paper that showed optical lasers to be possible,[3] this comment was made: ". . . . unless some radically new approach is found, they cannot be pushed to wavelengths much shorter than those in the ultraviolet region." However, a recent consideration of this question suggests that, if any fundamental limit indeed exists to laser action, it lies in the vicinity of the threshold for pair production.[4]

An obvious practical difficulty in ex-

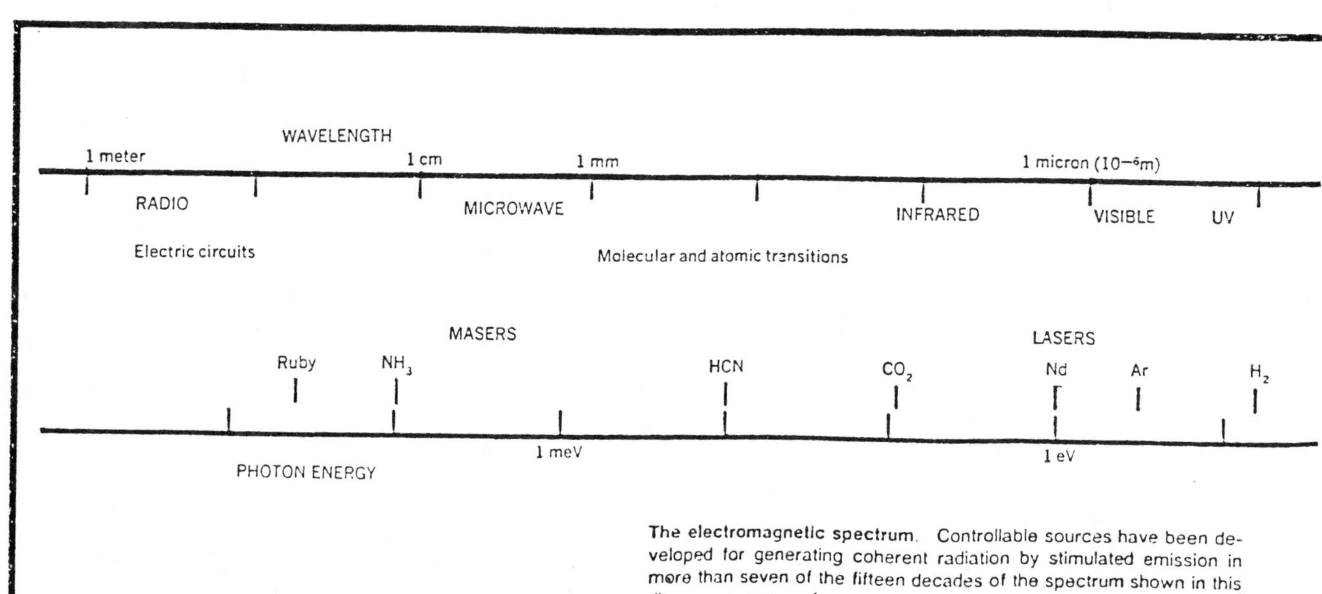

The electromagnetic spectrum. Controllable sources have been developed for generating coherent radiation by stimulated emission in more than seven of the fifteen decades of the spectrum shown in this diagram; success of current efforts to develop soft x-ray lasers would

Development of a "graser" may be possible if ways can be found to achieve Mössbauer transitions and population inversion simultaneously in nuclear isomers.

G. C. Baldwin and R. V. Khokhlov

tending the laser principle to higher frequencies is that of providing high stored-energy density. Nuclear reactions offer a new approach to this problem; in fact, nuclear transitions offer the only hope for laser action at wavelengths shorter than 1 Å.

The possibility of a nuclear laser, often termed a "graser" (for "gamma-ray laser") or a "gaser," was recognized early in the 1960's,[5-9] and proposals were made to stimulate Mössbauer transitions in nuclides prepared by neutron bombardment, chemical isolation and crystallization. Obviously, long transition lifetimes would be required if these operations were to be completed before loss of population inversion by decay. It was soon realized that long-lived isomers involve greater difficulty because of the narrow natural linewidth.[5,3] After this difficulty became apparent and attempts to circumvent it seemed unfruitful,[11] interest waned and the idea remained dormant until about two years ago,[12] when it became evident that the linewidth-versus-lifetime dilemma is not really fundamental, and can probably be overcome.

Some critics suggest that we await success in development of x-ray lasers, which is conceded to be extremely difficult, before attempting to develop gamma-ray lasers. However, the difficulties attending graser development are quite distinct from those of x-ray lasers; these difficulties, formidable as they may seem, may be overcome through research in certain specific topics that we shall identify during the course of this article.

Probable characteristics of grasers

Although the ultimate form and operating characteristics of grasers cannot be described at this stage, it is possible to make some general assertions that will probably turn out to be correct. In particular, grasers will operate without mirrors, they will probably be single-pulse devices, they will be pumped by capture[7,9,14] of neutrons, they will use Mössbauer transitions, and their photon energy will be in the 5 to 200-keV range.

Nuclear isomers. Because of extremely short lifetimes of the electric dipole transitions that emit characteristic x radiation, it appears unlikely that atomic states can be excited in sufficient density for lasing in this region of the spectrum; prohibitively high pump power density would be needed to establish population inversion. Nuclear transitions are available, however, with far longer lifetimes, and exoergic nuclear reactions can be employed to pump these transitions.

Figure 2 shows selected parts of the

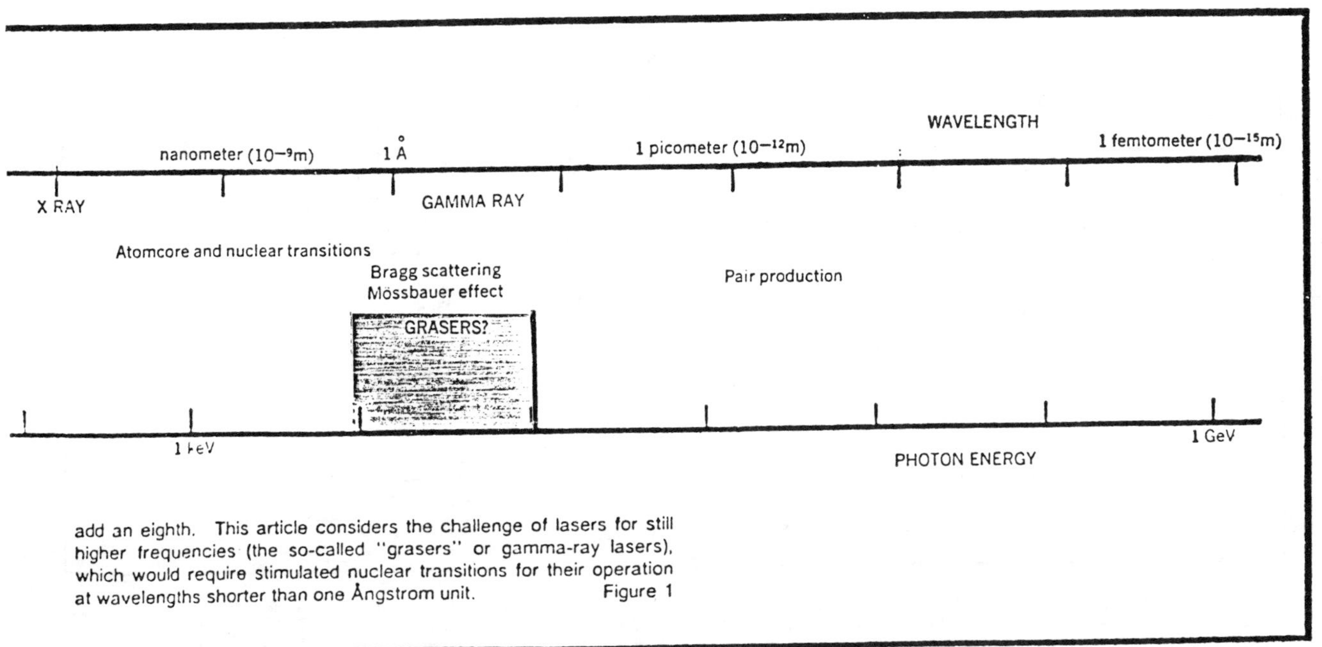

add an eighth. This article considers the challenge of lasers for still higher frequencies (the so-called "grasers" or gamma-ray lasers), which would require stimulated nuclear transitions for their operation at wavelengths shorter than one Ångstrom unit. Figure 1 energy level scheme[13] for two typical examples of isomeric transitions, Ta^{181} and In^{114} (we do not mean to imply that these particular isomers are suitable for graser application).

In general, the formation of states of high angular momentum (which will be relatively long-lived) is not only possible, but probable, in the radiative decay of a highly excited compound nucleus, following its formation in a nuclear reaction. Isomer production ratios, unfortunately, are rarely known—although several cases are known (for example, In^{114}) in which formation of the upper isomer is more probable than of the lower, so leading to population inversion. There are several isomeric nuclei (In^{114}, Zn^{69}) in which the lower of two excited states has the shorter lifetime—another condition leading to population inversion. We shall show below that it is also possible to isolate nuclei in either of two isomeric states by physical methods.

Radiative transitions are possible between any pair of isomeric nuclear levels (except in the case of $I = 0 \rightarrow I = 0$) but, in many cases, internal conversion is more probable than gamma emission. Occasionally, beta decay from isomeric levels competes with gamma emission and internal conversion. Those properties of isomeric states most significant to the graser problem are lifetime τ, spin I, production cross sections, transition energy E, branching ratio β, and internal conversion coefficient α.

Beam formation. In the absence of a resonator, the geometry and transparency of the active medium together determine the ability of an amplifying medium to form a directed beam of stimulated radiation (figure 3). An elongated solid, such as the whisker crystals that have been proposed,[8] is required for this purpose.

If I_0 denotes the average in all directions of the gamma radiation from the graser body, the intensity I on its axis of greatest extension will be increased by the gain factor

$$G = I/I_0 = [(\kappa - \mu)L]^{-1} \exp[(\kappa - \mu)L - 1] \quad (1)$$

in which

κ = coefficient of stimulation, cm^{-1}

μ = coefficient of nonresonant removal, cm^{-1}

L = total length

Ordinarily, κ is essentially zero, and the only observable effect is self-absorption of spontaneously emitted radiation. At any instant, few modes of the radiation field contain photons, and those that do are singly populated.

If κ exceeds μ sufficiently, there will be modes that contain many photons, populated to extents determined by the locations of the various initiating spontaneous emission events and the interplay of stimulation and absorption, governed by the coefficients κ and μ. Selection of the sense of beam propagation is possible by traveling wave methods[15] in which adjacent elements of the medium are made multiplying at successive instants of time.

Coefficient of removal. We first inquire concerning the coefficient of nonresonant removal, μ. (Resonant absorption is encompassed in our definition of κ.) Elements of medium atomic number interact with gamma radiation of energy less than 200 keV principally by photoelectric absorption; in light elements the principal interaction is Compton scattering. The cross sections for these interactions are several orders of magnitude lower than nuclear resonance cross sections observed in Mössbauer experiments.[10,16]

Nonresonant removal does eventually exceed the maximum possible resonance cross section as the photon energy is increased;[4] but not in the energy range we are considering, where several orders of magnitude separate these cross sections.

It has been suggested that nonresonant photon losses may be reduced further in one of two ways: either by embedding the isomeric nuclei at low concentration in a crystal host of low atomic number (for example, Be)[14], or by the Borrmann effect.[8,17] In the latter, Bragg scattering gives rise to a spatially periodic modulation of the amplitude of an electromagnetic wave, such that wave modes exist with electric field nodes at the lattice planes; such modes have greatly diminished photoelectric absorption.[18] It might be objected that the interaction with nuclei would also be reduced, since they are located at the lattice nodes; however, it has been shown[19] that stimulated emission is not reduced for nuclear isomeric transitions, which are of multipole order higher than electric dipole. Thus, when the direction of greatest extension of the solid coincides with a Bragg direction, the ratio μ/κ can be reduced by

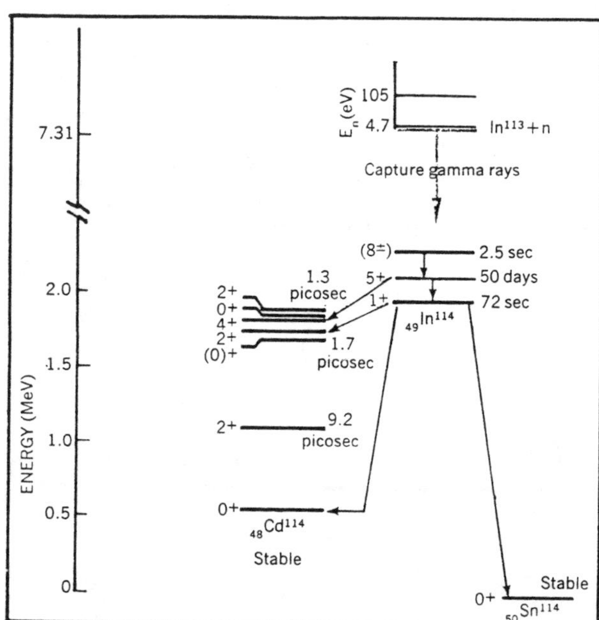

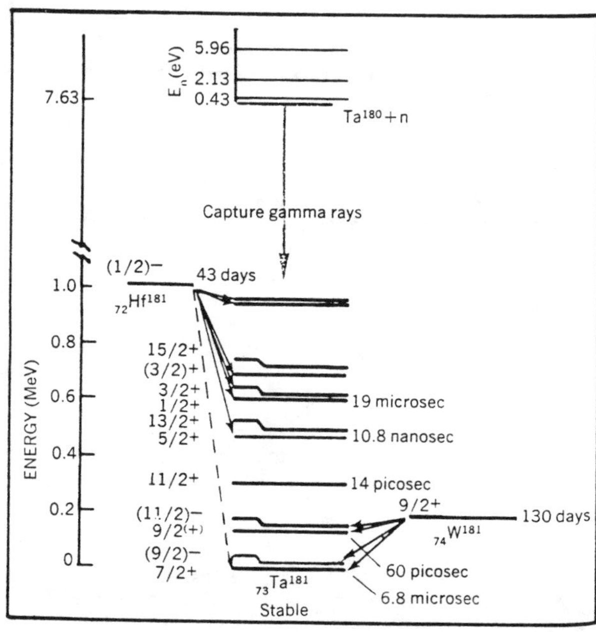

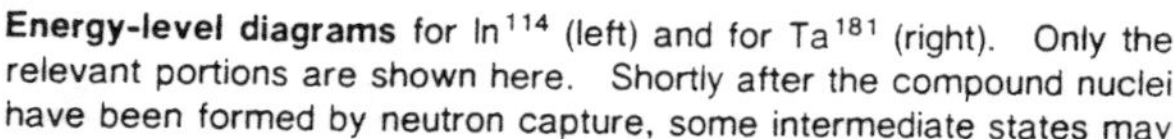

Energy-level diagrams for In^{114} (left) and for Ta^{181} (right). Only the relevant portions are shown here. Shortly after the compound nuclei have been formed by neutron capture, some intermediate states may be temporarily population-inverted. The two lowest states of In^{114} are an extreme example of this phenomenon. The 6.8-microsecond state of Ta^{181} is a Mössbauer isomer. Figure 2 at least two orders of magnitude.[19] The Borrmann effect, by singling out certain modes, offers the prospect of eventually making a resonator for gamma radiation.

Coefficient of stimulation. The coefficient of stimulated emission for recoilless gamma emission is

$$\kappa = N^* \sigma \tag{2}$$

where

$$N^* = N_2 - (g_1/g_2)N_1 \tag{3}$$

is the net inversion density between an upper state 2 and a lower state 1, with statistical weights respectively g_2 and g_1, and

$$\sigma = \frac{\lambda^2}{2\pi} \frac{f}{\Gamma\tau} \frac{\beta}{1+\alpha} \tag{4}$$

is the maximum value of the resonance cross section for a Mössbauer transition. Here

λ = wavelength of the radiation;
Γ = total linewidth;
τ = the effective lifetime of the transition, which if the two levels are both unstable, is the reciprocal of the sum of their respective reciprocal lifetimes;
β = branching ratio for the isomeric transition;
α = internal conversion coefficient; and
f = the "recoilless" Mössbauer fraction (Debye-Waller factor).

(Note that we employ the convention used in laser theory of applying the statistical weight factor to the population rather than to the cross section, instead of the convention common in Mössbauer work.)

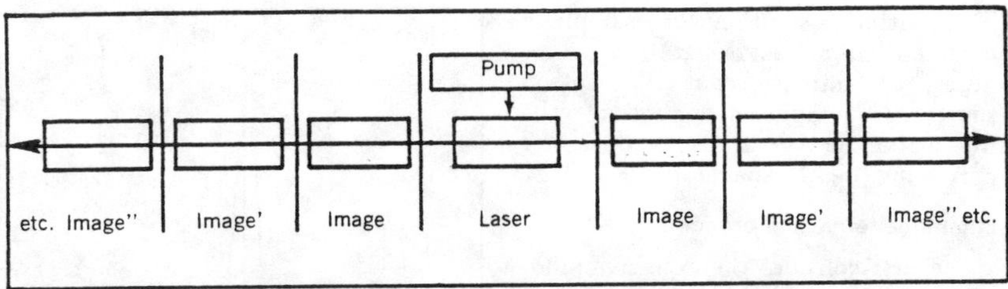

Mirror "resonators" extend the active medium in the majority of conventional lasers by an array of images, so that spontaneous emission into the axial direction receives greatest amplification. In the absence of mirrors, we extend the active medium itself—the so-called "amplified spontaneous emission lasers." Whisker crystals have been proposed for this purpose. Figure 3

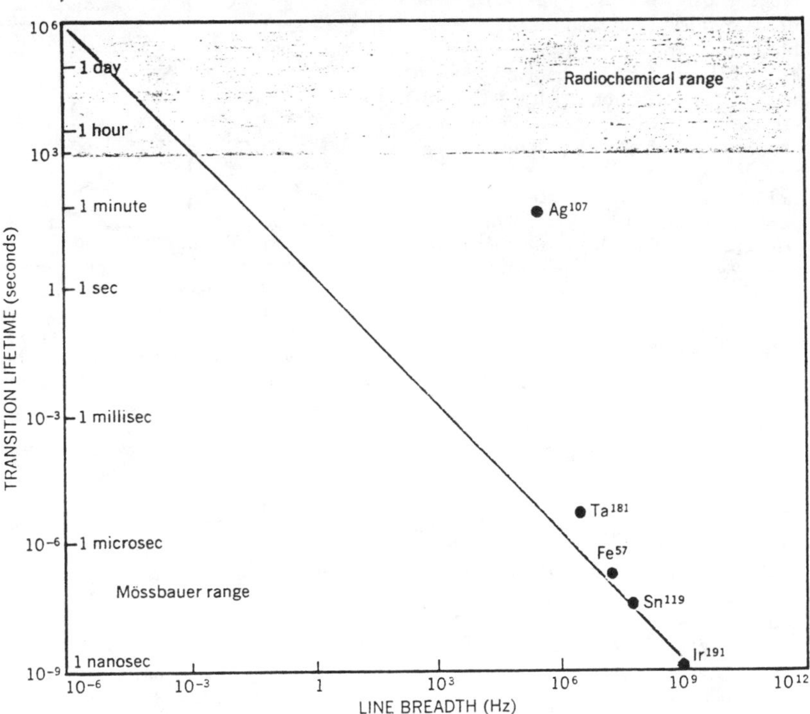

Lifetime versus bandwidth. The relationship of mean lifetime of a radiative transition to the frequency bandwidth of the radiation shown by the slanting colored line is for an unbroadened transition. The points show measured values, and indicate inhomogeneous broadening of long-lived isomeric transitions. The figure also indicates the range of isomer lifetimes in which line broadening does not interfere with observing Mössbauer effects, and also the range in which population inversion can be achieved by radiochemical procedures. Figure 4

Linewidth and transition lifetime

Figure 4 shows linewidth Γ as a function of transition lifetime τ. The solid, slanting line represents the natural width, τ^{-1}, of an unbroadened line. Homogeneous broadening through the factor $(1 + \alpha)\beta^{-1}$ causes the natural width of actual transitions to be somewhat greater than shown by this line; its effect appears in the cross section formula, equation 4.

The points in figure 4, experimental values from nuclear resonance absorption measurements on the indicated isotopes,[10] show that additional broadening is often present. For lifetimes longer than 10^{-5} seconds, the linewidth Γ appears to become independent of τ, so that $(\Gamma\tau)^{-1}$ decreases, reducing the resonance cross section at longer lifetimes (figure 5). For this reason, Mössbauer experiments are not performed with transitions of lifetime greater than 10 microseconds. For lifetimes shorter than 10^{-6} sec, the product $\Gamma\tau$ in equation 4 is essentially unity. Transitions in this lifetime range, showing a strong Mössbauer effect, would satisfy the condition for stimulated emission gain if inverted populations of the states could be generated. Under the usual conditions of Mössbauer experiments, however, only a very small number of excited nuclei are ever present simultaneously either in the source or in the absorber. It is the factor N^*, rather than σ, that requires attention if transitions in this lifetime range are to be used in grasers. This is indicated in the margin of the figure as the "Mössbauer range."

Figure 4 also indicates, along the margin, a range of lifetimes for which it is feasible to generate a condition of population inversion by neutron bombardment from conventional reactor sources, followed by conventional techniques of radiochemistry to isolate the transmuted material ("Szilard-Chalmers separation").[7]

A gap, nearly nine orders of magnitude, separates the "Mössbauer range" and the "radiochemical range" of nuclear transition lifetimes. To make a graser we must close this gap.

Proposed approaches

There are, consequently, two principal approaches to development of gamma ray lasers:

- Use long-lived isomers, and reduce or eliminate mechanisms that contribute to the total line breadth;[6,12]
- Use transitions in the Mössbauer range that can be inverted directly without chemical procedures by means of extremely intense pumping sources.[14,20]

Because neither approach may bridge the entire gap in figure 4, a combination of these approaches could be the most likely ultimate solution; for example, a combination of fast separation procedures.[20,21] intense pulsed neutron sources,[22,23] rapid assembly of the Mössbauer body.[21] and procedures for narrowing the Mössbauer line.[12,24–26]

Inhomogeneous line broadening

We first consider the excessive inhomogeneous linewidth of long-lived transitions.[5] Until about two years ago it was not evident that this problem could be resolved. Today it appears, not merely that the mechanisms that inhomogeneously perturb the Mössbauer line are known, but also that it is possible in principle to reduce the effect of each of them. The mechanisms include temperature broadening, hyperfine interactions between nuclei and locally generated fields, and gravitational broadening.

There are two contributions to temperature broadening, one of which, the second-order Doppler effect,[27] arises from gradients of temperature (more strictly, from gradients in the ratio of local temperature to Debye temperature). The second type of temperature broadening[28] is associated with local fluctuations in the value of the mean square lattice vibrational energy. Calculations[24] show that these two effects are reducible to insignificance at temperatures below 1 K.

Difficulty may be experienced with localized heating from radioactive decay of the isomer. A filamentary form for the graser body, such as the whisker crystals we mentioned earlier, assists in maintaining a low uniform temperature.

Temperature broadening, therefore, is not an insurmountable problem.

Three types of hyperfine interaction also contribute to the inhomogeneous line breadth.[24] All are manifestations of the finite volume of the nucleus; they are associated, respectively, with its magnetic dipole moment, electric quadrupole moment, and radius. They contribute inhomogeneous line breadths in the range 10^4–10^6 sec^{-1}, and so are responsible for the trend evident in figure 2. Two of the hyperfine interactions are associated with nuclear spin.

The magnetic moments of isomeric states differ, and each may differ from that of other nuclei in the solid; therefore, even when the spins are aligned by a strong magnetic field at low temperature, inhomogeneous broadening occurs because of the random nature of that part of the local magnetic field which is created by nearby nuclei.

Recent nuclear magnetic resonance experiments show that the nuclear dipole–dipole interaction can be averaged to zero[29] by application of a cycle of radiofrequency $\pi/2$ pulses that reorient the nuclear moments. Reductions of linewidth of nearly four orders of magnitude have been achieved in nuclear magnetic resonance experiments with this technique.[30]

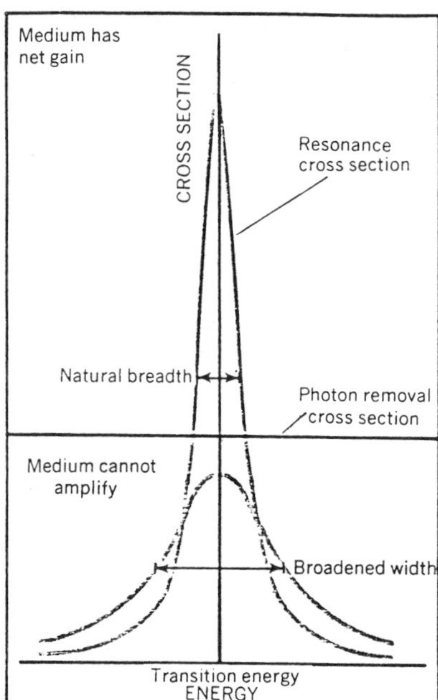

Broadening of the gamma-ray line reduces the maximum value of the effective resonance cross section; if it is thereby brought below the value needed to overcome losses, there can be no net gain. Figure 5

The same principle should be applicable to narrowing the gamma-ray line,[12,24] and therefore to extending the lifetime range accessible to the Mössbauer effect. We must note two significant facts, however:

First, two levels are involved in gamma-ray transitions, with unequal spins. Thus, to narrow the line, two different cycles of perturbing magnetic field pulses of unequal frequencies must be employed simultaneously.[24]

Second, the technique is limited to transitions of lifetime much greater than the period of the rf-pulse sequence, which, in turn, must be much greater than the Larmor precession period of either spin state. Thus, although rf perturbation will not be useful in conventional Mössbauer measurements with lifetimes near 10^{-5} sec, it should yield a significant effect in experiments of the Bizina[31] type, which used a long-lived transition in Ag^{107}.

The dipole–dipole interaction of nuclear spins that have been aligned by a strong magnetic field is governed by a Hamiltonian function of the form[29]

$$[\mathbf{I} \cdot \mathbf{I}' - 3I_zI_z'](r - r')^{-3}$$

summed over all interacting pairs of spins (lower-lower, lower-upper, and upper-upper) in the crystal. The interaction of nuclear quadrupole moments with electric field gradients in the crystal can be represented by a Hamiltonian in which the spin operators appear in similar form;[32] the Hamiltonian is

$$(\mathbf{I} \cdot \mathbf{I} - 3I_zI_z)$$

It follows that the same cycle of 90-deg rotations of nuclear spin that reduces the dipole–dipole interaction should also reduce the quadrupole breadth.[24] It may be noted further that the strong polarizing field can be internal in origin.

A third type of hyperfine interaction, inhomogeneous monopole shift[33] (also commonly called the "chemical shift" or the "isomer shift"), arises because the electron density at the nuclear site is not zero, and, furthermore, is modified by nearby chemical inhomogeneities or defects in the crystal lattice; in an isomeric transition, the nuclear volume changes, and with it, the interaction of nuclear charge with electrons lying within the nuclear volume.[33]

Estimates of the permissible concentration of lattice defects suggest that, with continued improvements in the art of growing perfect crystals, the monopole broadening contributed by lattice defects can be reduced to a tolerable amount.[24]

However, it may be possible to develop a technique with external radiofrequency fields that can compensate inhomogeneous chemical broadening as well. Owing to the so-called "Fermi contact interaction," there can be a net spin density at the nucleus. As long as minor changes of spin density and of the total s-electron density are proportional to each other, both can be affected by chemical inhomogeneities in a similar way. The hyperfine splitting produced by an internal magnetic field associated with electron spin density can be adjusted by varying an external radiofrequency field,[25] and this offers the possibility of compensating monopole shift by hyperfine splitting, for some single component of the hyperfine structure. That one component, then, would not be broadened by inhomogeneous chemical shifts. Although the cross section for stimulation of one component is lower than the theoretical maximum for an unsplit, unbroadened gamma-ray line, the increase in cross section from narrowing of a selected hyperfine component is a much greater effect.

The third contributor to inhomogeneous line broadening is the effect of gravity. Research on the Mössbauer effect has been closely associated with the gravitational red shift for many years,[10] and we know that the shift in transition frequency apparent to two nuclei with transition energy E, differing in gravitational potential by $\Delta\Phi$ is[5]

$$\Delta\omega = [\Delta\Phi/Mc^2][E/\hbar] \qquad (5)$$

For horizontal propagation in standard gravity this effect would limit the maximum vertical dimension of a graser body that could contribute to a growing wave, so that, for long-lived isomers, a diffraction limitation must be considered.

If we require that gravitational broadening not exceed the remaining part of the total linewidth, Γ′, the vertical dimension of a graser body with its axis horizontal in a gravitational field of acceleration g cannot exceed

$$\delta z < \hbar c^2 \Gamma' / gE = \lambda c \Gamma' / g$$

where E is the transition energy and λ the corresponding wavelength. To reduce losses by diffraction, the transverse (vertical) dimension should be made many times the wavelength; in other words, $\delta z/\lambda$ must be a large number, but less than $\Gamma' c/g$. Even in standard gravity, it is apparent that gravitational broadening is not the principal problem, since Γ′ is of the order of 10^5 $\sec^{-1}$ for the hyperfine interactions.

Moreover, elimination of gravity is a commonplace art today. The compensation of gravitational shift by temperature gradient[7] or even by deliberate chemical shift is also possible.

Thus, we see that all the interactions that inhomogeneously broaden the gamma-ray line are understood, and it appears likely that each can be eventually controlled, reduced, compensated or perhaps even eliminated.

It is difficult to estimate, without experimental evidence, the extent to which the linewidth can be reduced, and therefore, to decide whether this approach alone will suffice to close the lifetime gap and so make graser action feasible. We shall therefore next consider what advances are possible if we use the alternative approach, via short-lived transitions.

Transitions in the Mossbauer range

Many isomeric transitions of lifetime shorter than about 10^{-5} sec have resonance cross sections sufficient to be observable above a background of nonresonant absorption.[10] Producing population inversion, without destroying the conditions essential to the Mössbauer effect, is the problem with these transitions.

Although conventional Mössbauer transitions necessarily involve the ground state, for a graser there need be no such restriction, and, in fact, recoilless transitions between excited states would be preferable. Since Mössbauer cross sections of megabarns exist, the actual concentration of excited nuclei needed for observable gain can be as low as 10^{18} cm^{-3}. The total number also can be small, say 10^{13} or 10^{14}; however, the excitation process must be able to generate excited states in concentrations of this order of magnitude *within the mean lifetime of the transition;* reaction rates per unit volume of the order of 10^{23} cm^{-3} $\sec^{-1}$, or higher, would be required of a *direct* excitation process to satisfy this criterion.

Assuming parent isotopes in normal concentration and a 10-barn effective cross section for inversion, we would need a neutron flux of the order of 10^{24} cm^{-2} $\sec^{-1}$ to excite the nuclear inversion. This number usually suffices to discourage consideration of the short-lived graser possibility. Considerably higher neutron fluxes are indeed produced in nuclear explosions, but we prefer a less drastic method!

Nevertheless, it has been shown[14] that long filaments of beryllium containing approximately 100 parts per million of a parent isotope might be pumped by an explosive burst of neutrons to a lasing condition before their temperature would rise sufficiently (above 300 K) to destroy the Mössbauer effect.

Furthermore, current research on thermonuclear fusion demonstrates that intense laser irradiation of matter can compress it to extremely high densities[34] and, at the high temperatures and high electric fields in the resultant plasma, neutrons are generated. We also know that compression of fissile material in this way can lead to many orders of magnitude reduction in its critical mass,[22,23] so that nuclear fission explosions can be "miniaturized."

One suggestion for a neutron-pumped graser that uses transitions in the Mössbauer range[35] is to combine the neutron source—an annular region of fissile material, compressed by a cylindrical array of convergent laser beams—coaxial with a long filament of graser material—beryllium with a small admixture of a parent isotopic material.[14] Traveling-wave excitation[15] is achieved by so timing the arrival of laser light at the fissile layer (figure 6), that the region of criticality advances at velocity c. Material damage from neutron recoil in the graser filament, essential to moderating the neutron energies, may be a serious problem in this scheme.

We would not need to go to this extreme if it were possible to furnish excitation at one site and transfer it rapidly to another site at increased concentration, as in the long-lived isomer approach. In fact, one proposal[36] suggests that we transfer excitation from bombarded material to a smaller volume at the lasing site, by means of resonant absorption at the second site. As this must be followed by a transition to an unoccupied upper sublevel of the ground state, the temperature at the second site must be extremely low.

Approaches involving material transfer

It may be unlikely that excitation, separation and reassembly of isomeric material can be carried out rapidly enough to allow use of transitions in the Mössbauer range. However, the restriction to lifetimes of hours or more, inherent in the early graser proposals[5-9] (which were based on radiochemical procedures) need not apply today.

If we grant the possibility of appreciable reduction of the inhomogeneous linewidth, perhaps by procedures suggested in earlier sections, but find that we still cannot bridge the gap of figure 4, there remains the possibility of combining line-narrowing methods with faster methods of chemical separation and, preferably, with more intense neutron sources.

Conceivably, recoil of nuclei trans-

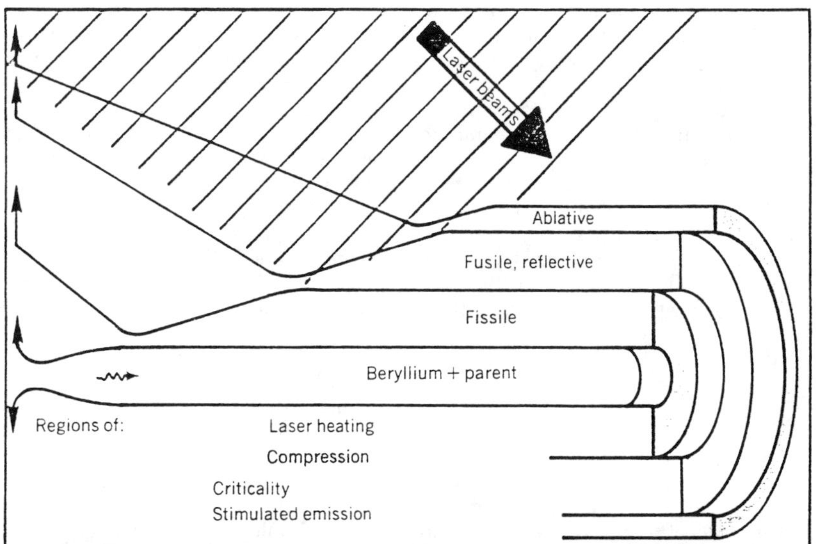

A conceptual graser employing transitions in the short (Mössbauer) lifetime range, pumped by a traveling wave of laser-driven fission. The reflecting material and the central beryllium core moderate neutrons generated in compressed fissile material; last to be compressed, the beryllium acts as a "flux trap" for neutrons, which excite isomeric states in target material. Figure 6 muted in the neutron burst might be used to transport them to a nearby surface, but quantitative estimates of the efficiency of the transplantation process have not been encouraging. Use of finely divided parent material in a scavenging gas stream has been proposed[20] for increasing the efficiency of the recoil separation process, with deposition of the active material upon a chemically active surface.

Recent progress in the separation of isotopes by photochemical reactions involving the use of tuned lasers offers the prospect of extremely rapid and specific isolation of nuclear isomeric material. We know that, because of their unequal spins, isomeric nuclear states have different optical spectra;[37] these differences are sufficient to provide a basis for quantitative separation. One obvious method is two-step photoionization,[38,39] in which the first step is absorption of sharply tuned laser light by one component of the hyperfine structure of the upper isomeric level, not present in the spectrum of the lower isomeric state. If this step is followed by rapid photoionization, by means of intense ultraviolet light, the upper-state isomer can be extracted and deposited by ion epitaxy on a nearby host surface[21] to form the laser material (figure 7). Many cases of *isotope* separation by laser radiation[40] have been reported; the principle is also directly applicable to *isomer* separation.

This proposal, suitable for transitions in the range from a few milliseconds to several seconds, involves many processes, hitherto untested; most of the data needed to evaluate it are unavailable. However, one attempt at an analysis concludes that this approach may be feasible.[21]

The most serious questions may turn out to concern, not the feasibility of the component steps, but their compatibility—that is, the possibility of nearly simultaneous excitation and separation, involving intense neutron bombardment, tuned lasers and an electrode system for implantation, with line narrowing, requiring cryogenic apparatus, intense magnetic fields, radiofrequency pulse generators and low gravity, establishing thereby conditions in the graser body conducive to a Mössbauer effect. Admittedly, it does seem to be a very difficult undertaking, if so many elements must be involved.

Research required

Realization of stimulated emission in nuclei evidently requires prior investigations into a variety of problems. We believe that this research should be undertaken with the stated objective of working toward development of gamma-ray lasers, rather than awaiting the normal course of developments in laser science and technology.

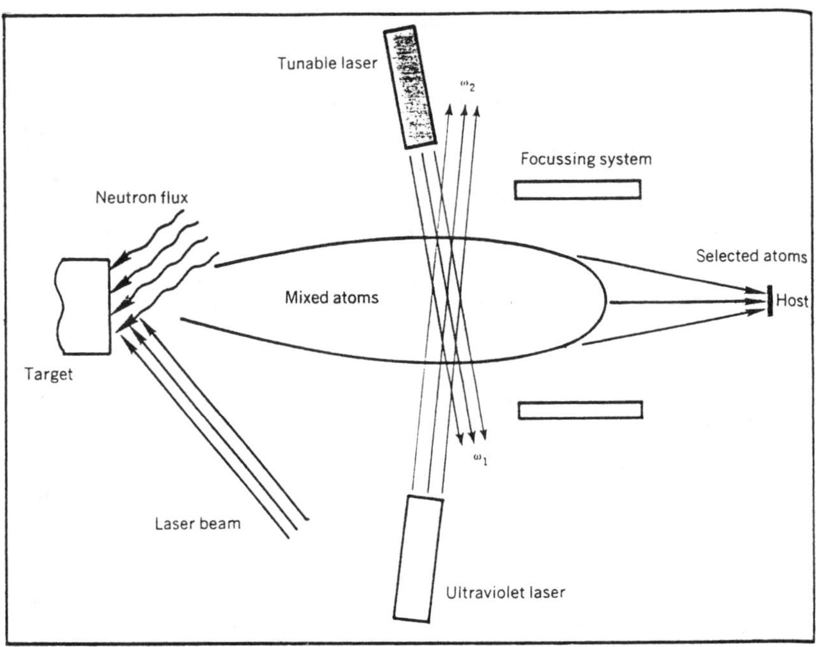

This graser system would employ transitions in an intermediate lifetime range, with laser vaporization of a neutron-bombarded target, photoexcitation and ionization of atoms containing the upper isomeric state, and electrical deposition by ion epitaxy onto a nearby host crystal to form the laser material. (Courtesy of V. S. Letokhov.) Figure 7

For example, despite decades of research on nuclear isomerism, data needed for calculating the cross section for stimulated emission are adequate in only those few exceptional isomers, mainly of long lifetime, for which measurements of internal conversion coefficients, production ratios and branching schemes could be made conveniently.

Nuclear properties alone do not suffice for selecting appropriate isomers; chemical form and crystallographic properties are equally important. Ability to isolate and concentrate the isomer and to assemble it within a crystalline host can be developed only through experimentation with the graser objective in mind.

Although the theoretical basis of the possibility of narrowing the gamma-ray line needs further development, even now it should be possible to attempt to demonstrate line narrowing in experiments of the Bizina[31] type. Such experiments will be significant in connection with the hypothesis of a universal quantum of length.[41]

Those properties that are significant to the Mössbauer effect need to be studied in material prepared by implantation and in matter which has been subjected to intense neutron bombardment immediately prior to the measurements.

The development of intense neutron sources (for example, by laser compression techniques) needs to be encouraged. Neutron exposure within the isomer transition lifetime is the significant parameter that characterizes the neutron source. Most of the development of pulsed neutron sources has concentrated on achieving pulse widths much shorter than the graser pump requires. Higher neutron intensity would greatly diminish demands on chemical separation yields.

We shall need to develop new methods for demonstrating stimulated emission at gamma wavelengths, probably based upon the statistical time structure of the gamma-ray counting rate in a photoelectric detector.[7]

Each of these ordinarily unrelated fields of investigation is closely interrelated to the others through the common requirement of graser development.

Nevertheless, each area of research promises dividends to science and technology; We might develop intense neutron sources, find new procedures for radioisotope production, or stimulate new applications of the Mössbauer effect.

Why develop a graser?

Early in this article, we asserted that development of a graser would be an extremely difficult and challenging task. The following sections amply confirmed that statement!

Is it worth the effort, and if so, is this the time to begin?

We believe it is worthwhile, because of the great potential for important application of radiation with enhanced coherence in this spectral region. In every region of the spectrum in which coherent sources exist, they have greatly multiplied the usefulness of radiation. Gamma rays have many important applications, because of their short wavelength, high penetrating power and ability to ionize. Controllable and directable sources of such radiation in which phase as well as intensity have significance, would greatly multiply its uses.

However, detailed speculation upon specific applications is clearly impossible at this stage, because the form, performance, output characteristics, cost—even the existence—of a graser are obviously impossible to describe at this stage of our knowledge, beyond the few characteristics enumerated above.

Moreover, it is well known that the most significant applications of new devices are rarely foreseen. No one, for example, in 1958 could have predicted the use of lasers in computers, surgery, nuclear fusion, isotope separation, and so on.

The most exciting possibility for coherent radiation in this short wavelength range is that of holography, which might permit direct observation of the structure of molecules, crystals, proteins, genes. Before this could be done, of course, one would need to solve the equally challenging problem of recording the hologram on a sufficiently fine scale.

Even coarse-grained gamma-ray holograms would be useful in radiographic inspection of thick material, however.

Precision frequency measurement, based on interferometric techniques made possible by coherent sources, now extends from very low frequency into the visible range; its extension into the nuclear region would greatly increase the precision with which fundamental nuclear constants are known.

Nonlinear optics has developed into a major field of current research, which has begun to make important contributions to technology, communication and metrology. Nonlinear optics exploits the high intensity of some laser sources and the exceptionally high coherence of others, so that very weak effects of nonlinearities become observable, either by higher-order intensity dependence or by coherently combined weak contributions from a medium of large extent. One can expect, by analogy, a new field of nonlinear nuclear physics to emerge if nonlinear (for example, multi-photon, stimulated Raman) processes are made possible by intense graser sources.

All of these, and the unforeseen applications that will ultimately prove the most rewarding, await resolution of the basic questions we have tried to identify here.

Admittedly, we have not given a recipe for constructing a graser, nor have we even proved that it is possible. We have demonstrated, however, that dogmatic assertions as to its impossibility are unwarranted.

* * *

The authors wish to express their appreciation to V. I. Goldanskii, Yu. Il'inskii, Yu. M. Kagan and V. S. Letokhov, who have read the manuscript and made helpful suggestions. One of us (Baldwin) wishes to acknowledge useful discussions with P. Casabella, H. M. Clark, D. Eccleshall, M. Maley, K. J. Miller, I. Preiss, R. Reeves, W. K. Rhim, R. Schnibman, R. Strong and J. Temperley.

This article is an adaptation of papers presented at the Spring Meeting of the Optical Society of America, in Washington D.C., April 1974 (Baldwin), and at the Eighth International Conference on Quantum Electronics, in San Francisco, June 1974 (Khokhlov).

References

1. A. Einstein, Phys. Zeitschr. **18,** 121, (1917); B. Lengyel, *Lasers,* Wiley, New York, (1962); section 3, pages 3–10; A. Yariv, *Quantum Electronics,* Wiley, New York (1967), pages 208–210.
2. L. Landau, E. Lifschitz, *Electrodynamics of Continuous Media,* English trans. by J. B. Sykes and J. S. Bell, Addison-Wesley, Reading, Mass., (1960); page 377.
3. A. L. Schawlow, C. H. Townes, Phys. Rev. **112,** 1949 (1958).
4. G. C. Baldwin, in *Laser Interaction and Related Plasma Phenomena,* Vol. 3, (H. Schwarz, H. Hora, eds.) Plenum, New York (1974), pages 875–888.
5. W. Vali, V. Vali, Proc. IEEE **51,** 182 (1963).
6. B. V. Chirikov, Sov. Phys.—JETP **17,** 1355 (1963).
7. G. C. Baldwin, J. P. Neissel, J. H. Terhune, L. Tonks, Trans. Am. Nucl. Soc. **6,** 176 (1963).
8. G. C. Baldwin, J. P. Neissel, J. H. Terhune, L. Tonks, Proc. IEEE **51,** 1247 (1963).
9. Unpublished reports on this subject include: L. Rivlin, Soviet Patent Disclosure Jan. 1961, cited by Chirikov in reference 6; G. C. Baldwin, J. P. Neissel, L. Tonks, Patent Disclosure October 1961 and Internal General Electric Reports 62GL22, 62GL178, February and December 1962; B. Podolsky, J. Mize, C. Carpenter, AVCO Internal Report 63AVCO-109, August 1963; R. Babcock, S. Ruby, L. Epstein, Westinghouse Report, December 1963. US Patents related to stimulated emission in nuclear states include: Baldwin et al, 3 234 099; Vali et al, 3 281 600; Eerckens, 3 430 046; Piekenbrock, 3 557 370.
10. *Mössbauer Effect,* (Selected reprints), American Association of Physics Teachers (1963).
11. J. H. Terhune, G. C. Baldwin, Phys. Rev. Lett. **14,** 589 (1965).
12. R. V. Khokhlov, Sov Phys—JETP Lett. **15,** 414 (1972); Paper A4, Proc. VII IQEC, Montreal, May 1972.
13. *Nuclear Data Sheets,* edited by the Nuclear Data Group, Oak Ridge National Laboratory (W. J. Horen, Director), published by Academic Press, New York; contains frequently revised compilations of isomer properties.
14. V. I. Goldanskii, Yu. Kagan, Sov. Phys.—JETP **37,** 49 (1973).
15. J. D. Shipman, Jr, Appl. Phys. Lett. **10,** 3 (1967).
16. G. W. Grodstein, "X-Ray Attenuation Coefficients from 10 keV to 100 MeV," NBS-583, Nat. Bur. Stds., Washington, 1957.
17. G. Borrmann, Zeits. Phys. **42,** 157 (1941).
18. P. P. Ewald, Rev. Mod. Phys. **37,** 46 (1965); B. Batterman, H. Cole, Rev. Mod. Phys. **36,** 681 (1964).
19. Yu. Kagan, Sov. Phys.—JETP Lett. **20,** 11 (1974).
20. V. I. Goldanskii, Yu. Kagan, Sov. Phys.—Uspekhi **16,** Jan.–Feb., 1974; Proc. Vth Int. Conf. on Mössbauer Spectroscopy, Bratislava, Sept. 1973.
21. V. S. Letokhov, Sov. Phys.—JETP **37,** 787 (1973); III Vavilov Conference on Nonlinear Optics, Novosibirsk, June 1973.
22. G. A. Askaryan, V. A. Namiot, M. S. Rabinovich, Sov. Phys.—JETP Lett. **17,** 424 (1973).
23. F. Winterberg, Proc. 3rd RPI Workshop Conference on Laser/Plasma Interaction, August 1973 (H. Schwarz, ed.) Plenum, New York (1974).
24. Yu. Il'inskii, R. V. Khokhlov, Sov. Phys.—Uspekhi **16,** Jan.–Feb. 1974.
25. V. I. Goldanskii, S. V. Karyagin, V. A. Namiot, Sov. Phys.—JETP Lett. **19,** 324 (1974).
26. Yu. Kagan, Sov. Phys.—JETP Lett. **19,** 373 (1974).
27. R. V. Pound, G. A. Rebka, Jr, Phys. Rev. Lett. **4,** 274 (1960); B. D. Josephson, Phys. Rev. Lett. **4,** 341 (1960).
28. Yu. Kagan, Sov. Phys.—JETP **47,** 366 (1964).
29. U. Haeberlen, J. S. Waugh, Phys. Rev. **175,** 453 (1968).
30. W. K. Rhim, D. D. Elleman, R. W. Vaughan, J. Chem. Phys. **59,** 3740 (1973).
31. G. Bizina, A. Beda, N. Burgov, A. Davydov, Sov. Phys.—JETP **18,** 973 (1964).
32. H. G. Dehmelt, Am. J. Phys. **22,** 110 (1954).
33. O. C. Kistner, A. W. Sunyar, Phys. Rev. Lett. **4,** 412 (1960).
34. J. Nuckolls, L. Wood, A. Thiessen, G. Zimmermann, Nature **239,** 139 (1972).
35. G. C. Baldwin, Laser Focus, March 1974, page 43.
36. V. I. Goldanskii, Yu. Kagan, V. A. Namiot, Sov. Phys.—JETP Lett. **18,** 34 (1973).
37. A. C. Melissinos, S. P. Davis, Phys. Rev. **115,** 130 (1958).
38. R. V. Ambartzumian, V. S. Letokhov, IEEE Jour. Quant. Elect. QE-**7,** 305 (1974); Appl. Optics **11,** 354 (1972).
39. V. S. Letokhov, Science **114,** 4 (1973).
40. PHYSICS TODAY, September 1974, page 17.
41. C. A. Mead, Phys. Rev. **143,** 990 (1966).

□

Appendix I. Additional Bibliography

X-Ray Lasers, Raymond C. Elton, Academic Press, San Diego (1990). *(This book traces the development of short wavelength lasers, with emphasis on the path leading toward x-ray lasers.)*

Short Wavelength Lasers and Their Applications, C. Yamanaka, ed., Springer-Verlag, Berlin (1988). *(This is a proceedings from a 1987 Japanese conference. It has brief papers on x-ray lasers, FELs, excimer lasers, and their applications.)*

Short Wavelength Coherent Radiation: Generation and Applications, D.T. Attwood and J. Bokor, eds., American Institute of Physics, New York (1986); AIP Conf. Proc. No. 147. *(This is one of a series of conference paper collections on short wavelength laser research. The papers are brief and give the status of the research. Not all of the proceedings of this conference series are included here.)*

Tunable Lasers, L.F. Mollenaur and J.C. White, eds., Springer-Verlag, Heidelberg (1984). *(Contains valuable work on nonlinear processes for short wavelength generation.)*

Excimer Lasers, Second Edition, C.K. Rhodes, ed., Springer-Verlag, Berlin (1984). *(This is an edited book consisting of very complete tutorial-review papers on the basic topics important to excimer lasers. The chapters are done by experts in the subject matter.)*

Laser Techniques in the Extreme Ultraviolet, S.E. Harris and T.B. Lucatorto, eds., American Institute of Physics, New York (1984); AIP Conf. Proc. No. 119. *(This is another in the AIP conference series on short wavelength lasers.)*

Gas Lasers, Applied Atomic Collision Physics Vol. 3, E.W. McDaniel and William L. Nighan, eds., Academic Press, New York (1982). *(This is an excellent book on gas lasers, especially the physics of gas lasers, with considerable [about 50%] treatment of excimer lasers. The introductory chapter by David Huestis is highly recommended as an overview of gas laser physics.)*

Table of Laser Lines in Gases and Vapors, Second Edition, R. Beck, W. English, and K. Gurs, eds., Springer-Verlag, Berlin (1978). *(This useful little book compiled most of the laser lines observed from gases and vapors along with reference to the original research. Its usefulness inspired the beginnings of such a table for short wavelength lasers included as an appendix at the end of this book.)*

The following journal articles would have been included as reprints in the main text were it not for the space limitations. These are important papers and should quickly become part of a new researcher's library. Reference to them (most without annotation) is given here for further reading for those interested.

R.M.J. Cotterill, "Universal planar x-ray resonator," *Appl. Phys. Lett.* 12, 403-404 (1968).

R.D. Deslattes, "X-ray monochromators and resonators from single crystals," *Appl. Phys. Lett.* 12, 133-135 (1968).

R.W. Dreyfus, R.T. Hodgson, "Electron-beam excitation of the nitrogen laser," *Appl. Phys. Lett.* 20(5), 195-197 (March 1, 1972).

K.G. Whitney, J. Davis, "Use of intense relativistic electron beams to pump VUV lasers," *J. Appl. Phys.* 46, 4103-4105 (1975).

T.S. Axelrod, "Inner-shell photoionization-pumped x-ray lasers. Sulfur," *Phys. Rev.* 13, 376-382 (1976).

D.A. Copeland, H. Mahr, C.L. Tang, "Threshold and rate equation considerations for a H^+-Cs charge-exchange laser," *IEEE J. Quantum Electron.* QE-12, 665-673 (1976).

D.A. Copeland, C.L. Tang, "Photon-assisted nonresonant charge exchange: a simple molecular model," *J. Chem. Phys.* 65, 3161-3171 (1976).

J.G. Eden, J. Golden, R.A. Mahaffey, J.A. Pasour, R.W. Waynant, "Efficient XeF laser excited by a proton beam," *Appl. Phys. Lett.* 35, 133-136 (1979).

J.K. Rice, G.C. Tisone, E.L. Patterson, "Oscillator performance and energy extraction from a KrF laser pumped by a high-intensity relativistic electron beam," *IEEE J. Quantum Electron.* QE-16, 1315-1326 (1980).

G.C. Baldwin, J.C. Solem, and V.I. Gol'danskii, "Approaches to the development of gamma-ray lasers," *Rev. Mod. Phys.* 53, 687-745 (1981). *(This sixty-plus page review paper is too lengthy to reprint here, but it represents a comprehensive review of the problems that must be solved if gamma ray lasers are to be developed.)*

C.A. Nicolaides, Y. Komninos, "Possibility for VUV and x-ray tunable atomic lasers," *Chem. Phys. Lett.* 80, 463-468 (1981).

U. Feldman, A.K. Bhatia, S. Suckewer, "Short wavelength laser calculations for electron pumping in neon-like krypton (Kr XXVII)," *J. Appl. Phys.* 54, 2188-2197 (1983).

D.L. Matthews, P. Hagelstein, E.M. Campbell, A. Toor, R.L. Kauffman, L. Koppel, W. Halsey, D. Phillion, R. Price, "Laser-heated x-ray flashlamp brightness measurements," *IEEE J. Quantum Electron.* QE-19, 1786-1794 (1983).

C.A. Nicolaides, "Radiative autoionization--a proposal for the construction of short-wavelength lasers," *IEEE J. Quantum Electron.* QE-19, 1781-1785 (1983).

F.L. Cochran, J. David, J.P. Apruzese, "X-ray lasing in a Na/Ne plasma environment," *J. Appl. Phys.* 57, 27-32 (1985).

F. Kannari, M. Obaara, T. Fujioka, "An advanced kinetic model of electron-beam-excited KrF lasers including the vibrational relaxation in $KrF^*(B)$ and collisional mixing of $KrF^*(B,C)$," *J. Appl. Phys.* 57, 4309-4322 (1985).

M.C. Richardson, R. Epstein, O. Barnouin, P.A. Jaanimagi, R. Keck, H.G. Kim, R.S. Marjoribanks, S. Noyes, J.M. Soures, B. Yaakobi, "Multibeam, laser imploded cylindrical plasmas," *Phys. Rev.* A 33, pp. 1246-1253 (1987).

Appendix II. Table of Laser Lines Below 400 nm

This table of laser lines has been assembled from the references available to the editors. Please communicate additions or errors directly to them so that an updated list can be given in the future. The atomic and molecular notation used here denotes ionization state, i.e., the roman numeral following the element specifies the ionization stage plus one (Xe III is doubly ionized xenon, etc.), and P represents a para-hydrogen molecule.

λ (nm)	Specie
5.03	Yb XLIII
6.58	Eu XXXVI
7.10	Eu XXXVI
8.1	F IX
8.3	Cl XV
8.44	Yb XLIII
8.48	Eu XXXVI
10.04	Eu XXXVI
10.46	Eu XXXVI
10.57	Al XI
10.64	Mo XXXIII
12.55	Mg X
12.79	Mg X
13.10	Mo XXXIII
13.27	Mo XXXIII
13.94	Mo XXXIII
15.47	Al XI
15.50	Y XXX
15.71	Al XI
15.98	Sr XXIX

λ (nm)	Specie
16.41	Sr XXIX
16.65	Sr XXIX
18.2	C VI
18.24	Se XXV
19.64	Ge XXII
20.64	Se XXV
20.98	Se XXV
22.03	Se XXV
22.07	Cu XX
23.22	Ge XXII
23.63	Ge XXII
24.73	Ge XXII
26.29	Se XXV
27.94	Cu XX
28.47	Cu XX
28.65	Ge XXII
96.9	Cs
108.9	Xe III
109.816	H_2 P
110.205	H_2 P

λ (nm)	Specie
111.336	D_2
111.515	H_2 P
111.894	H_2 P
113.770	D_2
113.864	HD
114.154	HD
114.462	H_2 P
114.757	D_2
114.862	H_2 P
115.198	HD
115.650	D_2
115.840	D_2
115.976	H_2
116.003	H_2 P
116.136	H_2
116.390	H_2 P
116.617	H_2
117.436	H_2
117.456	H_2 P
117.586	H_2

λ (nm)	Specie
117.806	HD
117.830	H_2 P
118.050	H_2
118.811	D_2
118.936	H_2
118.995	HD
119.005	D_2
119.281	HD
119.753	D_2
119.940	D_2
120.103	HD
120.497	H_2
120.536	H_2 P
120.640	D_2
120.668	H_2
120.821	D_2
120.929	H_2 P
121.125	HD
121.734	H_2
121.767	H_2 P

λ (nm)	Specie
121.900	H_2
121.946	H_2 P
122.143	H_2 P
122.358	H_2
122.800	D_2
122.837	HD
122.874	H_2 P
123.004	H_2
123.230	H_2 P
123.556	D_2
123.833	H_2 P
123.956	H_2
124.167	H_2 P
124.239	D_2
124.412	D_2
124.567	HD
124.620	H_2 P
124.831	D_2
124.997	D_2
125.202	H_2 P
125.276	HD
125.329	D_2
126.1	Ar_2
126.839	H_2 P
127.0	Zn III
130.334	HD
130.363	D_2
130.6	Zn III
131.9	Zn III
133.856	H_2 P
134.226	H_2
134.590	D_2
135.507	HD
135.984	H_2 P
136.799	H_2 P
138.879	D_2
139.895	H_2 P
140.264	H_2
140.728	H_2 P
140.770	HD
143.217	D_2
143.262	H_2 P
143.622	H_2
143.757	H_2 P
144.049	H_2
144.061	H_2 P
145.7	Kr2
146.017	H_2 P
146.383	H_2
146.411	H_2 P
146.841	H_2 P
148.652	H_2 P
148.843	HD
149.171	H_2 P
149.42	H_2
149.522	H_2
151.359	HD
151.570	H_2 P
151.867	H_2
151.994	H_2 P
152.325	H_2
152.989	HD
153.494	H_2 P
154.493	H_2 P
154.82	C IV
155.010	H_2 P
155.08	C IV
155.345	H_2
156.201	HD
156.55	H_2
156.629	H_2 P
156.644	H_2 P
156.725	H_2
156.753	H_2 P
157.136	HD
157.199	H_2
157.242	HD
157.267	HD
157.43	H_2
157.434	H_2 P
157.5	F2
157.585	D_2
157.739	H_2
157.771	H_2 P
157.919	H_2
157.998	H_2 P
157.998	H_2
158.008	HD
158.077	H_2
158.085	HD
158.110	H_2 P
158.140	H_2 P
158.185	HD
158.253	HD
158.305	HD
158.634	D_2
158.642	D_2
158.675	D_2
158.714	D_2
158.720	D_2
158.899	H_2 P
158.90	D_2
158.983	D_2
159.130	D_2
159.131	H_2
159.137	D_2
159.226	D_2
159.23	D_2
159.257	D_2
159.340	H_2 P
159.340	H_2
159.378	HD
159.524	HD
159.606	H_2
159.713	HD
159.926	H_2 P
160.044	D_2
160.086	D_2
160.210	D_2
160.233	HD
160.236	H_2 P
160.354	D_2
160.365	HD
160.448	H_2

λ (nm)	Specie
160.465	HD
160.496	HD
160.569	HD
160.578	D_2
160.594	H_2 P
160.623	H_2 P
160.623	H_2
160.63	D_2
160.647	HD
160.648	HD
160.650	D_2
160.674	HD
160.681	D_2
160.692	HD
160.747	HD
160.751	H_2
160.769	D_2
160.794	HD
160.827	HD
160.829	H_2 P
160.829	H_2
160.839	H_2
160.844	H_2 P
160.848	D_2
160.893	HD
160.902	H_2
160.955	D_2
160.961	H_2 P
161.005	HD
161.019	H_2 P
161.033	H_2 P
161.033	H_2
161.075	D_2
161.080	D_2
161.131	HD
161.147	D_2
161.165	H_2 P
161.165	D_2
161.166	H_2
161.171	D_2
161.198	D_2
161.236	D_2
161.251	D_2
161.257	D_2
161.318	H_2 P
161.318	D_2
161.319	H_2
161.320	D_2
161.324	D_2
161.412	D_2
161.48	H_2
161.485	H_2 P
161.65	H_2
161.658	D_2
172.2	Xe_2
175.0	ArCl
175.641	Kr IV
181.085	CO
183.243	Kr V
184.340	Ar IV
187.831	CO
189.784	CO
193.3	ArF
194.9623	Kr IV
195.006	CO
195.027	Kr IV
196.808	Kr IV
197.013	CO
201.8424	Ne IV
202.2186	Ne IV
205.1082	Kr IV
206.5	KrBr
206.5304	Ne IV
211.3982	Ar IV
217.7705	Ne III
218.0858	Ne III
219.1916	Kr IV
222.9	KrCl
223.2442	Xe IV
224.34	Ag II
224.8840	Ar IV
225.4638	Kr IV
226.57	Ne V
227.74	Ag II
228.5793	Ne IV
231.5357	Xe IV
233.8478	Kr IV
235.7980	Ne IV
237.3200	Ne IV
241.7843	Kr IV
242.8	Au
247.3398	Ne III
247.718	Xe III
248.1	KrF
248.4	KrF
248.5	KrF
248.58	Cu II
249.5	KrF
250.63	Cu II
251.3298	Ar IV
252.6664	Xe IV
253.37	Au II
259.05	Cu II
259.88	Cu II
260.9982	Ne III
261.34	Ne III
261.65	Au II
262.1377	Ar III
262.4882	Ar III
263.267	Cl III
263.898	S V
264.0	D V
264.9357	Kr IV
266.4398	Kr IV
267.6	Au
267.7918	Ne III
267.8690	Ne III
269.1939	Xe III
274.1380	Kr IV
275.3884	Ar III
275.958	F III
277.7634	Ne III
278.139	O V
281.8	XeBr

λ (nm)	Specie
282.25	Au II
282.612	F IV
284.70	Au II
285.5374	Ar III
286.21	Ag II
286.33	Au II
286.6726	Ar III
288.4216	Ar III
288.82	Au II
289.33	Au II
291.2924	Ar IV
291.5	Br_2
291.82	Au II
292.6227	Ar IV
295.94	Au II
298.37	Xe IV
298.378	O III
299.26	Ag II
300.2642	Ar III
302.405	Ar III
304.713	O III
304.9704	Kr III
305.484	Ar III
306.345	O IV
307.92	XeCl
307.9738	Xe III
308.16	XeCl
308.80	AgII
312.151	F III
321.2	Au
312.4363	Kr III

λ (nm)	Specie
315.756	N_2
315.778	N_2
315.798	N_2
315.803	N_2
315.816	N_2
315.827	N_2
315.832	N_2
315.844	N_2
315.853	N_2
315.861	N_2
315.870	N_2
315.874	N_2
315.883	N_2
315.891	N_2
315.900	N_2
315.911	N_2
315.919	N_2
317.413	F III
318.06	Ag II
319.146	Cl III
320.276	F I
323.9512	Kr III
324.6922	Xe IV
325.0	Cd II
330.5957	Xe IV
330.599	Xe III
331.9745	Ne II
332.3745	Ne II
332.437	Ne II
332.486	S III
332.717	Ne II

λ (nm)	Specie
332.923	Ne II
333.0869	Xe IV
333.114	Ne III
333.613	Ar III
334.472	Ar II
334.5446	Ne II
334.769	P IV
334.974	Xe IV
335.849	Ar III
336.4909	N_2
336.5425	N_2
336.5478	N_2
336.6913	N_2
336.734	N_2+
336.9541	N_2
336.9552	N_2
336.9769	N_2
336.9823	N_2
336.9835	N_2
336.9907	N_2
337.0027	N_2
337.0075	N_2
337.0081	N_2
337.0137	N_2
337.0174	N_2
337.0288	N_2
337.0295	N_2
337.0312	N_2
337.0381	N_2
337.0438	N_2
337.0466	N_2

λ (nm)	Specie
337.0474	N_2
337.0555	N_2
337.0562	N_2
337.0608	N_2
337.0619	N_2
337.0665	N_2
337.0677	N_2
337.0714	N_2
337.0726	N_2
337.0749	N_2
337.0758	N_2
337.0782	N_2
337.0797	N_2
337.0812	N_2
337.0816	N_2
337.0826	N_2
337.0919	N_2
337.0986	N_2
337.1037	N_2
337.1075	N_2
337.1082	N_2
337.1113	N_2
337.1121	N_2
337.1135	N_2
337.1143	N_2
337.1172	N_2
337.1266	N_2
337.1307	N_2
337.1366	N_2
337.1392	N_2
337.1421	N_2

λ (nm)	Specie
337.1429	N_2
337.496	Kr III
337.8256	Ne II
338.128	O IV
338.133	O IV
338.554	O IV
338.6428	N_2
339.2799	Ne II
339.287	Cl III
339.320	Ne II
339.343	Cl III
342.0	I_2
342.3	I_2
342.4	I_2
342.8	I_2
345.134	B II
345.4248	Xe III
347.867	N IV
348.296	N IV
348.322	Xe IV
348.75	XeF
349.737	S III
350.7420	Kr III
350.91	XeF
350.97	XeF

λ (nm)	Specie
351.112	Ar III
351.14	XeF
351.418	Ar III
353.004	Cl III
353.05	XeF
353.54	XeF
356.069	Cl III
356.423	Kr III
357.5460	N_2
357.5798	N_2
357.5980	N_2
357.6112	N_2
357.6194	N_2
357.6250	N_2
357.6320	N_2
357.6571	N_2
357.661	Ar II
357.6613	N_2
357.6778	N_2
357.6899	N_2
357.6955	N_2
358.744	Al II
359.661	Xe III
360.210	Cl III
361.283	Cl III

λ (nm)	Specie
362.268	Cl III
363.789	Ar III
363.954	Pb
364.5478	Xe IV
366.921	Xe III
370.52	Ar III
370.941	S III
371.309	Ne II
372.046	Cl III
374.571	Xe III
374.882	Cl III
374.949	O II
375.467	O III
375.979	Xe IV
375.988	O III
378.0990	Xe III
379.532	Ar III
380.322	Xe IV
380.4	N_2
382.62	Ag II
385.829	Ar III
388.05	Ag II
397.302	Xe IV
399.501	N II

Author Index

Subject Index